Table of Problem-Solving Strategies

Note for users of the five-volume edition:
Volume 1 (pp. 1–443) includes chapters 1–15.
Volume 2 (pp. 444–559) includes chapters 16–19.
Volume 3 (pp. 560–719) includes chapters 20–24.
Volume 4 (pp. 720–1101) includes chapters 25–36.
Volume 5 (pp. 1102–1279) includes chapters 36–42.

Chapters 37–42 are not in the Standard Edition.

Brief Contents

Randall D. Knight

Physics for Scientists and Engineers
A Strategic Approach with Modern Physics

Custom Edition for Penn State University
Physics 214

Taken from:
*Physics for Scientists and Engineers: A Strategic Approach
with Modern Physics,* Third Edition
by Randall D. Knight

Cover Art: Courtesy of Pearson Learning Solutions.

Taken from:

Physics for Scientists and Engineers: A Strategic Approach with Modern Physics, Third Edition
by Randall D. Knight
Copyright © 2013, 2008, 2004 by Pearson Education, Inc.
Boston, Massachusetts 02116

This special edition published in cooperation with Pearson Learning Solutions.

All trademarks, service marks, registered trademarks, and registered service marks are the property of their respective owners and are used herein for identification purposes only.

Pearson Learning Solutions, 501 Boylston Street, Suite 900, Boston, MA 02116
A Pearson Education Company
www.pearsoned.com

Printed in the United States of America

1 2 3 4 5 6 7 8 9 10 VOCR 18 17 16 15 14

000200010271909930

MS

ISBN 10: 1-269-91956-3
ISBN 13: 978-1-269-91956-2

About the Author

Randy Knight has taught introductory physics for over 30 years at Ohio State University and California Polytechnic University, where he is currently Professor of Physics. Professor Knight received a bachelor's degree in physics from Washington University in St. Louis and a Ph.D. in physics from the University of California, Berkeley. He was a post-doctoral fellow at the Harvard-Smithsonian Center for Astrophysics before joining the faculty at Ohio State University. It was at Ohio State that he began to learn about the research in physics education that, many years later, led to this book.

Professor Knight's research interests are in the field of lasers and spectroscopy, and he has published over 25 research papers. He also directs the environmental studies program at Cal Poly, where, in addition to introductory physics, he teaches classes on energy, oceanography, and environmental issues. When he's not in the classroom or in front of a computer, you can find Randy hiking, sea kayaking, playing the piano, or spending time with his wife Sally and their seven cats.

Builds problem-solving skills and confidence...

... through a carefully structured and research-proven program of problem-solving techniques and practice materials.

At the heart of the problem-solving instruction is the consistent 4-step MODEL/ VISUALIZE/ SOLVE/ ASSESS approach, used throughout the book and all supplements. *Problem-Solving Strategies* provide detailed guidance for particular topics and categories of problems, often drawing on key skills outlined in the step-by-step procedures of *Tactics Boxes*. Problem-Solving Strategies and Tactics Boxes are also illustrated in dedicated MasteringPhysics *Skill-Builder Tutorials*.

PROBLEM-SOLVING
STRATEGY 10.1   **Conservation of mechanical energy**

1 MODEL Choose a system that is isolated and has no friction or other losses of mechanical energy.

2 VISUALIZE Draw a before-and-after pictorial representation. Define symbols, list known values, and identify what you're trying to find.

3 SOLVE The mathematical representation is based on the law of conservation of mechanical energy:

$$K_f + U_f = K_i + U_i$$

4 ASSESS Check that your result has the correct units, is reasonable, and answers the question.

Exercise 8

TACTICS
BOX 9.1   **Drawing a before-and-after pictorial representation**

EXAMPLE 4.15 **Analyzing rotational data**

You've been assigned the task of measuring the start-up characteristics of a large industrial motor. After several seconds, when the motor has reached full speed, you know that the angular acceleration will be zero, but you hypothesize that the angular acceleration may be constant during the first couple of seconds as the motor speed increases. To find out, you attach a shaft encoder to the 3.0-cm-diameter axle. A shaft encoder is a device that converts the angular position of a shaft or axle to a signal that can be read by a computer. After setting the computer program to read four values a second, you start the motor and acquire the following data:

Time (s)	Angle(°)
0.00	0
0.25	16
0.50	69
0.75	161
1.00	267
1.25	428
1.50	620

a. Do the data support your hypothesis of a constant angular acceleration? If so, what is the angular acceleration? If not, is the angular acceleration increasing or decreasing with time?
b. A 76-cm-diameter blade is attached to the motor shaft. At what time does the acceleration of the tip of the blade reach 10 m/s²?

1 MODEL The axle is rotating with nonuniform circular motion. Model the tip of the blade as a particle.

2 VISUALIZE FIGURE 4.38 shows that the blade tip has both a tangential and a radial acceleration.

$\alpha = 2m$. If the graph is not a straight line, our observation of whether it curves upward or downward will tell us whether the angular acceleration us increasing or decreasing.

FIGURE 4.39 is the graph of θ versus t^2, and it confirms our hypothesis that the motor starts up with constant angular acceleration. The best-fit line, found using a spreadsheet, gives a slope of 274.6°/s². The units come not from the spreadsheet but by looking at the units of rise (°) over run (s²) because we're graphing t^2 on the x-axis). Thus the angular acceleration is

$$\alpha = 2m = 549.2°/s^2 \times \frac{\pi \, rad}{180°} = 9.6 \, rad/s^2$$

where we used $180° = \pi$ rad to convert to SI units of rad/s².

FIGURE 4.39 Graph of θ versus t^2 for the motor shaft.

y = 274.6x + 0.1

Best-fit line

b. The magnitude of the linear acceleration is

$$a = \sqrt{a_r^2 + a_t^2}$$

Worked Examples walk the student carefully through detailed solutions, focusing on underlying reasoning and common pitfalls to avoid.

NEW! *Data-based Examples* (shown here) help students with the skill of drawing conclusions from laboratory data.

NEW! *Challenge Examples* illustrate how to integrate multiple concepts and use more sophisticated reasoning.

CHALLENGE EXAMPLE 10.10   **A rebounding pendulum**

A 200 g steel ball hangs on a 1.0-m-long string. The ball is pulled sideways so that the string is at a 45° angle, then released. At the very bottom of its swing the ball strikes a 500 g steel paperweight that is resting on a frictionless table. To what angle does the ball rebound?

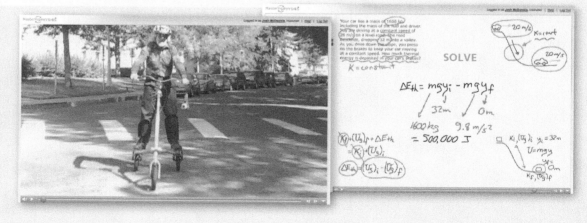

NEW! The Mastering Study Area also has *Video Tutor Solutions*, created by Randy Knight's College Physics co-author Brian Jones. These engaging and helpful videos walk students through a representative problem for each main topic, often starting with a qualitative overview in the context of a lab- or real-world demo.

Promotes deeper understanding...

... using powerful techniques from multimedia learning theory that focus and structure student learning, and improve engagement and retention.

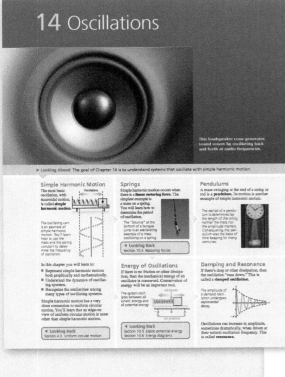

NEW! *Illustrated Chapter Previews* give an overview of the upcoming ideas for each chapter, setting them in context, explaining their utility, and tying them to existing knowledge (through *Looking Back* references).

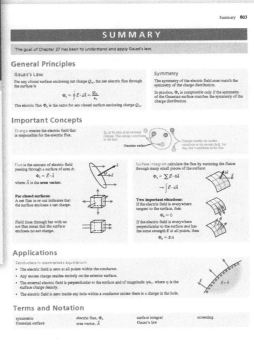

Critically acclaimed *Visual Chapter Summaries* and *Part Knowledge Structures* consolidate understanding by providing key concepts and principles in words, math, and figures and organizing these into a hierarchy.

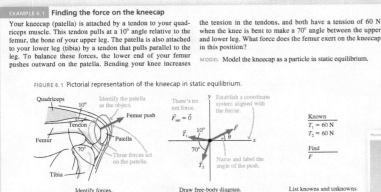

NEW! *Life-science and bioengineering examples* provide general interest, and specific context for biosciences students.

NEW! *PhET Simulations and Tutorials* allow students to explore real-life phenomena and discover the underlying physics. Sixteen tutorials are provided in the MasteringPhysics item library, and 76 PhET simulations are available in the Study Area and Pearson eText, along with the comprehensive library of ActivPhysics applets and applet-based tutorials.

NEW! *Video Tutor Demonstrations* feature "pause-and-predict" demonstrations of key physics concepts and incorporate assessment as the student progresses to actively engage them in understanding the key conceptual ideas underlying the physics principles.

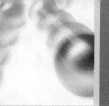

Provides research-enhanced problems...

... extensively class-tested and calibrated using MasteringPhysics data.

Data captured by MasteringPhysics® has been thoroughly analyzed by the author to ensure an optimal range of difficulty (indicated in the textbook using a three-bar rating), problem types, and topic coverage are being met.

56. ‖ A uniform rod of mass M and length L swings as a pendulum on a pivot at distance $L/4$ from one end of the rod. Find an expression for the frequency f of small-angle oscillations.

57. ‖ A solid sphere of mass M and radius R is suspended from a thin rod, as shown in FIGURE P14.57. The sphere can swing back and forth at the bottom of the rod. Find an expression for the frequency f of small-angle oscillations.

FIGURE P14.57

An ***increased emphasis on symbolic answers*** encourages students to work algebraically.

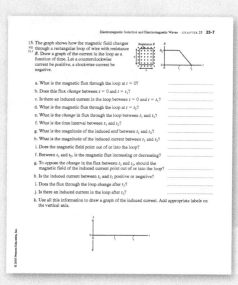

15. The graph shows how the magnetic field changes through a rectangular loop of wire with resistance R. Draw a graph of the current in the loop as a function of time. Let a counterclockwise current be positive, a clockwise current be negative.

a. What is the magnetic flux through the loop at $t = 0$?
b. Does this flux *change* between $t = 0$ and $t = t_1$?
c. Is there an induced current in the loop between $t = 0$ and $t = t_1$?
d. What is the magnetic flux through the loop at $t = t_2$?
e. What is the *change* in flux through the loop between t_1 and t_2?
f. What is the time interval between t_1 and t_2?
g. What is the magnitude of the induced emf between t_1 and t_2?
h. What is the magnitude of the induced current between t_1 and t_2?
i. Does the magnetic field point out of or into the loop?
f. Between t_1 and t_2, is the magnetic flux increasing or decreasing?
g. To oppose the *change* in the flux between t_1 and t_2, should the magnetic field of the induced current point out of or into the loop?
h. Is the induced current between t_1 and t_2 positive or negative?
i. Does the flux through the loop change after t_2?
j. Is there an induced current in the loop after t_2?
k. Use all this information to draw a graph of the induced current. Add appropriate labels on the vertical axis.

58. ‖ A geologist needs to determine the local value of g. Unfortunately, his only tools are a meter stick, a saw, and a stopwatch. He starts by hanging the meter stick from one end and measuring its frequency as it swings. He then saws off 20 cm—using the centimeter markings—and measures the frequency again. After two more cuts, these are his data:

Length (cm)	Frequency (Hz)
100	0.61
80	0.67
60	0.79
40	0.96

Use the best-fit line of an appropriate graph to determine the local value of g.

NEW! ***Data-based end-of-chapter problems*** allow students to practice drawing conclusions from data (as demonstrated in the new data-based examples in the text).

59. ‖ Interestingly, there have been several studies using cadavers to determine the moments of inertia of human body parts, information that is important in biomechanics. In one study, the center of mass of a 5.0 kg lower leg was found to be 18 cm from the knee. When the leg was allowed to pivot at the knee and swing freely as a pendulum, the oscillation frequency was 1.6 Hz. What

NEW! ***BIO problems*** are set in life-science, bioengineering, or biomedical contexts.

NEW! ***Student Workbook exercises*** help students work through a full solution symbolically, structured around the relevant textbook Problem-Solving Strategy.

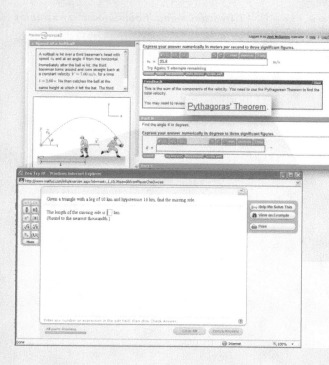

Pythagoras' Theorem

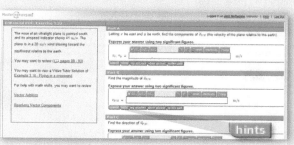

NEW! ***Enhanced end-of-chapter problems*** in MasteringPhysics now offer additional support such as problem-solving strategy hints, relevant math review and practice, links to the eText, and links to the related ***Video Tutor Solution***.

NEW! ***Math Remediation*** found within selected tutorials provide just-in-time math help and allow students to brush up on the most important mathematical concepts needed to successfully complete assignments. This new feature links students directly to math review and practice helping students make the connection between math and physics.

Make a difference with MasteringPhysics...

... the most effective and widely used online science tutorial, homework, and assessment system available.

MasteringPHYSICS www.masteringphysics.com

Pre-Built Assignments. For every chapter in the book, MasteringPhysics provides pre-built assignments that cover the material with a tested mix of tutorials and end-of-chapter problems of graded difficulty. Professors may use these assignments as-is or take them as a starting point for modification.

NEW! **Quizzing and Testing Enhancements.** These include options to:
- Hide item titles.
- Add password protection.
- Limit access to completed assignments.
- Randomize question order in an assignment.

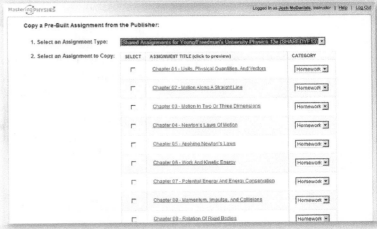

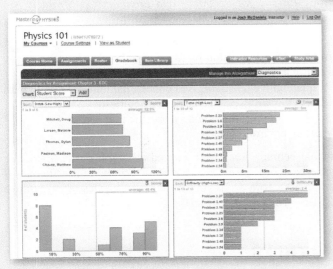

Class Performance on Assignment. Click on a problem to see which step your students struggled with most, and even their most common wrong answers. Compare results at every stage with the national average or with your previous class.

Gradebook

- Every assignment is graded automatically.
- Shades of red highlight vulnerable students and challenging assignments.
- The **Gradebook Diagnostics** screen provides your favorite weekly diagnostics, summarizing grade distribution, improvement in scores over the course, and much more.

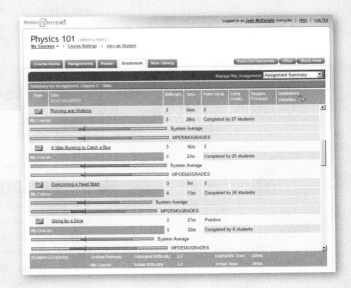

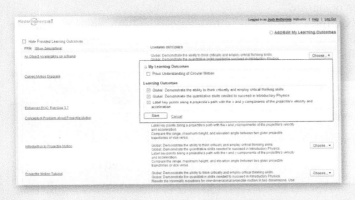

NEW! **Learning Outcomes.** In addition to being able to create your own learning outcomes to associate with questions in an assignment, you can now select content that is tagged to a large number of publisher-provided learning outcomes. You can also print or export student results based on learning outcomes for your own use or to incorporate into reports for your administration.

Preface to the Instructor

In 2003 we published *Physics for Scientists and Engineers: A Strategic Approach*. This was the first comprehensive introductory textbook built from the ground up on research into how students can more effectively learn physics. The development and testing that led to this book had been partially funded by the National Science Foundation. This first edition quickly became the most widely adopted new physics textbook in more than 30 years, meeting widespread critical acclaim from professors and students. For the second edition, and now the third, we have built on the research-proven instructional techniques introduced in the first edition and the extensive feedback from thousands of users to take student learning even further.

Objectives

My primary goals in writing *Physics for Scientists and Engineers: A Strategic Approach* have been:

- To produce a textbook that is more focused and coherent, less encyclopedic.
- To move key results from physics education research into the classroom in a way that allows instructors to use a range of teaching styles.
- To provide a balance of quantitative reasoning and conceptual understanding, with special attention to concepts known to cause student difficulties.
- To develop students' problem-solving skills in a systematic manner.
- To support an active-learning environment.

These goals and the rationale behind them are discussed at length in the *Instructor Guide* and in my small paperback book, *Five Easy Lessons: Strategies for Successful Physics Teaching*. Please request a copy from your local Pearson sales representative if it is of interest to you (ISBN 978-0-8053-8702-5).

FIVE EASY LESSONS
Strategies for Successful
Physics Teaching

RANDALL D. KNIGHT

What's New to This Edition

For this third edition, we continue to apply the best results from educational research, and to refine and tailor them for this course and its students. At the same time, the extensive feedback we've received has led to many changes and improvements to the text, the figures, and the end-of-chapter problems. These include:

- New illustrated **Chapter Previews** give a visual overview of the upcoming ideas, set them in context, explain their utility, and tie them to existing knowledge (through **Looking Back** references). These previews build on the cognitive psychology concept of an "advance organizer."
- New **Challenge Examples** illustrate how to integrate multiple concepts and use more sophisticated reasoning in problem-solving, ensuring an optimal range of worked examples for students to study in preparation for homework problems.
- New **Data-based Examples** help students with the skill of drawing conclusions from laboratory data. Designed to supplement lab-based instruction, these examples also help students in general with mathematical reasoning, graphical interpretation, and assessment of results.

End-of-chapter problem enhancements include the following:

- **Data from Mastering Physics® have been thoroughly analyzed** to ensure an optimal range of difficulty, problem types, and topic coverage. In addition, the wording of every problem has been reviewed for clarity. Roughly 20% of the end-of-chapter problems are new or significantly revised.

- **Data-based problems** allow students to practice drawing conclusions from data (as demonstrated in the new data-based examples in the text).
- **An increased emphasis on symbolic answers** encourages students to work algebraically. The *Student Workbook* also contains new exercises to help students work through symbolic solutions.
- **Bio problems** are set in life-science, bioengineering, or biomedical contexts.

Targeted content changes have been carefully implemented throughout the book. These include:

- **Life-science and bioengineering worked examples and applications** focus on the physics of life-science situations in order to serve the needs of life-science students taking a calculus-based physics class.
- **Descriptive text throughout has been streamlined** to focus the presentation and generate a shorter text.
- The chapter on *Modern Optics and Matter Waves* has been re-worked into Chapters 38 and 39 to streamline the coverage of this material.

At the front of the book, you'll find an illustrated walkthrough of the new pedagogical features in this third edition. The *Preface to the Student* demonstrates how all the book's features are designed to help your students.

Textbook Organization

The 42-chapter extended edition (ISBN 978-0-321-73608-6/0-321-73608-7) of *Physics for Scientists and Engineers* is intended for a three-semester course. Most of the 36-chapter standard edition (ISBN 978-0-321-75294-9/0-321-75294-5), ending with relativity, can be covered in two semesters, although the judicious omission of a few chapters will avoid rushing through the material and give students more time to develop their knowledge and skills.

There's a growing sentiment that quantum physics is quickly becoming the province of engineers, not just scientists, and that even a two-semester course should include a reasonable introduction to quantum ideas. The *Instructor Guide* outlines a couple of routes through the book that allow most of the quantum physics chapters to be included in a two-semester course. I've written the book with the hope that an increasing number of instructors will choose one of these routes.

The full textbook is divided into seven parts: Part I: *Newton's Laws*, Part II: *Conservation Laws*, Part III: *Applications of Newtonian Mechanics*, Part IV: *Thermodynamics*, Part V: *Waves and Optics*, Part VI: *Electricity and Magnetism*, and Part VII: *Relativity and Quantum Physics*. Although I recommend covering the parts in this order (see below), doing so is by no means essential. Each topic is self-contained, and Parts III–VI can be rearranged to suit an instructor's needs. To facilitate a reordering of topics, the full text is available in the five individual volumes listed in the margin.

Organization Rationale: Thermodynamics is placed before waves because it is a continuation of ideas from mechanics. The key idea in thermodynamics is energy, and moving from mechanics into thermodynamics allows the uninterrupted development of this important idea. Further, waves introduce students to functions of two variables, and the mathematics of waves is more akin to electricity and magnetism than to mechanics. Thus moving from waves to fields to quantum physics provides a gradual transition of ideas and skills.

The purpose of placing optics with waves is to provide a coherent presentation of wave physics, one of the two pillars of classical physics. Optics as it is presented in introductory physics makes no use of the properties of electromagnetic fields. There's little reason other than historical tradition to delay optics until after E&M.

- **Extended edition,** with modern physics (ISBN 978-0-321-73608-6 / 0-321-73608-7): Chapters 1–42.
- **Standard edition** (ISBN 978-0-321-75294-9 / 0-321-75294-5): Chapters 1–36.
- **Volume 1** (ISBN 978-0-321-75291-8 / 0-321-75291-0) covers mechanics: Chapters 1–15.
- **Volume 2** (ISBN 978-0-321-75318-2 / 0-321-75318-6) covers thermodynamics: Chapters 16–19.
- **Volume 3** (ISBN 978-0-321-75317-5 / 0-321-75317-8) covers waves and optics: Chapters 20–24.
- **Volume 4** (ISBN 978-0-321-75316-8 / 0-321-75316-X) covers electricity and magnetism, plus relativity: Chapters 25–36.
- **Volume 5** (ISBN 978-0-321-75315-1 / 0-321-75315-1) covers relativity and quantum physics: Chapters 36–42.
- **Volumes 1–5** boxed set (ISBN 978-0-321-77265-7 / 0-321-77265-2).

The documented difficulties that students have with optics are difficulties with waves, not difficulties with electricity and magnetism. However, the optics chapters are easily deferred until the end of Part VI for instructors who prefer that ordering of topics.

The Student Workbook

A key component of *Physics for Scientists and Engineers: A Strategic Approach* is the accompanying *Student Workbook*. The workbook bridges the gap between textbook and homework problems by providing students the opportunity to learn and practice skills prior to using those skills in quantitative end-of-chapter problems, much as a musician practices technique separately from performance pieces. The workbook exercises, which are keyed to each section of the textbook, focus on developing specific skills, ranging from identifying forces and drawing free-body diagrams to interpreting wave functions.

The workbook exercises, which are generally qualitative and/or graphical, draw heavily upon the physics education research literature. The exercises deal with issues known to cause student difficulties and employ techniques that have proven to be effective at overcoming those difficulties. The workbook exercises can be used in class as part of an active-learning teaching strategy, in recitation sections, or as assigned homework. More information about effective use of the *Student Workbook* can be found in the *Instructor Guide*.

Available versions: Extended (ISBN 978-0-321-75308-3/0-321-75308-9), Standard (ISBN 978-0-321-75309-0/0-321-75309-7), Volume 1 (ISBN 978-0-321-75314-4/0-321-75314-3), Volume 2 (ISBN 978-0-321-75313-7/0-321-75313-5), Volume 3 (ISBN 978-0-321-75312-0/0-321-75310-0), Volume 4 (ISBN 978-0-321-75311-3/0-321-75311-9), and Volume 5 (ISBN 978-0-321-75310-6/0-321-75310-0).

Instructor Supplements

- The **Instructor Guide for *Physics for Scientists and Engineers*** (ISBN 978-0-321-74765-5/0-321-74765-8) offers detailed comments and suggested teaching ideas for every chapter, an extensive review of what has been learned from physics education research, and guidelines for using active-learning techniques in your classroom. This invaluable guide is available on the Instructor Resource DVD, and via download, either from the MasteringPhysics Instructor Area or from the Instructor Resource Center (www.pearsonhighered.com/educator).

- The **Instructor Solutions** (ISBN 978-0-321-76940-4/0-321-76940-6), written by the author, Professor Larry Smith (Snow College), and Brett Kraabel (Ph.D., University of California, Santa Barbara), provide *complete* solutions to all the end-of-chapter problems. The solutions follow the four-step Model/Visualize/Solve/Assess procedure used in the Problem-Solving Strategies and in all worked examples. The solutions are available by chapter as editable Word® documents and as PDFs for your own use or for posting on your password-protected course website. Also provided are PDFs of handwritten solutions to all of the exercises in the *Student Workbook*, written by Professor James Andrews and Brian Garcar (Youngstown State University). All solutions are available

only via download, either from the MasteringPhysics Instructor Area or from the Instructor Resource Center (www.pearsonhighered.com/educator).

- The cross-platform **Instructor Resource DVD** (ISBN 978-0-321-75456-1/0-321-75456-5) provides a comprehensive library of more than 220 applets from **ActivPhysics OnLine** and 76 **PhET simulations**, as well as all figures, photos, tables, summaries, and key equations from the textbook in JPEG format. In addition, all the Problem-Solving Strategies, Tactics Boxes, and Key Equations are provided in editable Word format. PowerPoint® **Lecture Outlines** with embedded **Classroom Response System "Clicker" Questions** (including reading quizzes) are also provided.

- **MasteringPhysics®** (www.masteringphysics.com) is the most advanced, educationally effective, and widely used physics homework and tutorial system in the world. Eight years in development, it provides instructors with a library of extensively pre-tested end-of-chapter problems and rich, multipart, multistep tutorials that incorporate a wide variety of answer types, wrong answer feedback, individualized help (comprising hints or simpler sub-problems upon request), all driven by the largest metadatabase of student problem-solving in the world. NSF-sponsored published research (and subsequent studies) show that MasteringPhysics has dramatic educational results. MasteringPhysics allows instructors to build wide-ranging homework assignments of just the right difficulty and length and provides them with efficient tools to analyze in unprecedented detail both class trends and the work of any student.

MasteringPhysics routinely provides instant and individualized feedback and guidance to more than 100,000 students every day. A wide range of tools and support make MasteringPhysics fast and easy for instructors and students to learn to use. Extensive class tests show that by the end of their course, an unprecedented nine of ten students recommend MasteringPhysics as their preferred way to study physics and do homework.

For the third edition of *Physics for Scientists and Engineers,* MasteringPhysics now has the following functionalities:

- **Learning Outcomes:** In addition to being able to create their own learning outcomes to associate with questions in an assignment, professors can now select content that is tagged to a large number of publisher-provided learning outcomes. They can also print or export student results based on learning outcomes for their own use or to incorporate into reports for their administration.
- **Quizzing and Testing Enhancements:** These include options to hide item titles, add password protection, limit access to completed assignments, and to randomize question order in an assignment.
- **Math Remediation:** Found within selected tutorials, special links provide just-in-time math help and allow students to brush up on the most important mathematical concepts needed to successfully complete assignments. This new feature links students directly to math

review and practice helping students make the connection between math and physics.

- **Enhanced End-of-Chapter Problems:** A subset of homework problems now offer additional support such as problem-solving strategy hints, relevant math review and practice, links to the eText, and links to the related Video Tutor Solution.

- **ActivPhysics OnLine™** (accessed through the Self Study area within www.masteringphysics.com) provides a comprehensive library of more than 220 tried and tested ActivPhysics core applets updated for web delivery using the latest online technologies. In addition, it provides a suite of highly regarded applet-based tutorials developed by education pioneers Alan Van Heuvelen and Paul D'Alessandris.

The online exercises are designed to encourage students to confront misconceptions, reason qualitatively about physical processes, experiment quantitatively, and learn to think critically. The highly acclaimed ActivPhysics OnLine companion workbooks help students work through complex concepts and understand them more clearly. The applets from the ActivPhysics OnLine library are also available on the Instructor Resource DVD for this text.

- The **Test Bank** (ISBN 978-0-321-74766-2/0-321-74766-6) contains more than 2,000 high-quality problems, with a range of multiple-choice, true/false, short-answer, and regular homework-type questions. Test files are provided both in TestGen (an easy-to-use, fully networkable program for creating and editing quizzes and exams) and Word format. They are available only via download, either from the MasteringPhysics Instructor Area or from the Instructor Resource Center (www.pearsonhighered.com/educator).

Student Supplements

- The **Student Solutions Manuals Chapters 1–19** (ISBN 978-0-321-74767-9/0-321-74767-4) and **Chapters 20–42** (ISBN 978-0-321-77269-5/0-321-77269-5), written by the author, Professor Larry Smith (Snow College), and Brett Kraabel (Ph.D., University of California, Santa Barbara), provide *detailed* solutions to more than half of the odd-numbered end-of-chapter problems. The solutions follow the four-step Model/Visualize/Solve/Assess procedure used in the Problem-Solving Strategies and in all worked examples.
- **MasteringPhysics®** (www.masteringphysics.com) is a homework, tutorial, and assessment system based on years of research into how students work physics problems and precisely where they need help. Studies show that students who use MasteringPhysics significantly increase their scores compared to handwritten homework. MasteringPhysics achieves this

improvement by providing students with instantaneous feedback specific to their wrong answers, simpler subproblems upon request when they get stuck, and partial credit for their method(s). This individualized, 24/7 Socratic tutoring is recommended by 9 out of 10 students to their peers as the most effective and time-efficient way to study.

- **Pearson eText** is available through MasteringPhysics, either automatically when MasteringPhysics is packaged with new books, or available as a purchased upgrade online. Allowing students access to the text wherever they have access to the Internet, Pearson eText comprises the full text, including figures that can be enlarged for better viewing. With eText, students are also able to pop up definitions and terms to help with vocabulary and the reading of the material. Students can also take notes in eText using the annotation feature at the top of each page.

- **Pearson Tutor Services** (www.pearsontutorservices.com) Each student's subscription to MasteringPhysics also contains complimentary access to Pearson Tutor Services, powered by Smarthinking, Inc. By logging in with their MasteringPhysics ID and password, they will be connected to highly qualified e-instructors who provide additional interactive online tutoring on the major concepts of physics. Some restrictions apply; offer subject to change.
- **(MP) ActivPhysics OnLine™** (accessed through the Self Study area within www.masteringphysics.com)

provides students with a suite of highly regarded applet-based tutorials (see above). The following workbooks help students work through complex concepts and understand them more clearly:

- **ActivPhysics OnLine Workbook, Volume 1: Mechanics • Thermal Physics • Oscillations & Waves** (ISBN 978-0-8053-9060-5/0-8053-9060-X)
- **ActivPhysics OnLine Workbook, Volume 2: Electricity & Magnetism • Optics • Modern Physics** (ISBN 978-0-8053-9061-2/0-8053-9061-8)

Acknowledgments

I have relied upon conversations with and, especially, the written publications of many members of the physics education research community. Those who may recognize their influence include Arnold Arons, Uri Ganiel, Ibrahim Halloun, Richard Hake, Ken Heller, Paula Heron, David Hestenes, Leonard Jossem, Jill Larkin, Priscilla Laws, John Mallinckrodt, Kandiah Manivannan, Lillian McDermott and members of the Physics Education Research Group at the University of Washington, David Meltzer, Edward "Joe" Redish, Fred Reif, Jeffery Saul, Rachel Scherr, Bruce Sherwood, Josip Slisko, David Sokoloff, Richard Steinberg, Ronald Thornton, Sheila Tobias, Alan Van Heuleven, and Michael Wittmann. John Rigden, founder and director of the Introductory University Physics Project, provided the impetus that got me started down this path. Early development of the materials was supported by the National Science Foundation as the *Physics for the Year 2000* project; their support is gratefully acknowledged.

I especially want to thank my editor Jim Smith, development editor Alice Houston, project editor Martha Steele, and all the other staff at Pearson for their enthusiasm and hard work on this project. Production project manager Beth Collins, Rose Kernan and the team at Nesbitt Graphics, Inc., and photo researcher Eric Schrader get a good deal of the credit for making this complex project all come together. Larry Smith and Brett Kraabel have done an outstanding job of checking the solutions to every end-of-chapter problem and updating the *Instructor Solutions Manual*. Jim Andrews and Brian Garcar must be thanked for so carefully writing out the solutions to *The Student Workbook* exercises, and Jason Harlow for putting together the Lecture Outlines. In addition to the reviewers and classroom testers listed below, who gave invaluable feedback, I am particularly grateful to Charlie Hibbard for his close scrutiny of every word and figure.

Finally, I am endlessly grateful to my wife Sally for her love, encouragement, and patience, and to our many cats, past and present, who understand clearly that their priority is not deadlines but "Pet me, pet me, pet me."

Randy Knight, September 2011
rknight@calpoly.edu

Reviewers and Classroom Testers

Special thanks go to our third edition review panel: Kyle Altman, Taner Edis, Kent Fisher, Marty Gelfand, Elizabeth George, Jason Harlow, Bob Jacobsen, David Lee, Gary Morris, Eric Murray, and Bruce Schumm.

Gary B. Adams, *Arizona State University*
Ed Adelson, *Ohio State University*
Kyle Altmann, *Elon University*
Wayne R. Anderson, *Sacramento City College*
James H. Andrews, *Youngstown State University*
Kevin Ankoviak, *Las Positas College*
David Balogh, *Fresno City College*
Dewayne Beery, *Buffalo State College*
Joseph Bellina, *Saint Mary's College*
James R. Benbrook, *University of Houston*
David Besson, *University of Kansas*

Randy Bohn, *University of Toledo*
Richard A. Bone, *Florida International University*
Gregory Boutis, *York College*
Art Braundmeier, *University of Southern Illinois, Edwardsville*
Carl Bromberg, *Michigan State University*
Meade Brooks, *Collin College*
Douglas Brown, *Cabrillo College*
Ronald Brown, *California Polytechnic State University, San Luis Obispo*
Mike Broyles, *Collin County Community College*
Debra Burris, *University of Central Arkansas*
James Carolan, *University of British Columbia*
Michael Chapman, *Georgia Tech University*
Norbert Chencinski, *College of Staten Island*
Kristi Concannon, *King's College*

Sean Cordry, *Northwestern College of Iowa*
Robert L. Corey, *South Dakota School of Mines*
Michael Crescimanno, *Youngstown State University*
Dennis Crossley, *University of Wisconsin–Sheboygan*
Wei Cui, *Purdue University*
Robert J. Culbertson, *Arizona State University*
Danielle Dalafave, *The College of New Jersey*
Purna C. Das, *Purdue University North Central*
Chad Davies, *Gordon College*
William DeGraffenreid, *California State University–Sacramento*
Dwain Desbien, *Estrella Mountain Community College*
John F. Devlin, *University of Michigan, Dearborn*
John DiBartolo, *Polytechnic University*
Alex Dickison, *Seminole Community College*
Chaden Djalali, *University of South Carolina*
Margaret Dobrowolska, *University of Notre Dame*
Sandra Doty, *Denison University*
Miles J. Dresser, *Washington State University*
Charlotte Elster, *Ohio University*
Robert J. Endorf, *University of Cincinnati*
Tilahun Eneyew, *Embry-Riddle Aeronautical University*
F. Paul Esposito, *University of Cincinnati*
John Evans, *Lee University*
Harold T. Evensen, *University of Wisconsin–Platteville*
Michael R. Falvo, *University of North Carolina*
Abbas Faridi, *Orange Coast College*
Nail Fazleev, *University of Texas–Arlington*
Stuart Field, *Colorado State University*
Daniel Finley, *University of New Mexico*
Jane D. Flood, *Muhlenberg College*
Michael Franklin, *Northwestern Michigan College*
Jonathan Friedman, *Amherst College*
Thomas Furtak, *Colorado School of Mines*
Alina Gabryszewska-Kukawa, *Delta State University*
Lev Gasparov, *University of North Florida*
Richard Gass, *University of Cincinnati*
J. David Gavenda, *University of Texas, Austin*
Stuart Gazes, *University of Chicago*
Katherine M. Gietzen, *Southwest Missouri State University*
Robert Glosser, *University of Texas, Dallas*
William Golightly, *University of California, Berkeley*
Paul Gresser, *University of Maryland*
C. Frank Griffin, *University of Akron*
John B. Gruber, *San Jose State University*
Stephen Haas, *University of Southern California*
John Hamilton, *University of Hawaii at Hilo*
Jason Harlow, *University of Toronto*
Randy Harris, *University of California, Davis*
Nathan Harshman, *American University*
J. E. Hasbun, *University of West Georgia*
Nicole Herbots, *Arizona State University*
Jim Hetrick, *University of Michigan–Dearborn*
Scott Hildreth, *Chabot College*
David Hobbs, *South Plains College*
Laurent Hodges, *Iowa State University*

Mark Hollabaugh, *Normandale Community College*
John L. Hubisz, *North Carolina State University*
Shane Hutson, *Vanderbilt University*
George Igo, *University of California, Los Angeles*
David C. Ingram, *Ohio University*
Bob Jacobsen, *University of California, Berkeley*
Rong-Sheng Jin, *Florida Institute of Technology*
Marty Johnston, *University of St. Thomas*
Stanley T. Jones, *University of Alabama*
Darrell Judge, *University of Southern California*
Pawan Kahol, *Missouri State University*
Teruki Kamon, *Texas A&M University*
Richard Karas, *California State University, San Marcos*
Deborah Katz, *U.S. Naval Academy*
Miron Kaufman, *Cleveland State University*
Katherine Keilty, *Kingwood College*
Roman Kezerashvili, *New York City College of Technology*
Peter Kjeer, *Bethany Lutheran College*
M. Kotlarchyk, *Rochester Institute of Technology*
Fred Krauss, *Delta College*
Cagliyan Kurdak, *University of Michigan*
Fred Kuttner, *University of California, Santa Cruz*
H. Sarma Lakkaraju, *San Jose State University*
Darrell R. Lamm, *Georgia Institute of Technology*
Robert LaMontagne, *Providence College*
Eric T. Lane, *University of Tennessee–Chattanooga*
Alessandra Lanzara, *University of California, Berkeley*
Lee H. LaRue, *Paris Junior College*
Sen-Ben Liao, *Massachusetts Institute of Technology*
Dean Livelybrooks, *University of Oregon*
Chun-Min Lo, *University of South Florida*
Olga Lobban, *Saint Mary's University*
Ramon Lopez, *Florida Institute of Technology*
Vaman M. Naik, *University of Michigan, Dearborn*
Kevin Mackay, *Grove City College*
Carl Maes, *University of Arizona*
Rizwan Mahmood, *Slippery Rock University*
Mani Manivannan, *Missouri State University*
Richard McCorkle, *University of Rhode Island*
James McDonald, *University of Hartford*
James McGuire, *Tulane University*
Stephen R. McNeil, *Brigham Young University–Idaho*
Theresa Moreau, *Amherst College*
Gary Morris, *Rice University*
Michael A. Morrison, *University of Oklahoma*
Richard Mowat, *North Carolina State University*
Eric Murray, *Georgia Institute of Technology*
Taha Mzoughi, *Mississippi State University*
Scott Nutter, *Northern Kentucky University*
Craig Ogilvie, *Iowa State University*
Benedict Y. Oh, *University of Wisconsin*
Martin Okafor, *Georgia Perimeter College*
Halina Opyrchal, *New Jersey Institute of Technology*
Yibin Pan, *University of Wisconsin–Madison*
Georgia Papaefthymiou, *Villanova University*
Peggy Perozzo, *Mary Baldwin College*

Preface to the Student

From Me to You

The most incomprehensible thing about the universe is that it is comprehensible.
   —Albert Einstein

The day I went into physics class it was death.
   —Sylvia Plath, *The Bell Jar*

Let's have a little chat before we start. A rather one-sided chat, admittedly, because you can't respond, but that's OK. I've talked with many of your fellow students over the years, so I have a pretty good idea of what's on your mind.

What's your reaction to taking physics? Fear and loathing? Uncertainty? Excitement? All of the above? Let's face it, physics has a bit of an image problem on campus. You've probably heard that it's difficult, maybe downright impossible unless you're an Einstein. Things that you've heard, your experiences in other science courses, and many other factors all color your *expectations* about what this course is going to be like.

It's true that there are many new ideas to be learned in physics and that the course, like college courses in general, is going to be much faster paced than science courses you had in high school. I think it's fair to say that it will be an *intense* course. But we can avoid many potential problems and difficulties if we can establish, here at the beginning, what this course is about and what is expected of you—and of me!

Just what is physics, anyway? Physics is a way of thinking about the physical aspects of nature. Physics is not better than art or biology or poetry or religion, which are also ways to think about nature; it's simply different. One of the things this course will emphasize is that physics is a human endeavor. The ideas presented in this book were not found in a cave or conveyed to us by aliens; they were discovered and developed by real people engaged in a struggle with real issues. I hope to convey to you something of the history and the process by which we have come to accept the principles that form the foundation of today's science and engineering.

You might be surprised to hear that physics is not about "facts." Oh, not that facts are unimportant, but physics is far more focused on discovering *relationships* that exist between facts and *patterns* that exist in nature than on learning facts for their own sake. As a consequence, there's not a lot of memorization when you study physics. Some—there are still definitions and equations to learn—but less than in many other courses. Our emphasis, instead, will be on thinking and reasoning. This is important to factor into your expectations for the course.

Perhaps most important of all, *physics is not math!* Physics is much broader. We're going to look for patterns and relationships in nature, develop the logic that relates different ideas, and search for the reasons *why* things happen as they do. In doing so, we're going to stress qualitative reasoning, pictorial and graphical reasoning, and reasoning by analogy. And yes, we will use math, but it's just one tool among many.

It will save you much frustration if you're aware of this physics–math distinction up front. Many of you, I know, want to find a formula and plug numbers into it—that is,

(a) X-ray diffraction pattern

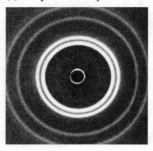

(b) Electron diffraction pattern

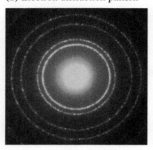

to do a math problem. Maybe that worked in high school science courses, but it is *not* what this course expects of you. We'll certainly do many calculations, but the specific numbers are usually the last and least important step in the analysis.

Physics is about recognizing patterns. For example, the top photograph is an x-ray diffraction pattern showing how a focused beam of x rays spreads out after passing through a crystal. The bottom photograph shows what happens when a focused beam of electrons is shot through the same crystal. What does the obvious similarity in these two photographs tell us about the nature of light and the nature of matter?

As you study, you'll sometimes be baffled, puzzled, and confused. That's perfectly normal and to be expected. Making mistakes is OK too *if* you're willing to learn from the experience. No one is born knowing how to do physics any more than he or she is born knowing how to play the piano or shoot basketballs. The ability to do physics comes from practice, repetition, and struggling with the ideas until you "own" them and can apply them yourself in new situations. There's no way to make learning effortless, at least for anything worth learning, so expect to have some difficult moments ahead. But also expect to have some moments of excitement at the joy of discovery. There will be instants at which the pieces suddenly click into place and you *know* that you understand a powerful idea. There will be times when you'll surprise yourself by successfully working a difficult problem that you didn't think you could solve. My hope, as an author, is that the excitement and sense of adventure will far outweigh the difficulties and frustrations.

Getting the Most Out of Your Course

Many of you, I suspect, would like to know the "best" way to study for this course. There is no best way. People are different, and what works for one student is less effective for another. But I do want to stress that *reading the text* is vitally important. Class time will be used to clarify difficulties and to develop tools for using the knowledge, but your instructor will *not* use class time simply to repeat information in the text. The basic knowledge for this course is written down on these pages, and the *number-one expectation* is that you will read carefully and thoroughly to find and learn that knowledge.

Despite there being no best way to study, I will suggest *one* way that is successful for many students. It consists of the following four steps:

1. **Read each chapter *before* it is discussed in class.** I cannot stress too strongly how important this step is. Class attendance is much more effective if you are prepared. When you first read a chapter, focus on learning new vocabulary, definitions, and notation. There's a list of terms and notations at the end of each chapter. Learn them! You won't understand what's being discussed or how the ideas are being used if you don't know what the terms and symbols mean.

2. **Participate actively in class.** Take notes, ask and answer questions, and participate in discussion groups. There is ample scientific evidence that *active participation* is much more effective for learning science than passive listening.

3. **After class, go back for a careful re-reading of the chapter.** In your second reading, pay closer attention to the details and the worked examples. Look for the *logic* behind each example (I've highlighted this to make it clear), not just at what formula is being used. Do the *Student Workbook* exercises for each section as you finish your reading of it.

4. **Finally, apply what you have learned to the homework problems at the end of each chapter.** I strongly encourage you to form a study group with two or three classmates. There's good evidence that students who study regularly with a group do better than the rugged individualists who try to go it alone.

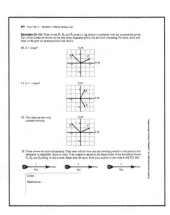

Did someone mention a workbook? The companion *Student Workbook* is a vital part of the course. Its questions and exercises ask you to reason *qualitatively,* to use graphical information, and to give explanations. It is through these exercises that you will learn what the concepts mean and will practice the reasoning skills appropriate to the chapter. You will then have acquired the baseline knowledge and confidence you need *before* turning to the end-of-chapter homework problems. In sports or in music, you would never think of performing before you practice, so why would you want to do so in physics? The workbook is where you practice and work on basic skills.

Many of you, I know, will be tempted to go straight to the homework problems and then thumb through the text looking for a formula that seems like it will work. That approach will not succeed in this course, and it's guaranteed to make you frustrated and discouraged. Very few homework problems are of the "plug and chug" variety where you simply put numbers into a formula. To work the homework problems successfully, you need a better study strategy—either the one outlined above or your own—that helps you learn the concepts and the relationships between the ideas.

A traditional guideline in college is to study two hours outside of class for every hour spent in class, and this text is designed with that expectation. Of course, two hours is an average. Some chapters are fairly straightforward and will go quickly. Others likely will require much more than two study hours per class hour.

Getting the Most Out of Your Textbook

Your textbook provides many features designed to help you learn the concepts of physics and solve problems more effectively.

- **TACTICS BOXES** give step-by-step procedures for particular skills, such as interpreting graphs or drawing special diagrams. Tactics Box steps are explicitly illustrated in subsequent worked examples, and these are often the starting point of a full *Problem-Solving Strategy*.

TACTICS
BOX 5.3 **Drawing a free-body diagram**

❶ **Identify all forces acting on the object.** This step was described in Tactics Box 5.2.
❷ **Draw a coordinate system.** Use the axes defined in your pictorial representation.
❸ **Represent the object as a dot at the origin of the coordinate axes.** This is the particle model.
❹ **Draw vectors representing each of the identified forces.** This was described in Tactics Box 5.1. Be sure to label each force vector.
❺ **Draw and label the *net force* vector $\vec{F}_{net}$.** Draw this vector beside the diagram, not on the particle. Or, if appropriate, write $\vec{F}_{net} = \vec{0}$. Then check that $\vec{F}_{net}$ points in the same direction as the acceleration vector $\vec{a}$ on your motion diagram.

Exercises 24–29

TACTICS
BOX 32.3 **Evaluating line integrals**

❶ If $\vec{B}$ is everywhere perpendicular to a line, the line integral of $\vec{B}$ is

$$\int_i^f \vec{B} \cdot d\vec{s} = 0$$

❷ If $\vec{B}$ is everywhere tangent to a line of length l *and* has the same magnitude B at every point, then

$$\int_i^f \vec{B} \cdot d\vec{s} = Bl$$

Exercises 23–24

■ PROBLEM-SOLVING STRATEGIES are provided for each broad class of problems—problems characteristic of a chapter or group of chapters. The strategies follow a consistent four-step approach to help you develop confidence and proficient problem-solving skills: MODEL, VISUALIZE, SOLVE, ASSESS.

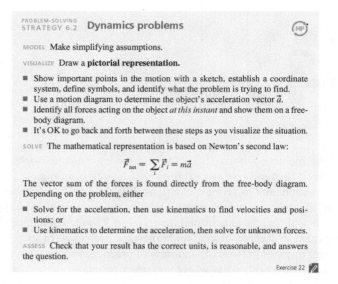

PROBLEM-SOLVING
STRATEGY 6.2 **Dynamics problems**

MODEL Make simplifying assumptions.

VISUALIZE Draw a **pictorial representation.**

■ Show important points in the motion with a sketch, establish a coordinate system, define symbols, and identify what the problem is trying to find.
■ Use a motion diagram to determine the object's acceleration vector $\vec{a}$.
■ Identify all forces acting on the object *at this instant* and show them on a free-body diagram.
■ It's OK to go back and forth between these steps as you visualize the situation.

SOLVE The mathematical representation is based on Newton's second law:

$$\vec{F}_{net} = \sum_i \vec{F}_i = m\vec{a}$$

The vector sum of the forces is found directly from the free-body diagram. Depending on the problem, either

■ Solve for the acceleration, then use kinematics to find velocities and positions; or
■ Use kinematics to determine the acceleration, then solve for unknown forces.

ASSESS Check that your result has the correct units, is reasonable, and answers the question.

Exercise 22

■ Worked EXAMPLES illustrate good problem-solving practices through the consistent use of the four-step problem-solving approach and, where appropriate, the Tactics Box steps. The worked examples are often very detailed and carefully lead you through the *reasoning* behind the solution as well as the numerical calculations. A careful study of the reasoning will help you apply the concepts and techniques to the new and novel problems you will encounter in homework assignments and on exams.

■ NOTE ▶ paragraphs alert you to common mistakes and point out useful tips for tackling problems.

■ STOP TO THINK questions embedded in the chapter allow you to quickly assess whether you've understood the main idea of a section. A correct answer will give you confidence to move on to the next section. An incorrect answer will alert you to re-read the previous section.

■ Blue annotations on figures help you better understand what the figure is showing. They will help you to interpret graphs; translate between graphs, math, and pictures; grasp difficult concepts through a visual analogy; and develop many other important skills.

■ *Pencil sketches* provide practical examples of the figures you should draw yourself when solving a problem.

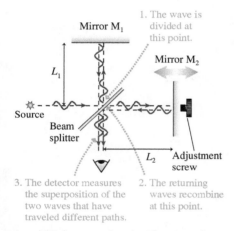

1. The wave is divided at this point.

2. The returning waves recombine at this point.

3. The detector measures the superposition of the two waves that have traveled different paths.

Annotated FIGURE showing the operation of the Michelson interferometer.

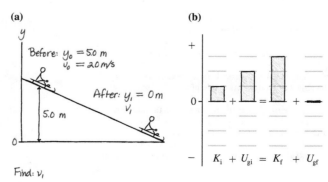

Pencil-sketch FIGURE showing a toboggan going down a hill and its energy bar chart.

- Each chapter begins with a *Chapter Preview*, a visual outline of the chapter ahead with recommendations of important topics you should review from previous chapters. A few minutes spent with the Preview will help you organize your thoughts so as to get the most out of reading the chapter.
- Schematic *Chapter Summaries* help you organize what you have learned into a hierarchy, from general principles (top) to applications (bottom). Side-by-side pictorial, graphical, textual, and mathematical representations are used to help you translate between these key representations.
- *Part Overviews* and *Summaries* provide a global framework for what you are learning. Each part begins with an overview of the chapters ahead and concludes with a broad summary to help you to connect the concepts presented in that set of chapters. KNOWLEDGE STRUCTURE tables in the Part Summaries, similar to the Chapter Summaries, help you to see the forest rather than just the trees.

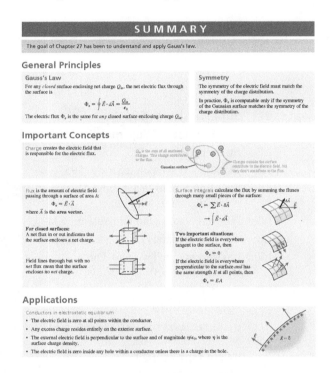

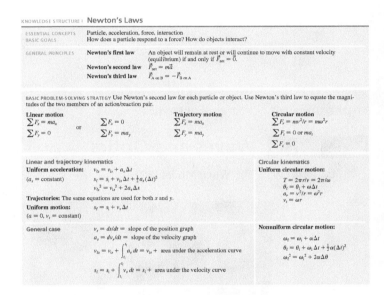

Now that you know more about what is expected of you, what can you expect of me? That's a little trickier because the book is already written! Nonetheless, the book was prepared on the basis of what I think my students throughout the years have expected—and wanted—from their physics textbook. Further, I've listened to the extensive feedback I have received from thousands of students like you, and their instructors, who used the first and second editions of this book.

You should know that these course materials—the text and the workbook—are based on extensive research about how students learn physics and the challenges they face. The effectiveness of many of the exercises has been demonstrated through extensive class testing. I've written the book in an informal style that I hope you will find appealing and that will encourage you to do the reading. And, finally, I have endeavored to make clear not only that physics, as a technical body of knowledge, is relevant to your profession but also that physics is an exciting adventure of the human mind.

I hope you'll enjoy the time we're going to spend together.

Detailed Contents

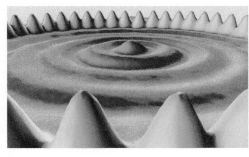

Introduction

Journey into Physics

Said Alice to the Cheshire cat,
"Cheshire-Puss, would you tell me, please, which way I ought to go from here?"
"That depends a good deal on where you want to go," said the Cat.
"I don't much care where—" said Alice.
"Then it doesn't matter which way you go," said the Cat.
 —Lewis Carroll, *Alice in Wonderland*

Have you ever wondered about questions such as

> Why is the sky blue?

> Why is glass an insulator but metal a conductor?

> What, really, is an atom?

These are the questions of which physics is made. Physicists try to understand the universe in which we live by observing the phenomena of nature—such as the sky being blue—and by looking for patterns and principles to explain these phenomena. Many of the discoveries made by physicists, from electromagnetic waves to nuclear energy, have forever altered the ways in which we live and think.

You are about to embark on a journey into the realm of physics. It is a journey in which you will learn about many physical phenomena and find the answers to questions such as the ones posed above. Along the way, you will also learn how to use physics to analyze and solve many practical problems.

As you proceed, you are going to see the methods by which physicists have come to understand the laws of nature. The ideas and theories of physics are not arbitrary; they are firmly grounded in experiments and measurements. By the time you finish this text, you will be able to recognize the *evidence* upon which our present knowledge of the universe is based.

Which Way Should We Go?

We are rather like Alice in Wonderland, here at the start of the journey, in that we must decide which way to go. Physics is an immense body of knowledge, and without specific goals it would not much matter which topics we study. But unlike Alice, we *do* have some particular destinations that we would like to visit.

The physics that provides the foundation for all of modern science and engineering can be divided into three broad categories:

- Particles and energy.
- Fields and waves.
- The atomic structure of matter.

A particle, in the sense that we'll use the term, is an idealization of a physical object. We will use particles to understand how objects move and how they interact with each other. One of the most important properties of a particle or a collection of particles is *energy*. We will study energy both for its value in understanding physical processes and because of its practical importance in a technological society.

A scanning tunneling microscope allows us to "see" the individual atoms on a surface. One of our goals is to understand how an image such as this is made.

Particles are discrete, localized objects. Although many phenomena can be understood in terms of particles and their interactions, the long-range interactions of gravity, electricity, and magnetism are best understood in terms of *fields,* such as the gravitational field and the electric field. Rather than being discrete, fields spread continuously through space. Much of the second half of this book will be focused on understanding fields and the interactions between fields and particles.

Certainly one of the most significant discoveries of the past 500 years is that matter consists of atoms. Atoms and their properties are described by quantum physics, but we cannot leap directly into that subject and expect that it would make any sense. To reach our destination, we are going to have to study many other topics along the way—rather like having to visit the Rocky Mountains if you want to drive from New York to San Francisco. All our knowledge of particles and fields will come into play as we end our journey by studying the atomic structure of matter.

The Route Ahead

Here at the beginning, we can survey the route ahead. Where will our journey take us? What scenic vistas will we view along the way?

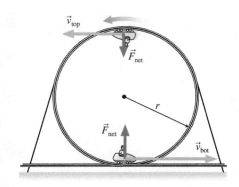

Parts I and II, *Newton's Laws* and *Conservation Laws,* form the basis of what is called *classical mechanics.* Classical mechanics is the study of motion. (It is called *classical* to distinguish it from the modern theory of motion at the atomic level, which is called *quantum mechanics.*) The first two parts of this textbook establish the basic language and concepts of motion. Part I will look at motion in terms of *particles* and *forces.* We will use these concepts to study the motion of everything from accelerating sprinters to orbiting satellites. Then, in Part II, we will introduce the ideas of *momentum* and *energy.* These concepts—especially energy—will give us a new perspective on motion and extend our ability to analyze motion.

Part III, *Applications of Newtonian Mechanics,* will pause to look at four important applications of classical mechanics: Newton's theory of gravity, rotational motion, oscillatory motion, and the motion of fluids. Only oscillatory motion is a prerequisite for later chapters. Your instructor may choose to cover some or all of the other chapters, depending upon the time available, but your study of Parts IV–VII will not be hampered if these chapters are omitted.

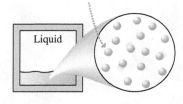

Atoms are held close together by weak molecular bonds, but they can slide around each other.

Liquid

Part IV, *Thermodynamics,* extends the ideas of particles and energy to systems such as liquids and gases that contain vast numbers of particles. Here we will look for connections between the *microscopic* behavior of large numbers of atoms and the *macroscopic* properties of bulk matter. You will find that some of the properties of gases that you know from chemistry, such as the ideal gas law, turn out to be direct consequences of the underlying atomic structure of the gas. We will also expand the concept of energy and study how energy is transferred and utilized.

Waves are ubiquitous in nature, whether they be large-scale oscillations like ocean waves, the less obvious motions of sound waves, or the subtle undulations of light waves and matter waves that go to the heart of the atomic structure of matter. In **Part V,** *Waves and Optics,* we will emphasize the unity of wave physics and find that many diverse wave phenomena can be analyzed with the same concepts and mathematical language. Light waves are of special interest, and we will end this portion of our journey with an exploration of optical instruments, ranging from microscopes and telescopes to that most important of all optical instruments—your eye.

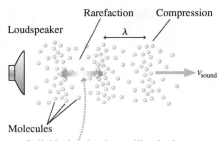

Individual molecules oscillate back and forth with displacement D. As they do so, the compressions propagate forward at speed v_{sound}. Because compressions are regions of higher pressure, a sound wave can be thought of as a pressure wave.

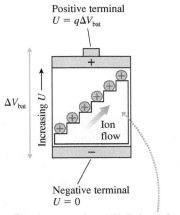

The charge escalator "lifts" charge from the negative side to the positive side. Charge q gains energy $\Delta U = q\Delta V_{bat}$.

Part VI, *Electricity and Magnetism,* is devoted to the *electromagnetic force,* one of the most important forces in nature. In essence, the electromagnetic force is the "glue" that holds atoms together. It is also the force that makes this the "electronic age." We'll begin this part of the journey with simple observations of static electricity. Bit by bit, we'll be led to the basic ideas behind electrical circuits, to magnetism, and eventually to the discovery of electromagnetic waves.

Part VII is *Relativity and Quantum Physics.* We'll start by exploring the strange world of Einstein's theory of *relativity,* a world in which space and time aren't quite what they appear to be. Then we will enter the microscopic domain of *atoms,* where the behaviors of light and matter are at complete odds with what our common sense tells us is possible. Although the mathematics of quantum theory quickly gets beyond the level of this text, and time will be running out, you will see that the quantum theory of atoms and nuclei explains many of the things that you learned simply as rules in chemistry.

We will not have visited all of physics on our travels. There just isn't time. Many exciting topics, ranging from quarks to black holes, will have to remain unexplored. But this particular journey need not be the last. As you finish this text, you will have the background and the experience to explore new topics further in more advanced courses or for yourself.

With that said, let us take the first step.

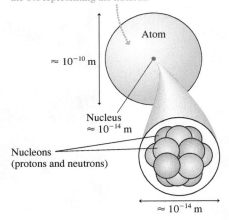

This picture of an atom would need to be 10 m in diameter if it were drawn to the same scale as the dot representing the nucleus.

Waves and Optics

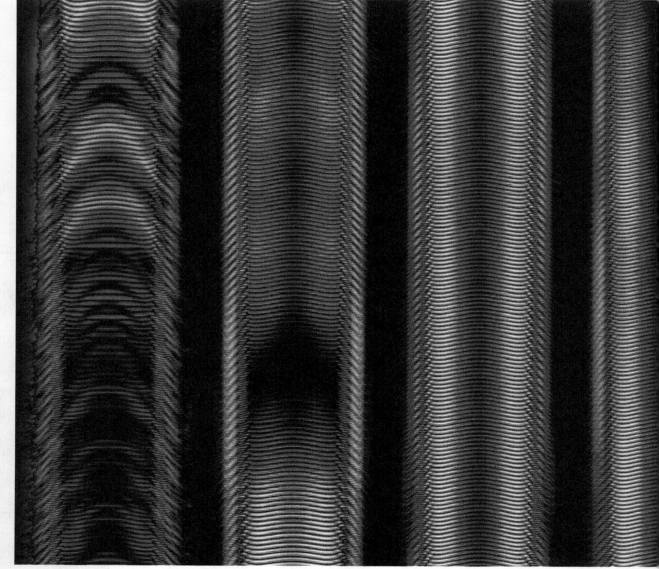

The song of a humpback whale can travel hundreds of kilometers underwater. This graph uses a procedure called wavelet analysis to study the frequency structure of a humpback whale song.

OVERVIEW

The Wave Model

Parts I–IV of this text have been primarily about the physics of particles. You've seen that macroscopic systems ranging from balls and rockets to a gas of molecules can be thought of as particles or as systems of particles. A *particle* is one of the two fundamental models of classical physics. The other, to which we now turn our attention, is a *wave.*

Waves are ubiquitous in nature. Familiar examples of waves include

- Undulating ripples on a pond.
- The swaying ground of an earthquake.
- A vibrating guitar string.
- The sweet sound of a flute.
- The colors of the rainbow.

The physics of waves is the subject of Part V, the next stage of our journey. Despite the great diversity of types and sources of waves, a single, elegant physical theory is capable of describing them all. Our exploration of wave phenomena will call upon sound waves, light waves, and vibrating strings for examples, but our goal is to emphasize the unity and coherence of the ideas that are common to *all* types of waves.

A wave, in contrast with a particle, is diffuse, spread out, not to be found at a single point in space. We will start with waves traveling outward through some medium, like the spreading ripples after a pebble hits a pool of water. These are called *traveling waves.* An investigation of what happens when waves travel through each other will lead us to *standing waves,* which are essential for understanding phenomena ranging from those as common as musical instruments and water sloshing in a tub to as complex as lasers and the electrons in atoms. We'll also study one of the most important defining characteristics of waves—their ability to exhibit *interference.*

Three chapters will be devoted to light and optics, perhaps the most important application of waves. Although light is an electromagnetic wave, your understanding of these chapters will depend on nothing more than the "waviness" of light. You can study these chapters either before or after your study of electricity and magnetism in Part VI. The electromagnetic aspects of light waves will be taken up in Chapter 34.

Our investigation of light will be aided by a second model, the *ray model,* in which light travels in straight lines, reflects from mirrors, and is focused by lenses. Many practical applications of optics, from the camera to the telescope, are best understood with the ray model of light.

In fact, that you're able to read this book at all is due to the first optical instrument you ever used—your eyes. We will investigate the optics of the eye, learn how the cornea and lens form an image on the retina, and see how glasses or contact lenses can be used to correct the image if it is out of focus.

20 Traveling Waves

This surfer is "catching a wave." At the same time, he's seeing light waves and hearing sound waves.

▶ **Looking Ahead** The goal of Chapter 20 is to learn the basic properties of traveling waves.

The Wave Model

A **wave** is a disturbance traveling through a medium. Our goal is to develop a model —the wave model—that describes the basic properties of all waves.

The wave propagates, but the particles of the medium don't. The water molecules simply oscillate up and down as the ripples spread outward.

Two Types of Waves

You'll find that waves come in two basic types:

Transverse waves: The displacement is perpendicular to the direction of travel.

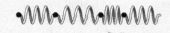

Longitudinal waves: The displacement is parallel to the direction of travel.

Sound and Light

Two types of waves are especially important: sound and light.
- Sound waves are longitudinal waves.
- Light waves are transverse waves.

You'll learn that the colors of visible light correspond to different wavelengths.

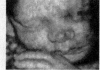

Ultrasound images are made with very-high-frequency sound waves.

Wave Properties

You'll learn that a wave is characterized by three basic properties:
- **Wave speed**: How fast it travels through the medium.
- **Wavelength**: The distance between two neighboring crests.
- **Frequency**: The number of oscillations per second.

You'll also see that wave motion is closely related to simple harmonic motion.

◀ **Looking Back**
Sections 14.1 and 14.2 Properties of simple harmonic motion

Intensity and Loudness

Waves carry energy. The rate at which a wave delivers energy to a surface is the **intensity** of the wave.

Your ears are sensitive to a remarkable range of intensities. You'll learn to use the logarithmic **decibel** scale to characterize the loudness of a sound.

Focusing the sun's light into a smaller area increases its intensity.

The Doppler Effect

The frequency and wavelength of a wave are shifted when there is relative motion between the source and the observer of the waves. This is called the **Doppler effect.**

The pitch of the ambulance siren drops as it races past you. The frequency is shifted up as it approaches, then shifted down as it recedes.

20.1 The Wave Model

Balls, cars, and rockets obviously differ from one another, but the general features of their motions are well described by the *particle model* of Parts I–IV. In Part V we will explore the basic properties of waves with a **wave model,** emphasizing those aspects of wave behavior common to all waves. Although water waves, sound waves, and light waves are clearly different, the wave model will allow us to understand many of the important features they have in common.

The wave model is built around the idea of a **traveling wave,** which is an organized disturbance traveling with a well-defined wave speed. We'll begin our study of traveling waves by looking at two distinct wave motions.

Two types of traveling waves

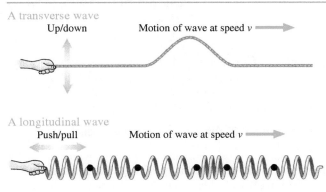

A transverse wave
Up/down   Motion of wave at speed v ⟶

A **transverse wave** is a wave in which the displacement is *perpendicular* to the direction in which the wave travels. For example, a wave travels along a string in a horizontal direction while the particles that make up the string oscillate vertically. Electromagnetic waves are also transverse waves because the electromagnetic fields oscillate perpendicular to the direction in which the wave travels.

A longitudinal wave
Push/pull   Motion of wave at speed v ⟶

In a **longitudinal wave,** the particles in the medium move *parallel* to the direction in which the wave travels. Here we see a chain of masses connected by springs. If you give the first mass in the chain a sharp push, a disturbance travels down the chain by compressing and expanding the springs. Sound waves in gases and liquids are the most well known examples of longitudinal waves.

We can also classify waves on the basis of what is "waving":

1. **Mechanical waves** travel only within a material *medium,* such as air or water. Two familiar mechanical waves are sound waves and water waves.
2. **Electromagnetic waves,** from radio waves to visible light to x rays, are a self-sustaining oscillation of the *electromagnetic field.* Electromagnetic waves require no material medium and can travel through a vacuum.

The **medium** of a mechanical wave is the substance through or along which the wave moves. For example, the medium of a water wave is the water, the medium of a sound wave is the air, and the medium of a wave on a stretched string is the string. A medium must be *elastic.* That is, a restoring force of some sort brings the medium back to equilibrium after it has been displaced or disturbed. The tension in a stretched string pulls the string back straight after you pluck it. Gravity restores the level surface of a lake after the wave generated by a boat has passed by.

As a wave passes through a medium, the atoms of the medium—we'll simply call them the particles of the medium—are displaced from equilibrium. This is a **disturbance** of the medium. The water ripples of FIGURE 20.1 are a disturbance of the water's surface. A pulse traveling down a string is a disturbance, as are the wake of a boat and the sonic boom created by a jet traveling faster than the speed of sound. **The disturbance of a wave is an *organized* motion of the particles in the medium,** in contrast to the *random* molecular motions of thermal energy.

FIGURE 20.1 Ripples on a pond are a traveling wave.

The disturbance is the rippling of the water's surface.

The water is the medium.

Wave Speed

A wave disturbance is created by a *source.* The source of a wave might be a rock thrown into water, your hand plucking a stretched string, or an oscillating loudspeaker cone pushing on the air. Once created, the disturbance travels outward through the medium at the **wave speed** v. This is the speed with which a ripple moves across the water or a pulse travels down a string.

NOTE ▶ The disturbance propagates through the medium, but **the medium as a whole does not move!** The ripples on the pond (the disturbance) move outward from the splash of the rock, but there is no outward flow of water from the splash. Likewise, the particles of a string oscillate up and down but do not move in the direction of a pulse traveling along the string. **A wave transfers energy, but it does not transfer any material or substance outward from the source.** ◀

As an example, we'll prove in Section 20.3 that the wave speed on a string stretched with tension T_s is

$$v_{string} = \sqrt{\frac{T_s}{\mu}} \quad \text{(wave speed on a stretched string)} \quad (20.1)$$

where μ is the string's **linear density,** its mass-to-length ratio:

$$\mu = \frac{m}{L} \quad (20.2)$$

The SI unit of linear density is kg/m. A fat string has a larger value of μ than a skinny string made of the same material. Similarly, a steel wire has a larger value of μ than a plastic string of the same diameter. We'll assume that strings are *uniform,* meaning the linear density is the same everywhere along the length of the string.

NOTE ▶ The subscript s on the symbol T_s for the string's tension distinguishes it from the symbol T for the *period* of oscillation. ◀

Equation 20.1 is the wave *speed,* not the wave velocity, so v_{string} always has a positive value. Every point on a wave travels with this speed. You can increase the wave speed either by *increasing* the string's tension (make it tighter) or by *decreasing* the string's linear density (make it skinnier). We'll examine the implications for stringed musical instruments in Chapter 21.

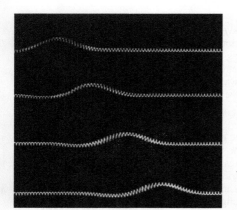

This sequence of photographs shows a wave pulse traveling along a spring.

EXAMPLE 20.1 **Measuring the linear density**

In a laboratory experiment, one end of a metal wire is connected to a motion sensor. The wire is stretched horizontally to a pulley 1.50 m away, then attached to a hanging mass that provides tension. A mechanical pick plucks the horizontal segment of the wire right at the pulley, creating a small wave pulse that travels along the wire. The plucking motion starts a timer that is stopped by the motion sensor when the pulse reaches the end of the wire. Changing the hanging mass changes the time required for the pulse to travel the length of the wire. The data are as follows:

Mass (kg)	Time (ms)
0.50	31
1.00	23
1.50	18
2.00	15
2.50	14

Use the data to determine the wire's linear density.

MODEL The wave pulse is a traveling wave on a stretched string. The hanging mass is in static equilibrium.

VISUALIZE FIGURE 20.2 is a pictorial representation.

SOLVE The wave speed on the wire is determined by the wire's linear density μ and tension T_s. The hanging mass is in static

FIGURE 20.2 A wave pulse on the wire.

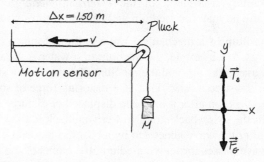

equilibrium, with no net force, so we see from the free-body diagram that the tension in the wire is $T_s = F_G = Mg$. Squaring both sides of Equation 20.1 gives

$$v^2 = \left(\frac{\Delta x}{\Delta t}\right)^2 = \frac{T_s}{\mu} = \frac{Mg}{\mu}$$

Mass M is the independent variable that we've changed, each time measuring the pulse travel time Δt, so we can rearrange the wave-speed equation as

$$(\Delta t)^2 = \frac{\mu (\Delta x)^2}{g} \frac{1}{M}$$

Theory predicts that a graph of the *square* of the travel time versus the *inverse* of the hanging mass should be a straight line passing through the origin with slope $\mu(\Delta x)^2/g$. The graph of FIGURE 20.3, with the times converted from ms to s, is indeed linear with a *y*-intercept of zero. The slope of the best-fit line is seen to be 4.85×10^{-4} kg s^2 (recall that spreadsheets and graphing calculators display this as 4.85E–04), from which we find the wire's linear density:

$$\mu = \frac{g \times \text{slope}}{(\Delta x)^2} = 0.0021 \text{ kg/m} = 2.1 \text{ g/m}$$

ASSESS A meter of thin wire is likely to have a mass of a few grams, so a linear density of a few g/m seems reasonable.

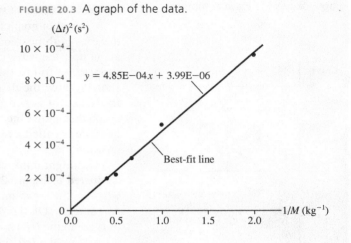

FIGURE 20.3 A graph of the data.

The wave speed on a string is a property of the string—its tension and linear density. In general, **the wave speed is a property** *of the medium.* The wave speed depends on the restoring forces within the medium but not at all on the shape or size of the pulse, how the pulse was generated, or how far it has traveled.

STOP TO THINK 20.1 Which of the following actions would make a pulse travel faster along a stretched string? More than one answer may be correct. If so, give all that are correct.

a. Move your hand up and down more quickly as you generate the pulse.
b. Move your hand up and down a larger distance as you generate the pulse.
c. Use a heavier string of the same length, under the same tension.
d. Use a lighter string of the same length, under the same tension.
e. Stretch the string tighter to increase the tension.
f. Loosen the string to decrease the tension.
g. Put more force into the wave.

20.2 One-Dimensional Waves

To understand waves we must deal with functions of *two* variables. Until now, we have been concerned with quantities that depend only on time, such as $x(t)$ or $v(t)$. Functions of the one variable t are all right for a particle because a particle is only in one place at a time, but a wave is not localized. It is spread out through space at each instant of time. To describe a wave mathematically requires a function that specifies not only an instant of time (when) but also a point in space (where).

Rather than leaping into mathematics, we will start by thinking about waves graphically. Consider the wave pulse shown moving along a stretched string in FIGURE 20.4. (We will consider somewhat artificial triangular and square-shaped pulses in this section to make clear where the edges of the pulse are.) The graph shows the string's displacement Δy at a particular instant of time t_1 as a function of position x along the string. This is a "snapshot" of the wave, much like what you might make with a camera whose shutter is opened briefly at t_1. A graph that shows the wave's displacement as a function of position at a single instant of time is called a **snapshot graph.** For a wave on a string, a snapshot graph is literally a picture of the wave at this instant.

FIGURE 20.5 shows a sequence of snapshot graphs as the wave of Figure 20.4 continues to move. These are like successive frames from a movie. Notice that the wave

FIGURE 20.4 A snapshot graph of a wave pulse on a string.

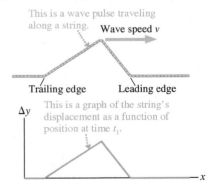

FIGURE 20.5 A sequence of snapshot graphs shows the wave in motion.

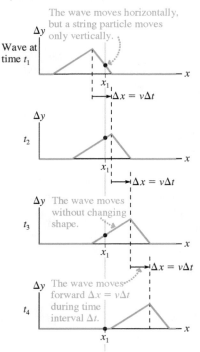

pulse moves forward distance $\Delta x = v\Delta t$ during the time interval Δt. That is, the wave moves with constant speed.

A snapshot graph tells only half the story. It tells us *where* the wave is and how it varies with position, but only at one instant of time. It gives us no information about how the wave *changes* with time. As a different way of portraying the wave, suppose we follow the dot marked on the string in Figure 20.5 and produce a graph showing how the displacement of this dot changes with time. The result, shown in FIGURE 20.6, is a displacement-versus-time graph at a single position in space. A graph that shows the wave's displacement as a function of time at a single position in space is called a **history graph.** It tells the history of that particular point in the medium.

You might think we have made a mistake; the graph of Figure 20.6 is reversed compared to Figure 20.5. It is not a mistake, but it requires careful thought to see why. As the wave moves toward the dot, the steep *leading edge* causes the dot to rise quickly. On the displacement-versus-time graph, *earlier* times (smaller values of t) are to the *left* and later times (larger t) to the right. Thus the leading edge of the wave is on the *left* side of the Figure 20.6 history graph. As you move to the right on Figure 20.6 you see the slowly falling *trailing edge* of the wave as it moves past the dot at later times.

The snapshot graph of Figure 20.4 and the history graph of Figure 20.6 portray complementary information. The snapshot graph tells us how things look throughout all of space, but at only one instant of time. The history graph tells us how things look at all times, but at only one position in space. We need them both to have the full story of the wave. An alternative representation of the wave is the series of graphs in FIGURE 20.7, where we can get a clearer sense of the wave moving forward. But graphs like these are essentially impossible to draw by hand, so it is necessary to move back and forth between snapshot graphs and history graphs.

FIGURE 20.6 A history graph for the dot on the string in Figure 20.5.

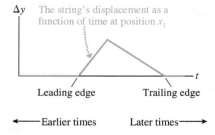

FIGURE 20.7 An alternative look at a traveling wave.

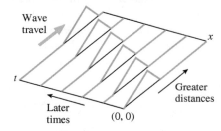

EXAMPLE 20.2 **Finding a history graph from a snapshot graph**

FIGURE 20.8 is a snapshot graph at $t = 0$ s of a wave moving to the right at a speed of 2.0 m/s. Draw a history graph for the position $x = 8.0$ m.

FIGURE 20.8 A snapshot graph at $t = 0$ s.

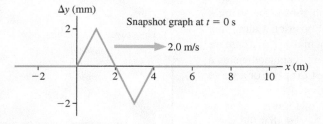

MODEL This is a wave traveling at constant speed. The pulse moves 2.0 m to the right every second.

VISUALIZE The snapshot graph of Figure 20.8 shows the wave at all points on the x-axis at $t = 0$ s. You can see that nothing is happening at $x = 8.0$ m at this instant of time because the wave has not yet reached $x = 8.0$ m. In fact, at $t = 0$ s the leading edge of the wave is still 4.0 m away from $x = 8.0$ m. Because the wave is traveling at 2.0 m/s, it will take 2.0 s for the leading edge to reach $x = 8.0$ m. Thus the history graph for $x = 8.0$ m will be zero until $t = 2.0$ s. The first part of the wave causes a *downward* displacement of the medium, so immediately after $t = 2.0$ s the displacement at $x = 8.0$ m will be negative. The negative portion of the wave pulse is 2.0 m wide and takes 1.0 s to pass $x = 8.0$ m, so the midpoint of the pulse reaches $x = 8.0$ m at $t = 3.0$ s. The positive portion takes another 1.0 s to go past, so the trailing edge of the pulse arrives at $t = 4.0$ s. You could also note that the trailing edge was initially 8.0 m away from $x = 8.0$ m and needed 4.0 s to travel that distance at 2.0 m/s. The displacement at $x = 8.0$ m returns to zero at $t = 4.0$ s and remains zero for all later times. This information is all portrayed on the history graph of FIGURE 20.9.

FIGURE 20.9 The corresponding history graph at $x = 8.0$ m.

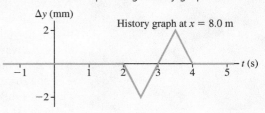

STOP TO THINK 20.2   The graph at the right is the history graph at $x = 4.0$ m of a wave traveling to the right at a speed of 2.0 m/s. Which is the history graph of this wave at $x = 0$ m?

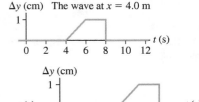

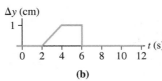

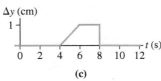

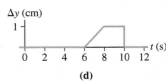

Longitudinal Waves

For a wave on a string, a transverse wave, the snapshot graph is literally a picture of the wave. Not so for a longitudinal wave, where the particles in the medium are displaced parallel to the direction in which the wave is traveling. Thus the displacement is Δx rather than Δy, and a snapshot graph is a graph of Δx versus x.

FIGURE 20.10a is a snapshot graph of a longitudinal wave, such as a sound wave. It's purposefully drawn to have the same shape as the string wave in Example 20.2. Without practice, it's not clear what this graph tells us about the particles in the medium.

FIGURE 20.10 Visualizing a longitudinal wave.

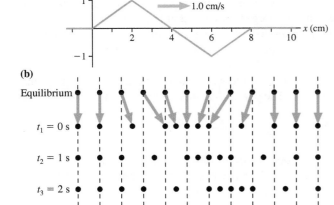

To help you find out, FIGURE 20.10b provides a tool for visualizing longitudinal waves. In the second row, we've used information from the graph to displace the particles in the medium to the right or to the left of their equilibrium positions. For example, the particle at $x = 1.0$ cm has been displaced 0.5 cm to the right because the snapshot graph shows $\Delta x = 0.5$ cm at $x = 1.0$ cm. We now have a picture of the longitudinal wave pulse at $t_1 = 0$ s. You can see that the medium is compressed to higher density at the center of the pulse and, to compensate, expanded to lower density at the leading and trailing edges. Two more lines show the medium at $t_2 = 1$ s and $t_3 = 2$ s so that you can see the wave propagating through the medium at 1.0 cm/s.

You've probably seen or participated in "the wave" at a sporting event. The wave moves around the stadium, but the people (the medium) simply undergo small displacements from their equilibrium positions.

The Displacement

A traveling wave causes the particles of the medium to be displaced from their equilibrium positions. Because one of our goals is to develop a mathematical representation to describe all types of waves, we'll use the generic symbol D to stand for the *displacement* of a wave of any type. But what do we mean by a "particle" in the medium? And what about electromagnetic waves, for which there is no medium?

For a string, where the atoms stay fixed relative to each other, you can think of either the atoms themselves or very small segments of the string as being the particles of the medium. D is then the perpendicular displacement Δy of a point on the string. For a sound wave, D is the longitudinal displacement Δx of a small volume of fluid. For any other mechanical wave, D is the appropriate displacement. Even electromagnetic waves can be described within the same mathematical representation if D is interpreted as a yet-undefined *electromagnetic field strength*, a "displacement" in a more abstract sense as an electromagnetic wave passes through a region of space.

Because the displacement of a particle in the medium depends both on *where* the particle is (position x) and on *when* you observe it (time t), D must be a function of the two variables x and t. That is,

$D(x, t)$ = the displacement at time t of a particle at position x

The values of *both* variables—where and when—must be specified before you can evaluate the displacement D.

20.3 Sinusoidal Waves

A wave source that oscillates with simple harmonic motion (SHM) generates a **sinusoidal wave.** For example, a loudspeaker cone that oscillates in SHM radiates a sinusoidal sound wave. The sinusoidal electromagnetic waves broadcast by television and FM radio stations are generated by electrons oscillating back and forth in the antenna wire with SHM. **The frequency f of the wave is the frequency of the oscillating source.**

FIGURE 20.11 shows a sinusoidal wave moving through a medium. The source of the wave, which is undergoing vertical SHM, is located at $x = 0$. Notice how the wave crests move with steady speed toward larger values of x at later times t.

FIGURE 20.12a is a history graph for a sinusoidal wave, showing the displacement of the medium at one point in space. Each particle in the medium undergoes simple harmonic motion with frequency f, so this graph of SHM is identical to the graphs you learned to work with in Chapter 14. The *period* of the wave, shown on the graph, is the time interval for one cycle of the motion. The period is related to the wave frequency f by

$$T = \frac{1}{f} \tag{20.3}$$

exactly as in simple harmonic motion. The **amplitude** A of the wave is the maximum value of the displacement. The crests of the wave have displacement $D_{\text{crest}} = A$ and the troughs have displacement $D_{\text{trough}} = -A$.

FIGURE 20.11 A sinusoidal wave moving along the *x*-axis.

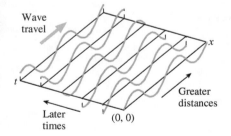

FIGURE 20.12 History and snapshot graphs for a sinusoidal wave.

(a) A history graph at one point in space

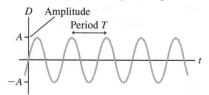

(b) A snapshot graph at one instant of time

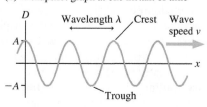

Displacement versus time is only half the story. FIGURE 20.12b shows a snapshot graph for the same wave at one instant in time. Here we see the wave stretched out in space, moving to the right with speed v. An important characteristic of a sinusoidal wave is that it is periodic *in space* as well as in time. As you move from left to right along the "frozen" wave in the snapshot graph, the disturbance repeats itself over and over. The distance spanned by one cycle of the motion is called the **wavelength** of the wave. Wavelength is symbolized by λ (lowercase Greek lambda) and, because it is a length, it is measured in units of meters. The wavelength is shown in Figure 20.12b as the distance between two crests, but it could equally well be the distance between two troughs.

NOTE ▶ Wavelength is the spatial analog of period. The period T is the *time* in which the disturbance at a single point in space repeats itself. The wavelength λ is the *distance* in which the disturbance at one instant of time repeats itself. ◀

The Fundamental Relationship for Sinusoidal Waves

There is an important relationship between the wavelength and the period of a wave. FIGURE 20.13 shows this relationship through five snapshot graphs of a sinusoidal wave at time increments of one-quarter of the period T. One full period has elapsed between the first graph and the last, which you can see by observing the motion at a fixed point on the x-axis. Each point in the medium has undergone exactly one complete oscillation.

The critical observation is that the wave crest marked by an arrow has moved one full wavelength between the first graph and the last. That is, **during a time interval of exactly one period T, each crest of a sinusoidal wave travels forward a distance of exactly one wavelength λ.** Because speed is distance divided by time, the wave speed must be

$$v = \frac{\text{distance}}{\text{time}} = \frac{\lambda}{T} \qquad (20.4)$$

Because $f = 1/T$, it is customary to write Equation 20.4 in the form

$$v = \lambda f \qquad (20.5)$$

Although Equation 20.5 has no special name, it is *the* fundamental relationship for periodic waves. When using it, keep in mind the *physical* meaning that **a wave moves forward a distance of one wavelength during a time interval of one period.**

NOTE ▶ Wavelength and period are defined only for *periodic* waves, so Equations 20.4 and 20.5 apply only to periodic waves. A wave pulse has a wave speed, but it doesn't have a wavelength or a period. Hence Equations 20.4 and 20.5 cannot be applied to wave pulses. ◀

Because the wave speed is a property of the medium while the wave frequency is a property of the source, it is often useful to write Equation 20.5 as

$$\lambda = \frac{v}{f} = \frac{\text{property of the medium}}{\text{property of the source}} \qquad (20.6)$$

The wavelength is a *consequence* of a wave of frequency f traveling through a medium in which the wave speed is v.

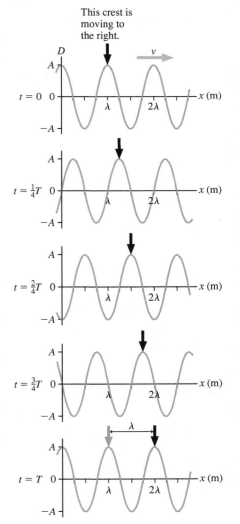

FIGURE 20.13 A series of snapshot graphs at time increments of one-quarter of the period T.

During a time interval of exactly one period, the crest has moved forward exactly one wavelength.

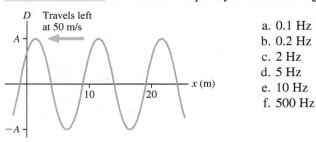

STOP TO THINK 20.3   What is the frequency of this traveling wave?

a. 0.1 Hz
b. 0.2 Hz
c. 2 Hz
d. 5 Hz
e. 10 Hz
f. 500 Hz

The Mathematics of Sinusoidal Waves

FIGURE 20.14 A sinusoidal wave is "frozen" at $t = 0$.

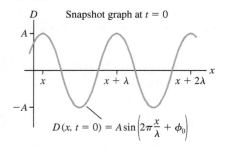

$$D(x, t = 0) = A \sin\left(2\pi \frac{x}{\lambda} + \phi_0\right)$$

FIGURE 20.14 shows a snapshot graph at $t = 0$ of a sinusoidal wave. The sinusoidal function that describes the displacement of this wave is

$$D(x, t = 0) = A \sin\left(2\pi \frac{x}{\lambda} + \phi_0\right) \tag{20.7}$$

where the notation $D(x, t = 0)$ means that we've frozen the time at $t = 0$ to make the displacement a function of only x. The term ϕ_0 is a *phase constant* that characterizes the initial conditions. (We'll return to the phase constant momentarily.)

The function of Equation 20.7 is periodic with period λ. We can see this by writing

$$D(x + \lambda) = A \sin\left(2\pi \frac{(x + \lambda)}{\lambda} + \phi_0\right) = A \sin\left(2\pi \frac{x}{\lambda} + \phi_0 + 2\pi \text{ rad}\right)$$

$$= A \sin\left(2\pi \frac{x}{\lambda} + \phi_0\right) = D(x)$$

where we used the fact that $\sin(a + 2\pi \text{ rad}) = \sin a$. In other words, the disturbance created by the wave at $x + \lambda$ is exactly the same as the disturbance at x.

The next step—and it's an important step to graph—is to set the wave in motion. We can do this by replacing x in Equation 20.7 with $x - vt$. To see why this works, recall that the wave moves distance vt during time t. In other words, whatever displacement the wave has at position x at time t, the wave must have had that same displacement at position $x - vt$ at the earlier time $t = 0$. Mathematically, this idea can be captured by writing

$$D(x, t) = D(x - vt, t = 0) \tag{20.8}$$

Make sure you understand how this statement describes a wave moving in the positive x-direction at speed v.

This is what we were looking for. $D(x, t)$ is the general function describing the traveling wave. It's found by taking the function that describes the wave at $t = 0$—the function of Equation 20.7—and replacing x with $x - vt$. Thus the displacement equation of a sinusoidal wave traveling in the positive x-direction at speed v is

$$D(x, t) = A \sin\left(2\pi \frac{x - vt}{\lambda} + \phi_0\right) = A \sin\left(2\pi \left(\frac{x}{\lambda} - \frac{t}{T}\right) + \phi_0\right) \tag{20.9}$$

In the last step we used $v = \lambda f = \lambda/T$ to write $v/\lambda = 1/T$. The function of Equation 20.9 is not only periodic in space with period λ, it is also periodic in time with period T. That is, $D(x, t + T) = D(x, t)$.

It will be useful to introduce two new quantities. First, recall from simple harmonic motion the *angular frequency*

$$\omega = 2\pi f = \frac{2\pi}{T} \tag{20.10}$$

The units of ω are rad/s, although many textbooks use simply s^{-1}.

You can see that ω is 2π times the reciprocal of the period in time. This suggests that we define an analogous quantity, called the **wave number** k, that is 2π times the reciprocal of the period in space:

$$k = \frac{2\pi}{\lambda} \tag{20.11}$$

The units of k are rad/m, although many textbooks use simply m^{-1}.

NOTE ▶ The wave number k is *not* a spring constant, even though it uses the same symbol. This is a most unfortunate use of symbols, but every major textbook and professional tradition uses the same symbol k for these two very different meanings, so we have little choice but to follow along. ◀

We can use the fundamental relationship $v = \lambda f$ to find an analogous relationship between ω and k:

$$v = \lambda f = \frac{2\pi}{k}\frac{\omega}{2\pi} = \frac{\omega}{k} \tag{20.12}$$

which is usually written

$$\omega = vk \tag{20.13}$$

Equation 20.13 contains no new information. It is a variation of Equation 20.5, but one that is convenient when working with k and ω.

If we use the definitions of Equations 20.10 and 20.11, Equation 20.9 for the displacement can be written

$$D(x, t) = A\sin(kx - \omega t + \phi_0) \tag{20.14}$$
(sinusoidal wave traveling in the positive x-direction)

A sinusoidal wave traveling in the negative x-direction is $A\sin(kx + \omega t + \phi_0)$. Equation 20.14 is graphed versus x and t in FIGURE 20.15.

Just as it did for simple harmonic motion, the phase constant ϕ_0 characterizes the initial conditions. At $(x, t) = (0\text{ m}, 0\text{ s})$ Equation 20.14 becomes

$$D(0\text{ m}, 0\text{ s}) = A\sin\phi \tag{20.15}$$

Different values of ϕ_0 describe different initial conditions for the wave.

FIGURE 20.15 Interpreting the equation of a sinusoidal traveling wave.

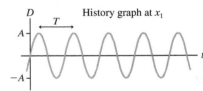

If x is fixed, $D(x_1, t) = A\sin(kx_1 - \omega t + \phi_0)$ gives a sinusoidal history graph at one point in space, x_1. It repeats every T s.

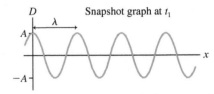

If t is fixed, $D(x, t_1) = A\sin(kx - \omega t_1 + \phi_0)$ gives a sinusoidal snapshot graph at one instant of time, t_1. It repeats every λ m.

EXAMPLE 20.3 **Analyzing a sinusoidal wave**

A sinusoidal wave with an amplitude of 1.00 cm and a frequency of 100 Hz travels at 200 m/s in the positive x-direction. At $t = 0$ s, the point $x = 1.00$ m is on a crest of the wave.

a. Determine the values of A, v, λ, k, f, ω, T, and ϕ_0 for this wave.
b. Write the equation for the wave's displacement as it travels.
c. Draw a snapshot graph of the wave at $t = 0$ s.

VISUALIZE The snapshot graph will be sinusoidal, but we must do some numerical analysis before we know how to draw it.

SOLVE a. There are several numerical values associated with a sinusoidal traveling wave, but they are not all independent. From the problem statement itself we learn that

$$A = 1.00\text{ cm} \qquad v = 200\text{ m/s} \qquad f = 100\text{ Hz}$$

We can then find:

$$\lambda = v/f = 2.00\text{ m}$$

$$k = 2\pi/\lambda = \pi\text{ rad/m or } 3.14\text{ rad/m}$$

Continued

$$\omega = 2\pi f = 628 \text{ rad/s}$$

$$T = 1/f = 0.0100 \text{ s} = 10.0 \text{ ms}$$

The phase constant ϕ_0 is determined by the initial conditions. We know that a wave crest, with displacement $D = A$, is passing $x_0 = 1.00$ m at $t_0 = 0$ s. Equation 20.14 at x_0 and t_0 is

$$D(x_0, t_0) = A = A \sin\left(k(1.00 \text{ m}) + \phi_0\right)$$

This equation is true only if $\sin\left(k(1.00 \text{ m}) + \phi_0\right) = 1$, which requires

$$k(1.00 \text{ m}) + \phi_0 = \frac{\pi}{2} \text{ rad}$$

Solving for the phase constant gives

$$\phi_0 = \frac{\pi}{2} \text{ rad} - (\pi \text{ rad/m})(1.00 \text{ m}) = -\frac{\pi}{2} \text{ rad}$$

b. With the information gleaned from part a, the wave's displacement is

$$D(x, t) = 1.00 \text{ cm} \times$$

$$\sin\left[(3.14 \text{ rad/m})x - (628 \text{ rad/s})t - \pi/2 \text{ rad}\right]$$

Notice that we included units with A, k, ω, and ϕ_0.

c. We know that $x = 1.00$ m is a wave crest at $t = 0$ s and that the wavelength is $\lambda = 2.00$ m. Because the origin is $\lambda/2$ away from the crest at $x = 1.00$ m, we expect to find a wave trough at $x = 0$. This is confirmed by calculating $D(0 \text{ m}, 0 \text{ s}) = (1.00 \text{ cm}) \sin(-\pi/2 \text{ rad}) = -1.00$ cm. FIGURE 20.16 is a snapshot graph that portrays this information.

FIGURE 20.16 A snapshot graph at $t = 0$ s of the sinusoidal wave of Example 20.3.

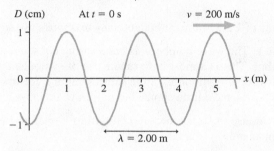

Wave Motion on a String

The displacement equation, Equation 20.14, allows us to learn more about wave motion on a string. As a wave travels along the x-axis, the points on the string oscillate back and forth in the y-direction. The displacement D of a point on the string is simply that point's y-coordinate, so Equation 20.14 for a string wave is

$$y(x, t) = A \sin(kx - \omega t + \phi_0) \tag{20.16}$$

The velocity of a particle on the string—**which is not the same as the velocity of the wave along the string**—is the time derivative of Equation 20.16:

$$v_y = \frac{dy}{dt} = -\omega A \cos(kx - \omega t + \phi_0) \tag{20.17}$$

The maximum velocity of a small segment of the string is $v_{\text{max}} = \omega A$. This is the same result we found for simple harmonic motion because the motion of the string particles is simple harmonic motion. FIGURE 20.17 shows velocity vectors *of the particles* at different points on a sinusoidal wave.

NOTE ▶ Creating a wave of larger amplitude increases the speed of particles in the medium, but it does *not* change the speed of the wave *through* the medium. ◀

Pursuing this line of thought, we can derive an expression for the wave speed along the string. FIGURE 20.18 shows a small segment of the string with length $\Delta x \ll \lambda$ right at a crest of the wave. You can see that the string's tension exerts a downward force on this piece of the string, pulling it back to equilibrium. Newton's second law for this small segment of string is

$$(F_{\text{net}})_y = ma_y = (\mu \Delta x)a_y \tag{20.18}$$

where we used the string's linear density μ to write the mass as $m = \mu \Delta x$.

FIGURE 20.17 A snapshot graph of a wave on a string with vectors showing the velocity *of the string* at various points.

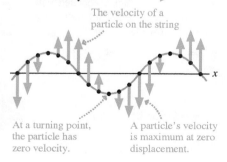

The velocity of the wave ⟶

The velocity of a particle on the string

At a turning point, the particle has zero velocity.

A particle's velocity is maximum at zero displacement.

From simple harmonic motion, we know that this point of maximum displacement is also the point of maximum acceleration. The acceleration of a point on the string is the time derivative of Equation 20.17:

$$a_y = \frac{dv_y}{dt} = -\omega^2 A \sin(kx - \omega t + \phi_0) \tag{20.19}$$

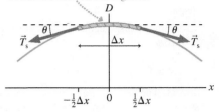

FIGURE 20.18 A small segment of string at the crest of a wave.

A small segment of the string at the crest of the wave. Because of the curvature of the string, the tension forces exert a net downward force on this segment.

Thus the acceleration at the crest of the wave is $a_y = -\omega^2 A$. But the angular frequency ω with which the particles of the string oscillate is related to the wave's speed v along the string by Equation 20.13, $\omega = vk$. Thus

$$a_y = -\omega^2 A = -v^2 k^2 A \tag{20.20}$$

A large wave speed causes the particles of the string to oscillate more quickly and thus to have a larger acceleration.

You can see from Figure 20.18 that the y-component of the tension is $T_s \sin\theta$, where θ is the angle of the string at $x = \frac{1}{2}\Delta x$. θ is a *negative* angle because it is below the x-axis. This segment of string is pulled from both ends, so

$$(F_{\text{net}})_y = 2T_s \sin\theta \tag{20.21}$$

The angle θ is very small because $\Delta x \ll \lambda$, so we can use the small-angle approximation ($\sin u \approx \tan u$ if $u \ll 1$) to write

$$(F_{\text{net}})_y \approx 2T_s \tan\theta \tag{20.22}$$

where $\tan\theta$ is the slope of the string at $x = \frac{1}{2}\Delta x$.

At this specific instant, with the crest of the wave at $x = 0$, the equation of the string is

$$y = A\cos(kx)$$

The slope of the string at $x = \frac{1}{2}\Delta x$ is the derivative evaluated at that point:

$$\tan\theta = \frac{dy}{dx}\bigg|_{\text{at } \Delta x/2} = -kA\sin(kx)\big|_{\text{at } \Delta x/2} = -kA\sin\left(\frac{k\Delta x}{2}\right)$$

Now $\Delta x \ll \lambda$, so $k\Delta x/2 = \pi\Delta x/\lambda \ll 1$. Thus the small-angle approximation ($\sin u \approx u$ if $u \ll 1$) of the slope is

$$\tan\theta \approx -kA\left(\frac{k\Delta x}{2}\right) = -\frac{k^2 A \Delta x}{2} \tag{20.23}$$

If we substitute this expression for $\tan\theta$ into Equation 20.22, we find that the net force on this little piece of string is

$$(F_{\text{net}})_y = -k^2 A T_s \Delta x \tag{20.24}$$

Now we can use Equation 20.20 for a_y and Equation 20.24 for $(F_{\text{net}})_y$ in Newton's second law. With these substitutions, Equation 20.18 becomes

$$(F_{\text{net}})_y = -k^2 A T_s \Delta x = (\mu\Delta x)a_y = -v^2 k^2 A\mu\Delta x \tag{20.25}$$

The term $-k^2 A\Delta x$ cancels, and we're left with

$$v = \sqrt{\frac{T_s}{\mu}} \tag{20.26}$$

This was the result that we stated, without proof, in Equation 20.1. Although we've derived Equation 20.26 with the assumption of a sinusoidal wave, the wave speed does not depend on the shape of the wave. Thus any wave on a stretched string will have this wave speed.

EXAMPLE 20.4 **Generating a sinusoidal wave**

A very long string with $\mu = 2.0$ g/m is stretched along the x-axis with a tension of 5.0 N. At $x = 0$ m it is tied to a 100 Hz simple harmonic oscillator that vibrates perpendicular to the string with an amplitude of 2.0 mm. The oscillator is at its maximum positive displacement at $t = 0$ s.

a. Write the displacement equation for the traveling wave on the string.
b. At $t = 5.0$ ms, what is the string's displacement at a point 2.7 m from the oscillator?

MODEL The oscillator generates a sinusoidal traveling wave on a string. The displacement of the wave has to match the displacement of the oscillator at $x = 0$ m.

SOLVE a. The equation for the displacement is

$$D(x, t) = A \sin(kx - \omega t + \phi_0)$$

with A, k, ω, and ϕ_0 to be determined. The wave amplitude is the same as the amplitude of the oscillator that generates the wave, so $A = 2.0$ mm. The oscillator has its maximum displacement $y_{\text{osc}} = A = 2.0$ mm at $t = 0$ s, thus

$$D(0 \text{ m}, 0 \text{ s}) = A \sin(\phi_0) = A$$

This requires the phase constant to be $\phi_0 = \pi/2$ rad. The wave's frequency is $f = 100$ Hz, the frequency of the source;

therefore the angular frequency is $\omega = 2\pi f = 200\pi$ rad/s. We still need $k = 2\pi/\lambda$, but we do not know the wavelength. However, we have enough information to determine the wave speed, and we can then use either $\lambda = v/f$ or $k = \omega/v$. The speed is

$$v = \sqrt{\frac{T_s}{\mu}} = \sqrt{\frac{5.0 \text{ N}}{0.0020 \text{ kg/m}}} = 50 \text{ m/s}$$

Using v, we find $\lambda = 0.50$ m and $k = 2\pi/\lambda = 4\pi$ rad/m. Thus the wave's displacement equation is

$$D(x, t) = (2.0 \text{ mm}) \times$$
$$\sin\left[2\pi\left((2.0 \text{ m}^{-1})x - (100 \text{ s}^{-1})t\right) + \pi/2 \text{ rad}\right]$$

Notice that we have separated out the 2π. This step is not essential, but for some problems it makes subsequent steps easier.

b. The wave's displacement at $t = 5.0$ ms $= 0.0050$ s is

$$D(x, t = 5.0 \text{ ms}) = (2.0 \text{ mm}) \sin(4\pi x - \pi \text{ rad} + \pi/2 \text{ rad})$$
$$= (2.0 \text{ mm}) \sin(4\pi x - \pi/2 \text{ rad})$$

At $x = 2.7$ m (calculator set to radians!), the displacement is

$$D(2.7 \text{ m}, 5.0 \text{ ms}) = 1.6 \text{ mm}$$

20.4 Waves in Two and Three Dimensions

Suppose you were to take a photograph of ripples spreading on a pond. If you mark the location of the *crests* on the photo, your picture would look like FIGURE 20.19a. The lines that locate the crests are called **wave fronts,** and they are spaced precisely one wavelength apart. The diagram shows only a single instant of time, but you can imagine a movie in which you would see the wave fronts moving outward from the source at speed v. A wave like this is called a **circular wave.** It is a two-dimensional wave that spreads across a surface.

Although the wave fronts are circles, you would hardly notice the curvature if you observed a small section of the wave front very, very far away from the source. The wave fronts would appear to be parallel lines, still spaced one wavelength apart and traveling at speed v. A good example is an ocean wave reaching a beach. Ocean waves are generated by storms and wind far out at sea, hundreds or thousands of miles away. By the time they reach the beach where you are working on your tan, the crests appear to be straight lines. An aerial view of the ocean would show a wave diagram like FIGURE 20.19b.

Many waves of interest, such as sound waves or light waves, move in three dimensions. For example, loudspeakers and lightbulbs emit **spherical waves.** That is, the crests of the wave form a series of concentric spherical shells separated by the wavelength λ. In essence, the waves are three-dimensional ripples. It will still be useful to draw wave-front diagrams such as Figure 20.19, but now the circles are slices through the spherical shells locating the wave crests.

If you observe a spherical wave very, very far from its source, the small piece of the wave front that you can see is a little patch on the surface of a very large sphere. If the radius of the sphere is sufficiently large, you will not notice the curvature and this little patch of the wave front appears to be a plane. FIGURE 20.20 illustrates the idea of a **plane wave.**

FIGURE 20.19 The wave fronts of a circular or spherical wave.

(a)

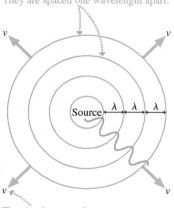

Wave fronts are the crests of the wave. They are spaced one wavelength apart.

The circular wave fronts move outward from the source at speed v.

(b)

Very far away from the source, small sections of the wave fronts appear to be straight lines.

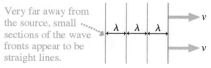

To visualize a plane wave, imagine standing on the *x*-axis facing a sound wave as it comes toward you from a very distant loudspeaker. Sound is a longitudinal wave, so the particles of medium oscillate toward you and away from you. If you were to locate all of the particles that, at one instant of time, were at their maximum displacement toward you, they would all be located in a plane perpendicular to the travel direction. This is one of the wave fronts in Figure 20.20, and all the particles in this plane are doing exactly the same thing at that instant of time. This plane is moving toward you at speed *v*. There is another plane one wavelength behind it where the molecules are also at maximum displacement, yet another two wavelengths behind the first, and so on.

Because a plane wave's displacement depends on *x* but not on *y* or *z*, the displacement function $D(x, t)$ describes a plane wave just as readily as it does a one-dimensional wave. Once you specify a value for *x*, the displacement is the same at every point in the *yz*-plane that slices the *x*-axis at that value (i.e., one of the planes shown in Figure 20.20).

NOTE ▶ There are no perfect plane waves in nature, but many waves of practical interest can be modeled as plane waves. ◀

We can describe a circular wave or a spherical wave by changing the mathematical description from $D(x, t)$ to $D(r, t)$, where *r* is the radial distance measured outward from the source. Then the displacement of the medium will be the same at every point on a spherical surface. In particular, a sinusoidal spherical wave with wave number *k* and angular frequency ω is written

$$D(r, t) = A(r)\sin(kr - \omega t + \phi_0) \tag{20.27}$$

Other than the change of *x* to *r*, the only difference is that the amplitude is now a function of *r*. A one-dimensional wave propagates with no change in the wave amplitude. But circular and spherical waves spread out to fill larger and larger volumes of space. To conserve energy, an issue we'll look at later in the chapter, the wave's amplitude has to decrease with increasing distance *r*. This is why sound and light decrease in intensity as you get farther from the source. We don't need to specify exactly how the amplitude decreases with distance, but you should be aware that it does.

Phase and Phase Difference

The quantity $(kx - \omega t + \phi_0)$ is called the **phase** of the wave, denoted ϕ. The phase of a wave will be an important concept in Chapters 21 and 22, where we will explore the consequences of adding various waves together. For now, we can note that the wave fronts seen in Figures 20.19 and 20.20 are "surfaces of constant phase." To see this, use the phase to write the displacement as simply $D(x, t) = A\sin\phi$. Because each point on a wave front has the same displacement, the phase must be the same at every point.

It will be useful to know the *phase difference* $\Delta\phi$ between two different points on a sinusoidal wave. FIGURE 20.21 shows two points on a sinusoidal wave at time *t*. The phase difference between these points is

$$\Delta\phi = \phi_2 - \phi_1 = (kx_2 - \omega t + \phi_0) - (kx_1 - \omega t + \phi_0)$$
$$= k(x_2 - x_1) = k\Delta x = 2\pi\frac{\Delta x}{\lambda} \tag{20.28}$$

That is, **the phase difference between two points on a wave depends on only the ratio of their separation Δx to the wavelength λ.** For example, two points on a wave separated by $\Delta x = \frac{1}{2}\lambda$ have a phase difference $\Delta\phi = \pi$ rad.

An important consequence of Equation 20.28 is that **the phase difference between two adjacent wave fronts is $\Delta\phi = 2\pi$ rad.** This follows from the fact that two adjacent wave fronts are separated by $\Delta x = \lambda$. This is an important idea. Moving from one crest of the wave to the next corresponds to changing the *distance* by λ and changing the *phase* by 2π rad.

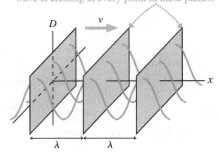

FIGURE 20.20 A plane wave.

Very far from the source, small segments of spherical wave fronts appear to be planes. The wave is cresting at every point in these planes.

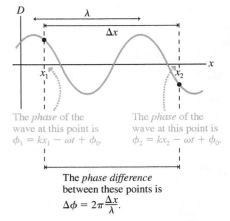

FIGURE 20.21 The phase difference between two points on a wave.

The *phase* of the wave at this point is $\phi_1 = kx_1 - \omega t + \phi_0$.

The *phase* of the wave at this point is $\phi_2 = kx_2 - \omega t + \phi_0$.

The *phase difference* between these points is $\Delta\phi = 2\pi\frac{\Delta x}{\lambda}$.

EXAMPLE 20.5   **The phase difference between two points on a sound wave**

A 100 Hz sound wave travels with a wave speed of 343 m/s.

a. What is the phase difference between two points 60.0 cm apart along the direction the wave is traveling?

b. How far apart are two points whose phase differs by 90°?

MODEL Treat the wave as a plane wave traveling in the positive x-direction.

SOLVE a. The phase difference between two points is

$$\Delta\phi = 2\pi\frac{\Delta x}{\lambda}$$

In this case, $\Delta x = 60.0$ cm $= 0.600$ m. The wavelength is

$$\lambda = \frac{v}{f} = \frac{343 \text{ m/s}}{100 \text{ Hz}} = 3.43 \text{ m}$$

and thus

$$\Delta\phi = 2\pi\frac{0.600 \text{ m}}{3.43 \text{ m}} = 0.350\pi \text{ rad} = 63.0°$$

b. A phase difference $\Delta\phi = 90°$ is $\pi/2$ rad. This will be the phase difference between two points when $\Delta x/\lambda = \frac{1}{4}$, or when $\Delta x = \lambda/4$. Here, with $\lambda = 3.43$ m, $\Delta x = 85.8$ cm.

ASSESS The phase difference increases as Δx increases, so we expect the answer to part b to be larger than 60 cm.

STOP TO THINK 20.4 What is the phase difference between the crest of a wave and the adjacent trough?

a. -2π rad   b. 0 rad   c. $\pi/4$ rad

d. $\pi/2$ rad   e. π rad   f. 3π rad

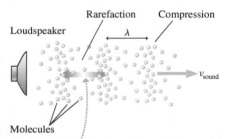

FIGURE 20.22 A sound wave in a fluid is a sequence of compressions and rarefactions. The variation in density and the amount of motion have been greatly exaggerated.

Individual molecules oscillate back and forth with displacement D. As they do so, the compressions propagate forward at speed v_{sound}. Because compressions are regions of higher pressure, a sound wave can be thought of as a pressure wave.

TABLE 20.1 The speed of sound

Medium	Speed (m/s)
Air (0°C)	331
Air (20°C)	343
Helium (0°C)	970
Ethyl alcohol	1170
Water	1480
Granite	6000
Aluminum	6420

20.5 Sound and Light

Although there are many kinds of waves in nature, two are especially significant for us as humans. These are sound waves and light waves, the basis of hearing and seeing.

Sound Waves

We usually think of sound waves traveling in air, but sound can travel through any gas, through liquids, and even through solids. FIGURE 20.22 shows a loudspeaker cone vibrating back and forth in a fluid such as air or water. Each time the cone moves forward, it collides with the molecules and pushes them closer together. A half cycle later, as the cone moves backward, the fluid has room to expand and the density decreases a little. These regions of higher and lower density (and thus higher and lower pressure) are called **compressions** and **rarefactions.**

This periodic sequence of compressions and rarefactions travels outward from the loudspeaker as a longitudinal sound wave. When the wave reaches your ear, the oscillating pressure causes your eardrum to vibrate. These vibrations are transferred into your inner ear and perceived as sound.

Your ears are able to detect sinusoidal sound waves with frequencies between about 20 Hz and about 20,000 Hz, or 20 kHz. Low frequencies are perceived as "low pitch" bass notes, while high frequencies are heard as "high pitch" treble notes. Your high-frequency range of hearing can deteriorate either with age or as a result of exposure to loud sounds that damage the ear.

The speed of sound waves depends on the properties of the medium. A thermodynamic analysis of the compressions and expansions shows that the wave speed in a gas depends on the temperature and on the molecular mass of the gas. For air at room temperature (20°C),

$$v_{\text{sound}} = 343 \text{ m/s} \qquad \text{(sound speed in air at 20°C)}$$

The speed of sound is a little lower at lower temperatures and a little higher at higher temperatures. Liquids and solids are less compressible than air, and that makes the speed of sound in those media higher than in air. Table 20.1 gives the speed of sound in several substances.

A speed of 343 m/s is high, but not extraordinarily so. A distance as small as 100 m is enough to notice a slight delay between when you see something, such as a person hammering a nail, and when you hear it. The time required for sound to travel 1 km is $t = (1000 \text{ m})/(343 \text{ m/s}) \approx 3$ s. You may have learned to estimate the distance to a bolt of lightning by timing the number of seconds between when you see the flash and when you hear the thunder. Because sound takes 3 s to travel 1 km, the time divided by 3 gives the distance in kilometers. Or, in English units, the time divided by 5 gives the distance in miles.

Sound waves exist at frequencies well above 20 kHz, even though humans can't hear them. These are called *ultrasonic* frequencies. Oscillators vibrating at frequencies of many MHz generate the ultrasonic waves used in ultrasound medical imaging. A 3 MHz wave traveling through water (which is basically what your body is) at a sound speed of 1480 m/s has a wavelength of about 0.5 mm. It is this very small wavelength that allows ultrasound to image very small objects. We'll see why when we study *diffraction* in Chapter 22.

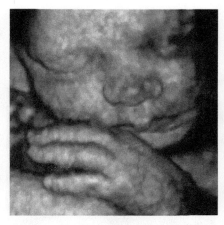

This ultrasound image is an example of using high-frequency sound waves to "see" within the human body.

EXAMPLE 20.6 **Sound wavelengths**

What are the wavelengths of sound waves at the limits of human hearing and at the midrange frequency of 500 Hz? Notes sung by human voices are near 500 Hz, as are notes played by striking keys near the center of a piano keyboard.

MODEL Assume a room temperature of 20°C.

SOLVE We can use the fundamental relationship $\lambda = v/f$ to find the wavelengths for sounds of various frequencies:

$$f = 20 \text{ Hz} \qquad \lambda = \frac{343 \text{ m/s}}{20 \text{ Hz}} = 17 \text{ m}$$

$$f = 500 \text{ Hz} \qquad \lambda = \frac{343 \text{ m/s}}{500 \text{ Hz}} = 0.69 \text{ m}$$

$$f = 20{,}000 \text{ Hz} \qquad \lambda = \frac{343 \text{ m/s}}{20{,}000 \text{ Hz}} = 0.017 \text{ m} = 1.7 \text{ cm}$$

ASSESS The wavelength of a 20 kHz note is a small 1.7 cm while, at the other extreme, a 20 Hz note has a huge wavelength of 17 m! This is because a wave moves forward one wavelength during a time interval of one period, and a wave traveling at 343 m/s can move 17 m during the $\frac{1}{20}$ s period of a 20 Hz note. The 69 cm wavelength of a 500 Hz note is more of a "human scale." You might note that most musical instruments are a meter or a little less in size. This is not a coincidence. You will see in the next chapter how the wavelength produced by a musical instrument is related to its size.

Electromagnetic Waves

A light wave is an *electromagnetic wave,* an oscillation of the electromagnetic field. Other electromagnetic waves, such as radio waves, microwaves, and ultraviolet light, have the same physical characteristics as light waves even though we cannot sense them with our eyes. It is easy to demonstrate that light will pass unaffected through a container from which all the air has been removed, and light reaches us from distant stars through the vacuum of interstellar space. Such observations raise interesting but difficult questions. If light can travel through a region in which there is no matter, then what is the *medium* of a light wave? What is it that is waving?

It took scientists over 50 years, most of the 19th century, to answer this question. We will examine the answers in more detail in Part IV after we introduce the ideas of electric and magnetic fields. For now we can say that light waves are a "self-sustaining oscillation of the electromagnetic field." That is, the displacement D is an electric or magnetic field. Being self-sustaining means that electromagnetic waves require *no material medium* in order to travel; hence electromagnetic waves are not mechanical waves. Fortunately, we can learn about the wave properties of light without having to understand electromagnetic fields.

It was predicted theoretically in the late 19th century, and has been subsequently confirmed, that all electromagnetic waves travel through vacuum with the same speed, called the *speed of light.* The value of the speed of light is

$$v_{\text{light}} = c = 299{,}792{,}458 \text{ m/s} \qquad \text{(electromagnetic wave speed in vacuum)}$$

where the special symbol c is used to designate the speed of light. (This is the c in Einstein's famous formula $E = mc^2$.) Now *this* is really moving—about one million times faster than the speed of sound in air!

NOTE ▶ $c = 3.00 \times 10^8$ m/s is the appropriate value to use in calculations. ◀

White light passing through a prism is spread out into a band of colors called the *visible spectrum.*

The wavelengths of light are extremely small. You will learn in Chapter 22 how these wavelengths are determined, but for now we will note that visible light is an electromagnetic wave with a wavelength (in air) in the range of roughly 400 nm (400×10^{-9} m) to 700 nm (700×10^{-9} m). Each wavelength is perceived as a different color, with the longer wavelengths seen as orange or red light and the shorter wavelengths seen as blue or violet light. A prism is able to spread the different wavelengths apart, from which we learn that "white light" is all the colors, or wavelengths, combined. The spread of colors seen with a prism, or seen in a rainbow, is called the *visible spectrum.*

If the wavelengths of light are unbelievably small, the oscillation frequencies are unbelievably large. The frequency for a 600 nm wavelength of light (orange) is

$$f = \frac{v}{\lambda} = \frac{3.00 \times 10^8 \text{ m/s}}{600 \times 10^{-9} \text{ m}} = 5.00 \times 10^{14} \text{ Hz}$$

The frequencies of light waves are roughly a factor of a trillion (10^{12}) higher than sound frequencies.

Electromagnetic waves exist at many frequencies other than the rather limited range that our eyes detect. One of the major technological advances of the 20th century was learning to generate and detect electromagnetic waves at many frequencies, ranging from low-frequency radio waves to the extraordinarily high frequencies of x rays. FIGURE 20.23 shows that the visible spectrum is a small slice of the much broader **electromagnetic spectrum.**

FIGURE 20.23 The electromagnetic spectrum from 10^6 Hz to 10^{18} Hz.

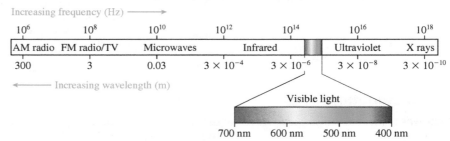

EXAMPLE 20.7 Traveling at the speed of light

A satellite exploring Jupiter transmits data to the earth as a radio wave with a frequency of 200 MHz. What is the wavelength of the electromagnetic wave, and how long does it take the signal to travel 800 million kilometers from Jupiter to the earth?

SOLVE Radio waves are sinusoidal electromagnetic waves traveling with speed c. Thus

$$\lambda = \frac{c}{f} = \frac{3.00 \times 10^8 \text{ m/s}}{2.00 \times 10^8 \text{ Hz}} = 1.5 \text{ m}$$

The time needed to travel 800×10^6 km $= 8.0 \times 10^{11}$ m is

$$\Delta t = \frac{\Delta x}{c} = \frac{8.0 \times 10^{11} \text{ m}}{3.00 \times 10^8 \text{ m/s}} = 2700 \text{ s} = 45 \text{ min}$$

The Index of Refraction

Light waves travel with speed c in a vacuum, but they slow down as they pass through transparent materials such as water or glass or even, to a very slight extent, air. The slowdown is a consequence of interactions between the electromagnetic field of the wave and the electrons in the material. The speed of light in a material is characterized by the material's **index of refraction** n, defined as

$$n = \frac{\text{speed of light in a vacuum}}{\text{speed of light in the material}} = \frac{c}{v} \tag{20.29}$$

The index of refraction of a material is always greater than 1 because $v < c$. A vacuum has $n = 1$ exactly. Table 20.2 shows the index of refraction for several materials. You can see that liquids and solids have larger indices of refraction than gases.

NOTE ▶ An accurate value for the index of refraction of air is relevant only in very precise measurements. We will assume $n_{air} = 1.00$ in this text. ◀

If the speed of a light wave changes as it enters into a transparent material, such as glass, what happens to the light's frequency and wavelength? Because $v = \lambda f$, either λ or f or both have to change when v changes.

As an analogy, think of a sound wave in the air as it impinges on the surface of a pool of water. As the air oscillates back and forth, it periodically pushes on the surface of the water. These pushes generate the compressions of the sound wave that continues on into the water. Because each push of the air causes one compression of the water, the frequency of the sound wave in the water must be *exactly the same* as the frequency of the sound wave in the air. In other words, **the frequency of a wave is the frequency of the source. It does not change as the wave moves from one medium to another.**

The same is true for electromagnetic waves; the frequency does not change as the wave moves from one material to another.

FIGURE 20.24 shows a light wave passing through a transparent material with index of refraction n. As the wave travels through vacuum it has wavelength λ_{vac} and frequency f_{vac} such that $\lambda_{vac} f_{vac} = c$. In the material, $\lambda_{mat} f_{mat} = v = c/n$. The frequency does not change as the wave enters ($f_{mat} = f_{vac}$), so the wavelength must. The wavelength in the material is

$$\lambda_{mat} = \frac{v}{f_{mat}} = \frac{c}{n f_{mat}} = \frac{c}{n f_{vac}} = \frac{\lambda_{vac}}{n} \qquad (20.30)$$

The wavelength in the transparent material is less than the wavelength in vacuum. This makes sense. Suppose a marching band is marching at one step per second at a speed of 1 m/s. Suddenly they slow their speed to $\frac{1}{2}$ m/s but maintain their march at one step per second. The only way to go slower while marching at the same pace is to take *smaller steps*. When a light wave enters a material, the only way it can go slower while oscillating at the same frequency is to have a *smaller wavelength*.

TABLE 20.2 Typical indices of refraction

Material	Index of refraction
Vacuum	1 exactly
Air	1.0003
Water	1.33
Glass	1.50
Diamond	2.42

FIGURE 20.24 Light passing through a transparent material with index of refraction n.

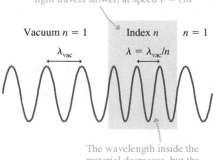

A transparent material in which light travels slower, at speed $v = c/n$

Vacuum $n = 1$ Index n $n = 1$

λ_{vac} $\lambda = \lambda_{vac}/n$

The wavelength inside the material decreases, but the frequency doesn't change.

EXAMPLE 20.8   **Light traveling through glass**

Orange light with a wavelength of 600 nm is incident upon a 1.00-mm-thick glass microscope slide.

a. What is the light speed in the glass?
b. How many wavelengths of the light are inside the slide?

SOLVE a. From Table 20.2 we see that the index of refraction of glass is $n_{glass} = 1.50$. Thus the speed of light in glass is

$$v_{glass} = \frac{c}{n_{glass}} = \frac{3.00 \times 10^8 \text{ m/s}}{1.50} = 2.00 \times 10^8 \text{ m/s}$$

b. The wavelength inside the glass is

$$\lambda_{glass} = \frac{\lambda_{vac}}{n_{glass}} = \frac{600 \text{ nm}}{1.50} = 400 \text{ nm} = 4.00 \times 10^{-7} \text{ m}$$

N wavelengths span a distance $d = N\lambda$, so the number of wavelengths in $d = 1.00$ mm is

$$N = \frac{d}{\lambda} = \frac{1.00 \times 10^{-3} \text{ m}}{4.00 \times 10^{-7} \text{ m}} = 2500$$

ASSESS The fact that 2500 wavelengths fit within 1 mm shows how small the wavelengths of light are.

STOP TO THINK 20.5   A light wave travels through three transparent materials of equal thickness. Rank in order, from largest to smallest, the indices of refraction n_a, n_b, and n_c.

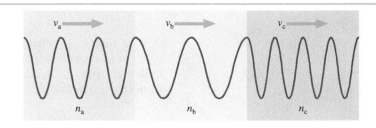

20.6 Power, Intensity, and Decibels

A traveling wave transfers energy from one point to another. The sound wave from a loudspeaker sets your eardrum into motion. Light waves from the sun warm the earth. The *power* of a wave is the rate, in joules per second, at which the wave transfers energy. As you learned in Chapter 11, power is measured in watts. A loudspeaker might emit 2 W of power, meaning that energy in the form of sound waves is radiated at the rate of 2 joules per second. A lightbulb might emit 5 W, or 5 J/s, of visible light. (In fact, this is about right for a so-called 100 watt bulb, with the other 95 W of power being emitted as heat, or infrared radiation, rather than as visible light.)

Imagine doing two experiments with a lightbulb that emits 5 W of visible light. In the first, you hang the bulb in the center of a room and allow the light to illuminate the walls. In the second experiment, you use mirrors and lenses to "capture" the bulb's light and focus it onto a small spot on one wall. This is what a computer projector does. The energy emitted by the bulb is the same in both cases, but, as you know, the light is much brighter when focused onto a small area. We would say that the focused light is more *intense* than the diffuse light that goes in all directions. Similarly, a loudspeaker that beams its sound forward into a small area produces a louder sound in that area than a speaker of equal power that radiates the sound in all directions. Quantities such as brightness and loudness depend not only on the rate of energy transfer, or power, but also on the *area* that receives that power.

FIGURE 20.25 shows a wave impinging on a surface of area a. The surface is perpendicular to the direction in which the wave is traveling. This might be a real, physical surface, such as your eardrum or a photovoltaic cell, but it could equally well be a mathematical surface in space that the wave passes right through. If the wave has power P, we define the **intensity** I of the wave to be

$$I = \frac{P}{a} = \text{power-to-area ratio} \qquad (20.31)$$

The SI units of intensity are W/m². Because intensity is a power-to-area ratio, a wave focused into a small area will have a larger intensity than a wave of equal power that is spread out over a large area.

FIGURE 20.25 Plane waves of power P impinge on area a with intensity $I = P/a$.

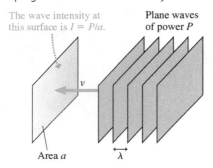

The wave intensity at this surface is $I = P/a$.

Plane waves of power P

v

Area a

λ

The intensity of a laser beam

A helium-neon laser, the kind that provides the familiar red light of classroom demonstrations and supermarket checkout scanners, emits 1.0 mW of light power into a 1.0-mm-diameter laser beam. What is the intensity of the laser beam?

MODEL The laser beam is a light wave.

SOLVE The light waves of the laser beam pass through a mathematical surface that is a circle of diameter 1.0 mm. The intensity of the laser beam is

$$I = \frac{P}{a} = \frac{P}{\pi r^2} = \frac{0.0010 \text{ W}}{\pi (0.00050 \text{ m})^2} = 1300 \text{ W/m}^2$$

ASSESS This is roughly the intensity of sunlight at noon on a summer day. The difference between the sun and a small laser is not their intensities, which are about the same, but their powers. The laser has a small power of 1 mW. It can produce a very intense wave only because the area through which the wave passes is very small. The sun, by contrast, radiates a total power $P_{\text{sun}} \approx 4 \times 10^{26}$ W. This immense power is spread through *all* of space, producing an intensity of 1400 W/m² at a distance of 1.5×10^{11} m, the radius of the earth's orbit.

If a source of spherical waves radiates uniformly in all directions, then, as FIGURE 20.26 shows, the power at distance r is spread uniformly over the surface of a sphere of radius r. The surface area of a sphere is $a = 4\pi r^2$, so the intensity of a uniform spherical wave is

$$I = \frac{P_{\text{source}}}{4\pi r^2} \qquad \text{(intensity of a uniform spherical wave)} \qquad (20.32)$$

The inverse-square dependence of r is really just a statement of energy conservation. The source emits energy at the rate P joules per second. The energy is spread over a larger and larger area as the wave moves outward. Consequently, the energy *per unit area* must decrease in proportion to the surface area of a sphere.

If the intensity at distance r_1 is $I_1 = P_{source}/4\pi r_1^2$ and the intensity at r_2 is $I_2 = P_{source}/4\pi r_2^2$, then you can see that the intensity *ratio* is

$$\frac{I_1}{I_2} = \frac{r_2^2}{r_1^2} \tag{20.33}$$

You can use Equation 20.33 to compare the intensities at two distances from a source without needing to know the power of the source.

NOTE ▶ Wave intensities are strongly affected by reflections and absorption. Equations 20.32 and 20.33 apply to situations such as the light from a star or the sound from a firework exploding high in the air. Indoor sound does *not* obey a simple inverse-square law because of the many reflecting surfaces. ◀

For a sinusoidal wave, each particle in the medium oscillates back and forth in simple harmonic motion. You learned in Chapter 14 that a particle in SHM with amplitude A has energy $E = \frac{1}{2}kA^2$, where k is the spring constant of the medium, not the wave number. It is this oscillatory energy of the medium that is transferred, particle to particle, as the wave moves through the medium.

Because a wave's intensity is proportional to the rate at which energy is transferred through the medium, and because the oscillatory energy in the medium is proportional to the *square* of the amplitude, we can infer that

$$I \propto A^2 \tag{20.34}$$

That is, **the intensity of a wave is proportional to the square of its amplitude.** If you double the amplitude of a wave, you increase its intensity by a factor of 4.

Human hearing spans an extremely wide range of intensities, from the *threshold of hearing* at $\approx 1 \times 10^{-12}$ W/m^2 (at midrange frequencies) to the *threshold of pain* at ≈ 10 W/m^2. If we want to make a scale of loudness, it's convenient and logical to place the zero of our scale at the threshold of hearing. To do so, we define the **sound intensity level,** expressed in **decibels** (dB), as

$$\beta = (10 \text{ dB}) \log_{10}\left(\frac{I}{I_0}\right) \tag{20.35}$$

where $I_0 = 1.0 \times 10^{-12}$ W/m^2. The symbol β is the Greek letter beta. Notice that β is computed as a base-10 logarithm, not a natural logarithm.

The decibel is named after Alexander Graham Bell, inventor of the telephone. Sound intensity level is actually dimensionless because it's formed from the ratio of two intensities, so decibels are just a *name* to remind us that we're dealing with an intensity *level* rather than a true intensity.

Right at the threshold of hearing, where $I = I_0$, the sound intensity level is

$$\beta = (10 \text{ dB}) \log_{10}\left(\frac{I_0}{I_0}\right) = (10 \text{ dB}) \log_{10}(1) = 0 \text{ dB}$$

Note that 0 dB doesn't mean no sound; it means that, for most people, no sound is heard. Dogs have more sensitive hearing than humans, and most dogs can easily perceive a 0 dB sound. The sound intensity level at the pain threshold is

$$\beta = (10 \text{ dB}) \log_{10}\left(\frac{10 \text{ W/m}^2}{10^{-12} \text{ W/m}^2}\right) = (10 \text{ dB}) \log_{10}(10^{13}) = 130 \text{ dB}$$

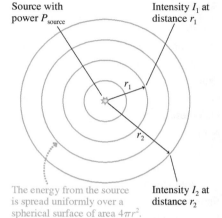

FIGURE 20.26 A source emitting uniform spherical waves.

Source with power P_{source}

Intensity I_1 at distance r_1

r_1

r_2

The energy from the source is spread uniformly over a spherical surface of area $4\pi r^2$.

Intensity I_2 at distance r_2

TABLE 20.3 Sound intensity levels of common sounds

Sound	β (dB)
Threshold of hearing	0
Person breathing, at 3 m	10
A whisper, at 1 m	20
Quiet room	30
Outdoors, no traffic	40
Quiet restaurant	50
Normal conversation, at 1 m	60
Busy traffic	70
Vacuum cleaner, for user	80
Niagara Falls, at viewpoint	90
Snowblower, at 2 m	100
Stereo, at maximum volume	110
Rock concert	120
Threshold of pain	130

The major point to notice is that the sound intensity level increases by 10 dB each time the actual intensity increases by a *factor* of 10. For example, the sound intensity level increases from 70 dB to 80 dB when the sound intensity increases from 10^{-5} W/m² to 10^{-4} W/m². Perception experiments find that sound is perceived as "twice as loud" when the intensity increases by a factor of 10. In terms of decibels, we can say that the perceived loudness of a sound doubles with each increase in the sound intensity level by 10 dB.

Table 20.3 gives the sound intensity levels for a number of sounds. Although 130 dB is the threshold of pain, quieter sounds can damage your hearing. A fairly short exposure to 120 dB can cause damage to the hair cells in the ear, but lengthy exposure to sound intensity levels of over 85 dB can produce damage as well.

EXAMPLE 20.10 **Blender noise**

The blender making a smoothie produces a sound intensity level of 83 dB. What is the intensity of the sound? What will the sound intensity level be if a second blender is turned on?

SOLVE We can solve Equation 20.35 for the sound intensity, finding $I = I_0 \times 10^{\beta/10 \text{ dB}}$. Here we used the fact that 10 raised to a power is an "antilogarithm." In this case,

$$I = (1.0 \times 10^{-12} \text{ W/m}^2) \times 10^{8.3} = 2.0 \times 10^{-4} \text{ W/m}^2$$

A second blender doubles the sound power and thus raises the intensity to $I = 4.0 \times 10^{-4}$ W/m². The new sound intensity level is

$$\beta = (10 \text{ dB}) \log_{10}\left(\frac{4.0 \times 10^{-4} \text{ W/m}^2}{1.0 \times 10^{-12} \text{ W/m}^2}\right) = 86 \text{ dB}$$

ASSESS In general, doubling the actual sound intensity increases the decibel level by 3 dB.

STOP TO THINK 20.6 Four trumpet players are playing the same note. If three of them suddenly stop, the sound intensity level decreases by

a. 40 dB   b. 12 dB   c. 6 dB   d. 4 dB

20.7 The Doppler Effect

Our final topic for this chapter is an interesting effect that occurs when you are in motion relative to a wave source. It is called the *Doppler effect*. You've likely noticed that the pitch of an ambulance's siren drops as it goes past you. Why?

FIGURE 20.27a shows a source of sound waves moving away from Pablo and toward Nancy at a steady speed v_s. The subscript s indicates that this is the speed of the source, not the speed of the waves. The source is emitting sound waves of frequency f_0 as it travels. The figure is a motion diagram showing the position of the source at times $t = 0$, T, $2T$, and $3T$, where $T = 1/f_0$ is the period of the waves.

Nancy measures the frequency of the wave emitted by the *approaching source* to be f_+. At the same time, Pablo measures the frequency of the wave emitted by the *receding source* to be f_-. Our task is to relate f_+ and f_- to the source frequency f_0 and speed v_s.

After a wave crest leaves the source, its motion is governed by the properties of the medium. That is, the motion of the source cannot affect a wave that has already been emitted. Thus each circular wave front in FIGURE 20.27b is centered on the point from which it was emitted. The wave crest from point 3 was emitted just as this figure was made, but it hasn't yet had time to travel any distance.

The wave crests are bunched up in the direction the source is moving, stretched out behind it. The distance between one crest and the next is one wavelength, so the wavelength λ_+ Nancy measures is *less* than the wavelength $\lambda_0 = v/f_0$ that would be emitted if the source were at rest. Similarly, λ_- behind the source is larger than λ_0.

FIGURE 20.27 A motion diagram showing the wave fronts emitted by a source as it moves to the right at speed v_s.

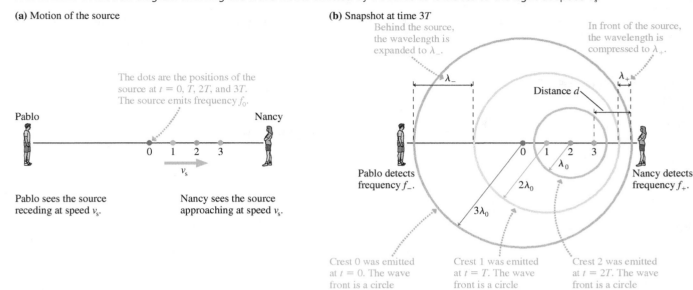

(a) Motion of the source

The dots are the positions of the source at $t = 0$, T, $2T$, and $3T$. The source emits frequency f_0.

Pablo   Nancy

0 1 2 3

v_s

Pablo sees the source receding at speed v_s.

Nancy sees the source approaching at speed v_s.

(b) Snapshot at time $3T$

Behind the source, the wavelength is expanded to λ_-.

In front of the source, the wavelength is compressed to λ_+.

λ_-

Distance d

λ_+

λ_0

0 1 2 3

$2\lambda_0$

$3\lambda_0$

Pablo detects frequency f_-.

Nancy detects frequency f_+.

Crest 0 was emitted at $t = 0$. The wave front is a circle centered on point 0.

Crest 1 was emitted at $t = T$. The wave front is a circle centered on point 1.

Crest 2 was emitted at $t = 2T$. The wave front is a circle centered on point 2.

These crests move through the medium at the wave speed v. Consequently, the frequency $f_+ = v/\lambda_+$ detected by the observer whom the source is approaching is *higher* than the frequency f_0 emitted by the source. Similarly, $f_- = v/\lambda_-$ detected behind the source is *lower* than frequency f_0. This change of frequency when a source moves relative to an observer is called the **Doppler effect.**

The distance labeled d in Figure 20.27b is the difference between how far the wave has moved and how far the source has moved at time $t = 3T$. These distances are

$$\Delta x_{\text{wave}} = vt = 3vT$$
$$\Delta x_{\text{source}} = v_s t = 3v_s T \tag{20.36}$$

The distance d spans three wavelengths; thus the wavelength of the wave emitted by an approaching source is

$$\lambda_+ = \frac{d}{3} = \frac{\Delta x_{\text{wave}} - \Delta x_{\text{source}}}{3} = \frac{3vT - 3v_s T}{3} = (v - v_s)T \tag{20.37}$$

You can see that our arbitrary choice of three periods was not relevant because the 3 cancels. The frequency detected in Nancy's direction is

$$f_+ = \frac{v}{\lambda_+} = \frac{v}{(v - v_s)T} = \frac{v}{(v - v_s)}f_0 \tag{20.38}$$

where $f_0 = 1/T$ is the frequency of the source and is the frequency you would detect if the source were at rest. We'll find it convenient to write the detected frequency as

$$f_+ = \frac{f_0}{1 - v_s/v} \qquad \text{(Doppler effect for an approaching source)}$$

$$\tag{20.39}$$

$$f_- = \frac{f_0}{1 + v_s/v} \qquad \text{(Doppler effect for a receding source)}$$

Proof of the second version, for the frequency f_- of a receding source, is similar. You can see that $f_+ > f_0$ in front of the source, because the denominator is less than 1, and $f_- < f_0$ behind the source.

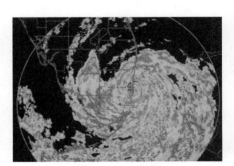

Doppler weather radar uses the Doppler shift of reflected radar signals to measure wind speeds and thus better gauge the severity of a storm.

EXAMPLE 20.11 **How fast are the police traveling?**

A police siren has a frequency of 550 Hz as the police car approaches you, 450 Hz after it has passed you and is receding. How fast are the police traveling? The temperature is 20°C.

MODEL The siren's frequency is altered by the Doppler effect. The frequency is f_+ as the car approaches and f_- as it moves away.

SOLVE To find v_s, we rewrite Equations 20.39 as

$$f_0 = (1 + v_s/v)f_-$$
$$f_0 = (1 - v_s/v)f_+$$

We subtract the second equation from the first, giving

$$0 = f_- - f_+ + \frac{v_s}{v}(f_- + f_+)$$

This is easily solved to give

$$v_s = \frac{f_+ - f_-}{f_+ + f_-}v = \frac{100 \text{ Hz}}{1000 \text{ Hz}}\,343 \text{ m/s} = 34.3 \text{ m/s}$$

ASSESS If you now solve for the siren frequency when at rest, you will find $f_0 = 495$ Hz. Surprisingly, the at-rest frequency is not halfway between f_- and f_+.

A Stationary Source and a Moving Observer

Suppose the police car in Example 20.11 is at rest while you drive toward it at 34.3 m/s. You might think that this is equivalent to having the police car move toward you at 34.3 m/s, but it isn't. Mechanical waves move through a medium, and the Doppler effect depends not just on how the source and the observer move with respect to each other but also on how they move with respect to the medium. We'll omit the proof, but it's not hard to show that the frequencies heard by an observer moving at speed v_o relative to a stationary source emitting frequency f_0 are

$$f_+ = (1 + v_o/v)f_0 \quad \text{(observer approaching a source)}$$
$$f_- = (1 - v_o/v)f_0 \quad \text{(observer receding from a source)}$$

(20.40)

A quick calculation shows that the frequency of the police siren as you approach it at 34.3 m/s is 545 Hz, not the 550 Hz you heard as it approached you at 34.3 m/s.

The Doppler Effect for Light Waves

The Doppler effect is observed for all types of waves, not just sound waves. If a source of light waves is receding from you, the wavelength λ_- that you detect is longer than the wavelength λ_0 emitted by the source.

Although the reason for the Doppler shift for light is the same as for sound waves, there is one fundamental difference. We derived Equations 20.39 for the Doppler-shifted frequencies by measuring the wave speed v relative to the medium. For electromagnetic waves in empty space, there is no medium. Consequently, we need to turn to Einstein's theory of relativity to determine the frequency of light waves from a moving source. The result, which we state without proof, is

$$\lambda_- = \sqrt{\frac{1 + v_s/c}{1 - v_s/c}}\,\lambda_0 \quad \text{(receding source)}$$

(20.41)

$$\lambda_+ = \sqrt{\frac{1 - v_s/c}{1 + v_s/c}}\,\lambda_0 \quad \text{(approaching source)}$$

Here v_s is the speed of the source *relative to* the observer.

The light waves from a receding source are shifted to longer wavelengths ($\lambda_- > \lambda_0$). Because the longest visible wavelengths are perceived as the color red, the light from a receding source is **red shifted**. That is *not* to say that the light is red, simply that its wavelength is shifted toward the red end of the spectrum. If $\lambda_0 = 470$ nm (blue) light emitted by a rapidly receding source is detected at $\lambda_- = 520$ nm (green), we would say that the light has been red shifted. Similarly, light from an approaching source is **blue shifted**, meaning that the detected wavelengths are shorter than the emitted wavelengths ($\lambda_+ < \lambda_0$) and thus are shifted toward the blue end of the spectrum.

EXAMPLE 20.12 Measuring the velocity of a galaxy

Hydrogen atoms in the laboratory emit red light with wavelength 656 nm. In the light from a distant galaxy, this "spectral line" is observed at 691 nm. What is the speed of this galaxy relative to the earth?

MODEL The observed wavelength is longer than the wavelength emitted by atoms at rest with respect to the observer (i.e., red shifted), so we are looking at light emitted from a galaxy that is receding from us.

SOLVE Squaring the expression for λ_- in Equations 20.41 and solving for v_s give

$$
\begin{aligned}
v_s &= \frac{(\lambda_-/\lambda_0)^2 - 1}{(\lambda_-/\lambda_0)^2 + 1}c \\
&= \frac{(691 \text{ nm}/656 \text{ nm})^2 - 1}{(691 \text{ nm}/656 \text{ nm})^2 + 1}c \\
&= 0.052c = 1.56 \times 10^7 \text{ m/s}
\end{aligned}
$$

ASSESS The galaxy is moving away from the earth at about 5% of the speed of light!

In the 1920s, an analysis of the red shifts of many galaxies led the astronomer Edwin Hubble to the conclusion that the galaxies of the universe are *all* moving apart from each other. Extrapolating backward in time must bring us to a point when all the matter of the universe—and even space itself, according to the theory of relativity—began rushing out of a primordial fireball. Many observations and measurements since have given support to the idea that the universe began in a *Big Bang* about 14 billion years ago.

As an example, FIGURE 20.28 is a Hubble Space Telescope picture of a *quasar*, short for *quasistellar object*. Quasars are extraordinarily powerful sources of light and radio waves. The light reaching us from quasars is highly red shifted, corresponding in some cases to objects that are moving away from us at greater than 90% of the speed of light. Astronomers have determined that some quasars are 10 to 12 *billion* light years away from the earth, hence the light we see was emitted when the universe was only about 25% of its present age. Today, the red shifts of distant quasars and supernovae (exploding stars) are being used to refine our understanding of the structure and evolution of the universe.

FIGURE 20.28 A Hubble Space Telescope picture of a quasar.

STOP TO THINK 20.7 Amy and Zack are both listening to the source of sound waves that is moving to the right. Compare the frequencies each hears.

a. $f_{Amy} > f_{Zack}$
b. $f_{Amy} = f_{Zack}$
c. $f_{Amy} < f_{Zack}$

Amy 10 m/s f_0 10 m/s 10 m/s Zack

CHALLENGE EXAMPLE 20.13 Decreasing the sound

The loudspeaker on a homecoming float—mounted on a pole—is stuck playing an annoying 210 Hz tone. When the speaker is 10 m away, you measure the sound to be a loud 95 dB at 208 Hz. How long will it take for the sound intensity level to drop to a tolerable 55 dB?

MODEL The source is on a pole, so model the sound waves as uniform spherical waves. Assume a temperature of 20°C.

SOLVE The 208 Hz frequency you measure is less than the 210 Hz frequency that was emitted, so the float must be moving away from you. The Doppler effect for a receding source is

$$ f_- = \frac{f_0}{1 + v_s/v} $$

We can solve this to find the speed of the float:

$$ v_s = \left(\frac{f_0}{f_-} - 1\right)v = \left(\frac{210 \text{ Hz}}{208 \text{ Hz}} - 1\right) \times 343 \text{ m/s} = 3.3 \text{ m/s} $$

The sound intensity of a spherical wave decreases with the inverse square of the distance from the source. A sound intensity level β corresponds to an intensity $I = I_0 \times 10^{\beta/10 \text{ dB}}$, where $I_0 = 1.0 \times 10^{-12} \text{ W/m}^2$. At the initial 95 dB, the intensity is

$$ I_1 = I_0 \times 10^{9.5} = 3.2 \times 10^{-3} \text{ W/m}^2 $$

At the desired 55 dB, the intensity will have dropped to

$$ I_2 = I_0 \times 10^{5.5} = 3.2 \times 10^{-7} \text{ W/m}^2 $$

The intensity ratio is related to the distances by

$$ \frac{I_1}{I_2} = \frac{r_2^2}{r_1^2} $$

Thus the sound will have dropped to 55 dB when the distance to the speaker is

$$ r_2 = \sqrt{\frac{I_1}{I_2}} r_1 = \sqrt{10^4} \times 10 \text{ m} = 1000 \text{ m} $$

The float has to travel $\Delta x = 990$ m, which will take

$$ \Delta t = \frac{\Delta x}{v_s} = \frac{990 \text{ m}}{3.3 \text{ m/s}} = 300 \text{ s} = 5.0 \text{ min} $$

ASSESS To drop the sound intensity level by 40 dB requires decreasing the intensity by a factor of 10^4. And with the intensity depending on the inverse square of the distance, that requires increasing the distance by a factor of 100. Floats don't move very fast—3.3 m/s is about 7 mph—so needing several minutes to travel the ≈ 1000 m seems reasonable.

SUMMARY

The goal of Chapter 20 has been to learn the basic properties of traveling waves.

General Principles

The Wave Model

This model is based on the idea of a traveling wave, which is an organized disturbance traveling at a well-defined **wave speed** v.

- In transverse waves the displacement is perpendicular to the direction in which the wave travels.

- In longitudinal waves the particles of the medium move parallel to the direction in which the wave travels.

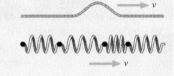

A wave transfers **energy,** but no material or substance is transferred outward from the source.

Two basic types of waves:

- Mechanical waves travel through a material medium such as water or air.

- Electromagnetic waves require no material medium and can travel through a vacuum.

For mechanical waves, such as sound waves and waves on strings, the speed of the wave is a property of the medium. Speed does not depend on the size or shape of the wave.

Important Concepts

The **displacement** D of a wave is a function of both position (where) and time (when).

- A snapshot graph shows the wave's displacement as a function of position at a single instant of time.

- A history graph shows the wave's displacement as a function of time at a single point in space.

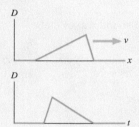

For a transverse wave on a string, the snapshot graph is a picture of the wave. The displacement of a longitudinal wave is parallel to the motion; thus the snapshot graph of a longitudinal sound wave is *not* a picture of the wave.

Sinusoidal waves are periodic in both time (period T) and space (wavelength λ):

$$D(x, t) = A \sin\left[2\pi(x/\lambda - t/T) + \phi_0\right]$$
$$= A \sin(kx - \omega t + \phi_0)$$

where A is the **amplitude,** $k = 2\pi/\lambda$ is the **wave number,** $\omega = 2\pi f = 2\pi/T$ is the **angular frequency,** and ϕ_0 is the **phase constant** that describes initial conditions.

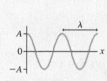

| One-dimensional waves | Two- and three-dimensional waves |

The fundamental relationship for any sinusoidal wave is $v = \lambda f$.

Applications

- **String** (transverse): $v = \sqrt{T_s/\mu}$

- **Sound** (longitudinal): $v = 343$ m/s in 20°C air

- **Light** (transverse): $v = c/n$, where $c = 3.00 \times 10^8$ m/s is the speed of light in a vacuum and n is the material's **index of refraction**

The wave intensity is the power-to-area ratio: $I = P/a$

For a circular or spherical wave: $I = P_{source}/4\pi r^2$

The sound intensity level is

$$\beta = (10 \text{ dB}) \log_{10}(I/1.0 \times 10^{-12} \text{ W/m}^2)$$

The Doppler effect occurs when a wave source and detector are moving with respect to each other: the frequency detected differs from the frequency f_0 emitted.

Approaching source

$$f_+ = \frac{f_0}{1 - v_s/v}$$

Observer approaching a source

$$f_+ = (1 + v_o/v)f_0$$

Receding source

$$f_- = \frac{f_0}{1 + v_s/v}$$

Observer receding from a source

$$f_- = (1 - v_o/v)f_0$$

The Doppler effect for light uses a result derived from the theory of relativity.

Terms and Notation

wave model	wave speed, v	wave front	index of refraction, n
traveling wave	linear density, μ	circular wave	intensity, I
transverse wave	snapshot graph	spherical wave	sound intensity level, β
longitudinal wave	history graph	plane wave	decibels
mechanical waves	sinusoidal wave	phase, ϕ	Doppler effect
electromagnetic waves	amplitude, A	compression	red shifted
medium	wavelength, λ	rarefaction	blue shifted
disturbance	wave number, k	electromagnetic spectrum	

CONCEPTUAL QUESTIONS

1. The three wave pulses in FIGURE Q20.1 travel along the same stretched string. Rank in order, from largest to smallest, their wave speeds v_a, v_b, and v_c. Explain.

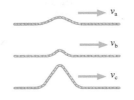

FIGURE Q20.1

2. A wave pulse travels along a stretched string at a speed of 200 cm/s. What will be the speed if:
   a. The string's tension is doubled?
   b. The string's mass is quadrupled (but its length is unchanged)?
   c. The string's length is quadrupled (but its mass is unchanged)?
   Note: Each part is independent and refers to changes made to the original string.

3. FIGURE Q20.3 is a history graph showing the displacement as a function of time at one point on a string. Did the displacement at this point reach its maximum of 2 mm *before* or *after* the interval of time when the displacement was a constant 1 mm?

FIGURE Q20.3

4. FIGURE Q20.4 shows a snapshot graph *and* a history graph for a wave pulse on a stretched string. They describe the same wave from two perspectives.
   a. In which direction is the wave traveling? Explain.
   b. What is the speed of this wave?

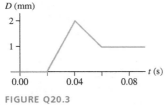

FIGURE Q20.4

5. Rank in order, from largest to smallest, the wavelengths λ_a, λ_b, and λ_c for sound waves having frequencies $f_a = 100$ Hz, $f_b = 1000$ Hz, and $f_c = 10,000$ Hz. Explain.

6. A sound wave with wavelength λ_0 and frequency f_0 moves into a new medium in which the speed of sound is $v_1 = 2v_0$. What are the new wavelength λ_1 and frequency f_1? Explain.

7. What are the amplitude, wavelength, frequency, and phase constant of the traveling wave in FIGURE Q20.7?

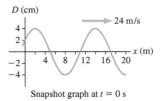

FIGURE Q20.7

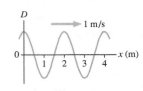

FIGURE Q20.8

8. FIGURE Q20.8 is a snapshot graph of a sinusoidal wave at $t = 1.0$ s. What is the phase constant of this wave?

9. FIGURE Q20.9 shows the wave fronts of a circular wave. What is the phase difference between (a) points A and B, (b) points C and D, and (c) points E and F?

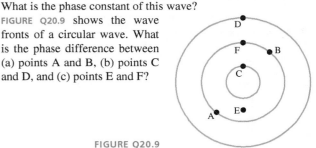

FIGURE Q20.9

10. Sound wave A delivers 2 J of energy in 2 s. Sound wave B delivers 10 J of energy in 5 s. Sound wave C delivers 2 mJ of energy in 1 ms. Rank in order, from largest to smallest, the sound powers P_A, P_B, and P_C of these three sound waves. Explain.

11. One physics professor talking produces a sound intensity level of 52 dB. It's a frightening idea, but what would be the sound intensity level of 100 physics professors talking simultaneously?

12. You are standing at $x = 0$ m, listening to a sound that is emitted at frequency f_0. The graph of FIGURE Q20.12 shows the frequency you hear during a 4-second interval. Which of the following describes the sound source? Explain your choice.
   A. It moves from left to right and passes you at $t = 2$ s.
   B. It moves from right to left and passes you at $t = 2$ s.
   C. It moves toward you but doesn't reach you. It then reverses direction at $t = 2$ s.
   D. It moves away from you until $t = 2$ s. It then reverses direction and moves toward you but doesn't reach you.

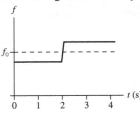

FIGURE Q20.12

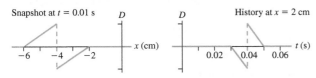

EXERCISES AND PROBLEMS

Problems labeled [ ] integrate material from earlier chapters.

Exercises

Section 20.1 The Wave Model

1. | The wave speed on a string is 150 m/s when the tension is 75 N. What tension will give a speed of 180 m/s?
2. | The wave speed on a string under tension is 200 m/s. What is the speed if the tension is halved?
3. || A 25 g string is under 20 N of tension. A pulse travels the length of the string in 50 ms. How long is the string?

Section 20.2 One-Dimensional Waves

4. || Draw the history graph $D(x = 0 \text{ m}, t)$ at $x = 0$ m for the wave shown in FIGURE EX20.4.

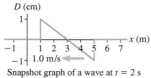
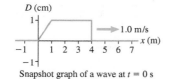

Snapshot graph of a wave at $t = 2$ s   Snapshot graph of a wave at $t = 0$ s

FIGURE EX20.4   **FIGURE EX20.5**

5. || Draw the history graph $D(x = 5.0 \text{ m}, t)$ at $x = 5.0$ m for the wave shown in FIGURE EX20.5.
6. || Draw the snapshot graph $D(x, t = 0 \text{ s})$ at $t = 0$ s for the wave shown in FIGURE EX20.6.

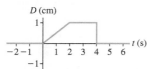

History graph of a wave at $x = 2$ m   History graph of a wave at $x = 0$ m
Wave moving to the left at 1.0 m/s   Wave moving to the right at 1.0 m/s

FIGURE EX20.6   **FIGURE EX20.7**

7. || Draw the snapshot graph $D(x, t = 1.0 \text{ s})$ at $t = 1.0$ s for the wave shown in FIGURE EX20.7.
8. || FIGURE EX20.8 is the snapshot graph at $t = 0$ s of a *longitudinal* wave. Draw the corresponding picture of the particle positions, as was done in Figure 20.10b. Let the equilibrium spacing between the particles be 1.0 cm.

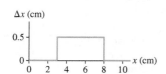

FIGURE EX20.8

9. || FIGURE EX20.9 is a picture at $t = 0$ s of the particles in a medium as a longitudinal wave is passing through. The equilibrium spacing between the particles is 1.0 cm. Draw the snapshot graph $D(x, t = 0 \text{ s})$ of this wave at $t = 0$ s.

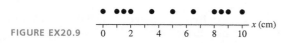

FIGURE EX20.9

Section 20.3 Sinusoidal Waves

10. | A wave travels with speed 200 m/s. Its wave number is 1.5 rad/m. What are its (a) wavelength and (b) frequency?
11. | A wave has angular frequency 30 rad/s and wavelength 2.0 m. What are its (a) wave number and (b) wave speed?
12. | The displacement of a wave traveling in the positive x-direction is $D(x, t) = (3.5 \text{ cm}) \sin(2.7x - 124t)$, where x is in m and t is in s. What are the (a) frequency, (b) wavelength, and (c) speed of this wave?
13. | The displacement of a wave traveling in the negative y-direction is $D(y, t) = (5.2 \text{ cm}) \sin(5.5y + 72t)$, where y is in m and t is in s. What are the (a) frequency, (b) wavelength, and (c) speed of this wave?
14. | What are the amplitude, frequency, and wavelength of the wave in FIGURE EX20.14?

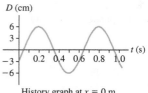

History graph at $x = 0$ m
Wave traveling left at 2.0 m/s

FIGURE EX20.14

Section 20.4 Waves in Two and Three Dimensions

15. | A spherical wave with a wavelength of 2.0 m is emitted from the origin. At one instant of time, the phase at $r = 4.0$ m is π rad. At that instant, what is the phase at $r = 3.5$ m and at $r = 4.5$ m?
16. | A circular wave travels outward from the origin. At one instant of time, the phase at $r_1 = 20$ cm is 0 rad and the phase at $r_2 = 80$ cm is 3π rad. What is the wavelength of the wave?
17. || A loudspeaker at the origin emits a 120 Hz tone on a day when the speed of sound is 340 m/s. The phase difference between two points on the x-axis is 5.5 rad. What is the distance between these two points?
18. || A sound source is located somewhere along the x-axis. Experiments show that the same wave front simultaneously reaches listeners at $x = -7.0$ m and $x = +3.0$ m.
    a. What is the x-coordinate of the source?
    b. A third listener is positioned along the positive y-axis. What is her y-coordinate if the same wave front reaches her at the same instant it does the first two listeners?

Section 20.5 Sound and Light

19. || A hammer taps on the end of a 4.00-m-long metal bar at room temperature. A microphone at the other end of the bar picks up two pulses of sound, one that travels through the metal and one that travels through the air. The pulses are separated in time by 9.00 ms. What is the speed of sound in this metal?
20. || a. What is the wavelength of a 2.0 MHz ultrasound wave traveling through aluminum?
    b. What frequency of electromagnetic wave would have the same wavelength as the ultrasound wave of part a?

21. | a. What is the frequency of an electromagnetic wave with a wavelength of 20 cm?
    b. What would be the wavelength of a sound wave in water with the same frequency as the electromagnetic wave of part a?

22. | a. What is the frequency of blue light that has a wavelength of 450 nm?
    b. What is the frequency of red light that has a wavelength of 650 nm?
    c. What is the index of refraction of a material in which the red-light wavelength is 450 nm?

23. | a. An FM radio station broadcasts at a frequency of 101.3 MHz. What is the wavelength?
    b. What is the frequency of a sound source that produces the same wavelength in 20°C air?

24. | a. Telephone signals are often transmitted over long distances by microwaves. What is the frequency of microwave radiation with a wavelength of 3.0 cm?
    b. Microwave signals are beamed between two mountaintops 50 km apart. How long does it take a signal to travel from one mountaintop to the other?

25. ‖ a. How long does it take light to travel through a 3.0-mm-thick piece of window glass?
    b. Through what thickness of water could light travel in the same amount of time?

26. ‖ Cell phone conversations are transmitted by high-frequency radio waves. Suppose the signal has wavelength 35 cm while traveling through air. What are the (a) frequency and (b) wavelength as the signal travels through 3-mm-thick window glass into your room?

27. | A light wave has a 670 nm wavelength in air. Its wavelength in a transparent solid is 420 nm.
    a. What is the speed of light in this solid?
    b. What is the light's frequency in the solid?

Section 20.6 Power, Intensity, and Decibels

28. ‖ A sound wave with intensity 2.0×10^{-3} W/m² is perceived to be modestly loud. Your eardrum is 6.0 mm in diameter. How much energy will be transferred to your eardrum while listening to this sound for 1.0 min?
BIO

29. ‖ The intensity of electromagnetic waves from the sun is 1.4 kW/m² just above the earth's atmosphere. Eighty percent of this reaches the surface at noon on a clear summer day. Suppose you think of your back as a 30 cm × 50 cm rectangle. How many joules of solar energy fall on your back as you work on your tan for 1.0 h?

30. ‖ A concert loudspeaker suspended high above the ground emits 35 W of sound power. A small microphone with a 1.0 cm² area is 50 m from the speaker.
    a. What is the sound intensity at the position of the microphone?
    b. How much sound energy impinges on the microphone each second?

31. ‖ During takeoff, the sound intensity level of a jet engine is 140 dB at a distance of 30 m. What is the sound intensity level at a distance of 1.0 km?

32. | The sun emits electromagnetic waves with a power of 4.0×10^{26} W. Determine the intensity of electromagnetic waves from the sun just outside the atmospheres of Venus, the earth, and Mars.

33. | What are the sound intensity levels for sound waves of intensity (a) 3.0×10^{-6} W/m² and (b) 3.0×10^{-2} W/m²?

34. | What are the intensities of sound waves with sound intensity levels (a) 46 dB and (b) 103 dB?

35. ‖ A loudspeaker on a tall pole broadcasts sound waves equally in all directions. What is the speaker's power output if the sound intensity level is 90 dB at a distance of 20 m?

Section 20.7 The Doppler Effect

36. | A friend of yours is loudly singing a single note at 400 Hz while racing toward you at 25.0 m/s on a day when the speed of sound is 340 m/s.
    a. What frequency do you hear?
    b. What frequency does your friend hear if you suddenly start singing at 400 Hz?

37. | An opera singer in a convertible sings a note at 600 Hz while cruising down the highway at 90 km/h. What is the frequency heard by
    a. A person standing beside the road in front of the car?
    b. A person on the ground behind the car?

38. ‖ A bat locates insects by emitting ultrasonic "chirps" and then listening for echoes from the bugs. Suppose a bat chirp has a frequency of 25 kHz. How fast would the bat have to fly, and in what direction, for you to just barely be able to hear the chirp at 20 kHz?
BIO

39. | A mother hawk screeches as she dives at you. You recall from biology that female hawks screech at 800 Hz, but you hear the screech at 900 Hz. How fast is the hawk approaching?

Problems

40. ‖ The displacement of a traveling wave is

$$D(x, t) = \begin{cases} 1 \text{ cm} & \text{if } |x - 3t| \leq 1 \\ 0 \text{ cm} & \text{if } |x - 3t| > 1 \end{cases}$$

where x is in m and t in s.
    a. Draw displacement-versus-position graphs from $x = -2$ m to $x = 12$ m at 1 s intervals from $t = 0$ s to $t = 3$ s.
    b. Determine the wave speed from the graphs. Explain.
    c. Determine the wave speed from the equation for $D(x, t)$. Does it agree with your answer to part b?

41. ‖ FIGURE P20.41 is a history graph at $x = 0$ m of a wave traveling in the positive x-direction at 4.0 m/s.
    a. What is the wavelength?
    b. What is the phase constant of the wave?
    c. Write the displacement equation for this wave.

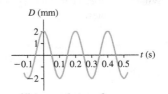

History graph at $x = 0$ m
Wave traveling right at 4.0 m/s

FIGURE P20.41

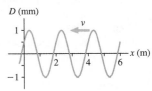

Snapshot graph at $t = 0$ s

FIGURE P20.42

42. ‖ FIGURE P20.42 is a snapshot graph at $t = 0$ s of a 5.0 Hz wave traveling to the left.
    a. What is the wave speed?
    b. What is the phase constant of the wave?
    c. Write the displacement equation for this wave.

43. ‖ A wave travels along a string at speed v_0. What will be the speed if the string is replaced by one made of the same material and under the same tension but having twice the radius?

44. | String 1 in FIGURE P20.44 has linear density 2.0 g/m and string 2 has linear density 4.0 g/m. A student sends pulses in both directions by quickly pulling up on the knot, then releasing it. What should the string lengths L_1 and L_2 be if the pulses are to reach the ends of the strings simultaneously?

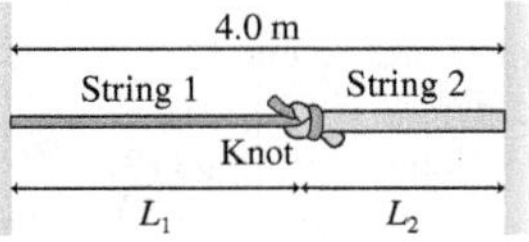

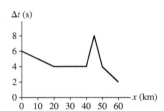

FIGURE P20.44

45. ‖ Ships measure the distance to the ocean bottom with sonar. A pulse of sound waves is aimed at the ocean bottom, then sensitive microphones listen for the echo. FIGURE P20.45 shows the delay time as a function of the ship's position as it crosses 60 km of ocean. Draw a graph of the ocean bottom. Let the ocean surface define $y = 0$ and ocean bottom have negative values of y. This way your graph will be a picture of the ocean bottom. The speed of sound in ocean water varies slightly with temperature, but you can use 1500 m/s as an average value.

FIGURE P20.45

46. ‖ Oil explorers set off explosives to make loud sounds, then listen for the echoes from underground oil deposits. Geologists suspect that there is oil under 500-m-deep Lake Physics. It's known that Lake Physics is carved out of a granite basin. Explorers detect a weak echo 0.94 s after exploding dynamite at the lake surface. If it's really oil, how deep will they have to drill into the granite to reach it?

47. ‖ One cue your hearing system uses to localize a sound (i.e., to
BIO tell where a sound is coming from) is the slight difference in the arrival times of the sound at your ears. Your ears are spaced approximately 20 cm apart. Consider a sound source 5.0 m from the center of your head along a line 45° to your right. What is the difference in arrival times? Give your answer in microseconds. **Hint:** You are looking for the difference between two numbers that are nearly the same. What does this near equality imply about the necessary precision during intermediate stages of the calculation?

48. ‖ A helium-neon laser beam has a wavelength in air of 633 nm. It takes 1.38 ns for the light to travel through 30 cm of an unknown liquid. What is the wavelength of the laser beam in the liquid?

49. | A 440 Hz sound wave in 20°C air propagates into the water of a swimming pool. What are the wave's (a) frequency and (b) wavelength in the water?

50. ‖ Earthquakes are essentially sound waves—called seismic waves—traveling through the earth. Because the earth is solid, it can support both longitudinal and transverse seismic waves. The speed of longitudinal waves, called P waves, is 8000 m/s. Transverse waves, called S waves, travel at a slower 4500 m/s.

A seismograph records the two waves from a distant earthquake. If the S wave arrives 2.0 min after the P wave, how far away was the earthquake? You can assume that the waves travel in straight lines, although actual seismic waves follow more complex routes.

51. ‖ A sound wave is described by $D(y, t) = (0.0200 \text{ mm}) \times \sin[(8.96 \text{ rad/m})y + (3140 \text{ rad/s})t + \pi/4 \text{ rad}]$, where y is in m and t is in s.
   a. In what direction is this wave traveling?
   b. Along which axis is the air oscillating?
   c. What are the wavelength, the wave speed, and the period of oscillation?

52. ‖ A wave on a string is described by $D(x, t) = (3.0 \text{ cm}) \times \sin[2\pi(x/(2.4 \text{ m}) + t/(0.20 \text{ s}) + 1)]$, where x is in m and t is in s.
   a. In what direction is this wave traveling?
   b. What are the wave speed, the frequency, and the wave number?
   c. At $t = 0.50$ s, what is the displacement of the string at $x = 0.20$ m?

53. ‖ A wave on a string is described by $D(x, t) = (2.00 \text{ cm}) \times \sin[(12.57 \text{ rad/m})x - (638 \text{ rad/s})t]$, where x is in m and t in s. The linear density of the string is 5.00 g/m. What are
   a. The string tension?
   b. The maximum displacement of a point on the string?
   c. The maximum speed of a point on the string?

54. | Write the displacement equation for a sinusoidal wave that is traveling in the negative y-direction with wavelength 50 cm, speed 4.0 m/s, and amplitude 5.0 cm. Assume $\phi_0 = 0$.

55. | Write the displacement equation for a sinusoidal wave that is traveling in the positive x-direction with frequency 200 Hz, speed 400 m/s, amplitude 0.010 mm, and phase constant $\pi/2$ rad.

56. | A string with linear density 2.0 g/m is stretched along the positive x-axis with tension 20 N. One end of the string, at $x = 0$ m, is tied to a hook that oscillates up and down at a frequency of 100 Hz with a maximum displacement of 1.0 mm. At $t = 0$ s, the hook is at its lowest point.
   a. What are the wave speed on the string and the wavelength?
   b. What are the amplitude and phase constant of the wave?
   c. Write the equation for the displacement $D(x, t)$ of the traveling wave?
   d. What is the string's displacement at $x = 0.50$ m and $t = 15$ ms?

57. ‖ FIGURE P20.57 shows a snapshot graph of a wave traveling to the right along a string at 45 m/s. At this instant, what is the velocity of points 1, 2, and 3 on the string?

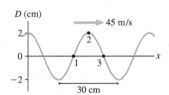

FIGURE P20.57

58. ‖ FIGURE P20.58 shows two masses hanging from a steel wire. The mass of the wire is 60.0 g. A wave pulse travels along the wire from point 1 to point 2 in 24.0 ms. What is mass m?

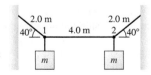

FIGURE P20.58

59. ‖ A wire is made by welding together two metals having different densities. FIGURE P20.59 shows a 2.00-m-long section of wire centered on the junction, but the wire extends much farther in both directions. The wire is placed under 2250 N tension, then a 1500 Hz wave with an amplitude of 3.00 mm is sent down the wire. How many wavelengths (complete cycles) of the wave are in this 2.00-m-long section of the wire?

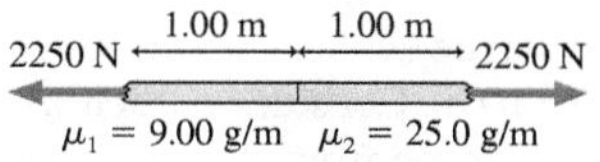

FIGURE P20.59

2250 N $\longleftarrow$ 1.00 m $\longrightarrow$ 1.00 m $\longrightarrow$ 2250 N

$\mu_1 = 9.00$ g/m $\mu_2 = 25.0$ g/m

60. ‖ The string in FIGURE P20.60 has linear density μ. Find an expression in terms of M, μ and θ for the speed of waves on the string.

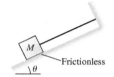

FIGURE P20.60

M Frictionless θ

61. ‖ A string that is under 50.0 N of tension has linear density 5.0 g/m. A sinusoidal wave with amplitude 3.0 cm and wavelength 2.0 m travels along the string. What is the maximum speed of a particle on the string?

62. ‖ A sinusoidal wave travels along a stretched string. A particle on the string has a maximum speed of 2.0 m/s and a maximum acceleration of 200 m/s^2. What are the frequency and amplitude of the wave?

63. ‖ a. A 100 W lightbulb produces 5.0 W of visible light. (The other 95 W are dissipated as heat and infrared radiation.) What is the light intensity on a wall 2.0 m away from the lightbulb?
    b. A krypton laser produces a cylindrical red laser beam 2.0 mm in diameter with 5.0 W of power. What is the light intensity on a wall 2.0 m away from the laser?

64. ‖ An AM radio station broadcasts with a power of 25 kW at a frequency of 920 kHz. Estimate the intensity of the radio wave at a point 10 km from the broadcast antenna.

65. ‖ LASIK eye surgery uses pulses of laser light to shave off
BIO tissue from the cornea, reshaping it. A typical LASIK laser emits a 1.0-mm-diameter laser beam with a wavelength of 193 nm. Each laser pulse lasts 15 ns and contains 1.0 mJ of light energy
    a. What is the power of one laser pulse?
    b. During the very brief time of the pulse, what is the intensity of the light wave?

66. ‖ The sound intensity 50 m from a wailing tornado siren is 0.10 W/m^2.
    a. What is the intensity at 1000 m?
    b. The weakest intensity likely to be heard over background noise is ≈ 1 μW/m^2. Estimate the maximum distance at which the siren can be heard.

67. ‖ The sound intensity level 5.0 m from a large power saw is 100 dB. At what distance will the sound be a more tolerable 80 dB?

68. ‖ Two loudspeakers on elevated platforms are at opposite ends of a field. Each broadcasts equally in all directions. The sound intensity level at a point halfway between the loudspeakers is 75.0 dB. What is the sound intensity level at a point one-quarter of the way from one speaker to the other along the line joining them?

69. ‖ Your ears are sensitive to differences in pitch, but they are not
BIO very sensitive to differences in intensity. You are not capable of detecting a difference in sound intensity level of less than 1 dB. By what factor does the sound intensity increase if the sound intensity level increases from 60 dB to 61 dB?

70. ‖‖ The intensity of a sound source is described by an inverse-square law only if the source is very small (a point source) and only if the waves can travel unimpeded in all directions. For an extended source or in a situation where obstacles absorb or reflect the waves, the intensity at distance r can often be expressed as $I = cP_{source}/r^x$, where c is a constant and the exponent x—which would be 2 for an ideal spherical wave—depends on the situation. In one such situation, you use a sound meter to measure the sound intensity level at different distances from a source, acquiring the following data:

Distance (m)	Intensity level (dB)
1	100
3	93
10	85
30	78
100	70

Use the best-fit line of an appropriate graph to determine the exponent x that characterizes this sound source.

71. ‖‖ A mad doctor believes that baldness can be cured by warming the scalp with sound waves. His patients sit underneath the Bald-o-Matic loudspeakers, where their heads are bathed with 93 dB of soothing 800 Hz sound waves. Suppose we model a bald head as a 16-cm-diameter hemisphere. If 0.10 J of sound energy is considered an appropriate "dose," how many minutes should each therapy session last?

72. ‖ A physics professor demonstrates the Doppler effect by tying a 600 Hz sound generator to a 1.0-m-long rope and whirling it around her head in a horizontal circle at 100 rpm. What are the highest and lowest frequencies heard by a student in the classroom?

73. ‖ Show that the Doppler frequency f_- of a receding source is $f_- = f_0/(1 + v_s/v)$.

74. ‖ A starship approaches its home planet at a speed of $0.1c$. When it is 54×10^6 km away, it uses its green laser beam ($\lambda = 540$ nm) to signal its approach.
    a. How long does the signal take to travel to the home planet?
    b. At what wavelength is the signal detected on the home planet?

75. ‖ Wavelengths of light from a distant galaxy are found to be 0.5% longer than the corresponding wavelengths measured in a terrestrial laboratory. Is the galaxy approaching or receding from the earth? At what speed?

76. ‖ You have just been pulled over for running a red light, and the police officer has informed you that the fine will be $250. In desperation, you suddenly recall an idea that your physics professor recently discussed in class. In your calmest voice, you tell the officer that the laws of physics prevented you from knowing that the light was red. In fact, as you drove toward it, the light was Doppler shifted to where it appeared green to you. "OK," says the officer, "Then I'll ticket you for speeding. The fine is $1 for every 1 km/h over the posted speed limit of 50 km/h." How big is your fine? Use 650 nm as the wavelength of red light and 540 nm as the wavelength of green light.

Challenge Problems

77. One way to monitor global warming is to measure the average temperature of the ocean. Researchers are doing this by measuring the time it takes sound pulses to travel underwater over large distances. At a depth of 1000 m, where ocean temperatures hold steady near 4°C, the average sound speed is 1480 m/s. It's known from laboratory measurements that the sound speed increases 4.0 m/s for every 1.0°C increase in temperature. In one experiment, where sounds generated near California are detected in the South Pacific, the sound waves travel 8000 km. If the smallest time change that can be reliably detected is 1.0 s, what is the smallest change in average temperature that can be measured?

78. The G string on a guitar is a 0.46-mm-diameter steel string with a linear density of 1.3 g/m. When the string is properly tuned to 196 Hz, the wave speed on the string is 250 m/s. Tuning is done by turning the tuning screw, which slowly tightens—and stretches—the string. By how many mm does a 75-cm-long G string stretch when it's first tuned?

79. A rope of mass m and length L hangs from a ceiling.
    a. Show that the wave speed on the rope a distance y above the lower end is $v = \sqrt{gy}$.
    b. Show that the time for a pulse to travel the length of the string is $\Delta t = 2\sqrt{L/g}$.

80. Some modern optical devices are made with glass whose index of refraction changes with distance from the front surface. FIGURE CP20.80 shows the index of refraction as a function of the distance into a slab of glass of thickness L. The index of refraction increases linearly from n_1 at the front surface to n_2 at the rear surface.

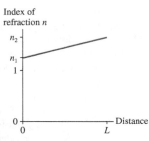

FIGURE CP20.80

a. Find an expression for the time light takes to travel through this piece of glass.
b. Evaluate your expression for a 1.0-cm-thick piece of glass for which $n_1 = 1.50$ and $n_2 = 1.60$.

81. A water wave is a *shallow-water wave* if the water depth d is less than $\approx \lambda/10$. It is shown in hydrodynamics that the speed of a shallow-water wave is $v = \sqrt{gd}$, so waves slow down as they move into shallower water. Ocean waves, with wavelengths of typically 100 m, are shallow-water waves when the water depth is less than ≈ 10 m. Consider a beach where the depth increases linearly with distance from the shore until reaching a depth of 5.0 m at a distance of 100 m. How long does it take a wave to move the last 100 m to the shore? Assume that the waves are so small that they don't break before reaching the shore.

82. An important characteristic of the heart, one used to diagnose heart disease, is the *pressure difference* between the blood pressure inside the heart and the blood pressure in the aorta, the large artery leading away from the heart. The blood inside the heart is essentially at rest, but it speeds up significantly as it enters the aorta—and its speed can be measured by using the Doppler shift of reflected ultrasound.
    a. The Doppler effect enters twice in calculating the frequency of the reflection from a moving object. Suppose the object's speed v_o is very small compared to the wave speed v. Show that a good approximation for the *Doppler shift*—the difference between the reflected frequency and the incident frequency—is

    $$\Delta f = 2f_0 \frac{v_o}{v}$$

    b. A doctor using 2.5 MHz ultrasound measures a 6000 Hz Doppler shift as the ultrasound reflects from blood ejected from the heart into the aorta. What is the blood pressure difference, in mm of Hg, between the inside of the heart and the aorta? Assume the patient is lying down so that there is no height difference between the heart and the aorta. The density of blood is 1060 kg/m³.

STOP TO THINK ANSWERS

Stop to Think 20.1: d and e. The wave speed depends on properties of the medium, not on how you generate the wave. For a string, $v = \sqrt{T_s/\mu}$. Increasing the tension or decreasing the linear density (lighter string) will increase the wave speed.

Stop to Think 20.2: b. The wave is traveling to the right at 2.0 m/s, so each point on the wave passes $x = 0$ m, the point of interest, 2.0 s before reaching $x = 4.0$ m. The graph has the same shape, but everything happens 2.0 s earlier.

Stop to Think 20.3: d. The wavelength—the distance between two crests—is seen to be 10 m. The frequency is $f = v/\lambda = (50 \text{ m/s})/(10 \text{ m}) = 5$ Hz.

Stop to Think 20.4: e. A crest and an adjacent trough are separated by $\lambda/2$. This is a phase difference of π rad.

Stop to Think 20.5: $n_c > n_a > n_b$. $\lambda = \lambda_{vac}/n$, so a shorter wavelength corresponds to a larger index of refraction.

Stop to Think 20.6: c. Any factor-of-2 change in intensity changes the sound intensity level by 3 dB. One trumpet is $\frac{1}{4}$ the original number, so the intensity has decreased by two factors of 2.

Stop to Think 20.7: c. Zack hears a higher frequency as he and the source approach. Amy is moving with the source, so $f_{Amy} = f_0$.

21 Superposition

This swirl of colors is due to a very thin layer of oil. Oil is clear. The colors arise from the interference of reflected light waves.

▶ **Looking Ahead** The goal of Chapter 21 is to understand and use the idea of superposition.

Standing Waves

Standing waves are created from the superposition of traveling waves bouncing back and forth between the edges of the medium.

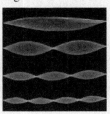

Standing waves occur in well-defined patterns called **modes,** each with its own distinct frequency. Some points on the wave, called **nodes,** do not oscillate at all.

You'll learn how to calculate the frequencies and wavelengths of standing waves on strings and in air.

Superposition

Waves can pass through each other—a characteristic that distinguishes waves from particles. As they do, their displacements add together. This is called the **principle of superposition**.

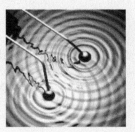

These water waves are exhibiting superposition as the ripples pass through each other.

You'll learn to analyze the response of the medium when two waves pass through each other.

Interference

When two sources emit waves of the same wavelength and frequency, the overlapped waves create an **interference pattern.**

You'll learn to interpret interference patterns such as this one. The two black dots are the sources of the waves.

Constructive interference occurs where the waves add to make a larger wave. *Destructive interference* is where the waves cancel to make a smaller wave.

Applications

You'll learn how standing waves determine the notes of a guitar and other musical instruments...

...and how interference is used to design antireflection coatings for lenses.

◀ **Looking Back**
Section 20.5 Sound waves

◀ **Looking Back**
Sections 20.2–20.4 Properties of traveling waves

Beats

The superposition of two waves of slightly different frequency produces a soft-loud-soft-loud-... modulation of the intensity called **beats.**

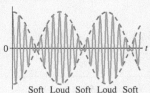

Soft Loud Soft Loud Soft

Beats are easily demonstrated with sound waves, but the concept is used in applications from ultrasonics to telecommunications.

21.1 The Principle of Superposition

FIGURE 21.1a shows two baseball players, Alan and Bill, at batting practice. Unfortunately, someone has turned the pitching machines so that pitching machine A throws baseballs toward Bill while machine B throws toward Alan. If two baseballs are launched at the same time, and with the same speed, they collide at the crossing point. Two particles cannot occupy the same point of space at the same time.

FIGURE 21.1 Unlike particles, two waves can pass directly through each other.

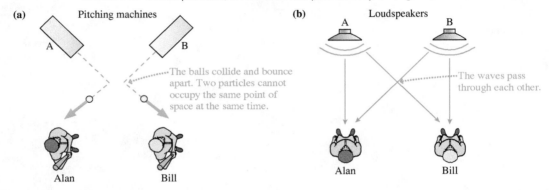

But waves, unlike particles, can pass directly through each other. In FIGURE 21.1b Alan and Bill are listening to the stereo system in the locker room after practice. Because both hear the music quite well, the sound wave that travels from loudspeaker A toward Bill must pass through the wave traveling from loudspeaker B toward Alan. What happens to the medium at a point where two waves are present simultaneously?

If wave 1 displaces a particle in the medium by D_1 and wave 2 *simultaneously* displaces it by D_2, the net displacement of the particle is simply $D_1 + D_2$. This is a very important idea because it tells us how to combine waves. It is known as the *principle of superposition.*

> **Principle of superposition** When two or more waves are *simultaneously* present at a single point in space, the displacement of the medium at that point is the sum of the displacements due to each individual wave.

When one object is placed on top of another, the two are said to be *superimposed.* But through some quirk in the English language, the result of superimposing objects is called a *superposition,* without the syllable "im." When one wave is "placed" on top of another wave, we have a superposition of waves.

Mathematically, the net displacement of a particle in the medium is

$$D_{net} = D_1 + D_2 + \cdots = \sum_i D_i \tag{21.1}$$

where D_i is the displacement that would be caused by wave i alone. We will make the simplifying assumption that the displacements of the individual waves are along the same line so that we can add displacements as scalars rather than vectors.

To use the principle of superposition you must know the displacement caused by each wave if traveling alone. Then you go through the medium *point by point* and add the displacements due to each wave *at that point* to find the net displacement at that point. The outcome will be different at each and every point in the medium because the displacements are different at each point.

To illustrate, FIGURE 21.2 shows snapshot graphs taken 1 s apart of two waves traveling at the same speed (1 m/s) in opposite directions along a string. The principle of superposition comes into play wherever the waves overlap. The solid line is the sum *at each point* of the two displacements at that point. This is the displacement that you would actually observe as the two waves pass through each other.

FIGURE 21.2 The superposition of two waves on a string as they pass through each other.

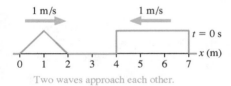

Two waves approach each other.

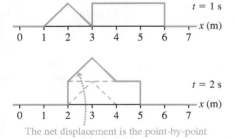

The net displacement is the point-by-point summation of the individual waves.

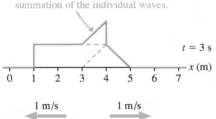

Both waves emerge unchanged.

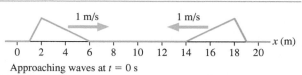

STOP TO THINK 21.1 Two pulses on a string approach each other at speeds of 1 m/s. What is the shape of the string at $t = 6$ s?

Approaching waves at $t = 0$ s

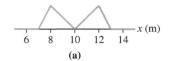

(a)

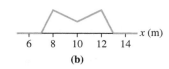

(b)

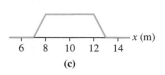

(c)

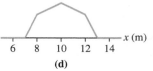

(d)

21.2 Standing Waves

FIGURE 21.3 is a time-lapse photograph of a *standing wave* on a vibrating string. It's not obvious from the photograph, but this is actually a superposition of two waves. To understand this, consider two sinusoidal waves **with the same frequency, wavelength, and amplitude** traveling in opposite directions. For example, FIGURE 21.4a shows two waves on a string, and FIGURE 21.4b shows nine snapshot graphs, at intervals of $\frac{1}{8}T$. The dots identify two of the crests to help you visualize the wave movement.

At *each point,* the net displacement—the superposition—is found by adding the red displacement and the green displacement. FIGURE 21.4c shows the result. It is the wave you would actually observe. The blue dot shows that the blue wave is moving neither right nor left. The wave of Figure 21.4c is called a **standing wave** because the crests and troughs "stand in place" as the wave oscillates.

FIGURE 21.3 A vibrating string is an example of a standing wave.

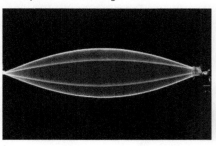

FIGURE 21.4 The superposition of two sinusoidal waves traveling in opposite directions.

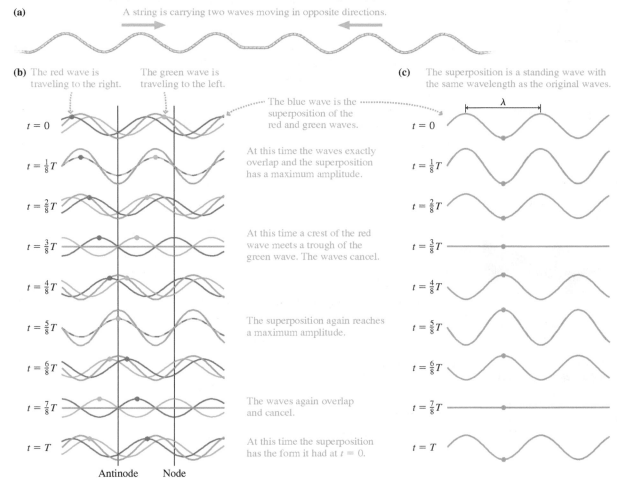

FIGURE 21.5 Standing waves are often represented as they would be seen in a time-lapse photograph.

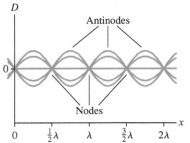

The nodes and antinodes are spaced λ/2 apart.

FIGURE 21.6 The intensity of a standing wave is maximum at the antinodes, zero at the nodes.

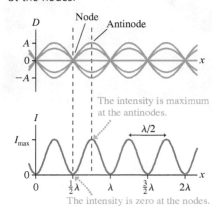

The intensity is maximum at the antinodes.

The intensity is zero at the nodes.

This photograph shows the Tacoma Narrows suspension bridge on the day in 1940 when it experienced a catastrophic standing-wave oscillation that led to its collapse. Aerodynamic forces caused the amplitude of a particular resonant mode of the bridge to increase dramatically until the bridge failed. In this photo, the red line shows the original line of the deck of the bridge. You can clearly see the large amplitude of the oscillation and the node at the center of the span.

Nodes and Antinodes

FIGURE 21.5 has collapsed the nine graphs of Figure 21.4b into a single graphical representation of a standing wave. Compare this to the Figure 21.3 photograph of a vibrating string. A striking feature of a standing-wave pattern is the existence of **nodes,** points that *never move!* **The nodes are spaced λ/2 apart.** Halfway between the nodes are the points where the particles in the medium oscillate with maximum displacement. These points of maximum amplitude are called **antinodes,** and you can see that they are also spaced λ/2 apart.

It seems surprising and counterintuitive that some particles in the medium have no motion at all. To understand how this happens, look carefully at the two traveling waves in Figure 21.4a. You will see that the nodes occur at points where at *every instant* of time the displacements of the two traveling waves have equal magnitudes but *opposite signs.* Thus the superposition of the displacements at these points is always zero. The antinodes correspond to points where the two displacements have equal magnitudes and the *same sign* at all times.

Two waves 1 and 2 are said to be *in phase* at a point where D_1 is *always* equal to D_2. The superposition at that point yields a wave whose amplitude is twice that of the individual waves. This is called a point of *constructive interference.* The antinodes of a standing wave are points of constructive interference between the two traveling waves.

In contrast, two waves are said to be *out of phase* at points where D_1 is *always* equal to $-D_2$. Their superposition gives a wave with zero amplitude—no wave at all! This is a point of *destructive interference.* The nodes of a standing wave are points of destructive interference. We will defer the main discussion of constructive and destructive interference until later in this chapter, but you'll then recognize that you're seeing constructive and destructive interference at the antinodes and nodes of a standing wave.

In Chapter 20 you learned that the *intensity* of a wave is proportional to the square of the amplitude: $I \propto A^2$. You can see in FIGURE 21.6 that maximum intensity occurs at the antinodes and that the intensity is zero at the nodes. If this is a sound wave, the loudness is maximum at the antinodes and zero at the nodes. A standing light wave is bright at the antinodes, dark at the nodes. The key idea is that **the intensity is maximum at points of constructive interference and zero at points of destructive interference.**

The Mathematics of Standing Waves

A sinusoidal wave traveling to the right along the *x*-axis with angular frequency $\omega = 2\pi f$, wave number $k = 2\pi/\lambda$, and amplitude a is

$$D_R = a \sin(kx - \omega t) \tag{21.2}$$

An equivalent wave traveling to the left is

$$D_L = a \sin(kx + \omega t) \tag{21.3}$$

We previously used the symbol A for the wave amplitude, but here we will use a lowercase a to represent the amplitude of each individual wave and reserve A for the amplitude of the net wave.

According to the principle of superposition, the net displacement of the medium when both waves are present is the sum of D_R and D_L:

$$D(x, t) = D_R + D_L = a \sin(kx - \omega t) + a \sin(kx + \omega t) \tag{21.4}$$

We can simplify Equation 21.4 by using the trigonometric identity

$$\sin(\alpha \pm \beta) = \sin \alpha \cos \beta \pm \cos \alpha \sin \beta$$

Doing so gives

$$D(x, t) = a(\sin kx \cos \omega t - \cos kx \sin \omega t) + a(\sin kx \cos \omega t + \cos kx \sin \omega t)$$
$$= (2a \sin kx) \cos \omega t \tag{21.5}$$

It is useful to write Equation 21.5 as

$$D(x, t) = A(x) \cos \omega t \qquad (21.6)$$

where the **amplitude function** $A(x)$ is defined as

$$A(x) = 2a \sin kx \qquad (21.7)$$

The amplitude reaches a maximum value $A_{max} = 2a$ at points where $\sin kx = 1$.

The displacement $D(x, t)$ given by Equation 21.6 is neither a function of $x - vt$ nor a function of $x + vt$; hence it is *not* a traveling wave. Instead, the $\cos \omega t$ term in Equation 21.6 describes a medium in which each point oscillates in simple harmonic motion with frequency $f = \omega/2\pi$. The function $A(x) = 2a \sin kx$ gives the amplitude of the oscillation for a particle at position x.

FIGURE 21.7 graphs Equation 21.6 at several different instants of time. Notice that the graphs are identical to those of Figure 21.5, showing us that Equation 21.6 is the mathematical description of a standing wave.

The nodes of the standing wave are the points at which the amplitude is zero. They are located at positions x for which

$$A(x) = 2a \sin kx = 0 \qquad (21.8)$$

The sine function is zero if the angle is an integer multiple of π rad, so Equation 21.8 is satisfied if

$$kx_m = \frac{2\pi x_m}{\lambda} = m\pi \qquad m = 0, 1, 2, 3, \ldots \qquad (21.9)$$

Thus the position x_m of the mth node is

$$x_m = m\frac{\lambda}{2} \qquad m = 0, 1, 2, 3, \ldots \qquad (21.10)$$

You can see that the spacing between two adjacent nodes is $\lambda/2$, in agreement with Figure 21.6. The nodes are *not* spaced by λ, as you might have expected.

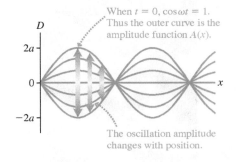

FIGURE 21.7 The net displacement resulting from two counter-propagating sinusoidal waves.

When $t = 0$, $\cos \omega t = 1$. Thus the outer curve is the amplitude function $A(x)$.

The oscillation amplitude changes with position.

EXAMPLE 21.1 **Node spacing on a string**

A very long string has a linear density of 5.0 g/m and is stretched with a tension of 8.0 N. 100 Hz waves with amplitudes of 2.0 mm are generated at the ends of the string.

a. What is the node spacing along the resulting standing wave?
b. What is the maximum displacement of the string?

MODEL Two counter-propagating waves of equal frequency create a standing wave.

VISUALIZE The standing wave will look like Figure 21.5.

SOLVE a. The speed of the waves on the string is

$$v = \sqrt{\frac{T_s}{\mu}} = \sqrt{\frac{8.0\ N}{0.0050\ kg/m}} = 40\ m/s$$

and the wavelength is

$$\lambda = \frac{v}{f} = \frac{40\ m/s}{100\ Hz} = 0.40\ m = 40\ cm$$

Thus the spacing between adjacent nodes is $\lambda/2 = 20$ cm.
b. The maximum displacement is $A_{max} = 2a = 4.0$ mm.

21.3 Standing Waves on a String

Wiggling both ends of a very long string is not a practical way to generate standing waves. Instead, as in the photograph in Figure 21.3, standing waves are usually seen on a string that is fixed at both ends. To understand why this condition causes standing waves, we need to examine what happens when a traveling wave encounters a discontinuity.

FIGURE 21.8a on the next page shows a *discontinuity* between a string with a larger linear density and one with a smaller linear density. The tension is the same in both strings, so the wave speed is slower on the left, faster on the right. Whenever a wave encounters a discontinuity, some of the wave's energy is *transmitted* forward and some is *reflected*.

FIGURE 21.8 A wave reflects when it encounters a discontinuity or a boundary.

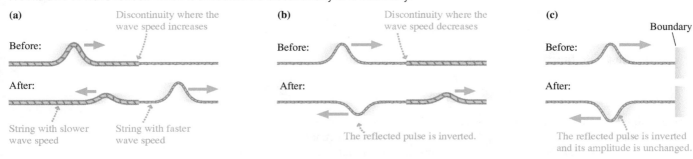

(a) Discontinuity where the wave speed increases

Before:

After:

String with slower wave speed   String with faster wave speed

(b) Discontinuity where the wave speed decreases

Before:

After:

The reflected pulse is inverted.

(c) Boundary

Before:

After:

The reflected pulse is inverted and its amplitude is unchanged.

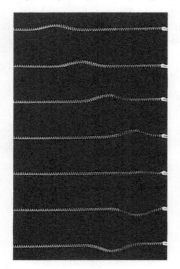

FIGURE 21.9 A strobe photo of a pulse traveling along a rope-like spring.

Light waves exhibit an analogous behavior when they encounter a piece of glass. Most of the light wave's energy is transmitted through the glass, which is why glass is transparent, but a small amount of energy is reflected. That is how you see your reflection dimly in a storefront window.

In FIGURE 21.8b, an incident wave encounters a discontinuity at which the wave speed decreases. In this case, the reflected pulse is *inverted*. A positive displacement of the incident wave becomes a negative displacement of the reflected wave. Because $\sin(\phi + \pi) = -\sin\phi$, we say that the reflected wave has a *phase change of π upon reflection*. This aspect of reflection will be important later in the chapter when we look at the interference of light waves.

The wave in FIGURE 21.8c reflects from a *boundary*. You can think of this as Figure 21.8b in the limit that the string on the right becomes infinitely massive. Thus the reflection in Figure 21.8c looks like that of Figure 21.8b with one exception: Because there is no transmitted wave, *all* the wave's energy is reflected. Hence **the amplitude of a wave reflected from a boundary is unchanged.** FIGURE 21.9 is a sequence of strobe photos in which you see a pulse on a rope-like spring reflecting from a boundary at the right of the photo. The reflected pulse is inverted but otherwise unchanged.

Creating Standing Waves

FIGURE 21.10 shows a string of length L tied at $x = 0$ and $x = L$. If you wiggle the string in the middle, sinusoidal waves travel outward in both directions and soon reach the boundaries. Because the speed of a reflected wave does not change, **the wavelength and frequency of a reflected sinusoidal wave are unchanged.** Consequently, reflections at the ends of the string cause two waves of *equal amplitude and wavelength* to travel in opposite directions along the string. As we've just seen, these are the conditions that cause a standing wave!

To connect the mathematical analysis of standing waves in Section 21.2 with the physical reality of a string tied down at the ends, we need to impose *boundary conditions*. A **boundary condition** is a mathematical statement of any constraint that *must* be obeyed at the boundary or edge of a medium. Because the string is tied down at the ends, the displacements at $x = 0$ and $x = L$ must be zero at all times. Thus the standing-wave boundary conditions are $D(x = 0, t) = 0$ and $D(x = L, t) = 0$. Stated another way, we require nodes at both ends of the string.

We found that the displacement of a standing wave is $D(x, t) = (2a \sin kx) \cos \omega t$. This equation already satisfies the boundary condition $D(x = 0, t) = 0$. That is, the origin has already been located at a node. The second boundary condition, at $x = L$, requires $D(x = L, t) = 0$. This condition will be met at all times if

$$2a \sin kL = 0 \quad \text{(boundary condition at } x = L) \quad (21.11)$$

Equation 21.11 will be true if $\sin kL = 0$, which in turn requires

$$kL = \frac{2\pi L}{\lambda} = m\pi \qquad m = 1, 2, 3, 4, \ldots \quad (21.12)$$

kL must be a multiple of $m\pi$, but $m = 0$ is excluded because L can't be zero.

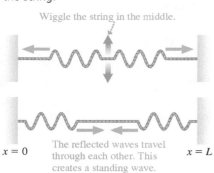

FIGURE 21.10 Reflections at the two boundaries cause a standing wave on the string.

Wiggle the string in the middle.

$x = 0$ The reflected waves travel through each other. This creates a standing wave. $x = L$

For a string of fixed length L, the only quantity in Equation 21.12 that can vary is λ. That is, the boundary condition is satisfied only if the wavelength has one of the values

$$\lambda_m = \frac{2L}{m} \qquad m = 1, 2, 3, 4, \ldots \qquad (21.13)$$

A standing wave can exist on the string *only* if its wavelength is one of the values given by Equation 21.13. The mth possible wavelength $\lambda_m = 2L/m$ is just the right size so that its mth node is located at the end of the string (at $x = L$).

NOTE ▶ Other wavelengths, which would be perfectly acceptable wavelengths for a traveling wave, cannot exist as a *standing* wave of length L because they cannot meet the boundary conditions requiring a node at each end of the string. ◀

If standing waves are possible only for certain wavelengths, then only a few specific oscillation frequencies are allowed. Because $\lambda f = v$ for a sinusoidal wave, the oscillation frequency corresponding to wavelength λ_m is

$$f_m = \frac{v}{\lambda_m} = \frac{v}{2L/m} = m\frac{v}{2L} \qquad m = 1, 2, 3, 4, \ldots \qquad (21.14)$$

The lowest allowed frequency

$$f_1 = \frac{v}{2L} \qquad \text{(fundamental frequency)} \qquad (21.15)$$

which corresponds to wavelength $\lambda_1 = 2L$, is called the **fundamental frequency** of the string. The allowed frequencies can be written in terms of the fundamental frequency as

$$f_m = mf_1 \qquad m = 1, 2, 3, 4, \ldots \qquad (21.16)$$

The allowed standing-wave frequencies are all integer multiples of the fundamental frequency. The higher-frequency standing waves are called **harmonics,** with the $m = 2$ wave at frequency f_2 called the *second harmonic,* the $m = 3$ wave called the *third harmonic,* and so on.

FIGURE 21.11 graphs the first four possible standing waves on a string of fixed length L. These possible standing waves are called the **modes** of the string, or sometimes the *normal modes.* Each mode, numbered by the integer m, has a unique wavelength and frequency. Keep in mind that these drawings simply show the *envelope,* or outer edge, of the oscillations. The string is continuously oscillating at all positions between these edges, as we showed in more detail in Figure 21.5.

There are three things to note about the modes of a string.

1. m is the number of *antinodes* on the standing wave, not the number of nodes. You can tell a string's mode of oscillation by counting the number of antinodes.
2. The *fundamental mode,* with $m = 1$, has $\lambda_1 = 2L$, not $\lambda_1 = L$. Only half of a wavelength is contained between the boundaries, a direct consequence of the fact that the spacing between nodes is $\lambda/2$.
3. The frequencies of the normal modes form a series: $f_1, 2f_1, 3f_1, 4f_1, \ldots$. The fundamental frequency f_1 can be found as the *difference* between the frequencies of any two adjacent modes. That is, $f_1 = \Delta f = f_{m+1} - f_m$.

FIGURE 21.12 is a time-exposure photograph of the $m = 3$ standing wave on a string. The nodes and antinodes are quite distinct. The string vibrates three times faster for the $m = 3$ mode than for the fundamental $m = 1$ mode.

FIGURE 21.11 The first four modes for standing waves on a string of length L.

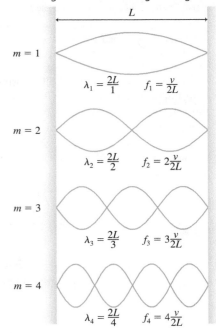

FIGURE 21.12 Time-exposure photograph of the $m = 3$ standing-wave mode on a stretched string.

EXAMPLE 21.2 Measuring g

Standing-wave frequencies can be measured very accurately. Consequently, standing waves are often used in experiments to make accurate measurements of other quantities. One such experiment, shown in FIGURE 21.13, uses standing waves to measure the free-fall acceleration g. A heavy mass is suspended from a 1.65-m-long, 5.85 g steel wire; then an oscillating magnetic field (because steel is magnetic) is used to excite the $m = 3$ standing wave on the wire. Measuring the frequency for different masses yields the following data:

FIGURE 21.13 An experiment to measure g with standing waves.

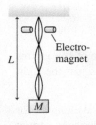

Mass (kg)	f_3 (Hz)
2.00	68
4.00	97
6.00	117
8.00	135
10.00	152

Analyze these data to determine the local value of g.

MODEL The hanging mass creates tension in the wire. This establishes the wave speed along the wire and thus the frequencies of standing waves. Masses of a few kg might stretch the wire a mm or so, but that doesn't change the length L until the third decimal place. The mass of the wire itself is insignificant in comparison to that of the hanging mass. We'll be justified in determining g to three significant figures.

SOLVE The frequency of the third harmonic is

$$f_3 = \frac{3}{2}\frac{v}{L}$$

The wave speed on the wire is

$$v = \sqrt{\frac{T_s}{\mu}} = \sqrt{\frac{Mg}{m/L}} = \sqrt{\frac{MgL}{m}}$$

where Mg is the weight of the hanging mass, and thus the tension in the wire, while m is the mass of the wire. Combining these two equations, we have

$$f_3 = \frac{3}{2}\sqrt{\frac{Mg}{mL}} = \frac{3}{2}\sqrt{\frac{g}{mL}}\sqrt{M}$$

Squaring both sides gives

$$f_3^2 = \frac{9g}{4mL}M$$

A graph of the square of the standing-wave frequency versus mass M should be a straight line passing through the origin with slope $9g/4mL$. We can use the experimental slope to determine g.

FIGURE 21.14 is a graph of f_3^2 versus M. The slope of the best-fit line is 2289 $kg^{-1}s^{-2}$, from which we find

$$g = \text{slope} \times \frac{4mL}{9}$$

$$= 2289\ kg^{-1}s^{-2} \times \frac{4(0.00585\ \text{kg})(1.65\ \text{m})}{9} = 9.82\ \text{m/s}^2$$

FIGURE 21.14 Graph of the data.

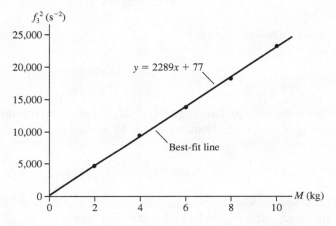

ASSESS The fact that the graph is linear and passes through the origin confirms our model. This is an important reason for having multiple data points rather than using only one mass.

STOP TO THINK 21.2 A standing wave on a string vibrates as shown at the right. Suppose the string tension is quadrupled while the frequency and the length of the string are held constant. Which standing-wave pattern is produced?

Original standing wave

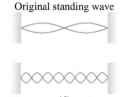

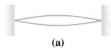

(a)

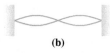

(b)

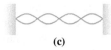

(c)

(d)

Standing Electromagnetic Waves

Because electromagnetic waves are transverse waves, a standing electromagnetic wave is very much like a standing wave on a string. Standing electromagnetic waves can be established between two parallel mirrors that reflect light back and forth. The mirrors are boundaries, analogous to the boundaries at the ends of a string. In fact, this is exactly how a laser operates. The two facing mirrors in FIGURE 21.15 form what is called a *laser cavity*.

Because the mirrors act like the points to which a string is tied, the light wave must have a node at the surface of each mirror. One of the mirrors is only partially reflective, to allow some light to escape and form the laser beam, but this doesn't affect the boundary condition.

Because the boundary conditions are the same, Equations 21.13 and 21.14 for λ_m and f_n apply to a laser just as they do to a vibrating string. The primary difference is the size of the wavelength. A typical laser cavity has a length $L \approx 30$ cm, and visible light has a wavelength $\lambda \approx 600$ nm. The standing light wave in a laser cavity has a mode number m that is approximately

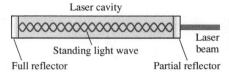

FIGURE 21.15 A laser contains a standing light wave between two parallel mirrors.

Laser cavity

Standing light wave

Full reflector   Partial reflector

Laser beam

$$m = \frac{2L}{\lambda} \approx \frac{2 \times 0.30 \text{ m}}{6.00 \times 10^{-7} \text{ m}} = 1{,}000{,}000$$

In other words, the standing light wave inside a laser cavity has approximately one million antinodes! This is a consequence of the very short wavelength of light.

EXAMPLE 21.3 **The standing light wave inside a laser**

Helium-neon lasers emit the red laser light commonly used in classroom demonstrations and supermarket checkout scanners. A helium-neon laser operates at a wavelength of precisely 632.9924 nm when the spacing between the mirrors is 310.372 mm.

a. In which mode does this laser operate?
b. What is the next longest wavelength that could form a standing wave in this laser cavity?

MODEL The light wave forms a standing wave between the two mirrors.

VISUALIZE The standing wave looks like Figure 21.15.

SOLVE a. We can use $\lambda_m = 2L/m$ to find that m (the mode) is

$$m = \frac{2L}{\lambda_m} = \frac{2(0.310372 \text{ m})}{6.329924 \times 10^{-7} \text{ m}} = 980{,}650$$

There are 980,650 antinodes in the standing light wave.
b. The next longest wavelength that can fit in this laser cavity will have one fewer node. It will be the $m = 980{,}649$ mode and its wavelength will be

$$\lambda = \frac{2L}{m} = \frac{2(0.310372 \text{ m})}{980{,}649} = 632.9930 \text{ nm}$$

ASSESS The wavelength increases by a mere 0.0006 nm when the mode number is decreased by 1.

Microwaves, with a wavelength of a few centimeters, can also set up standing waves. This is not always good. If the microwaves in a microwave oven form a standing wave, there are nodes where the electromagnetic field intensity is always zero. These nodes cause cold spots where the food does not heat. Although designers of microwave ovens try to prevent standing waves, ovens usually do have cold spots spaced $\lambda/2$ apart at nodes in the microwave field. A turntable in a microwave oven keeps the food moving so that no part of your dinner remains at a node.

21.4 Standing Sound Waves and Musical Acoustics

A long, narrow column of air, such as the air in a tube or pipe, can support a *longitudinal* standing sound wave. Longitudinal waves are somewhat trickier than string waves because a graph—showing displacement *parallel* to the tube—is not a picture of the wave.

To illustrate the ideas, FIGURE 21.16 on the next page is a series of three graphs and pictures that show the $m = 2$ standing wave inside a column of air closed at both ends. We call this a *closed-closed tube*. The air at the closed ends cannot oscillate because the air molecules are pressed up against the wall, unable to move; hence **a closed end of a column of air must be a displacement node.** Thus the boundary conditions— nodes at the ends—are the same as for a standing wave on a string.

Although the graph looks familiar, it is now a graph of *longitudinal* displacement. At $t = 0$, positive displacements in the left half and negative displacements in the right half cause all the air molecules to converge at the center of the tube. The density and pressure rise at the center and fall at the ends—a *compression* and *rarefaction* in the terminology of Chapter 20. A half cycle later, the molecules have rushed to the ends

FIGURE 21.16 This time sequence of graphs and pictures illustrates the $m = 2$ standing sound wave in a closed-closed tube of air.

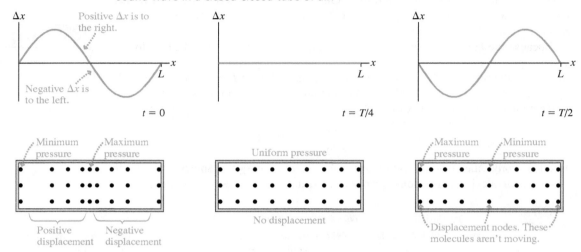

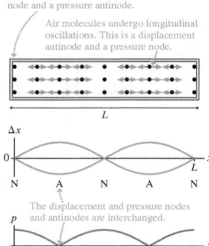

FIGURE 21.17 The $m = 2$ longitudinal standing wave can be represented as a displacement wave or as a pressure wave.

The closed end is a displacement node and a pressure antinode.

Air molecules undergo longitudinal oscillations. This is a displacement antinode and a pressure node.

The displacement and pressure nodes and antinodes are interchanged.

The pressure is oscillating around atmospheric pressure p_{atmos}.

of the tube. Now the pressure is maximum at the ends, minimum in the center. Try to visualize the air molecules sloshing back and forth this way.

FIGURE 21.17 combines these illustrations into a single picture showing where the molecules are oscillating (antinodes) and where they're not (nodes). A graph of the displacement Δx looks just like the $m = 2$ graph of a standing wave on a string. Because the boundary conditions are the same, the possible wavelengths and frequencies of standing waves in a closed-closed tube are the same as for a string of the same length.

It is often useful to think of sound as a *pressure wave* rather than a displacement wave, and the bottom graph in Figure 21.17 shows the $m = 2$ pressure standing wave in a closed-closed tube. Notice that the pressure is oscillating around p_{atmos}, its equilibrium value. **The nodes and antinodes of the pressure wave are interchanged with those of the displacement wave,** and a careful study of Figure 21.16 reveals why. The gas molecules are alternately pushed up against the ends of the tube, then pulled away, causing the pressure at the closed ends to oscillate with maximum amplitude—an antinode.

EXAMPLE 21.4 Singing in the shower

A shower stall is 2.45 m (8 ft) tall. For what frequencies less than 500 Hz are there standing sound waves in the shower stall?

MODEL The shower stall, to a first approximation, is a column of air 2.45 m long. It is closed at the ends by the ceiling and floor. Assume a 20°C speed of sound.

VISUALIZE A standing sound wave will have nodes at the ceiling and the floor. The $m = 2$ mode will look like Figure 21.17 rotated 90°.

SOLVE The fundamental frequency for a standing sound wave in this air column is

$$f_1 = \frac{v}{2L} = \frac{343 \text{ m/s}}{2(2.45 \text{ m})} = 70 \text{ Hz}$$

The possible standing-wave frequencies are integer multiples of the fundamental frequency. These are 70 Hz, 140 Hz, 210 Hz, 280 Hz, 350 Hz, 420 Hz, and 490 Hz.

ASSESS The many possible standing waves in a shower cause the sound to *resonate,* which helps explain why some people like to sing in the shower. Our approximation of the shower stall as a one-dimensional tube is actually a bit too simplistic. A three-dimensional analysis would find additional modes, making the "sound spectrum" even richer.

Air columns closed at both ends are of limited interest unless, as in Example 21.4, you are inside the column. Columns of air that *emit* sound are open at one or both ends. Many musical instruments fit this description. For example, a flute is a tube of air open at both ends. The flutist blows across one end to create a standing wave inside the tube, and a note of that frequency is emitted from both ends of the flute. (The blown end of a flute is open on the side, rather than across the tube. That is necessary for practical reasons of how flutes are played, but from a physics perspective this is the "end" of the tube because it opens the tube to the atmosphere.) A trumpet, however, is open at the bell end but is *closed* by the player's lips at the other end.

You saw earlier that a wave is partially transmitted and partially reflected at a discontinuity. When a sound wave traveling through a tube of air reaches an open end, some of the wave's energy is transmitted out of the tube to become the sound that you hear and some portion of the wave is reflected back into the tube. These reflections, analogous to the reflection of a string wave from a boundary, allow standing sound waves to exist in a tube of air that is open at one or both ends.

Not surprisingly, the *boundary condition* at the open end of a column of air is not the same as the boundary condition at a closed end. The air pressure at the open end of a tube is constrained to match the atmospheric pressure of the surrounding air. Consequently, the open end of a tube must be a pressure node. Because pressure nodes and antinodes are interchanged with those of the displacement wave, **an open end of an air column is required to be a displacement antinode.** (A careful analysis shows that the antinode is actually just outside the open end, but for our purposes we'll assume the antinode is exactly at the open end.)

FIGURE 21.18 shows displacement and pressure graphs of the first three standing-wave modes of a tube closed at both ends (a *closed-closed tube*), a tube open at both ends (an *open-open tube*), and a tube open at one end but closed at the other (an *open-closed tube*), all with the same length L. Notice the pressure and displacement boundary conditions. The standing wave in the open-open tube looks like the closed-closed tube except that the positions of the nodes and antinodes are interchanged. In both cases there are m half-wavelength segments between the ends; thus the wavelengths and frequencies of an open-open tube and a closed-closed tube are the same as those of a string tied at both ends:

FIGURE 21.18 The first three standing sound wave modes in columns of air with different boundary conditions.

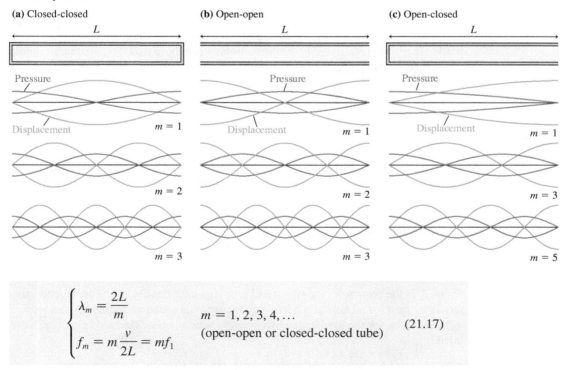

$$\begin{cases} \lambda_m = \dfrac{2L}{m} \\ f_m = m\dfrac{v}{2L} = mf_1 \end{cases} \quad \begin{matrix} m = 1, 2, 3, 4, \ldots \\ \text{(open-open or closed-closed tube)} \end{matrix} \quad (21.17)$$

The open-closed tube is different. The fundamental mode has only one-quarter of a wavelength in a tube of length L; hence the $m = 1$ wavelength is $\lambda_1 = 4L$. This is twice the λ_1 wavelength of an open-open or a closed-closed tube. Consequently, **the fundamental frequency of an open-closed tube is half that of an open-open or a closed-closed tube of the same length.** It will be left as a homework problem for you to show that the possible wavelengths and frequencies of an open-closed tube of length L are

$$\begin{cases} \lambda_m = \dfrac{4L}{m} \\[2mm] f_m = m\dfrac{v}{4L} = mf_1 \end{cases} \quad \begin{array}{l} m = 1, 3, 5, 7, \ldots \\ \text{(open-closed tube)} \end{array} \qquad (21.18)$$

Notice that m in Equation 21.18 takes on only *odd* values.

EXAMPLE 21.5 **Resonances of the ear canal**

The eardrum, which transmits sounds vibrations to the sensory organs of the inner ear, lies at the end of the ear canal. For adults, the ear canal is about 2.5 cm in length. What frequency standing waves can occur in the ear canal that are within the range of human hearing? The speed of sound in the warm air of the ear canal is 350 m/s.

MODEL The ear canal is open to the air at one end, closed by the eardrum at the other. We can model it as an open-closed tube. The standing waves will be those of Figure 21.18c.

SOLVE The lowest standing-wave frequency is the fundamental frequency for a 2.5-cm-long open-closed tube:

$$f_1 = \frac{v}{4L} = \frac{350 \text{ m/s}}{4(0.025 \text{ m})} = 3500 \text{ Hz}$$

Standing waves also occur at the harmonics, but an open-closed tube has only odd harmonics. These are

$$f_3 = 3f_1 = 10{,}500 \text{ Hz}$$
$$f_5 = 5f_1 = 17{,}500 \text{ Hz}$$

Higher harmonics are beyond the range of human hearing, as discussed in Section 20.5.

ASSESS The ear canal is short, so we expected the standing-wave frequencies to be relatively high. The air in your ear canal responds readily to sounds at these frequencies—what we call a *resonance* of the ear canal—and transmits theses sounds to the eardrum. Consequently, your ear actually is slightly more sensitive to sounds with frequencies around 3500 Hz and 10,500 Hz than to sounds at nearby frequencies.

STOP TO THINK 21.3 An open-open tube of air supports standing waves at frequencies of 300 Hz and 400 Hz and at no frequencies between these two. The second harmonic of this tube has frequency

a. 100 Hz   b. 200 Hz   c. 400 Hz   d. 600 Hz   e. 800 Hz

Musical Instruments

An important application of standing waves is to musical instruments. Instruments such as the guitar, the piano, and the violin have strings fixed at the ends and tightened to create tension. A disturbance generated on the string by plucking, striking, or bowing it creates a standing wave on the string.

The fundamental frequency of a vibrating string is

$$f_1 = \frac{v}{2L} = \frac{1}{2L}\sqrt{\frac{T_s}{\mu}}$$

where T_s is the tension in the string and μ is its linear density. The fundamental frequency is the musical note you hear when the string is sounded. Increasing the tension in the string raises the fundamental frequency, which is how stringed instruments are tuned.

NOTE ▶ v is the wave speed *on the string,* not the speed of sound in air. ◀

For the guitar or the violin, the strings are all the same length and under approximately the same tension. Were that not the case, the neck of the instrument would tend to twist toward the side of higher tension. The strings have different frequencies because they differ in linear density: The lower-pitched strings are "fat" while the higher-pitched strings are "skinny." This difference changes the frequency by changing the wave speed. *Small* adjustments are then made in the tension to bring each string to the exact desired frequency. Once the instrument is tuned, you play it by using your fingertips to alter the effective length of the string. As you shorten the string's length, the frequency and pitch go up.

A piano covers a much wider range of frequencies than a guitar or violin. This range cannot be produced by changing only the linear densities of the strings. The high end would have strings too thin to use without breaking, and the low end would have solid rods rather than flexible wires! So a piano is tuned through a combination of changing the linear density *and* the length of the strings. The bass note strings are not only fatter, they are also longer.

With a wind instrument, blowing into the mouthpiece creates a standing sound wave inside a tube of air. The player changes the notes by using her fingers to cover holes or open valves, changing the length of the tube and thus its frequency. The fact that the holes are on the side makes very little difference; the first open hole becomes an antinode because the air is free to oscillate in and out of the opening.

A wind instrument's frequency depends on the speed of sound *inside* the instrument. But the speed of sound depends on the temperature of the air. When a wind player first blows into the instrument, the air inside starts to rise in temperature. This increases the sound speed, which in turn raises the instrument's frequency for each note until the air temperature reaches a steady state. Consequently, wind players must "warm up" before tuning their instrument.

Many wind instruments have a "buzzer" at one end of the tube, such as a vibrating reed on a saxophone or vibrating lips on a trombone. Buzzers generate a continuous range of frequencies rather than single notes, which is why they sound like a "squawk" if you play on just the mouthpiece without the rest of the instrument. When a buzzer is connected to the body of the instrument, most of those frequencies cause no response of the air molecules. But the frequency from the buzzer that matches the fundamental frequency of the instrument causes the buildup of a large-amplitude response at just that frequency—a standing-wave resonance. This is the energy input that generates and sustains the musical note.

The strings on a harp vibrate as standing waves. Their frequencies determine the notes that you hear.

EXAMPLE 21.6 Flutes and clarinets

A clarinet is 66.0 cm long. A flute is nearly the same length, with 63.5 cm between the hole the player blows across and the end of the flute. What are the frequencies of the lowest note and the next higher harmonic on a flute and on a clarinet? The speed of sound in warm air is 350 m/s.

MODEL The flute is an open-open tube, open at the end as well as at the hole the player blows across. A clarinet is an open-closed tube because the player's lips and the reed seal the tube at the upper end.

SOLVE The lowest frequency is the fundamental frequency. For the flute, an open-open tube, this is

$$f_1 = \frac{v}{2L} = \frac{350 \text{ m/s}}{2(0.635 \text{ m})} = 275 \text{ Hz}$$

The clarinet, an open-closed tube, has

$$f_1 = \frac{v}{4L} = \frac{350 \text{ m/s}}{4(0.660 \text{ m})} = 133 \text{ Hz}$$

The next higher harmonic on the flute's open-open tube is $m = 2$ with frequency $f_2 = 2f_1 = 550$ Hz. An open-closed tube has only odd harmonics, so the next higher harmonic of the clarinet is $f_3 = 3f_1 = 399$ Hz.

ASSESS The clarinet plays a much lower note than the flute—musically, about an octave lower—because it is an open-closed tube. It's worth noting that neither of our fundamental frequencies is exactly correct because our open-open and open-closed tube models are a bit too simplified to adequately describe a real instrument. However, both calculated frequencies are close because our models do capture the essence of the physics.

A vibrating string plays the musical note corresponding to the fundamental frequency f_1, so stringed instruments must use several strings to obtain a reasonable range of notes. In contrast, wind instruments can sound at the second or third harmonic of the tube of air (f_2 or f_3). These higher frequencies are sounded by *overblowing* (flutes, brass instruments) or with keys that open small holes to encourage the formation of an antinode at that point (clarinets, saxophones). The controlled use of these higher harmonics gives wind instruments a wide range of notes.

21.5 Interference in One Dimension

One of the most basic characteristics of waves is the ability of two waves to combine into a single wave whose displacement is given by the principle of superposition. The pattern resulting from the superposition of two waves is often called **interference.** A standing wave is the interference pattern produced when two waves of equal frequency travel in opposite directions. In this section we will look at the interference of two waves traveling in the *same* direction.

FIGURE 21.19 Two overlapped waves travel along the x-axis.

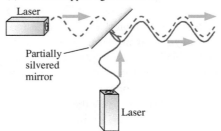 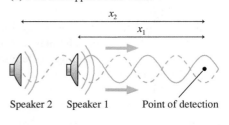

FIGURE 21.19a shows two light waves impinging on a partially silvered mirror. Such a mirror partially transmits and partially reflects each wave, causing two *overlapped* light waves to travel along the x-axis to the right of the mirror. Or consider the two loudspeakers in FIGURE 21.19b. The sound wave from loudspeaker 2 passes just to the side of loudspeaker 1; hence two overlapped sound waves travel to the right along the x-axis. We want to find out what happens when two overlapped waves travel in the same direction along the same axis.

Figure 21.19b shows a point on the x-axis where the overlapped waves are detected, either by your ear or by a microphone. This point is distance x_1 from loudspeaker 1 and distance x_2 from loudspeaker 2. (We will use loudspeakers and sound waves for most of our examples, but our analysis is valid for any wave.) What is the amplitude of the combined waves at this point?

Throughout this section, **we will assume that the waves are sinusoidal, have the same frequency and amplitude, and travel to the right along the x-axis.** Thus we can write the displacements of the two waves as

$$D_1(x_1, t) = a\sin(kx_1 - \omega t + \phi_{10}) = a\sin\phi_1$$
$$D_2(x_2, t) = a\sin(kx_2 - \omega t + \phi_{20}) = a\sin\phi_2$$
(21.19)

where ϕ_1 and ϕ_2 are the *phases* of the waves. Both waves have the same wave number $k = 2\pi/\lambda$ and the same angular frequency $\omega = 2\pi f$.

The phase constants ϕ_{10} and ϕ_{20} are characteristics of *the sources,* not the medium. FIGURE 21.20 shows snapshot graphs at $t = 0$ of waves emitted by three sources with phase constants $\phi_0 = 0$ rad, $\phi_0 = \pi/2$ rad, and $\phi_0 = \pi$ rad. You can see that **the phase constant tells us what the source is doing at $t = 0$.** For example, a loudspeaker at its center position and moving backward at $t = 0$ has $\phi_0 = 0$ rad. Looking back at Figure 21.19b, you can see that loudspeaker 1 has phase constant $\phi_{10} = 0$ rad and loudspeaker 2 has $\phi_{20} = \pi$ rad.

NOTE ▶ We will often consider *identical sources,* by which we mean that $\phi_{20} = \phi_{10}$. That is, the sources oscillate in phase. ◀

Let's examine overlapped waves graphically before diving into the mathematics. FIGURE 21.21 shows two important situations. In part a, the crests of the two waves are aligned as they travel along the x-axis. In part b, the crests of one wave align with the troughs of the other wave. The graphs and the wave fronts are slightly displaced from

FIGURE 21.20 Waves from three sources having phase constants $\phi_0 = 0$ rad, $\phi_0 = \pi/2$ rad, and $\phi_0 = \pi$ rad.

(a) Snapshot graph at $t = 0$ for $\phi_0 = 0$ rad

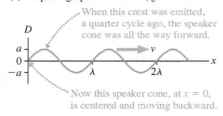

(b) Snapshot graph at $t = 0$ for $\phi_0 = \pi/2$ rad

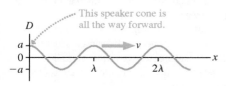

(c) Snapshot graph at $t = 0$ for $\phi_0 = \pi$ rad

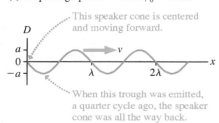

each other so that you can see what each wave is doing, but the *physical situation* is one in which the waves are traveling *on top of* each other. Recall, from Chapter 20, that the wave fronts shown in the middle panel locate the crests of the waves.

The two waves of FIGURE 21.21a have the same displacement at every point: $D_1(x) = D_2(x)$. Two waves that are aligned crest to crest and trough to trough are said to be **in phase**. Waves that are in phase march along "in step" with each other.

When we combine two in-phase waves, using the principle of superposition, the net displacement at each point is twice the displacement of each individual wave. The superposition of two waves to create a traveling wave with an amplitude *larger* than either individual wave is called **constructive interference**. When the waves are exactly in phase, giving $A = 2a$, we have *maximum constructive interference*.

In FIGURE 21.21b, where the crests of one wave align with the troughs of the other, the waves march along "out of step" with $D_1(x) = -D_2(x)$ at every point. Two waves that are aligned crest to trough are said to be *180° out of phase* or, more generally, just **out of phase**. A superposition of two waves to create a wave with an amplitude smaller than either individual wave is called **destructive interference**. In this case, because $D_1 = -D_2$, the net displacement is *zero* at *every point* along the axis. The combination of two waves that cancel each other to give no wave is called *perfect destructive interference*.

NOTE ▶ Perfect destructive interference occurs only if the two waves have equal wavelengths and amplitudes, as we're assuming. Two waves of unequal amplitudes can interfere destructively, but the cancellation won't be perfect. ◀

The Phase Difference

To understand interference, we need to focus on the *phases* of the two waves, which are

$$\phi_1 = kx_1 - \omega t + \phi_{10}$$
$$\phi_2 = kx_2 - \omega t + \phi_{20}$$
(21.20)

The difference between the two phases ϕ_1 and ϕ_2, called the **phase difference** $\Delta\phi$, is

$$\Delta\phi = \phi_2 - \phi_1 = (kx_2 - \omega t + \phi_{20}) - (kx_1 - \omega t + \phi_{10})$$

$$= k(x_2 - x_1) + (\phi_{20} - \phi_{10})$$
(21.21)

$$= 2\pi \frac{\Delta x}{\lambda} + \Delta\phi_0$$

You can see that there are two contributions to the phase difference. $\Delta x = x_2 - x_1$, the distance between the two sources, is called **path-length difference**. It is the extra distance traveled by wave 2 on the way to the point where the two waves are combined. $\Delta\phi_0 = \phi_{20} - \phi_{10}$ is the *inherent phase difference* between the sources.

The condition of being in phase, where crests are aligned with crests and troughs with troughs, is $\Delta\phi = 0, 2\pi, 4\pi$, or any integer multiple of 2π rad. Thus the condition for maximum constructive interference is

Maximum constructive interference:
$$\Delta\phi = 2\pi \frac{\Delta x}{\lambda} + \Delta\phi_0 = m \cdot 2\pi \text{ rad} \qquad m = 0, 1, 2, 3, \ldots$$
(21.22)

For identical sources, which have $\Delta\phi_0 = 0$ rad, maximum constructive interference occurs when $\Delta x = m\lambda$. That is, **two identical sources produce maximum constructive interference when the path-length difference is an integer number of wavelengths.**

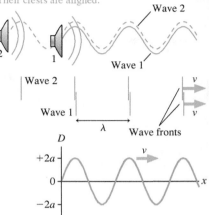

FIGURE 21.21 Constructive and destructive interference of two waves traveling along the x-axis.

(a) Constructive interference

These two waves are in phase. Their crests are aligned.

Their superposition produces a traveling wave moving to the right with amplitude $2a$. This is maximum constructive interference.

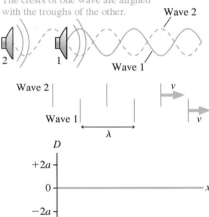

(b) Destructive interference

These two waves are out of phase. The crests of one wave are aligned with the troughs of the other.

Their superposition produces a wave with zero amplitude. This is perfect destructive interference.

FIGURE 21.22 Two identical sources one wavelength apart.

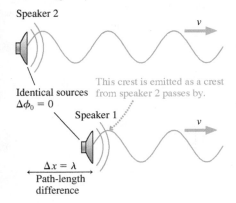

Speaker 2

Identical sources
$\Delta\phi_0 = 0$

This crest is emitted as a crest from speaker 2 passes by.

Speaker 1

$\Delta x = \lambda$
Path-length difference

The two waves are in phase ($\Delta\phi = 2\pi$ rad) and interfere constructively.

FIGURE 21.22 shows two identical sources (i.e., the two loudspeakers are doing the same thing at the same time), so $\Delta\phi_0 = 0$ rad. The path-length difference Δx is the extra distance traveled by the wave from loudspeaker 2 before it combines with loudspeaker 1. In this case, $\Delta x = \lambda$. Because a wave moves forward exactly one wavelength during one period, loudspeaker 1 emits a crest exactly as a crest of wave 2 passes by. The two waves are "in step," with $\Delta\phi = 2\pi$ rad, so the two waves interfere constructively to produce a wave of amplitude $2a$.

Perfect destructive interference, where the crests of one wave are aligned with the troughs of the other, occurs when two waves are *out of phase*, meaning that $\Delta\phi = \pi$, 3π, 5π, or any odd multiple of π rad. Thus the condition for perfect destructive interference is

Perfect destructive interference:

$$\Delta\phi = 2\pi\frac{\Delta x}{\lambda} + \Delta\phi_0 = \left(m + \frac{1}{2}\right) \cdot 2\pi \text{ rad} \qquad m = 0, 1, 2, 3, \ldots \qquad (21.23)$$

For identical sources, which have $\Delta\phi_0 = 0$ rad, perfect destructive interference occurs when $\Delta x = (m + \frac{1}{2})\lambda$. **That is, two identical sources produce perfect destructive interference when the path-length difference is a half-integer number of wavelengths.**

Two waves can be out of phase because the sources are located at different positions, because the sources themselves are out of phase, or because of a combination of these two. FIGURE 21.23 illustrates these ideas by showing three different ways in which two waves interfere destructively. Each of these three arrangements creates waves with $\Delta\phi = \pi$ rad.

FIGURE 21.23 Destructive interference three ways.

(a) The sources are out of phase.

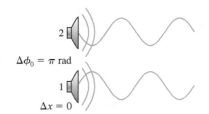

$\Delta\phi_0 = \pi$ rad

$\Delta x = 0$

(b) Identical sources are separated by half a wavelength.

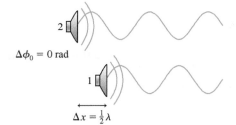

$\Delta\phi_0 = 0$ rad

$\Delta x = \frac{1}{2}\lambda$

(c) The sources are both separated and partially out of phase.

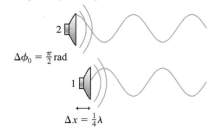

$\Delta\phi_0 = \frac{\pi}{2}$ rad

$\Delta x = \frac{1}{4}\lambda$

NOTE ▶ Don't confuse the phase difference of the waves ($\Delta\phi$) with the phase difference of the sources ($\Delta\phi_0$). It is $\Delta\phi$, the phase difference of the waves, that governs interference. ◀

EXAMPLE 21.7 **Interference between two sound waves**

You are standing in front of two side-by-side loudspeakers playing sounds of the same frequency. Initially there is almost no sound at all. Then one of the speakers is moved slowly away from you. The sound intensity increases as the separation between the speakers increases, reaching a maximum when the speakers are 0.75 m apart. Then, as the speaker continues to move, the intensity starts to decrease. What is the distance between the speakers when the sound intensity is again a minimum?

MODEL The changing sound intensity is due to the interference of two overlapped sound waves.

VISUALIZE Moving one speaker relative to the other changes the phase difference between the waves.

SOLVE A minimum sound intensity implies that the two sound waves are interfering destructively. Initially the loudspeakers are side by side, so the situation is as shown in Figure 21.23a with $\Delta x = 0$ and $\Delta\phi_0 = \pi$ rad. That is, the speakers themselves are out of phase. Moving one of the speakers does not change $\Delta\phi_0$, but it does change the path-length difference Δx and thus increases the overall phase difference $\Delta\phi$. Constructive interference, causing maximum intensity, is reached when

$$\Delta\phi = 2\pi\frac{\Delta x}{\lambda} + \Delta\phi_0 = 2\pi\frac{\Delta x}{\lambda} + \pi = 2\pi \text{ rad}$$

where we used $m = 1$ because this is the first separation giving constructive interference. The speaker separation at which this occurs is $\Delta x = \lambda/2$. This is the situation shown in FIGURE 21.24.

Because $\Delta x = 0.75$ m is $\lambda/2$, the sound's wavelength is $\lambda = 1.50$ m. The next point of destructive interference, with $m = 1$, occurs when

$$\Delta\phi = 2\pi\frac{\Delta x}{\lambda} + \Delta\phi_0 = 2\pi\frac{\Delta x}{\lambda} + \pi = 3\pi \text{ rad}$$

Thus the distance between the speakers when the sound intensity is again a minimum is

$$\Delta x = \lambda = 1.50 \text{ m}$$

ASSESS A separation of λ gives constructive interference for two *identical* speakers ($\Delta\phi_0 = 0$). Here the phase difference of π rad between the speakers (one is pushing forward as the other pulls back) gives destructive interference at this separation.

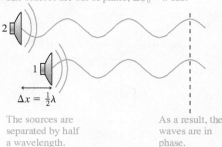

FIGURE 21.24 Two out-of-phase sources generate waves that are in phase if the sources are one half-wavelength apart.

The sources are out of phase, $\Delta\phi_0 = \pi$ rad.

$\Delta x = \frac{1}{2}\lambda$

The sources are separated by half a wavelength.

As a result, the waves are in phase.

STOP TO THINK 21.4 Two loudspeakers emit waves with $\lambda = 2.0$ m. Speaker 2 is 1.0 m in front of speaker 1. What, if anything, can be done to cause constructive interference between the two waves?

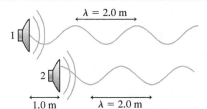

$\lambda = 2.0$ m

1.0 m

$\lambda = 2.0$ m

a. Move speaker 1 forward (to the right) 1.0 m.
b. Move speaker 1 forward (to the right) 0.5 m.
c. Move speaker 1 backward (to the left) 0.5 m.
d. Move speaker 1 backward (to the left) 1.0 m.
e. Nothing. The situation shown already causes constructive interference.
f. Constructive interference is not possible for any placement of the speakers.

21.6 The Mathematics of Interference

Let's look more closely at the superposition of two waves. As two waves of equal amplitude and frequency travel together along the x-axis, the net displacement of the medium is

$$D = D_1 + D_2 = a\sin(kx_1 - \omega t + \phi_{10}) + a\sin(kx_2 - \omega t + \phi_{20})$$
$$= a\sin\phi_1 + a\sin\phi_2 \qquad (21.24)$$

where the phases ϕ_1 and ϕ_2 were defined in Equation 21.20.

A useful trigonometric identity is

$$\sin\alpha + \sin\beta = 2\cos\left[\tfrac{1}{2}(\alpha - \beta)\right]\sin\left[\tfrac{1}{2}(\alpha + \beta)\right] \qquad (21.25)$$

This identity is certainly not obvious, although it is easily proven by working backward from the right side. We can use this identity to write the net displacement of Equation 21.24 as

$$D = \left[2a\cos\left(\frac{\Delta\phi}{2}\right)\right]\sin(kx_{\text{avg}} - \omega t + (\phi_0)_{\text{avg}}) \qquad (21.26)$$

where $\Delta\phi = \phi_2 - \phi_1$ is the phase difference between the two waves, exactly as in Equation 21.21. $x_{\text{avg}} = (x_1 + x_2)/2$ is the average distance to the two sources and $(\phi_0)_{\text{avg}} = (\phi_{10} + \phi_{20})/2$ is the average phase constant of the sources.

The sine term shows that the superposition of the two waves is still a traveling wave. An observer would see a sinusoidal wave moving along the x-axis with the *same* wavelength and frequency as the original waves.

FIGURE 21.25 The interference of two waves for three different values of the phase difference.

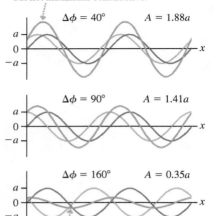

For $\Delta\phi = 40°$, the interference is constructive but not maximum constructive.

For $\Delta\phi = 160°$, the interference is destructive but not perfect destructive.

But how *big* is this wave compared to the two original waves? They each had amplitude a, but the amplitude of their superposition is

$$A = \left| 2a\cos\left(\frac{\Delta\phi}{2}\right) \right| \qquad (21.27)$$

where we have used an absolute value sign because amplitudes must be positive. Depending upon the phase difference of the two waves, the amplitude of their superposition can be anywhere from zero (perfect destructive interference) to $2a$ (maximum constructive interference).

The amplitude has its maximum value $A = 2a$ if $\cos(\Delta\phi/2) = \pm 1$. This occurs when

$$\Delta\phi = m \cdot 2\pi \qquad \text{(maximum amplitude } A = 2a) \qquad (21.28)$$

where m is an integer. Similarly, the amplitude is zero if $\cos(\Delta\phi/2) = 0$, which occurs when

$$\Delta\phi = \left(m + \tfrac{1}{2}\right) \cdot 2\pi \qquad \text{(minimum amplitude } A = 0) \qquad (21.29)$$

Equations 21.28 and 21.29 are identical to the conditions of Equations 21.22 and 21.23 for constructive and destructive interference. We initially found these conditions by considering the alignment of the crests and troughs. Now we have confirmed them with an algebraic addition of the waves.

It is entirely possible, of course, that the two waves are neither exactly in phase nor exactly out of phase. Equation 21.27 allows us to calculate the amplitude of the superposition for any value of the phase difference. As an example, FIGURE 21.25 shows the calculated interference of two waves that differ in phase by 40°, by 90°, and by 160°.

EXAMPLE 21.8 **More interference of sound waves**

Two loudspeakers emit 500 Hz sound waves with an amplitude of 0.10 mm. Speaker 2 is 1.00 m behind speaker 1, and the phase difference between the speakers is 90°. What is the amplitude of the sound wave at a point 2.00 m in front of speaker 1?

MODEL The amplitude is determined by the interference of the two waves. Assume that the speed of sound has a room-temperature (20°C) value of 343 m/s.

SOLVE The amplitude of the sound wave is

$$A = \left| 2a\cos(\Delta\phi/2) \right|$$

where $a = 0.10$ mm and the phase difference between the waves is

$$\Delta\phi = \phi_2 - \phi_1 = 2\pi\frac{\Delta x}{\lambda} + \Delta\phi_0$$

The sound's wavelength is

$$\lambda = \frac{v}{f} = \frac{343 \text{ m/s}}{500 \text{ Hz}} = 0.686 \text{ m}$$

Distances $x_1 = 2.00$ m and $x_2 = 3.00$ m are measured from the speakers, so the path-length difference is $\Delta x = 1.00$ m. We're given that the inherent phase difference between the speakers is $\Delta\phi_0 = \pi/2$ rad. Thus the phase difference at the observation point is

$$\Delta\phi = 2\pi\frac{\Delta x}{\lambda} + \Delta\phi_0 = 2\pi\frac{1.00 \text{ m}}{0.686 \text{ m}} + \frac{\pi}{2} \text{ rad} = 10.73 \text{ rad}$$

and the amplitude of the wave at this point is

$$A = \left| 2a\cos\left(\frac{\Delta\phi}{2}\right) \right| = \left| (0.200 \text{ mm})\cos\left(\frac{10.73}{2}\right) \right| = 0.121 \text{ mm}$$

ASSESS The interference is constructive because $A > a$, but less than maximum constructive interference.

Application: Thin-Film Optical Coatings

The shimmering colors of soap bubbles and oil slicks, as seen in the photo at the beginning of the chapter, are due to the interference of light waves. In fact, the idea of light-wave interference in one dimension has an important application in the optics industry, namely the use of **thin-film optical coatings**. These films, less than 1 μm (10^{-6} m) thick, are placed on glass surfaces, such as lenses, to control reflections from the glass. Antireflection coatings on the lenses in cameras, microscopes, and other optical equipment are examples of thin-film coatings.

FIGURE 21.26 shows a light wave of wavelength λ approaching a piece of glass that has been coated with a transparent film of thickness d whose index of refraction is n. The air-film boundary is a discontinuity at which the wave speed suddenly decreases, and you saw earlier, in Figure 21.8, that a discontinuity causes a reflection. Most of the light is transmitted into the film, but a little bit is reflected.

Furthermore, you saw in Figure 21.8 that the wave reflected from a discontinuity at which the speed decreases is *inverted* with respect to the incident wave. For a sinusoidal wave, which we're now assuming, the inversion is represented mathematically as a phase shift of π rad. The speed of a light wave decreases when it enters a material with a *larger* index of refraction. Thus **a light wave that reflects from a boundary at which the index of refraction increases has a phase shift of π rad.** There is no phase shift for the reflection from a boundary at which the index of refraction decreases. The reflection in Figure 21.26 is from a boundary between air ($n_{air} = 1.00$) and a transparent film with $n_{film} > n_{air}$, so the reflected wave is inverted due to the phase shift of π rad.

When the transmitted wave reaches the glass, most of it continues on into the glass but a portion is reflected back to the left. We'll assume that the index of refraction of the glass is larger than that of the film, $n_{glass} > n_{film}$, so this reflection also has a phase shift of π rad. This second reflection, after traveling back through the film, passes back into the air. There are now *two* equal-frequency waves traveling to the left, and these waves will interfere. If the two reflected waves are *in phase,* they will interfere constructively to cause a *strong reflection.* If the two reflected waves are *out of phase,* they will interfere destructively to cause a *weak reflection* or, if their amplitudes are equal, *no reflection* at all.

This suggests practical uses for thin-film optical coatings. The reflections from glass surfaces, even if weak, are often undesirable. For example, reflections degrade the performance of optical equipment. These reflections can be eliminated by coating the glass with a film whose thickness is chosen to cause *destructive* interference of the two reflected waves. This is an *antireflection coating.*

The amplitude of the reflected light depends on the phase difference between the two reflected waves. This phase difference is

$$\Delta\phi = \phi_2 - \phi_1 = (kx_2 + \phi_{20} + \pi \text{ rad}) - (kx_1 + \phi_{10} + \pi \text{ rad})$$
$$= 2\pi \frac{\Delta x}{\lambda_f} + \Delta\phi_0 \qquad (21.30)$$

where we explicitly included the reflection phase shift of each wave. In this case, because *both* waves had a phase shift of π rad, the reflection phase shifts cancel.

The wavelength λ_f is the wavelength *in the film* because that's where the path-length difference Δx occurs. You learned in Chapter 20 that the wavelength in a transparent material with index of refraction n is $\lambda_f = \lambda/n$, where the unsubscripted λ is the wavelength in vacuum or air. That is, λ is the wavelength that we measure on "our" side of the air-film boundary.

The path-length difference between the two waves is $\Delta x = 2d$ because wave 2 travels through the film *twice* before rejoining wave 1. The two waves have a common origin—the initial division of the incident wave at the front surface of the film—so the inherent phase difference is $\Delta\phi_0 = 0$. Thus the phase difference of the two reflected waves is

$$\Delta\phi = 2\pi \frac{2d}{\lambda/n} = 2\pi \frac{2nd}{\lambda} \qquad (21.31)$$

The interference is constructive, causing a strong reflection, when $\Delta\phi = m \cdot 2\pi$ rad. So when both reflected waves have a phase of π rad, constructive interference occurs for wavelengths

$$\lambda_C = \frac{2nd}{m} \qquad m = 1, 2, 3, \ldots \qquad \text{(constructive interference)} \quad (21.32)$$

FIGURE 21.26 The two reflections, one from the coating and one from the glass, interfere.

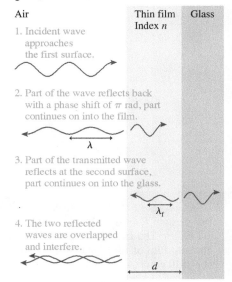

Air   Thin film   Glass
                      Index n

1. Incident wave approaches the first surface.

2. Part of the wave reflects back with a phase shift of π rad, part continues on into the film.

λ

3. Part of the transmitted wave reflects at the second surface, part continues on into the glass.

λ_f

4. The two reflected waves are overlapped and interfere.

d

Antireflection coatings use the interference of light waves to nearly eliminate reflections from glass surfaces.

You will notice that m starts with 1, rather than 0, in order to give meaningful results. Destructive interference, with minimum reflection, requires $\Delta\phi = \left(m - \frac{1}{2}\right) \cdot 2\pi$ rad. This—again, when both waves have a phase shift of π rad—occurs for wavelengths

$$\lambda_D = \frac{2nd}{m - \frac{1}{2}} \qquad m = 1, 2, 3, \ldots \qquad \text{(destructive interference)} \quad (21.33)$$

We've used $m - \frac{1}{2}$, rather than $m + \frac{1}{2}$, so that m can start with 1 to match the condition for constructive interference.

NOTE ▶ The exact condition for constructive or destructive interference is satisfied for only a few discrete wavelengths λ. Nonetheless, reflections are strongly enhanced (nearly constructive interference) for a range of wavelengths near λ_C. Likewise, there is a range of wavelengths near λ_D for which the reflection is nearly canceled. ◀

EXAMPLE 21.9 **Designing an antireflection coating**

Magnesium fluoride (MgF_2) is used as an antireflection coating on lenses. The index of refraction of MgF_2 is 1.39. What is the thinnest film of MgF_2 that works as an antireflection coating at $\lambda = 510$ nm, near the center of the visible spectrum?

MODEL Reflection is minimized if the two reflected waves interfere destructively.

SOLVE The film thicknesses that cause destructive interference at wavelength λ are

$$d = \left(m - \frac{1}{2}\right)\frac{\lambda}{2n}$$

The thinnest film has $m = 1$. Its thickness is

$$d = \frac{\lambda}{4n} = \frac{510 \text{ nm}}{4(1.39)} = 92 \text{ nm}$$

The film thickness is significantly less than the wavelength of visible light!

ASSESS The reflected light is completely eliminated (perfect destructive interference) only if the two reflected waves have equal amplitudes. In practice, they don't. Nonetheless, the reflection is reduced from $\approx 4\%$ of the incident intensity for "bare glass" to well under 1%. Furthermore, the intensity of reflected light is much reduced across most of the visible spectrum (400–700 nm), even though the phase difference deviates more and more from π rad as the wavelength moves away from 510 nm. It is the increasing reflection at the ends of the visible spectrum ($\lambda \approx 400$ nm and $\lambda \approx 700$ nm), where $\Delta\phi$ deviates significantly from π rad, that gives a reddish-purple tinge to the lenses on cameras and binoculars. Homework problems will let you explore situations where only one of the two reflections has a reflection phase shift of π rad.

21.7 Interference in Two and Three Dimensions

Ripples on a lake move in two dimensions. The glow from a lightbulb spreads outward as a spherical wave. A circular or spherical wave can be written

$$D(r, t) = a\sin(kr - \omega t + \phi_0) \tag{21.34}$$

FIGURE 21.27 A circular or spherical wave.

The wave fronts are crests, separated by λ.

Troughs are halfway between wave fronts.

Source

λ

v

r

This graph shows the displacement of the medium.

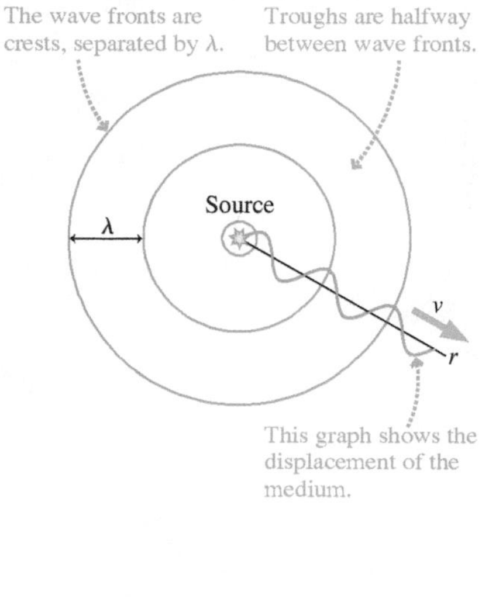

where r is the distance measured outward from the source. Equation 21.34 is our familiar wave equation with the one-dimensional coordinate x replaced by a more general radial coordinate r. Strictly speaking, the amplitude a of a circular or spherical wave diminishes as r increases. However, we will assume that a remains essentially constant over the region in which we study the wave. FIGURE 21.27 shows the wave-front diagram for a circular or spherical wave. Recall that the wave fronts represent the *crests* of the wave and are spaced by the wavelength λ.

What happens when two circular or spherical waves overlap? For example, imagine two paddles oscillating up and down on the surface of a pond. We will assume that the two paddles oscillate with the same frequency and amplitude and that they are in phase. FIGURE 21.28 shows the wave fronts of the two waves. The ripples overlap as they travel, and, as was the case in one dimension, this causes interference.

Constructive interference with $A = 2a$ occurs where two crests align or two troughs align. Several locations of constructive interference are marked in Figure 21.28. Intersecting wave fronts are points where two crests are aligned. It's a bit harder to visualize, but two troughs are aligned when a midpoint between two wave fronts is overlapped with another midpoint between two wave fronts. Destructive interference with $A = 0$ occurs where the crest of one wave aligns with a trough of the other wave. Several points of destructive interference are also indicated in Figure 21.28.

A picture on a page is static, but **the wave fronts are in motion.** Try to imagine the wave fronts of Figure 21.28 expanding outward as new circular rings are born at the sources. The waves will move forward half a wavelength during half a period, causing the crests in Figure 21.28 to be replaced by troughs while the troughs become crests.

The important point to recognize is that **the motion of the waves does not affect the points of constructive and destructive interference.** Points in the figure where two crests overlap will become points where two troughs overlap, but this overlap is still constructive interference. Similarly, points in the figure where a crest and a trough overlap will become a point where a trough and a crest overlap—still destructive interference.

The mathematical description of interference in two or three dimensions is very similar to that of one-dimensional interference. The net displacement of a particle in the medium is

$$D = D_1 + D_2 = a\sin(kr_1 - \omega t + \phi_{10}) + a\sin(kr_2 - \omega t + \phi_{20}) \quad (21.35)$$

The only difference between Equation 21.35 and the earlier one-dimensional Equation 21.24 is that the linear coordinates x_1 and x_2 have been changed to radial coordinates r_1 and r_2. Thus our conclusions are unchanged. The superposition of the two waves yields a wave traveling outward with amplitude

$$A = \left| 2a\cos\left(\frac{\Delta\phi}{2}\right) \right| \quad (21.36)$$

where the phase difference, with x replaced by r, is now

$$\Delta\phi = 2\pi\frac{\Delta r}{\lambda} + \Delta\phi_0 \quad (21.37)$$

The term $2\pi(\Delta r/\lambda)$ is the phase difference that arises when the waves travel different distances from the sources to the point at which they combine. Δr itself is the *path-length difference*. As before, $\Delta\phi_0$ is any inherent phase difference of the sources themselves.

Maximum constructive interference with $A = 2a$ occurs, just as in one dimension, at those points where $\cos(\Delta\phi/2) = \pm 1$. Similarly, perfect destructive interference occurs at points where $\cos(\Delta\phi/2) = 0$. The conditions for constructive and destructive interference are

Maximum constructive interference:

$$\Delta\phi = 2\pi\frac{\Delta r}{\lambda} + \Delta\phi_0 = m \cdot 2\pi$$

$$m = 0, 1, 2, \ldots \quad (21.38)$$

Perfect destructive interference:

$$\Delta\phi = 2\pi\frac{\Delta r}{\lambda} + \Delta\phi_0 = \left(m + \frac{1}{2}\right) \cdot 2\pi$$

For two identical sources (i.e., sources that oscillate in phase with $\Delta\phi_0 = 0$), the conditions for constructive and destructive interference are simple:

Constructive: $\Delta r = m\lambda$

Destructive: $\Delta r = \left(m + \frac{1}{2}\right)\lambda$ (identical sources)   (21.39)

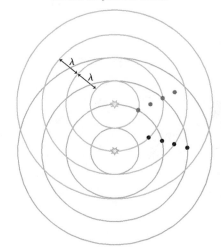

FIGURE 21.28 The overlapping ripple patterns of two sources. Several points of constructive and destructive interference are noted.

Two in-phase sources emit circular or spherical waves.

• Points of constructive interference. A crest is aligned with a crest, or a trough with a trough.

• Points of destructive interference. A crest is aligned with a trough of another wave.

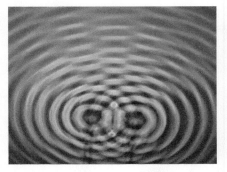

Two overlapping water waves create an interference pattern.

• At A, $\Delta r_A = \lambda$, so this is a point of constructive interference.

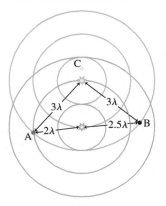

• At B, $\Delta r_B = \frac{1}{2}\lambda$, so this is a point of destructive interference.

The waves from two identical sources interfere constructively at points where the path-length difference is an integer number of wavelengths because, for these values of Δr, crests are aligned with crests and troughs with troughs. **The waves interfere destructively at points where the path-length difference is a half-integer number of wavelengths** because, for these values of Δr, crests are aligned with troughs. These two statements are the essence of interference.

NOTE ▶ Equation 21.39 applies only if the sources are in phase. If the sources are not in phase, you must use the more general Equation 21.38 to locate the points of constructive and destructive interference. ◀

Wave fronts are spaced exactly one wavelength apart; hence we can measure the distances r_1 and r_2 simply by counting the rings in the wave-front pattern. In FIGURE 21.29, which is based on Figure 21.28, point A is distance $r_1 = 3\lambda$ from the first source and $r_2 = 2\lambda$ from the second. The path-length difference is $\Delta r_A = 1\lambda$, the condition for the maximum constructive interference of identical sources. Point B has $\Delta r_B = \frac{1}{2}\lambda$, so it is a point of perfect destructive interference.

NOTE ▶ Interference is determined by Δr, the path-length *difference,* rather than by r_1 or r_2. ◀

STOP TO THINK 21.5 The interference at point C in Figure 21.29 is

a. Maximum constructive.
c. Perfect destructive.
e. There is no interference at point C.

b. Constructive, but less than maximum.
d. Destructive, but not perfect.

We can now locate the points of maximum constructive interference, for which $\Delta r = m\lambda$, by drawing a line through *all* the points at which $\Delta r = 0$, another line through all the points at which $\Delta r = \lambda$, and so on. These lines, shown in red in FIGURE 21.30, are called **antinodal lines.** They are analogous to the antinodes of a standing wave, hence the name. An antinode is a *point* of maximum constructive interference; for circular waves, oscillation at maximum amplitude occurs along a continuous *line.* Similarly, destructive interference occurs along lines called **nodal lines.** The displacement is *always zero* along these lines, just as it is at a node in a standing-wave pattern.

FIGURE 21.30 The points of constructive and destructive interference fall along antinodal and nodal lines.

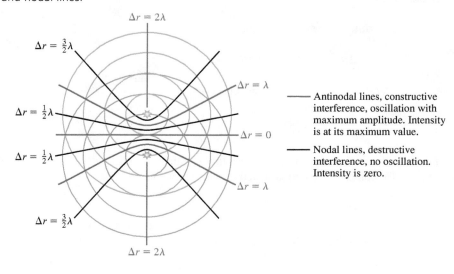

A Problem-Solving Strategy for Interference Problems

The information in this section is the basis of a strategy for solving interference problems. This strategy applies equally well to interference in one dimension if you use Δx instead of Δr.

PROBLEM-SOLVING
STRATEGY 21.1 **Interference of two waves**

MODEL Make simplifying assumptions, such as assuming waves are circular and of equal amplitude.

VISUALIZE Draw a picture showing the sources of the waves and the point where the waves interfere. Give relevant dimensions. Identify the distances r_1 and r_2 from the sources to the point. Note any phase difference $\Delta\phi_0$ between the two sources.

SOLVE The interference depends on the path-length difference $\Delta r = r_2 - r_1$ and the source phase difference $\Delta\phi_0$.

Constructive: $\quad \Delta\phi = 2\pi\dfrac{\Delta r}{\lambda} + \Delta\phi_0 = m \cdot 2\pi$

$\qquad\qquad\qquad\qquad\qquad\qquad\qquad\qquad m = 0, 1, 2, \ldots$

Destructive: $\quad \Delta\phi = 2\pi\dfrac{\Delta r}{\lambda} + \Delta\phi_0 = \left(m + \dfrac{1}{2}\right) \cdot 2\pi$

For identical sources ($\Delta\phi_0 = 0$), the interference is maximum constructive if $\Delta r = m\lambda$, perfect destructive if $\Delta r = \left(m + \frac{1}{2}\right)\lambda$.

ASSESS Check that your result has the correct units, is reasonable, and answers the question.

Exercise 18

EXAMPLE 21.10 **Two-dimensional interference between two loudspeakers**

Two loudspeakers in a plane are 2.0 m apart and in phase with each other. Both emit 700 Hz sound waves into a room where the speed of sound is 341 m/s. A listener stands 5.0 m in front of the loudspeakers and 2.0 m to one side of the center. Is the interference at this point maximum constructive, perfect destructive, or in between? How will the situation differ if the loudspeakers are out of phase?

MODEL The two speakers are sources of in-phase, spherical waves. The overlap of these waves causes interference.

VISUALIZE FIGURE 21.31 shows the loudspeakers and defines the distances r_1 and r_2 to the point of observation. The figure includes dimensions and notes that $\Delta\phi_0 = 0$ rad.

FIGURE 21.31 Pictorial representation of the interference between two loudspeakers.

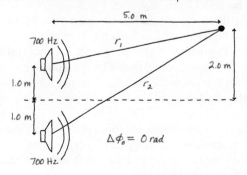

SOLVE It's not r_1 and r_2 that matter, but the *difference* Δr between them. From the geometry of the figure we can calculate that

$$r_1 = \sqrt{(5.0\text{ m})^2 + (1.0\text{ m})^2} = 5.10\text{ m}$$

$$r_2 = \sqrt{(5.0\text{ m})^2 + (3.0\text{ m})^2} = 5.83\text{ m}$$

Thus the path-length difference is $\Delta r = r_2 - r_1 = 0.73$ m. The wavelength of the sound waves is

$$\lambda = \frac{v}{f} = \frac{341\text{ m/s}}{700\text{ Hz}} = 0.487\text{ m}$$

In terms of wavelengths, the path-length difference is $\Delta r/\lambda = 1.50$, or

$$\Delta r = \frac{3}{2}\lambda$$

Because the sources are in phase ($\Delta\phi_0 = 0$), this is the condition for *destructive* interference. If the sources were out of phase ($\Delta\phi_0 = \pi$ rad), then the phase difference of the waves at the listener would be

$$\Delta\phi = 2\pi\frac{\Delta r}{\lambda} + \Delta\phi_0 = 2\pi\left(\frac{3}{2}\right) + \pi\text{ rad} = 4\pi\text{ rad}$$

This is an integer multiple of 2π rad, so in this case the interference would be *constructive*.

ASSESS Both the path-length difference *and* any inherent phase difference of the sources must be considered when evaluating interference.

Picturing Interference

A *contour map* is a useful way to visualize an interference pattern. FIGURE 21.32a shows the superposition of the waves from two identical sources ($\Delta\phi_0 = 0$) emitting waves with $\lambda = 1$ m. The sources, indicated with black dots, are located two wavelengths apart at $y = \pm 1$ m. Positive displacements are shown in red, with the deepest red representing the maximum displacement of the wave at this instant in time. These are the points where the crests of the individual waves interfere constructively to give $D = 2a$. Negative displacements are blue, with the darkest blue being the most negative displacement of the wave. These are also points of constructive interference, with two troughs overlapping to give $D = -2a$.

FIGURE 21.32 A contour map of the interference pattern of two sources. The graph on the right side of each figure shows the wave intensity along a vertical line at $x = 4$ m.

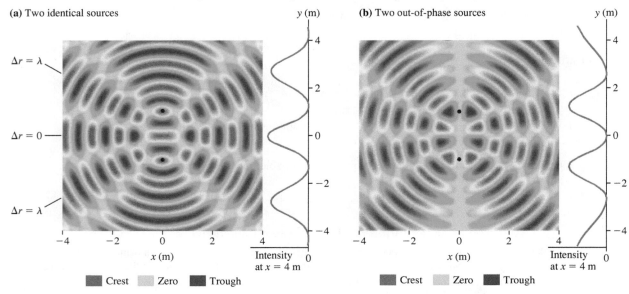

(a) Two identical sources

(b) Two out-of-phase sources

To understand this figure, try to visualize the waves expanding outward from the center. The red-blue-red-blue-red-··· pattern of crests and troughs moves outward along the antinodal lines as a *traveling wave* of amplitude $A = 2a$. Nothing ever happens along the nodal lines, where the amplitude is always zero.

Suppose you were to observe the *intensity* of the wave as it crosses the vertical line at $x = 4$ m on the right edge of the figure. If, for example, these are sound waves, you could listen to (or measure with a microphone) the sound intensity as you walk from $(x, y) = (4\text{ m}, -4\text{ m})$ at the bottom of the figure to $(x, y) = (4\text{ m}, 4\text{ m})$ at the top. The intensity is zero as you cross the nodal lines at $y \approx \pm 1$ m $\left(\Delta r = \frac{1}{2}\lambda\right)$. The intensity is maximum at the antinodal lines at $y = 0$ ($\Delta r = 0$) and $y \approx \pm 2.5$ m ($\Delta r = \lambda$), where a wave of maximum amplitude streams out from the sources.

The intensity is shown in the rather unusual graph on the right side of Figure 21.32a. It is unusual in the sense that the intensity, the quantity of interest, is graphed to the left. The peaks are the points of constructive interference, where you would measure maximum amplitude. The zeros are points of destructive interference, where the intensity is zero.

FIGURE 21.32b is a contour map of the interference pattern produced by the same two sources but with the sources themselves now out of phase ($\Delta\phi_0 = \pi$ rad). We'll leave the investigation of this figure to you, but notice that the nodal and antinodal lines are reversed from those of Figure 21.32a.

EXAMPLE 21.11 **The intensity of two interfering loudspeakers**

Two loudspeakers in a plane are 6.0 m apart and in phase. They emit equal-amplitude sound waves with a wavelength of 1.0 m. Each speaker alone creates sound with intensity I_0. An observer at point A is 10 m in front of the plane containing the two loudspeakers and centered between them. A second observer at point B is 10 m directly in front of one of the speakers. In terms of I_0, what are the intensity I_A at point A and the intensity I_B at point B?

MODEL The two speakers are sources of in-phase waves. The overlap of these waves causes interference.

VISUALIZE **FIGURE 21.33** shows the two loudspeakers and the two points of observation. Distances r_1 and r_2 are defined for point B.

FIGURE 21.33 Pictorial representation of the interference between two loudspeakers.

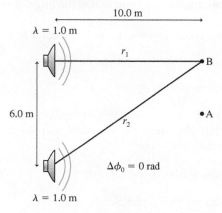

SOLVE Let the amplitude of the wave from each speaker be a. The intensity of a wave is proportional to the square of the amplitude,

so the intensity of each speaker alone is $I_0 = ca^2$, where c is an unknown proportionality constant. Point A is a point of constructive interference because the speakers are in phase ($\Delta\phi_0 = 0$) and the path-length difference is $\Delta r = 0$. The amplitude at this point is given by Equation 21.36:

$$A_A = \left|2a\cos\left(\frac{\Delta\phi}{2}\right)\right| = 2a\cos(0) = 2a$$

Consequently, the intensity at this point is

$$I_A = cA_A^2 = c(2a)^2 = 4ca^2 = 4I_0$$

The intensity at A is four times that of either speaker played alone. At point B, the path-length difference is

$$\Delta r = \sqrt{(10.0\ \text{m})^2 + (6.0\ \text{m})^2} - 10.0\ \text{m} = 1.662\ \text{m}$$

The phase difference of the waves at this point is

$$\Delta\phi = 2\pi\frac{\Delta r}{\lambda} = 2\pi\frac{1.662\ \text{m}}{1.0\ \text{m}} = 10.44\ \text{rad}$$

Consequently, the amplitude at B is

$$A_B = \left|2a\cos\left(\frac{\Delta\phi}{2}\right)\right| = |2a\cos(5.22\ \text{rad})| = 0.972a$$

Thus the intensity at this point is

$$I_B = cA_B^2 = c(0.972a)^2 = 0.95ca^2 = 0.95I_0$$

ASSESS Although B is directly in front of one of the speakers, superposition of the two waves results in an intensity that is less than it would be if this speaker played alone.

STOP TO THINK 21.6 These two loudspeakers are in phase. They emit equal-amplitude sound waves with a wavelength of 1.0 m. At the point indicated, is the interference maximum constructive, perfect destructive, or something in between?

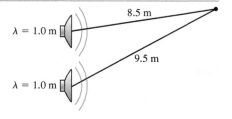

21.8 Beats

Thus far we have looked at the superposition of sources having the same wavelength and frequency. We can also use the principle of superposition to investigate a phenomenon that is easily demonstrated with two sources of slightly different frequency.

If you listen to two sounds with very different frequencies, such as a high note and a low note, you hear two distinct tones. But if the frequency difference is very small, just one or two hertz, then you hear a single tone whose intensity is *modulated* once or twice every second. That is, the sound goes up and down in volume, loud, soft, loud, soft, ..., making a distinctive sound pattern called **beats**.

Consider two sinusoidal waves traveling along the x-axis with angular frequencies $\omega_1 = 2\pi f_1$ and $\omega_2 = 2\pi f_2$. The two waves are

$$D_1 = a\sin(k_1 x - \omega_1 t + \phi_{10})$$
$$D_2 = a\sin(k_2 x - \omega_2 t + \phi_{20})$$

(21.40)

where the subscripts 1 and 2 indicate that the frequencies, wave numbers, and phase constants of the two waves may be different.

To simplify the analysis, let's make several assumptions:

1. The two waves have the same amplitude a,
2. A detector, such as your ear, is located at the origin ($x = 0$),
3. The two sources are in phase ($\phi_{10} = \phi_{20}$), and
4. The source phases happen to be $\phi_{10} = \phi_{20} = \pi$ rad.

None of these assumptions is essential to the outcome. All could be otherwise and we would still come to basically the same conclusion, but the mathematics would be far messier. Making these assumptions allows us to emphasize the physics with the least amount of mathematics.

With these assumptions, the two waves as they reach the detector at $x = 0$ are

$$D_1 = a\sin(-\omega_1 t + \pi) = a\sin\omega_1 t$$
$$D_2 = a\sin(-\omega_2 t + \pi) = a\sin\omega_2 t$$

(21.41)

where we've used the trigonometric identity $\sin(\pi - \theta) = \sin\theta$. The principle of superposition tells us that the *net* displacement of the medium at the detector is the sum of the displacements of the individual waves. Thus

$$D = D_1 + D_2 = a(\sin\omega_1 t + \sin\omega_2 t)$$

(21.42)

Earlier, for interference, we used the trigonometric identity

$$\sin\alpha + \sin\beta = 2\cos\left[\tfrac{1}{2}(\alpha - \beta)\right]\sin\left[\tfrac{1}{2}(\alpha + \beta)\right]$$

We can use this identity again to write Equation 21.42 as

$$D = 2a\cos\left[\tfrac{1}{2}(\omega_1 - \omega_2)t\right]\sin\left[\tfrac{1}{2}(\omega_1 + \omega_2)t\right]$$
$$= \left[2a\cos(\omega_{\text{mod}}t)\right]\sin(\omega_{\text{avg}}t)$$

(21.43)

where $\omega_{\text{avg}} = \tfrac{1}{2}(\omega_1 + \omega_2)$ is the *average* angular frequency and $\omega_{\text{mod}} = \tfrac{1}{2}(\omega_1 - \omega_2)$ is called the *modulation frequency*.

We are interested in the situation when the two frequencies are very nearly equal: $\omega_1 \approx \omega_2$. In that case, ω_{avg} hardly differs from either ω_1 or ω_2 while ω_{mod} is very near to—but not exactly—zero. When ω_{mod} is very small, the term $\cos(\omega_{\text{mod}}t)$ oscillates *very* slowly. We have grouped it with the $2a$ term because, together, they provide a slowly changing "amplitude" for the rapid oscillation at frequency ω_{avg}.

FIGURE 21.34 is a history graph of the wave at the detector ($x = 0$). It shows the oscillation of the air against your eardrum at frequency $f_{\text{avg}} = \omega_{\text{avg}}/2\pi = \tfrac{1}{2}(f_1 + f_2)$. This oscillation determines the note you hear; it differs little from the two notes at frequencies f_1 and f_2. We are especially interested in the time-dependent amplitude, shown as a dashed line, that is given by the term $2a\cos(\omega_{\text{mod}}t)$. This periodically varying amplitude is called a **modulation** of the wave, which is where ω_{mod} gets its name.

As the amplitude rises and falls, the sound alternates as loud, soft, loud, soft, and so on. But that is exactly what you hear when you listen to beats! The alternating loud and soft sounds arise from the two waves being alternately in phase and out of phase, causing constructive and then destructive interference.

FIGURE 21.34 Beats are caused by the superposition of two waves of nearly identical frequency.

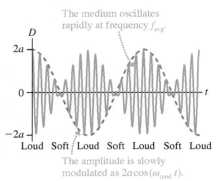

The medium oscillates rapidly at frequency f_{avg}.

Loud Soft Loud Soft Loud Soft Loud

The amplitude is slowly modulated as $2a\cos(\omega_{\text{mod}}t)$.

Imagine two people walking side by side at just slightly different paces. Initially both of their right feet hit the ground together, but after a while they get out of step. A little bit later they are back in step and the process alternates. The sound waves are doing the same. Initially the crests of each wave, of amplitude a, arrive together at your ear and the net displacement is doubled to $2a$. But after a while the two waves, being of slightly different frequency, get out of step and a crest of one arrives with a trough of the other. When this happens, the two waves cancel each other to give a net displacement of zero. This process alternates over and over, loud and soft.

Notice, from the figure, that the sound intensity rises and falls *twice* during one cycle of the modulation envelope. Each "loud-soft-loud" is one beat, so the **beat frequency** f_{beat}, which is the number of beats per second, is *twice* the modulation frequency $f_{mod} = \omega_{mod}/2\pi$. From the above definition of ω_{mod}, the beat frequency is

$$f_{beat} = 2f_{mod} = 2\frac{\omega_{mod}}{2\pi} = 2 \cdot \frac{1}{2}\left(\frac{\omega_1}{2\pi} - \frac{\omega_2}{2\pi}\right) = f_1 - f_2 \qquad (21.44)$$

where, to keep f_{beat} from being negative, we will always let f_1 be the larger of the two frequencies. The beat frequency is simply the *difference* between the two individual frequencies.

EXAMPLE 21.12 **Detecting bats with beats**

The little brown bat is a common species in North America. It emits echolocation pulses at a frequency of 40 kHz, well above the range of human hearing. To allow researchers to "hear" these bats, the bat detector shown in FIGURE 21.35 combines the bat's sound wave at frequency f_1 with a wave of frequency f_2 from a tunable oscillator. The resulting beat frequency is then amplified and sent to a loudspeaker. To what frequency should the tunable oscillator be set to produce an audible beat frequency of 3 kHz?

SOLVE Combining two waves with different frequencies gives a beat frequency

$$f_{beat} = f_1 - f_2$$

A beat frequency will be generated at 3 kHz if the oscillator frequency and the bat frequency *differ* by 3 kHz. An oscillator frequency of either 37 kHz or 43 kHz will work nicely.

ASSESS The electronic circuitry of radios, televisions, and cell phones makes extensive use of *mixers* to generate difference frequencies.

FIGURE 21.35 The operation of a bat detector.

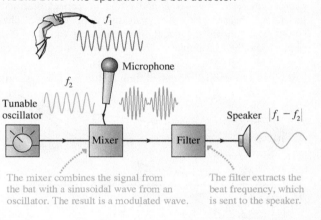

The mixer combines the signal from the bat with a sinusoidal wave from an oscillator. The result is a modulated wave.

The filter extracts the beat frequency, which is sent to the speaker.

Beats aren't limited to sound waves. FIGURE 21.36 shows a graphical example of beats. Two "fences" of slightly different frequencies are superimposed on each other. The difference in the two frequencies is two lines per inch. You can confirm, with a ruler, that the figure has two "beats" per inch, in agreement with Equation 21.44.

Beats are important in many other situations. For example, you have probably seen movies where rotating wheels seem to turn slowly backward. Why is this? Suppose the movie camera is shooting at 30 frames per second but the wheel is rotating 32 times per second. The combination of the two produces a "beat" of 2 Hz, meaning that the wheel appears to rotate only twice per second. The same is true if the wheel is rotating 28 times per second, but in this case, where the wheel frequency slightly lags the camera frequency, it appears to rotate *backward* twice per second!

FIGURE 21.36 A graphical example of beats.

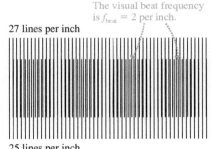

The visual beat frequency is $f_{beat} = 2$ per inch.

27 lines per inch

25 lines per inch

You hear three beats per second when two sound tones are generated. The frequency of one tone is 610 Hz. The frequency of the other is

a. 604 Hz	b. 607 Hz	c. 613 Hz
d. 616 Hz	e. Either a or d.	f. Either b or c.

CHALLENGE EXAMPLE 21.13   **An airplane landing system**

Your firm has been hired to design a system that allows airplane pilots to make instrument landings in rain or fog. You've decided to place two radio transmitters 50 m apart on either side of the runway. These two transmitters will broadcast the same frequency, but out of phase with each other. This will cause a nodal line to extend straight off the end of the runway. As long as the airplane's receiver is silent, the pilot knows she's directly in line with the runway. If she drifts to one side or the other, the radio will pick up a signal and sound a warning beep. To have sufficient accuracy, the first intensity maxima need to be 60 m on either side of the nodal line at a distance of 3.0 km. What frequency should you specify for the transmitters?

MODEL   The two transmitters are sources of out-of-phase, circular waves. The overlap of these waves produces an interference pattern.

VISUALIZE   For out-of-phase sources, the center line—with zero path-length difference—is a nodal line of perfect destructive interference because the two signals always arrive out of phase. FIGURE 21.37 shows the nodal line, extending straight off the runway, and the first antinodal line—the points of maximum con-

FIGURE 21.37 Pictorial representation of the landing system.

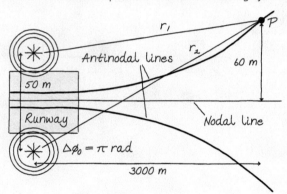

structive interference—on either side. Comparing this to Figure 21.30, where the two sources were in phase, you can see that the nodal and antinodal lines have been reversed.

SOLVE   Point P, 60 m to the side at a distance of 3000 m, needs to be a point of maximum constructive interference. The distances are

$$r_1 = \sqrt{(3000 \text{ m})^2 + (60 \text{ m} - 25 \text{ m})^2} = 3000.204 \ m$$
$$r_2 = \sqrt{(3000 \text{ m})^2 + (60 \text{ m} + 25 \text{ m})^2} = 3001.204 \ m$$

We needed to keep several extra significant figures because we're looking for the difference between two numbers that are almost the same. The path-length difference at P is

$$\Delta r = r_2 - r_1 = 1.000 \text{ m}$$

We know, for out-of-phase transmitters, that the phase difference of the sources is $\Delta\phi_0 = \pi$ rad. The first maximum will occur where the phase difference between the waves is $\Delta\phi = 1 \cdot 2\pi$ rad. Thus the condition that we must satisfy at P is

$$\Delta\phi = 2\pi \text{ rad} = 2\pi \frac{\Delta r}{\lambda} + \pi \text{ rad}$$

Solving for λ, we find

$$\lambda = 2 \Delta r = 2.00 \text{ m}$$

Consequently, the required frequency is

$$f = \frac{c}{\lambda} = \frac{3.00 \times 10^8 \text{ m/s}}{2.00 \text{ m}} = 1.50 \times 10^8 \text{ Hz} = 150 \text{ MHz}$$

ASSESS   150 MHz is slightly higher than the frequencies of FM radio ($\approx$ 100 MHz) but is well within the radio frequency range. Notice that the condition to be satisfied at P is that the path-length difference must be $\frac{1}{2}\lambda$. This makes sense. A path-length difference of $\frac{1}{2}\lambda$ contributes π rad to the phase difference. When combined with the π rad from the out-of-phase sources, the total phase difference of 2π rad creates constructive interference.

SUMMARY

The goal of Chapter 21 has been to understand and use the idea of superposition.

General Principles

Principle of Superposition

The displacement of a medium when more than one wave is present is the sum of the displacements due to each individual wave.

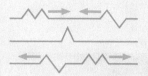

Important Concepts

Standing waves are due to the superposition of two traveling waves moving in opposite directions.

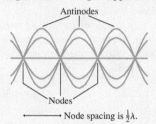

Antinodes

Nodes

Node spacing is $\frac{1}{2}\lambda$.

The amplitude at position x is

$$A(x) = 2a \sin kx$$

where a is the amplitude of each wave.

The boundary conditions determine which standing-wave frequencies and wavelengths are allowed. The allowed standing waves are **modes** of the system.

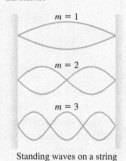

$m = 1$

$m = 2$

$m = 3$

Standing waves on a string

Interference

In general, the superposition of two or more waves into a single wave is called interference.

Maximum constructive interference occurs where crests are aligned with crests and troughs with troughs. These waves are in phase. The maximum displacement is $A = 2a$.

Perfect destructive interference occurs where crests are aligned with troughs. These waves are out of phase. The amplitude is $A = 0$.

Interference depends on the phase difference $\Delta\phi$ between the two waves.

Constructive: $\Delta\phi = 2\pi\dfrac{\Delta r}{\lambda} + \Delta\phi_0 = m \cdot 2\pi$

Destructive: $\Delta\phi = 2\pi\dfrac{\Delta r}{\lambda} + \Delta\phi_0 = \left(m + \dfrac{1}{2}\right) \cdot 2\pi$

Δr is the path-length difference of the two waves, and $\Delta\phi_0$ is any phase difference between the sources. For identical sources (in phase, $\Delta\phi_0 = 0$):

Interference is constructive if the path-length difference $\Delta r = m\lambda$.

Interference is destructive if the path-length difference $\Delta r = \left(m + \frac{1}{2}\right)\lambda$.

The amplitude at a point where the phase difference is $\Delta\phi$ is $A = \left|2a\cos\left(\dfrac{\Delta\phi}{2}\right)\right|$.

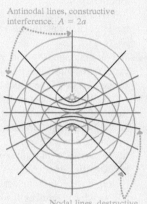

Antinodal lines, constructive interference. $A = 2a$

Nodal lines, destructive interference. $A = 0$

Applications

Boundary conditions

Strings, electromagnetic waves, and sound waves in closed-closed tubes must have nodes at both ends:

$$\lambda_m = \frac{2L}{m} \qquad f_m = m\frac{v}{2L} = mf_1$$

where $m = 1, 2, 3, \ldots$.

The frequencies and wavelengths are the same for a sound wave in an open-open tube, which has antinodes at both ends.

A sound wave in an open-closed tube must have a node at the closed end but an antinode at the open end. This leads to

$$\lambda_m = \frac{4L}{m} \qquad f_m = m\frac{v}{4L} = mf_1$$

where $m = 1, 3, 5, 7, \ldots$.

Beats (loud-soft-loud-soft modulations of intensity) occur when two waves of slightly different frequency are superimposed.

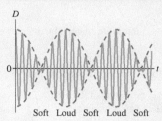

Soft Loud Soft Loud Soft

The beat frequency between waves of frequencies f_1 and f_2 is

$$f_{\text{beat}} = f_1 - f_2$$

Terms and Notation

principle of superposition	mode	path-length difference, Δx or Δr
standing wave	interference	thin-film optical coating
node	in phase	antinodal line
antinode	constructive interference	nodal line
amplitude function, $A(x)$	out of phase	beats
boundary condition	destructive interference	modulation
fundamental frequency, f_1	phase difference, $\Delta \phi$	beat frequency, f_{beat}
harmonic		

CONCEPTUAL QUESTIONS

1. FIGURE Q21.1 shows a standing wave oscillating on a string at frequency f_0.
   a. What mode (m-value) is this?
   b. How many antinodes will there be if the frequency is doubled to $2f_0$?

FIGURE Q21.1

2. If you take snapshots of a standing wave on a string, there are certain instants when the string is totally flat. What has happened to the energy of the wave at those instants?

3. FIGURE Q21.3 shows the displacement of a standing sound wave in a 32-cm-long horizontal tube of air open at both ends.
   a. What mode (m-value) is this?
   b. Are the air molecules moving horizontally or vertically? Explain.
   c. At what distances from the left end of the tube do the molecules oscillate with maximum amplitude?
   d. At what distances from the left end of the tube does the air pressure oscillate with maximum amplitude?

D

0 ——————— x (cm)
                32

FIGURE Q21.3

4. An organ pipe is tuned to exactly 384 Hz when the room temperature is 20°C. If the room temperature later increases to 22°C, does the pipe's frequency increase, decrease, or stay the same? Explain.

5. If you pour liquid into a tall, narrow glass, you may hear sound with a steadily rising pitch. What is the source of the sound? And why does the pitch rise as the glass fills?

6. A flute filled with helium will, until the helium escapes, play notes at a much higher pitch than normal. Why?

7. In music, two notes are said to be an *octave* apart when one note is exactly twice the frequency of the other. Suppose you have a guitar string playing frequency f_0. To increase the frequency by an octave, to $2f_0$, by what factor would you have to (a) increase the tension or (b) decrease the length?

8. FIGURE Q21.8 is a snapshot graph of two plane waves passing through a region of space. Each wave has a 2.0 mm amplitude and the same wavelength. What is the net displacement of the medium at points a, b, and c?

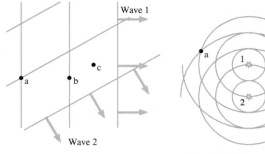

FIGURE Q21.8   FIGURE Q21.9

9. FIGURE Q21.9 shows the circular waves emitted by two in-phase sources. Are points a, b, and c points of maximum constructive interference or perfect destructive interference? Explain.

10. A trumpet player hears 5 beats per second when she plays a note and simultaneously sounds a 440 Hz tuning fork. After pulling her tuning valve out to slightly increase the length of her trumpet, she hears 3 beats per second against the tuning fork. Was her initial frequency 435 Hz or 445 Hz? Explain.

EXERCISES AND PROBLEMS

Problems labeled [ ] integrate material from earlier chapters.

Exercises

Section 21.1 The Principle of Superposition

1. | FIGURE EX21.1 is a snapshot graph at $t = 0$ s of two waves approaching each other at 1.0 m/s. Draw six snapshot graphs, stacked vertically, showing the string at 1 s intervals from $t = 1$ s to $t = 6$ s.

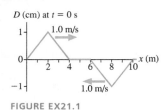

FIGURE EX21.1

2. | FIGURE EX21.2 is a snapshot graph at $t = 0$ s of two waves approaching each other at 1.0 m/s. Draw six snapshot graphs, stacked vertically, showing the string at 1 s intervals from $t = 1$ s to $t = 6$ s.

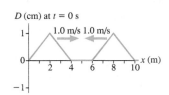

FIGURE EX21.2

3. ‖ FIGURE EX21.3 is a snapshot graph at $t = 0$ s of two waves approaching each other at 1.0 m/s. Draw four snapshot graphs, stacked vertically, showing the string at $t = 2, 4, 6,$ and 8 s.

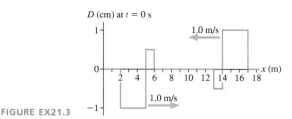

FIGURE EX21.3

4. ‖ FIGURE EX21.4a is a snapshot graph at $t = 0$ s of two waves approaching each other at 1.0 m/s.
   a. At what time was the snapshot graph in FIGURE EX21.4b taken?
   b. Draw a history graph of the string at $x = 5.0$ m from $t = 0$ s to $t = 6$ s.

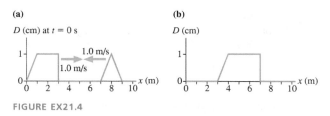

FIGURE EX21.4

Section 21.2 Standing Waves

Section 21.3 Standing Waves on a String

5. ‖ FIGURE EX21.5 is a snapshot graph at $t = 0$ s of two waves moving to the right at 1.0 m/s. The string is fixed at $x = 8.0$ m. Draw four snapshot graphs, stacked vertically, showing the string at $t = 2, 4, 6,$ and 8 s.

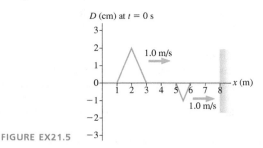

FIGURE EX21.5

6. ‖ FIGURE EX21.6 shows a standing wave oscillating at 100 Hz on a string. What is the wave speed?

FIGURE EX21.6   FIGURE EX21.7

7. ‖ FIGURE EX21.7 shows a standing wave on a 2.0-m-long string that has been fixed at both ends and tightened until the wave speed is 40 m/s. What is the frequency?

8. ‖ FIGURE EX21.8 shows a standing wave that is oscillating at frequency f_0.
   a. How many antinodes will there be if the frequency is doubled to $2f_0$? Explain.

FIGURE EX21.8

b. If the tension in the string is increased by a factor of four, for what frequency, in terms of f_0, will the string continue to oscillate as a standing wave with four antinodes?

9. │ a. What are the three longest wavelengths for standing waves on a 240-cm-long string that is fixed at both ends?
   b. If the frequency of the second-longest wavelength is 50 Hz, what is the frequency of the third-longest wavelength?

10. │ Standing waves on a 1.0-m-long string that is fixed at both ends are seen at successive frequencies of 36 Hz and 48 Hz.
    a. What are the fundamental frequency and the wave speed?
    b. Draw the standing-wave pattern when the string oscillates at 48 Hz.

11. ‖ A heavy piece of hanging sculpture is suspended by a 90-cm-long, 5.0 g steel wire. When the wind blows hard, the wire hums at its fundamental frequency of 80 Hz. What is the mass of the sculpture?

12. │ A carbon dioxide laser is an infrared laser. A CO_2 laser with a cavity length of 53.00 cm oscillates in the $m = 100,000$ mode. What are the wavelength and frequency of the laser beam?

Section 21.4 Standing Sound Waves and Musical Acoustics

13. │ What are the three longest wavelengths for standing sound waves in a 121-cm-long tube that is (a) open at both ends and (b) open at one end, closed at the other?

14. │ FIGURE EX21.14 shows a standing sound wave in an 80-cm-long tube. The tube is filled with an unknown gas. What is the speed of sound in this gas?

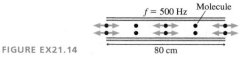

FIGURE EX21.14

15. ‖ The fundamental frequency of an open-open tube is 1500 Hz when the tube is filled with 0°C helium. What is its frequency when filled with 0°C air?

16. │ We can make a simple model of the human vocal tract as an BIO open-closed tube extending from the opening of the mouth to the diaphragm. What is the length of this tube if its fundamental frequency equals a typical speech frequency of 250 Hz? The speed of sound in the warm air is 350 m/s.

17. ‖ The lowest note on a grand piano has a frequency of 27.5 Hz. The entire string is 2.00 m long and has a mass of 400 g. The vibrating section of the string is 1.90 m long. What tension is needed to tune this string properly?

18. ‖ A violin string is 30 cm long. It sounds the musical note A (440 Hz) when played without fingering. How far from the end of the string should you place your finger to play the note C (523 Hz)?

Section 21.5 Interference in One Dimension

Section 21.6 The Mathematics of Interference

19. ‖ Two loudspeakers emit sound waves along the x-axis. The sound has maximum intensity when the speakers are 20 cm apart. The sound intensity decreases as the distance between the speakers is increased, reaching zero at a separation of 60 cm.
    a. What is the wavelength of the sound?
    b. If the distance between the speakers continues to increase, at what separation will the sound intensity again be a maximum?

20. ‖ Two loudspeakers in a 20°C room emit 686 Hz sound waves along the x-axis.
    a. If the speakers are in phase, what is the smallest distance between the speakers for which the interference of the sound waves is perfectly destructive?
    b. If the speakers are out of phase, what is the smallest distance between the speakers for which the interference of the sound waves is maximum constructive?

21. | What is the thinnest film of MgF_2 ($n = 1.39$) on glass that produces a strong reflection for orange light with a wavelength of 600 nm?

22. ‖ A very thin oil film ($n = 1.25$) floats on water ($n = 1.33$). What is the thinnest film that produces a strong reflection for green light with a wavelength of 500 nm?

Section 21.7 Interference in Two and Three Dimensions

23. ‖ FIGURE EX21.23 shows the circular wave fronts emitted by two wave sources.
    a. Are these sources in phase or out of phase? Explain.
    b. Make a table with rows labeled P, Q, and R and columns labeled r_1, r_2, Δr, and C/D. Fill in the table for points P, Q, and R, giving the distances as multiples of λ and indicating, with a C or a D, whether the interference at that point is constructive or destructive.

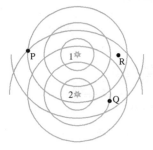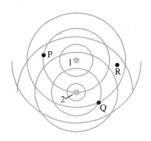

FIGURE EX21.23   FIGURE EX21.24

24. ‖ FIGURE EX21.24 shows the circular wave fronts emitted by two wave sources.
    a. Are these sources in phase or out of phase? Explain.
    b. Make a table with rows labeled P, Q, and R and columns labeled r_1, r_2, Δr, and C/D. Fill in the table for points P, Q, and R, giving the distances as multiples of λ and indicating, with a C or a D, whether the interference at that point is constructive or destructive.

25. ‖ Two in-phase speakers 2.0 m apart in a plane are emitting 1800 Hz sound waves into a room where the speed of sound is 340 m/s. Is the point 4.0 m in front of one of the speakers, perpendicular to the plane of the speakers, a point of maximum constructive interference, perfect destructive interference, or something in between?

26. ‖ Two out-of-phase radio antennas at $x = \pm 300$ m on the x-axis are emitting 3.0 MHz radio waves. Is the point $(x, y) = (300$ m, 800 m$)$ a point of maximum constructive interference, perfect destructive interference, or something in between?

Section 21.8 Beats

27. | Two strings are adjusted to vibrate at exactly 200 Hz. Then the tension in one string is increased slightly. Afterward, three beats per second are heard when the strings vibrate at the same time. What is the new frequency of the string that was tightened?

28. | A flute player hears four beats per second when she compares her note to a 523 Hz tuning fork (the note C). She can match the frequency of the tuning fork by pulling out the "tuning joint" to lengthen her flute slightly. What was her initial frequency?

29. | Two microwave signals of nearly equal wavelengths can generate a beat frequency if both are directed onto the same microwave detector. In an experiment, the beat frequency is 100 MHz. One microwave generator is set to emit microwaves with a wavelength of 1.250 cm. If the second generator emits the longer wavelength, what is that wavelength?

Problems

30. ‖ Two waves on a string travel in opposite directions at 100 m/s. FIGURE P21.30 shows a snapshot graph of the string at $t = 0$ s, when the two waves are overlapped, and a snapshot graph of the left-traveling wave at $t = 0.050$ s. Draw a snapshot graph of the right-traveling wave at $t = 0.050$ s.

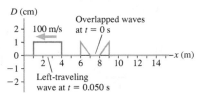

FIGURE P21.30

31. | A 2.0-m-long string vibrates at its second-harmonic frequency with a maximum amplitude of 2.0 cm. One end of the string is at $x = 0$ cm. Find the oscillation amplitude at $x = 10, 20, 30, 40,$ and 50 cm.

32. ‖ A string vibrates at its third-harmonic frequency. The amplitude at a point 30 cm from one end is half the maximum amplitude. How long is the string?

33. ‖ A string of length L vibrates at its fundamental frequency. The amplitude at a point $\frac{1}{4}L$ from one end is 2.0 cm. What is the amplitude of each of the traveling waves that form this standing wave?

34. ‖ Two sinusoidal waves with equal wavelengths travel along a string in opposite directions at 3.0 m/s. The time between two successive instants when the antinodes are at maximum height is 0.25 s. What is the wavelength?

35. ‖ BIO Tendons are, essentially, elastic cords stretched between two fixed ends. As such, they can support standing waves. A woman has a 20-cm-long Achilles tendon—connecting the heel to a muscle in the calf—with a cross-section area of 90 mm². The density of tendon tissue is 1100 kg/m³. For a reasonable tension of 500 N, what will be the fundamental frequency of her Achilles tendon?

36. ‖ BIO Biologists think that some spiders "tune" strands of their web to give enhanced response at frequencies corresponding to those at which desirable prey might struggle. Orb spider web silk has a typical diameter of 20 μm, and spider silk has a density of 1300 kg/m³. To have a fundamental frequency at 100 Hz, to what tension must a spider adjust a 12-cm-long strand of silk?

37. ‖ A particularly beautiful note reaching your ear from a rare Stradivarius violin has a wavelength of 39.1 cm. The room is slightly warm, so the speed of sound is 344 m/s. If the string's linear density is 0.600 g/m and the tension is 150 N, how long is the vibrating section of the violin string?

38. ‖ A violinist places her finger so that the vibrating section of a 1.0 g/m string has a length of 30 cm, then she draws her bow across it. A listener nearby in a 20°C room hears a note with a wavelength of 40 cm. What is the tension in the string?

39. ‖ A steel wire is used to stretch the spring of FIGURE P21.39. An oscillating magnetic field drives the steel wire back and forth. A standing wave with three antinodes is created when the spring is stretched 8.0 cm. What stretch of the spring produces a standing wave with two antinodes?

FIGURE P21.39   Steel wire   Pull
                     Spring

40. ‖ Astronauts visiting Planet X have a 250-cm-long string whose mass is 5.00 g. They tie the string to a support, stretch it horizontally over a pulley 2.00 m away, and hang a 4.00 kg mass on the free end. Then the astronauts begin to excite standing waves on the horizontal portion of the string. Their data are as follows:

m	Frequency (Hz)
1	31
2	66
3	95
4	130
5	162

Use the best-fit line of an appropriate graph to determine the value of g, the free-fall acceleration on Planet X.

41. ‖ A 75 g bungee cord has an equilibrium length of 1.20 m. The cord is stretched to a length of 1.80 m, then vibrated at 20 Hz. This produces a standing wave with two antinodes. What is the spring constant of the bungee cord?

42. ‖ A metal wire under tension T_0 vibrates at its fundamental frequency. For what tension will the second-harmonic frequency be the same as the fundamental frequency at tension T_0?

43. ‖‖ In a laboratory experiment, one end of a horizontal string is tied to a support while the other end passes over a frictionless pulley and is tied to a 1.5 kg sphere. Students determine the frequencies of standing waves on the horizontal segment of the string, then they raise a beaker of water until the hanging 1.5 kg sphere is completely submerged. The frequency of the fifth harmonic with the sphere submerged exactly matches the frequency of the third harmonic before the sphere was submerged. What is the diameter of the sphere?

44. ‖‖ What is the fundamental frequency of the steel wire in FIGURE P21.44?

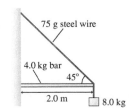

FIGURE P21.44

75 g steel wire

4.0 kg bar
      45°
   2.0 m   8.0 kg

45. ‖ The two strings in FIGURE P21.45 are of equal length and are being driven at equal frequencies. The linear density of the left string is μ_0. What is the linear density of the right string?

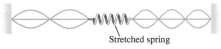

Stretched spring

FIGURE P21.45

46. | Microwaves pass through a small hole into the "microwave cavity" of FIGURE P21.46. What frequencies between 10 GHz and 20 GHz will create standing waves in the cavity?

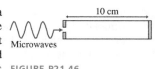

Microwaves

FIGURE P21.46

47. ‖ An open-open organ pipe is 78.0 cm long. An open-closed pipe has a fundamental frequency equal to the third harmonic of the open-open pipe. How long is the open-closed pipe?

48. | A narrow column of 20°C air is found to have standing waves at frequencies of 390 Hz, 520 Hz, and 650 Hz and at no frequencies in between these. The behavior of the tube at frequencies less than 390 Hz or greater than 650 Hz is not known.
    a. Is this an open-open tube or an open-closed tube? Explain.
    b. How long is the tube?

49. ‖ Deep-sea divers often breathe a mixture of helium and oxygen to avoid getting the "bends" from breathing high-pressure nitrogen. The helium has the side effect of making the divers' voices sound odd. Although your vocal tract can be roughly described as an open-closed tube, the way you hold your mouth and position your lips greatly affects the standing-wave frequencies of the vocal tract. This is what allows different vowels to sound different. The "ee" sound is made by shaping your vocal tract to have standing-wave frequencies at, normally, 270 Hz and 2300 Hz. What will these frequencies be for a helium-oxygen mixture in which the speed of sound at body temperature is 750 m/s? The speed of sound in air at body temperature is 350 m/s.

50. ‖ In 1866, the German scientist Adolph Kundt developed a technique for accurately measuring the speed of sound in various gases. A long glass tube, known today as a Kundt's tube, has a vibrating piston at one end and is closed at the other. Very finely ground particles of cork are sprinkled in the bottom of the tube before the piston is inserted. As the vibrating piston is slowly moved forward, there are a few positions that cause the cork particles to collect in small, regularly spaced piles along the bottom. FIGURE P21.50 shows an experiment in which the tube is filled with pure oxygen and the piston is driven at 400 Hz. What is the speed of sound in oxygen?

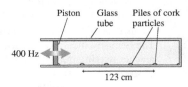

Piston Glass   Piles of cork
        tube   particles

400 Hz

     123 cm

FIGURE P21.50

51. ‖ The 40-cm-long tube of FIGURE P21.51 has a 40-cm-long insert that can be pulled in and out. A vibrating tuning fork is held next to the tube. As the insert is slowly pulled out, the sound from the tuning fork creates standing waves in the tube when the total length L is 42.5 cm, 56.7 cm, and 70.9 cm. What is the frequency of the tuning fork? Assume $v_{sound} = 343$ m/s.

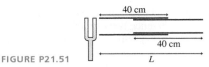

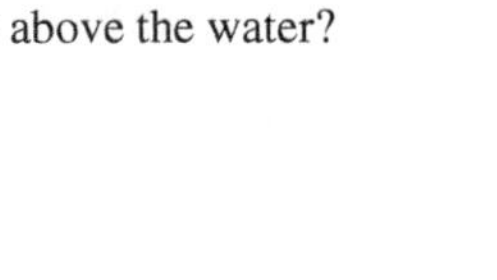

40 cm

40 cm

FIGURE P21.51 L

52. ‖ A 1.0-m-tall vertical tube is filled with 20°C water. A tuning fork vibrating at 580 Hz is held just over the top of the tube as the water is slowly drained from the bottom. At what water heights, measured from the bottom of the tube, will there be a standing wave in the tube above the water?

53. ‖ A 25-cm-long wire with a linear density of 20 g/m passes across the open end of an 85-cm-long open-closed tube of air. If the wire, which is fixed at both ends, vibrates at its fundamental frequency, the sound wave it generates excites the second vibrational mode of the tube of air. What is the tension in the wire? Assume $v_{sound} = 340$ m/s.

54. ‖ A longitudinal standing wave can be created in a long, thin aluminum rod by stroking the rod with very dry fingers. This is often done as a physics demonstration, creating a high-pitched, very annoying whine. From a wave perspective, the standing wave is equivalent to a sound standing wave in an open-open tube. As FIGURE P21.54 shows, both ends of the rod are anti-nodes. What is the fundamental frequency of a 2.0-m-long aluminum rod?

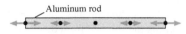
Aluminum rod

FIGURE P21.54

55. ‖ An old mining tunnel disappears into a hillside. You would like to know how long the tunnel is, but it's too dangerous to go inside. Recalling your recent physics class, you decide to try setting up standing-wave resonances inside the tunnel. Using your subsonic amplifier and loudspeaker, you find resonances at 4.5 Hz and 6.3 Hz, and at no frequencies between these. It's rather chilly inside the tunnel, so you estimate the sound speed to be 335 m/s. Based on your measurements, how far is it to the end of the tunnel?

56. ‖ Analyze the standing sound waves in an open-closed tube to show that the possible wavelengths and frequencies are given by Equation 21.18.

57. ‖‖ Two in-phase loudspeakers emit identical 1000 Hz sound waves along the x-axis. What distance should one speaker be placed behind the other for the sound to have an amplitude 1.5 times that of each speaker alone?

58. ‖ Two loudspeakers emit sound waves of the same frequency along the x-axis. The amplitude of each wave is a. The sound intensity is minimum when speaker 2 is 10 cm behind speaker 1. The intensity increases as speaker 2 is moved forward and first reaches maximum, with amplitude $2a$, when it is 30 cm in front of speaker 1. What is
    a. The wavelength of the sound?
    b. The phase difference between the two loudspeakers?
    c. The amplitude of the sound (as a multiple of a) if the speakers are placed side by side?

59. ‖‖ Two loudspeakers emit sound waves along the x-axis. A listener in front of both speakers hears a maximum sound intensity when speaker 2 is at the origin and speaker 1 is at $x = 0.50$ m. If speaker 1 is slowly moved forward, the sound intensity decreases and then increases, reaching another maximum when speaker 1 is at $x = 0.90$ m.
    a. What is the frequency of the sound? Assume $v_{sound} = 340$ m/s.
    b. What is the phase difference between the speakers?

60. ‖ A sheet of glass is coated with a 500-nm-thick layer of oil ($n = 1.42$).
    a. For what *visible* wavelengths of light do the reflected waves interfere constructively?
    b. For what *visible* wavelengths of light do the reflected waves interfere destructively?
    c. What is the color of reflected light? What is the color of transmitted light?

61. ‖ A manufacturing firm has hired your company, Acoustical Consulting, to help with a problem. Their employees are complaining about the annoying hum from a piece of machinery. Using a frequency meter, you quickly determine that the machine emits a rather loud sound at 1200 Hz. After investigating, you tell the owner that you cannot solve the problem entirely, but you can at least improve the situation by eliminating reflections of this sound from the walls. You propose to do this by installing mesh screens in front of the walls. A portion of the sound will reflect from the mesh; the rest will pass through the mesh and reflect from the wall. How far should the mesh be placed in front of the wall for this scheme to work?

62. ‖ A soap bubble is essentially a very thin film of water ($n = 1.33$) surrounded by air. The colors that you see in soap bubbles are produced by interference.
    a. Derive an expression for the wavelengths λ_C for which constructive interference causes a strong reflection from a soap bubble of thickness d.
       Hint: Think about the reflection phase shifts at both boundaries.
    b. What visible wavelengths of light are strongly reflected from a 390-nm-thick soap bubble? What color would such a soap bubble appear to be?

63. ‖ Two radio antennas are separated by 2.0 m. Both broadcast identical 750 MHz waves. If you walk around the antennas in a circle of radius 10 m, how many maxima will you detect?

64. ‖ You are standing 2.5 m directly in front of one of the two loudspeakers shown in FIGURE P21.64. They are 3.0 m apart and both are playing a 686 Hz tone in phase. As you begin to walk directly away from the speaker, at what distances from the speaker do you hear a *minimum* sound intensity? The room temperature is 20°C.

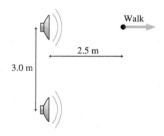
Walk
2.5 m
3.0 m

FIGURE P21.64

65. ‖ Two loudspeakers in a plane, 5.0 apart, are playing the same frequency. If you stand 12.0 m in front of the plane of the speakers, centered between them, you hear a sound of maximum intensity. As you walk parallel to the plane of the speakers, staying 12.0 m in front of them, you first hear a minimum of sound intensity when you are directly in front of one of the speakers. What is the frequency of the sound? Assume a sound speed of 340 m/s.

66. ‖ Two in-phase loudspeakers are located at (x, y) coordinates $(-3.0$ m, $+2.0$ m$)$ and $(-3.0$ m, -2.0 m$)$. They emit identical sound waves with a 2.0 m wavelength and amplitude a. Determine the amplitude of the sound at the five positions on the y-axis ($x = 0$) with $y = 0.0$ m, 0.5 m, 1.0 m, 1.5 m, and 2.0 m.

67. ‖ Two identical loudspeakers separated by distance Δx each emit sound waves of wavelength λ and amplitude a along the x-axis. What is the minimum value of the ratio $\Delta x/\lambda$ for which the amplitude of their superposition is also a?

68. ‖ Two radio antennas are 100 m apart along a north-south line. They broadcast identical radio waves at a frequency of 3.0 MHz. Your job is to monitor the signal strength with a hand-held receiver. To get to your first measuring point, you walk 800 m east from the midpoint between the antennas, then 600 m north.
    a. What is the phase difference between the waves at this point?
    b. Is the interference at this point maximum constructive, perfect destructive, or somewhere in between? Explain.
    c. If you now begin to walk farther north, does the signal strength increase, decrease, or stay the same? Explain.

69. ‖ The three identical loudspeakers in FIGURE P21.69 play a 170 Hz tone in a room where the speed of sound is 340 m/s. You are standing 4.0 m in front of the middle speaker. At this point, the amplitude of the wave from each speaker is a.
    a. What is the amplitude at this point?
    b. How far must speaker 2 be moved to the left to produce a maximum amplitude at the point where you are standing?
    c. When the amplitude is maximum, by what factor is the sound intensity greater than the sound intensity from a single speaker?

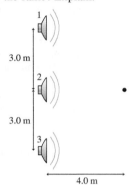

FIGURE P21.69

70. | Piano tuners tune pianos by listening to the beats between the *harmonics* of two different strings. When properly tuned, the note A should have a frequency of 440 Hz and the note E should be at 659 Hz.
    a. What is the frequency difference between the third harmonic of the A and the second harmonic of the E?
    b. A tuner first tunes the A string very precisely by matching it to a 440 Hz tuning fork. She then strikes the A and E strings simultaneously and listens for beats between the harmonics. What beat frequency indicates that the E string is properly tuned?
    c. The tuner starts with the tension in the E string a little low, then tightens it. What is the frequency of the E string when she hears four beats per second?

71. ‖ A flutist assembles her flute in a room where the speed of sound is 342 m/s. When she plays the note A, it is in perfect tune with a 440 Hz tuning fork. After a few minutes, the air inside her flute has warmed to where the speed of sound is 346 m/s.
    a. How many beats per second will she hear if she now plays the note A as the tuning fork is sounded?
    b. How far does she need to extend the "tuning joint" of her flute to be in tune with the tuning fork?

72. ‖ Two loudspeakers face each other from opposite walls of a room. Both are playing exactly the same frequency, thus setting up a standing wave with distance $\lambda/2$ between antinodes. Assume that λ is much less than the room width, so there are many antinodes.
    a. Yvette starts at one speaker and runs toward the other at speed v_Y. As the does so, she hears a loud-soft-loud modulation of the sound intensity. From your perspective, as you sit at rest in the room, Yvette is running through the nodes and antinodes of the standing wave. Find an expression for the number of sound maxima she hears per second.

b. From Yvette's perspective, the two sound waves are Doppler shifted. They're not the same frequency, so they don't create a standing wave. Instead, she hears a loud-soft-loud modulation of the sound intensity because of beats. Find an expression for the beat frequency that Yvette hears.
    c. Are your answers to parts a and b the same or different? *Should* they be the same or different?

73. ‖ Two loudspeakers emit 400 Hz notes. One speaker sits on the ground. The other speaker is in the back of a pickup truck. You hear eight beats per second as the truck drives away from you. What is the truck's speed?

Challenge Problems

74. a. The frequency of a standing wave on a string is f when the string's tension is T_s. If the tension is changed by the *small* amount ΔT_s, without changing the length, show that the frequency changes by an amount Δf such that

$$\frac{\Delta f}{f} = \frac{1}{2}\frac{\Delta T_s}{T_s}$$

b. Two identical strings vibrate at 500 Hz when stretched with the same tension. What percentage increase in the tension of one of the strings will cause five beats per second when both strings vibrate simultaneously?

75. A 280 Hz sound wave is directed into one end of the trombone slide seen in FIGURE CP21.75. A microphone is placed at the other end to record the intensity of sound waves that are transmitted through the tube. The straight sides of the slide are 80 cm in length and 10 cm apart with a semicircular bend at the end. For what slide extensions s will the microphone detect a maximum of sound intensity?

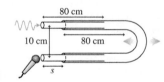

FIGURE CP21.75

76. As the captain of the scientific team sent to Planet Physics, one of your tasks is to measure g. You have a long, thin wire labeled 1.00 g/m and a 1.25 kg weight. You have your accurate space cadet chronometer but, unfortunately, you seem to have forgotten a meter stick. Undeterred, you first find the midpoint of the wire by folding it in half. You then attach one end of the wire to the wall of your laboratory, stretch it horizontally to pass over a pulley at the midpoint of the wire, then tie the 1.25 kg weight to the end hanging over the pulley. By vibrating the wire, and measuring time with your chronometer, you find that the wire's second-harmonic frequency is 100 Hz. Next, with the 1.25 kg weight still tied to one end of the wire, you attach the other end to the ceiling to make a pendulum. You find that the pendulum requires 314 s to complete 100 oscillations. Pulling out your trusty calculator, you get to work. What value of g will you report back to headquarters?

77. When mass M is tied to the bottom of a long, thin wire suspended from the ceiling, the wire's second-harmonic frequency is 200 Hz. Adding an additional 1.0 kg to the hanging mass increases the second-harmonic frequency to 245 Hz. What is M?

78. Ultrasound has many medical applications, one of which is to
    BIO monitor fetal heartbeats by reflecting ultrasound off a fetus in the
    womb.
    a. Consider an object moving at speed v_o toward an at-rest
       source that is emitting sound waves of frequency f_0. Show
       that the reflected wave (i.e., the echo) that returns to the
       source has a Doppler-shifted frequency

    $$f_{echo} = \left(\frac{v + v_o}{v - v_o}\right) f_0$$

       where v is the speed of sound in the medium.
    b. Suppose the object's speed is much less than the wave speed:
       $v_o \ll v$. Then $f_{echo} \approx f_0$, and a microphone that is sensitive to
       these frequencies will detect a beat frequency if it listens to
       f_0 and f_{echo} simultaneously. Use the binomial approximation
       and other appropriate approximations to show that the beat
       frequency is $f_{beat} \approx (2v_o/v)f_0$.
    c. The reflection of 2.40 MHz ultrasound waves from the surface
       of a fetus's beating heart is combined with the 2.40 MHz wave
       to produce a beat frequency that reaches a maximum of 65 Hz.
       What is the maximum speed of the surface of the heart? The
       speed of ultrasound waves within the body is 1540 m/s.
    d. Suppose the surface of the heart moves in simple harmonic
       motion at 90 beats/min. What is the amplitude in mm of the
       heartbeat?

79. A water wave is called a *deep-water wave* if the water's depth
    is more than one-quarter of the wavelength. Unlike the waves
    we've considered in this chapter, the speed of a deep-water wave
    depends on its wavelength:

    $$v = \sqrt{\frac{g\lambda}{2\pi}}$$

    Longer wavelengths travel faster. Let's apply this to standing
    waves. Consider a diving pool that is 5.0 m deep and 10.0 m
    wide. Standing water waves can set up across the width of the
    pool. Because water sloshes up and down at the sides of the pool,
    the boundary conditions require antinodes at $x = 0$ and $x = L$.
    Thus a standing water wave resembles a standing sound wave in
    an open-open tube.
    a. What are the wavelengths of the first three standing-wave
       modes for water in the pool? Do they satisfy the condition for
       being deep-water waves? Draw a graph of each.

b. What are the wave speeds for each of these waves?
c. Derive a general expression for the frequencies f_m of the possible standing waves. Your expression should be in terms of
   m, g, and L.
d. What are the oscillation *periods* of the first three standing-
   wave modes?

80. The broadcast antenna of an
    AM radio station is located at
    the edge of town. The station
    owners would like to beam all
    of the energy into town and
    none into the countryside, but
    a single antenna radiates en-
    ergy equally in all directions.
    FIGURE CP21.80 shows two par-
    allel antennas separated by dis-
    tance L. Both antennas broadcast a signal at wavelength λ, but
    antenna 2 can delay its broadcast relative to antenna 1 by a time
    interval Δt in order to create a phase difference $\Delta\phi_0$ between
    the sources. Your task is to find values of L and Δt such that the
    waves interfere constructively on the town side and destructively
    on the country side.
       Let antenna 1 be at $x = 0$. The wave that travels to the right is
    $a\sin[2\pi(x/\lambda - t/T)]$. The left wave is $a\sin[2\pi(-x/\lambda - t/T)]$.
    (It must be this, rather than $a\sin[2\pi(x/\lambda + t/T)]$, so that the
    two waves match at $x = 0$.) Antenna 2 is at $x = L$. It broadcasts
    wave $a\sin[2\pi((x - L)/\lambda - t/T) + \phi_{20}]$ to the right and wave
    $a\sin[2\pi(-(x - L)/\lambda - t/T) + \phi_{20}]$ to the left.
    a. What is the smallest value of L for which you can create per-
       fect constructive interference on the town side and perfect
       destructive interference on the country side? Your answer
       will be a multiple or fraction of the wavelength λ.
    b. What phase constant ϕ_{20} of antenna 2 is needed?
    c. What fraction of the oscillation period T must Δt be to pro-
       duce the proper value of ϕ_{20}?
    d. Evaluate both L and Δt for the realistic AM radio frequency
       of 1000 KHz.
    Comment: This is a simple example of what is called a *phased
    array*, where phase differences between identical emitters are
    used to "steer" the radiation in a particular direction. Phased ar-
    rays are widely used in radar technology.

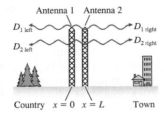

FIGURE CP21.80

STOP TO THINK ANSWERS

Stop to Think 21.1: c. The figure shows the two waves at $t = 6$ s and
their superposition. The superposition is the *point-by-point* addition
of the displacements of the two individual waves.

x (m)
0 2 4 6 8 10 12 14 16 18 20

Stop to Think 21.2: a. The allowed standing-wave frequencies are
$f_m = m(v/2L)$, so the mode number of a standing wave of frequency
f is $m = 2Lf/v$. Quadrupling T_s increases the wave speed v by a factor
of 2. The initial mode number was 2, so the new mode number is 1.

Stop to Think 21.3: b. 300 Hz and 400 Hz are allowed standing
waves, but they are not f_1 and f_2 because 400 Hz $\neq 2 \times$ 300 Hz.
Because there's a 100 Hz difference between them, these must be

$f_3 = 3 \times 100$ Hz and $f_4 = 4 \times 100$ Hz, with a fundamental frequency
$f_1 = 100$ Hz. Thus the second harmonic is $f_2 = 2 \times 100$ Hz $=$
200 Hz.

Stop to Think 21.4: c. Shifting the top wave 0.5 m to the left aligns
crest with crest and trough with trough.

Stop to Think 21.5: a. $r_1 = 0.5\lambda$ and $r_2 = 2.5\lambda$, so $\Delta r = 2.0\lambda$. This
is the condition for maximum constructive interference.

Stop to Think 21.6: Maximum constructive. The path-length difference is $\Delta r = 1.0$ m $= \lambda$. For identical sources, interference is constructive when Δr is an integer multiple of λ.

Stop to Think 21.7: f. The beat frequency is the difference between
the two frequencies.

22 Wave Optics

The vivid colors of this peacock—which change as you see the feathers from different angles—are not due to pigments. Instead, the colors are due to the interference of light waves.

▶ **Looking Ahead** The goal of Chapter 22 is to understand and apply the wave model of light.

Models of Light

You'll learn that light has aspects of both waves and particles. We'll introduce three models of light:

The **wave model** of light—the subject of this chapter—allows us to understand the colors of a soap bubble.

To understand the focusing of light by a contact lens, Chapter 23 will introduce a **ray model** in which light travels in particle-like straight lines.

Solar cells generate electricity from sunlight. The **photon model** of Part VII will be most appropriate for understanding this aspect of light.

◀ **Looking Back**
Sections 20.4–20.6 Wave fronts, phase, and intensity

Diffraction

Diffraction is the ability of waves to spread out after going through small holes or around corners. The diffraction of light indicates that light is a wave.

The "ripples" around the edges of this razor blade—back lit with a blue laser beam—are due to the diffraction of light.

The Diffraction Grating

A **diffraction grating** is a periodic array of closely spaced holes or slits or grooves. You'll learn how a diffraction grating sends different wavelengths off at different angles.

The microscopic pits in this DVD act as a diffraction grating, breaking white light into its component colors.

Diffraction gratings are the basis for *spectroscopy*, an important tool for determining the composition of materials by the wavelengths they emit.

Double-Slit Interference

You'll learn that an interference pattern is formed when light shines on an opaque screen with two narrow, closely spaced slits. This also shows that light is a wave.

Interference fringes from green light passing through two closely spaced slits

◀ **Looking Back**
Section 21.7 Interference

Interferometry

Today, the controlled interference of light has applications that include optical computing, precision measurements in engineering, holography, and observing movements of the earth's crust.

Interference fringes such as these can be used to monitor vibrations and displacements of only a few nanometers.

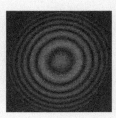

22.1 Light and Optics

The study of light is called **optics.** But what is light? The first Greek scientists did not make a distinction between light and vision. Light, to them, was inseparable from seeing. But gradually there arose a view that light actually "exists," that light is some sort of physical entity that is present regardless of whether or not someone is looking. But if light is a physical entity, what is it? What are its characteristics? Is it a wave, similar to sound? Or is light a collection of small particles that blows by like the wind?

Newton, in addition to his pioneering work in mathematics and mechanics in the 1660s, investigated the nature of light. Newton knew that a water wave, after passing through an opening, *spreads out* to fill the space behind the opening. You can see this in FIGURE 22.1a, where plane waves, approaching from the left, spread out in circular arcs after passing through a hole in a barrier. This inexorable spreading of waves is the phenomenon called **diffraction.** Diffraction is a sure sign that whatever is passing through the hole is a wave.

In contrast, FIGURE 22.1b shows that sunlight makes a sharp-edged shadow after passing through a door. We don't see sunlight light spreading out in circular arcs. This behavior is exactly what you would expect if light consists of particles traveling in straight lines. Some particles would pass through the door to make a bright area on the floor, others would be blocked and cause the well-defined shadow. This reasoning led Newton to the conclusion that light consists of very small, light, fast particles that he called *corpuscles.*

The situation changed dramatically in 1801, when the English scientist Thomas Young announced that he had produced *interference* between two waves of light. Young's experiment, which we will analyze in the next section, was painstakingly difficult with the technology of his era. Nonetheless, Young's experiment quickly settled the debate in favor of a wave theory of light because interference is a distinctly wave-like phenomenon.

But if light is a wave, what is waving? This was the question that Young posed to the 19th century. It was ultimately established that light is an *electromagnetic wave,* an oscillation of the electromagnetic field requiring no material medium in which to travel. Further, as we have already seen, visible light is just one small slice out of a vastly broader *electromagnetic spectrum.*

But this satisfying conclusion was soon undermined by new discoveries at the start of the 20th century. Albert Einstein's introduction of the concept of the *photon*—a wave having certain particle-like characteristics—marked the end of *classical physics* and the beginning of a new era called *quantum physics.* Equally important, Einstein's theory marked yet another shift in our age-old effort to understand light.

Models of Light

Light is a real physical entity, but the nature of light is elusive. Light is the chameleon of the physical world. Under some circumstances, light acts like particles traveling in straight lines. But change the circumstances, and light shows the same kinds of wave-like behavior as sound waves or water waves. Change the circumstances yet again, and light exhibits behavior that is neither wave-like nor particle-like but has characteristics of both.

Rather than an all-encompassing "theory of light," it will be better to develop three **models of light.** Each model successfully explains the behavior of light within a certain domain—that is, within a certain range of physical situations. Our task will be twofold:

1. To develop clear and distinct models of light.
2. To learn the conditions and circumstances for which each model is valid.

We'll begin with a brief summary of all three models.

FIGURE 22.1 Water waves spread out behind a small hole in a barrier, but light passing through a doorway makes a sharp-edged shadow.

(a) Plane waves approach from the left.

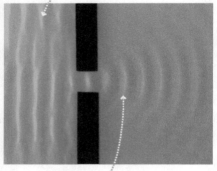

Circular waves spread out on the right.

(b)

A beam of sunlight has a sharp edge.

Three models of light

The Wave Model

The wave model of light is responsible for the widely known "fact" that light is a wave. Indeed, under many circumstances light exhibits the same behavior as sound or water waves. Lasers and electro-optical devices are best described by the wave model of light. Some aspects of the wave model were introduced in Chapters 20 and 21, and it is the primary focus of this chapter.

The Ray Model

An equally well-known "fact" is that light travels in straight lines. These straight-line paths are called *light rays*. The properties of prisms, mirrors, and lenses are best understood in terms of light rays. Unfortunately, it's difficult to reconcile "light travels in straight lines" with "light is a wave." For the most part, waves and rays are mutually exclusive models of light. One of our important tasks will be to learn when each model is appropriate. Ray optics is the subject of Chapters 23 and 24.

The Photon Model

Modern technology is increasingly reliant on quantum physics. In the quantum world, light behaves like neither a wave nor a particle. Instead, light consists of *photons* that have both wave-like and particle-like properties. Much of the quantum theory of light is beyond the scope of this textbook, but we will take a peek at some of the important ideas in Part VII.

22.2 The Interference of Light

Newton might have reached a different conclusion had he seen the experiment depicted in FIGURE 22.2. Here light of a single wavelength (or color) passes through a "window"—a narrow slit—that is only 0.1 mm wide, about twice the width of a human hair. The image shows how the light appears on a viewing screen 2 m behind the slit. If light consists of corpuscles traveling in straight lines, as Newton thought, we should see a narrow strip of light, about 0.1 mm wide, with dark shadows on either side. Instead, we see a band of light extending over about 2.5 cm, a distance much wider than the aperture, with dimmer patches of light extending even farther on either side.

If you compare Figure 22.2 to the water wave of Figure 22.1, you see that *the light is spreading out* behind the 0.1-mm-wide hole. The light is exhibiting diffraction, the sure signature of waviness. We will look at diffraction in more detail later in the chapter. For now, we merely need the *observation* that light does, indeed, spread out behind a hole that is sufficiently small.

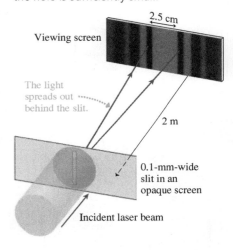

FIGURE 22.2 Light, just like a water wave, does spread out behind a hole *if* the hole is sufficiently small.

Young's Double-Slit Experiment

Rather than one small hole, suppose we use two. FIGURE 22.3a shows an experiment in which a laser beam is aimed at an opaque screen containing two long, narrow slits that are very close together. This pair of slits is called a **double slit,** and in a typical

FIGURE 22.3 A double-slit interference experiment.

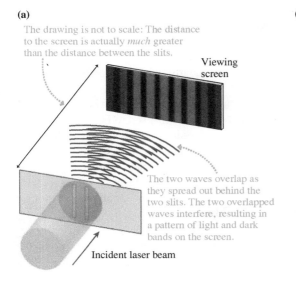

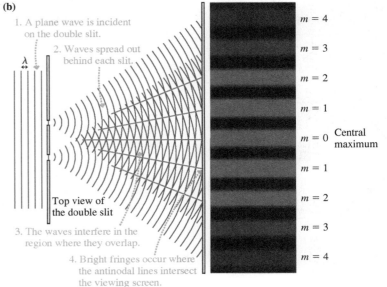

experiment they are ≈ 0.1 mm wide and spaced ≈ 0.5 mm apart. We will assume that the laser beam illuminates both slits equally, and any light passing through the slits impinges on a viewing screen. This is the essence of Young's experiment of 1801, although he used sunlight rather than a laser.

What should we expect to see on the screen? FIGURE 22.3b is a view from above the experiment, looking down on the top ends of the slits and the top edge of the viewing screen. Because the slits are very narrow, **light spreads out behind each slit** as it did in Figure 22.2, and these two spreading waves overlap in the region between the slits and the screen.

The primary conclusion of Chapter 21 was that two overlapped waves of equal wavelength produce interference. In fact, Figure 22.3b is equivalent to the waves emitted by two loudspeakers, a situation we analyzed in Section 21.7. (It is very useful to compare Figure 22.3b with Figures 21.30 and 21.32a.) Nothing in that analysis depended on what type of wave it was, so the conclusions apply equally well to two overlapped light waves. If light really is a wave, we should see interference between the two light waves over the small region, typically a few centimeters wide, where they overlap on the viewing screen.

The image in Figure 22.3b shows how the screen looks. As expected, the light is intense at points where an antinodal line intersects the screen. There is no light at all at points where a nodal line intersects the screen. These alternating bright and dark bands of light, due to constructive and destructive interference, are called **interference fringes.** The fringes are numbered $m = 0, 1, 2, 3, \ldots$, going outward from the center. The brightest fringe, at the midpoint of the viewing screen, with $m = 0$, is called the **central maximum.**

STOP TO THINK 22.1 Suppose the viewing screen in Figure 22.3 is moved closer to the double slit. What happens to the interference fringes?

a. They get brighter but otherwise do not change.
b. They get brighter and closer together.
c. They get brighter and farther apart.
d. They get out of focus.
e. They fade out and disappear.

Analyzing Double-Slit Interference

Figure 22.3 showed qualitatively how interference is produced behind a double slit by the overlap of the light waves spreading out behind each slit. Now let's analyze the experiment more carefully. FIGURE 22.4 shows a double-slit experiment in which the spacing between the two slits is d and the distance to the viewing screen is L. We will assume that L is *very* much larger than d. Consequently, we don't see the individual slits in the upper part of Figure 22.4.

Let P be a point on the screen at angle θ. Our goal is to determine whether the interference at P is constructive, destructive, or in between. The insert to Figure 22.4 shows the individual slits and the paths from these slits to point P. Because P is so far away on this scale, the two paths are virtually parallel, both at angle θ. Both slits are illuminated by the *same* wave front from the laser; hence the slits act as sources of identical, in-phase waves ($\Delta\phi_0 = 0$). You learned in Chapter 21 that constructive interference between the waves from in-phase sources occurs at points for which the path-length difference $\Delta r = r_2 - r_1$ is an integer number of wavelengths:

$$\Delta r = m\lambda \qquad m = 0, 1, 2, 3, \ldots \qquad \text{(constructive interference)} \qquad (22.1)$$

Thus the interference at point P is constructive, producing a bright fringe, if $\Delta r = m\lambda$ at that point.

FIGURE 22.4 Geometry of the double-slit experiment.

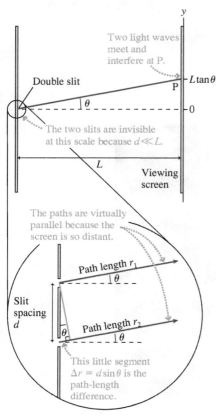

The midpoint on the viewing screen at $y = 0$ is equally distant from both slits ($\Delta r = 0$) and thus is a point of constructive interference. This is the bright fringe identified as the central maximum in Figure 22.3b. The path-length difference increases as you move away from the center of the screen, and the $m = 1$ fringes occur at the points where $\Delta r = 1\lambda$—that is, where one wave has traveled exactly one wavelength farther than the other. In general, **the mth bright fringe occurs where the wave from one slit travels m wavelengths farther than the wave from the other slit and thus $\Delta r = m\lambda$.**

You can see from the magnified portion of Figure 22.4 that the wave from the lower slit travels an extra distance

$$\Delta r = d \sin \theta \qquad (22.2)$$

If we use this in Equation 22.1, we find that bright fringes (constructive interference) occur at angles θ_m such that

$$\Delta r = d \sin \theta_m = m\lambda \qquad m = 0, 1, 2, 3, \ldots \qquad (22.3)$$

We added the subscript m to denote that θ_m is the angle of the mth bright fringe, starting with $m = 0$ at the center.

In practice, the angle θ in a double-slit experiment is very small ($<1°$). We can use the small-angle approximation $\sin \theta \approx \theta$, where θ must be in radians, to write Equation 22.3 as

$$\theta_m = m \frac{\lambda}{d} \qquad m = 0, 1, 2, 3, \ldots \qquad \text{(angles of bright fringes)} \quad (22.4)$$

This gives the angular positions *in radians* of the bright fringes in the interference pattern.

It's usually easier to measure distances rather than angles, so we can also specify point P by its position on a y-axis with the origin directly across from the midpoint between the slits. You can see from Figure 22.4 that

$$y = L \tan \theta \qquad (22.5)$$

Using the small-angle approximation once again, this time in the form $\tan \theta \approx \theta$, we can substitute θ_m from Equation 22.4 for $\tan \theta_m$ in Equation 22.1 to find that the mth bright fringe occurs at position

$$y_m = \frac{m\lambda L}{d} \qquad m = 0, 1, 2, 3, \ldots \qquad \text{(positions of bright fringes)} \quad (22.6)$$

The interference pattern is symmetrical, so there is an mth bright fringe at the same distance on both sides of the center. You can see this in Figure 22.3b. As we've noted, **the $m = 1$ fringes occur at points on the screen where the light from one slit travels exactly one wavelength farther than the light from the other slit.**

NOTE ▶ Equations 22.4 and 22.6 do *not* apply to the interference of sound waves from two loudspeakers. The approximations we've used (small angles, $L \gg d$) are usually not valid for the much longer wavelengths of sound waves. ◀

Equation 22.6 predicts that **the interference pattern is a series of equally spaced bright lines** on the screen, exactly as shown in Figure 22.3b. How do we know the fringes are equally spaced? The **fringe spacing** between the m fringe and the $m + 1$ fringe is

$$\Delta y = y_{m+1} - y_m = \frac{(m + 1)\lambda L}{d} - \frac{m\lambda L}{d} = \frac{\lambda L}{d} \qquad (22.7)$$

Because Δy is independent of m, *any* two adjacent bright fringes have the same spacing.

The dark fringes in the image are bands of destructive interference. You learned in Chapter 21 that destructive interference occurs at positions where the path-length difference of the waves is a half-integer number of wavelengths:

$$\Delta r = \left(m + \frac{1}{2}\right)\lambda \qquad m = 0, 1, 2, \dots \qquad \text{(destructive interference)} \qquad (22.8)$$

We can use Equation 22.2 for Δr and the small-angle approximation to find that the dark fringes are located at positions

$$y'_m = \left(m + \frac{1}{2}\right)\frac{\lambda L}{d} \qquad m = 0, 1, 2, \dots \qquad \text{(positions of dark fringes)} \qquad (22.9)$$

We have used y'_m, with a prime, to distinguish the location of the mth minimum from the mth maximum at y_m. You can see from Equation 22.9 that **the dark fringes are located exactly halfway between the bright fringes.**

EXAMPLE 22.1 **Double-slit interference of a laser beam**

Light from a helium-neon laser ($\lambda = 633$ nm) illuminates two slits spaced 0.40 mm apart. A viewing screen is 2.0 m behind the slits. What are the distances between the two $m = 2$ bright fringes and between the two $m = 2$ dark fringes?

MODEL Two closely spaced slits produce a double-slit interference pattern.

VISUALIZE The interference pattern looks like the image of Figure 22.3b. It is symmetrical, with $m = 2$ bright fringes at equal distances on both sides of the central maximum.

SOLVE The positions of the bright fringes are given by Equation 22.6. The $m = 2$ bright fringe is located at position

$$y_m = \frac{m\lambda L}{d} = \frac{2(633 \times 10^{-9}\ \text{m})(2.0\ \text{m})}{4.0 \times 10^{-4}\ \text{m}} = 6.3\ \text{mm}$$

Each of the $m = 2$ fringes is 6.3 mm from the central maximum; so the distance between the two $m = 2$ bright fringes is 12.6 mm. The $m = 2$ dark fringe is located at

$$y'_m = \left(m + \frac{1}{2}\right)\frac{\lambda L}{d} = 7.9\ \text{mm}$$

Thus the distance between the two $m = 2$ dark fringes is 15.8 mm.

ASSESS Because the fringes are counted outward from the center, the $m = 2$ bright fringe occurs *before* the $m = 2$ dark fringe.

EXAMPLE 22.2 **Measuring the wavelength of light**

A double-slit interference pattern is observed on a screen 1.0 m behind two slits spaced 0.30 mm apart. Ten bright fringes span a distance of 1.7 cm. What is the wavelength of the light?

MODEL It is not always obvious which fringe is the central maximum. Slight imperfections in the slits can make the interference fringe pattern less than ideal. However, you do not need to identify the $m = 0$ fringe because you can make use of the fact that the fringe spacing Δy is uniform. Ten bright fringes have *nine* spaces between them (not ten—be careful!).

VISUALIZE The interference pattern looks like the image of Figure 22.3b.

SOLVE The fringe spacing is

$$\Delta y = \frac{1.7\ \text{cm}}{9} = 1.89 \times 10^{-3}\ \text{m}$$

Using this fringe spacing in Equation 22.7, we find that the wavelength is

$$\lambda = \frac{d}{L}\Delta y = 5.7 \times 10^{-7}\ \text{m} = 570\ \text{nm}$$

It is customary to express the wavelengths of visible light in nanometers. Be sure to do this as you solve problems.

ASSESS Young's double-slit experiment not only demonstrated that light is a wave, it provided a means for measuring the wavelength. You learned in Chapter 20 that the wavelengths of visible light span the range 400–700 nm. These lengths are smaller than we can easily comprehend. A wavelength of 570 nm, which is in the middle of the visible spectrum, is only about 1% of the diameter of a human hair.

STOP TO THINK 22.2 Light of wavelength λ_1 illuminates a double slit, and interference fringes are observed on a screen behind the slits. When the wavelength is changed to λ_2, the fringes get closer together. Is λ_2 larger or smaller than λ_1?

Intensity of the Double-Slit Interference Pattern

Equations 22.6 and 22.9 locate the positions of maximum and zero intensity. To complete our analysis we need to calculate the light *intensity* at every point on the screen. All the tools we need to do this calculation were developed in Chapters 20 and 21.

You learned in Chapter 20 that the wave intensity I is proportional to the square of the wave's amplitude. The light spreading out behind a *single* slit produces the wide band of light that you saw in Figure 22.2. The intensity in this band of light is $I_1 = ca^2$, where a is the light-wave amplitude at the screen due to *one* wave and c is a proportionality constant.

If there were no interference, the light intensity due to two slits would be twice the intensity of one slit: $I_2 = 2I_1 = 2ca^2$. In other words, two slits would cause the broad band of light on the screen to be twice as bright. But that's not what happens. Instead, the superposition of the two light waves creates bright and dark interference fringes.

We found in Chapter 21 (Equation 21.36) that the net amplitude of two superimposed waves is

$$A = \left| 2a\cos\left(\frac{\Delta\phi}{2}\right) \right| \qquad (22.10)$$

where a is the amplitude of each individual wave. Because the sources (i.e., the two slits) are in phase, the phase difference $\Delta\phi$ at the point where the two waves are combined is due only to the path-length difference: $\Delta\phi = 2\pi(\Delta r/\lambda)$. Using Equation 22.2 for Δr, along with the small-angle approximation and Equation 22.5 for y, we find the phase difference at position y on the screen to be

$$\Delta\phi = 2\pi\frac{\Delta r}{\lambda} = 2\pi\frac{d\sin\theta}{\lambda} \approx 2\pi\frac{d\tan\theta}{\lambda} = \frac{2\pi d}{\lambda L}y \qquad (22.11)$$

Substituting Equation 22.11 into Equation 22.10, we find the wave amplitude at position y to be

$$A = \left| 2a\cos\left(\frac{\pi d}{\lambda L}y\right) \right| \qquad (22.12)$$

Consequently, the light intensity at position y on the screen is

$$I = cA^2 = 4ca^2\cos^2\left(\frac{\pi d}{\lambda L}y\right) \qquad (22.13)$$

But ca^2 is I_1, the light intensity of a single slit. Thus the intensity of the double-slit interference pattern at position y is

$$I_{\text{double}} = 4I_1\cos^2\left(\frac{\pi d}{\lambda L}y\right) \qquad (22.14)$$

FIGURE 22.5a is a graph of the double-slit intensity versus position y. Notice the unusual orientation of the graph, with the intensity increasing toward the *left* so that the y-axis can match the experimental layout. You can see that the intensity oscillates between dark fringes ($I_{\text{double}} = 0$) and bright fringes ($I_{\text{double}} = 4I_1$). The maxima occur at points where $y_m = m\lambda L/d$. This is what we found earlier for the positions of the bright fringes, so Equation 22.14 is consistent with our initial analysis.

One curious feature is that the light intensity at the maxima is $I = 4I_1$, four times the intensity of the light from each slit alone. You might think that two slits would make the light twice as intense as one slit, but interference leads to a different result. Mathematically, two slits make the *amplitude* twice as big at points of constructive interference ($A = 2a$), so the intensity increases by a factor of $2^2 = 4$. Physically, this is conservation of energy. The line labeled $2I_1$ in Figure 22.5a is the uniform intensity that two slits would produce *if* the waves did not interfere. Interference does not change the amount of light energy coming through the two slits, but it does redistribute the light energy on the viewing screen. You can see that the *average* intensity of the

FIGURE 22.5 Intensity of the interference fringes in a double-slit experiment.

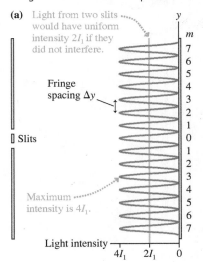

(a) Light from two slits would have uniform intensity $2I_1$ if they did not interfere.

Fringe spacing Δy

Slits

Maximum intensity is $4I_1$.

Light intensity

$4I_1 \quad 2I_1 \quad 0$

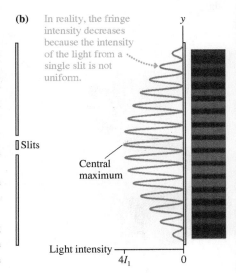

(b) In reality, the fringe intensity decreases because the intensity of the light from a single slit is not uniform.

Slits

Central maximum

Light intensity

$4I_1 \quad 0$

oscillating curve is $2I_1$, but the intensity of the bright fringes gets pushed up from $2I_1$ to $4I_1$ in order for the intensity of the dark fringes to drop from $2I_1$ to 0.

There is still one problem. Equation 22.14 predicts that all interference fringes are equally bright, but you saw in Figure 22.3b that the fringes decrease in brightness as you move away from the center. The erroneous prediction stems from our assumption that the amplitude a of the wave from each slit is constant across the screen. This isn't really true. A more detailed calculation, in which the amplitude gradually decreases as you move away from the center, finds that Equation 22.14 is correct if I_1 slowly decreases as y increases.

FIGURE 22.5b summarizes this analysis by graphing the light intensity (Equation 22.14) with I_1 slowly decreasing as y increases. Comparing this graph to the image, you can see that the wave model of light has provided an excellent description of Young's double-slit interference experiment.

22.3 The Diffraction Grating

Suppose we were to replace the double slit with an opaque screen that has N closely spaced slits. When illuminated from one side, each of these slits becomes the source of a light wave that diffracts, or spreads out, behind the slit. Such a multi-slit device is called a **diffraction grating.** The light intensity pattern on a screen behind a diffraction grating is due to the interference of N overlapped waves.

FIGURE 22.6 shows a diffraction grating in which N slits are equally spaced a distance d apart. This is a top view of the grating, as we look down on the experiment, and the slits extend above and below the page. Only 10 slits are shown here, but a practical grating will have hundreds or even thousands of slits. Suppose a plane wave of wavelength λ approaches from the left. The crest of a plane wave arrives *simultaneously* at each of the slits, causing the wave emerging from each slit to be in phase with the wave emerging from every other slit. Each of these emerging waves spreads out, just like the light wave in Figure 22.2, and after a short distance they all overlap with each other and interfere.

We want to know how the interference pattern will appear on a screen behind the grating. The light wave at the screen is the superposition of N waves, from N slits, as they spread and overlap. As we did with the double slit, we'll assume that the distance L to the screen is very large in comparison with the slit spacing d; hence the path followed by the light from one slit to a point on the screen is *very nearly* parallel to the path followed by the light from neighboring slits. The paths cannot be perfectly parallel, of course, or they would never meet to interfere, but the slight deviation from perfect parallelism is too small to notice. You can see in Figure 22.6 that the wave from one slit travels distance $\Delta r = d\sin\theta$ more than the wave from the slit above it and $\Delta r = d\sin\theta$ less than the wave below it. This is the same reasoning we used in Figure 22.4 to analyze the double-slit experiment.

Figure 22.6 is a magnified view of the slits. FIGURE 22.7 steps back to where we can see the viewing screen. If the angle θ is such that $\Delta r = d\sin\theta = m\lambda$, where m is an integer, then the light wave arriving at the screen from one slit will be *exactly in phase* with the light waves arriving from the two slits next to it. But each of those waves is in phase with waves from the slits next to them, and so on until we reach the end of the grating. In other words, N **light waves, from N different slits, will *all* be in phase** with each other when they arrive at a point on the screen at angle θ_m such that

$$d\sin\theta_m = m\lambda \qquad m = 0, 1, 2, 3, \ldots \qquad (22.15)$$

The screen will have bright constructive-interference fringes at the values of θ_m given by Equation 22.15. We say that the light is "diffracted at angle θ_m."

Because it's usually easier to measure distances rather than angles, the position y_m of the mth maximum is

$$y_m = L\tan\theta_m \qquad \text{(positions of bright fringes)} \qquad (22.16)$$

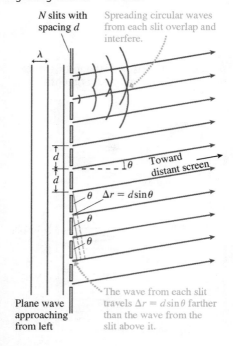

FIGURE 22.6 Top view of a diffraction grating with $N = 10$ slits.

N slits with spacing d

Spreading circular waves from each slit overlap and interfere.

λ

d

θ Toward distant screen

$\theta \quad \Delta r = d\sin\theta$

θ

θ

Plane wave approaching from left

The wave from each slit travels $\Delta r = d\sin\theta$ farther than the wave from the slit above it.

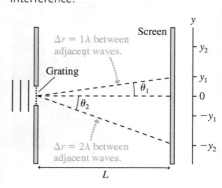

FIGURE 22.7 Angles of constructive interference.

$\Delta r = 1\lambda$ between adjacent waves.

Screen

y

y_2

Grating

θ_1

y_1

0

θ_2

$-y_1$

$\Delta r = 2\lambda$ between adjacent waves.

$-y_2$

L

The integer m is called the **order** of the diffraction. For example, light diffracted at θ_2 would be the second-order diffraction. Practical gratings, with very small values for d, display only a few orders. Because d is usually very small, it is customary to character- ize a grating by the number of *lines per millimeter*. Here "line" is synonymous with "slit," so the number of lines per millimeter is simply the inverse of the slit spacing d in millimeters.

NOTE ▶ The condition for constructive interference in a grating of N slits is identical to Equation 22.4 for just two slits. Equation 22.15 is simply the requirement that the path-length difference between adjacent slits, be they two or N, is $m\lambda$. But unlike the angles in double-slit interference, the angles of constructive interference from a diffraction grating are generally *not* small angles. The reason is that the slit spacing d in a diffraction grating is so small that λ/d is not a small number. Thus you *cannot* use the small-angle approximation to simplify Equations 22.15 and 22.16. ◀

The wave amplitude at the points of constructive interference is Na because N waves of amplitude a combine in phase. Because the intensity depends on the square of the amplitude, the intensities of the bright fringes of a diffraction grating are

$$I_{\text{max}} = N^2 I_1 \qquad (22.17)$$

where, as before, I_1 is the intensity of the wave from a single slit. Equation 22.17 is consistent with our prior conclusion that the intensity of a bright fringe in a double-slit interference experiment is four times the intensity of the light from each slit alone. You can see that the fringe intensities increase rapidly as the number of slits increases.

Not only do the fringes get brighter as N increases, they also get narrower. This is again a matter of conservation of energy. If the light waves did not interfere, the inten- sity from N slits would be NI_1. Interference increases the intensity of the bright fringes by an extra factor of N, so to conserve energy the width of the bright fringes must be proportional to $1/N$. For a realistic diffraction grating, with $N > 100$, the interference pattern consists of a small number of *very* bright and *very* narrow fringes while most of the screen remains dark. FIGURE 22.8a shows the interference pattern behind a diffrac- tion grating both graphically and with a simulation of the viewing screen. A compari- son with Figure 22.5b shows that the bright fringes of a diffraction grating are much sharper and more distinct than the fringes of a double slit.

Because the bright fringes are so distinct, diffraction gratings are used for mea- suring the wavelengths of light. Suppose the incident light consists of two slightly different wavelengths. Each wavelength will be diffracted at a slightly different angle and, if N is sufficiently large, we'll see two distinct fringes on the screen. FIGURE 22.8b illustrates this idea. By contrast, the bright fringes in a double-slit experiment are too broad to distinguish the fringes of one wavelength from those of the other.

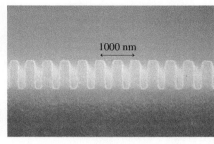

A microscopic side-on look at a diffraction grating.

FIGURE 22.8 The interference pattern behind a diffraction grating.

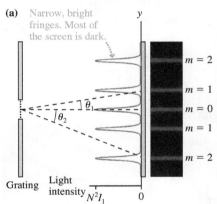

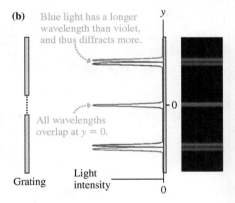

EXAMPLE 22.3   **Measuring wavelengths emitted by sodium atoms**

Light from a sodium lamp passes through a diffraction grating having 1000 slits per millimeter. The interference pattern is viewed on a screen 1.000 m behind the grating. Two bright yellow fringes are visible 72.88 cm and 73.00 cm from the central maximum. What are the wavelengths of these two fringes?

VISUALIZE This is the situation shown in Figure 22.8b. The two fringes are very close together, so we expect the wavelengths to be only slightly different. No other yellow fringes are mentioned, so we will assume these two fringes are the first-order diffraction ($m = 1$).

SOLVE The distance y_m of a bright fringe from the central maxi- mum is related to the diffraction angle by $y_m = L\tan\theta_m$. Thus the diffraction angles of these two fringes are

$$\theta_1 = \tan^{-1}\left(\frac{y_1}{L}\right) = \begin{cases} 36.08° & \text{fringe at 72.88 cm} \\ 36.13° & \text{fringe at 73.00 cm} \end{cases}$$

These angles must satisfy the interference condition $d\sin\theta_1 = \lambda$, so the wavelengths are $\lambda = d\sin\theta_1$. What is d? If a 1 mm length of the grating has 1000 slits, then the spacing from one slit to the next must be 1/1000 mm, or $d = 1.000 \times 10^{-6}$ m. Thus the wave- lengths creating the two bright fringes are

$$\lambda = d\sin\theta_1 = \begin{cases} 589.0 \text{ nm} & \text{fringe at 72.88 cm} \\ 589.6 \text{ nm} & \text{fringe at 73.00 cm} \end{cases}$$

ASSESS We had data accurate to four significant figures, and all four were necessary to distinguish the two wavelengths.

The science of measuring the wavelengths of atomic and molecular emissions is called **spectroscopy.** The two sodium wavelengths in this example are called the *sodium doublet,* a name given to two closely spaced wavelengths emitted by the atoms of one element. This doublet is an identifying characteristic of sodium. Because no other element emits these two wavelengths, the doublet can be used to identify the presence of sodium in a sample of unknown composition, even if sodium is only a very minor constituent. This procedure is called *spectral analysis.*

Reflection Gratings

We have analyzed what is called a *transmission grating,* with many parallel slits. In practice, most diffraction gratings are manufactured as *reflection gratings.* The simplest reflection grating, shown in FIGURE 22.9a, is a mirror with hundreds or thousands of narrow, parallel grooves cut into the surface. The grooves divide the surface into many parallel reflective stripes, each of which, when illuminated, becomes the source of a spreading wave. Thus an incident light wave is divided into N overlapped waves. The interference pattern is exactly the same as the interference pattern of light transmitted through N parallel slits.

Naturally occurring reflection gratings are responsible for some forms of color in nature. As the micrograph of FIGURE 22.9b shows, a peacock feather consists of nearly parallel rods of melanin. These act as a reflection grating and create the ever-changing, multicolored hues of iridescence as the angle between the grating and your eye changes. The iridescence of some insects is due to diffraction from parallel microscopic ridges on the shell.

The rainbow of colors reflected from the surface of a DVD is a similar display of interference. The surface of a DVD is smooth plastic with a mirror-like reflective coating in which millions of microscopic holes, each about 1 μm in diameter, encode digital information. From an optical perspective, the array of holes in a shiny surface is a two-dimensional version of the reflection grating shown in Figure 22.9a. Reflection gratings can be manufactured at very low cost simply by stamping holes or grooves into a reflective surface, and these are widely sold as toys and novelty items. Rainbows of color are seen as each wavelength of white light is diffracted at a unique angle.

FIGURE 22.9 Reflection gratings.

(a) Incident light   Different wavelengths diffracted at different angles

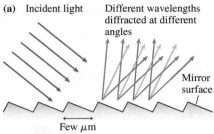

Mirror surface

Few μm

A reflection grating can be made by cutting parallel grooves in a mirror surface. These can be very precise, for scientific use, or mass produced in plastic.

(b)

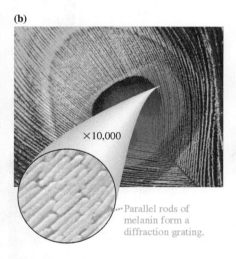

×10,000

Parallel rods of melanin form a diffraction grating.

STOP TO THINK 22.3   White light passes through a diffraction grating and forms rainbow patterns on a screen behind the grating. For each rainbow,

   a. The red side is on the right, the violet side on the left.
   b. The red side is on the left, the violet side on the right.
   c. The red side is closest to the center of the screen, the violet side is farthest from the center.
   d. The red side is farthest from the center of the screen, the violet side is closest to the center.

22.4 Single-Slit Diffraction

We opened this chapter with a photograph (Figure 22.1a) of a water wave passing through a hole in a barrier, then spreading out on the other side. You then saw an image (Figure 22.2) showing that light, after passing through a very narrow slit, also spreads out on the other side. This phenomenon is called *diffraction.* We're now ready to look at the details of diffraction.

FIGURE 22.10 shows the experimental arrangement for observing the diffraction of light through a narrow slit of width *a.* Diffraction through a tall, narrow slit is known as **single-slit diffraction.** A viewing screen is placed distance *L* behind the slit, and we will assume that $L \gg a$. The light pattern on the viewing screen consists of a *central maximum*

FIGURE 22.10 A single-slit diffraction experiment.

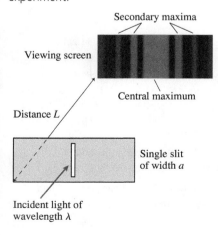

Secondary maxima

Viewing screen

Central maximum

Distance *L*

Single slit of width *a*

Incident light of wavelength λ

flanked by a series of weaker **secondary maxima** and dark fringes. Notice that the central maximum is significantly broader than the secondary maxima. It is also significantly brighter than the secondary maxima, although that is hard to tell here because this image has been overexposed to make the secondary maxima show up better.

Huygens' Principle

Our analysis of the superposition of waves from distinct sources, such as two loudspeakers or the two slits in a double-slit experiment, has tacitly assumed that the sources are *point sources,* with no measurable extent. To understand diffraction, we need to think about the propagation of an *extended* wave front. This is a problem first considered by the Dutch scientist Christiaan Huygens, a contemporary of Newton who argued that light is a wave.

Huygens lived before a mathematical theory of waves had been developed, so he developed a geometrical model of wave propagation. His idea, which we now call **Huygens' principle,** has two steps:

1. Each point on a wave front is the source of a spherical *wavelet* that spreads out at the wave speed.
2. At a later time, the shape of the wave front is the line tangent to all the wavelets.

FIGURE 22.11 illustrates Huygens' principle for a plane wave and a spherical wave. As you can see, the line tangent to the wavelets of a plane wave is a plane that has propagated to the right. The line tangent to the wavelets of a spherical wave is a larger sphere.

Huygens' principle is a visual device, not a theory of waves. Nonetheless, the full mathematical theory of waves, as it developed in the 19th century, justifies Huygens' basic idea, although it is beyond the scope of this textbook to prove it.

Analyzing Single-Slit Diffraction

FIGURE 22.12a shows a wave front passing through a narrow slit of width a. According to Huygens' principle, each point on the wave front can be thought of as the source of a spherical wavelet. These wavelets overlap and interfere, producing the diffraction pattern seen on the viewing screen. The full mathematical analysis, using *every* point on the wave front, is a fairly difficult problem in calculus. We'll be satisfied with a geometrical analysis based on just a few wavelets.

FIGURE 22.12b shows the paths of several wavelets that travel straight ahead to the central point on the screen. (The screen is *very* far to the right in this magnified view of the slit.) The paths are very nearly parallel to each other, thus all the wavelets travel the same distance and arrive at the screen *in phase* with each other. The *constructive interference* between these wavelets produces the central maximum of the diffraction pattern at $\theta = 0$.

FIGURE 22.11 Huygens' principle applied to the propagation of plane waves and spherical waves.

(a) Plane wave

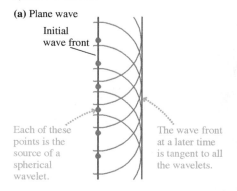

Each of these points is the source of a spherical wavelet.

The wave front at a later time is tangent to all the wavelets.

(b) Spherical wave

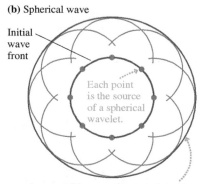

Each point is the source of a spherical wavelet.

The wave front at a later time is tangent to all the wavelets.

FIGURE 22.12 Each point on the wave front is a source of spherical wavelets. The superposition of these wavelets produces the diffraction pattern on the screen.

(a)   Greatly magnified view of slit

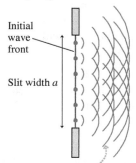

Initial wave front

Slit width a

The wavelets from each point on the initial wave front overlap and interfere, creating a diffraction pattern on the screen.

(b)

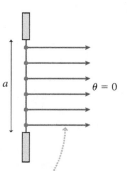

a $\theta = 0$

The wavelets going straight forward all travel the same distance to the screen. Thus they arrive in phase and interfere constructively to produce the central maximum.

(c)

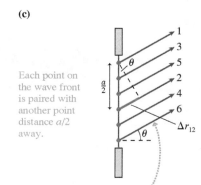

Each point on the wave front is paired with another point distance $a/2$ away.

θ

1
3
5
2
4
6

Δr_{12}

θ

These wavelets all meet on the screen at angle θ. Wavelet 2 travels distance $\Delta r_{12} = (a/2)\sin\theta$ farther than wavelet 1.

The situation is different at points away from the center. Wavelets 1 and 2 in FIGURE 22.12c start from points that are distance $a/2$ apart. If the angle is such that Δr_{12}, the extra distance traveled by wavelet 2, happens to be $\lambda/2$, then wavelets 1 and 2 arrive out of phase and interfere destructively. But if Δr_{12} is $\lambda/2$, then the difference Δr_{34} between paths 3 and 4 and the difference Δr_{56} between paths 5 and 6 are also $\lambda/2$. Those pairs of wavelets also interfere destructively. The superposition of all the wavelets produces perfect destructive interference.

Figure 22.12c shows six wavelets, but our conclusion is valid for any number of wavelets. The key idea is that **every point on the wave front can be paired with another point distance $a/2$ away.** If the path-length difference is $\lambda/2$, the wavelets originating at these two points arrive at the screen out of phase and interfere destructively. When we sum the displacements of all N wavelets, they will—pair by pair—add to zero. The viewing screen at this position will be dark. This is the main idea of the analysis, one worth thinking about carefully.

You can see from Figure 22.12c that $\Delta r_{12} = (a/2)\sin\theta$. This path-length difference will be $\lambda/2$, the condition for destructive interference, if

$$\Delta r_{12} = \frac{a}{2}\sin\theta_1 = \frac{\lambda}{2} \qquad (22.18)$$

or, equivalently, if $a\sin\theta_1 = \lambda$.

NOTE ▶ Equation 22.18 cannot be satisfied if the slit width a is less than the wavelength λ. If a wave passes through an opening smaller than the wavelength, the central maximum of the diffraction pattern expands to where it *completely* fills the space behind the opening. There are no minima or dark spots at any angle. This situation is uncommon for light waves, because λ is so small, but quite common in the diffraction of sound and water waves. ◀

We can extend this idea to find other angles of perfect destructive interference. Suppose each wavelet is paired with another wavelet from a point $a/4$ away. If Δr between these wavelets is $\lambda/2$, then all N wavelets will again cancel in pairs to give complete destructive interference. The angle θ_2 at which this occurs is found by replacing $a/2$ in Equation 22.18 with $a/4$, leading to the condition $a\sin\theta_2 = 2\lambda$. This process can be continued, and we find that the general condition for complete destructive interference is

$$a\sin\theta_p = p\lambda \qquad p = 1, 2, 3, \ldots \qquad (22.19)$$

When $\theta_p \ll 1$ rad, which is almost always true for light waves, we can use the small-angle approximation to write

$$\theta_p = p\frac{\lambda}{a} \qquad p = 1, 2, 3, \ldots \qquad \text{(angles of dark fringes)} \qquad (22.20)$$

Equation 22.20 gives the angles *in radians* to the dark minima in the diffraction pattern of Figure 22.10. Notice that $p = 0$ is explicitly *excluded*. $p = 0$ corresponds to the straight-ahead position at $\theta = 0$, but you saw in Figures 22.10 and 22.12b that $\theta = 0$ is the central *maximum*, not a minimum.

NOTE ▶ It is perhaps surprising that Equations 22.19 and 22.20 are *mathematically* the same as the condition for the mth *maximum* of the double-slit interference pattern. But the physical meaning here is quite different. Equation 22.20 locates the *minima* (dark fringes) of the single-slit diffraction pattern. ◀

You might think that we could use this method of pairing wavelets from different points on the wave front to find the maxima in the diffraction pattern. Why not take two points on the wave front that are distance $a/2$ apart, find the angle at which their wavelets are in phase and interfere constructively, then sum over all points on the wave front? There is a subtle but important distinction. FIGURE 22.13 shows six vector

FIGURE 22.13 Destructive interference by pairs leads to net destructive interference, but constructive interference by pairs does *not* necessarily lead to net constructive interference.

(a)

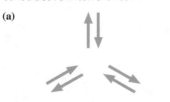

Each pair of vectors interferes destructively. The vector sum of all six vectors is zero.

(b)

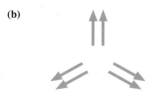

Each pair of vectors interferes constructively. Even so, the vector sum of all six vectors is zero.

arrows. The arrows in FIGURE 22.13a are arranged in pairs such that the two members of each pair cancel. The sum of all six vectors is clearly the zero vector $\vec{0}$, representing destructive interference. This is the procedure we used in Figure 22.12c to arrive at Equation 22.18.

The arrows in FIGURE 22.13b are arranged in pairs such that the two members of each pair point in the same direction—constructive interference! Nonetheless, the sum of all six vectors is still $\vec{0}$. To have N waves interfere constructively requires more than simply having constructive interference between pairs. Each pair must also be in phase with every other pair, a condition not satisfied in Figure 22.13b. Constructive interference by pairs does *not* necessarily lead to net constructive interference. It turns out that there is no simple formula to locate the maxima of a single-slit diffraction pattern.

It is possible, although beyond the scope of this textbook, to calculate the entire light intensity pattern. The results of such a calculation are shown graphically in FIGURE 22.14. You can see the bright central maximum at $\theta = 0$, the weaker secondary maxima, and the dark points of destructive interference at the angles given by Equation 22.20. Compare this graph to the image of Figure 22.10 and make sure you see the agreement between the two.

FIGURE 22.14 A graph of the intensity of a single-slit diffraction pattern.

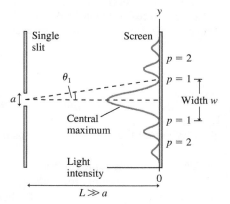

EXAMPLE 22.4   Diffraction of a laser through a slit

Light from a helium-neon laser ($\lambda = 633$ nm) passes through a narrow slit and is seen on a screen 2.0 m behind the slit. The first minimum in the diffraction pattern is 1.2 cm from the central maximum. How wide is the slit?

MODEL   A narrow slit produces a single-slit diffraction pattern. A displacement of only 1.2 cm in a distance of 200 cm means that angle θ_1 is certainly a small angle.

VISUALIZE   The intensity pattern will look like Figure 22.14.

SOLVE   We can use the small-angle approximation to find that the angle to the first minimum is

$$\theta_1 = \frac{1.2 \text{ cm}}{200 \text{ cm}} = 0.00600 \text{ rad} = 0.344°$$

The first minimum is at angle $\theta_1 = \lambda/a$, from which we find that the slit width is

$$a = \frac{\lambda}{\theta_1} = \frac{633 \times 10^{-9} \text{ m}}{6.00 \times 10^{-3} \text{ rad}} = 1.1 \times 10^{-4} \text{ m} = 0.11 \text{ mm}$$

ASSESS   This is typical of the slit widths used to observe single-slit diffraction. You can see that the small-angle approximation is well satisfied.

The Width of a Single-Slit Diffraction Pattern

We'll find it useful, as we did for the double slit, to measure positions on the screen rather than angles. The position of the pth dark fringe, at angle θ_p, is $y_p = L \tan\theta_p$, where L is the distance from the slit to the viewing screen. Using Equation 22.20 for θ_p and the small-angle approximation $\tan\theta_p \approx \theta_p$, we find that the dark fringes in the single-slit diffraction pattern are located at

$$y_p = \frac{p\lambda L}{a} \qquad p = 1, 2, 3, \dots \qquad \text{(positions of dark fringes)} \qquad (22.21)$$

A diffraction pattern is dominated by the central maximum, which is much brighter than the secondary maxima. The width w of the central maximum, shown in Figure 22.14, is defined as the distance between the two $p = 1$ minima on either side of the central maximum. Because the pattern is symmetrical, the width is simply $w = 2y_1$. This is

$$w = \frac{2\lambda L}{a} \qquad \text{(single slit)} \qquad (22.22)$$

The width of the central maximum is *twice* the spacing $\lambda L/a$ between the dark fringes on either side. The farther away the screen (larger L), the wider the pattern of light on it becomes. In other words, the light waves are *spreading out* behind the slit, and they fill a wider and wider region as they travel farther.

An important implication of Equation 22.22, one contrary to common sense, is that a narrower slit (smaller a) causes a *wider* diffraction pattern. **The smaller the opening you squeeze a wave through, the *more* it spreads out on the other side.**

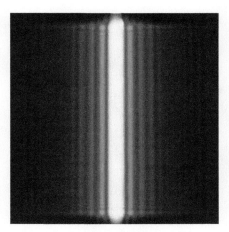

The central maximum of this single-slit diffraction pattern appears white because it is overexposed. The width of the central maximum is clear.

EXAMPLE 22.5 **Determining the wavelength**

Light passes through a 0.12-mm-wide slit and forms a diffraction pattern on a screen 1.00 m behind the slit. The width of the central maximum is 0.85 cm. What is the wavelength of the light?

SOLVE From Equation 22.22, the wavelength is

$$\lambda = \frac{aw}{2L} = \frac{(1.2 \times 10^{-4}\text{ m})(0.0085\text{ m})}{2(1.00\text{ m})}$$

$$= 5.1 \times 10^{-7}\text{ m} = 510\text{ nm}$$

STOP TO THINK 22.4 The figure shows two single-slit diffraction patterns. The distance between the slit and the viewing screen is the same in both cases. Which of the following (perhaps more than one) could be true?

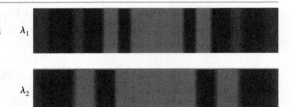

a. The slits are the same for both; $\lambda_1 > \lambda_2$.
b. The slits are the same for both; $\lambda_2 > \lambda_1$.
c. The wavelengths are the same for both; $a_1 > a_2$.
d. The wavelengths are the same for both; $a_2 > a_1$.
e. The slits and the wavelengths are the same for both; $p_1 > p_2$.
f. The slits and the wavelengths are the same for both; $p_2 > p_1$.

22.5 Circular-Aperture Diffraction

Diffraction occurs if a wave passes through an opening of any shape. Diffraction by a single slit establishes the basic ideas of diffraction, but a common situation of practical importance is diffraction of a wave by a **circular aperture.** Circular diffraction is mathematically more complex than diffraction from a slit, and we will present results without derivation.

Consider some examples. A loudspeaker cone generates sound by the rapid oscillation of a diaphragm, but the sound wave must pass through the circular aperture defined by the outer edge of the speaker cone before it travels into the room beyond. This is diffraction by a circular aperture. Telescopes and microscopes are the reverse. Light waves from outside need to enter the instrument. To do so, they must pass through a circular lens. In fact, the performance limit of optical instruments is determined by the diffraction of the circular openings through which the waves must pass. This is an issue we'll look at in Chapter 24.

FIGURE 22.15 shows a circular aperture of diameter D. Light waves passing through this aperture spread out to generate a *circular* diffraction pattern. You should compare this to Figure 22.10 for a single slit to note the similarities and differences. The diffraction pattern still has a *central maximum,* now circular, and it is surrounded by a series of secondary bright fringes.

FIGURE 22.15 The diffraction of light by a circular opening.

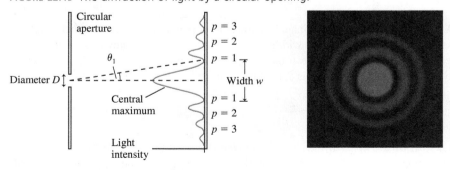

Angle θ_1 locates the first minimum in the intensity, where there is perfect destructive interference. A mathematical analysis of circular diffraction finds

$$\theta_1 = \frac{1.22\lambda}{D} \tag{22.23}$$

where D is the *diameter* of the circular opening. Equation 22.23 has assumed the small-angle approximation, which is almost always valid for the diffraction of light but usually is *not* valid for the diffraction of longer-wavelength sound waves.

Within the small-angle approximation, the width of the central maximum is

$$w = 2y_1 = 2L \tan \theta_1 \approx \frac{2.44 \lambda L}{D} \quad \text{(circular aperture)} \quad (22.24)$$

The diameter of the diffraction pattern increases with distance L, showing that light spreads out behind a circular aperture, but it decreases if the size D of the aperture is increased.

EXAMPLE 22.6 | **Shining a laser through a circular hole**

Light from a helium-neon laser ($\lambda = 633$ nm) passes through a 0.50-mm-diameter hole. How far away should a viewing screen be placed to observe a diffraction pattern whose central maximum is 3.0 mm in diameter?

SOLVE Equation 22.24 gives us the appropriate screen distance:

$$L = \frac{wD}{2.44\lambda} = \frac{(3.0 \times 10^{-3}\,\text{m})(5.0 \times 10^{-4}\,\text{m})}{2.44(633 \times 10^{-9}\,\text{m})} = 0.97\,\text{m}$$

The Wave and Ray Models of Light

We opened this chapter by noting that there are three models of light, each useful within a certain range of circumstances. We are now at a point where we can establish an important condition that separates the wave model of light from the ray model of light.

When light passes through an opening of size a, the angle of the first diffraction minimum is

$$\theta_1 = \sin^{-1}\left(\frac{\lambda}{a}\right) \quad (22.25)$$

Equation 22.25 is for a slit, but the result is very nearly the same if a is the diameter of a circular aperture. Regardless of the shape of the opening, **the factor that determines how much a wave spreads out behind an opening is the ratio λ/a, the size of the wavelength compared to the size of the opening.**

FIGURE 22.16 illustrates the difference between a wave whose wavelength is much smaller than the size of the opening and a second wave whose wavelength is comparable to the opening. A wave with $\lambda/a \approx 1$ quickly spreads to fill the region behind the opening. Light waves, because of their very short wavelength, almost always have $\lambda/a \ll 1$ and diffract to produce a slowly spreading "beam" of light.

Now we can better appreciate Newton's dilemma. With everyday-sized openings, sound and water waves have $\lambda/a \approx 1$ and diffract to fill the space behind the opening. Consequently, this is what we come to expect for the behavior of waves. Newton saw no evidence of this for light passing through openings. We see now that light really does spread out behind an opening, but the very small λ/a ratio usually makes the diffraction pattern too small to see. Diffraction begins to be discernible only when the size of the opening is a fraction of a millimeter or less. If we wanted the diffracted light wave to *fill* the space behind the opening ($\theta_1 \approx 90°$), as a sound wave does, we would need to reduce the size of the opening to $a \approx 0.001$ mm! Although holes this small can be made today, with the processes used to make integrated circuits, the light passing through such a small opening is too weak to be seen by the eye.

FIGURE 22.17 shows light passing through a hole of diameter D. According to the ray model, light rays passing through the hole travel straight ahead to create a bright circular spot of diameter D on a viewing screen. This is the *geometric image* of the slit. In reality, diffraction causes the light to spread out behind the slit, but—and this is the important point—**we will not notice the spreading if it is less than the diameter D of the geometric image.** That is, we will not be aware of diffraction unless the bright spot on the screen increases in diameter.

FIGURE 22.16 The diffraction of a long-wavelength wave and a short-wavelength wave through the same opening.

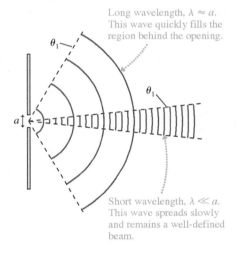

Long wavelength, $\lambda \approx a$. This wave quickly fills the region behind the opening.

Short wavelength, $\lambda \ll a$. This wave spreads slowly and remains a well-defined beam.

FIGURE 22.17 Diffraction will be noticed only if the bright spot on the screen is wider than D.

If light travels in straight lines, the image on the screen is the same size as the hole. Diffraction will not be noticed unless the light spreads over a diameter larger than D.

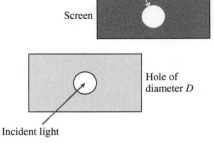

Screen

Hole of diameter D

Incident light

This idea provides a reasonable criterion for when to use ray optics and when to use wave optics:

- If the spreading due to diffraction is less than the size of the opening, use the ray model and think of light as traveling in straight lines.
- If the spreading due to diffraction is greater than the size of the opening, use the wave model of light.

The crossover point between these two regimes occurs when the spreading due to diffraction is equal to the size of the opening. The central-maximum width of a circular-aperture diffraction pattern is $w = 2.44\lambda L/D$. If we equate this diffraction width to the diameter of the aperture itself, we have

$$\frac{2.44\lambda L}{D_c} = D_c \qquad (22.26)$$

where the subscript c on D_c indicates that this is the crossover between the ray model and the wave model. Because we're making an estimate—the change from the ray model to the wave model is gradual, not sudden—to one significant figure, we find

$$D_c \approx \sqrt{2\lambda L} \qquad (22.27)$$

This is the diameter of a circular aperture whose diffraction pattern, at distance L, has width $w = D$. We know that visible light has $\lambda \approx 500$ nm, and a typical distance in laboratory work is $L \approx 1$ m. For these values,

$$D_c \approx 1 \text{ mm}$$

This brings us to an important and very practical conclusion, presented in Tactics Box 22.1.

TACTICS
BOX 22.1   **Choosing a model of light**

❶ When visible light passes through openings smaller than about 1 mm in size, diffraction effects are usually important. Use the wave model of light.
❷ When visible light passes through openings larger than about 1 mm in size, diffraction effects are usually not important. Use the ray model of light.

Openings ≈ 1 mm in size are a gray area. Whether one should use a ray model or a wave model will depend on the precise values of λ and L. We'll avoid such ambiguous cases in this book, sticking with examples and homework that fall clearly within the wave model or the ray model. Lenses and mirrors, in particular, are almost always >1 mm in size. We will study the optics of lenses and mirrors in the chapter on ray optics. This chapter on wave optics deals with objects and openings <1 mm in size.

22.6 Interferometers

Scientists and engineers have devised many ingenious methods for using interference to control the flow of light and to make very precise measurements with light waves. A device that makes practical use of interference is called an **interferometer.**

Interference requires two waves of *exactly* the same wavelength. One way of guaranteeing that two waves have exactly equal wavelengths is to divide one wave into two parts of smaller amplitude. Later, at a different point in space, the two parts are recombined. Interferometers are based on the division and recombination of a single wave.

To illustrate the idea, FIGURE 22.18 shows an *acoustical interferometer*. A sound wave is sent into the left end of the tube. The wave splits into two parts at the junction, and waves of smaller amplitude travel around each side. Distance L can be changed by sliding the upper tube in and out like a trombone. After traveling distances r_1 and r_2, the waves recombine and their superposition travels out to the microphone. The sound emerging from the right end has maximum intensity, zero intensity, or somewhere in between depending on the phase difference between the two waves as they recombine.

The two waves traveling through the interferometer started from the *same* source, the loudspeaker; hence the phase difference $\Delta\phi_0$ between the wave sources is automatically zero. The phase difference $\Delta\phi$ between the recombined waves is due entirely to the different distances they travel. Consequently, the conditions for constructive and destructive interference are those we found in Chapter 21 for identical sources:

FIGURE 22.18 An acoustical interferometer.

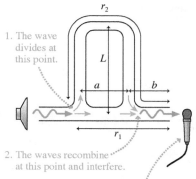

1. The wave divides at this point.

2. The waves recombine at this point and interfere.

3. The microphone detects the superposition of the two waves that traveled different distances.

$$\text{Constructive:} \quad \Delta r = m\lambda$$
$$\text{Destructive:} \quad \Delta r = \left(m + \frac{1}{2}\right)\lambda \qquad m = 0, 1, 2, \ldots \qquad (22.28)$$

The distance each wave travels is easily found from Figure 22.18:

$$r_1 = a + b$$
$$r_2 = L + a + L + b = 2L + a + b$$

Thus the path-length difference between the waves is $\Delta r = r_2 - r_1 = 2L$, and the conditions for constructive and destructive interference are

$$\text{Constructive:} \quad L = m\frac{\lambda}{2}$$
$$\text{Destructive:} \quad L = \left(m + \frac{1}{2}\right)\frac{\lambda}{2} \qquad m = 0, 1, 2, \ldots \qquad (22.29)$$

The interference conditions involve $\lambda/2$ rather than just λ because the wave following the upper path travels distance L *twice,* once up and once down. The upper wave travels a full wavelength λ farther than the lower wave when $L = \lambda/2$.

The interferometer is used by recording the alternating maxima and minima in the sound as the top tube is pulled out and L changes. The interference changes from a maximum to a minimum and back to a maximum every time L increases by half a wavelength. FIGURE 22.19 is a graph of the sound intensity at the microphone as L is increased. You can see, from Equation 22.29, that the number Δm of maxima appearing as the length changes by ΔL is

$$\Delta m = \frac{\Delta L}{\lambda/2} \qquad (22.30)$$

Equation 22.30 is the basis for measuring wavelengths very accurately.

FIGURE 22.19 Interference maxima and minima alternate as the slide on an acoustical interferometer is withdrawn.

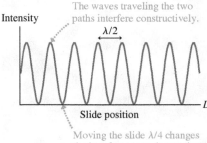

The waves traveling the two paths interfere constructively.

Intensity

Slide position

Moving the slide $\lambda/4$ changes the interference to destructive.

EXAMPLE 22.7 **Measuring the wavelength of sound**

A loudspeaker broadcasts a sound wave into an acoustical interferometer. The interferometer is adjusted so that the output sound intensity is a maximum, then the slide is slowly withdrawn. Exactly 10 new maxima appear as the slide moves 31.52 cm. What is the wavelength of the sound wave?

MODEL An interferometer produces a new maximum each time L increases by $\lambda/2$, causing the path-length difference Δr to increase by λ.

SOLVE Using Equation 22.30, we have

$$\lambda = \frac{2\Delta L}{\Delta m} = \frac{2(31.52 \text{ cm})}{10} = 6.304 \text{ cm}$$

ASSESS The wavelength can be determined to four significant figures because the distance was measured to four significant figures.

The Michelson Interferometer

FIGURE 22.20 A Michelson interferometer.

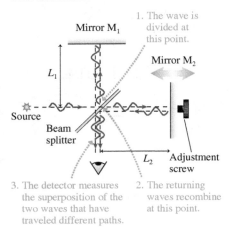

1. The wave is divided at this point.

Mirror M_1

Mirror M_2

L_1

Source

Beam splitter

L_2 Adjustment screw

3. The detector measures the superposition of the two waves that have traveled different paths.

2. The returning waves recombine at this point.

FIGURE 22.20 A Michelson interferometer.

Albert Michelson, the first American scientist to receive a Nobel Prize, invented an optical interferometer analogous to the acoustical interferometer. In the Michelson interferometer of FIGURE 22.20, the light wave is divided by a **beam splitter,** a partially silvered mirror that reflects half the light but transmits the other half. The two waves then travel toward mirrors M_1 and M_2. Half of the wave reflected from M_1 is transmitted through the beam splitter, where it recombines with the reflected half of the wave returning from M_2. The superimposed waves travel on to a light detector, originally a human observer but now more likely an electronic photodetector.

Mirror M_2 can be moved forward or backward by turning a precision screw. This is equivalent to pulling out the slide on the acoustical interferometer. The waves travel distances $r_1 = 2L_1$ and $r_2 = 2L_2$, with the factors of 2 appearing because the waves travel to the mirrors and back again. Thus the path-length difference between the two waves is

$$\Delta r = 2L_2 - 2L_1 \tag{22.31}$$

The condition for constructive interference is $\Delta r = m\lambda$; hence constructive interference occurs when

$$\text{Constructive:} \quad L_2 - L_1 = m\frac{\lambda}{2} \quad m = 0, 1, 2, \ldots \tag{22.32}$$

This result is essentially identical to Equation 22.29 for an acoustical interferometer. Both divide a wave, send the two smaller waves along two paths that differ in length by Δr, then recombine the two waves at a detector.

You might expect the interferometer output to be either "bright" or "dark." Instead, a viewing screen shows the pattern of circular interference fringes seen in FIGURE 22.21. Our analysis was for light waves that impinge on the mirrors exactly perpendicular to the surface. In an actual experiment, some of the light waves enter the interferometer at slightly different angles and, as a result, the recombined waves have slightly altered path-length differences Δr. These waves cause the alternating bright and dark fringes as you move outward from the center of the pattern. Their analysis will be left to more advanced courses in optics. Equation 22.32 is valid at the *center* of the circular pattern; thus there is a bright central spot when Equation 22.32 is true.

If mirror M_2 is moved by turning the screw, the central spot in the fringe pattern alternates between bright and dark. The output recorded by a detector looks exactly like the alternating loud and soft sounds shown in Figure 22.19. Suppose the interferometer is adjusted to produce a bright central spot. The next bright spot will appear when M_2 has moved half a wavelength, increasing the path-length difference by one full wavelength. The number Δm of maxima appearing as M_2 moves through distance ΔL_2 is

$$\Delta m = \frac{\Delta L_2}{\lambda/2} \tag{22.33}$$

FIGURE 22.21 Photograph of the interference fringes produced by a Michelson interferometer.

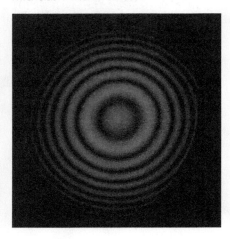

Very precise wavelength measurements can be made by moving the mirror while counting the number of new bright spots appearing at the center of the pattern. The number Δm is counted and known exactly. The only limitation on how precisely λ can be measured this way is the precision with which distance ΔL_2 can be measured. Unlike λ, which is microscopic, ΔL_2 is typically a few millimeters, a macroscopic distance that can be measured very accurately using precision screws, micrometers, and other techniques. Michelson's invention provided a way to transfer the precision of macroscopic distance measurements to an equal precision for the wavelength of light.

EXAMPLE 22.8 **Measuring the wavelength of light**

An experimenter uses a Michelson interferometer to measure one of the wavelengths of light emitted by neon atoms. She slowly moves mirror M_2 until 10,000 new bright central spots have appeared. (In a modern experiment, a photodetector and computer would eliminate the possibility of experimenter error while counting.) She then measures that the mirror has moved a distance of 3.164 mm. What is the wavelength of the light?

MODEL An interferometer produces a new maximum each time L_2 increases by $\lambda/2$.

SOLVE The mirror moves $\Delta L_2 = 3.164$ mm $= 3.164 \times 10^{-3}$ m. We can use Equation 22.33 to find

$$\lambda = \frac{2\Delta L_2}{\Delta m} = 6.328 \times 10^{-7} \text{ m} = 632.8 \text{ nm}$$

ASSESS A measurement of ΔL_2 accurate to four significant figures allowed us to determine λ to four significant figures. This happens to be the neon wavelength that is emitted as the laser beam in a helium-neon laser.

STOP TO THINK 22.5 A Michelson interferometer using light of wavelength λ has been adjusted to produce a bright spot at the center of the interference pattern. Mirror M_1 is then moved distance λ toward the beam splitter while M_2 is moved distance λ away from the beam splitter. How many bright-dark-bright fringe shifts are seen?

a. 0   b. 1   c. 2   d. 4
e. 8   f. It's not possible to say without knowing λ.

Holography

No discussion of wave optics would be complete without mentioning holography, which has both scientific and artistic applications. The basic idea is a simple extension of interferometry.

FIGURE 22.22a shows how a **hologram** is made. A beam splitter divides a laser beam into two waves. One wave illuminates the object of interest. The light scattered by this object is a very complex wave, but it is the wave you would see if you looked at the object from the position of the film. The other wave, called the *reference beam,* is reflected directly toward the film. The scattered light and the reference beam meet at the film and interfere. The film records their interference pattern.

The interference patterns we've looked at in this chapter have been simple patterns of stripes and circles because the light waves have been well-behaved plane waves and spherical waves. The light wave scattered by the object in Figure 22.22a is exceedingly complex. As a result, the interference pattern recorded on the film—the hologram—is a seemingly random pattern of whorls and blotches. FIGURE 22.22b is an enlarged photograph of a portion of a hologram. It's certainly not obvious that information is stored in this pattern, but it is.

A hologram.

FIGURE 22.22 Holography is an important application of wave optics.

(a) Recording a hologram

The interference between the scattered light and the reference beam is recorded on the film.

Film
Plane waves
Reference beam
Laser
Beam splitter
Object beam
Object
The scattered light has a complex wave front.

(b) A hologram

An enlarged photo of the developed film. This is the hologram.

(c) Playing a hologram

The diffraction of the laser beam through the light and dark patches of the film reconstructs the original scattered wave.

Hologram (developed film)
An observer "sees" the object as if it were here.
Laser beam along the reference beam direction

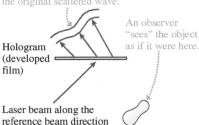

The hologram is "played" by sending just the reference beam through it, as seen in FIGURE 22.2c. The reference beam diffracts through the transparent parts of the hologram, just as it would through the slits of a diffraction grating. Amazingly, the diffracted wave is *exactly the same* as the light wave that had been scattered by the object! In other words, the diffracted reference beam *reconstructs* the original scattered wave. As you look at this diffracted wave, from the far side of the hologram, you "see" the object exactly as if it were there. The view is three dimensional because, by moving your head with respect to the hologram, you can see different portions of the wave front.

CHALLENGE EXAMPLE 22.9 **Measuring the index of refraction of a gas**

A Michelson interferometer uses a helium-neon laser with wavelength $\lambda_{vac} = 633$ nm. In one arm, the light passes through a 4.00-cm-thick glass cell. Initially the cell is evacuated, and the interferometer is adjusted so that the central spot is a bright fringe. The cell is then slowly filled to atmospheric pressure with a gas. As the cell fills, 43 bright-dark-bright fringe shifts are seen and counted. What is the index of refraction of the gas at this wavelength?

MODEL Adding one additional wavelength to the round trip causes one bright-dark-bright fringe shift. Changing the length of the arm is one way to add wavelengths, but not the only way. Increasing the index of refraction also adds wavelengths because light has a shorter wavelength when traveling through a material with a larger index of refraction.

VISUALIZE FIGURE 22.23 shows a Michelson interferometer with a cell of thickness d in one arm.

FIGURE 22.23 Measuring the index of refraction.

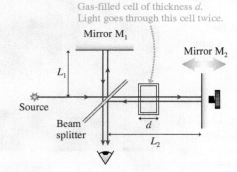

Gas-filled cell of thickness d. Light goes through this cell twice.

SOLVE To begin, all the air is pumped out of the cell. As light travels from the beam splitter to the mirror and back, the number of wavelengths inside the cell is

$$m_1 = \frac{2d}{\lambda_{vac}}$$

where the 2 appears because the light passes through the cell twice.

The cell is then filled with gas at 1 atm pressure. Light travels slower in the gas, $v = c/n$, and you learned in Chapter 20 that the reduction in speed decreases the wavelength to λ_{vac}/n. With the cell filled, the number of wavelengths spanning distance d is

$$m_2 = \frac{2d}{\lambda} = \frac{2d}{\lambda_{vac}/n}$$

The physical distance has not changed, but the number of wavelengths along the path has. Filling the cell has increased the path by

$$\Delta m = m_2 - m_1 = (n - 1)\frac{2d}{\lambda_{vac}}$$

wavelengths. Each increase of one wavelength causes one bright-dark-bright fringe shift at the output. Solving for n, we find

$$n = 1 + \frac{\lambda_{vac}\Delta m}{2d} = 1 + \frac{(6.33 \times 10^{-7}\text{ m})(43)}{2(0.0400\text{ m})} = 1.00034$$

ASSESS This may seem like a six-significant-figure result, but there are really only two. What we're measuring is not n but $n - 1$. We know the fringe count to two significant figures, and that has allowed us to compute $n - 1 = \lambda_{vac}\Delta m/2d = 3.4 \times 10^{-4}$.

SUMMARY

The goal of Chapter 22 has been to understand and apply the wave model of light.

General Principles

Huygens' principle says that each point on a wave front is the source of a spherical wavelet. The wave front at a later time is tangent to all the wavelets.

Diffraction is the spreading of a wave after it passes through an opening.

Constructive and destructive interference are due to the overlap of two or more waves as they spread behind openings.

Important Concepts

The wave model of light considers light to be a wave propagating through space. Diffraction and interference are important.

The ray model of light considers light to travel in straight lines like little particles. Diffraction and interference are not important.

Diffraction is important when the width of the diffraction pattern of an aperture equals or exceeds the size of the aperture. For a circular aperture, the crossover between the ray and wave models occurs for an opening of diameter $D_c \approx \sqrt{2\lambda L}$.

In practice, $D_c \approx 1$ mm for visible light. Thus

- Use the wave model when light passes through openings < 1 mm in size. Diffraction effects are usually important.
- Use the ray model when light passes through openings > 1 mm in size. Diffraction is usually not important.

Applications

Single slit of width a.
A bright **central maximum** of width

$$w = \frac{2\lambda L}{a}$$

is flanked by weaker **secondary maxima.**
Dark fringes are located at angles such that

$$a\sin\theta_p = p\lambda \qquad p = 1, 2, 3, \ldots$$

If $\lambda/a \ll 1$, then from the small-angle approximation

$$\theta_p = \frac{p\lambda}{a} \qquad y_p = \frac{p\lambda L}{a}$$

Circular aperture of diameter D.
A bright central maximum of diameter

$$w = \frac{2.44\lambda L}{D}$$

is surrounded by circular secondary maxima.
The first dark fringe is located at

$$\theta_1 = \frac{1.22\lambda}{D} \qquad y_1 = \frac{1.22\lambda L}{D}$$

For an aperture of any shape, a smaller opening causes a more rapid spreading of the wave behind the opening.

Interference due to wave-front division

Waves overlap as they spread out behind slits. Constructive interference occurs along antinodal lines. Bright fringes are seen where the antinodal lines intersect the viewing screen.

Double slit with separation d.
Equally spaced bright fringes are located at

$$\theta_m = \frac{m\lambda}{d} \qquad y_m = \frac{m\lambda L}{d} \qquad m = 0, 1, 2, \ldots$$

The **fringe spacing** is $\Delta y = \dfrac{\lambda L}{d}$

Diffraction grating with slit spacing d.
Very bright and narrow fringes are located at angles and positions

$$d\sin\theta_m = m\lambda \qquad y_m = L\tan\theta_m$$

Interference due to amplitude division

An interferometer divides a wave, lets the two waves travel different paths, then recombines them. Interference is constructive if one wave travels an integer number of wavelengths more or less than the other wave. The difference can be due to an actual path-length difference or to a different index of refraction.

Michelson interferometer

The number of bright-dark-bright fringe shifts as mirror M_2 moves distance ΔL_2 is

$$\Delta m = \frac{\Delta L_2}{\lambda/2}$$

Terms and Notation

optics	photon model	diffraction grating	Huygens' principle
diffraction	double slit	order, m	circular aperture
models of light	interference fringes	spectroscopy	interferometer
wave model	central maximum	single-slit diffraction	beam splitter
ray model	fringe spacing, Δy	secondary maxima	hologram

CONCEPTUAL QUESTIONS

1. FIGURE Q22.1 shows light waves passing through two closely spaced, narrow slits. The graph shows the intensity of light on a screen behind the slits. Reproduce these graph axes, including the zero and the tick marks locating the double-slit fringes, then draw a graph to show how the light-intensity pattern will appear if the right slit is blocked, allowing light to go through only the left slit. Explain your reasoning.

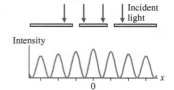

FIGURE Q22.1

2. In a double-slit interference experiment, which of the following actions (perhaps more than one) would cause the fringe spacing to increase? (a) Increasing the wavelength of the light. (b) Increasing the slit spacing. (c) Increasing the distance to the viewing screen. (d) Submerging the entire experiment in water.

3. FIGURE Q22.3 shows the viewing screen in a double-slit experiment. Fringe C is the central maximum. What will happen to the fringe spacing if
   a. The wavelength of the light is decreased?
   b. The spacing between the slits is decreased?
   c. The distance to the screen is decreased?
   d. Suppose the wavelength of the light is 500 nm. How much farther is it from the dot on the screen in the center of fringe E to the left slit than it is from the dot to the right slit?

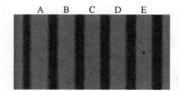

FIGURE Q22.3

4. FIGURE Q22.3 is the interference pattern seen on a viewing screen behind 2 slits. Suppose the 2 slits were replaced by 20 slits having the same spacing d between adjacent slits.
   a. Would the number of fringes on the screen increase, decrease, or stay the same?
   b. Would the fringe spacing increase, decrease, or stay the same?
   c. Would the width of each fringe increase, decrease, or stay the same?
   d. Would the brightness of each fringe increase, decrease, or stay the same?

5. FIGURE Q22.5 shows the light intensity on a viewing screen behind a single slit of width a. The light's wavelength is λ. Is $\lambda < a$, $\lambda = a$, $\lambda > a$, or is it not possible to tell? Explain.

FIGURE Q22.5   FIGURE Q22.6

6. FIGURE Q22.6 shows the light intensity on a viewing screen behind a circular aperture. What happens to the width of the central maximum if
   a. The wavelength of the light is increased?
   b. The diameter of the aperture is increased?
   c. How will the screen appear if the aperture diameter is less than the light wavelength?

7. Narrow, bright fringes are observed on a screen behind a diffraction grating. The entire experiment is then immersed in water. Do the fringes on the screen get closer together, get farther apart, remain the same, or disappear? Explain.

8. a. Green light shines through a 100-mm-diameter hole and is observed on a screen. If the hole diameter is increased by 20%, does the circular spot of light on the screen decrease in diameter, increase in diameter, or stay the same? Explain.
   b. Green light shines through a 100-μm-diameter hole and is observed on a screen. If the hole diameter is increased by 20%, does the circular spot of light on the screen decrease in diameter, increase in diameter, or stay the same? Explain.

9. A Michelson interferometer using 800 nm light is adjusted to have a bright central spot. One mirror is then moved 200 nm forward, the other 200 nm back. Afterward, is the central spot bright, dark, or in between? Explain.

10. A Michelson interferometer is set up to display constructive interference (a bright central spot in the fringe pattern of Figure 22.21) using light of wavelength λ. If the wavelength is changed to $\lambda/2$, does the central spot remain bright, does the central spot become dark, or do the fringes disappear? Explain. Assume the fringes are viewed by a detector sensitive to both wavelengths.

EXERCISES AND PROBLEMS

Problems labeled ▓▓▓ integrate material from earlier chapters.

Exercises

Section 22.2 The Interference of Light

1. | Two narrow slits 80 μm apart are illuminated with light of wavelength 600 nm. What is the angle of the $m = 3$ bright fringe in radians? In degrees?

2. | A double slit is illuminated simultaneously with orange light of wavelength 600 nm and light of an unknown wavelength. The $m = 4$ bright fringe of the unknown wavelength overlaps the $m = 3$ bright orange fringe. What is the unknown wavelength?

3. | Light of wavelength 500 nm illuminates a double slit, and the interference pattern is observed on a screen. At the position of the $m = 2$ bright fringe, how much farther is it to the more distant slit than to the nearer slit?

4. | A double-slit experiment is performed with light of wavelength 600 nm. The bright interference fringes are spaced 1.8 mm apart on the viewing screen. What will the fringe spacing be if the light is changed to a wavelength of 400 nm?

5. ‖ Light of 600 nm wavelength illuminates a double slit. The intensity pattern shown in FIGURE EX22.5 is seen on a screen 2.0 m behind the slits. What is the spacing (in mm) between the slits?

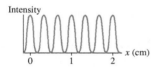

FIGURE EX22.5

6. ‖ Light from a sodium lamp ($\lambda = 589$ nm) illuminates two narrow slits. The fringe spacing on a screen 150 cm behind the slits is 4.0 mm. What is the spacing (in mm) between the two slits?

7. ‖ In a double-slit experiment, the slit separation is 200 times the wavelength of the light. What is the angular separation (in degrees) between two adjacent bright fringes?

8. ‖ A double-slit interference pattern is created by two narrow slits spaced 0.20 mm apart. The distance between the first and the fifth minimum on a screen 60 cm behind the slits is 6.0 mm. What is the wavelength (in nm) of the light used in this experiment?

Section 22.3 The Diffraction Grating

9. | A 4.0-cm-wide diffraction grating has 2000 slits. It is illuminated by light of wavelength 550 nm. What are the angles (in degrees) of the first two diffraction orders?

10. ‖ A diffraction grating produces a first-order maximum at an angle of 20.0°. What is the angle of the second-order maximum?

11. ‖ Light of wavelength 600 nm illuminates a diffraction grating. The second-order maximum is at angle 39.5°. How many lines per millimeter does this grating have?

12. ‖ The two most prominent wavelengths in the light emitted by a hydrogen discharge lamp are 656 nm (red) and 486 nm (blue). Light from a hydrogen lamp illuminates a diffraction grating with 500 lines/mm, and the light is observed on a screen 1.5 m behind the grating. What is the distance between the first-order red and blue fringes?

13. ‖ A helium-neon laser ($\lambda = 633$ nm) illuminates a diffraction grating. The distance between the two $m = 1$ bright fringes is 32 cm on a screen 2.0 m behind the grating. What is the spacing between slits of the grating?

14. | A diffraction grating is illuminated simultaneously with red light of wavelength 660 nm and light of an unknown wavelength. The fifth-order maximum of the unknown wavelength exactly overlaps the third-order maximum of the red light. What is the unknown wavelength?

Section 22.4 Single-Slit Diffraction

15. | A helium-neon laser ($\lambda = 633$ nm) illuminates a single slit and is observed on a screen 1.5 m behind the slit. The distance between the first and second minima in the diffraction pattern is 4.75 mm. What is the width (in mm) of the slit?

16. | In a single-slit experiment, the slit width is 200 times the wavelength of the light. What is the width (in mm) of the central maximum on a screen 2.0 m behind the slit?

17. | The central maximum of a single slit has width 4000λ when viewed on a screen 1.0 m behind the slit. How wide (in mm) is the slit?

18. ‖ Light of 600 nm wavelength illuminates a single slit. The intensity pattern shown in FIGURE EX22.18 is seen on a screen 2.0 m behind the slits. What is the width (in mm) of the slit?

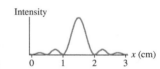

FIGURE EX22.18

19. ‖ A 0.50-mm-wide slit is illuminated by light of wavelength 500 nm. What is the width (in mm) of the central maximum on a screen 2.0 m behind the slit?

20. ‖ You need to use your cell phone, which broadcasts an 800 MHz signal, but you're behind two massive, radio-wave-absorbing buildings that have only a 15 m space between them. What is the angular width, in degrees, of the electromagnetic wave after it emerges from between the buildings?

21. | The opening to a cave is a tall, 30-cm-wide crack. A bat that is preparing to leave the cave emits a 30 kHz ultrasonic chirp. How wide is the "sound beam" 100 m outside the cave opening? Use $v_{sound} = 340$ m/s.

Section 22.5 Circular-Aperture Diffraction

22. ‖ A 0.50-mm-diameter hole is illuminated by light of wavelength 500 nm. What is the width (in mm) of the central maximum on a screen 2.0 m behind the slit?

23. | Infrared light of wavelength 2.5 μm illuminates a 0.20-mm-diameter hole. What is the angle of the first dark fringe in radians? In degrees?

24. | You want to photograph a circular diffraction pattern whose central maximum has a diameter of 1.0 cm. You have a helium-neon laser ($\lambda = 633$ nm) and a 0.12-mm-diameter pinhole. How far behind the pinhole should you place the screen that's to be photographed?

25. || Light from a helium-neon laser ($\lambda = 633$ nm) passes through a circular aperture and is observed on a screen 4.0 m behind the aperture. The width of the central maximum is 2.5 cm. What is the diameter (in mm) of the hole?

Section 22.6 Interferometers

26. | A Michelson interferometer uses red light with a wavelength of 656.45 nm from a hydrogen discharge lamp. How many bright-dark-bright fringe shifts are observed if mirror M_2 is moved exactly 1 cm?

27. | Moving mirror M_2 of a Michelson interferometer a distance of 100 μm causes 500 bright-dark-bright fringe shifts. What is the wavelength of the light?

28. || A Michelson interferometer uses light whose wavelength is known to be 602.446 nm. Mirror M_2 is slowly moved while exactly 33,198 bright-dark-bright fringe shifts are observed. What distance has M_2 moved? Be sure to give your answer to an appropriate number of significant figures.

29. | A Michelson interferometer uses light from a sodium lamp. Sodium atoms emit light having wavelengths 589.0 nm and 589.6 nm. The interferometer is initially set up with both arms of equal length ($L_1 = L_2$), producing a bright spot at the center of the interference pattern. How far must mirror M_2 be moved so that one wavelength has produced one more new maximum than the other wavelength?

Problems

30. | FIGURE P22.30 shows the light intensity on a screen 2.5 m behind an aperture. The aperture is illuminated with light of wavelength 600 nm.
    a. Is the aperture a single slit or a double slit? Explain.
    b. If the aperture is a single slit, what is its width? If it is a double slit, what is the spacing between the slits?

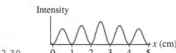
Intensity
FIGURE P22.30 x (cm)   0 1 2 3 4 5

31. | FIGURE P22.31 shows the light intensity on a screen 2.5 m behind an aperture. The aperture is illuminated with light of wavelength 600 nm.
    a. Is the aperture a single slit or a double slit? Explain.
    b. If the aperture is a single slit, what is its width? If it is a double slit, what is the spacing between the slits?

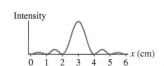
Intensity
FIGURE P22.31 x (cm)   0 1 2 3 4 5 6

32. || Light from a helium-neon laser ($\lambda = 633$ nm) is used to illuminate two narrow slits. The interference pattern is observed on a screen 3.0 m behind the slits. Twelve bright fringes are seen, spanning a distance of 52 mm. What is the spacing (in mm) between the slits?

33. || FIGURE P22.33 shows the light intensity on a screen behind a double slit. The slit spacing is 0.20 mm and the wavelength of the light is 600 nm. What is the distance from the slits to the screen?

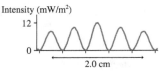
Intensity (mW/m^2)
12
0
FIGURE P22.33   2.0 cm

34. || FIGURE P22.33 shows the light intensity on a screen behind a double slit. The slit spacing is 0.20 mm and the screen is 2.0 m behind the slits. What is the wavelength (in nm) of the light?

35. | FIGURE P22.33 shows the light intensity on a screen behind a double slit. Suppose one slit is covered. What will be the light intensity at the center of the screen due to the remaining slit?

36. ||| A laser beam with a wavelength of 524 nm is exactly perpendicular to a screen having two narrow slits spaced 0.150 mm apart. Interference fringes, including a central maximum, are observed on a viewing screen 1.00 m away. The direction of the laser beam is then slowly rotated by 1.0° around an axis parallel to the slits until it makes an 89.0° angle with the screen. How far does the central maximum move on the viewing screen?

37. ||| A double-slit experiment is set up using a helium-neon laser ($\lambda = 633$ nm). Then a very thin piece of glass ($n = 1.50$) is placed over one of the slits. Afterward, the central point on the screen is occupied by what had been the $m = 10$ dark fringe. How thick is the glass?

38. || A diffraction grating having 500 lines/mm diffracts visible light at 30°. What is the light's wavelength?

39. || Helium atoms emit light at several wavelengths. Light from a helium lamp illuminates a diffraction grating and is observed on a screen 50.0 cm behind the grating. The emission at wavelength 501.5 nm creates a first-order bright fringe 21.90 cm from the central maximum. What is the wavelength of the bright fringe that is 31.60 cm from the central maximum?

40. || A triple-slit experiment consists of three narrow slits, equally spaced by distance d and illuminated by light of wavelength λ. Each slit alone produces intensity I_1 on the viewing screen at distance L.
    a. Consider a point on the distant viewing screen such that the path-length difference between any two adjacent slits is λ. What is the intensity at this point?
    b. What is the intensity at a point where the path-length difference between any two adjacent slits is $\lambda/2$?

41. || Because sound is a wave, it's possible to make a diffraction grating for sound from a large board of sound-absorbing material with several parallel slits cut for sound to go through. When 10 kHz sound waves pass through such a grating, listeners 10 m from the grating report "loud spots" 1.4 m on both sides of center. What is the spacing between the slits? Use 340 m/s for the speed of sound.

42. || A diffraction grating with 600 lines/mm is illuminated with light of wavelength 500 nm. A very wide viewing screen is 2.0 m behind the grating.
    a. What is the distance between the two $m = 1$ bright fringes?
    b. How many bright fringes can be seen on the screen?

43. || A 500 line/mm diffraction grating is illuminated by light of wavelength 510 nm. How many bright fringes are seen on a 2.0-m-wide screen located 2.0 m behind the grating?

44. || White light (400–700 nm) incident on a 600 line/mm diffraction grating produces rainbows of diffracted light. What is the width of the first-order rainbow on a screen 2.0 m behind the grating?

45. ‖ For your science fair project you need to design a diffraction grating that will disperse the visible spectrum (400–700 nm) over 30.0° in first order.
    a. How many lines per millimeter does your grating need?
    b. What is the first-order diffraction angle of light from a sodium lamp ($\lambda = 589$ nm)?

46. ‖ FIGURE P22.46 shows the interference pattern on a screen 1.0 m behind an 800 line/mm diffraction grating. What is the wavelength (in nm) of the light?

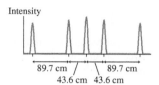

Intensity

89.7 cm   89.7 cm

FIGURE P22.46   43.6 cm 43.6 cm

47. ‖ FIGURE P22.46 shows the interference pattern on a screen 1.0 m behind a diffraction grating. The wavelength of the light is 600 nm. How many lines per millimeter does the grating have?

48. ‖ Light from a sodium lamp ($\lambda = 589$ nm) illuminates a narrow slit and is observed on a screen 75 cm behind the slit. The distance between the first and third dark fringes is 7.5 mm. What is the width (in mm) of the slit?

49. | The wings of some beetles
BIO have closely spaced parallel lines of melanin, causing the wing to act as a reflection grating. Suppose sunlight shines straight onto a beetle wing. If the melanin lines on the wing are spaced 2.0 μm apart, what is the first-order diffraction angle for green light ($\lambda = 550$ nm)?

50. | If sunlight shines straight onto a peacock feather, the feather
BIO appears bright blue when viewed from 15° on either side of the incident beam of light. The blue color is due to diffraction from parallel rods of melanin in the feather barbules, as was shown in the photograph on page 636. Other wavelengths in the incident light are diffracted at different angles, leaving only the blue light to be seen. The average wavelength of blue light is 470 nm. Assuming this to be the first-order diffraction, what is the spacing of the melanin rods in the feather?

51. ‖ You've found an unlabeled diffraction grating. Before you can use it, you need to know how many lines per mm it has. To find out, you illuminate the grating with light of several different wavelengths and then measure the distance between the two first-order bright fringes on a viewing screen 150 cm behind the grating. Your data are as follows:

Wavelength (nm)	Distance (cm)
430	109.6
480	125.4
530	139.8
580	157.2
630	174.4
680	194.8

Use the best-fit line of an appropriate graph to determine the number of lines per mm.

52. ‖ A diffraction grating has slit spacing d. Fringes are viewed on a screen at distance L. What wavelength of light produces a first-order fringe on the viewing screen at distance L from the center of the screen?

53. | For what slit-width-to-wavelength ratio does the first minimum of a single-slit diffraction pattern appear at (a) 30°, (b) 60°, and (c) 90°?

54. ‖ Light from a helium-neon laser ($\lambda = 633$ nm) is incident on a single slit. What is the largest slit width for which there are no minima in the diffraction pattern?

55. ‖ FIGURE P22.55 shows the light intensity on a screen behind a single slit. The slit width is 0.20 mm and the screen is 1.5 m behind the slit. What is the wavelength (in nm) of the light?

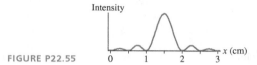

Intensity

FIGURE P22.55   0   1   2   3 x (cm)

56. ‖ FIGURE P22.55 shows the light intensity on a screen behind a single slit. The wavelength of the light is 600 nm and the slit width is 0.15 mm. What is the distance from the slit to the screen?

57. ‖ FIGURE P22.55 shows the light intensity on a screen behind a circular aperture. The wavelength of the light is 500 nm and the screen is 1.0 m behind the slit. What is the diameter (in mm) of the aperture?

58. ‖ Light from a helium-neon laser ($\lambda = 633$ nm) illuminates a circular aperture. It is noted that the diameter of the central maximum on a screen 50 cm behind the aperture matches the diameter of the geometric image. What is the aperture's diameter (in mm)?

59. ‖ One day, after pulling down your window shade, you notice that sunlight is passing through a pinhole in the shade and making a small patch of light on the far wall. Having recently studied optics in your physics class, you're not too surprised to see that the patch of light seems to be a circular diffraction pattern. It appears that the central maximum is about 1 cm across, and you estimate that the distance from the window shade to the wall is about 3 m. Estimate (a) the average wavelength of the sunlight (in nm) and (b) the diameter of the pinhole (in mm).

60. | A radar for tracking aircraft broadcasts a 12 GHz microwave beam from a 2.0-m-diameter circular radar antenna. From a wave perspective, the antenna is a circular aperture through which the microwaves diffract.
    a. What is the diameter of the radar beam at a distance of 30 km?
    b. If the antenna emits 100 kW of power, what is the average microwave intensity at 30 km?

61. ‖ Scientists use *laser range-finding* to measure the distance to the moon with great accuracy. A brief laser pulse is fired at the moon, then the time interval is measured until the "echo" is seen by a telescope. A laser beam spreads out as it travels because it diffracts through a circular exit as it leaves the laser. In order for the reflected light to be bright enough to detect, the laser spot on the moon must be no more than 1.0 km in diameter. Staying within this diameter is accomplished by using a special large-diameter laser. If $\lambda = 532$ nm, what is the minimum diameter of the circular opening from which the laser beam emerges? The earth-moon distance is 384,000 km.

62. ‖ Light of wavelength 600 nm passes though two slits separated by 0.20 mm and is observed on a screen 1.0 m behind the slits. The location of the central maximum is marked on the screen and labeled $y = 0$.
    a. At what distance, on either side of $y = 0$, are the $m = 1$ bright fringes?
    b. A very thin piece of glass is then placed in one slit. Because light travels slower in glass than in air, the wave passing through the glass is delayed by 5.0×10^{-16} s in comparison to the wave going through the other slit. What fraction of the period of the light wave is this delay?
    c. With the glass in place, what is the phase difference $\Delta\phi_0$ between the two waves as they leave the slits?
    d. The glass causes the interference fringe pattern on the screen to shift sideways. Which way does the central maximum move (toward or away from the slit with the glass) and by how far?

63. ‖ A 600 line/mm diffraction grating is in an empty aquarium tank. The index of refraction of the glass walls is $n_{glass} = 1.50$. A helium-neon laser ($\lambda = 633$ nm) is outside the aquarium. The laser beam passes through the glass wall and illuminates the diffraction grating.
    a. What is the first-order diffraction angle of the laser beam?
    b. What is the first-order diffraction angle of the laser beam after the aquarium is filled with water ($n_{water} = 1.33$)?

64. | You've set up a Michelson interferometer with a helium-neon laser ($\lambda = 632.8$ nm). After adjusting mirror M_2 to produce a bright spot at the center of the pattern, you carefully move M_2 away from the beam splitter while counting 1200 new bright spots at the center. Then you put the laser away. Later another student wants to restore the interferometer to its starting condition, but he mistakenly sets up a hydrogen discharge lamp and uses the 656.5 nm emission from hydrogen atoms. He then counts 1200 new bright spots while slowly moving M_2 back toward the beam splitter. What is the net displacement of M_2 when he is done? Is M_2 now closer to or farther from the beam splitter?

65. ‖ A Michelson interferometer operating at a 600 nm wavelength has a 2.00-cm-long glass cell in one arm. To begin, the air is pumped out of the cell and mirror M_2 is adjusted to produce a bright spot at the center of the interference pattern. Then a valve is opened and air is slowly admitted into the cell. The index of refraction of air at 1.00 atm pressure is 1.00028. How many bright-dark-bright fringe shifts are observed as the cell fills with air?

66. | A 0.10-mm-thick piece of glass is inserted into one arm of a Michelson interferometer that is using light of wavelength 500 nm. This causes the fringe pattern to shift by 200 fringes. What is the index of refraction of this piece of glass?

67. ‖ Optical computers require microscopic optical switches to turn signals on and off. One device for doing so, which can be implemented in an integrated circuit, is the *Mach-Zender interferometer* seen in FIGURE P22.67. Light from an on-chip infrared laser ($\lambda = 1.000 \ \mu m$) is split into two waves that travel equal distances around the arms of the interferometer. One arm passes through an *electro-optic crystal,* a transparent material that can change its index of refraction in response to an applied voltage. Suppose both arms are exactly the same length and the crystal's index of refraction with no applied voltage is 1.522.
    a. With no voltage applied, is the output bright (switch closed, optical signal passing through) or dark (switch open, no signal)? Explain.

b. What is the first index of refraction of the electro-optic crystal larger than 1.522 that changes the optical switch to the state opposite the state you found in part a?

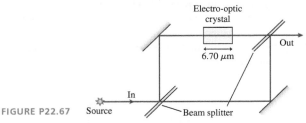

FIGURE P22.67

68. ‖ To illustrate one of the ideas of holography in a simple way, consider a diffraction grating with slit spacing d. The small-angle approximation is usually not valid for diffraction gratings, because d is only slightly larger than λ, but assume that the λ/d ratio of this grating is small enough to make the small-angle approximation valid.
    a. Use the small-angle approximation to find an expression for the fringe spacing on a screen at distance L behind the grating.
    b. Rather than a screen, suppose you place a piece of film at distance L behind the grating. The bright fringes will expose the film, but the dark spaces in between will leave the film unexposed. After being developed, the film will be a series of alternating light and dark stripes. What if you were to now "play" the film by using it as a diffraction grating? In other words, what happens if you shine the same laser through the film and look at the film's diffraction pattern on a screen at the same distance L? Demonstrate that the film's diffraction pattern is a reproduction of the original diffraction grating.

Challenge Problems

69. A helium-neon laser ($\lambda = 633$ nm) is built with a glass tube of inside diameter 1.0 mm, as shown in FIGURE CP22.69. One mirror is partially transmitting to allow the laser beam out. An electrical discharge in the tube causes it to glow like a neon light. From an optical perspective, the laser beam is a light wave that diffracts out through a 1.0-mm-diameter circular opening.
    a. Can a laser beam be *perfectly* parallel, with no spreading? Why or why not?
    b. The angle θ_1 to the first minimum is called the *divergence angle* of a laser beam. What is the divergence angle of this laser beam?
    c. What is the diameter (in mm) of the laser beam after it travels 3.0 m?
    d. What is the diameter of the laser beam after it travels 1.0 km?

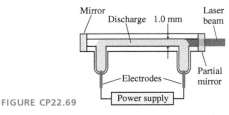

FIGURE CP22.69

70. The intensity at the central maximum of a double-slit interference pattern is $4I_1$. The intensity at the first minimum is zero. At what fraction of the distance from the central maximum to the first minimum is the intensity I_1?

71. Light consisting of two nearly equal wavelengths $\lambda + \Delta\lambda$ and λ, where $\Delta\lambda \ll \lambda$, is incident on a diffraction grating. The slit separation of the grating is d.

    a. Show that the angular separation of these two wavelengths in the mth order is

    $$\Delta\theta = \frac{\Delta\lambda}{\sqrt{(d/m)^2 - \lambda^2}}$$

    b. Sodium atoms emit light at 589.0 nm and 589.6 nm. What are the first-order and second-order angular separations (in degrees) of these two wavelengths for a 600 line/mm grating?

72. FIGURE CP22.72 shows two nearly overlapped intensity peaks of the sort you might produce with a diffraction grating (see Figure 22.8b). As a practical matter, two peaks can just barely be resolved if their spacing Δy equals the width w of each peak, where w is measured at half of the peak's height. Two peaks closer together than w will merge into a single peak. We can use this idea to understand the *resolution* of a diffraction grating.

    a. In the small-angle approximation, the position of the $m = 1$ peak of a diffraction grating falls at the same location as the $m = 1$ fringe of a double slit: $y_1 = \lambda L/d$. Suppose two wavelengths differing by $\Delta\lambda$ pass through a grating at the same time. Find an expression for Δy, the separation of their first-order peaks.

    b. We noted that the widths of the bright fringes are proportional to $1/N$, where N is the number of slits in the grating. Let's hypothesize that the fringe width is $w = y_1/N$. Show that this is true for the double-slit pattern. We'll then assume it to be true as N increases.

    c. Use your results from parts a and b together with the idea that $\Delta y_{min} = w$ to find an expression for $\Delta\lambda_{min}$, the minimum wavelength separation (in first order) for which the diffraction fringes can barely be resolved.

    d. Ordinary hydrogen atoms emit red light with a wavelength of 656.45 nm. In deuterium, which is a "heavy" isotope of hydrogen, the wavelength is 656.27 nm. What is the minimum number of slits in a diffraction grating that can barely resolve these two wavelengths in the first-order diffraction pattern?

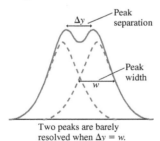

FIGURE CP22.72

Peak separation

Peak width

Δy

w

Two peaks are barely resolved when $\Delta y = w$.

73. The diffraction grating analysis in this chapter assumed that the incident light is normal to the grating. FIGURE CP22.73 shows a plane wave approaching a diffraction grating at angle ϕ.

    a. Show that the angles θ_m for constructive interference are given by the grating equation

    $$d(\sin\theta_m + \sin\phi) = m\lambda$$

    where $m = 0, \pm 1, \pm 2, \ldots$. Angles are considered positive if they are above the horizontal line, negative if below it.

    b. The two first-order maxima, $m = +1$ and $m = -1$, are no longer symmetrical about the center. Find θ_1 and θ_{-1} for 500 nm light incident on a 600 line/mm grating at $\phi = 30°$.

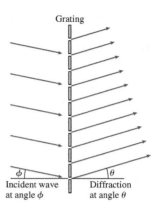

Grating

FIGURE CP22.73

Incident wave at angle ϕ Diffraction at angle θ

74. FIGURE CP22.74 shows light of wavelength λ incident at angle ϕ on a *reflection* grating of spacing d. We want to find the angles θ_m at which constructive interference occurs.

    a. The figure shows paths 1 and 2 along which two waves travel and interfere. Find an expression for the path-length difference $\Delta r = r_2 - r_1$.

    b. Using your result from part a, find an equation (analogous to Equation 22.15) for the angles θ_m at which diffraction occurs when the light is incident at angle ϕ. Notice that m can be a negative integer in your expression, indicating that path 2 is shorter than path 1.

    c. Show that the zeroth-order diffraction is simply a "reflection." That is, $\theta_0 = \phi$.

    d. Light of wavelength 500 nm is incident at $\phi = 40°$ on a reflection grating having 700 reflection lines/mm. Find all angles θ_m at which light is diffracted. Negative values of θ_m are interpreted as an angle left of the vertical.

    e. Draw a picture showing a *single* 500 nm light ray incident at $\phi = 40°$ and showing all the diffracted waves at the correct angles.

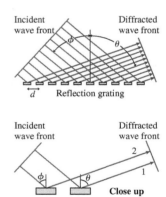

Incident wave front   Diffracted wave front

ϕ θ

d Reflection grating

Incident wave front   Diffracted wave front

ϕ θ 2   1

Close up

FIGURE CP22.74 d

75. The pinhole camera of FIGURE CP22.75 images distant objects by allowing only a narrow bundle of light rays to pass through the hole and strike the film. If light consisted of particles, you could make the image sharper and sharper (at the expense of getting dimmer and dimmer) by making the aperture smaller and smaller. In practice, diffraction of light

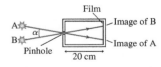

Film

Image of B

α

A

B

Pinhole   Image of A

20 cm

FIGURE CP22.75

by the circular aperture limits the maximum sharpness that can be obtained. Consider two distant points of light, such as two distant streetlights. Each will produce a circular diffraction pattern on the film. The two images can just barely be resolved if the central maximum of one image falls on the first dark fringe of the other image. (This is called Rayleigh's criterion, and we will explore its implication for optical instruments in Chapter 24.)

a. Optimum sharpness of one image occurs when the diameter of the central maximum equals the diameter of the pinhole. What is the optimum hole size for a pinhole camera in which the film is 20 cm behind the hole? Assume $\lambda = 550$ nm, an average value for visible light.
b. For this hole size, what is the angle α (in degrees) between two distant sources that can barely be resolved?
c. What is the distance between two street lights 1 km away that can barely be resolved?

STOP TO THINK ANSWERS

Stop to Think 22.1: b. The antinodal lines seen in Figure 22.3b are diverging.

Stop to Think 22.2: Smaller. Shorter-wavelength light doesn't spread as rapidly as longer-wavelength light. The fringe spacing Δy is directly proportional to the wavelength λ.

Stop to Think 22.3: d. Larger wavelengths have larger diffraction angles. Red light has a larger wavelength than violet light, so red light is diffracted farther from the center.

Stop to Think 22.4: b or c. The width of the central maximum, which is proportional to λ/a, has increased. This could occur either because the wavelength has increased or because the slit width has decreased.

Stop to Think 22.5: d. Moving M_1 in by λ decreases r_1 by 2λ. Moving M_2 out by λ increases r_2 by 2λ. These two actions together change the path length by $\Delta r = 4\lambda$.

23 Ray Optics

The observation that light travels in straight lines—*light rays*—will help us understand the physics of lenses and prisms.

▶ **Looking Ahead** The goals of Chapter 23 are to understand and apply the ray model of light.

The Ray Model of Light

The ray model applies when light interacts with objects that are very large compared to the wavelength. You'll learn that...

...light rays travel in straight lines unless they are...

...reflected by a surface or...

...refracted at a boundary.

Light rays can also be *scattered* or *absorbed* by the medium they travel through.

Reflection

Light rays can bounce, or **reflect,** off a surface. There are two important cases:

Specular reflection, like from a mirror.

Diffuse reflection, like from the page of this book.

You'll learn to use the *law of reflection.*

Refraction

When light rays travel from one medium to another, they change directions, or **refract,** at the boundary.

Refraction causes the laser beam to change direction as it goes through the prism.

You'll learn to use *Snell's law* to find the angles on both sides.

◀ **Looking Back**
Section 20.5 Index of refraction

Images Formed by Lenses and Mirrors

You'll discover how lenses and mirrors form **images.** We'll start with a graphical method called **ray tracing.**

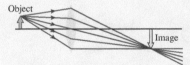

Ray tracing shows how this lens forms a *real image* on the opposite side of the lens from the object.

We'll then develop the **thin-lens equation** for more quantitative results.

A magnifying glass creates a *virtual image* that you see by looking through the lens.

We'll use the same graphical and mathematical techniques to understand how curved mirrors create images.

The passenger-side rearview mirror is curved, allowing you to see a wider field of view.

23.1 The Ray Model of Light

A flashlight makes a beam of light through the night's darkness. Sunbeams stream into a darkened room through a small hole in the shade. Laser beams are even more well defined. Our everyday experience that light travels in straight lines is the basis of the *ray model* of light.

The ray model is an oversimplification of reality but nonetheless is very useful within its range of validity. In particular, the ray model of light is valid as long as any apertures through which the light passes (lenses, mirrors, and holes) are very large compared to the wavelength of light. In that case, diffraction and other wave aspects of light are negligible and can be ignored. The analysis of Section 22.5 found that the crossover between wave optics and ray optics occurs for apertures ≈ 1 mm in diameter. Lenses and mirrors are almost always larger than 1 mm, so the ray model of light is an excellent basis for the practical optics of image formation.

To begin, let us define a **light ray** as a line in the direction along which light energy is flowing. A light ray is an abstract idea, not a physical entity or a "thing." Any narrow beam of light, such as the laser beam in FIGURE 23.1, is actually a bundle of many parallel light rays. You can think of a single light ray as the limiting case of a laser beam whose diameter approaches zero. Laser beams are good approximations of light rays, certainly adequate for demonstrating ray behavior, but any real laser beam is a bundle of many parallel rays.

The following table outlines five basic ideas and assumptions of the ray model of light.

FIGURE 23.1 A laser beam or beam of sunlight is a bundle of parallel light rays.

Light rays

Direction of travel

A beam of light

The ray model of light

Light rays travel in straight lines.

Light travels through a transparent material in straight lines called light rays. The speed of light is $v = c/n$, where n is the index of refraction of the material.

Light rays can cross.

Light rays do not interact with each other. Two rays can cross without either being affected in any way.

A light ray travels forever unless it interacts with matter.

A light ray continues forever unless it has an interaction with matter that causes the ray to change direction or to be absorbed. Light interacts with matter in four different ways:

- At an interface between two materials, light can be either *reflected* or *refracted*.
- Within a material, light can be either *scattered* or *absorbed*.

These interactions are discussed later in the chapter.

Material 1   Material 2

Reflection

Refraction

Scattering

Absorption

An object is a source of light rays.

An **object** is a source of light rays. Rays originate from *every* point on the object, and each point sends rays in *all* directions. We make no distinction between self-luminous objects and reflective objects.

The eye sees by focusing a diverging bundle of rays.

Diverging bundle of rays

Eye

The eye "sees" an object when *diverging* bundles of rays from each point on the object enter the pupil and are focused to an image on the retina. (Imaging is discussed later in the chapter.) From the movements the eye's lens has to make to focus the image, your brain determines the point from which the rays originated, and you perceive the object as being at that point.

Objects

FIGURE 23.2 illustrates the idea that objects can be either *self-luminous,* such as the sun, flames, and lightbulbs, or *reflective.* Most objects are reflective. A tree, unless it is on fire, is seen or photographed by virtue of reflected sunlight or reflected skylight. People, houses, and this page in the book reflect light from self-luminous sources. In this chapter we are concerned not with how the light originates but with how it behaves after leaving the object.

Light rays from an object are emitted in all directions, but you are not *aware* of light rays unless they enter the pupil of your eye. Consequently, most light rays go completely unnoticed. For example, light rays travel from the sun to the tree in Figure 23.2, but you're not aware of these unless the tree reflects some of them into your eye. Or consider a laser beam. You've probably noticed that it's almost impossible to see a laser beam from the side unless there's dust in the air. The dust scatters a few of the light rays toward your eye, but in the absence of dust you would be completely unaware of a very powerful light beam traveling past you. **Light rays exist independently of whether you are seeing them.**

FIGURE 23.3 shows two idealized sets of light rays. The diverging rays from a **point source** are emitted in all directions. It is useful to think of each point on an object as a point source of light rays. A **parallel bundle** of rays could be a laser beam. Alternatively it could represent a *distant object,* an object such as a star so far away that the rays arriving at the observer are essentially parallel to each other.

Ray Diagrams

Rays originate from *every* point on an object and travel outward in *all* directions, but a diagram trying to show all these rays would be hopelessly messy and confusing. To simplify the picture, we usually use a **ray diagram** showing only a few rays. For example, FIGURE 23.4 is a ray diagram showing only a few rays leaving the top and bottom points of the object and traveling to the right. These rays will be sufficient to show us how the object is imaged by lenses or mirrors.

> NOTE ▶ Ray diagrams are the basis for a *pictorial representation* that we'll use throughout this chapter. Be careful not to think that a ray diagram shows all of the rays. The rays shown on the diagram are just a subset of the infinitely many rays leaving the object. ◀

Apertures

A popular form of entertainment during ancient Roman times was a visit to a **camera obscura,** Latin for "dark room." As FIGURE 23.5a shows, a camera obscura was a darkened room with a single, small hole to the outside world. After their eyes became dark adapted, visitors could see a dim but full-color image of the outside world displayed on the back wall of the room. However, the image was upside down! The *pinhole camera* is a miniature version of the camera obscura.

A hole through which light passes is called an **aperture.** FIGURE 23.5b uses the ray model of light passing through a small aperture to explain how the camera obscura works. Each point on an object emits light rays in all directions, but only a very few of these rays pass through the aperture and reach the back wall. As the figure illustrates, the geometry of the rays causes the image to be upside down.

Actually, as you may have realized, each *point* on the object illuminates a small but extended *patch* on the wall. This is because the non-zero size of the aperture—needed for the image to be bright enough to see—allows several rays from each point on the object to pass through at slightly different angles. As a result, the image is slightly blurred and out of focus. (Diffraction also becomes an issue if the hole gets too small.) We'll later discover how a modern camera, with a lens, improves on the camera obscura.

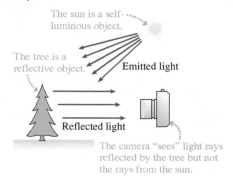

FIGURE 23.2 Self-luminous and reflective objects.

The sun is a self-luminous object.

The tree is a reflective object.

Emitted light

Reflected light

The camera "sees" light rays reflected by the tree but not the rays from the sun.

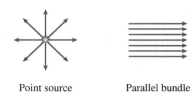

FIGURE 23.3 Point sources and parallel bundles represent idealized objects.

Point source   Parallel bundle

FIGURE 23.4 A ray diagram simplifies the situation by showing only a few rays.

These are just a few of the infinitely many rays leaving the object.

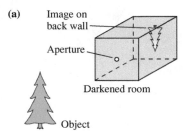

FIGURE 23.5 A camera obscura.

(a)   Image on back wall

Aperture

Darkened room

Object

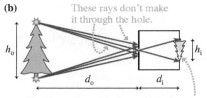

(b)   These rays don't make it through the hole.

h_o h_i

d_o d_i

The image is upside down. If the hole is sufficiently small, each point on the image corresponds to one point on the object.

FIGURE 23.6 Light through an aperture.

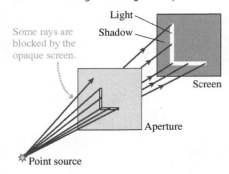

Some rays are
blocked by the
opaque screen.

You can see from the similar triangles in Figure 23.5b that the object and image heights are related by

$$\frac{h_i}{h_o} = \frac{d_i}{d_o} \qquad (23.1)$$

where d_o is the distance to the object and d_i is the depth of the camera obscura. Any realistic camera obscura has $d_i < d_o$; thus the image is smaller than the object.

We can apply the ray model to more complex apertures, such as the L-shaped aperture in FIGURE 23.6. The pattern of light on the screen is found by tracing all the straight-line paths—the ray trajectories—that start from the point source and pass through the aperture. We will see an enlarged L on the screen, with a sharp boundary between the image and the dark shadow.

STOP TO THINK 23.1 A long, thin lightbulb illuminates a vertical aperture. Which pattern of light do you see on a viewing screen behind the aperture?

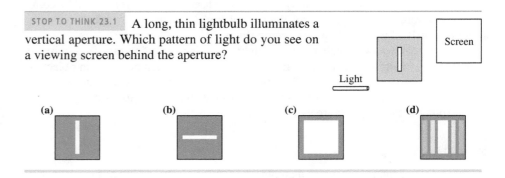

23.2 Reflection

Reflection of light is a familiar, everyday experience. You see your reflection in the bathroom mirror first thing every morning, reflections in your car's rearview mirror as you drive to school, and the sky reflected in puddles of standing water. Reflection from a flat, smooth surface, such as a mirror or a piece of polished metal, is called **specular reflection,** from *speculum,* the Latin word for "mirror."

FIGURE 23.7a shows a bundle of parallel light rays reflecting from a mirror-like surface. You can see that the incident and reflected rays are both in a plane that is normal, or perpendicular, to the reflective surface. A three-dimensional perspective accurately shows the relationship between the light rays and the surface, but figures such as this are hard to draw by hand. Instead, it is customary to represent reflection with the simpler pictorial representation of FIGURE 23.7b. In this figure,

FIGURE 23.7 Specular reflection of light.

(a) The incident and reflected rays lie
in the plane of incidence, a plane
perpendicular to the surface.

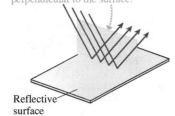

Reflective
surface

(b)

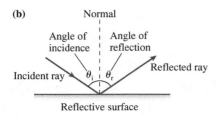

- The plane of the page is the *plane of incidence*, the plane containing both incident and reflected rays. The reflective surface extends into the page.
- A *single* light ray represents the entire bundle of parallel rays. This is oversimplified, but it keeps the figure and the analysis clear.

The angle θ_i between the ray and a line perpendicular to the surface—the *normal* to the surface—is called the **angle of incidence.** Similarly, the **angle of reflection** θ_r is the angle between the reflected ray and the normal to the surface. The **law of reflection,** easily demonstrated with simple experiments, states that

1. The incident ray and the reflected ray are in the same plane normal to the surface, and
2. The angle of reflection equals the angle of incidence: $\theta_r = \theta_i$.

NOTE ▶ Optics calculations *always* use the angle measured from the normal, not the angle between the ray and the surface. ◀

EXAMPLE 23.1 **Light reflecting from a mirror**

A dressing mirror on a closet door is 1.50 m tall. The bottom is 0.50 m above the floor. A bare lightbulb hangs 1.00 m from the closet door, 2.50 m above the floor. How long is the streak of reflected light across the floor?

MODEL Treat the lightbulb as a point source and use the ray model of light.

FIGURE 23.8 Pictorial representation of the light rays reflecting from a mirror.

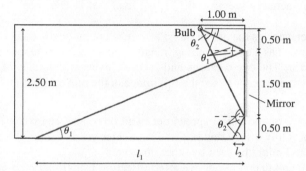

VISUALIZE FIGURE 23.8 is a pictorial representation of the light rays. We need to consider only the two rays that strike the edges of the mirror. All other reflected rays will fall between these two.

SOLVE Figure 23.8 has used the law of reflection to set the angles of reflection equal to the angles of incidence. Other angles have been identified with simple geometry. The two angles of incidence are

$$\theta_1 = \tan^{-1}\left(\frac{0.50 \text{ m}}{1.00 \text{ m}}\right) = 26.6°$$

$$\theta_2 = \tan^{-1}\left(\frac{2.00 \text{ m}}{1.00 \text{ m}}\right) = 63.4°$$

The distances to the points where the rays strike the floor are then

$$l_1 = \frac{2.00 \text{ m}}{\tan\theta_1} = 4.00 \text{ m}$$

$$l_2 = \frac{0.50 \text{ m}}{\tan\theta_2} = 0.25 \text{ m}$$

Thus the length of the light streak is $l_1 - l_2 = 3.75$ m.

Diffuse Reflection

Most objects are seen by virtue of their reflected light. For a "rough" surface, the law of reflection $\theta_r = \theta_i$ is obeyed at each point but the irregularities of the surface cause the reflected rays to leave in many random directions. This situation, shown in FIGURE 23.9, is called **diffuse reflection.** It is how you see this page, the wall, your hand, your friend, and so on.

By a "rough" surface, we mean a surface that is rough or irregular in comparison to the wavelength of light. Because visible-light wavelengths are ≈ 0.5 μm, any surface with texture, scratches, or other irregularities larger than 1 μm will cause diffuse reflection rather than specular reflection. A piece of paper may feel quite smooth to your hand, but a microscope would show that the surface consists of distinct fibers much larger than 1 μm. By contrast, the irregularities on a mirror or a piece of polished metal are much smaller than 1 μm.

FIGURE 23.9 Diffuse reflection from an irregular surface.

Each ray obeys the law of reflection at that point, but the irregular surface causes the reflected rays to leave in many random directions.

Magnified view of surface

The Plane Mirror

One of the most commonplace observations is that you can see yourself in a mirror. How? FIGURE 23.10a shows rays from point source P reflecting from a mirror. Consider the particular ray shown in FIGURE 23.10b. The reflected ray travels along a line that passes through point P′ on the "back side" of the mirror. Because $\theta_r = \theta_i$, simple geometry dictates that P′ is the same distance behind the mirror as P is in front of the mirror. That is, $s' = s$.

FIGURE 23.10 The light rays reflecting from a plane mirror.

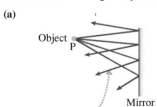

(a)

Rays from P reflect from the mirror. Each ray obeys the law of reflection.

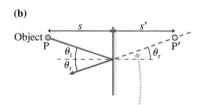

(b)

This reflected ray appears to have been traveling along a line that passed through point P′.

(c) Object distance Image distance

The reflected rays *all* diverge from P′, which appears to be the source of the reflected rays. Your eye collects the bundle of diverging rays and "sees" the light coming from P′.

The location of point P′ in Figure 23.10b is independent of the value of θ_i. Consequently, as FIGURE 23.10c shows, **the reflected rays all *appear* to be coming from point P′.** For a plane mirror, the distance $s′$ to point P′ is equal to the object distance s:

$$s′ = s \quad \text{(plane mirror)} \quad (23.2)$$

If rays diverge from an object point P and interact with a mirror so that the reflected rays diverge from point P′ and *appear* to come from P′, then we call P′ a **virtual image** of point P. The image is "virtual" in the sense that no rays actually leave P′, which is in darkness behind the mirror. But as far as your eye is concerned, the light rays act exactly *as if* the light really originated at P′. So while you may say "I see P in the mirror," what you are actually seeing is the virtual image of P. Distance $s′$ is the *image distance*.

For an extended object, such as the one in FIGURE 23.11, each point on the object from which rays strike the mirror has a corresponding image point an equal distance on the opposite side of the mirror. The eye captures and focuses diverging bundles of rays from each point of the image in order to see the full image in the mirror. Two facts are worth noting:

1. Rays from each point on the object spread out in all directions and strike *every point* on the mirror. Only a very few of these rays enter your eye, but the other rays are very real and might be seen by other observers.
2. Rays from points P and Q enter your eye after reflecting from *different* areas of the mirror. This is why you can't always see the full image of an object in a very small mirror.

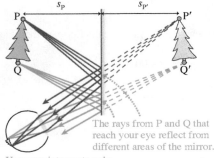

FIGURE 23.11 Each point on the extended object has a corresponding image point an equal distance on the opposite side of the mirror.

The rays from P and Q that reach your eye reflect from different areas of the mirror.

Your eye intercepts only a very small fraction of all the reflected rays.

EXAMPLE 23.2 **How high is the mirror?**

If your height is h, what is the shortest mirror on the wall in which you can see your full image? Where must the top of the mirror be hung?

MODEL Use the ray model of light.

VISUALIZE FIGURE 23.12 is a pictorial representation of the light rays. We need to consider only the two rays that leave your head and feet and reflect into your eye.

SOLVE Let the distance from your eyes to the top of your head be l_1 and the distance to your feet be l_2. Your height is $h = l_1 + l_2$. A light ray from the top of your head that reflects from the mirror at $\theta_r = \theta_i$ and enters your eye must, by congruent triangles, strike the mirror a distance $\frac{1}{2}l_1$ above your eyes. Similarly, a ray from your foot to your eye strikes the mirror a distance $\frac{1}{2}l_2$ below your eyes. The distance between these two points on the mirror is $\frac{1}{2}l_1 + \frac{1}{2}l_2 = \frac{1}{2}h$. A ray from anywhere else on your body will reach your eye if it strikes the mirror between these two points. Pieces of the mirror outside these two points are irrelevant, not because rays don't strike them but because the reflected rays don't reach your

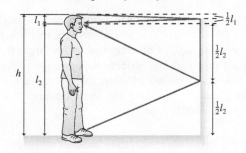

FIGURE 23.12 Pictorial representation of light rays from your head and feet reflecting into your eye.

eye. Thus the shortest mirror in which you can see your full reflection is $\frac{1}{2}h$. But this will work only if the top of the mirror is hung midway between your eyes and the top of your head.

ASSESS It is interesting that the answer does not depend on how far you are from the mirror.

STOP TO THINK 23.2 Two plane mirrors form a right angle. How many images of the ball can you see in the mirrors?

a. 1
b. 2
c. 3
d. 4

Observer

23.3 Refraction

Two things happen when a light ray is incident on a smooth boundary between two transparent materials, such as the boundary between air and glass:

1. Part of the light *reflects* from the boundary, obeying the law of reflection. This is how you see reflections from pools of water or storefront windows, even though water and glass are transparent.

2. Part of the light continues into the second medium. It is *transmitted* rather than reflected, but the transmitted ray changes direction as it crosses the boundary. The transmission of light from one medium to another, but with a change in direction, is called **refraction.**

The photograph of FIGURE 23.13 shows the refraction of a light beam as it passes through a glass prism. Notice that the ray direction changes as the light enters and leaves the glass. Our goal in this section is to understand refraction, so we will usually ignore the weak reflection and focus on the transmitted light.

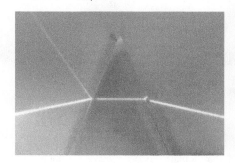

FIGURE 23.13 A light beam refracts twice in passing through a glass prism. You can see a weak reflection from the left surface of the prism.

NOTE ▶ A transparent material through which light travels is called the *medium.* This term has to be used with caution. The material does affect the light speed, but a transparent material differs from the medium of a sound or water wave in that particles of the medium do *not* oscillate as a light wave passes through. For a light wave it is the electromagnetic field that oscillates. ◀

FIGURE 23.14a shows the refraction of light rays in a parallel beam of light, such as a laser beam, and rays from a point source. It's good to remember that an infinite number of rays are incident on the boundary, but our analysis will be simplified if we focus on a single light ray. FIGURE 23.14b is a ray diagram showing the refraction of a single ray at a boundary between medium 1 and medium 2. Let the angle between the ray and the normal be θ_1 in medium 1 and θ_2 in medium 2. For the medium in which the ray is approaching the boundary, this is the *angle of incidence* as we've previously defined it. The angle on the transmitted side, *measured from the normal,* is called the **angle of refraction.** Notice that θ_1 is the angle of incidence in Figure 23.14b and the angle of refraction in FIGURE 23.14c, where the ray is traveling in the opposite direction, even though the value of θ_1 has not changed.

FIGURE 23.14 Refraction of light rays.

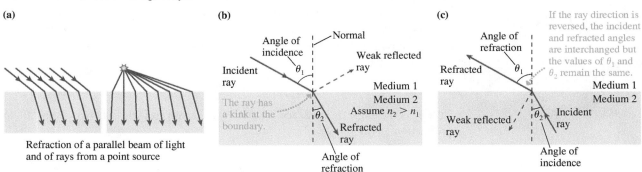

(a)

Refraction of a parallel beam of light and of rays from a point source

(b)

Angle of incidence — Normal

Incident ray

θ_1

Weak reflected ray

Medium 1

The ray has a kink at the boundary.

θ_2

Medium 2

Assume $n_2 > n_1$

Refracted ray

Angle of refraction

(c)

If the ray direction is reversed, the incident and refracted angles are interchanged but the values of θ_1 and θ_2 remain the same.

Angle of refraction

Refracted ray

θ_1

Medium 1

Medium 2

Weak reflected ray

θ_2

Incident ray

Angle of incidence

Refraction was first studied experimentally by the Arab scientist Ibn Al-Haitham, in about the year 1000, and later by the Dutch scientist Willebrord Snell. **Snell's law** says that when a ray refracts between medium 1 and medium 2, having indices of refraction n_1 and n_2, the ray angles θ_1 and θ_2 in the two media are related by

$$n_1 \sin \theta_1 = n_2 \sin \theta_2 \qquad \text{(Snell's law of refraction)} \qquad (23.3)$$

Notice that Snell's law does not mention which is the incident angle and which the refracted angle.

The Index of Refraction

To Snell and his contemporaries, n was simply an "index of the refractive power" of a transparent substance. The relationship between the index of refraction and the speed of light was not recognized until the development of a wave theory of light in the 19th century. Theory predicts, and experiment confirms, that light travels through a transparent medium, such as glass or water, at a speed *less* than its speed c in vacuum. In Section 20.5, we defined the *index of refraction n* of a transparent medium as

$$n = \frac{c}{v_{\text{medium}}} \tag{23.4}$$

where v_{medium} is the light speed in the medium. This implies, of course, that $v_{\text{medium}} = c/n$. The index of refraction of a medium is always $n > 1$ except for vacuum, which has $n = 1$ exactly.

Table 23.1 shows measured values of n for several materials. There are many types of glass, each with a slightly different index of refraction, so we will keep things simple by accepting $n = 1.50$ as a typical value. Notice that cubic zirconia, used to make costume jewelry, has an index of refraction much higher than glass, although not equal to diamond.

We can accept Snell's law as simply an empirical discovery about light. Alternatively, and perhaps surprisingly, we can use the wave model of light to justify Snell's law. The key ideas we need are:

■ Wave fronts represent the crests of waves. They are spaced one wavelength apart.
■ The wavelength in a medium with index of refraction n is $\lambda = \lambda_{\text{vac}}/n$, where λ_{vac} is the vacuum wavelength.
■ Wave fronts are perpendicular to the wave's direction of travel. Consequently, wave fronts are perpendicular to rays.
■ The wave fronts have to stay lined up as a wave crosses from one medium into another.

FIGURE 23.15 shows what happens as a wave crosses the boundary between two media, where we're assuming $n_2 > n_1$. **Because the wavelengths differ on opposite sides of the boundary, the wave fronts can stay lined up only if the waves in the two media are traveling in different directions.** In other words, the wave must refract at the boundary to keep the crests of the wave aligned.

To analyze Figure 23.15, consider the segment of boundary of length l between the two dots. This segment is the common hypotenuse of two right triangles. From the upper triangle, which has one side of length λ_1, we see

$$l = \frac{\lambda_1}{\sin \theta_1} \tag{23.5}$$

where θ_1 is the angle of incidence. Similarly, the lower triangle, where θ_2 is the angle of refraction, gives

$$l = \frac{\lambda_2}{\sin \theta_2} \tag{23.6}$$

Equating these two expressions for l, and using $\lambda_1 = \lambda_{\text{vac}}/n_1$ and $\lambda_2 = \lambda_{\text{vac}}/n_2$, we find

$$\frac{\lambda_{\text{vac}}}{n_1 \sin \theta_1} = \frac{\lambda_{\text{vac}}}{n_2 \sin \theta_2} \tag{23.7}$$

Equation 23.7 can be true only if

$$n_1 \sin \theta_1 = n_2 \sin \theta_2 \tag{23.8}$$

which is Snell's law.

TABLE 23.1 Indices of refraction

Medium	n
Vacuum	1.00 exactly
Air (actual)	1.0003
Air (accepted)	1.00
Water	1.33
Ethyl alcohol	1.36
Oil	1.46
Glass (typical)	1.50
Polystyrene plastic	1.59
Cubic zirconia	2.18
Diamond	2.41
Silicon (infrared)	3.50

FIGURE 23.15 Snell's law is a consequence of the wave model of light.

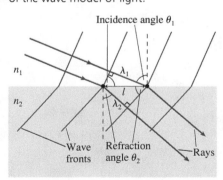

Examples of Refraction

Look back at Figure 23.14. As the ray in Figure 23.14b moves from medium 1 to medium 2, where $n_2 > n_1$, it bends closer to the normal. In Figure 23.14c, where the ray moves from medium 2 to medium 1, it bends away from the normal. This is a general conclusion that follows from Snell's law:

■ When a ray is transmitted into a material with a higher index of refraction, it bends toward the normal.
■ When a ray is transmitted into a material with a lower index of refraction, it bends away from the normal.

This rule becomes a central idea in a procedure for analyzing refraction problems.

**TACTICS
BOX 23.1 Analyzing refraction**

❶ **Draw a ray diagram.** Represent the light beam with one ray.
❷ **Draw a line normal to the boundary.** Do this at each point where the ray intersects a boundary.
❸ **Show the ray bending in the correct direction.** The angle is larger on the side with the smaller index of refraction. This is the qualitative application of Snell's law.
❹ **Label angles of incidence and refraction.** Measure all angles from the normal.
❺ **Use Snell's law.** Calculate the unknown angle or unknown index of refraction.

Exercises 11–15

EXAMPLE 23.3 Deflecting a laser beam

A laser beam is aimed at a 1.0-cm-thick sheet of glass at an angle 30° above the glass.

a. What is the laser beam's direction of travel in the glass?
b. What is its direction in the air on the other side?
c. By what distance is the laser beam displaced?

MODEL Represent the laser beam with a single ray and use the ray model of light.

VISUALIZE FIGURE 23.16 is a pictorial representation in which the first four steps of Tactics Box 23.1 are identified. Notice that the angle of incidence is $\theta_1 = 60°$, not the 30° value given in the problem.

FIGURE 23.16 The ray diagram of a laser beam passing through a sheet of glass.

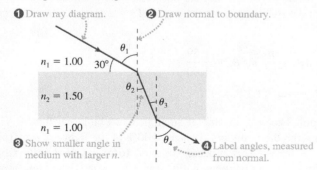

SOLVE a. Snell's law, the final step in the Tactics Box, is $n_1 \sin\theta_1 = n_2 \sin\theta_2$. Using $\theta_1 = 60°$, we find that the direction of travel in the glass is

$$\theta_2 = \sin^{-1}\left(\frac{n_1 \sin\theta_1}{n_2}\right) = \sin^{-1}\left(\frac{\sin 60°}{1.5}\right)$$

$$= \sin^{-1}(0.577) = 35.3°$$

b. Snell's law at the second boundary is $n_2 \sin\theta_3 = n_1 \sin\theta_4$. You can see from Figure 23.16 that the interior angles are equal: $\theta_3 = \theta_2 = 35.3°$. Thus the ray emerges back into the air traveling at angle

$$\theta_4 = \sin^{-1}\left(\frac{n_2 \sin\theta_3}{n_1}\right) = \sin^{-1}(1.5 \sin 35.3°)$$

$$= \sin^{-1}(0.867) = 60°$$

This is the same as θ_1, the original angle of incidence. The glass doesn't change the direction of the laser beam.

c. Although the exiting laser beam is parallel to the initial laser beam, it has been displaced sideways by distance d. **FIGURE 23.17** on the next page shows the geometry for finding d. From trigonometry, $d = l \sin\phi$. Further, $\phi = \theta_1 - \theta_2$ and $l = t/\cos\theta_2$, where t is the thickness of the glass. Combining these gives

Continued

$$d = l\sin\phi = \frac{t}{\cos\theta_2}\sin(\theta_1 - \theta_2)$$

$$= \frac{(1.0 \text{ cm})\sin 24.7°}{\cos 35.3°} = 0.51 \text{ cm}$$

The glass causes the laser beam to be displaced sideways by 0.51 cm.

ASSESS The laser beam exits the glass still traveling in the same direction as it entered. This is a general result for light traveling through a medium with parallel sides. Notice that the displacement d becomes zero in the limit $t \rightarrow 0$. This will be an important observation when we get to lenses.

FIGURE 23.17 The laser beam is deflected sideways by distance d.

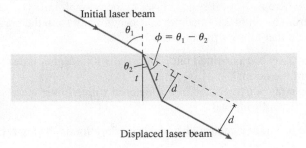

EXAMPLE 23.4 **Measuring the index of refraction**

FIGURE 23.18 shows a laser beam deflected by a 30°-60°-90° prism. What is the prism's index of refraction?

FIGURE 23.18 A prism deflects a laser beam.

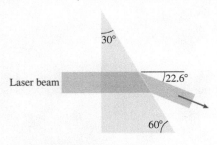

MODEL Represent the laser beam with a single ray and use the ray model of light.

VISUALIZE FIGURE 23.19 uses the steps of Tactics Box 23.1 to draw a ray diagram. The ray is incident perpendicular to the front face of the prism ($\theta_{\text{incident}} = 0°$), thus it is transmitted through the first boundary without deflection. At the second boundary it is especially important to *draw the normal to the surface* at the point of incidence and to *measure angles from the normal*.

SOLVE From the geometry of the triangle you can find that the laser's angle of incidence on the hypotenuse of the prism is

FIGURE 23.19 Pictorial representation of a laser beam passing through the prism.

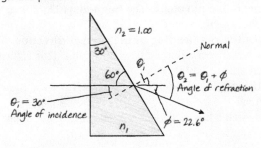

θ_1 and θ_2 are measured from the normal.

$\theta_1 = 30°$, the same as the apex angle of the prism. The ray exits the prism at angle θ_2 such that the deflection is $\phi = \theta_2 - \theta_1 = 22.6°$. Thus $\theta_2 = 52.6°$. Knowing both angles and $n_2 = 1.00$ for air, we can use Snell's law to find n_1:

$$n_1 = \frac{n_2\sin\theta_2}{\sin\theta_1} = \frac{1.00\sin 52.6°}{\sin 30°} = 1.59$$

ASSESS Referring to the indices of refraction in Table 23.1, we see that the prism is made of plastic.

Total Internal Reflection

FIGURE 23.20 The blue laser beam undergoes total internal reflection inside the prism.

What would have happened in Example 23.4 if the prism angle had been 45° rather than 30°? The light rays would approach the rear surface of the prism at an angle of incidence $\theta_1 = 45°$. When we try to calculate the angle of refraction at which the ray emerges into the air, we find

$$\sin\theta_2 = \frac{n_1}{n_2}\sin\theta_1 = \frac{1.59}{1.00}\sin 45° = 1.12$$

$$\theta_2 = \sin^{-1}(1.12) = \text{???}$$

Angle θ_2 doesn't compute because the sine of an angle can't be larger than 1. The ray is unable to refract through the boundary. Instead, 100% of the light *reflects* from the boundary back into the prism. This process is called **total internal reflection,** often abbreviated TIR. That it really happens is illustrated in FIGURE 23.20. Here three laser beams enter a prism from the left. The bottom two refract out through the right side of the prism. The blue beam, which is incident on the prism's top face, undergoes total internal reflection and then emerges through the right surface.

FIGURE 23.21 shows several rays leaving a point source in a medium with index of refraction n_1. The medium on the other side of the boundary has $n_2 < n_1$. As we've seen, crossing a boundary into a material with a lower index of refraction causes the ray to bend away from the normal. Two things happen as angle θ_1 increases. First, the refraction angle θ_2 approaches 90°. Second, the fraction of the light energy transmitted decreases while the fraction reflected increases.

A **critical angle** is reached when $\theta_2 = 90°$. Because $\sin 90° = 1$, Snell's law $n_1 \sin \theta_c = n_2 \sin 90°$ gives the critical angle of incidence as

$$\theta_c = \sin^{-1}\left(\frac{n_2}{n_1}\right) \qquad (23.9)$$

The refracted light vanishes at the critical angle and the reflection becomes 100% for any angle $\theta_1 \geq \theta_c$. The critical angle is well defined because of our assumption that $n_2 < n_1$. **There is no critical angle and no total internal reflection if $n_2 > n_1$.**

As a quick example, the critical angle in a typical piece of glass at the glass-air boundary is

$$\theta_{c\,\text{glass}} = \sin^{-1}\left(\frac{1.00}{1.50}\right) = 42°$$

The fact that the critical angle is less than 45° has important applications. For example, FIGURE 23.22 shows a pair of binoculars. The lenses are much farther apart than your eyes, so the light rays need to be brought together before exiting the eyepieces. Rather than using mirrors, which get dirty and require alignment, binoculars use a pair of prisms on each side. Thus the light undergoes two total internal reflections and emerges from the eyepiece. (The actual arrangement is a little more complex than in Figure 23.22, to avoid left-right reversals, but this illustrates the basic idea.)

FIGURE 23.21 Refraction and reflection of rays as the angle of incidence increases.

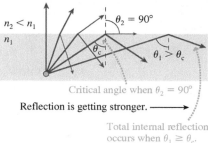

The angle of incidence is increasing.
Transmission is getting weaker.

Critical angle when $\theta_2 = 90°$

Reflection is getting stronger.

Total internal reflection occurs when $\theta_1 \geq \theta_c$.

FIGURE 23.22 Binoculars and other optical instruments make use of total internal reflection.

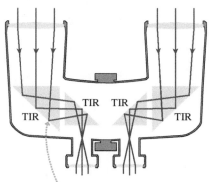

Angles of incidence exceed the critical angle.

EXAMPLE 23.5 **Total internal reflection**

A lightbulb is set in the bottom of a 3.0-m-deep swimming pool. What is the diameter of the circle of light seen on the water's surface from above?

MODEL Represent the lightbulb as a point source and use the ray model of light.

VISUALIZE FIGURE 23.23 is a pictorial representation of the light rays. The lightbulb emits rays at all angles, but only some of the rays refract into the air where they can be seen from above. Rays striking the surface at greater than the critical angle undergo TIR and remain within the water. The diameter of the circle of light is the distance between the two points at which rays strike the surface at the critical angle.

SOLVE From trigonometry, the circle diameter is $D = 2h\tan\theta_c$, where h is the depth of the water. The critical angle for a water-air boundary is $\theta_c = \sin^{-1}(1.00/1.33) = 48.7°$. Thus

$$D = 2(3.0\text{ m})\tan 48.7° = 6.8\text{ m}$$

FIGURE 23.23 Pictorial representation of the rays leaving a lightbulb at the bottom of a swimming pool.

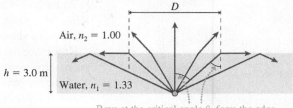

Air, $n_2 = 1.00$

$h = 3.0$ m

Water, $n_1 = 1.33$

Rays at the critical angle θ_c form the edge of the circle of light seen from above.

Fiber Optics

The most important modern application of total internal reflection is the transmission of light through optical fibers. FIGURE 23.24a on the next page shows a laser beam shining into the end of a long, narrow-diameter glass tube. The light rays pass easily from the air into the glass, but they then impinge on the inside wall of the glass tube at an angle

FIGURE 23.24 Light rays are confined within an optical fiber by total internal reflection.

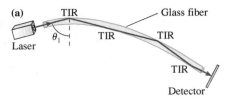

(a)

(b)

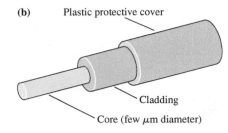

of incidence θ_1 approaching 90°. This is well above the critical angle, so the laser beam undergoes TIR and remains inside the glass. The laser beam continues to "bounce" its way down the tube as if the light were inside a pipe. Indeed, optical fibers are sometimes called "light pipes." The rays are *below* the critical angle ($\theta_1 \approx 0$) when they finally reach the end of the fiber, thus they refract out without difficulty and can be detected.

While a simple glass tube can transmit light, reliance on a glass-air boundary is not sufficiently reliable for commercial use. Any small scratch on the side of the tube alters the rays' angle of incidence and allows leakage of light. FIGURE 23.24b shows the construction of a practical optical fiber. A small-diameter glass *core* is surrounded by a layer of glass *cladding*. The glasses used for the core and the cladding have $n_{core} > n_{cladding}$; thus light undergoes TIR at the core-cladding boundary and remains confined within the core. This boundary is not exposed to the environment and hence retains its integrity even under adverse conditions.

Even glass of the highest purity is not perfectly transparent. Absorption in the glass, even if very small, causes a gradual decrease in light intensity. The glass used for the core of optical fibers has a minimum absorption at a wavelength of 1.3 μm, in the infrared, so this is the laser wavelength used for long-distance signal transmission. Light at this wavelength can travel hundreds of kilometers through a fiber without significant loss.

STOP TO THINK 23.3 A light ray travels from medium 1 to medium 3 as shown. For these media,

a. $n_3 > n_1$ b. $n_3 = n_1$ c. $n_3 < n_1$
d. We can't compare n_1 to n_3 without knowing n_2.

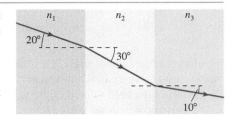

23.4 Image Formation by Refraction

If you see a fish that appears to be swimming close to the front window of the aquarium, but then look through the side of the aquarium, you'll find that the fish is actually farther from the window than you thought. Why is this?

To begin, recall that vision works by focusing a diverging bundle of rays onto the retina. The point from which the rays diverge is where you perceive the object to be. FIGURE 23.25a shows how you would see a fish out of water at distance d.

Now place the fish back into the aquarium at the same distance d. For simplicity, we'll ignore the glass wall of the aquarium and consider the water-air boundary. (The thin glass of a typical window has only a very small effect on the refraction of the rays and doesn't change the conclusions.) Light rays again leave the fish, but this time they refract at the water-air boundary. Because they're going from a higher to a lower index of refraction, the rays refract *away from* the normal. FIGURE 23.25b shows the consequences.

A bundle of diverging rays still enters your eye, but now these rays are diverging from a closer point, at distance d'. As far as your eye and brain are concerned, it's exactly *as if* the rays really originate at distance d', and this is the location at which you "see" the fish. **The object appears closer than it really is because of the refraction of light at the boundary.**

We found that the rays reflected from a mirror diverge from a point that is not the object point. We called that point a *virtual image*. Similarly, if rays from an object point P refract at a boundary between two media such that the rays then diverge from a point P′ and *appear* to come from P′, we call P′ a virtual image of point P. The virtual image of the fish is what you see.

Let's examine this image formation a bit more carefully. FIGURE 23.26 shows a boundary between two transparent media having indices of refraction n_1 and n_2. Point P, a source of light rays, is the object. Point P′, from which the rays *appear* to diverge, is

FIGURE 23.25 Refraction of the light rays causes a fish in the aquarium to be seen at distance d'.

(a) A fish out of water

The rays that reach the eye are diverging from this point, the object.

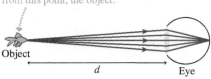

(b) A fish in the aquarium

Refraction causes the rays to bend at the boundary.

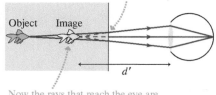

Now the rays that reach the eye are diverging from this point, the image.

the virtual image of P. Distance s is called the **object distance.** Our goal is to determine distance s', the **image distance. Both are measured from the boundary.**

A line perpendicular to the boundary is called the **optical axis.** Consider a ray leaving the object at angle θ_1 with respect to the optical axis. θ_1 is also the angle of incidence at the boundary, where the ray refracts into the second medium at angle θ_2. By tracing the refracted ray backward, you can see that θ_2 is also the angle between the refracted ray and the optical axis at point P'.

The distance l is common to both the incident and the refracted rays, and you can see that $l = s \tan\theta_1 = s' \tan\theta_2$. Thus

$$s' = \frac{\tan\theta_1}{\tan\theta_2} s \qquad (23.10)$$

Snell's law relates the sines of angles θ_1 and θ_2; that is,

$$\frac{\sin\theta_1}{\sin\theta_2} = \frac{n_2}{n_1} \qquad (23.11)$$

In practice, the angle between any of these rays and the optical axis is very small because the size of the pupil of your eye is very much less than the distance between the object and your eye. (The angles in the figure have been greatly exaggerated.) Rays that are nearly *parallel* to the *axis* are called **paraxial rays.** The small-angle approximation $\sin\theta \approx \tan\theta \approx \theta$, where θ is in radians, can be applied to paraxial rays. Consequently,

$$\frac{\tan\theta_1}{\tan\theta_2} \approx \frac{\sin\theta_1}{\sin\theta_2} = \frac{n_2}{n_1} \qquad (23.12)$$

Using this result in Equation 23.10, we find that the image distance is

$$s' = \frac{n_2}{n_1} s \qquad (23.13)$$

NOTE ▶ The fact that the result for s' is independent of θ_1 implies that *all* paraxial rays appear to diverge from the same point P'. This property of the diverging rays is essential in order to have a well-defined image. ◀

This section has given us a first look at image formation via refraction. We will extend this idea to image formation with lenses in Section 23.6.

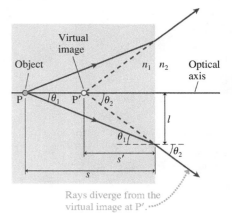

FIGURE 23.26 Finding the virtual image P' of an object at P. We've assumed $n_1 > n_2$.

Virtual image
Object
n_1 n_2 Optical axis
P θ_1 P' θ_2
l
θ_1 θ_2
s'
s
Rays diverge from the virtual image at P'.

| EXAMPLE 23.6 | **An air bubble in a window** |

A fish and a sailor look at each other through a 5.0-cm-thick glass porthole in a submarine. There happens to be an air bubble right in the center of the glass. How far behind the surface of the glass does the air bubble appear to the fish? To the sailor?

MODEL Represent the air bubble as a point source and use the ray model of light.

VISUALIZE Paraxial light rays from the bubble refract into the air on one side and into the water on the other. The ray diagram looks like Figure 23.26.

SOLVE The index of refraction of the glass is $n_1 = 1.50$. The bubble is in the center of the window, so the object distance from

either side of the window is $s = 2.5$ cm. From the water side, the fish sees the bubble at an image distance

$$s' = \frac{n_2}{n_1} s = \frac{1.33}{1.50}(2.5 \text{ cm}) = 2.2 \text{ cm}$$

This is the apparent depth of the bubble. The sailor, in air, sees the bubble at an image distance

$$s' = \frac{n_2}{n_1} s = \frac{1.00}{1.50}(2.5 \text{ cm}) = 1.7 \text{ cm}$$

ASSESS The image distance is *less* for the sailor because of the *larger* difference between the two indices of refraction.

23.5 Color and Dispersion

One of the most obvious visual aspects of light is the phenomenon of color. Yet color, for all its vivid sensation, is not inherent in the light itself. Color is a *perception*, not a physical quantity. Color is associated with the wavelength of light, but the fact that we see light with a wavelength of 650 nm as "red" tells us how our visual system responds

FIGURE 23.27 Newton used prisms to study color.

(a)

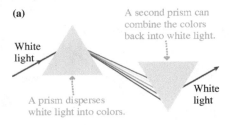

White light

A second prism can combine the colors back into white light.

White light

A prism disperses white light into colors.

(b)

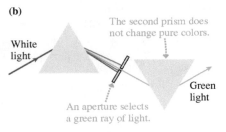

White light

The second prism does not change pure colors.

Green light

An aperture selects a green ray of light.

TABLE 23.2 A brief summary of the visible spectrum of light

Color	Approximate wavelength
Deepest red	700 nm
Red	650 nm
Green	550 nm
Blue	450 nm
Deepest violet	400 nm

FIGURE 23.28 Dispersion curves show how the index of refraction varies with wavelength.

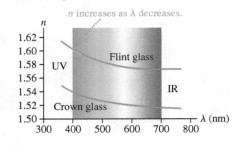

to electromagnetic waves of this wavelength. There is no "redness" associated with the light wave itself.

Most of the results of optics do not depend on color. We generally don't need to know the color of light—or, to be more precise, its wavelength—to use the laws of reflection and refraction. Nonetheless, color is an interesting subject, one worthy of a short digression.

Color

It has been known since antiquity that irregularly shaped glass and crystals cause sunlight to be broken into various colors. A common idea was that the glass or crystal somehow altered the properties of the light by *adding* color to the light. Newton suggested a different explanation. He first passed a sunbeam through a prism, producing the familiar rainbow of light. We say that the prism *disperses* the light. Newton's novel idea, shown in FIGURE 23.27a, was to use a second prism, inverted with respect to the first, to "reassemble" the colors. He found that the light emerging from the second prism was a beam of pure, white light.

But the emerging light beam is white only if *all* the rays are allowed to move between the two prisms. Blocking some of the rays with small obstacles, as in FIGURE 23.27b, causes the emerging light beam to have color. This suggests that color is associated with the light itself, not with anything that the prism is "doing" to the light. Newton tested this idea by inserting a small aperture between the prisms to pass only the rays of a particular color, such as green. If the prism alters the properties of light, then the second prism should change the green light to other colors. Instead, the light emerging from the second prism is unchanged from the green light entering the prism.

These and similar experiments show that

1. What we perceive as white light is a mixture of all colors. White light can be dispersed into its various colors and, equally important, mixing all the colors produces white light.
2. The index of refraction of a transparent material differs slightly for different colors of light. Glass has a slightly larger index of refraction for violet light than for green light or red light. Consequently, different colors of light refract at slightly different angles. A prism does not alter the light or add anything to the light; it simply causes the different colors that are inherent in white light to follow slightly different trajectories.

Dispersion

It was Thomas Young, with his two-slit interference experiment, who showed that different colors are associated with light of different wavelengths. The longest wavelengths are perceived as red light and the shortest as violet light. Table 23.2 is a brief summary of the *visible spectrum* of light. Visible-light wavelengths are used so frequently that it is well worth committing this short table to memory.

The slight variation of index of refraction with wavelength is known as **dispersion.** FIGURE 23.28 shows the *dispersion curves* of two common glasses. Notice that **n is larger when the wavelength is shorter,** thus violet light refracts more than red light.

EXAMPLE 23.7 **Dispersing light with a prism**

Example 23.4 found that a ray incident on a 30° prism is deflected by 22.6° if the prism's index of refraction is 1.59. Suppose this is the index of refraction of deep violet light and deep red light has an index of refraction of 1.54.

a. What is the deflection angle for deep red light?
b. If a beam of white light is dispersed by this prism, how wide is the rainbow spectrum on a screen 2.0 m away?

VISUALIZE Figure 23.19 showed the geometry. A ray of any wavelength is incident on the hypotenuse of the prism at $\theta_1 = 30°$.

SOLVE a. If $n_1 = 1.54$ for deep red light, the refraction angle is

$$\theta_2 = \sin^{-1}\left(\frac{n_1 \sin\theta_1}{n_2}\right) = \sin^{-1}\left(\frac{1.54 \sin 30°}{1.00}\right) = 50.4°$$

Example 23.4 showed that the deflection angle is $\phi = \theta_2 - \theta_1$, so deep red light is deflected by $\phi_{red} = 20.4°$. This angle is slightly smaller than the previously observed $\phi_{violet} = 22.6°$.

b. The entire spectrum is spread between $\phi_{red} = 20.4°$ and $\phi_{violet} = 22.6°$. The angular spread is

$$\delta = \phi_{violet} - \phi_{red} = 2.2° = 0.038 \text{ rad}$$

At distance r, the spectrum spans an arc length

$$s = r\delta = (2.0 \text{ m})(0.038 \text{ rad}) = 0.076 \text{ m} = 7.6 \text{ cm}$$

ASSESS The angle is so small that there's no appreciable difference between arc length and a straight line. The spectrum will be 7.6 cm wide at a distance of 2.0 m.

Rainbows

One of the most interesting sources of color in nature is the rainbow. The details get somewhat complicated, but FIGURE 23.29a shows that the basic cause of the rainbow is a combination of refraction, reflection, and dispersion.

Figure 23.29a might lead you to think that the top edge of a rainbow is violet. In fact, the top edge is red, and violet is on the bottom. The rays leaving the drop in Figure 23.29a are spreading apart, so they can't all reach your eye. As FIGURE 23.29b shows, a ray of red light reaching your eye comes from a drop *higher* in the sky than a ray of violet light. In other words, the colors you see in a rainbow refract toward your eye from different raindrops, not from the same drop. You have to look higher in the sky to see the red light than to see the violet light.

FIGURE 23.29 Light seen in a rainbow has undergone refraction + reflection + refraction in a raindrop.

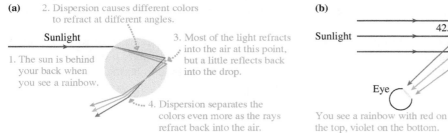

(a) 2. Dispersion causes different colors to refract at different angles.

Sunlight

1. The sun is behind your back when you see a rainbow.

3. Most of the light refracts into the air at this point, but a little reflects back into the drop.

4. Dispersion separates the colors even more as the rays refract back into the air.

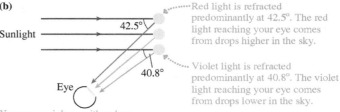

(b)

Sunlight

42.5°

40.8°

Eye

You see a rainbow with red on the top, violet on the bottom.

Red light is refracted predominantly at 42.5°. The red light reaching your eye comes from drops higher in the sky.

Violet light is refracted predominantly at 40.8°. The violet light reaching your eye comes from drops lower in the sky.

Colored Filters and Colored Objects

White light passing through a piece of green glass emerges as green light. A possible explanation would be that the green glass *adds* "greenness" to the white light, but Newton found otherwise. Green glass is green because it *absorbs* any light that is "not green." We can think of a piece of colored glass or plastic as a *filter* that removes all wavelengths except a chosen few.

If a green filter and a red filter are overlapped, as in FIGURE 23.30, *no* light gets through. The green filter transmits only green light, which is then absorbed by the red filter because it is "not red."

This behavior is true not just for glass filters, which transmit light, but for *pigments* that absorb light of some wavelengths but *reflect* light at other wavelengths. For example, red paint contains pigments reflecting light at wavelengths near 650 nm while absorbing all other wavelengths. Pigments in paints, inks, and natural objects are responsible for most of the color we observe in the world, from the red of lipstick to the blue of a bluebird's feathers.

As an example, FIGURE 23.31 on the next page shows the absorption curve of *chlorophyll*. Chlorophyll is essential for photosynthesis in green plants. The chemical reactions of photosynthesis are able to use red light and blue/violet light, thus chlorophyll absorbs red light and blue/violet light from sunlight and puts it to use. But

FIGURE 23.30 No light at all passes through both a green and a red filter.

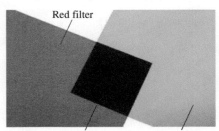

Red filter

Black where filters overlap Green filter

FIGURE 23.31 The absorption curve of chlorophyll.

Chlorophyll absorbs most of the red and blue/violet light for use in photosynthesis.

The green and yellow light that is not absorbed is reflected and gives plants their green color.

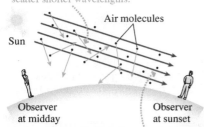

Sunsets are red because all the blue light has scattered as the sunlight passes through the atmosphere.

FIGURE 23.32 Rayleigh scattering by molecules in the air gives the sky and sunsets their color.

At midday the scattered light is mostly blue because molecules preferentially scatter shorter wavelengths.

Air molecules

Sun

Observer at midday   Observer at sunset

At sunset, when the light has traveled much farther through the atmosphere, the light is mostly red because the shorter wavelengths have been lost to scattering.

green and yellow light are not absorbed. Instead, to conserve energy, these wavelengths are mostly *reflected* to give the object a greenish-yellow color. When you look at the green leaves on a tree, you're seeing the light that was reflected because it *wasn't* needed for photosynthesis.

Light Scattering: Blue Skies and Red Sunsets

In the ray model of Section 23.1 we noted that light within a medium can be scattered or absorbed. As we've now seen, the absorption of light can be wavelength dependent and can create color in objects. What are the effects of scattering?

Light can scatter from small particles that are suspended in a medium. If the particles are large compared to the wavelengths of light—even though they may be microscopic and not readily visible to the naked eye—the light essentially reflects off the particles. The law of reflection doesn't depend on wavelength, so all colors are scattered equally. White light scattered from many small particles makes the medium appear cloudy and white. Two well-known examples are clouds, where micrometer-size water droplets scatter the light, and milk, which is a colloidal suspension of microscopic droplets of fats and proteins.

A more interesting aspect of scattering occurs at the atomic level. The atoms and molecules of a transparent medium are much smaller than the wavelengths of light, so they can't scatter light simply by reflection. Instead, the oscillating electric field of the light wave interacts with the electrons in each atom in such a way that the light is scattered. This atomic-level scattering is called **Rayleigh scattering.**

Unlike the scattering by small particles, Rayleigh scattering from atoms and molecules *does* depend on the wavelength. A detailed analysis shows that the intensity of scattered light depends inversely on the fourth power of the wavelength: $I_{\text{scattered}} \propto \lambda^{-4}$. This wavelength dependence explains why the sky is blue and sunsets are red.

As sunlight travels through the atmosphere, the λ^{-4} dependence of Rayleigh scattering causes the shorter wavelengths to be preferentially scattered. If we take 650 nm as a typical wavelength for red light and 450 nm for blue light, the intensity of scattered blue light relative to scattered red light is

$$\frac{I_{\text{blue}}}{I_{\text{red}}} = \left(\frac{650}{450}\right)^4 \approx 4$$

Four times more blue light is scattered toward us than red light and thus, as FIGURE 23.32 shows, the sky appears blue.

Because of the earth's curvature, sunlight has to travel much farther through the atmosphere when we see it at sunrise or sunset than it does during the midday hours. In fact, the path length through the atmosphere at sunset is so long that essentially all the short wavelengths have been lost due to Rayleigh scattering. Only the longer wavelengths remain—orange and red—and they make the colors of the sunset.

23.6 Thin Lenses: Ray Tracing

A camera obscura or a pinhole camera forms images on a screen, but the images are faint and not perfectly focused. The ability to create a bright, well-focused image is vastly improved by using a lens. A **lens** is a transparent material that uses refraction at *curved* surfaces to form an image from diverging light rays. We will defer a mathematical analysis of the refraction of lenses until the next section. First, we want to establish a pictorial method of understanding image formation. This method is called **ray tracing.**

FIGURE 23.33 Parallel light rays pass through a converging lens and a diverging lens.

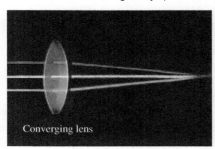 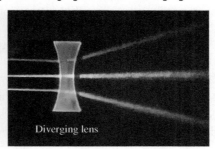

Converging lens   Diverging lens

FIGURE 23.33 shows parallel light rays entering two different lenses. The left lens, called a **converging lens,** causes the rays to refract *toward* the optical axis. The common point through which initially parallel rays pass is called the **focal point** of the lens. The distance of the focal point from the lens is called the **focal length** f of the lens. The right lens, called a **diverging lens,** refracts parallel rays *away from* the optical axis. This lens also has a focal point, but it is not as obvious.

NOTE ▶ A converging lens is thicker in the center than at the edges. A diverging lens is thicker at the edges than at the center. ◀

FIGURE 23.34 clarifies the situation. In the case of a diverging lens, a backward projection of the diverging rays shows that they *appear* to have started from the same point. This is the focal point of a diverging lens, and its distance from the lens is the focal length of the lens. In the next section we'll relate the focal length to the curvature and index of refraction of the lens, but now we'll use the practical definition that **the focal length is the distance from the lens at which rays parallel to the optical axis converge or from which they diverge.**

NOTE ▶ The focal length f is a property *of the lens,* independent of how the lens is used. The focal length characterizes a lens in much the same way that a mass m characterizes an object or a spring constant k characterizes a spring. ◀

Converging Lenses

These basic observations about lenses are enough to understand image formation by a thin lens. A **thin lens** is a lens whose thickness is very small in comparison to its focal length and in comparison to the object and image distances. We'll make the approximation that the thickness of a thin lens is zero and that the lens lies in a plane called the **lens plane.** Within this approximation, **all refraction occurs as the rays cross the lens plane, and all distances are measured from the lens plane.** Fortunately, the thin-lens approximation is quite good for most practical applications of lenses.

NOTE ▶ We'll *draw* lenses as if they have a thickness, because that is how we expect lenses to look, but our analysis will not depend on the shape or thickness of a lens. ◀

FIGURE 23.35 shows three important situations of light rays passing through a thin converging lens. Part a is familiar from Figure 23.34. If the direction of each of the rays in FIGURE 23.35a is reversed, Snell's law tells us that each ray will exactly retrace its path and emerge from the lens parallel to the optical axis. This leads to FIGURE 23.35b, which is the "mirror image" of part (a). Notice that the lens actually has *two* focal points, located at distances f on either side of the lens.

FIGURE 23.35c shows three rays passing through the *center* of the lens. At the center, the two sides of a lens are very nearly parallel to each other. Earlier, in Example 23.3, we found that a ray passing through a piece of glass with parallel sides is *displaced*

FIGURE 23.34 The focal lengths of converging and diverging lenses.

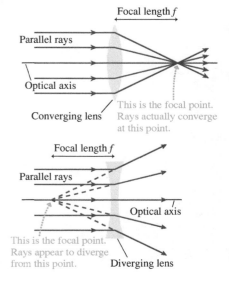

Focal length f

Parallel rays

Optical axis

This is the focal point. Rays actually converge at this point.

Converging lens

Focal length f

Parallel rays

Optical axis

This is the focal point. Rays appear to diverge from this point.

Diverging lens

FIGURE 23.35 Three important sets of rays passing through a thin converging lens.

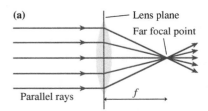

(a)   Lens plane

Far focal point

Parallel rays f

Any ray initially parallel to the optical axis will refract through the focal point on the far side of the lens.

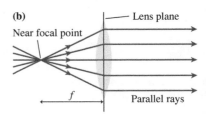

(b)   Lens plane

Near focal point

f Parallel rays

Any ray passing through the near focal point emerges from the lens parallel to the optical axis.

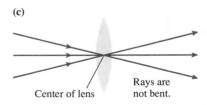

(c)

Center of lens   Rays are not bent.

Any ray directed at the center of the lens passes through in a straight line.

but *not bent* and that the displacement becomes zero as the thickness approaches zero. Consequently, a ray through the center of a thin lens, with zero thickness, is neither bent nor displaced but travels in a straight line.

These three situations form the basis for ray tracing.

Real Images

FIGURE 23.36 shows a lens and an object whose distance from the lens is larger than the focal length. Rays from point P on the object are refracted by the lens so as to converge at point P' on the opposite side of the lens. If rays diverge from an object point P and interact with a lens such that the refracted rays *converge* at point P', actually meeting at P', then we call P' a **real image** of point P. Contrast this with our prior definition of a *virtual image* as a point from which rays—which never meet—appear to *diverge*.

FIGURE 23.36 Rays from an object point P are refracted by the lens and converge to a real image at point P'.

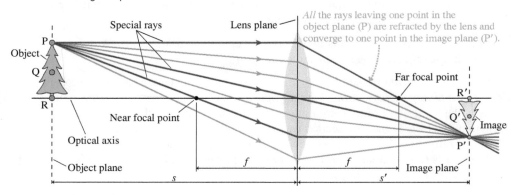

All points on the object that are in the same plane, the **object plane,** converge to image points in the **image plane.** Points Q and R in the object plane of Figure 23.36 have image points Q' and R' in the same plane as point P'. Once we locate *one* point in the image plane, such as point P', we know that the full image lies in the same plane.

There are two important observations to make about Figure 23.36. First, the image is upside down with respect to the object. This is called an **inverted image,** and it is a standard characteristic of real-image formation with a converging lens. Second, rays from point P *fill* the entire lens surface, and all portions of the lens contribute to the image. A larger lens will "collect" more rays and thus make a brighter image.

FIGURE 23.37 is a close-up view of the rays very near the image plane. The rays don't stop at P' unless we place a screen in the image plane. When we do so, we see a sharp, well-focused image on the screen. To focus an image, you must either move the screen to coincide with the image plane or move the lens or object to make the image plane coincide with the screen. For example, the focus knob on a projector moves the lens forward or backward until the image plane matches the screen position.

NOTE ▶ The ability to see a real image on a screen sets real images apart from *virtual* images. But keep in mind that we need not *see* a real image in order to *have* an image. A real image exists at a point in space where the rays converge even if there's no viewing screen in the image plane. ◀

Figure 23.36 highlights three "special rays" based on the three situations of Figure 23.35. These three rays alone are sufficient to locate the image point P'. That is, we don't need to draw all the rays shown in Figure 23.36. The procedure known as *ray tracing* consists of locating the image by the use of just these three rays.

FIGURE 23.37 A close-up look at the rays near the image plane.

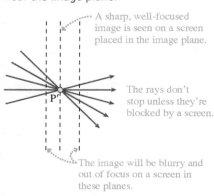

A sharp, well-focused image is seen on a screen placed in the image plane.

The rays don't stop unless they're blocked by a screen.

The image will be blurry and out of focus on a screen in these planes.

BOX 23.2 **Ray tracing for a converging lens**

❶ **Draw an optical axis.** Use graph paper or a ruler! Establish an appropriate scale.

❷ **Center the lens on the axis.** Mark and label the focal points at distance f on either side.

❸ **Represent the object with an upright arrow at distance s.** It's usually best to place the base of the arrow on the axis and to draw the arrow about half the radius of the lens.

❹ **Draw the three "special rays" from the tip of the arrow.** Use a straight edge.

   a. A ray parallel to the axis refracts through the far focal point.
   b. A ray that enters the lens along a line through the near focal point emerges parallel to the axis.
   c. A ray through the center of the lens does not bend.

❺ **Extend the rays until they converge.** This is the image point. Draw the rest of the image in the image plane. If the base of the object is on the axis, then the base of the image will also be on the axis.

❻ **Measure the image distance s'.** Also, if needed, measure the image height relative to the object height.

EXAMPLE 23.8   Finding the image of a flower

A 4.0-cm-diameter flower is 200 cm from the 50-cm-focal-length lens of a camera. How far should the light detector be placed behind the lens to record a well-focused image? What is the diameter of the image on the detector?

MODEL The flower is in the object plane. Use ray tracing to locate the image.

VISUALIZE FIGURE 23.38 shows the ray-tracing diagram and the steps of Tactics Box 23.2. The image has been drawn in the plane where the three special rays converge. You can see *from the drawing* that the image distance is $s' \approx 67$ cm. This is where the detector needs to be placed to record a focused image.

The heights of the object and image are labeled h and h'. The ray through the center of the lens is a straight line, thus the object and image both subtend the same angle θ. Using similar triangles,

$$\frac{h'}{s'} = \frac{h}{s}$$

Solving for h' gives

$$h' = h\frac{s'}{s} = (4.0 \text{ cm})\frac{67 \text{ cm}}{200 \text{ cm}} = 1.3 \text{ cm}$$

The flower's image has a diameter of 1.3 cm.

ASSESS We've been able to learn a great deal about the image from a simple geometric procedure.

FIGURE 23.38 Ray-tracing diagram for Example 23.8.

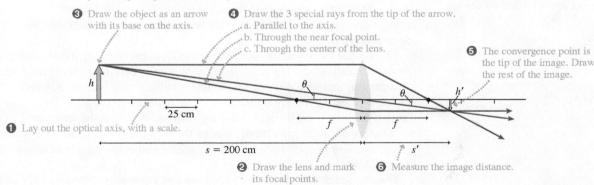

Lateral Magnification

The image can be either larger or smaller than the object, depending on the location and focal length of the lens. But there's more to a description of the image than just its size. We also want to know its *orientation* relative to the object. That is, is the image upright or inverted? It is customary to combine size and orientation information into a single number. The **lateral magnification** m is defined as

$$m = -\frac{s'}{s} \tag{23.14}$$

You just saw in Example 23.8 that the image-to-object height ratio is $h'/h = s'/s$. Consequently, we interpret the lateral magnification m as follows:

1. A positive value of m indicates that the image is upright relative to the object. A negative value of m indicates that the image is inverted relative to the object.
2. The absolute value of m gives the size ratio of the image and object: $h'/h = |m|$.

The lateral magnification in Example 23.8 would be $m = -0.33$, indicating that the image is inverted and 33% the size of the object.

NOTE ▶ The image-to-object height ratio is called *lateral* magnification to distinguish it from angular magnification, which we'll introduce in the next chapter. In practice, m is simply called "magnification" when there's no chance of confusion. Magnification can be less than 1, meaning that the image is smaller than the object. ◀

STOP TO THINK 23.4 A lens produces a sharply focused, inverted image on a screen. What will you see on the screen if the lens is removed?

a. The image will be inverted and blurry.
b. The image will be upright and sharp.
c. The image will be upright and blurry.
d. The image will be much dimmer but otherwise unchanged.
e. There will be no image at all.

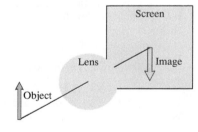

Virtual Images

The previous section considered a converging lens with the object at distance $s > f$. That is, the object was outside the focal point. What if the object is inside the focal point, at distance $s < f$? FIGURE 23.39 shows just this situation, and we can use ray tracing to analyze it.

The special rays initially parallel to the axis and through the center of the lens present no difficulties. However, a ray through the near focal point would travel toward the left and would never reach the lens! Referring back to Figure 23.35b, you can see that the rays emerging parallel to the axis entered the lens *along a line* passing through the near focal point. It's the angle of incidence on the lens that is important, not whether the light ray actually passes through the focal point. This was the basis for the wording of step 4b in Tactics Box 23.2 and is the third special ray shown in Figure 23.39.

You can see that the three refracted rays don't converge. Instead, all three rays appear to *diverge* from point P'. This is the situation we found for rays reflecting from

---

FIGURE 23.39 Rays from an object at distance $s < f$ are refracted by the lens and diverge to form a virtual image.

A ray *along a line* through the near focal point refracts parallel to the optical axis.

The refracted rays are diverging. They appear to come from point P'.

a mirror and for the rays refracting out of an aquarium. Point P′ is a *virtual image* of the object point P. Furthermore, it is an **upright image,** having the same orientation as the object.

The refracted rays, which are all to the right of the lens, *appear* to come from P′, but none of the rays were ever at that point. No image would appear on a screen placed in the image plane at P′. So what good is a virtual image?

Your eye collects and focuses bundles of diverging rays; thus, as FIGURE 23.40a shows, you can "see" a virtual image by looking *through* the lens. This is exactly what you do with a magnifying glass, producing a scene like the one in FIGURE 23.40b. In fact, you view a virtual image anytime you look *through* the eyepiece of an optical instrument such as a microscope or binoculars.

The image distance s' for a virtual image is defined to be a *negative number* ($s' < 0$), indicating that the image is on the opposite side of the lens from a real image. With this choice of sign, the definition of magnification, $m = -s'/s$, is still valid. A virtual image with negative s' has $m > 0$, thus the image is upright. This agrees with the rays in Figure 23.39 and the photograph of Figure 23.40b.

NOTE ▶ A lens thicker in the middle than at the edges is classified as a converging lens. The light rays from an object *can* converge to form a real image after passing through such a lens, but only if the object distance is larger than the focal length of the lens: $s > f$. If $s < f$, the rays leaving a converging lens are diverging to produce a virtual image. ◀

FIGURE 23.40 A converging lens is a magnifying glass when the object distance is less than *f*.

(a)

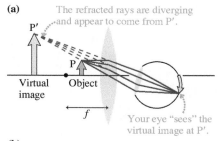

The refracted rays are diverging and appear to come from P′.

Your eye "sees" the virtual image at P′.

(b)

EXAMPLE 23.9 Magnifying a flower

To see a flower better, a naturalist holds a 6.0-cm-focal-length magnifying glass 4.0 cm from the flower. What is the magnification?

MODEL The flower is in the object plane. Use ray tracing to locate the image.

VISUALIZE FIGURE 23.41 shows the ray-tracing diagram. The three special rays diverge from the lens, but we can use a straightedge to extend the rays backward to the point from which they diverge. This point, the image point, is seen to be 12 cm to the left of the lens. Because this is a virtual image, the image distance is $s' = -12$ cm. Thus the magnification is

$$m = -\frac{s'}{s} = -\frac{-12 \text{ cm}}{4.0 \text{ cm}} = 3.0$$

The image is three times as large as the object and, because *m* is positive, upright.

FIGURE 23.41 Ray-tracing diagram for Example 23.9.

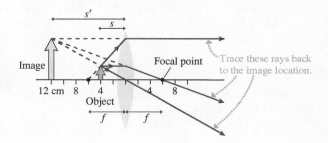

Trace these rays back to the image location.

Diverging Lenses

A lens thicker at the edges than in the middle is called a *diverging lens*. FIGURE 23.42 shows three important sets of rays passing through a diverging lens. These are based on Figures 23.33 and 23.34, where you saw that rays initially parallel to the axis diverge after passing through a diverging lens.

FIGURE 23.42 Three important sets of rays passing through a thin diverging lens.

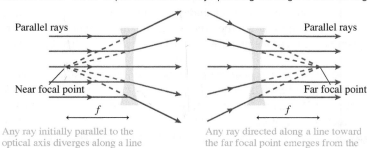

Any ray initially parallel to the optical axis diverges along a line through the near focal point.

Any ray directed along a line toward the far focal point emerges from the lens parallel to the optical axis.

Any ray directed at the center of the lens passes through in a straight line.

Ray tracing follows the steps of Tactics Box 23.2 for a converging lens *except* that two of the three special rays in step 4 are different.

TACTICS
BOX 23.3 **Ray tracing for a diverging lens**

❶–❸ **Follow steps 1 through 3 of Tactics Box 23.2.**
❹ **Draw the three "special rays" from the tip of the arrow.** Use a straight-edge.

   a. A ray parallel to the axis diverges along a line through the near focal point.
   b. A ray along a line toward the far focal point emerges parallel to the axis.
   c. A ray through the center of the lens does not bend.

❺ **Trace the diverging rays backward.** The point from which they are diverging is the image point, which is always a virtual image.
❻ **Measure the image distance *s'*.** This will be a negative number.

Exercise 28

EXAMPLE 23.10 **Demagnifying a flower**

A diverging lens with a focal length of 50 cm is placed 100 cm from a flower. Where is the image? What is its magnification?

MODEL The flower is in the object plane. Use ray tracing to locate the image.

VISUALIZE FIGURE 23.43 shows the ray-tracing diagram. The three special rays (labeled a, b, and c to match the Tactics Box) do not converge. However, they can be traced backward to an intersection ≈ 33 cm to the left of the lens. A virtual image is formed at *s'* = −33 cm with magnification

$$m = -\frac{s'}{s} = -\frac{-33\ \text{cm}}{100\ \text{cm}} = 0.33$$

The image, which can be seen by looking *through* the lens, is one-third the size of the object and upright.

FIGURE 23.43 Ray-tracing diagram for Example 23.10.

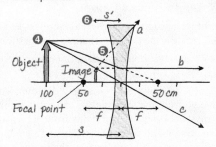

ASSESS Ray tracing with a diverging lens is somewhat trickier than with a converging lens, so this example is worth careful study.

Diverging lenses *always* make virtual images and, for this reason, are rarely used alone. However, they have important applications when used in combination with other lenses. Cameras, eyepieces, and eyeglasses often incorporate diverging lenses.

23.7 Thin Lenses: Refraction Theory

Ray tracing is a powerful visual approach for understanding image formation, but it doesn't provide precise information about the image location or image properties. We need to develop a quantitative relationship between the object distance *s* and the image distance *s'*.

To begin, FIGURE 23.44 shows a *spherical* boundary between two transparent media with indices of refraction n_1 and n_2. The sphere has radius of curvature *R*. Consider a ray that leaves object point P at angle α and later, after refracting, reaches point P'. Figure 23.44 has exaggerated the angles to make the picture clear, but we will restrict our analysis to *paraxial rays* traveling nearly parallel to the axis. For paraxial rays, all the angles are small and we can use the small-angle approximation.

FIGURE 23.44 Image formation due to refraction at a spherical surface. The angles are exaggerated.

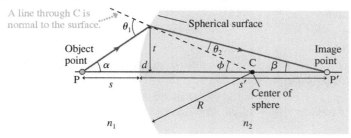

The ray from P is incident on the boundary at angle θ_1 and refracts into medium n_2 at angle θ_2, both measured from the normal to the surface at the point of incidence. Snell's law is $n_1 \sin\theta_1 = n_2 \sin\theta_2$, which in the small-angle approximation is

$$n_1\theta_1 = n_2\theta_2 \tag{23.15}$$

You can see from the geometry of Figure 23.44 that angles α, β, and ϕ are related by

$$\theta_1 = \alpha + \phi$$
$$\theta_2 = \phi - \beta \tag{23.16}$$

Using these expressions in Equation 23.15, we can write Snell's law as

$$n_1(\alpha + \phi) = n_2(\phi - \beta) \tag{23.17}$$

This is one important relationship between the angles.

The line of height t, from the axis to the point of incidence, is the vertical leg of three different right triangles having vertices at points P, C, and P'. Consequently,

$$\tan\alpha \approx \alpha = \frac{t}{s+d} \qquad \tan\beta \approx \beta = \frac{t}{s'-d} \qquad \tan\phi \approx \phi = \frac{t}{R-d} \tag{23.18}$$

But $d \to 0$ for paraxial rays, thus

$$\alpha = \frac{t}{s} \qquad \beta = \frac{t}{s'} \qquad \phi = \frac{t}{R} \tag{23.19}$$

This is the second important relationship that comes from Figure 23.44.

If we use the angles of Equation 23.19 in Equation 23.17, we find

$$n_1\left(\frac{t}{s} + \frac{t}{R}\right) = n_2\left(\frac{t}{R} - \frac{t}{s'}\right) \tag{23.20}$$

The t cancels, and we can rearrange Equation 23.20 to read

$$\frac{n_1}{s} + \frac{n_2}{s'} = \frac{n_2 - n_1}{R} \tag{23.21}$$

Equation 23.21 is independent of angle α. Consequently, **all paraxial rays leaving point P later converge at point P'.** If an object is located at distance s from a spherical refracting surface, an image will be formed at distance s' given by Equation 23.21.

Equation 23.21 was derived for a surface that is convex toward the object point, and the image is real. However, the result is also valid for virtual images or for surfaces that are concave toward the object point as long as we adopt the *sign convention* shown in Table 23.3.

Section 23.4 considered image formation due to refraction by a plane surface. There we found (in Equation 23.13) an image distance $s' = (n_2/n_1)s$. A plane can be thought of as a sphere in the limit $R \to \infty$, so we should be able to reach the same conclusion from Equation 23.21. As $R \to \infty$, the term $(n_2 - n_1)/R \to 0$ and Equation 23.21 becomes $s' = -(n_2/n_1)s$. This seems to differ from Equation 23.13, but it

TABLE 23.3 Sign convention for refracting surfaces

	Positive	Negative
R	Convex toward the object	Concave toward the object
s'	Real image, opposite side from object	Virtual image, same side as object

doesn't really. Equation 23.13 gives the actual distance to the image. Equation 23.21 is based on a sign convention in which virtual images have negative image distances, hence the minus sign.

EXAMPLE 23.11 **Image formation inside a glass rod**

One end of a 4.0-cm-diameter glass rod is shaped like a hemisphere. A small lightbulb is 6.0 cm from the end of the rod. Where is the bulb's image located?

MODEL Model the lightbulb as a point source of light and consider the paraxial rays that refract into the glass rod.

FIGURE 23.45 The curved surface refracts the light to form a real image.

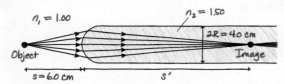

VISUALIZE FIGURE 23.45 shows the situation. $n_1 = 1.00$ for air and $n_2 = 1.50$ for glass.

SOLVE The radius of the surface is half the rod diameter, so $R = 2.0$ cm. Equation 23.21 is

$$\frac{1.00}{6.0 \text{ cm}} + \frac{1.50}{s'} = \frac{1.50 - 1.00}{2.0 \text{ cm}} = \frac{0.50}{2.0 \text{ cm}}$$

Solving for the image distance s' gives

$$\frac{1.50}{s'} = \frac{0.50}{2.0 \text{ cm}} - \frac{1.00}{6.0 \text{ cm}} = 0.0833 \text{ cm}^{-1}$$

$$s' = \frac{1.50}{0.0833} = 18 \text{ cm}$$

ASSESS This is a real image located 18 cm inside the glass rod.

EXAMPLE 23.12 **A goldfish in a bowl**

A goldfish lives in a spherical fish bowl 50 cm in diameter. If the fish is 10 cm from the near edge of the bowl, where does the fish appear when viewed from the outside?

MODEL Model the fish as a point source and consider the paraxial rays that refract from the water into the air. The thin glass wall has little effect and will be ignored.

FIGURE 23.46 The curved surface of a fish bowl produces a virtual image of the fish.

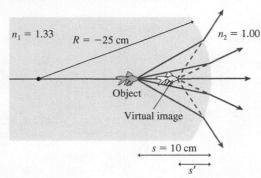

VISUALIZE FIGURE 23.46 shows the rays refracting *away* from the normal as they move from the water into the air. We expect to find a virtual image at a distance less than 10 cm.

SOLVE The object is in the water, so $n_1 = 1.33$ and $n_2 = 1.00$. The inner surface is concave (you can remember "concave" because it's like looking into a cave), so $R = -25$ cm. The object distance is $s = 10$ cm. Thus Equation 23.21 is

$$\frac{1.33}{10 \text{ cm}} + \frac{1.00}{s'} = \frac{1.00 - 1.33}{-25 \text{ cm}} = \frac{0.33}{25 \text{ cm}}$$

Solving for the image distance s' gives

$$\frac{1.00}{s'} = \frac{0.33}{25 \text{ cm}} - \frac{1.33}{10 \text{ cm}} = -0.12 \text{ cm}^{-1}$$

$$s' = \frac{1.00}{-0.12 \text{ cm}^{-1}} = -8.3 \text{ cm}$$

ASSESS The image is virtual, located to the left of the boundary. A person looking into the bowl will see a fish that appears to be 8.3 cm from the edge of the bowl.

STOP TO THINK 23.5 Which of these actions will move the real image point P′ farther from the boundary? More than one may work.

a. Increase the radius of curvature R.
b. Increase the index of refraction n.
c. Increase the object distance s.
d. Decrease the radius of curvature R.
e. Decrease the index of refraction n.
f. Decrease the object distance s.

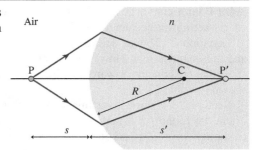

Lenses

The thin-lens approximation assumes rays refract one time, at the lens plane. In fact, as FIGURE 23.47 shows, rays refract *twice,* at spherical surfaces having radii of curvature R_1 and R_2. Let the lens have thickness t and be made of a material with index of refraction n. For simplicity, we'll assume that the lens is surrounded by air.

FIGURE 23.47 Image formation by a lens.

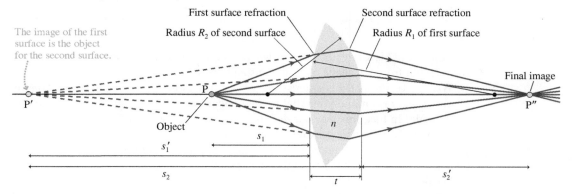

The object at point P is distance s_1 to the left of the lens. The first surface of the lens, of radius R_1, refracts the rays from P to create an image at point P′. We can use Equation 23.21 for a spherical surface to find the image distance s_1':

$$\frac{1}{s_1} + \frac{n}{s_1'} = \frac{n-1}{R_1} \tag{23.22}$$

where we used $n_1 = 1$ for the air and $n_2 = n$ for the lens. We'll assume that the image P′ is a virtual image, but this assumption isn't essential to the outcome.

With two refracting surfaces, the image P′ of the first surface becomes the object for the second surface. That is, the rays refracting at the second surface appear to have come from P′. Object distance s_2 from P′ to the second surface looks like it should be $s_2 = s_1' + t$, but P′ is a virtual image, so s_1' is a *negative* number. Thus the distance to the second surface is $s_2 = |s_1'| + t = t - s_1'$. We can find the image of P′ by a second application of Equation 23.21, but with a switch. The rays are incident on the surface from within the lens, so this time $n_1 = n$ and $n_2 = 1$. Consequently,

$$\frac{n}{t - s_1'} + \frac{1}{s_2'} = \frac{1-n}{R_2} \tag{23.23}$$

For a *thin lens,* which has $t \to 0$, Equation 23.23 becomes

$$-\frac{n}{s_1'} + \frac{1}{s_2'} = \frac{1-n}{R_2} = -\frac{n-1}{R_2} \tag{23.24}$$

Our goal is to find the distance s_2' to point P″, the image produced by the lens as a whole. This goal is easily reached if we simply add Equations 23.22 and 23.24, eliminating s_1' and giving

$$\frac{1}{s_1} + \frac{1}{s_2'} = \frac{n-1}{R_1} - \frac{n-1}{R_2} = (n-1)\left(\frac{1}{R_1} - \frac{1}{R_2}\right) \tag{23.25}$$

The numerical subscripts on s_1 and s_2' no longer serve a purpose. If we replace s_1 by s, the object distance from the lens, and s_2' by s', the image distance, Equation 23.25 becomes the *thin-lens equation:*

$$\frac{1}{s} + \frac{1}{s'} = \frac{1}{f} \qquad \text{(thin-lens equation)} \qquad (23.26)$$

where the *focal length* of the lens is

$$\frac{1}{f} = (n-1)\left(\frac{1}{R_1} - \frac{1}{R_2}\right) \qquad \text{(lens maker's equation)} \qquad (23.27)$$

Equation 23.27 is known as the *lens maker's equation*. It allows you to determine the focal length from the shape of a thin lens and the material used to make it.

We can verify that this expression for f really is the focal length of the lens by recalling that rays initially parallel to the optical axis pass through the focal point on the far side. In fact, this was our *definition* of the focal length of a lens. Parallel rays must come from an object extremely far away, with object distance $s \to \infty$ and thus $1/s = 0$. In that case, Equation 23.26 tells us that the parallel rays will converge at distance $s' = f$ on the far side of the lens, exactly as expected.

We derived the thin-lens equation and the lens maker's equation from the specific lens geometry shown in Figure 23.47, but the results are valid for any lens as long as all quantities are given appropriate signs. The sign convention used with Equations 23.26 and 23.27 is given in Table 23.4.

TABLE 23.4 Sign convention for thin lenses

	Positive	Negative
R_1, R_2	Convex toward the object	Concave toward the object
f	Converging lens, thicker in center	Diverging lens, thinner in center
s'	Real image, opposite side from object	Virtual image, same side as object

NOTE ▶ For a *thick lens,* where the thickness t is not negligible, we can solve Equations 23.22 and 23.23 in sequence to find the position of the image point P''. ◀

EXAMPLE 23.13 **Focal length of a meniscus lens**

What is the focal length of the glass *meniscus lens* shown in FIGURE 23.48? Is this a converging or diverging lens?

FIGURE 23.48 A meniscus lens.

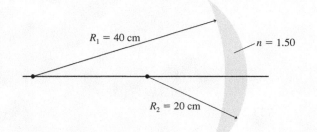

$R_1 = 40$ cm

$n = 1.50$

$R_2 = 20$ cm

SOLVE If the object is on the left, then the first surface has $R_1 = -40$ cm (concave toward the object) and the second surface has $R_2 = -20$ cm (also concave toward the object). The index of refraction of glass is $n = 1.50$, so the lens maker's equation is

$$\frac{1}{f} = (n-1)\left(\frac{1}{R_1} - \frac{1}{R_2}\right) = (1.50 - 1)\left(\frac{1}{-40 \text{ cm}} - \frac{1}{-20 \text{ cm}}\right)$$

$$= 0.0125 \text{ cm}^{-1}$$

Inverting this expression gives $f = 80$ cm. This is a converging lens, as seen both from the positive value of f and from the fact that the lens is thicker in the center.

Thin-Lens Image Formation

Although the thin-lens equation allows precise calculations, the lessons of ray tracing should not be forgotten. The most powerful tool of optical analysis is a combination of ray tracing, to gain an intuitive understanding of the ray trajectories, and the thin-lens equation.

EXAMPLE 23.14 **Designing a lens**

The objective lens of a microscope uses a planoconvex glass lens with the flat side facing the specimen. A real image is formed 160 mm behind the lens when the lens is 8.0 mm from the specimen. What is the radius of the lens's curved surface?

MODEL Treat the lens as a thin lens with the specimen as the object. The lens's focal length is given by the lens maker's equation.

VISUALIZE FIGURE 23.49 clarifies the shape of the lens and defines R_2. The index of refraction was taken from Table 23.1.

FIGURE 23.49 A planoconvex microscope lens.

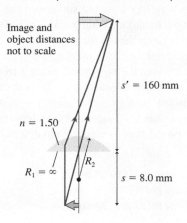

Image and object distances not to scale

$s' = 160$ mm

$n = 1.50$

R_2

$R_1 = \infty$

$s = 8.0$ mm

SOLVE We can use the lens maker's equation to solve for R_2 if we know the lens's focal length. Because we know both the object and image distances, we can use the thin-lens equation to find

$$\frac{1}{f} = \frac{1}{s} + \frac{1}{s'} = \frac{1}{8.0 \text{ mm}} + \frac{1}{160 \text{ mm}} = 0.131 \text{ mm}^{-1}$$

The focal length is $f = 1/(0.131 \text{ mm}^{-1}) = 7.6$ mm, but $1/f$ is all we need for the lens maker's equation. The front surface of the lens is planar, which we can consider a portion of a sphere with $R_1 \to \infty$. Consequently $1/R_1 = 0$. With this, we can solve the lens maker's equation for R_2:

$$\frac{1}{R_2} = \frac{1}{R_1} - \frac{1}{n-1}\frac{1}{f} = 0 - \left(\frac{1}{1.50 - 1}\right)(0.131 \text{ mm}^{-1})$$

$$= -0.262 \text{ mm}^{-1}$$

$$R_2 = -3.8 \text{ mm}$$

The minus sign appears because the curved surface is concave toward the object. Physically, the radius of the curved surface is 3.8 mm.

ASSESS The actual thickness of the lens has to be less than R_2, probably no more than about 1.0 mm. This thickness is significantly less than the object and image distances, so the thin-lens approximation is justified.

EXAMPLE 23.15 **A magnifying lens**

A stamp collector uses a magnifying lens that sits 2.0 cm above the stamp. The magnification is 4.0. What is the focal length of the lens?

FIGURE 23.50 Pictorial representation of a magnifying lens.

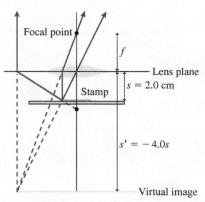

Focal point

f

Lens plane

$s = 2.0$ cm

Stamp

$s' = -4.0s$

Virtual image

MODEL A magnifying lens is a converging lens with the object distance less than the focal length ($s < f$). Assume it is a thin lens.

VISUALIZE FIGURE 23.50 shows the lens and a ray-tracing diagram. We do not need to know the actual shape of the lens, so the figure shows a generic converging lens.

SOLVE A virtual image is upright, so $m = +4.0$. The magnification is $m = -s'/s$, thus

$$s' = -4.0s = -(4.0)(2.0 \text{ cm}) = -8.0 \text{ cm}$$

We can use s and s' in the thin-lens equation to find the focal length:

$$\frac{1}{f} = \frac{1}{s} + \frac{1}{s'} = \frac{1}{2.0 \text{ cm}} + \frac{1}{-8.0 \text{ cm}} = 0.375 \text{ cm}^{-1}$$

$$f = 2.7 \text{ cm}$$

ASSESS $f > 2$ cm, as expected.

A lens forms a real image of a lightbulb, but the image of the bulb on a viewing screen is blurry because the screen is slightly in front of the image plane. To focus the image, should you move the lens toward the bulb or away from the bulb?

23.8 Image Formation with Spherical Mirrors

Curved mirrors—such as those used in telescopes, security and rearview mirrors, and searchlights—can be used to form images, and their images can be analyzed with ray diagrams similar to those used with lenses. We'll consider only the important case of **spherical mirrors,** whose surface is a section of a sphere.

Concave Mirrors

FIGURE 23.51 The focal point and focal length of a concave mirror.

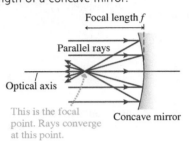

Focal length f

Parallel rays

Optical axis

This is the focal point. Rays converge at this point.

Concave mirror

FIGURE 23.51 shows a **concave mirror,** a mirror in which the edges curve *toward* the light source. Rays parallel to the optical axis reflect from the surface of the mirror so as to pass through a single point on the optical axis. This is the focal point of the mirror. The focal length is the distance from the mirror surface to the focal point. A concave mirror is analogous to a converging lens, but it has only one focal point.

Let's begin by considering the case where the object's distance s from the mirror is greater than the focal length ($s > f$), as shown in FIGURE 23.52. We see that the image is *real* (and inverted) because rays from the object point P converge at the image point P'. Although an infinite number of rays from P all meet at P', each ray obeying the law of reflection, you can see that three "special rays" are enough to determine the position and size of the image:

■ A ray parallel to the axis reflects through the focal point.
■ A ray through the focal point reflects parallel to the axis.
■ A ray striking the center of the mirror reflects at an equal angle on the opposite side of the axis.

These three rays also locate the image if $s < f$, but in that case the image is *virtual* and behind the mirror.

FIGURE 23.52 A real image formed by a concave mirror.

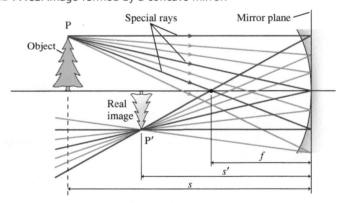

Convex Mirrors

FIGURE 23.53 The focal point and focal length of a convex mirror.

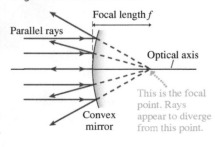

Focal length f

Parallel rays

Optical axis

This is the focal point. Rays appear to diverge from this point.

Convex mirror

FIGURE 23.53 shows parallel light rays approaching a mirror in which the edges curve *away from* the light source. This is called a **convex mirror.** In this case, the reflected rays appear to come from a point behind the mirror. This is the focal point for a convex mirror.

A common example of a convex mirror is a silvered ball, such as a tree ornament. You may have noticed that if you look at your reflection in such a ball, your image appears right-side-up but is quite small. As another example, FIGURE 23.54 shows a city skyline reflected in a polished metal sphere. Let's use ray tracing to understand why the skyscrapers all appear to be so small.

FIGURE 23.55 shows an object in front of a convex mirror. In this case, the reflected rays—each obeying the law of reflection—create an upright image of reduced height behind the mirror. We see that the image is virtual because no rays actually converge at the image point P′. Instead, diverging rays *appear* to come from this point. Once again, three special rays are enough to find the image.

FIGURE 23.54 A city skyline is reflected in this polished sphere.

FIGURE 23.55 A virtual image formed by a convex mirror.

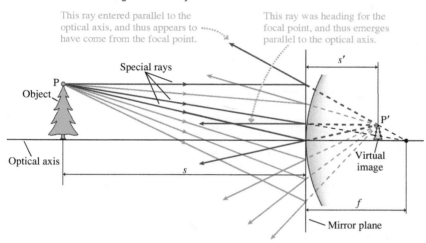

This ray entered parallel to the optical axis, and thus appears to have come from the focal point.

This ray was heading for the focal point, and thus emerges parallel to the optical axis.

Special rays

Object

P

Optical axis

s

s'

P′

Virtual image

f

Mirror plane

Convex mirrors are used for a variety of safety and monitoring applications, such as passenger-side rearview mirrors and the round mirrors used in stores to keep an eye on the customers. When an object is reflected in a convex mirror, the image appears smaller than the object itself. Because the image is, in a sense, a miniature version of the object, you can *see much more of it* within the edges of the mirror than you could with an equal-sized flat mirror.

TACTICS BOX 23.4   Ray tracing for a spherical mirror

❶ **Draw an optical axis.** Use graph paper or a ruler! Establish an appropriate scale.

❷ **Center the mirror on the axis.** Mark and label the focal point at distance f from the mirror's surface.

❸ **Represent the object with an upright arrow at distance s.** It's usually best to place the base of the arrow on the axis and to draw the arrow about half the radius of the mirror.

❹ **Draw the three "special rays" from the tip of the arrow.** Use a straight-edge.

  a. A ray parallel to the axis reflects through (concave) or away from (convex) the focal point.

  b. An incoming ray passing through (concave) or heading toward (convex) the focal point reflects parallel to the axis.

  c. A ray that strikes the center of the mirror reflects at an equal angle on the opposite side of the optical axis.

❺ **Extend the rays forward or backward until they converge.** This is the image point. Draw the rest of the image in the image plane. If the base of the object is on the axis, then the base of the image will also be on the axis.

❻ **Measure the image distance s'.** Also, if needed, measure the image height relative to the object height.

Exercises 32–33

EXAMPLE 23.16 | Analyzing a concave mirror

A 3.0-cm-high object is located 60 cm from a concave mirror. The mirror's focal length is 40 cm. Use ray tracing to find the position and height of the image.

MODEL Use the ray-tracing steps of Tactics Box 23.4.

VISUALIZE FIGURE 23.56 shows the steps of Tactics Box 23.4.

SOLVE We can use a ruler to find that the image position is $s' \approx 120$ cm in front of the mirror and its height is $h' \approx 6$ cm.

ASSESS The image is a *real* image because light rays converge at the image point.

FIGURE 23.56 Ray-tracing diagram for a concave mirror.

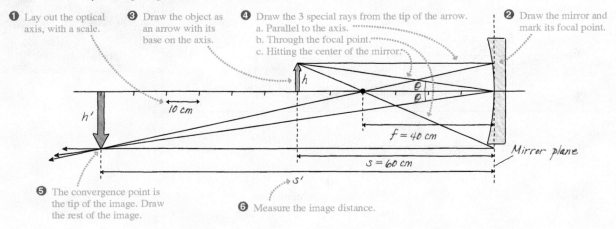

❶ Lay out the optical axis, with a scale.

❸ Draw the object as an arrow with its base on the axis.

❹ Draw the 3 special rays from the tip of the arrow.
 a. Parallel to the axis.
 b. Through the focal point.
 c. Hitting the center of the mirror.

❷ Draw the mirror and mark its focal point.

❺ The convergence point is the tip of the image. Draw the rest of the image.

❻ Measure the image distance.

The Mirror Equation

The thin-lens equation assumes lenses have negligible thickness (so a single refraction occurs in the lens plane) and the rays are nearly parallel to the optical axis (paraxial rays). If we make the same assumptions about spherical mirrors—the mirror has negligible thickness and so paraxial rays reflect at the mirror plane—then the object and image distances are related exactly as they were for thin lenses:

$$\frac{1}{s} + \frac{1}{s'} = \frac{1}{f} \qquad \text{(mirror equation)} \qquad (23.28)$$

The focal length of the mirror, as you can show as a homework problem, is related to the mirror's radius of curvature by

$$f = \frac{R}{2} \qquad (23.29)$$

TABLE 23.5 Sign convention for spherical mirrors

	Positive	Negative
R, f	Concave toward the object	Convex toward the object
s'	Real image, same side as object	Virtual image, opposite side from object

Table 23.5 shows the sign convention used with spherical mirrors. It differs from the convention for lenses, so you'll want to carefully compare this table to Table 23.4. A concave mirror (analogous to a converging lens) has a positive focal length while a convex mirror (analogous to a diverging lens) has a negative focal length. The lateral magnification of a spherical mirror is computed exactly as for a lens:

$$m = -\frac{s'}{s} \qquad (23.30)$$

EXAMPLE 23.17 | Analyzing a concave mirror

A 3.0-cm-high object is located 20 cm from a concave mirror. The mirror's radius of curvature is 80 cm. Determine the position, orientation, and height of the image.

MODEL Treat the mirror as a thin mirror.

VISUALIZE The mirror's focal length is $f = R/2 = +40$ cm, where we used the sign convention from Table 23.5. With the focal length known, the three special rays in FIGURE 23.57 show that the image is a magnified, virtual image behind the mirror.

FIGURE 23.57 Pictorial representation of Example 23.17.

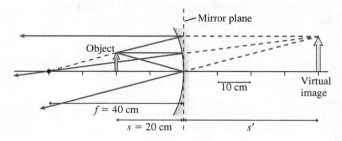

SOLVE The thin-mirror equation is

$$\frac{1}{20 \text{ cm}} + \frac{1}{s'} = \frac{1}{40 \text{ cm}}$$

This is easily solved to give $s' = -40$ cm, in agreement with the ray tracing. The negative sign tells us this is a virtual image behind the mirror. The magnification is

$$m = -\frac{-40 \text{ cm}}{20 \text{ cm}} = +2.0$$

Consequently, the image is 6.0 cm tall and upright.

ASSESS This is a virtual image because light rays diverge from the image point. You could see this enlarged image by standing behind the object and looking into the mirror. In fact, this is how magnifying cosmetic mirrors work.

STOP TO THINK 23.7   A concave mirror of focal length f forms an image of the moon. Where is the image located?

a. At the mirror's surface
b. Almost exactly a distance f behind the mirror
c. Almost exactly a distance f in front of the mirror
d. At a distance behind the mirror equal to the distance of the moon in front of the mirror

---

CHALLENGE EXAMPLE 23.18   **Optical fiber imaging**

An *endoscope* is a thin bundle of optical fibers that can be inserted through a bodily opening or small incision to view the interior of the body. As FIGURE 23.58 shows, an *objective* lens forms a real image on the entrance face of the fiber bundle. Individual fibers, using total internal reflection, transport the light to the exit face, where it emerges. The doctor (or a TV camera) observes the object by viewing the exit face through an *eyepiece* lens.

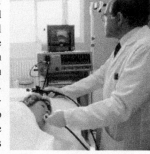

FIGURE 23.58 An endoscope.

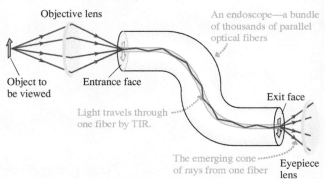

Consider an endoscope having a 3.0-mm-diameter objective lens with a focal length of 1.1 mm. These are typical values. The indices of refraction of the core and the cladding of the optical fibers are 1.62 and 1.50, respectively. To give maximum brightness, the objective lens is positioned so that, for an on-axis object, rays passing through the outer edge of the lens have the maximum angle of incidence for undergoing TIR in the fiber. How far should the objective lens be placed from the object the doctor wishes to view?

MODEL Represent the object as an on-axis point source and use the ray model of light.

VISUALIZE FIGURE 23.59 on the next page shows the real image being focused on the entrance face of the endoscope. Inside the fiber, rays that strike the cladding at an angle of incidence greater than the critical angle θ_c undergo TIR and stay in the fiber; rays are lost if their angle of incidence is less than θ_c. For maximum brightness, the lens is positioned so that a ray passing through the outer edge refracts into the fiber at the maximum angle of incidence θ_{max} for which TIR is possible. A smaller-diameter lens would sacrifice light-gathering power, whereas the outer rays from a larger-diameter lens would impinge on the core-cladding boundary at less than θ_c and would not undergo TIR. Note that the lens-to-fiber distance, although unknown, is fixed by the manufacturer and cannot be changed. Only object distance is under the doctor's control.

Continued

FIGURE 23.59 Magnified view of the entrance of an optical fiber.

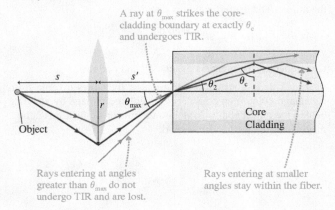

A ray at θ_{max} strikes the core-cladding boundary at exactly θ_c and undergoes TIR.

Object

Rays entering at angles greater than θ_{max} do not undergo TIR and are lost.

Rays entering at smaller angles stay within the fiber.

Core
Cladding

SOLVE We know the focal length of the lens. We can use the geometry of the ray at the critical angle to find the image distance s', then use the thin-lens equation to find the object distance s. The critical angle for TIR inside the fiber is

$$\theta_c = \sin^{-1}\left(\frac{n_{cladding}}{n_{core}}\right) = \sin^{-1}\left(\frac{1.50}{1.62}\right) = 67.8°$$

A ray incident on the core-cladding boundary at exactly the critical angle must have entered the fiber, at the entrance face, at angle $\theta_2 = 90° - \theta_c = 22.2°$. For optimum lens placement, this ray passed through the outer edge of the lens and was incident on the entrance face at angle θ_{max}. Snell's law at the entrance face is

$$n_{air} \sin\theta_{max} = 1.0 \cdot \sin\theta_{max} = n_{core} \sin\theta_2$$

and thus

$$\theta_{max} = \sin^{-1}(1.62 \sin 22.2°) = 37.7°$$

We know the lens radius, $r = 1.5$ mm, so the distance of the lens from the fiber—the image distance s'—is

$$s' = \frac{r}{\tan\theta_{max}} = \frac{1.5 \text{ mm}}{\tan(37.7°)} = 1.9 \text{ mm}$$

Now we can use the thin-lens equation to locate the object:

$$\frac{1}{s} = \frac{1}{f} - \frac{1}{s'} = \frac{1}{1.1 \text{ mm}} - \frac{1}{1.9 \text{ mm}}$$

$$s = 2.6 \text{ mm}$$

The doctor, viewing the exit face of the fiber bundle, will see a focused image when the objective lens is 2.6 mm from the object she wishes to view.

ASSESS The object and image distances are both greater than the focal length, which is correct for forming a real image.

SUMMARY

The goals of Chapter 23 have been to understand and apply the ray model of light.

General Principles

Reflection

Law of reflection: $\theta_r = \theta_i$

Reflection can be **specular** (mirror-like) or **diffuse** (from rough surfaces).

Plane mirrors: A virtual image is formed at P' with $s' = s$.

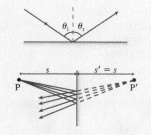

Refraction

Snell's law of refraction:

$$n_1 \sin\theta_1 = n_2 \sin\theta_2$$

Index of refraction is $n = c/v$. The ray is closer to the normal on the side with the larger index of refraction.

If $n_2 < n_1$, **total internal reflection** (TIR) occurs when the angle of incidence $\theta_1 \geq \theta_c = \sin^{-1}(n_2/n_1)$.

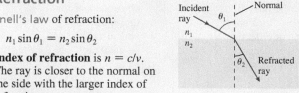

Important Concepts

The ray model of light

Light travels along straight lines, called **light rays,** at speed $v = c/n$.

A light ray continues forever unless an interaction with matter causes it to reflect, refract, scatter, or be absorbed.

Light rays come from **objects.** Each point on the object sends rays in all directions.

The eye sees an object (or an image) when diverging rays are collected by the pupil and focused on the retina.

▶ Ray optics is valid when lenses, mirrors, and apertures are larger than ≈ 1 mm.

Image formation

If rays diverge from P and interact with a lens or mirror so that the refracted rays *converge* at P', then P' is a real image of P.

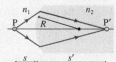

If rays diverge from P and interact with a lens or mirror so that the refracted/reflected rays *diverge* from P' and appear to come from P', then P' is a virtual image of P.

Spherical surface: Object and image distances are related by

$$\frac{n_1}{s} + \frac{n_2}{s'} = \frac{n_2 - n_1}{R}$$

Plane surface: $R \rightarrow \infty$, so $|s'/s| = n_2/n_1$.

Applications

Ray tracing

3 special rays in 3 basic situations:

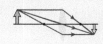 

| Converging lens Real image | Converging lens Virtual image | Diverging lens Virtual image |

Magnification $m = -\dfrac{s'}{s}$

m is $+$ for an upright image, $-$ for inverted.
The height ratio is $h'/h = |m|$.

Thin lenses

The image and object distances are related by

$$\frac{1}{s} + \frac{1}{s'} = \frac{1}{f}$$

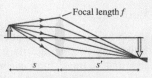

where the focal length is given by the lens maker's equation:

$$\frac{1}{f} = (n-1)\left(\frac{1}{R_1} - \frac{1}{R_2}\right)$$

R $+$ for surface convex toward object $-$ for concave
f $+$ for a converging lens $-$ for diverging
s' $+$ for a real image $-$ for virtual

Spherical mirrors

The image and object distances are related by

$$\frac{1}{s} + \frac{1}{s'} = \frac{1}{f}$$

R, f $+$ for concave mirror $-$ for convex
s' $+$ for a real image $-$ for virtual

Focal length $f = R/2$

Terms and Notation

light ray	diffuse reflection	dispersion	object plane
object	virtual image	Rayleigh scattering	image plane
point source	refraction	lens	inverted image
parallel bundle	angle of refraction	ray tracing	lateral magnification, m
ray diagram	Snell's law	converging lens	upright image
camera obscura	total internal reflection (TIR)	focal point	spherical mirror
aperture	critical angle, θ_c	focal length, f	concave mirror
specular reflection	object distance, s	diverging lens	convex mirror
angle of incidence	image distance, s'	thin lens	
angle of reflection	optical axis	lens plane	
law of reflection	paraxial rays	real image	

CONCEPTUAL QUESTIONS

1. If you turn on your car headlights during the day, the road ahead of you doesn't appear to get brighter. Why not?

2. Suppose you have two pinhole cameras. The first has a small round hole in the front. The second is identical except it has a square hole of the same area as the round hole in the first camera. Would the pictures taken by these two cameras, under the same conditions, be different in any obvious way? Explain.

3. You are looking at the image of a pencil in a mirror, as shown in FIGURE Q23.3.
   a. What happens to the image if the top half of the mirror, down to the midpoint, is covered with a piece of cardboard? Explain.
   b. What happens to the image if the bottom half of the mirror is covered with a piece of cardboard? Explain.

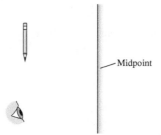

FIGURE Q23.3

4. One problem with using optical fibers for communication is that a light ray passing directly down the center of the fiber takes less time to travel from one end to the other than a ray taking a longer, zig-zag path. Thus light rays starting at the same time but traveling in slightly different directions reach the end of the fiber at different times. This problem can be solved by making the refractive index of the glass change gradually from a higher value in the center to a lower value near the edges of the fiber. Explain how this reduces the difference in travel times.

5. Suppose you looked at the sky on a clear day through pieces of red and blue plastic oriented as shown in FIGURE Q23.5. Describe the color and brightness of the light coming through sections 1, 2, and 3.

FIGURE Q23.5

6. A red card is illuminated by red light. What color will the card appear? What if it's illuminated by blue light?

7. The center of the galaxy is filled with low-density hydrogen gas. An astronomer wants to take a picture of the center of the galaxy. Will the view be better using ultraviolet light, visible light, or infrared light? (High-quality telescopes are available in all three spectral regions.) Explain.

8. Consider *one* point on an object near a lens.
   a. What is the minimum number of rays needed to locate its image point? Explain.
   b. How many rays from this point actually strike the lens and refract to the image point?

9. The object and lens in FIGURE Q23.9 are positioned to form a well-focused, inverted image on a viewing screen. Then a piece of cardboard is lowered just in front of the lens to cover the top half of the lens. Describe what you see on the screen when the cardboard is in place.

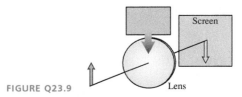

FIGURE Q23.9

10. FIGURE Q23.10 shows an object near a lens. The focal points are marked. Is there an image? If so, is the image real or virtual? Is it upright or inverted? If not, why not? Explain.

FIGURE Q23.10

11. A concave mirror brings the sun's rays to a focus in front of the mirror. Suppose the mirror is submerged in a swimming pool but still pointed up at the sun. Will the sun's rays be focused nearer to, farther from, or at the same distance from the mirror? Explain.

12. When you look at your reflection in the bowl of a spoon, it is upside down. Why?

EXERCISES AND PROBLEMS

Exercises

Section 23.1 The Ray Model of Light

1. ‖ a. How long (in ns) does it take light to travel 1.0 m in vacuum?
   b. What distance does light travel in water, glass, and cubic zirconia during the time that it travels 1.0 m in vacuum?

2. ‖ A point source of light illuminates an aperture 2.0 m away. A 12.0-cm-wide bright patch of light appears on a screen 1.0 m behind the aperture. How wide is the aperture?

3. ‖ A 5.0-cm-thick layer of oil is sandwiched between a 1.0-cm-thick sheet of glass and a 2.0-cm-thick sheet of polystyrene plastic. How long (in ns) does it take light incident perpendicular to the glass to pass through this 8.0-cm-thick sandwich?

4. ‖ A student has built a 15-cm-long pinhole camera for a science fair project. She wants to photograph her 180-cm-tall friend and have the image on the film be 5.0 cm high. How far should the front of the camera be from her friend?

Section 23.2 Reflection

5. | The mirror in FIGURE EX23.5 deflects a horizontal laser beam by 60°. What is the angle ϕ?

FIGURE EX23.5

6. | A light ray leaves point A in FIGURE EX23.6, reflects from the mirror, and reaches point B. How far below the top edge does the ray strike the mirror?

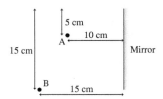

FIGURE EX23.6

7. ‖ The laser beam in FIGURE EX23.7 is aimed at the center of a rotating hexagonal mirror. How long is the streak of laser light as the reflected laser beam sweeps across the wall behind the laser?

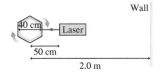

FIGURE EX23.7

8. ‖ At what angle ϕ should the laser beam in FIGURE EX23.8 be aimed at the mirrored ceiling in order to hit the midpoint of the far wall?

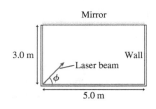

FIGURE EX23.8

9. ‖ It is 165 cm from your eyes to your toes. You're standing 200 cm in front of a tall mirror. How far is it from your eyes to the image of your toes?

Section 23.3 Refraction

10. ‖ A 1.0-cm-thick layer of water stands on a horizontal slab of glass. A light ray in the air is incident on the water 60° from the normal. What is the ray's direction of travel in the glass?

11. ‖ A costume jewelry pendant made of cubic zirconia is submerged in oil. A light ray strikes one face of the zirconia crystal at an angle of incidence of 25°. Once inside, what is the ray's angle with respect to the face of the crystal?

12. ‖ An underwater diver sees the sun 50° above horizontal. How high is the sun above the horizon to a fisherman in a boat above the diver?

13. | A laser beam in air is incident on a liquid at an angle of 53° with respect to the normal. The laser beam's angle in the liquid is 35°. What is the liquid's index of refraction?

14. ‖ The glass core of an optical fiber has an index of refraction 1.60. The index of refraction of the cladding is 1.48. What is the maximum angle a light ray can make with the wall of the core if it is to remain inside the fiber?

15. ‖ A thin glass rod is submerged in oil. What is the critical angle for light traveling inside the rod?

Section 23.4 Image Formation by Refraction

16. ‖ A fish in a flat-sided aquarium sees a can of fish food on the counter. To the fish's eye, the can looks to be 30 cm outside the aquarium. What is the actual distance between the can and the aquarium? (You can ignore the thin glass wall of the aquarium.)

17. | A biologist keeps a specimen of his favorite beetle embedded in a cube of polystyrene plastic. The hapless bug appears to be 2.0 cm within the plastic. What is the beetle's actual distance beneath the surface?

18. | A 150-cm-tall diver is standing completely submerged on the bottom of a swimming pool full of water. You are sitting on the end of the diving board, almost directly over her. How tall does the diver appear to be?

19. ‖ To a fish in an aquarium, the 4.00-mm-thick walls appear to be only 3.50 mm thick. What is the index of refraction of the walls?

Section 23.5 Color and Dispersion

20. ‖ A sheet of glass has $n_{\text{red}} = 1.52$ and $n_{\text{violet}} = 1.55$. A narrow beam of white light is incident on the glass at 30°. What is the angular spread of the light inside the glass?

21. | A narrow beam of white light is incident on a sheet of quartz. The beam disperses in the quartz, with red light ($\lambda \approx 700$ nm) traveling at an angle of 26.3° with respect to the normal and violet light ($\lambda \approx 400$ nm) traveling at 25.7°. The index of refraction of quartz for red light is 1.45. What is the index of refraction of quartz for violet light?

22. ‖ A hydrogen discharge lamp emits light with two prominent wavelengths: 656 nm (red) and 486 nm (blue). The light enters a flint-glass prism perpendicular to one face and then refracts through the hypotenuse back into the air. The angle between these two faces is 35°.
    a. Use Figure 23.28 to estimate to ±0.002 the index of refraction of flint glass at these two wavelengths.
    b. What is the angle (in degrees) between the red and blue light as it leaves the prism?
23. ‖ Infrared telescopes, which use special infrared detectors, are able to peer farther into star-forming regions of the galaxy because infrared light is not scattered as strongly as is visible light by the tenuous clouds of hydrogen gas from which new stars are created. For what wavelength of light is the scattering only 1% that of light with a visible wavelength of 500 nm?

Section 23.6 Thin Lenses: Ray Tracing

24. ‖ An object is 20 cm in front of a converging lens with a focal length of 10 cm. Use ray tracing to determine the location of the image. Is the image upright or inverted?
25. ‖ An object is 30 cm in front of a converging lens with a focal length of 5 cm. Use ray tracing to determine the location of the image. Is the image upright or inverted?
26. ‖ An object is 6 cm in front of a converging lens with a focal length of 10 cm. Use ray tracing to determine the location of the image. Is the image upright or inverted?
27. ‖ An object is 15 cm in front of a diverging lens with a focal length of −15 cm. Use ray tracing to determine the location of the image. Is the image upright or inverted?

Section 23.7 Thin Lenses: Refraction Theory

28. ‖ Find the focal length of the glass lens in FIGURE EX23.28.

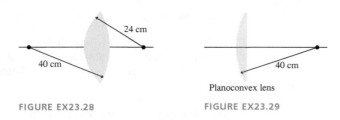

24 cm

40 cm   40 cm

Planoconvex lens

FIGURE EX23.28   FIGURE EX23.29

29. ‖ Find the focal length of the planoconvex polystyrene plastic lens in FIGURE EX23.29.
30. ‖ Find the focal length of the glass lens in FIGURE EX23.30.

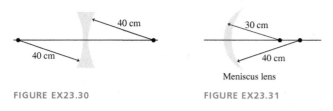

40 cm   30 cm

40 cm   40 cm

Meniscus lens

FIGURE EX23.30   FIGURE EX23.31

31. ‖ Find the focal length of the meniscus polystyrene plastic lens in FIGURE EX23.31.
32. ‖ An air bubble inside an 8.0-cm-diameter plastic ball is 2.0 cm from the surface. As you look at the ball with the bubble turned toward you, how far beneath the surface does the bubble appear to be?

33. ‖ A goldfish lives in a 50-cm-diameter spherical fish bowl. The fish sees a cat watching it. If the cat's face is 20 cm from the edge of the bowl, how far from the edge does the fish see it as being? (You can ignore the thin glass wall of the bowl.)
34. ‖ A 1.0-cm-tall candle flame is 60 cm from a lens with a focal length of 20 cm. What are the image distance and the height of the flame's image?

Section 23.8 Image Formation with Spherical Mirrors

35. ‖ An object is 40 cm in front of a concave mirror with a focal length of 20 cm. Use ray tracing to locate the image. Is the image upright or inverted?
36. ‖ An object is 12 cm in front of a concave mirror with a focal length of 20 cm. Use ray tracing to locate the image. Is the image upright or inverted?
37. ‖ An object is 30 cm in front of a convex mirror with a focal length of −20 cm. Use ray tracing to locate the image. Is the image upright or inverted?

Problems

38. ‖ An advanced computer sends information to its various parts via infrared light pulses traveling through silicon fibers. To acquire data from memory, the central processing unit sends a light-pulse request to the memory unit. The memory unit processes the request, then sends a data pulse back to the central processing unit. The memory unit takes 0.5 ns to process a request. If the information has to be obtained from memory in 2.0 ns, what is the maximum distance the memory unit can be from the central processing unit?
39. ‖ A red ball is placed at point A in FIGURE P23.39.
    a. How many images are seen by an observer at point O?
    b. What are the (x, y) coordinates of each image?

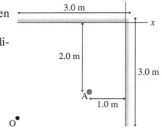

3.0 m

2.0 m

3.0 m

A
1.0 m

FIGURE P23.39   O

40. ‖ A laser beam is incident on the left mirror in FIGURE P23.40. Its initial direction is parallel to a line that bisects the mirrors. What is the angle φ of the reflected laser beam?

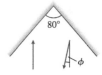

80°

φ

FIGURE P23.40

41. ‖ The place you get your hair cut has two nearly parallel mirrors 5.0 m apart. As you sit in the chair, your head is 2.0 m from the nearer mirror. Looking toward this mirror, you first see your face and then, farther away, the back of your head. (The mirrors need to be slightly nonparallel for you to be able to see the back of your head, but you can treat them as parallel in this problem.) How far away does the back of your head appear to be? Neglect the thickness of your head.
42. ‖ You're helping with an experiment in which a vertical cylinder will rotate about its axis by a very small angle. You need to devise a way to measure this angle. You decide to use what is called an *optical lever*. You begin by mounting a small mirror

on top of the cylinder. A laser 5.0 m away shoots a laser beam at the mirror. Before the experiment starts, the mirror is adjusted to reflect the laser beam directly back to the laser. Later, you measure that the reflected laser beam, when it returns to the laser, has been deflected sideways by 2.0 mm. Through how many degrees has the cylinder rotated?

43. ‖ A microscope is focused on a black dot. When a 1.00-cm-thick piece of plastic is placed over the dot, the microscope objective has to be raised 0.40 cm to bring the dot back into focus. What is the index of refraction of the plastic?

44. ‖ A light ray in air is incident on a transparent material whose index of refraction is n.
   a. Find an expression for the (non-zero) angle of incidence whose angle of refraction is half the angle of incidence.
   b. Evaluate your expression for light incident on glass.

45. ‖ The meter stick in FIGURE P23.45 lies on the bottom of a 100-cm-long tank with its zero mark against the left edge. You look into the tank at a 30° angle, with your line of sight just grazing the upper left edge of the tank. What mark do you see on the meter stick if the tank is (a) empty, (b) half full of water, and (c) completely full of water?

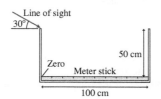

FIGURE P23.45

46. ‖ The 80-cm-tall, 65-cm-wide tank shown in FIGURE P23.46 is completely filled with water. The tank has marks every 10 cm along one wall, and the 0 cm mark is barely submerged. As you stand beside the opposite wall, your eye is level with the top of the water.
   a. Can you see the marks from the top of the tank (the 0 cm mark) going down, or from the bottom of the tank (the 80 cm mark) coming up? Explain.
   b. Which is the lowest or highest mark, depending on your answer to part a, that you can see?

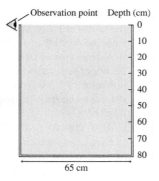

FIGURE P23.46

47. ‖ A 4.0-m-wide swimming pool is filled to the top. The bottom of the pool becomes completely shaded in the afternoon when the sun is 20° above the horizon. How deep is the pool?

48. ‖ It's nighttime, and you've dropped your goggles into a 3.0-m-deep swimming pool. If you hold a laser pointer 1.0 m above the edge of the pool, you can illuminate the goggles if the laser beam enters the water 2.0 m from the edge. How far are the goggles from the edge of the pool?

49. ‖ Shown from above in FIGURE P23.49 is one corner of a rectangular box filled with water. A laser beam starts 10 cm from side A of the container and enters the water at position x. You can ignore the thin walls of the container.
   a. If $x = 15$ cm, does the laser beam refract back into the air through side B or reflect from side B back into the water? Determine the angle of refraction or reflection.

b. Repeat part a for $x = 25$ cm.
c. Find the minimum value of x for which the laser beam passes through side B and emerges into the air.

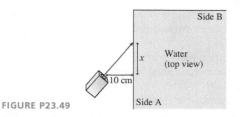

FIGURE P23.49

50. ‖ A fish is 20 m from the shore of a lake. A bonfire is burning on the edge of the lake nearest the fish.
   a. Does the fish need to be shallow (just below the surface) or very deep to see the light from the bonfire? Explain.
   b. What is the deepest or shallowest, depending on your answer to part a, that the fish can be and still see light from the fire?

51. ‖ Your supervisor asks you to measure the index of refraction of a piece of plastic. You notice that, because of scattering of the light, you can see the path of a laser beam through the plastic. You decide to shoot a laser beam toward the plastic at several different incident angles and measure the refraction angle in the plastic. Your data are as follows:

Incident angle	Refraction angle
15°	9°
30°	19°
45°	26°
60°	34°
75°	37°

Use the best-fit line of an appropriate graph to determine the plastic's index of refraction.

52. ‖‖ One of the contests at the school carnival is to throw a spear at an underwater target lying flat on the bottom of a pool. The water is 1.0 m deep. You're standing on a small stool that places your eyes 3.0 m above the bottom of the pool. As you look at the target, your gaze is 30° below horizontal. At what angle below horizontal should you throw the spear in order to hit the target? Your raised arm brings the spear point to the level of your eyes as you throw it, and over this short distance you can assume that the spear travels in a straight line rather than a parabolic trajectory.

53. ‖ White light is incident onto a 30° prism at the 40° angle shown in FIGURE P23.53. Violet light emerges perpendicular to the rear face of the prism. The index of refraction of violet light in this glass is 2.0% larger than the index of refraction of red light. At what angle ϕ does red light emerge from the rear face?

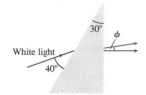

FIGURE P23.53

54. ‖ There's one angle of incidence β onto a prism for which the light inside an isosceles prism travels parallel to the base and emerges at angle β.

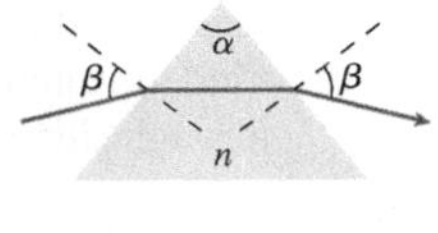

FIGURE P23.54

   a. Find an expression for β in terms of the prism's apex angle α and index of refraction n.

   b. A laboratory measurement finds that $\beta = 52.2°$ for a prism shaped like an equilateral triangle. What is the prism's index of refraction?

55. ‖ Paraxial light rays approach a transparent sphere parallel to an optical axis passing through the center of the sphere. The rays come to a focus on the far surface of the sphere. What is the sphere's index of refraction?

56. ‖ A 6.0-cm-diameter cubic zirconia sphere has an air bubble exactly in the center. As you look into the sphere, how far beneath the surface does the bubble appear to be?

57. ‖ A 1.0-cm-tall object is 10 cm in front of a converging lens that has a 30 cm focal length.

   a. Use ray tracing to find the position and height of the image. To do this accurately, use a ruler or paper with a grid. Determine the image distance and image height by making measurements on your diagram.

   b. Calculate the image position and height. Compare with your ray-tracing answers in part a.

58. ‖ A 2.0-cm-tall object is 40 cm in front of a converging lens that has a 20 cm focal length.

   a. Use ray tracing to find the position and height of the image. To do this accurately, use a ruler or paper with a grid. Determine the image distance and image height by making measurements on your diagram.

   b. Calculate the image position and height. Compare with your ray-tracing answers in part a.

59. ‖ A 1.0-cm-tall object is 75 cm in front of a converging lens that has a 30 cm focal length.

   a. Use ray tracing to find the position and height of the image. To do this accurately, use a ruler or paper with a grid. Determine the image distance and image height by making measurements on your diagram.

   b. Calculate the image position and height. Compare with your ray-tracing answers in part a.

60. ‖ A 2.0-cm-tall object is 15 cm in front of a converging lens that has a 20 cm focal length.

   a. Use ray tracing to find the position and height of the image. To do this accurately, use a ruler or paper with a grid. Determine the image distance and image height by making measurements on your diagram.

   b. Calculate the image position and height. Compare with your ray-tracing answers in part a.

61. ‖ A 1.0-cm-tall object is 60 cm in front of a diverging lens that has a −30 cm focal length.

   a. Use ray tracing to find the position and height of the image. To do this accurately, use a ruler or paper with a grid. Determine the image distance and image height by making measurements on your diagram.

   b. Calculate the image position and height. Compare with your ray-tracing answers in part a.

62. ‖ A 2.0-cm-tall object is 15 cm in front of a diverging lens that has a −20 cm focal length.

   a. Use ray tracing to find the position and height of the image. To do this accurately, use a ruler or paper with a grid.

Determine the image distance and image height by making measurements on your diagram.

   b. Calculate the image position and height. Compare with your ray-tracing answers in part a.

63. ‖ To determine the focal length of a lens, you place the lens in front of a small lightbulb and then adjust a viewing screen to get a sharply focused image. Varying the lens position produces the following data:

Bulb to lens (cm)	Lens to screen (cm)
20	61
22	47
24	39
26	37
28	32

Use the best-fit line of an appropriate graph to determine the focal length of the lens.

64. ‖ A 1.0-cm-tall object is 20 cm in front of a concave mirror that has a 60 cm focal length. Calculate the position and height of the image. State whether the image is in front of or behind the mirror, and whether the image is upright or inverted.

65. ‖ A 1.0-cm-tall object is 20 cm in front of a convex mirror that has a −60 cm focal length. Calculate the position and height of the image. State whether the image is in front of or behind the mirror, and whether the image is upright or inverted.

66. ‖ The illumination lights in an operating room use a concave
BIO mirror to focus an image of a bright lamp onto the surgical site. One such light uses a mirror with a 30 cm radius of curvature. If the mirror is 1.2 m from the patient, how far should the lamp be from the mirror?

67. ‖ A dentist uses a curved mirror to view the back side of teeth in
BIO the upper jaw. Suppose she wants an upright image with a magnification of 1.5 when the mirror is 1.2 cm from a tooth. Should she use a convex or a concave mirror? What focal length should it have?

68. ‖ A 2.0-cm-tall candle flame is 2.0 m from a wall. You happen to have a lens with a focal length of 32 cm. How many places can you put the lens to form a well-focused image of the candle flame on the wall? For each location, what are the height and orientation of the image?

69. ‖ A lightbulb is 3.0 m from a wall. What are the focal length and the position (measured from the bulb) of a lens that will form an image on the wall that is twice the size of the lightbulb?

70. ‖ a. Estimate the diameter of your eyeball.
BIO   b. Bring this page up to the closest distance at which the text is sharp—not the closest at which you can still read it, but the closest at which the letters remain sharp. If you wear glasses or contact lenses, leave them on. This distance is called the *near point* of your (possibly corrected) eye. Measure it.

   c. Estimate the effective focal length of your eye. The effective focal length includes the focusing due to the lens, the curvature of the cornea, and any corrections you wear. Ignore the effects of the fluid in your eye.

71. ‖ A slide projector needs to create a 98-cm-high image of a 2.0-cm-tall slide. The screen is 300 cm from the slide.

   a. What focal length does the lens need? Assume that it is a thin lens.

   b. How far should you place the lens from the slide?

72. ‖ A lens placed 10 cm in front of an object creates an upright image twice the height of the object. The lens is then moved along the optical axis until it creates an inverted image twice the height of the object. How far did the lens move?

73. ‖ An object is 60 cm from a screen. What are the radii of a symmetric converging plastic lens (i.e., two equally curved surfaces) that will form an image on the screen twice the height of the object?

74. ‖ A sports photographer has a 150-mm-focal-length lens on his camera. The photographer wants to photograph a sprinter running straight away from him at 5.0 m/s. What is the speed (in mm/s) of the sprinter's image at the instant the sprinter is 10 m in front of the lens?

75. ‖ A concave mirror has a 40 cm radius of curvature. How far from the mirror must an object be placed to create an upright image three times the height of the object?

76. ‖‖ A 2.0-cm-tall object is placed in front of a mirror. A 1.0-cm-tall upright image is formed behind the mirror, 150 cm from the object. What is the focal length of the mirror?

77. ‖ A spherical mirror of radius R has its center at C, as shown in FIGURE P23.77. A ray parallel to the axis reflects through F, the focal point. Prove that $f = R/2$ if $\phi \ll 1$ rad.

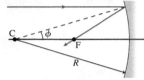

FIGURE P23.77

Challenge Problems

78. Consider a lens having index of refraction n_2 and surfaces with radii R_1 and R_2. The lens is immersed in a fluid that has index of refraction n_1.
    a. Derive a generalized lens maker's equation to replace Equation 23.27 when the lens is surrounded by a medium other than air. That is, when $n_1 \neq 1$.
    b. A symmetric converging glass lens (i.e., two equally curved surfaces) has two surfaces with radii of 40 cm. Find the focal length of this lens in air and the focal length of this lens in water.

79. FIGURE CP23.79 shows a light ray that travels from point A to point B. The ray crosses the boundary at position x, making angles θ_1 and θ_2 in the two media. Suppose that you did *not* know Snell's law.
    a. Write an expression for the *time t* it takes the light ray to travel from A to B. Your expression should be in terms of the distances a, b, and w; the variable x; and the indices of refraction n_1 and n_2.

b. The time depends on x. There's one value of x for which the light travels from A to B in the shortest possible time. We'll call it x_{min}. Write an expression (but don't try to solve it!) from which x_{min} could be found.

c. Now, by using the geometry of the figure, derive Snell's law from your answer to part b.

You've proven that Snell's law is equivalent to the statement that "light traveling between two points follows the path that requires the shortest time." This interesting way of thinking about refraction is called *Fermat's principle*.

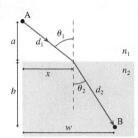

FIGURE P23.79

80. A fortune teller's "crystal ball" (actually just glass) is 10 cm in diameter. Her secret ring is placed 6.0 cm from the edge of the ball.
    a. An image of the ring appears on the opposite side of the crystal ball. How far is the image from the center of the ball?
    b. Draw a ray diagram showing the formation of the image.
    c. The crystal ball is removed and a thin lens is placed where the center of the ball had been. If the image is still in the same position, what is the focal length of the lens?

81. A beam of white light enters a transparent material. Wavelengths for which the index of refraction is n are refracted at angle θ_2. Wavelengths for which the index of refraction is $n + \delta n$, where $\delta n \ll n$, are refracted at angle $\theta_2 + \delta\theta$.
    a. Show that the angular separation in radians is $\delta\theta = -(\delta n/n)\tan\theta_2$.
    b. A beam of white light is incident on a piece of glass at 30.0°. Deep violet light is refracted 0.28° more than deep red light. The index of refraction for deep red light is known to be 1.552. What is the index of refraction for deep violet light?

82. Consider an object of thickness ds (parallel to the axis) in front of a lens or mirror. The image of the object has thickness ds'. Define the *longitudinal magnification* as $M = ds'/ds$. Prove that $M = -m^2$, where m is the lateral magnification.

STOP TO THINK ANSWERS

Stop to Think 23.1: c. The light spreads vertically as it goes through the vertical aperture. The light spreads horizontally due to different points on the horizontal lightbulb.

Stop to Think 23.2: c. There's one image behind the vertical mirror and a second behind the horizontal mirror. A third image in the corner arises from rays that reflect twice, once off each mirror.

Stop to Think 23.3: a. The ray travels closer to the normal in both media 1 and 3 than in medium 2, so n_1 and n_3 are both larger than n_2. The angle is smaller in medium 3 than in medium 1, so $n_3 > n_1$.

Stop to Think 23.4: e. The rays from the object are diverging. Without a lens, the rays cannot converge to form any kind of image on the screen.

Stop to Think 23.5: a, e, or f. Any of these will increase the angle of refraction θ_2.

Stop to Think 23.6: Away from. You need to decrease s' to bring the image plane onto the screen. s' is decreased by increasing s.

Stop to Think 23.7: c. A concave mirror forms a real image in front of the mirror. Because the object distance is $s \approx \infty$, the image distance is $s' \approx f$.

24 Optical Instruments

The world's greatest collection of telescopes is on the summit of Mauna Kea on the Big Island of Hawaii, towering 4200 m (13,800 ft) over the Pacific Ocean.

▶ **Looking Ahead** The goal of Chapter 24 is to understand some common optical instruments and their limitations.

Lenses in Combination

The "lenses" of optical instruments are always built with several individual lenses to give better optical performance.

A cross section of a typical camera lens shows that it is built of 5 individual lenses and an adjustable iris.

You'll learn how to analyze a system with multiple lenses.

Optical Systems That Magnify

Lenses and mirrors can be used to magnify objects both near and far. Optical instruments open a realm far beyond what the unaided eye can see.

A simple magnifying glass has a low magnification of only 2× or 3×.

A microscope uses two sets of lenses in combination to produce magnifications of up to 1000×.

Small telescopes use lenses; larger telescopes use a curved mirror as the primary optical element.

The Camera

A camera uses a lens to project a real image onto a light-sensitive detector.

Although a modern digital camera is very complex, at its heart it's just a light-tight box with a lens to focus the image.

You'll learn about focusing, zoom, and exposure.

◀ **Looking Back**
Sections 23.6–23.7 Ray tracing and image formation by lenses

The Human Eye

The human eye is much like a camera: The cornea and lens together focus a real image onto the retina.

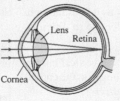

Lens
Retina
Cornea

You'll discover how eyeglasses and contact lenses are used to correct defects of vision.

Resolution of Lenses

Light passing through a lens undergoes diffraction, just like light passing through a circular hole. Diffraction limits a lens's ability to form a perfectly focused image.

An ideal lens would have focused the light to two points. Instead, we get two overlapped diffraction patterns.

You'll learn about *Rayleigh's criterion* for when two images can be resolved.

◀ **Looking Back**
Section 22.5 Circular diffraction

24.1 Lenses in Combination

Only the simplest magnifiers are built with a single lens of the sort we analyzed in Chapter 23. Optical instruments, such as microscopes and cameras, are invariably built with multiple lenses. The reason, as we'll see, is to improve the image quality.

The analysis of multi-lens systems requires only one new rule: **The image of the first lens acts as the object for the second lens.** To see why this is so, FIGURE 24.1 shows a simple telescope consisting of a large-diameter converging lens, called the *objective*, and a smaller converging lens used as the *eyepiece*. (We'll analyze telescopes more thoroughly later in the chapter.) Highlighted are the three special rays you learned to use in Chapter 23:

- A ray parallel to the optical axis refracts through the focal point.
- A ray through the focal point refracts parallel to the optical axis.
- A ray through the center of the lens is undeviated.

FIGURE 24.1 Ray-tracing diagram of a simple astronomical telescope.

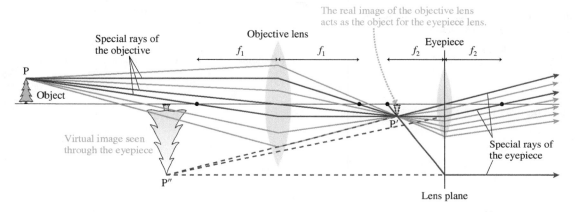

The rays passing through the objective converge to a real image at P′, but they don't stop there. Instead, light rays *diverge* from P′ as they approach the second lens. **As far as the eyepiece is concerned, the rays are coming from P′, and thus P′ acts as the object for the second lens.** The three special rays passing through the objective lens are sufficient to locate the image P′, but these rays are generally *not* the special rays for the second lens. However, other rays converging at P′ leave at the correct angles to be the special rays for the eyepiece. That is, a new set of special rays is drawn from P′ to the second lens and used to find the final image point P″.

NOTE ▶ One ray seems to "miss" the eyepiece lens, but this isn't a problem. All rays passing through the lens converge to (or diverge from) a single point, and the purpose of the special rays is to locate that point. To do so, we can let the special rays refract as they cross the *lens plane,* regardless of whether the physical lens really extends that far. ◀

EXAMPLE 24.1 **A camera lens**

The "lens" on a camera is usually a combination of two or more single lenses. Consider a camera in which light passes first through a diverging lens, with $f_1 = -120$ mm, then a converging lens, with $f_2 = 42$ mm, spaced 60 mm apart. A reasonable definition of the *effective focal length* of this lens combination is the focal length of a *single* lens that could produce an image in the same location if placed at the midpoint of the lens combination. A 10-cm-tall object is 500 mm from the first lens.

a. What are the location, size, and orientation of the image?
b. What is the effective focal length of the double-lens system used in this camera?

MODEL Each lens is a thin lens. The image of the first lens is the object for the second.

VISUALIZE The ray-tracing diagram of FIGURE 24.2 shows the production of a real, inverted image ≈ 55 mm behind the second lens.

Continued

SOLVE

a. $s_1 = 500$ mm is the object distance of the first lens. Its image, a virtual image, is found from the t hin-lens equation:

$$\frac{1}{s_1'} = \frac{1}{f_1} - \frac{1}{s_1} = \frac{1}{-120 \text{ mm}} - \frac{1}{500 \text{ mm}} = -0.0103 \text{ mm}^{-1}$$

$$s_1' = -97 \text{ mm}$$

This is consistent with the ray-tracing diagram. The image of the first lens now acts as the object for the second lens. Because the lenses are 60 mm apart, the object distance is $s_2 = 97$ mm + 60 mm = 157 mm. A second application of the thin-lens equation yields

$$\frac{1}{s_2'} = \frac{1}{f_2} - \frac{1}{s_2} = \frac{1}{42 \text{ mm}} - \frac{1}{157 \text{ mm}} = 0.0174 \text{ mm}^{-1}$$

$$s_2' = 57 \text{ mm}$$

The image of the lens combination is 57 mm behind the second lens. The lateral magnifications of the two lenses are

$$m_1 = -\frac{s_1'}{s_1} = -\frac{-97 \text{ cm}}{500 \text{ cm}} = 0.194$$

$$m_2 = -\frac{s_2'}{s_2} = -\frac{57 \text{ cm}}{157 \text{ cm}} = -0.363$$

The second lens magnifies the image of the first lens, which magnifies the object, so **the total magnification is the product of the individual magnifications:**

$$m = m_1 m_2 = -0.070$$

Thus the image is 57 mm behind the second lens, inverted (m is negative), and 0.70 cm tall.

b. If a single lens midway between these two lenses produced an image in the same plane, its object and image distances would be $s = 500$ mm + 30 mm = 530 mm and $s' = 57$ mm + 30 mm = 87 mm. A final application of the thin-lens equation gives the effective focal length:

$$\frac{1}{f_{\text{eff}}} = \frac{1}{s} + \frac{1}{s'} = \frac{1}{530 \text{ mm}} + \frac{1}{87 \text{ mm}} = 0.0134 \text{ mm}^{-1}$$

$$f_{\text{eff}} = 75 \text{ mm}$$

ASSESS This combination lens would be sold as a "75 mm lens."

FIGURE 24.2 Pictorial representation of a combination lens.

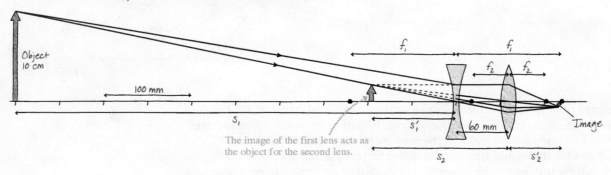

The image of the first lens acts as the object for the second lens.

STOP TO THINK 24.1   The second lens in this optical instrument

a. Causes the light rays to focus closer than they would with the first lens acting alone.
b. Causes the light rays to focus farther away than they would with the first lens acting alone.
c. Inverts the image but does not change where the light rays focus.
d. Prevents the light rays from reaching a focus.

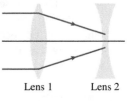

24.2 The Camera

A **camera,** shown in FIGURE 24.3, "takes a picture" by using a lens to form a real, inverted image on a light-sensitive detector in a light-tight box. Film was the detector of choice for well over a hundred years, but today's digital cameras use an electronic detector called a *charge-coupled device,* or CCD.

FIGURE 24.3 A camera.

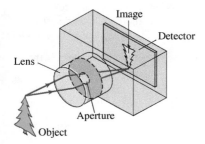

The camera "lens" is always a combination of two or more individual lenses. The simplest such lens, shown in FIGURE 24.4, consists of a converging lens and a somewhat weaker diverging lens. This combination of positive and negative lenses corrects some of the defects inherent in single lenses, as we'll discuss later in the chapter. As Example 24.1 suggested, we can model a combination lens as a single lens with an **effective focal length** (usually called simply "the focal length") f. A *zoom lens* changes the effective focal length by changing the spacing between the converging lens and the diverging lens; this is what happens when the lens barrel on your digital camera moves in and out as you use the zoom. A typical digital camera has a lens whose effective focal length can be varied from 6 mm to 18 mm, giving, as we'll see, a 3× zoom.

FIGURE 24.4 A simple camera lens is a combination lens.

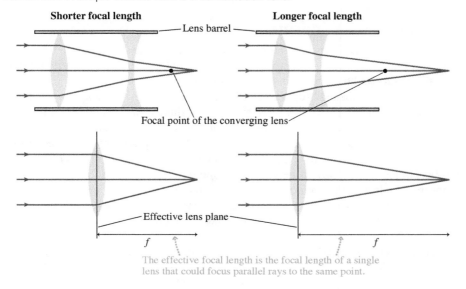

A camera must carry out two important functions: focus the image on the detector and control the exposure. Cameras are focused by moving the lens forward or backward until the image is well focused on the detector. Most modern cameras do this automatically, but older cameras required manual focusing.

EXAMPLE 24.2 **Focusing a camera**

Your digital camera lens, with an effective focal length of 10.0 mm, is focused on a flower 20.0 cm away. You then turn to take a picture of a distant landscape. How far, and in which direction, must the lens move to bring the landscape into focus?

MODEL Model the camera's combination lens as a single thin lens with $f = 10.0$ mm. Image and object distances are measured from the effective lens plane. Assume all the lenses in the combination move together as the camera refocuses.

SOLVE The flower is at object distance $s = 20.0$ cm $= 200$ mm. When the camera is focused, the image distance between the effective lens plane and the detector is found by solving the thin-lens equation $1/s + 1/s' = 1/f$ to give

$$s' = \left(\frac{1}{f} - \frac{1}{s}\right)^{-1} = \left(\frac{1}{10.0 \text{ mm}} - \frac{1}{200 \text{ mm}}\right)^{-1} = 10.5 \text{ mm}$$

The distant landscape is effectively at object distance $s = \infty$, so its image distance is $s' = f = 10.0$ mm. To refocus as you shift scenes, the lens must move 0.5 mm closer to the detector.

ASSESS The required motion of the lens is very small, about the diameter of the lead used in a mechanical pencil.

Zoom Lenses

For objects more than 10 focal lengths from the lens (roughly $s > 20$ cm for a typical digital camera), the approximation $s \gg f$ (and thus $1/s \ll 1/f$) leads to $s' \approx f$. In other words, objects more than about 10 focal lengths away are essentially "at infinity," and we know that the parallel rays from an infinitely distant object are focused one focal length behind the lens. For such an object, the lateral magnification of the image is

$$m = -\frac{s'}{s} \approx -\frac{f}{s} \qquad (24.1)$$

The magnification is much less than 1, because $s \gg f$, so the image on the detector is much smaller than the object itself. This comes as no surprise. More important, **the size of the image is directly proportional to the focal length of the lens.** We saw in Figure 24.4 that the effective focal length of a combination lens is easily changed by varying the distance between the individual lenses, and this is exactly how a zoom lens works. A lens that can be varied from $f_{min} = 6$ mm to $f_{max} = 18$ mm gives magnifications spanning a factor of 3, and that is why you see it specified as a 3× zoom lens.

Controlling the Exposure

The camera also must control the amount of light reaching the detector. Too little light results in photos that are *underexposed;* too much light gives *overexposed* pictures. Both the shutter and the lens diameter help control the exposure.

The *shutter* is "opened" for a selected amount of time as the image is recorded. Older cameras used a spring-loaded mechanical shutter that literally opened and closed; digital cameras electronically control the amount of time the detector is active. Either way, the exposure—the amount of light captured by the detector—is directly proportional to the time the shutter is open. Typical exposure times range from 1/1000 s or less for a sunny scene to 1/30 s or more for dimly lit or indoor scenes. The exposure time is generally referred to as the *shutter speed.*

The amount of light passing through the lens is controlled by an adjustable **aperture,** also called an *iris* because it functions much like the iris of your eye. The aperture sets the effective diameter D of the lens. The full area of the lens is used when the aperture is fully open, but a *stopped-down* aperture allows light to pass through only the central portion of the lens.

The light intensity on the detector is directly proportional to the area of the lens; a lens with twice as much area will collect and focus twice as many light rays from the object to make an image twice as bright. The lens area is proportional to the square of its diameter, so the intensity I is proportional to D^2. The light intensity—power per square meter—is also *inversely* proportional to the area of the image. That is, the light reaching the detector is more intense if the rays collected from the object are focused into a small area than if they are spread out over a large area. The lateral size of the image is proportional to the focal length of the lens, as we saw in Equation 24.1, so the *area* of the image is proportional to f^2 and thus I is proportional to $1/f^2$. Altogether, $I \propto D^2/f^2$.

By long tradition, the light-gathering ability of a lens is specified by its **f-number,** defined as

$$f\text{-number} = \frac{f}{D} \qquad (24.2)$$

The *f*-number of a lens may be written either as *f*/4.0, to mean that the *f*-number is 4.0, or as F4.0. The instruction manuals with some digital cameras call this the *aperture value* rather than the *f*-number. A digital camera in fully automatic mode does not display shutter speed or *f*-number, but that information is displayed if you set your camera to any of the other modes. For example, the display 1/125 F5.6 means that your camera is going to achieve the correct exposure by adjusting the diameter of the lens aperture to give *f*/D = 5.6 and by opening the shutter for 1/125 s. If your lens's effective focal length is 10 mm, the diameter of the lens aperture will be

$$D = \frac{f}{f\text{-number}} = \frac{10 \text{ mm}}{5.6} = 1.8 \text{ mm}$$

An iris can change the effective diameter of a lens and thus the amount of light reaching the detector.

NOTE ▶ The f in f-number is not the focal length f; it's just a name. And the / in $f/4$ does not mean division; it's just a notation. These both derive from the long history of photography. ◀

Because the aperture diameter is in the denominator of the f-number, a *larger-diameter* aperture, which gathers more light and makes a brighter image, has a *smaller* f-number. The light intensity on the detector is related to the lens's f-number by

$$I \propto \frac{D^2}{f^2} = \frac{1}{(f\text{-number})^2} \tag{24.3}$$

Historically, a lens's f-numbers could be adjusted in the sequence 2.0, 2.8, 4.0, 5.8, 8.0, 11, 16. Each differs from its neighbor by a factor of $\sqrt{2}$, so changing the lens by one "f stop" changed the light intensity by a factor of 2. A modern digital camera is able to adjust the f-number continuously.

The exposure, the total light reaching the detector while the shutter is open, depends on the product $I\Delta t_{\text{shutter}}$. A small f-number (large aperture diameter D) and short $\Delta t_{\text{shutter}}$ can produce the same exposure as a larger f-number (smaller aperture) and a longer $\Delta t_{\text{shutter}}$. It might not make any difference for taking a picture of a distant mountain, but action photography needs very short shutter times to "freeze" the action. Thus action photography requires a large-diameter lens with a small f-number.

Focal length and f-number information is stamped on a camera lens. This lens is labeled 5.8–23.2 mm 1:2.6–5.5. The first numbers are the range of focal lengths. They span a factor of 4, so this is a 4× zoom lens. The second numbers show that the minimum f-number ranges from $f/2.6$ (for the $f = 5.8$ mm focal length) to $f/5.5$ (for the $f = 23.2$ mm focal length).

EXAMPLE 24.3 **Capturing the action**

Before a race, a photographer finds that she can make a perfectly exposed photo of the track while using a shutter speed of 1/250 s and a lens setting of $f/8.0$. To freeze the sprinters as they go past, she plans to use a shutter speed of 1/1000 s. To what f-number must she set her lens?

MODEL The exposure depends on $I\Delta t_{\text{shutter}}$, and the light intensity depends inversely on the square of the f-number.

SOLVE Changing the shutter speed from 1/250 s to 1/1000 s will reduce the light reaching the detector by a factor of 4. To compensate, she needs to let 4 times as much light through the lens. Because $I \propto 1/(f\text{-number})^2$, the intensity will increase by a factor of 4 if she *decreases* the f-number by a factor of 2. Thus the correct lens setting is $f/4.0$.

ASSESS To keep the photo properly exposed, a decreased shutter time must be balanced by an increased lens aperture diameter.

The Detector

For traditional cameras, the light-sensitive detector is film. Today's digital cameras use an electronic light-sensitive surface called a *charge-coupled device* or **CCD**. A CCD consists of a rectangular array of many millions of small detectors called **pixels.** When light hits one of these pixels, it generates an electric charge proportional to the light intensity. Thus an image is recorded on the CCD in terms of little packets of charge. After the CCD has been exposed, the charges are read out, the signal levels are digitized, and the picture is stored in the digital memory of the camera.

FIGURE 24.5a shows a CCD "chip" and, schematically, the magnified appearance of the pixels on its surface. To record color information, different pixels are covered by red, green, or blue filters. A pixel covered by a green filter, for instance, records only the intensity of the green light hitting it. Later, the camera's microprocessor interpolates nearby colors to give each pixel an overall true color. The pixels are so small that the picture looks "smooth" even after some enlargement, but, as you can see in FIGURE 24.5b, sufficient magnification reveals the individual pixels.

FIGURE 24.5 The CCD detector used in a digital camera.

(a)   2500 × 2000 pixels

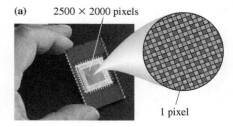

1 pixel

(b)

STOP TO THINK 24.2 A photographer has adjusted his camera for a correct exposure with a short-focal-length lens. He then decides to zoom in by increasing the focal length. To maintain a correct exposure without changing the shutter speed, the diameter of the lens aperture should

a. Be increased.   b. Be decreased.   c. Stay the same.

24.3 Vision

The human eye is a marvelous and intricate organ. If we leave the biological details to biologists and focus on the eye's optical properties, we find that it functions very much like a camera. Like a camera, the eye has refracting surfaces that focus incoming light rays, an adjustable iris to control the light intensity, and a light-sensitive detector.

FIGURE 24.6 shows the basic structure of the eye. It is roughly spherical, about 2.4 cm in diameter. The transparent **cornea,** which is somewhat more sharply curved, and the *lens* are the eye's refractive elements. The eye is filled with a clear, jellylike fluid called the *aqueous humor* (in front of the lens) and the *vitreous humor* (behind the lens). The indices of refraction of the aqueous and vitreous humors are 1.34, only slightly different from water. The lens, although not uniform, has an average index of 1.44. The **pupil,** a variable-diameter aperture in the **iris,** automatically opens and closes to control the light intensity. A fully dark-adapted eye can open to ≈ 8 mm, and the pupil closes down to ≈ 1.5 mm in bright sun. This corresponds to *f*-numbers from roughly *f*/3 to *f*/16, very similar to a camera.

FIGURE 24.6 The human eye.

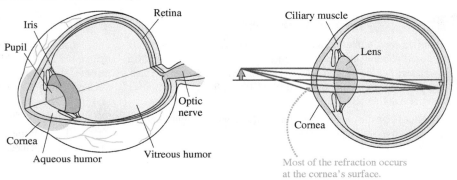

The eye's detector, the **retina,** consists of specialized light-sensitive cells called *rods* and *cones.* The rods, sensitive mostly to light and dark, are most important in very dim lighting. Color vision, which requires somewhat more light, is due to the cones, of which there are three types. FIGURE 24.7 shows the wavelength responses of the cones. They have overlapping ranges, especially the red- and green-sensitive cones, so two or even all three cones respond to light of any particular wavelength. The relative response of the different cones is interpreted by your brain as light of a particular color. Color is a *perception,* a response of our sensory and nervous systems, not something inherent in the light itself. Other animals, with slightly different retinal cells, can see ultraviolet or infrared wavelengths that we cannot see.

FIGURE 24.7 Wavelength sensitivity of the three types of cones in the human retina.

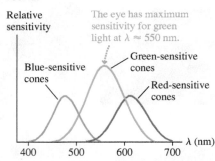

Focusing and Accommodation

The eye, like a camera, focuses light rays to an inverted image on the retina. Perhaps surprisingly, most of the refractive power of the eye is due to the cornea, not the lens. The cornea is a sharply curved, spherical surface, and you learned in Chapter 23 that images are formed by refraction at a spherical surface. The rather large difference between the index of refraction of air and that of the aqueous humor causes a significant refraction of light rays at the cornea. In contrast, there is much less difference between the indices of the lens and its surrounding fluid, so refraction at the lens surfaces is weak. The lens is important for fine-tuning, but the air-cornea boundary is responsible for the majority of the refraction.

You can recognize the power of the cornea if you open your eyes underwater. Everything is very blurry! When light enters the cornea through water, rather than through air, there's almost no difference in the indices of refraction at the surface. Light rays pass through the cornea with almost no refraction, so what little focusing ability you have while underwater is due to the lens alone.

A camera focuses by moving the lens. The eye focuses by changing the focal length of the lens, a feat it accomplishes by using the *ciliary muscles* to change the curvature of the lens surface. The ciliary muscles are relaxed when you look at a distant scene. Thus the lens surface is relatively flat and the lens has its longest focal length. As you shift your gaze to a nearby object, the ciliary muscles contract and cause the lens to bulge. This process, called **accommodation,** decreases the lens's radius of curvature and thus decreases its focal length.

The farthest distance at which a relaxed eye can focus is called the eye's **far point** (FP). The far point of a normal eye is infinity; that is, the eye can focus on objects extremely far away. The closest distance at which an eye can focus, using maximum accommodation, is the eye's **near point** (NP). (Objects can be *seen* closer than the near point, but they're not sharply focused on the retina.) Both situations are shown in FIGURE 24.8.

FIGURE 24.8 Normal vision of far and near objects.

The ciliary muscles are relaxed for distant vision.

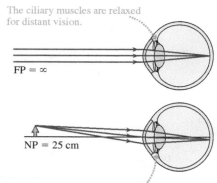

FP = ∞

NP = 25 cm

The ciliary muscles are contracted for near vision, causing the lens to curve more.

Vision Defects and Their Correction

The near point of normal vision is considered to be 25 cm, but the near point of any individual changes with age. The near point of young children can be as little as 10 cm. The "normal" 25 cm near point is characteristic of young adults, but the near point of most individuals begins to move outward by age 40 or 45 and can reach 200 cm by age 60. This loss of accommodation, which arises because the lens loses flexibility, is called **presbyopia.** Even if their vision is otherwise normal, individuals with presbyopia need reading glasses to bring their near point back to 25 or 30 cm, a comfortable distance for reading.

Presbyopia is known as a *refractive error* of the eye. Two other common refractive errors are *hyperopia* and *myopia.* All three can be corrected with lenses—either eyeglasses or contact lenses—that assist the eye's focusing. Corrective lenses are prescribed not by their focal length but by their **power.** The power of a lens is the inverse of its focal length:

$$\text{Power of a lens} = P = \frac{1}{f} \qquad (24.4)$$

A lens with more power (shorter focal length) causes light rays to refract through a larger angle. The SI unit of lens power is the **diopter,** abbreviated D, defined as $1 \text{ D} = 1 \text{ m}^{-1}$. Thus a lens with $f = 50 \text{ cm} = 0.50 \text{ m}$ has power $P = 2.0 \text{ D}$.

A person who is *farsighted* can see faraway objects (but even then must use some accommodation rather than a relaxed eye), but his near point is larger than 25 cm, often much larger, so he cannot focus on nearby objects. The cause of farsightedness—called **hyperopia**—is an eyeball that is too short for the refractive power of the cornea and lens. As FIGURES 24.9a and b on the next page show, no amount of accommodation allows the eye to focus on an object 25 cm away, the normal near point.

With hyperopia, the eye needs assistance to focus the rays from a near object onto the closer-than-normal retina. This assistance is obtained by adding refractive power with the positive (i.e., converging) lens shown in FIGURE 24.9c. To understand why this works, recall that the image of a first lens acts as the object for a second lens. The goal is to allow the person to focus on an object 25 cm away. If a corrective lens forms an upright, virtual image at the person's actual near point, that virtual image acts as an object for the eye itself and, with maximum accommodation, the eye can focus these rays onto the retina. Presbyopia, the loss of accommodation with age, is corrected in the same way.

The optometrist's prescription is −2.25 D for the right eye (top) and −2.50 D for the left (bottom), the minus sign indicating that these are diverging lenses. The optometrist doesn't write the D because the lens maker already knows that prescriptions are in diopters. Most people's eyes are not exactly the same, so each eye usually gets a different lens.

FIGURE 24.9 Hyperopia.

(a)

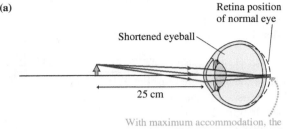

Shortened eyeball

Retina position
of normal eye

25 cm

With maximum accommodation, the
eye tries to focus the image behind the
actual retina. Thus the image is blurry.

(b)

Maximum accommodation

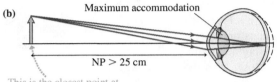

NP > 25 cm

This is the closest point at
which the eye can focus.

(c)

This is the actual object the
eye wants to see.

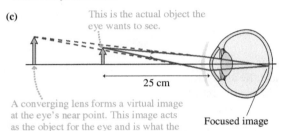

25 cm

A converging lens forms a virtual image
at the eye's near point. This image acts
as the object for the eye and is what the
eye actually focuses on.

Focused image

FIGURE 24.10 Myopia.

(a)

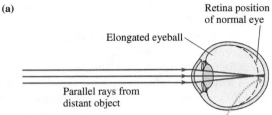

Elongated eyeball

Retina position
of normal eye

Parallel rays from
distant object

A fully relaxed eye focuses the image in front
of the actual retina. The image is blurry.

(b)

Fully relaxed

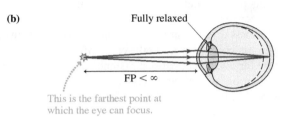

FP < ∞

This is the farthest point at
which the eye can focus.

(c)

The eye wants to see
a distant object.

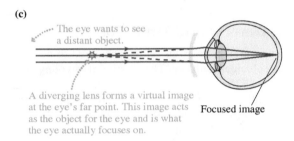

A diverging lens forms a virtual image
at the eye's far point. This image acts
as the object for the eye and is what
the eye actually focuses on.

Focused image

NOTE ▶ Figures 24.9 and 24.10 show the corrective lenses as they are actually shaped—called *meniscus lenses*—rather than with our usual lens shape. Nonetheless, the lens in Figure 24.9c is a converging lens because it's thicker in the center than at the edges. The lens in Figure 24.10c is a diverging lens because it's thicker at the edges than in the center. ◀

A person who is *nearsighted* can clearly see nearby objects when the eye is relaxed (and extremely close objects by using accommodation), but no amount of relaxation allows her to see distant objects. Nearsightedness—called **myopia**—is caused by an eyeball that is too long. As FIGURE 24.10a shows, rays from a distant object come to a focus in front of the retina and have begun to diverge by the time they reach the retina. The eye's far point, shown in FIGURE 24.10b, is less than infinity.

To correct myopia, we needed a diverging lens, as shown in FIGURE 24.10c, to slightly defocus the rays and move the image point back to the retina. To focus on a very distant object, the person needs a corrective lens that forms an upright, virtual image at her actual far point. That virtual image acts as an object for the eye itself and, when fully relaxed, the eye can focus these rays onto the retina.

EXAMPLE 24.4 **Correcting hyperopia**

Sanjay has hyperopia. The near point of his left eye is 150 cm. What prescription lens will restore normal vision?

MODEL Normal vision will allow Sanjay to focus on an object 25 cm away. In measuring distances, we'll ignore the small space between the lens and his eye.

SOLVE Because Sanjay can see objects at 150 cm, using maximum accommodation, we want a lens that creates a virtual image

at position $s' = -150$ cm (negative because it's a virtual image) of an object held at $s = 25$ cm. From the thin-lens equation,

$$\frac{1}{f} = \frac{1}{s} + \frac{1}{s'} = \frac{1}{0.25 \text{ m}} + \frac{1}{-1.50 \text{ m}} = 3.3 \text{ m}^{-1}$$

$1/f$ is the lens power, and m^{-1} are diopters. Thus the prescription is for a lens with power $P = 3.3$ D.

ASSESS Hyperopia is always corrected with a converging lens.

EXAMPLE 24.5 **Correcting myopia**

Martina has myopia. The far point of her left eye is 200 cm. What prescription lens will restore normal vision?

MODEL Normal vision will allow Martina to focus on a very distant object. In measuring distances, we'll ignore the small space between the lens and her eye.

SOLVE Because Martina can see objects at 200 cm with a fully relaxed eye, we want a lens that will create a virtual image at position $s' = -200$ cm (negative because it's a virtual image) of a distant object at $s = \infty$ cm. From the thin-lens equation,

$$\frac{1}{f} = \frac{1}{s} + \frac{1}{s'} = \frac{1}{\infty \text{ m}} + \frac{1}{-2.0 \text{ m}} = -0.5 \text{ m}^{-1}$$

Thus the prescription is for a lens with power $P = -0.5$ D.

ASSESS Myopia is always corrected with a diverging lens.

STOP TO THINK 24.3 You need to improvise a magnifying glass to read some very tiny print. Should you borrow the eyeglasses from your hyperopic friend or from your myopic friend?

a. The hyperopic friend
b. The myopic friend
c. Either will do.
d. Neither will work.

24.4 Optical Systems That Magnify

The camera, with its fast shutter speed, allows us to capture images of events that take place too quickly for our unaided eye to resolve. Another use of optical systems is to magnify—to see objects smaller or closer together than our eye can see.

The easiest way to magnify an object requires no extra optics at all; simply get closer! The closer you get, the bigger the object appears. Obviously the actual size of the object is unchanged as you approach it, so what exactly is getting "bigger"? Consider the green arrow in FIGURE 24.11a. We can determine the size of its image on the retina by tracing the ray that is undeviated as it passes through the center of a lens. (Here we're modeling the eye's optical system as one thin lens.) If we get closer to the arrow, now shown as red, we find the arrow makes a larger image on the retina. Our brain interprets the larger image as a larger-appearing object. The object's actual size doesn't change, but its *apparent size* gets larger as it gets closer.

Technically, we say that closer objects look larger because they subtend a larger angle θ, called the **angular size** of the object. The red arrow has a larger angular size than the green arrow, $\theta_2 > \theta_1$, so the red arrow looks larger and we can see more detail. But you can't keep increasing an object's angular size because you can't focus on the object if it's closer than your near point, which we'll take to be a normal 25 cm. FIGURE 24.11b defines the angular size θ_{NP} of an object at your near point. If the object's height is h and if we assume the small-angle approximation $\tan \theta \approx \theta$, the maximum angular size viewable by your unaided eye is

$$\theta_{NP} = \frac{h}{25 \text{ cm}} \tag{24.5}$$

Suppose we view the same object, of height h, through the single converging lens in FIGURE 24.12 on the next page. If the object's distance from the lens is less than the lens's focal length, we'll see an enlarged, upright image. Used in this way, the lens is called a **magnifier** or *magnifying glass*. The eye sees the virtual image subtending angle θ, and it can focus on this virtual image as long as the image distance is more than 25 cm. Within the small-angle approximation, the image subtends angle $\theta = h/s$. In practice, we usually want the image to be at distance $s' \approx \infty$ so that we can view it with a relaxed eye as a "distant object." This will be true if the object is very near the focal point: $s \approx f$. In this case, the image subtends angle

$$\theta = \frac{h}{s} \approx \frac{h}{f} \tag{24.6}$$

FIGURE 24.11 Angular size.

(a) Same object at two different distances

As the object gets closer, the angle it subtends becomes larger. Its *angular size* has increased.

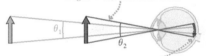

Further, the size of the image on the retina gets larger. The object's *apparent size* has increased.

(b)

h θ_{NP}

25 cm

Near point

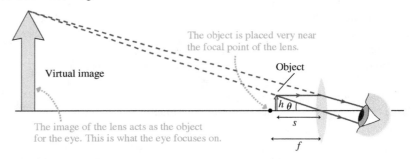

FIGURE 24.12 The magnifier.

Virtual image

The object is placed very near the focal point of the lens.

Object

The image of the lens acts as the object for the eye. This is what the eye focuses on.

Let's define the **angular magnification** M as

$$M = \frac{\theta}{\theta_{NP}} \tag{24.7}$$

Angular magnification is the increase in the *apparent size* of the object that you achieve by using a magnifying lens rather than simply holding the object at your near point. Substituting from Equations 24.5 and 24.6, we find the angular magnification of a magnifying glass is

$$M = \frac{25 \text{ cm}}{f} \tag{24.8}$$

The angular magnification depends on the focal length of the lens but not on the size of the object. Although it would appear we could increase angular magnification without limit by using lenses with shorter and shorter focal lengths, the inherent limitations of lenses we discuss in the next section limit the magnification of a simple lens to about 4×. Slightly more complex magnifiers with two lenses reach 20×, but beyond that one would use a microscope.

NOTE ▶ Don't confuse angular magnification with lateral magnification. Lateral magnification m compares the height of an object to the height of its image. The lateral magnification of a magnifying glass is $\approx \infty$ because the virtual image is at $s' \approx \infty$, but that doesn't make the object seem infinitely big. Its apparent size is determined by the angle subtended on your retina, and that angle remains finite. Thus angular magnification tells us how much bigger things appear. ◀

The Microscope

A microscope, whose major parts are shown in FIGURE 24.13a, can attain a magnification of up to 1000× by a *two-step* magnification process. A specimen to be observed is placed on the *stage* of the microscope, directly beneath the **objective,** a converging lens with a relatively short focal length. The objective creates a magnified real image that is further enlarged by the **eyepiece.** Both the objective and the eyepiece are complex combination lenses, but we'll model them as single thin lenses. It's common for a prism to bend the rays so that the eyepiece is at a comfortable viewing angle. However, we'll consider a simplified version of a microscope in which the light travels along a straight tube.

FIGURE 24.13b shows the optics in more detail. The object is placed just outside the focal point of the objective, which then creates a highly magnified real image with lateral magnification $m = -s'/s$. The object is so close to the focal point that $s \approx f_{obj}$ is an excellent approximation. In addition, the focal lengths of the objective and the eyepiece are much less than the tube length L, so $s' \approx L$ is another good approximation. With these approximations, the lateral magnification of the objective is

$$m_{obj} = -\frac{s'}{s} \approx -\frac{L}{f_{obj}} \tag{24.9}$$

FIGURE 24.13 The microscope.

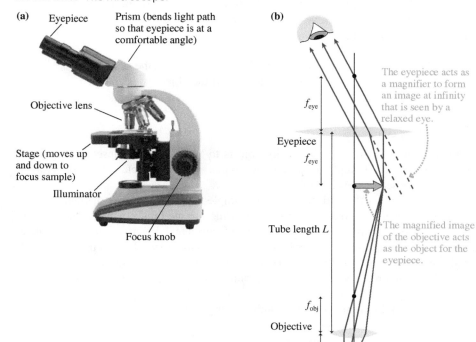

(a)

Eyepiece

Prism (bends light path so that eyepiece is at a comfortable angle)

Objective lens

Stage (moves up and down to focus sample)

Illuminator

Focus knob

(b)

The eyepiece acts as a magnifier to form an image at infinity that is seen by a relaxed eye.

f_{eye}

Eyepiece

f_{eye}

Tube length L

The magnified image of the objective acts as the object for the eyepiece.

f_{obj}

Objective

f_{obj}

The object is just beyond the focal point.

Object

The image of the objective acts as the object for the eyepiece, which functions as a simple magnifier. The angular magnification of the eyepiece is given by Equation 24.8, $M_{eye} = (25 \text{ cm})/f_{eye}$. Together, the objective and eyepiece produce a total angular magnification

$$M = m_{obj}M_{eye} = -\frac{L}{f_{obj}}\frac{25 \text{ cm}}{f_{eye}} \qquad (24.10)$$

The minus sign shows that the image seen in a microscope is inverted.

In practice, the magnifications of the objective (without the minus sign) and the eyepiece are stamped on the barrels. A set of objectives on a rotating turret might include 10×, 20×, 40×, and 100×. When combined with a 10× eyepiece, the microscope's total angular magnification ranges from 100× to 1000×. In addition, most biological microscopes are standardized with a tube length $L = 160$ mm. Thus a 40× objective has focal length $f_{obj} = 160$ mm/40 = 4.0 mm.

EXAMPLE 24.6 **Viewing blood cells**

A pathologist inspects a sample of 7-μm-diameter human blood cells under a microscope. She selects a 40× objective and a 10× eyepiece. What size object, viewed from 25 cm, has the same apparent size as a blood cell seen through the microscope?

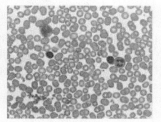

MODEL Angular magnification compares the magnified angular size to the angular size seen at the near-point distance of 25 cm.

SOLVE The microscope's angular magnification is $M = -(40) \times (10) = -400$. The magnified cells will have the same apparent size as an object $400 \times 7\ \mu$m $\approx$ 3 mm in diameter seen from a distance of 25 cm.

ASSESS 3 mm is about the size of a capital O in this textbook, so a blood cell seen through the microscope will have about the same apparent size as an O seen from a comfortable reading distance.

STOP TO THINK 24.4 A biologist rotates the turret of a microscope to replace a 20× objective with a 10× objective. To keep the same overall magnification, the focal length of the eyepiece must be

a. Doubled. b. Halved. c. Kept the same.
d. The magnification cannot be kept the same if the objective is changed.

The Telescope

A microscope magnifies small, nearby objects to look large. A telescope magnifies distant objects, which might be quite large, so that we can see details that are blended together when seen by eye.

FIGURE 24.14 shows the optical layout of a simple telescope. A large-diameter objective lens (larger lenses collect more light and thus can see fainter objects) collects the parallel rays from a distant object ($s = \infty$) and forms a real, inverted image at distance $s' = f_{obj}$. Unlike a microscope, which uses a short-focal-length objective, the focal length of a telescope objective is very nearly the length of the telescope tube. Then, just as in the microscope, the eyepiece functions as a simple magnifier. The viewer observes an inverted image, but that's not a serious problem in astronomy. Terrestrial telescopes use a different design to obtain an upright image.

FIGURE 24.14 A refracting telescope.

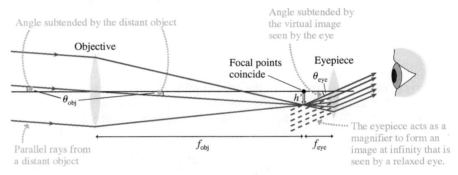

Suppose the distant object, as seen by the objective lens, subtends angle θ_{obj}. If the image seen through the eyepiece subtends a larger angle θ_{eye}, then the angular magnification is $M = \theta_{eye}/\theta_{obj}$. We can see from the undeviated ray passing through the center of the objective lens that (using the small-angle approximation)

$$\theta_{obj} \approx -\frac{h'}{f_{obj}}$$

where the minus sign indicates the inverted image. The image of height h' acts as the object for the eyepiece, and we can see that the final image observed by the viewer subtends angle

$$\theta_{eye} = \frac{h'}{f_{eye}}$$

Consequently, the angular magnification of a telescope is

$$M = \frac{\theta_{eye}}{\theta_{obj}} = -\frac{f_{obj}}{f_{eye}} \tag{24.11}$$

The angular magnification is simply the ratio of the objective focal length to the eyepiece focal length.

Because the stars and galaxies are so distant, light-gathering power is more important to astronomers than magnification. Large light-gathering power requires a large-diameter objective lens, but large lenses are not practical; they begin to sag under their own weight. Thus **refracting telescopes,** with two lenses, are relatively small. Serious astronomy is done with a **reflecting telescope,** such as the one shown in FIGURE 24.15.

A large-diameter mirror (the *primary mirror*) focuses the rays to form a real image, but, for practical reasons, a small flat mirror (the *secondary mirror*) reflects the rays sideways before they reach a focus. This moves the primary mirror's image out to the edge of the telescope where it can be viewed by an eyepiece on the side. None of these changes affects the overall analysis of the telescope, and its angular magnification is given by Equation 24.11 if f_{obj} is replaced by f_{pri}, the focal length of the primary mirror.

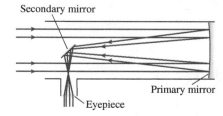

FIGURE 24.15 A reflecting telescope.

Secondary mirror

Primary mirror

Eyepiece

24.5 The Resolution of Optical Instruments

A camera *could* focus light with a single lens. A microscope objective *could* be built with a single lens. So why would anyone ever use a lens combination in place of a single lens? There are two primary reasons.

First, any lens has dispersion. That is, its index of refraction varies slightly with wavelength. Because the index of refraction for violet light is larger than for red light, a lens's focal length is shorter for violet light than for red light. Consequently, different colors of light come to a focus at slightly different distances from the lens. If red light is sharply focused on a viewing screen, then blue and violet wavelengths are not well focused. This imaging error, illustrated in FIGURE 24.16a, is called **chromatic aberration.**

Second, our analysis of thin lenses was based on paraxial rays traveling nearly parallel to the optical axis. A more exact analysis, taking all the rays into account, finds that rays incident on the outer edges of a spherical surface are not focused at exactly the same point as rays incident near the center. This imaging error, shown in FIGURE 24.16b, is called **spherical aberration.** Spherical aberration, which causes the image to be slightly blurred, gets worse as the lens diameter increases.

FIGURE 24.16 Chromatic aberration and spherical aberration prevent simple lenses from forming perfect images.

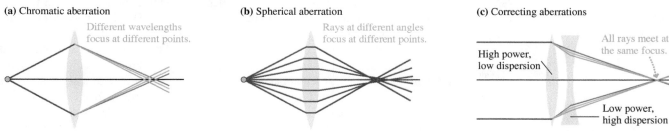

(a) Chromatic aberration

Different wavelengths focus at different points.

(b) Spherical aberration

Rays at different angles focus at different points.

(c) Correcting aberrations

High power, low dispersion

All rays meet at the same focus.

Low power, high dispersion

Fortunately, the chromatic and spherical aberrations of a converging lens and a diverging lens are in opposite directions. When a converging lens and a diverging lens are used in combination, their aberrations tend to cancel. A combination lens, such as the one in FIGURE 24.16c, can produce a much sharper focus than a single lens with the equivalent focal length. Consequently, most optical instruments use combination lenses rather than single lenses.

Diffraction Again

According to the ray model of light, a perfect lens (one with no aberrations) should be able to form a perfect image. But the ray model of light, though a very good model for lenses, is not an absolutely correct description of light. If we look closely, the wave aspects of light haven't entirely disappeared. In fact, the performance of optical equipment is limited by the diffraction of light.

FIGURE 24.17 A lens both focuses and diffracts the light passing through.

(a) A lens acts as a circular aperture.

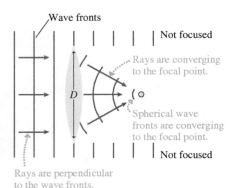

Wave fronts

Not focused

Rays are converging to the focal point.

D

Spherical wave fronts are converging to the focal point.

Not focused

Rays are perpendicular to the wave fronts.

(b) The aperture and focusing effects can be separated.

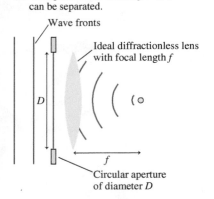

Wave fronts

Ideal diffractionless lens with focal length f

D

f

Circular aperture of diameter D

(c) The lens focuses the diffraction pattern in the focal plane.

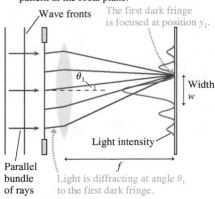

Wave fronts

The first dark fringe is focused at position y_1.

θ_1

Width w

Light intensity

Parallel bundle of rays

f

Light is diffracting at angle θ_1 to the first dark fringe.

FIGURE 24.17a shows a plane wave, with parallel light rays, being focused by a lens of diameter D. According to the ray model of light, a perfect lens would focus parallel rays to a perfect point. Notice, though, that only a piece of each wave front passes *through* the lens and gets focused. In effect, **the lens itself acts as a circular aperture** in an opaque barrier, allowing through only a portion of each wave front. Consequently, **the lens diffracts the light wave.** The diffraction is usually very small because D is usually much greater than the wavelength of the light; nonetheless, this small amount of diffraction is the limiting factor in how well the lens can focus the light.

FIGURE 24.17b separates the diffraction from the focusing by modeling the lens as an actual aperture of diameter D followed by an "ideal" diffractionless lens. You learned in Chapter 22 that a circular aperture produces a diffraction pattern with a bright central maximum surrounded by dimmer fringes. A converging lens brings this diffraction pattern to a focus in the image plane, as shown in **FIGURE 24.17c**. As a result, a perfect lens focuses parallel light rays not to a perfect point of light, as we expected, but to a small, circular diffraction pattern.

The angle to the first minimum of a circular diffraction pattern is $\theta_1 = 1.22\lambda/D$. The ray that passes through the center of a lens is not bent, so Figure 24.17c uses this ray to show that the position of the dark fringe is $y_1 = f\tan\theta_1 \approx f\theta_1$. Thus the width of the central maximum in the focal plane is

$$w_{min} \approx 2f\theta_1 = \frac{2.44\lambda f}{D} \qquad \text{(minimum spot size)} \qquad (24.12)$$

This is the **minimum spot size** to which a lens can focus light.

Lenses are often limited by aberrations, so not all lenses can focus parallel light rays to a spot this small. A well-crafted lens, for which Equation 24.12 is the minimum spot size, is called a *diffraction-limited lens*. No optical design can overcome the spreading of light due to diffraction, and it is because of this spreading that the image point has a minimum spot size. The image of an actual object, rather than of parallel rays, becomes a mosaic of overlapping diffraction patterns, so even the most perfect lens inevitably forms an image that is slightly fuzzy.

For various reasons, it is difficult to produce a diffraction-limited lens having a focal length that is much less than its diameter. The very best microscope objectives have $f \approx 0.5D$. This implies that **the smallest diameter to which you can focus a spot of light, no matter how hard you try, is $w_{min} \approx \lambda$.** This is a fundamental limit on the performance of optical equipment. Diffraction has very real consequences!

One example of these consequences is found in the manufacturing of integrated circuits. Integrated circuits are made by creating a "mask" showing all the components and their connections. A lens images this mask onto the surface of a semiconductor wafer that has been coated with a substance called *photoresist*. Bright areas in the mask expose the photoresist, and subsequent processing steps chemically etch away the exposed areas while leaving behind areas that had been in the shadows of the mask. This process is called *photolithography*.

The power of a microprocessor and the amount of memory in a memory chip depend on how small the circuit elements can be made. Diffraction dictates that a circuit element can be no smaller than the smallest spot to which light can be focused, which is roughly the wavelength of the light. If the mask is projected with ultraviolet light having $\lambda \approx 200$ nm, then the smallest elements on a chip are about 200 nm wide. This is, in fact, just about the current limit of technology.

EXAMPLE 24.7 | **Seeing stars**

A 12-cm-diameter telescope lens has a focal length of 1.0 m. What is the diameter of the image of a star in the focal plane if the lens is diffraction limited *and* if the earth's atmosphere is not a limitation?

MODEL Stars are so far away that they appear as points in space. An ideal diffractionless lens would focus their light to arbitrarily small points. Diffraction prevents this. Model the telescope lens as a 12-cm-diameter aperture in front of an ideal lens with a 1.0 m focal length.

SOLVE The minimum spot size in the focal plane of this lens is

$$w = \frac{2.44\lambda f}{D}$$

where D is the lens diameter. What is λ? Because stars emit white light, the *longest* wavelengths spread the most and determine the size of the image that is seen. If we use $\lambda = 700$ nm as the approximate upper limit of visible wavelengths, we find $w = 1.4 \times 10^{-5}$ m $= 14$ μm.

ASSESS This is certainly small, and it would appear as a point to your unaided eye. Nonetheless, the spot size would be easily noticed if it were recorded on film and enlarged. Turbulence and temperature effects in the atmosphere, the causes of the "twinkling" of stars, prevent ground-based telescopes from being this good, but space-based telescopes really are diffraction limited.

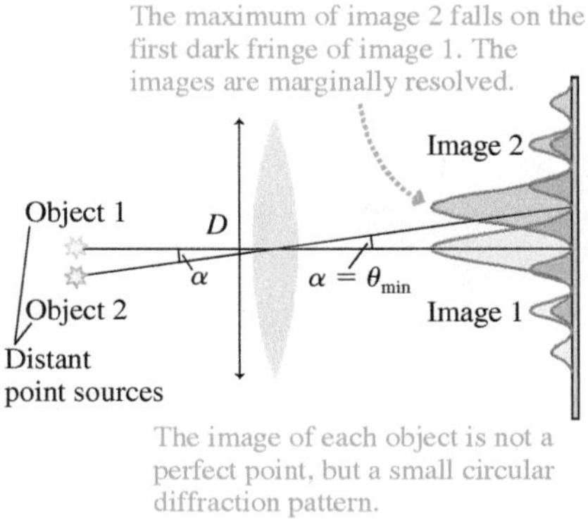

Resolution

Suppose you point a telescope at two nearby stars in a galaxy far, far away. If you use the best possible detector, will you be able to distinguish separate images for the two stars, or will they blur into a single blob of light? A similar question could be asked of a microscope. Can two microscopic objects, very close together, be distinguished if sufficient magnification is used? Or is there some size limit at which their images will blur together and never be separated? These are important questions about the *resolution* of optical instruments.

Because of diffraction, the image of a distant star is not a point but a circular diffraction pattern. Our question, then, really is: How close together can two diffraction patterns be before you can no longer distinguish them? One of the major scientists of the 19th century, Lord Rayleigh, studied this problem and suggested a reasonable rule that today is called **Rayleigh's criterion.**

FIGURE 24.18 shows two distant point sources being imaged by a lens of diameter D. The angular separation between the objects, as seen from the lens, is α. Rayleigh's criterion states that

- The two objects are resolvable if $\alpha > \theta_{min}$, where $\theta_{min} = \theta_1 = 1.22\lambda/D$ is the angle of the first dark fringe in the circular diffraction pattern.
- The two objects are not resolvable if $\alpha < \theta_{min}$ because their diffraction patterns are too overlapped.
- The two objects are marginally resolvable if $\alpha = \theta_{min}$. The central maximum of one image falls exactly on top of the first dark fringe of the other image. This is the situation shown in the figure.

FIGURE 24.19 shows enlarged photographs of the images of two point sources. The images are circular diffraction patterns, not points. The two images are close but distinct where the objects are separated by $\alpha > \theta_{min}$. Two objects really were recorded in the photo at the bottom, but their separation is $\alpha < \theta_{min}$ and their images have blended together. In the middle photo, with $\alpha = \theta_{min}$, you can see that the two images are just barely resolved.

The angle

$$\theta_{min} = \frac{1.22\lambda}{D} \qquad \text{(angular resolution of a lens)} \qquad (24.13)$$

is called the **angular resolution** of a lens. The angular resolution of a telescope depends on the diameter of the objective lens (or the primary mirror) and the wavelength of the light; magnification is not a factor. Two images will remain overlapped and unresolved no matter what the magnification if their angular separation is less than θ_{min}. For visible light, where λ is pretty much fixed, the only parameter over which the astronomer has any control is the diameter of the lens or mirror of the

FIGURE 24.18 Two images that are marginally resolved.

The maximum of image 2 falls on the first dark fringe of image 1. The images are marginally resolved.

Object 1
Object 2
Distant point sources
D
α
$\alpha = \theta_{min}$
Image 2
Image 1

The image of each object is not a perfect point, but a small circular diffraction pattern.

FIGURE 24.19 Enlarged photographs of the images of two point sources.

$\alpha > \theta_{min}$
Resolved

$\alpha = \theta_{min}$
Marginally resolved

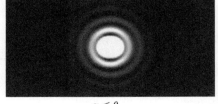

$\alpha < \theta_{min}$
Not resolved

The size of the features in an integrated circuit is limited by the diffraction of light.

telescope. The urge to build ever-larger telescopes is motivated, in part, by a desire to improve the angular resolution. (Another motivation is to increase the light-gathering power so as to see objects farther away.)

The performance of a microscope is also limited by the diffraction of light passing through the objective lens. Just as light cannot be focused to a spot smaller than about a wavelength, the most perfect microscope cannot resolve the features of objects that are smaller than a wavelength. Similarly, two objects separated by less than one wavelength—roughly 500 nm—will blur into a single object and cannot be resolved. Because atoms are approximately 0.1 nm in diameter, vastly smaller than the wavelength of visible or even ultraviolet light, there is no hope of ever seeing atoms with an optical microscope. This limitation is not simply a matter of needing a better design or more precise components; it is a fundamental limit set by the wave nature of the light with which we see.

STOP TO THINK 24.5   Four diffraction-limited lenses focus plane waves of light with the same wavelength λ. Rank in order, from largest to smallest, the spot sizes w_a to w_d.

$f = 10$ mm a $|$ 2 mm

$f = 5$ mm b $|$ 2 mm

$f = 10$ mm c $|$ 4 mm

$f = 24$ mm d $|$ 8 mm

CHALLENGE EXAMPLE 24.8   **Visual acuity**

The normal human eye has maximum visual acuity with a pupil diameter of about 3 mm. For larger pupils, acuity decreases due to increasing aberrations; for smaller pupils, acuity decreases due to increasing diffraction. If your pupil diameter is 2.0 mm, as it would be in bright light, what is the smallest-diameter circle that you should be able to see as a circle, rather than just an unresolved blob, on an eye chart at the standard distance of 20 ft? The index of refraction inside the eye is 1.33.

MODEL Assume that a 2.0-mm-diameter pupil is diffraction limited. Then the angular resolution is given by Rayleigh's criterion. Diffraction increases with wavelength, so the eye's acuity will be affected more by longer wavelengths than by shorter wavelengths. Consequently, assume that the light's wavelength in air is 600 nm.

VISUALIZE Let the diameter of the circle be d. FIGURE 24.20 shows the circle at distance $s = 20$ ft $= 6.1$ m. "Seeing the circle," shown edge-on, requires resolving the top and bottom lines as distinct.

FIGURE 24.20 Viewing a circle of diameter d.

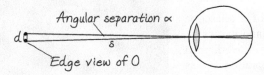

SOLVE The angular separation of the top and bottom lines of the circle is $\alpha = d/s$. Rayleigh's criterion says that a perfect lens with aperture D can just barely resolve these two lines if

$$\alpha = \frac{d}{s} = \theta_{min} = \frac{1.22\lambda_{eye}}{D} = \frac{1.22\lambda_{air}}{n_{eye}D}$$

The diffraction takes place inside the eye, where the wavelength is shortened to $\lambda_{eye} = \lambda_{air}/n_{eye}$. Thus the circle diameter that can barely be resolved with perfect vision is

$$d = \frac{1.22\lambda_{air}s}{n_{eye}D} = \frac{1.22(600 \times 10^{-9}\text{ m})(6.1\text{ m})}{(1.33)(0.0020\text{ m})} \approx 2\text{ mm}$$

That's about the height of a capital O in this book, so in principle you should—in very bright light—just barely be able to recognize it as an O at 20 feet.

ASSESS On an eye chart, the O on the line for 20/20 vision—the standard of excellent vision—is about 7 mm tall, so the calculated 2 mm, although in the right range, is a bit too small. There are three reasons. First, eye tests are done with medium-bright indoor lighting. Your acuity really does improve in light bright enough to reduce your pupil diameter to 2.0 mm. Second, although aberrations of the eye are reduced with a smaller pupil, they haven't vanished. And third, for a 2-mm-tall object at 20 ft, the size of the image on the retina is barely larger than the spacing between the cone cells, so the resolution of the "detector" is also a factor. Your eye is a very good optical instrument, but not perfect.

SUMMARY

The goal of Chapter 24 has been to understand some common optical instruments and their limitations.

Important Concepts

Lens Combinations

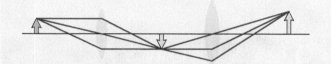

The image of the first lens acts as the object for the second lens.

Lens power: $P = \dfrac{1}{f}$ diopters, 1 D = 1 m^{-1}

Resolution

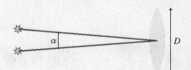

The angular resolution of a lens of diameter D is

$$\theta_{min} = 1.22\lambda/D$$

Rayleigh's criterion states that two objects separated by an angle α are marginally resolvable if $\alpha = \theta_{min}$.

Applications

Cameras

Forms a real, inverted image on a detector. The lens's **f-number** is

$$f\text{-number} = \frac{f}{D}$$

The light intensity on the detector is

$$I \propto \frac{1}{(f\text{-number})^2}$$

Magnifiers

For relaxed-eye viewing, the angular magnification is

$$M = \frac{25 \text{ cm}}{f}$$

For microscopes and telescopes, angular magnification, not lateral magnification, is the important characteristic. The eyepiece acts as a magnifier to view the image formed by the objective lens.

Vision

Refraction at the cornea is responsible for most of the focusing. The lens provides fine-tuning by changing its shape **(accommodation).**

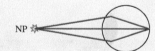

In normal vision, the eye can focus from a far point (FP) at ∞ (relaxed eye) to a near point (NP) at ≈ 25 cm (maximum accommodation).

- **Hyperopia** (farsightedness) is corrected with a converging lens.
- **Myopia** (nearsightedness) is corrected with a diverging lens.

Microscopes

The object is very close to the focal point of the objective. The total angular magnification is

$$M = -\frac{L}{f_{obj}} \frac{25 \text{ cm}}{f_{eye}}$$

The best possible spatial resolution of a microscope, limited by diffraction, is about one wavelength of light.

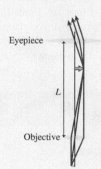

Focusing and spatial resolution

The minimum spot size to which a lens of diameter D can focus light is limited by diffraction to

$$w_{min} = \frac{2.44\lambda f}{D}$$

With the best lenses that can be manufactured, $w_{min} \approx \lambda$.

Telescopes

The object is very far from the objective.

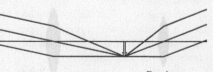

The total angular magnification is $M = -\dfrac{f_{obj}}{f_{eye}}$.

Terms and Notation

camera	iris	hyperopia	reflecting telescope
effective focal length, f	retina	myopia	chromatic aberration
aperture	accommodation	angular size	spherical aberration
f-number	far point	magnifier	minimum spot size, w_{min}
CCD	near point	angular magnification, M	Rayleigh's criterion
pixel	presbyopia	objective	angular resolution
cornea	power, P	eyepiece	
pupil	diopter, D	refracting telescope	

CONCEPTUAL QUESTIONS

1. Suppose a camera's exposure is correct when the lens has a focal length of 8.0 mm. Will the picture be overexposed, underexposed, or still correct if the focal length is "zoomed" to 16.0 mm without changing the diameter of the lens aperture? Explain.
2. A camera has a circular aperture immediately behind the lens. Reducing the aperture diameter to half its initial value will
   A. Make the image blurry.
   B. Cut off the outer half of the image and leave the inner half unchanged.
   C. Make the image less bright.
   D. All the above.
   Explain your choice.
3. Suppose you wanted special glasses designed to let you see underwater without a face mask. Should the glasses use a converging or diverging lens? Explain.
4. A friend lends you the eyepiece of his microscope to use on your own microscope. He claims the spatial resolution of your microscope will be halved, since his eyepiece has the same diameter as yours but twice the magnification. Is his claim valid? Explain.
5. A diffraction-limited lens can focus light to a 10-μm-diameter spot on a screen. Do the following actions make the spot diameter larger, make it smaller, or leave it unchanged?
   A. Decreasing the wavelength of the light.
   B. Decreasing the lens diameter.
   C. Decreasing the lens focal length.
   D. Decreasing the lens-to-screen distance.
6. To focus parallel light rays to the smallest possible spot, should you use a lens with a small f-number or a large f-number? Explain.
7. An astronomer is trying to observe two distant stars. The stars are marginally resolved when she looks at them through a filter that passes green light with a wavelength near 550 nm. Which of the following actions would improve the resolution? Assume that the resolution is not limited by the atmosphere.
   A. Changing the filter to a different wavelength. If so, should she use a shorter or a longer wavelength?
   B. Using a telescope with an objective lens of the same diameter but a different focal length. If so, should she select a shorter or a longer focal length?
   C. Using a telescope with an objective lens of the same focal length but a different diameter. If so, should she select a larger or a smaller diameter?
   D. Using an eyepiece with a different magnification. If so, should she select an eyepiece with more or less magnification?

EXERCISES AND PROBLEMS

Exercises

Section 24.1 Lenses in Combination

1. ‖ Two converging lenses with focal lengths of 40 cm and 20 cm are 10 cm apart. A 2.0-cm-tall object is 15 cm in front of the 40-cm-focal-length lens.
   a. Use ray tracing to find the position and height of the image. Do this accurately with a ruler or paper with a grid. Estimate the image distance and image height by making measurements on your diagram.
   b. Calculate the image position and height. Compare with your ray-tracing answers in part a.
2. ‖ A converging lens with a focal length of 40 cm and a diverging lens with a focal length of −40 cm are 160 cm apart. A 2.0-cm-tall object is 60 cm in front of the converging lens.
   a. Use ray tracing to find the position and height of the image. Do this accurately with a ruler or paper with a grid. Estimate the image distance and image height by making measurements on your diagram.
   b. Calculate the image position and height. Compare with your ray-tracing answers in part a.
3. ‖ A 2.0-cm-tall object is 20 cm to the left of a lens with a focal length of 10 cm. A second lens with a focal length of 15 cm is 30 cm to the right of the first lens.
   a. Use ray tracing to find the position and height of the image. Do this accurately with a ruler or paper with a grid. Estimate the image distance and image height by making measurements on your diagram.
   b. Calculate the image position and height. Compare with your ray-tracing answers in part a.

4. ‖ A 2.0-cm-tall object is 20 cm to the left of a lens with a focal length of 10 cm. A second lens with a focal length of 5 cm is 30 cm to the right of the first lens.
   a. Use ray tracing to find the position and height of the image. Do this accurately with a ruler or paper with a grid. Estimate the image distance and image height by making measurements on your diagram.
   b. Calculate the image position and height. Compare with your ray-tracing answers in part a.

5. ‖‖ A 2.0-cm-tall object is 20 cm to the left of a lens with a focal length of 10 cm. A second lens with a focal length of −5 cm is 30 cm to the right of the first lens.
   a. Use ray tracing to find the position and height of the image. Do this accurately with a ruler or paper with a grid. Estimate the image distance and image height by making measurements on your diagram.
   b. Calculate the image position and height. Compare with your ray-tracing answers in part a.

Section 24.2 The Camera

6. | A 2.0-m-tall man is 10 m in front of a camera with a 15-mm-focal-length lens. How tall is his image on the detector?

7. | What is the f-number of a lens with a 35 mm focal length and a 7.0-mm-diameter aperture?

8. | A 12-mm-focal-length lens has a 4.0-mm-diameter aperture. What is the aperture diameter of an 18-mm-focal-length lens with the same f-number?

9. | What is the aperture diameter of a 12-mm-focal-length lens set to $f/4.0$?

10. | A camera takes a properly exposed photo at $f/5.6$ and 1/125 s. What shutter speed should be used if the lens is changed to $f/4.0$?

11. ‖‖ A camera takes a properly exposed photo with a 3.0-mm-diameter aperture and a shutter speed of 1/125 s. What is the appropriate aperture diameter for a 1/500 s shutter speed?

Section 24.3 Vision

12. ‖ BIO Ramon has contact lenses with the prescription +2.0 D.
   a. What eye condition does Ramon have?
   b. What is his near point without the lenses?

13. | BIO Ellen wears eyeglasses with the prescription −1.0 D.
   a. What eye condition does Ellen have?
   b. What is her far point without the glasses?

14. | BIO What is the f-number of a relaxed eye with the pupil fully dilated to 8.0 mm? Model the eye as a single lens 2.4 cm in front of the retina.

Section 24.4 Optical Systems That Magnify

15. | A magnifier has a magnification of 5×. How far from the lens should an object be held so that its image is at the near-point distance of 25 cm?

16. ‖ A microscope has a 20 cm tube length. What focal-length objective will give total magnification 500× when used with a eyepiece having a focal length of 5.0 cm?

17. ‖ A standardized biological microscope has an 8.0-mm-focal-length objective. What focal-length eyepiece should be used to achieve a total magnification of 100×?

18. ‖ A 6.0-mm-diameter microscope objective has a focal length of 9.0 mm. What object distance gives a lateral magnification of −40?

19. | A 20× telescope has a 12-cm-diameter objective lens. What minimum diameter must the eyepiece lens have to collect all the light rays from an on-axis distant source?

20. ‖ A reflecting telescope is built with a 20-cm-diameter mirror having a 1.00 m focal length. It is used with a 10× eyepiece. What are (a) the magnification and (b) the f-number of the telescope?

Section 24.5 The Resolution of Optical Instruments

21. ‖ A scientist needs to focus a helium-neon laser beam ($\lambda = 633$ nm) to a 10-μm-diameter spot 8.0 cm behind a lens.
   a. What focal-length lens should she use?
   b. What minimum diameter must the lens have?

22. ‖ Two lightbulbs are 1.0 m apart. From what distance can these lightbulbs be marginally resolved by a small telescope with a 4.0-cm-diameter objective lens? Assume that the lens is diffraction limited and $\lambda = 600$ nm.

Problems

23. ‖ A 1.0-cm-tall object is located 4.0 cm to the left of a converging lens with a focal length of 5.0 cm. A diverging lens, of focal length −8.0 cm, is 12 cm to the right of the first lens. Find the position, size, and orientation of the final image.

24. | In FIGURE P24.24, are parallel rays from the left focused to a point? If so, on which side of the lens and at what distance?

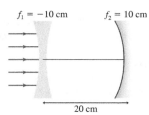

FIGURE P24.24

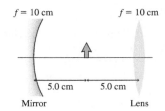

FIGURE P24.25

25. ‖ The rays leaving the two-component optical system of FIGURE P24.25 produce two distinct images of the 1.0-cm-tall object.
   a. What are the position (relative to the lens), orientation, and height of each image?
   b. Draw two ray diagrams, one for each image, showing how the images are formed.

26. | A common optical instrument in a laser laboratory is a *beam expander*. One type of beam expander is shown in FIGURE P24.26. The parallel rays of a laser beam of width w_1 enter from the left.
   a. For what lens spacing d does a parallel laser beam exit from the right?
   b. What is the width w_2 of the exiting laser beam?

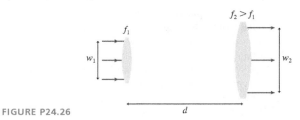

FIGURE P24.26

27. | A common optical instrument in a laser laboratory is a *beam expander*. One type of beam expander is shown in FIGURE P24.27. The parallel rays of a laser beam of width w_1 enter from the left.
    a. For what lens spacing d does a parallel laser beam exit from the right?
    b. What is the width w_2 of the exiting laser beam?

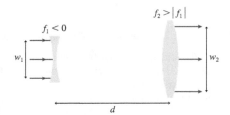

FIGURE P24.27

28. ‖ A 15-cm-focal-length converging lens is 20 cm to the right of a 7.0-cm-focal-length converging lens. A 1.0-cm-tall object is distance L to the left of the first lens.
    a. For what value of L is the final image of this two-lens system halfway between the two lenses?
    b. What are the height and orientation of the final image?

29. | A 1.0-cm-tall object is 110 cm from a screen. A diverging lens with focal length -20 cm is 20 cm in front of the object. What are the focal length and distance from the screen of a second lens that will produce a well-focused, 2.0-cm-tall image on the screen?

30. ‖ You use your 8× binoculars to focus on a 14-cm-long bird in a tree 18 m away from you. What angle (in degrees) does the image of the warbler subtend on your retina?

31. ‖ Yang can focus on objects 150 cm away with a relaxed eye.
    BIO With full accommodation, she can focus on objects 20 cm away. After her eyesight is corrected for distance vision, what will her near point be while wearing her glasses?

32. ‖ The cornea, a boundary between the air and the aqueous hu-
    BIO mor, has a 3.0 cm focal length when acting alone. What is its radius of curvature?

33. | The objective lens of a telescope is a symmetric glass lens with 100 cm radii of curvature. The eyepiece lens is also a symmetric glass lens. What are the radii of curvature of the eyepiece lens if the telescope's magnification is 20×?

34. ‖ You've been asked to build a telescope from a 2.0× magnifying lens and a 5.0× magnifying lens.
    a. What is the maximum magnification you can achieve?
    b. Which lens should be used as the objective? Explain.
    c. What will be the length of your telescope?

35. | Marooned on a desert island and with a lot of time on your hands, you decide to disassemble your glasses to make a crude telescope with which you can scan the horizon for rescuers. Luckily you're farsighted, and, like most people, your two eyes have different lens prescriptions. Your left eye uses a lens of power $+4.5$ D, and your right eye's lens is $+3.0$ D.
    a. Which lens should you use for the objective and which for the eyepiece? Explain.
    b. What will be the magnification of your telescope?
    c. How far apart should the two lenses be when you focus on distant objects?

36. ‖ You've been asked to build a 12× microscope from a 2.0× magnifying lens and a 4.0× magnifying lens.
    a. Which lens should be used as the objective?
    b. What will be the tube length of your microscope?

37. ‖ A microscope with a tube length of 180 mm achieves a total magnification of 800× with a 40× objective and a 20× eyepiece. The microscope is focused for viewing with a relaxed eye. How far is the sample from the objective lens?

38. | High-power lasers are used to cut and weld materials by focusing the laser beam to a very small spot. This is like using a magnifying lens to focus the sun's light to a small spot that can burn things. As an engineer, you have designed a laser cutting device in which the material to be cut is placed 5.0 cm behind the lens. You have selected a high-power laser with a wavelength of 1.06 μm. Your calculations indicate that the laser must be focused to a 5.0-μm-diameter spot in order to have sufficient power to make the cut. What is the minimum diameter of the lens you must install?

39. ‖ Once dark adapted, the pupil of your eye is approximately
    BIO 7 mm in diameter. The headlights of an oncoming car are 120 cm apart. If the lens of your eye is diffraction limited, at what distance are the two headlights marginally resolved? Assume a wavelength of 600 nm and that the index of refraction inside the eye is 1.33. (Your eye is not really good enough to resolve headlights at this distance, due both to aberrations in the lens and to the size of the receptors in your retina, but it comes reasonably close.)

40. ‖ The Hubble Space Telescope has a mirror diameter of 2.4 m. Suppose the telescope is used to photograph stars near the center of our galaxy, 30,000 light years away, using red light with a wavelength of 650 nm.
    a. What's the distance (in km) between two stars that are marginally resolved? The resolution of a reflecting telescope is calculated exactly the same as for a refracting telescope.
    b. For comparison, what is this distance as a multiple of the distance of Jupiter from the sun?

41. ‖ Alpha Centauri, the nearest star to our solar system, is 4.3 light years away. Assume that Alpha Centauri has a planet with an advanced civilization. Professor Dhg, at the planet's Astronomical Institute, wants to build a telescope with which he can find out whether any planets are orbiting our sun.
    a. What is the minimum diameter for an objective lens that will just barely resolve Jupiter and the sun? The radius of Jupiter's orbit is 780 million km. Assume $\lambda = 600$ nm.
    b. Building a telescope of the necessary size does not appear to be a major problem. What practical difficulties might prevent Professor Dhg's experiment from succeeding?

Challenge Problems

42. In FIGURE CP24.42, what are the position, height, and orientation of the final image? Give the position as a distance to the right or left of the lens.

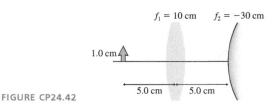

FIGURE CP24.42

43. Mars (6800 km diameter) is viewed through a telescope on a night when it is 1.1×10^8 km from the earth. Its angular size as seen through the eyepiece is 0.50°, the same size as the full moon seen by the naked eye. If the eyepiece focal length is 25 mm, how long is the telescope?

44. Your task in physics laboratory is to make a microscope from two lenses. One lens has a focal length of 2.0 cm, the other 1.0 cm. You plan to use the more powerful lens as the objective, and you want the eyepiece to be 16 cm from the objective.

   a. For viewing with a relaxed eye, how far should the sample be from the objective lens?

   b. What is the magnification of your microscope?

45. The lens shown in FIGURE CP24.45 is called an *achromatic doublet,* meaning that it has no chromatic aberration. The left side is flat, and all other surfaces have radii of curvature R.

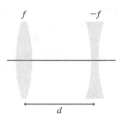

FIGURE CP24.45

   a. For parallel light rays coming from the left, show that the effective focal length of this two-lens system is $f = R/(2n_2 - n_1 - 1)$, where n_1 and n_2 are, respectively, the indices of refraction of the diverging and the converging lenses. Don't forget to make the thin-lens approximation.

   b. Because of dispersion, either lens alone would focus red rays and blue rays at different points. Define Δn_1 and Δn_2 as $n_{blue} - n_{red}$ for the two lenses. Find an expression for Δn_2 in terms of Δn_1 that makes $f_{blue} = f_{red}$ for the two-lens system. That is, the two-lens system does *not* exhibit chromatic aberration.

   c. Indices of refraction for two types of glass are given in the table. To make an achromatic doublet, which glass should you use for the converging lens and which for the diverging lens? Explain.

	n_{blue}	n_{red}
Crown glass	1.525	1.517
Flint glass	1.632	1.616

   d. What value of R gives a focal length of 10.0 cm?

46. FIGURE CP24.46 shows a simple zoom lens in which the magnitudes of both focal lengths are f. If the spacing $d < f$, the image of the converging lens falls on the right side of the diverging lens. Our procedure of letting the image of the first lens act as the object of the second lens will continue to work in this case if we use a *negative* object distance for the second lens. This is called a *virtual object.* Consider a very distant object ($s \approx \infty$ for the first lens) and define the effective focal length as the distance from the midpoint between the lenses to the final image.

   a. Show that the effective focal length is

$$f_{eff} = \frac{f^2 - fd + \frac{1}{2}d^2}{d}$$

   b. What is the zoom for a lens that can be adjusted from $d = \frac{1}{2}f$ to $d = \frac{1}{4}f$?

FIGURE CP24.46

Stop to Think 24.1: b. A diverging lens refracts rays away from the optical axis, so the rays will travel farther down the axis before converging.

Stop to Think 24.2: a. Because the shutter speed doesn't change, the f-number must remain unchanged. The f-number is f/D, so increasing f requires increasing D.

Stop to Think 24.3: a. A magnifier is a converging lens. Converging lenses are used to correct hyperopia.

Stop to Think 24.4: b. If the objective magnification is halved, the eyepiece magnification must be doubled. $M_{eye} = 25 \text{ cm}/f_{eye}$, so doubling M_{eye} requires halving f_{eye}.

Stop to Think 24.5: $w_a > w_d > w_b = w_c$. The spot size is proportional to f/D.

SUMMARY

V Waves and Optics

We end our study of waves a long distance from where we started. Who would have guessed, as we examined our first pulse on a string, that we would end up discussing the resolution of microscopes? But despite the wide disparity between string waves, sound waves, and light waves, a few key ideas have stayed with us throughout Part V: the principle of superposition, interference and diffraction, and standing waves. As part of your final study of waves, you should trace the influence of these ideas through the chapters of Part V.

One point we have tried to emphasize is the *unity* of wave physics. We did not need separate theories of string waves and sound waves and light waves. Instead, a few basic ideas enabled us to understand waves of all types. By focusing on similarities, we have been able to analyze vibrating guitar strings and anti-reflection coatings on lenses in a single part of this book.

Unfortunately, the physics of waves is not as easily summarized as the physics of particles. Newton's laws and the conservation laws are two very general sets of principles about particles, principles that allowed us to develop the powerful problem-solving strategies of Parts I and II. You probably noticed that we have not found any general problem-solving strategies for wave problems.

This is not to say that wave physics has no structure. Rather, the knowledge structure of waves and optics rests more heavily on *phenomena* than on general principles. Unlike the knowledge structure of Newtonian mechanics, which was a "pyramid of ideas," the knowledge structure of waves is a logical grouping of the major topics you studied. This is a different way of structuring knowledge, but it still provides you with a mental framework for analyzing and thinking about wave problems.

KNOWLEDGE STRUCTURE V Waves and Optics

ESSENTIAL CONCEPTS	Wave speed, wavelength, frequency, phase, wave front, and ray
BASIC GOALS	What are the distinguishing features of waves?
	How does a wave travel through a medium?
	How does a medium respond to the presence of more than one wave?
	What is light and what are its properties?
GENERAL PRINCIPLES	Principle of superposition
	$v = \lambda f$ for periodic waves

Traveling Waves

- The wave speed v is a property of the medium.
- The motion of particles in the medium is distinct from the motion of the wave.
- Snapshot graphs and history graphs show the same wave from different perspectives.
- The Doppler effect of shifted frequencies is observed whenever the wave source or the detector is moving.

Standing Waves

- Standing waves are the superposition of waves moving in opposite directions.
- Nodes and antinodes are spaced by $\lambda/2$.
- Only certain discrete frequencies are allowed, depending on the boundary conditions.

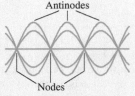

Antinodes

Nodes

Interference

- Interference is constructive—crests align with crests—if two waves are in phase: $\Delta\phi = 0, 2\pi, 4\pi, \ldots$. The wave is enhanced.
- Interference is destructive—crests align with troughs—if two waves are out of phase: $\Delta\phi = \pi, 3\pi, 5\pi, \ldots$. The wave is reduced.
- The phase difference depends on the path-length difference Δr and on any phase difference between the sources.
- Beats occur when $f_1 \neq f_2$.

Light and Optics

- The wave model, used for interference and diffraction, is appropriate when apertures are comparable in size to the wavelength.

Single-slit diffraction: 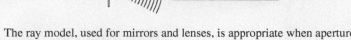   Double-slit interference: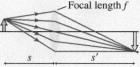

- The ray model, used for mirrors and lenses, is appropriate when apertures are much larger than the wavelength.
- Diffraction, a wave effect, limits the best possible resolution of a lens.

Focal length f

s s'

Tsunami!

In December 2004, an earthquake off the Indonesian coast produced a devastating water wave, a *tsunami,* that caused tremendous destruction and loss of life around the edges of the Indian Ocean, often thousands of miles from the earthquake's epicenter. The tsunami was a dramatic reminder of the power of the earth's forces and an impressive illustration of the energy carried by waves.

The Indian Ocean tsunami of 2004 was caused when a very large earthquake disrupted the seafloor along a fault line, pushing one side of the fault up several meters. This dramatic shift in the seafloor produced an almost instantaneous rise in the surface of the ocean above, much like giving a quick shake to one end of a rope. This was the disturbance that produced the tsunami. And just as shaking one end of rope causes a pulse to travel along it, the resulting water wave propagated throughout the Indian Ocean, as we see in the figure, carrying energy from the earthquake.

This computer simulation of the tsunami looks much like the ripples that spread out when you drop a pebble into a pond, but on an immensely larger scale. The individual wave pulses are up to 100 km wide, and the leading wave front spans more than 5000 km.

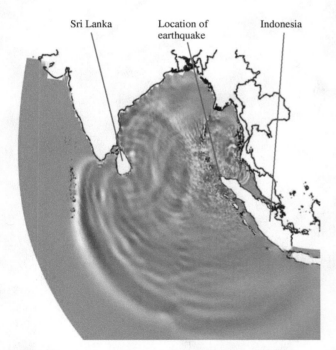

Sri Lanka   Location of earthquake   Indonesia

A frame from a computer simulation of the tsunami, showing the Indian Ocean about three hours after the earthquake. Notice the interference pattern to the east of Sri Lanka, where incoming waves and reflected waves are superimposed.

Technically, a tsunami is a "shallow-water wave," even in the deep ocean, because the scale of the wave (roughly 100 km) is much larger than the depth of the ocean (typically 4 km). Consequently, a tsunami travels differently than normal ocean waves. Unlike normal waves on the surface, whose speed is independent of depth, the speed of a shallow-water wave is determined by the depth of the ocean: The greater the depth, the greater the speed. In the deep ocean, a tsunami travels at hundreds of kilometers per hour, about the speed of a jet plane. This great speed allows a tsunami to cross oceans in only a few hours.

The height of the tsunami as it raced across the open ocean was about half a meter. Why should such a small wave—one that ships didn't even notice as it passed—be so fearsome? It's the width of the wave that matters. The wave pulse may have been only half a meter high, but it was about 100 km wide. In other words, the tsunami far from land was a half-meter-high, 100-km-wide wall of water. This is a tremendous amount of water displaced upward, and thus the tsunami was carrying a tremendous amount of energy.

As a tsunami nears shore, the ocean depth decreases and—because its speed is determined by depth—the tsunami begins to slow. This is when the awesome power of a tsunami begins to become apparent. As the leading edge of the wave slows, the trailing edge, still 100 km away and traveling much faster in deeper water, quickly begins to catch up. Water is nearly incompressible. As the width of the wave pulse decreases, the water begins to pile up higher and higher and the wave increases dramatically in height. The Indian Ocean tsunami had a height of up to 15 m (50 ft) as it came ashore.

Despite its height, a tsunami doesn't break and crash on the beach like a normal wave. The wave pulse may have narrowed dramatically from its 100 km width in the open ocean, but it is still several kilometers wide. Thus a tsunami reaching shore is more like a huge water surge than a typical wave—a wall of water that moves onto the shore and just keeps on coming. In many places, the Indian Ocean tsunami reached 2 km inland.

The impact of the Indian Ocean tsunami was devastating, but it was the first tsunami for which scientists were able to use satellites and ocean sensors to make planet-wide measurements. An analysis of the data, including computer simulations like the one seen here, has helped us better understand the physics of these ocean waves. We won't be able to stop future tsunamis, but with a better knowledge of how they are formed and how they travel, we will be better able to warn people to get out of their way.

Electricity and Magnetism

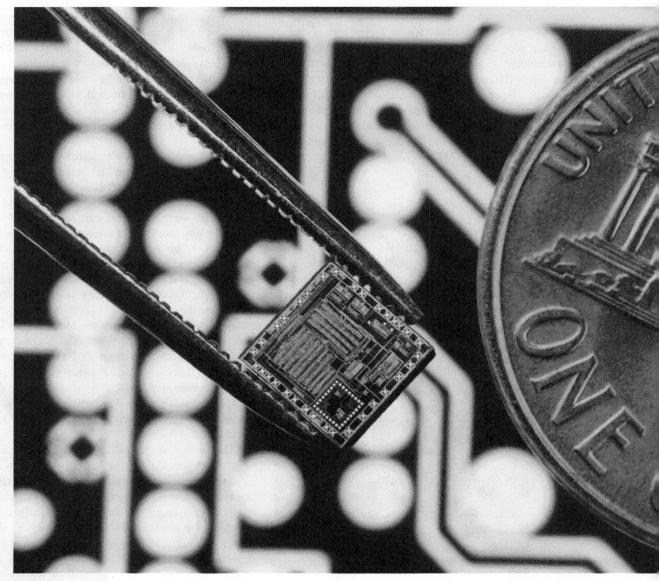

This integrated circuit contains millions of circuit elements. The density of circuit elements in integrated circuits has doubled about every 18 months for the past 30 years. Whether this trend continues depends on whether scientists and engineers can understand the physics of nano-scale electric circuits.

OVERVIEW

Phenomena and Theories

Amber, or fossilized tree resin, has long been prized for its beauty. Amber is of scientific interest today because biologists have learned how to recover DNA strands from million-year-old insects trapped in the resin. But amber has an ancient scientific connection as well. The Greek word for amber is *elektron.*

It has been known since antiquity that a piece of amber rubbed with fur can attract feathers or straw—seemingly magical powers to a pre-scientific society. It was also known to the ancient Greeks that certain stones from the region they called *Magnesia* could pick up pieces of iron. It is from these humble beginnings that we today have high-speed computers, lasers, and magnetic resonance imaging as well as such mundane modern-day miracles as the lightbulb.

The basic phenomena of electricity and magnetism are not as familiar as those of mechanics. You have spent your entire life exerting forces on objects and watching them move, but your experience with electricity and magnetism is probably much more limited. We will deal with this lack of experience by placing a large emphasis on the *phenomena* of electricity and magnetism.

We will begin by looking in detail at *electric charge* and the process of *charging* an object. It is easy to make systematic observations of how charges behave, and we will consider the forces between charges and how charges behave in different materials. Similarly, we will begin our study of magnetism by observing how magnets stick to some metals but not others and how magnets affect compass needles. But our most important observation will be that an electric current affects a compass needle in exactly the same way as a magnet. This observation, suggesting a close connection between electricity and magnetism, will eventually lead us to the discovery of electromagnetic waves.

Our goal in Part VI is to develop a theory to explain the phenomena of electricity and magnetism. The linchpin of our theory will be the entirely new concept of a *field.* Electricity and magnetism are about the long-range interactions of charges, both static charges and moving charges, and the field concept will help us understand how these interactions take place. We will want to know how fields are created by charges and how charges, in return, respond to the fields. Bit by bit, we will assemble a theory—based on the new concepts of electric and magnetic fields—that will allow us to understand, explain, and predict a wide range of electromagnetic behavior.

The story of electricity and magnetism is vast. The 19th-century formulation of the theory of electromagnetism, which led to sweeping revolutions in science and technology, has been called by no less than Einstein "the most important event in physics since Newton's time." Not surprisingly, all we can do in this text is develop some of the basic ideas and concepts, leaving many details and applications to later courses. Even so, our study of electricity and magnetism will explore some of the most exciting and important topics in physics.

34 Electromagnetic Fields and Waves

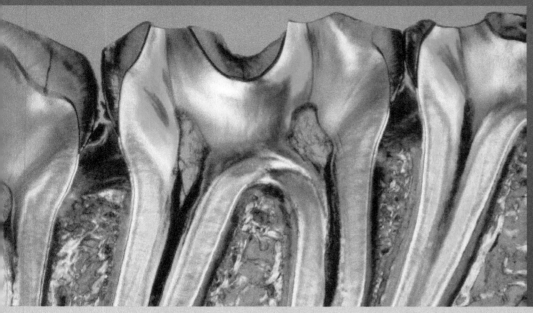

A thin section of molar teeth seen in polarized light. The rainbow of colors arises because different biological materials have different effects on the light's polarization.

▶ **Looking Ahead** The goal of Chapter 34 is to study the properties of electromagnetic fields and waves.

Maxwell's Theory of Electromagnetism

All of electricity and magnetism is based on four equations for the fields, called **Maxwell's equations,** and one equation that tells us how charges respond to fields.

Gauss's law: Charged particles create electric fields.

Faraday's law: Electric fields can also be created by changing magnetic fields.

Gauss's law for magnetism: There are no isolated magnetic poles.

Ampère-Maxwell law: Magnetic fields can be created by currents or by changing electric fields.

◀ **Looking Back**
Section 27.4 Gauss's law
Section 32.6 Ampère's law
Section 33.5 Faraday's law

Electric and magnetic fields exert forces on charged particles. When combined, the net force on charge q is called the **Lorentz force law:**

$$\vec{F} = q(\vec{E} + \vec{v} \times \vec{B})$$

Electromagnetic Waves

You'll learn that Maxwell's equations predict the existence of self-sustaining **electromagnetic waves** that travel through space without the presence of charges or currents.

- $\vec{E}$ and $\vec{B}$ are perpendicular to each other and to the direction of travel.
- In vacuum $v_{em} = 1/\sqrt{\epsilon_0 \mu_0} = c$, the speed of light.

Electromagnetic waves are often **polarized,** meaning that the electric field always oscillates in the same plane. You'll learn to calculate the intensity of light transmitted through a polarizing filter.

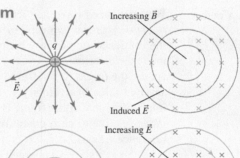

No light is transmitted through *crossed polarizers* whose axes are perpendicular to each other.

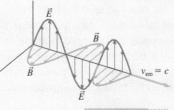

Field Transformations

Electric and magnetic fields turn out not to be separate, independent entities. Whether the field at a point is electric or magnetic depends on your motion relative to the charges and currents.

You'll learn how to transform the fields measured in reference frame A to a second frame B moving relative to A.

What are the fields of this charge?

◀ **Looking Back**
Section 4.4 Relative motion

34.1 *E* or *B*? It Depends on Your Perspective

FIGURE 34.1 Brittney carries a charge past Alec.

(a)

Brittney

Alec

Charge q moves with velocity $\vec{v}$ relative to Alec.

(b)

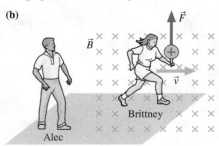

Brittney

Alec

Charge q moves through a magnetic field established by Alec.

It seems clear, after the last nine chapters, that charges create electric fields and that moving charges, or currents, create magnetic fields. But consider FIGURE 34.1a, where Brittney, carrying charge q, runs past Alec with velocity $\vec{v}$. Alec sees a moving charge, and he knows that this charge creates a magnetic field. But from Brittney's perspective, the charge is at rest. Stationary charges don't create magnetic fields, so Brittney claims that the magnetic field is zero. Is there, or is there not, a magnetic field?

Or what about the situation in FIGURE 34.1b? Now Brittney is carrying the charge through a magnetic field that Alec has created. Alec sees a charge moving in a magnetic field, so he knows there's a force $\vec{F} = q\vec{v} \times \vec{B}$ on the charge. But for Brittney the charge is still at rest. Stationary charges don't experience magnetic forces, so Brittney claims that $\vec{F} = \vec{0}$.

Now, we may be a bit uncertain about magnetic fields, but surely there can be no disagreement over forces. After all, forces cause observable and measurable effects, so Alec and Brittney should be able to agree on whether or not the charge experiences a force. Further, if Brittney runs with constant velocity, then both Alec and Brittney are in *inertial reference frames*. You learned in Chapter 4 that these are the reference frames in which Newton's laws are valid, so we can't say that there's anything abnormal or unusual about Alec's and Brittney's observations. We have a paradox.

This paradox has arisen because magnetic fields and forces depend on velocity, but we haven't looked at the issue of velocity *with respect to what* or velocity *as measured by whom*. The resolution of this paradox will lead us to the conclusion that $\vec{E}$ and $\vec{B}$ are not, as we've been assuming, separate and independent entities. They are closely intertwined.

Reference Frames

FIGURE 34.2 Reference frames A and B.

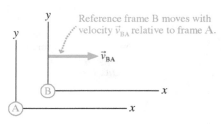

Reference frame B moves with velocity $\vec{v}_{BA}$ relative to frame A.

We introduced reference frames and relative motion in Chapter 4. To remind you, FIGURE 34.2 shows two reference frames labeled A and B. You can think of these as the reference frames in which Alec and Brittney, respectively, are at rest. Frame B moves with velocity $\vec{v}_{BA}$ with respect to frame A. That is, an observer (Alec) at rest in A sees the origin of B (Brittney) go past with velocity $\vec{v}_{BA}$. Of course, Brittney would say that Alec has velocity $\vec{v}_{AB} = -\vec{v}_{BA}$ relative to her reference frame. There's no implication that either frame is "at rest." All we know is that the two reference frames move relative to each other. We will stipulate that both reference frames are inertial reference frames, so $\vec{v}_{BA}$ is constant.

FIGURE 34.3 shows a charged particle C. Experimenters in frame A measure the motion of the particle and find that its velocity *relative to frame A* is $\vec{v}_{CA}$. At the same instant, experimenters in B find that the particle's velocity *relative to frame B* is $\vec{v}_{CB}$. In Chapter 4, we found that $\vec{v}_{CA}$ and $\vec{v}_{CB}$ are related by

$$\vec{v}_{CA} = \vec{v}_{CB} + \vec{v}_{BA} \qquad (34.1)$$

FIGURE 34.3 The particle's velocity is measured in both frame A and frame B.

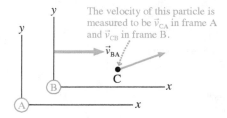

The velocity of this particle is measured to be $\vec{v}_{CA}$ in frame A and $\vec{v}_{CB}$ in frame B.

Equation 34.1, the *Galilean transformation of velocity*, tells us that the velocity of the particle relative to reference frame A is its velocity relative to frame B plus (vector addition!) the velocity of frame B relative to frame A.

Suppose the charged particle in Figure 34.3 is accelerating, as it would if acted on by a net force. How does its acceleration $\vec{a}_{CA}$, as measured by experimenters in frame A, compare to the acceleration $\vec{a}_{CB}$ measured in frame B? We can answer this question by taking the time derivative of Equation 34.1:

$$\frac{d\vec{v}_{CA}}{dt} = \frac{d\vec{v}_{CB}}{dt} + \frac{d\vec{v}_{BA}}{dt}$$

The derivatives of $\vec{v}_{CA}$ and $\vec{v}_{CB}$ are the particle's accelerations $\vec{a}_{CA}$ and $\vec{a}_{CB}$ in frames A and B, respectively. But $\vec{v}_{BA}$ is a *constant* velocity, so $d\vec{v}_{BA}/dt = \vec{0}$. Thus the Galilean transformation of acceleration is simply

$$\vec{a}_{CA} = \vec{a}_{CB} \qquad (34.2)$$

Brittney and Alec may measure different positions and velocities for a particle, but they *agree* on its acceleration. And if they agree on its acceleration, they must, by using Newton's second law, agree on the force acting on the particle. That is, **experimenters in all inertial reference frames agree about the force acting on a particle.** This conclusion is the key to understanding how different experimenters see electric and magnetic fields.

The Transformation of Electric and Magnetic Fields

Imagine that Alec has measured the electric field $\vec{E}_A$ and the magnetic field $\vec{B}_A$ in reference frame A. Our investigations thus far give us no reason to think that Brittney's measurements of the fields will differ from Alec's. After all, it seems like the fields are just "there," waiting to be measured. Thus our expectation is that Brittney, in frame B, will measure $\vec{E}_B = \vec{E}_A$ and $\vec{B}_B = \vec{B}_A$.

To find out if this is true, Alec establishes a region of space with a uniform magnetic field $\vec{B}_A$ but no electric field ($\vec{E}_A = \vec{0}$). Then, as shown in FIGURE 34.4, he shoots a positive charge q through the magnetic field. At an instant when q is moving horizontally with velocity $\vec{v}_{CA}$, Alec observes that the particle experiences force $\vec{F}_A = q(\vec{E}_A + \vec{v}_{CA} \times \vec{B}_A) = q\vec{v}_{CA} \times \vec{B}_A$. The direction of the force, given by the right-hand rule, is straight up.

Suppose that Brittney, in frame B, runs alongside the charge with the same velocity: $\vec{v}_{BA} = \vec{v}_{CA}$. To her, in frame B, the charge is at rest. Nonetheless, because both experimenters must agree about forces, Brittney *must* observe the same upward force on the charge that Alec observed. But there is *no* magnetic force on a stationary charge, so how can this be?

Because Brittney sees a stationary charge being acted on by an upward force, her only possible conclusion is that there is an upward-pointing *electric field*. After all, the electric field was initially defined in terms of the force experienced by a stationary charge. If the electric field in frame B is $\vec{E}_B$, then the force on the charge is $\vec{F}_B = q\vec{E}_B$. But we know that $\vec{F}_B = \vec{F}_A$, and Alec has already measured $\vec{F}_A = q\vec{v}_{CA} \times \vec{B}_A = q\vec{v}_{BA} \times \vec{B}_A$. Thus we're led to the conclusion that

$$\vec{E}_B = \vec{v}_{BA} \times \vec{B}_A \qquad (34.3)$$

As Brittney runs past Alec, she finds that at least part of Alec's magnetic field has become an electric field! **Whether a field is seen as "electric" or "magnetic" depends on the motion of the reference frame relative to the sources of the field.**

FIGURE 34.5 shows the situation from Brittney's perspective. There is a force on charge q, the same force that Alec measured in Figure 34.4, but Brittney attributes this force to an electric field rather than a magnetic field. (Brittney needs a moving charge to measure magnetic forces, so we'll need a different experiment to see whether or not there's a magnetic field in frame B.)

More generally, suppose that an experimenter in reference frame A creates both an electric field $\vec{E}_A$, and a magnetic field $\vec{B}_A$. A charge moving in A with velocity $\vec{v}_{CA}$ experiences the force $\vec{F}_A = q(\vec{E}_A + \vec{v}_{CA} \times \vec{B}_A)$ shown in FIGURE 34.6a on the next page. The charge is at rest in a reference frame B that moves with velocity $\vec{v}_{BA} = \vec{v}_{CA}$ so the force in B can be due only to an electric field: $\vec{F}_B = q\vec{E}_B$. Equating the forces, because experimenters in all inertial reference frames agree about forces, we find that

$$\vec{E}_B = \vec{E}_A + \vec{v}_{BA} \times \vec{B}_A \qquad (34.4)$$

FIGURE 34.4 A charged particle moves through a magnetic field in reference frame A and experiences a magnetic force.

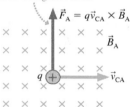

In A, the force on q is due to a magnetic field.

The situation in frame A

FIGURE 34.5 In frame B, the charge experiences an electric force.

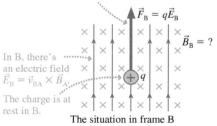

In B, the force on q is due to an electric field.

In B, there's an electric field $\vec{E}_B = \vec{v}_{BA} \times \vec{B}_A$.

The charge is at rest in B.

The situation in frame B

Equation 34.4 transforms the electric and magnetic fields measured in reference frame A into the electric field measured in a frame B that moves relative to A with velocity $\vec{v}_{BA}$. FIGURE 34.6b shows the outcome. Although we used a charge as a probe to find Equation 34.4, the equation is strictly about fields in different reference frames; it makes no mention of charges.

FIGURE 34.6 A charge in reference frame A experiences electric and magnetic forces. The charge experiences the same force in frame B, but it is due only to an electric field.

(a) The electric and magnetic fields in frame A

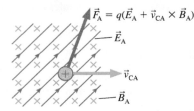

(b) The electric field in frame B, where the charged particle is at rest

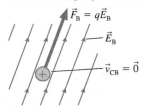

EXAMPLE 34.1 Transforming the electric field

A laboratory experimenter has created the parallel electric and magnetic fields $\vec{E} = 10{,}000\,\hat{\imath}$ V/m and $\vec{B} = 0.10\,\hat{\imath}$ T. A proton is shot into these fields with velocity $\vec{v} = 1.0 \times 10^5\,\hat{\jmath}$ m/s. What is the electric field in the proton's reference frame?

MODEL Let the laboratory be reference frame A and a frame moving with the proton be reference frame B. The relative velocity is $\vec{v}_{BA} = 1.0 \times 10^5\,\hat{\jmath}$ m/s.

VISUALIZE FIGURE 34.7 shows the geometry. The laboratory fields, now labeled A, are parallel to the x-axis while $\vec{v}_{BA}$ is in the y-direction. Thus $\vec{v}_{BA} \times \vec{B}_A$ points in the negative z-direction.

SOLVE $\vec{v}_{BA}$ and $\vec{B}_A$ are perpendicular, so the magnitude of $\vec{v}_{BA} \times \vec{B}_A$ is $(1.0 \times 10^5 \text{ m/s})(0.10 \text{ T})(\sin 90°) = 10{,}000$ V/m. Thus the electric field in frame B, the proton's frame, is

$$\vec{E}_B = \vec{E}_A + \vec{v}_{BA} \times \vec{B}_A = (10{,}000\,\hat{\imath} - 10{,}000\,\hat{k}) \text{ V/m}$$

$$= (14{,}000 \text{ V/m}, 45° \text{ below the } x\text{-axis})$$

FIGURE 34.7 Finding electric field $\vec{E}_B$.

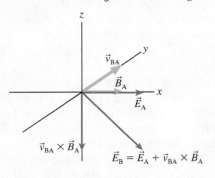

ASSESS The force on the proton is the same in both reference frames. But in the proton's reference frame that force is due entirely to an electric field tilted 45° below the x-axis.

To find a transformation equation for the magnetic field, FIGURE 34.8a shows charge q at rest in reference frame A. Alec measures the fields of a stationary point charge, which we know are

$$\vec{E}_A = \frac{1}{4\pi\epsilon_0} \frac{q}{r^2}\hat{r} \qquad \vec{B}_A = \vec{0}$$

What are the fields at this point in space as measured by Brittney in frame B? We can use Equation 34.4 to find $\vec{E}_B$. Because $\vec{B}_A = \vec{0}$, the electric field in frame B is

$$\vec{E}_B = \vec{E}_A = \frac{1}{4\pi\epsilon_0} \frac{q}{r^2}\hat{r} \tag{34.5}$$

In other words, Coulomb's law is still valid in a frame in which the point charge is moving.

But Brittney also measures a magnetic field $\vec{B}_B$, because, as seen in FIGURE 34.8b, charge q is moving in reference frame B. The magnetic field of a moving point charge is given by the Biot-Savart law:

$$\vec{B}_B = \frac{\mu_0}{4\pi} \frac{q}{r^2}\vec{v}_{CB} \times \hat{r} = -\frac{\mu_0}{4\pi} \frac{q}{r^2}\vec{v}_{BA} \times \hat{r} \tag{34.6}$$

where we used the fact that the charge's velocity in frame B is $\vec{v}_{CB} = -\vec{v}_{BA}$.

It will be useful to rewrite Equation 34.6 as

$$\vec{B}_B = -\frac{\mu_0}{4\pi}\frac{q}{r^2}\vec{v}_{BA} \times \hat{r} = -\epsilon_0\mu_0\vec{v}_{BA} \times \left(\frac{1}{4\pi\epsilon_0}\frac{q}{r^2}\hat{r}\right)$$

The expression in parentheses is simply $\vec{E}_A$, the electric field in frame A, so we have

$$\vec{B}_B = -\epsilon_0\mu_0\vec{v}_{BA} \times \vec{E}_A \qquad (34.7)$$

Equation 34.7 expresses the remarkable idea that **the Biot-Savart law for the magnetic field of a moving point charge is nothing other than the Coulomb electric field of a stationary point charge transformed into a moving reference frame.**

We will assert without proof that if the experimenters in frame A create a magnetic field $\vec{B}_A$ in addition to the electric field $\vec{E}_A$, then the magnetic field $\vec{B}_B$ measured in frame B is

$$\vec{B}_B = \vec{B}_A - \epsilon_0\mu_0\vec{v}_{BA} \times \vec{E}_A \qquad (34.8)$$

This is a general transformation matching Equation 34.4 for the electric field $\vec{E}_B$.

Notice something interesting. The constant μ_0 has units of T m/A; those of ϵ_0 are C²/N m². By definition, 1 T = 1 N/A m and 1 A = 1 C/s. Consequently, the units of $\epsilon_0\mu_0$ turn out to be s²/m². In other words, the quantity $1/\sqrt{\epsilon_0\mu_0}$, with units of m/s, is a speed. But what speed? The constants are well known from measurements of static electric and magnetic fields, so we can compute

$$\frac{1}{\sqrt{\epsilon_0\mu_0}} = \frac{1}{\sqrt{(8.85 \times 10^{-12}\,\text{C}^2/\text{N m}^2)(1.26 \times 10^{-6}\,\text{T m/A})}} = 3.00 \times 10^8\,\text{m/s}$$

Of all the possible values you might get from evaluating $1/\sqrt{\epsilon_0\mu_0}$, what are the chances it equals c, the speed of light? It is not a random coincidence. In Section 34.5 we'll show that electric and magnetic fields can exist as a *traveling wave*, and that the wave speed is predicted by the theory to be none other than

$$v_{em} = c = \frac{1}{\sqrt{\epsilon_0\mu_0}} \qquad (34.9)$$

For now, we'll go ahead and write $\epsilon_0\mu_0 = 1/c^2$. With this, our **Galilean field transformation equations** are

$$\vec{E}_B = \vec{E}_A + \vec{v}_{BA} \times \vec{B}_A$$
$$\vec{B}_B = \vec{B}_A - \frac{1}{c^2}\vec{v}_{BA} \times \vec{E}_A \qquad (34.10)$$

where $\vec{v}_{BA}$ is the velocity of reference frame B relative to frame A and where, to reiterate, the fields are measured *at the same point in space* by experimenters *at rest* in each reference frame.

NOTE ▶ We'll see shortly that these equations are valid only if $v_{BA} \ll c$. ◀

We can no longer believe that electric and magnetic fields have a separate, independent existence. Changing from one reference frame to another mixes and rearranges the fields. Different experimenters watching an event will agree on the outcome, such as the deflection of a charged particle, but they will ascribe it to different combinations of fields. Our conclusion is that **there is a single electromagnetic field that presents different faces, in terms of $\vec{E}$ and $\vec{B}$, to different viewers.**

FIGURE 34.8 A charge at rest in frame A is moving in frame B and creates a magnetic field $\vec{B}_B$.

(a) In frame A, the static charge creates an electric field but no magnetic field.

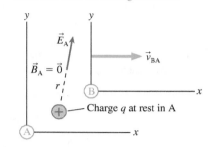

(b) In frame B, the moving charge creates both an electric and a magnetic field.

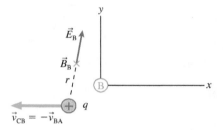

EXAMPLE 34.2 **Two views of a magnet**

The 1.0 T field of a large laboratory magnet points straight up. A rocket flies past the laboratory, parallel to the ground, at 1000 m/s. What are the fields between the magnet's pole tips as measured—very quickly!—by scientists on the rocket?

MODEL Let the laboratory be reference frame A and a frame moving with the rocket be reference frame B.

VISUALIZE FIGURE 34.9 shows the magnet and establishes the coordinate systems. The relative velocity is $\vec{v}_{BA} = 1000\,\hat{\imath}$ m/s.

FIGURE 34.9 The rocket and the magnet.

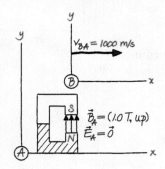

SOLVE The fields in the laboratory reference frame are $\vec{E}_A = \vec{0}$ and $\vec{B}_A = 1.0\,\hat{\jmath}$ T. Transforming the fields to the rocket's reference frame gives first, for the electric field,

$$\vec{E}_B = \vec{E}_A + \vec{v}_{BA} \times \vec{B}_A = \vec{v}_{BA} \times \vec{B}_A$$

From the right-hand rule, $\vec{v}_{BA} \times \vec{B}_A$ is out of the page, in the z-direction. $\vec{v}_{BA}$ and $\vec{B}_A$ are perpendicular, so

$$\vec{E}_B = v_{BA} B_A \hat{k} = 1000\,\hat{k}\text{ V/m}$$

Similarly, for the magnetic field,

$$\vec{B}_B = \vec{B}_A - \frac{1}{c^2}\vec{v}_{BA} \times \vec{E}_A = \vec{B}_A = 1.0\,\hat{\jmath}\text{ T}$$

Thus the rocket scientists measure

$$\vec{E}_B = 1000\,\hat{k}\text{ V/m} \quad\text{and}\quad \vec{B}_B = 1.0\,\hat{\jmath}\text{ T}$$

Almost Relativity

FIGURE 34.10 Two charges moving parallel to each other.

(a)

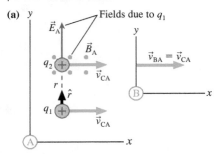

Fields seen in frame A

(b)

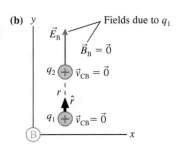

Fields seen in frame B

FIGURE 34.10a shows two positive charges moving side by side through frame A with velocity $\vec{v}_{CA}$. Charge q_1 creates an electric field and a magnetic field at the position of charge q_2. These are

$$\vec{E}_A = \frac{1}{4\pi\epsilon_0}\frac{q_1}{r^2}\hat{\jmath} \quad\text{and}\quad \vec{B}_A = \frac{\mu_0}{4\pi}\frac{q_1 v_{CA}}{r^2}\hat{k}$$

where r is the distance between the charges, and we've used $\hat{r} = \hat{\jmath}$ and $\vec{v} \times \hat{r} = v\hat{k}$.

How are the fields seen in frame B, which moves with $\vec{v}_{BA} = \vec{v}_{CA}$ and in which the charges are at rest? From the field transformation equations,

$$\vec{B}_B = \vec{B}_A - \frac{1}{c^2}\vec{v}_{BA} \times \vec{E}_A = \frac{\mu_0}{4\pi}\frac{q_1 v_{CA}}{r^2}\hat{k} - \frac{1}{c^2}\left(v_{CA}\hat{\imath} \times \frac{1}{4\pi\epsilon_0}\frac{q_1}{r^2}\hat{\jmath}\right)$$

$$= \frac{\mu_0}{4\pi}\frac{q_1 v_{CA}}{r^2}\left(1 - \frac{1}{\epsilon_0\mu_0 c^2}\right)\hat{k}$$

(34.11)

where we used $\hat{\imath} \times \hat{\jmath} = \hat{k}$. But $\epsilon_0\mu_0 = 1/c^2$, so the term in parentheses is zero and thus $\vec{B}_B = \vec{0}$. This result was expected because q_1 is at rest in frame B and shouldn't create a magnetic field.

The transformation of the electric field is similar:

$$\vec{E}_B = \vec{E}_A + \vec{v}_{BA} \times \vec{B}_A = \frac{1}{4\pi\epsilon_0}\frac{q_1}{r^2}\hat{\jmath} + v_{BA}\hat{\imath} \times \frac{\mu_0}{4\pi}\frac{q_1 v_{CA}}{r^2}\hat{k}$$

(34.12)

$$= \frac{1}{4\pi\epsilon_0}\frac{q_1}{r^2}(1 - \epsilon_0\mu_0 v_{BA}^2)\hat{\jmath} = \frac{1}{4\pi\epsilon_0}\frac{q_1}{r^2}\left(1 - \frac{v_{BA}^2}{c^2}\right)\hat{\jmath}$$

where we used $\hat{\imath} \times \hat{k} = -\hat{\jmath}$, $\vec{v}_{CA} = \vec{v}_{BA}$, and $\epsilon_0\mu_0 = 1/c^2$. FIGURE 34.10b shows the charges and fields in frame B.

But now we have a problem. In frame B where the two charges are at rest and separated by distance r, the electric field due to charge q_1 should be simply

$$\vec{E}_B = \frac{1}{4\pi\epsilon_0} \frac{q_1}{r^2} \hat{j}$$

The field transformation equations have given a "wrong" result for the electric field $\vec{E}_B$.

It turns out that the field transformations of Equations 34.10, which are based on Galilean relativity, aren't quite right. We would need Einstein's relativity—a topic that we'll take up in Chapter 36—to give the correct transformations. However, the Galilean field transformations in Equations 34.10 are equivalent to the relativistically correct transformations when $v \ll c$, in which case $v^2/c^2 \ll 1$. You can see that the two expressions for $\vec{E}_B$ do, in fact, agree if v_{BA}^2/c^2 can be neglected.

Thus our use of the field transformation equations has an additional rule: Set v^2/c^2 to zero. This is an acceptable rule for speeds $v < 10^7$ m/s. Even with this limitation, our investigation has provided us with a deeper understanding of electric and magnetic fields.

STOP TO THINK 34.1 The first diagram shows electric and magnetic fields in reference frame A. Which diagram shows the fields in frame B?

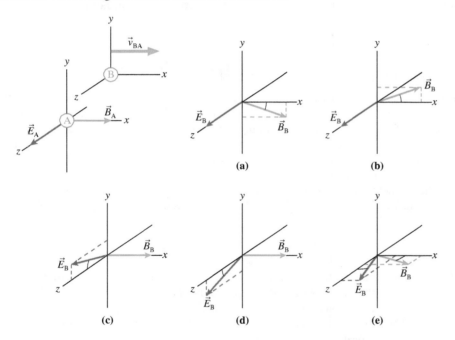

Faraday's Law Revisited

The transformation of electric and magnetic fields gives us new insight into Faraday's law. FIGURE 34.11a on the next page shows a reference frame A in which a conducting loop is moving with velocity $\vec{v}$ into a magnetic field. You learned in Chapter 33 that the magnetic field exerts a magnetic force $\vec{F}_B = q\vec{v} \times \vec{B} = (qvB, \text{upward})$ on the charges in the leading edge of the wire, creating an emf $\mathcal{E} = vLB$ and an induced current in the loop. We called this a *motional emf.*

How do things appear to an experimenter who is in frame B that moves with the loop at velocity $\vec{v}_{BA} = \vec{v}$ and for whom the loop is at rest? We have learned the important lesson that experimenters in different inertial reference frames agree about the outcome of any experiment; hence an experimenter in frame B agrees that there is an

FIGURE 34.11 A motional emf as seen in two different reference frames.

(a) Laboratory frame A

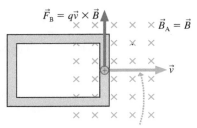

The loop is moving to the right.

(b) Loop frame B

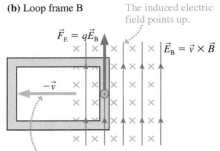

The magnetic field is moving to the left.

FIGURE 34.12 A Gaussian surface enclosing a charge.

Gaussian surface

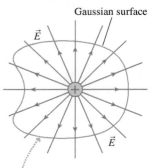

There is a net electric flux through this surface that encloses a charge.

FIGURE 34.13 There is no net flux through a Gaussian surface around a magnetic dipole.

Gaussian surface

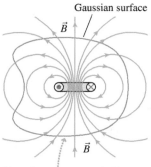

There is no net magnetic flux through this closed surface.

induced current in the loop. But the charges are at rest in frame B so there cannot be any magnetic force on them. How is the emf established in frame B?

We can use the field transformations to determine that the fields in frame B are

$$\vec{E}_B = \vec{E}_A + \vec{v} \times \vec{B}_A = \vec{v} \times \vec{B}$$
$$\vec{B}_B = \vec{B}_A - \frac{1}{c^2}\vec{v} \times \vec{E}_A = \vec{B}$$

(34.13)

where we used the fact that $\vec{E}_A = \vec{0}$ in frame A.

An experimenter in the loop's frame sees not only a magnetic field but also the electric field $\vec{E}_B$ shown in FIGURE 34.11b. The magnetic field exerts no force on the charges, because they're at rest in this frame, but the electric field does. The force on charge q is $\vec{F}_E = q\vec{E}_B = q\vec{v} \times \vec{B} = (qvB,$ upward). This is the same force as was measured in the laboratory frame, so it will cause the same emf and the same current. The outcome is identical, as we knew it had to be, but the experimenter in B attributes the emf to an electric field whereas the experimenter in A attributes it to a magnetic field.

Field $\vec{E}_B$ is, in fact, the *induced electric field* of Faraday's law. Faraday's law, fundamentally, is a statement that **a changing magnetic field creates an electric field.** But only in frame B, the frame of the loop, is the magnetic field changing. Thus the induced electric field is seen in the loop's frame but not in the laboratory frame.

34.2 The Field Laws Thus Far

Let's remind ourselves where we are in terms of discovering laws about the electromagnetic field. Gauss's law, which you studied in Chapter 27, states a very general property of the electric field. It says that charges create electric fields in such a way that the electric flux of the field is the same through *any* closed surface surrounding the charges. FIGURE 34.12 illustrates this idea by showing the field lines passing through a Gaussian surface enclosing a charge.

The mathematical statement of Gauss's law for the electric field says that for any *closed* surface enclosing total charge Q_{in}, the net electric flux through the surface is

$$(\Phi_e)_{\text{closed surface}} = \oint \vec{E} \cdot d\vec{A} = \frac{Q_{in}}{\epsilon_0}$$

(34.14)

The circle on the integral sign indicates that the integration is over a closed surface. Gauss's law is the first of what will turn out to be four *field equations.*

There's an analogous equation for magnetic fields, an equation we implied in Chapter 32—where we noted that isolated north or south poles do not exist—but didn't explicitly write it down. FIGURE 34.13 shows a Gaussian surface around a magnetic dipole. Magnetic field lines form continuous curves, without starting or stopping, so every field line leaving the surface at some point must reenter it at another. Consequently, the net magnetic flux over a *closed* surface is zero.

We've shown only one surface and one magnetic field, but this conclusion turns out to be a general property of magnetic fields. Because every north pole is accompanied by a south pole, we can't enclose a "net pole" within a surface. Thus Gauss's law for magnetic fields is

$$(\Phi_m)_{\text{closed surface}} = \oint \vec{B} \cdot d\vec{A} = 0$$

(34.15)

Equation 34.14 is the mathematical statement that Coulomb electric field lines start and stop on charges. Equation 34.15 is the mathematical statement that magnetic field lines form closed loops; they don't start or stop (i.e., there are no isolated magnetic poles).

These two versions of Gauss's law are important statements about what types of fields can and cannot exist. They will become two of Maxwell's equations.

The third field law we've established is Faraday's law:

$$\mathcal{E} = \oint \vec{E} \cdot d\vec{s} = -\frac{d\Phi_m}{dt} \tag{34.16}$$

where the line integral of $\vec{E}$ is around the closed curve that bounds the surface through which the magnetic flux Φ_m is calculated. Equation 34.16 is the mathematical statement that an electric field (and thus an emf $\mathcal{E}$) can also be created by a changing magnetic field. The correct use of Faraday's law requires a convention for determining when fluxes are positive and negative. The sign convention will be given in the next section, where we discuss the fourth and last field equation—an analogous equation for magnetic fields.

34.3 The Displacement Current

We introduced Ampère's law in Chapter 32 as an alternative to the Biot-Savart law for calculating the magnetic field of a current. Whenever total current $I_{through}$ passes through an area bounded by a closed curve, the line integral of the magnetic field around the curve is

$$\oint \vec{B} \cdot d\vec{s} = \mu_0 I_{through} \tag{34.17}$$

FIGURE 34.14 illustrates the geometry of Ampère's law. The sign of each current can be determined by using Tactics Box 34.1. In this case, $I_{through} = I_1 - I_2$.

FIGURE 34.14 Ampère's law relates the line integral of $\vec{B}$ around curve C to the current passing through surface S.

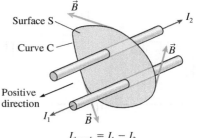

$$I_{through} = I_1 - I_2$$

TACTICS BOX 34.1 **Determining the signs of flux and current**

❶ For a surface S bounded by a closed curve C, choose either the clockwise (cw) or counterclockwise (ccw) direction around C.
❷ Curl the fingers of your *right* hand around the curve in the chosen direction, with your thumb perpendicular to the surface. Your thumb defines the positive direction.

■ A flux Φ through the surface is positive if the field is in the same direction as your thumb, negative if the field is in the opposite direction.

■ A current through the surface in the direction of your thumb is positive, in the direction opposite your thumb is negative.

Exercises 4–6

Ampère's law is the formal statement that **currents create magnetic fields.** Although Ampère's law can be used to calculate magnetic fields in situations with a high degree of symmetry, it is more important as a statement about what types of magnetic field can and cannot exist.

Something Is Missing

Nothing restricts the bounded surface of Ampère's law to being flat. It's not hard to see that any current passing through surface S_1 in FIGURE 34.15 on the next page must also pass through the curved surface S_2. To interpret Ampère's law properly, we have to say that the current $I_{through}$ is the net current passing through *any* surface S that is bounded by curve C.

FIGURE 34.15 The *net* current passing through the flat surface S_1 also passes through the curved surface S_2.

Closed curve C around wire

Surface S_1 Surface S_2

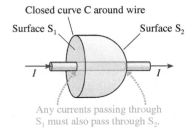

Any currents passing through S_1 must also pass through S_2.

Closed curve C around wire

S_1 S_2

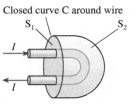

Even in this case, the *net* current through S_1, namely zero, matches the net current through S_2.

FIGURE 34.16 There is no current through surface S_2 as the capacitor charges, but there is a changing electric flux.

(a)   Cross section through a closed curve C around the wire

Current I passes through surface S_1.   No current passes through surface S_2.

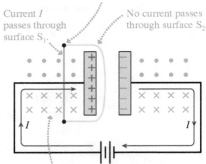

This is the magnetic field of the current I that is charging the capacitor.

(b)

Curve C S_2

S_1

$I = \dfrac{dQ}{dt}$ $I = \dfrac{dQ}{dt}$

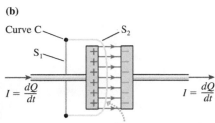

The electric flux Φ_e through surface S_2 increases as the capacitor charges.

But this leads to an interesting puzzle. FIGURE 34.16a shows a capacitor being charged. Current I, from the left, brings positive charge to the left capacitor plate. The same current carries charges away from the right capacitor plate, leaving the right plate negatively charged. This is a perfectly ordinary current in a conducting wire, and you can use the right-hand rule to verify that its magnetic field is as shown.

Curve C is a closed curve encircling the wire on the left. The current passes through surface S_1, a flat surface across C, and we could use Ampère's law to find that the magnetic field is that of a straight wire. But what happens if we try to use surface S_2 to determine $I_{through}$? Ampère's law says that we can consider *any* surface bounded by curve C, and surface S_2 certainly qualifies. But *no* current passes through S_2. Charges are brought to the left plate of the capacitor and charges are removed from the right plate, but *no* charge moves across the gap between the plates. Surface S_1 has $I_{through} = I$, but surface S_2 has $I_{through} = 0$. Another dilemma!

It would appear that Ampère's law is either wrong or incomplete. Maxwell was the first to recognize the seriousness of this problem. He noted that there may be no current passing through S_2, but, as FIGURE 34.16b shows, there is an electric flux Φ_e through S_2 due to the electric field inside the capacitor. Furthermore, this flux is *changing* with time as the capacitor charges and the electric field strength grows. Faraday had discovered the significance of a changing magnetic flux, but no one had considered a changing electric flux.

The current I passes through S_1, so Ampère's law applied to S_1 gives

$$\oint \vec{B} \cdot d\vec{s} = \mu_0 I_{through} = \mu_0 I$$

We believe this result because it gives the correct magnetic field for a current-carrying wire. Now the line integral depends only on the magnetic field at points on curve C, so its value won't change if we choose a different surface S to evaluate the current. The problem is with the right side of Ampère's law, which would incorrectly give zero if applied to surface S_2. We need to modify the right side of Ampère's law to recognize that an electric flux rather than a current passes through S_2.

The electric flux between two capacitor plates of surface area A is

$$\Phi_e = EA$$

The capacitor's electric field is $E = Q/\epsilon_0 A$; hence the flux is actually independent of the plate size:

$$\Phi_e = \frac{Q}{\epsilon_0 A} A = \frac{Q}{\epsilon_0} \tag{34.18}$$

The *rate* at which the electric flux is changing is

$$\frac{d\Phi_e}{dt} = \frac{1}{\epsilon_0} \frac{dQ}{dt} = \frac{I}{\epsilon_0} \tag{34.19}$$

where we used $I = dQ/dt$. The flux is changing with time at a rate directly proportional to the charging current I.

Equation 34.19 suggests that the quantity $\epsilon_0(d\Phi_e/dt)$ is in some sense "equivalent" to current I. Maxwell called the quantity

$$I_{\text{disp}} = \epsilon_0 \frac{d\Phi_e}{dt} \tag{34.20}$$

the **displacement current.** He had started with a fluid-like model of electric and magnetic fields, and the displacement current was analogous to the displacement of a fluid. The fluid model has since been abandoned, but the name lives on despite the fact that nothing is actually being displaced.

Maxwell hypothesized that the displacement current was the "missing" piece of Ampère's law, so he modified Ampère's law to read

$$\oint \vec{B} \cdot d\vec{s} = \mu_0(I_{\text{through}} + I_{\text{disp}}) = \mu_0\left(I_{\text{through}} + \epsilon_0 \frac{d\Phi_e}{dt}\right) \tag{34.21}$$

Equation 34.21 is now known as the Ampère-Maxwell law. When applied to Figure 34.16b, the Ampère-Maxwell law gives

$$S_1: \quad \oint \vec{B} \cdot d\vec{s} = \mu_0\left(I_{\text{through}} + \epsilon_0 \frac{d\Phi_e}{dt}\right) = \mu_0(I + 0) = \mu_0 I$$

$$S_2: \quad \oint \vec{B} \cdot d\vec{s} = \mu_0\left(I_{\text{through}} + \epsilon_0 \frac{d\Phi_e}{dt}\right) = \mu_0(0 + I) = \mu_0 I$$

where, for surface S_2, we used Equation 34.19 for $d\Phi_e/dt$. Surfaces S_1 and S_2 now both give the same result for the line integral of $\vec{B} \cdot d\vec{s}$ around the closed curve C.

NOTE ▶ The displacement current I_{disp} between the capacitor plates is numerically equal to the current I in the wires to and from the capacitor, so in some sense it allows "current" to be conserved all the way through the capacitor. Nonetheless, the displacement current is *not* a flow of charge. The displacement current is equivalent to a real current in that it creates the same magnetic field, but it does so with a changing electric flux rather than a flow of charge. ◀

The Induced Magnetic Field

Ordinary Coulomb electric fields are created by charges, but a second way to create an electric field is by having a changing magnetic field. That's Faraday's law. Ordinary magnetic fields are created by currents, but now we see that a second way to create a magnetic field is by having a changing electric field. Just as the electric field created by a changing $\vec{B}$ is called an induced electric field, the magnetic field created by a changing $\vec{E}$ is called an *induced magnetic field.*

FIGURE 34.17 shows the close analogy between induced electric fields, governed by Faraday's law, and induced magnetic fields, governed by the second term in the Ampère-Maxwell law. An increasing solenoid current causes an increasing magnetic field. The changing magnetic field, in turn, induces a circular electric field. The negative sign in Faraday's law dictates that the induced electric field direction is ccw when seen looking along the magnetic field direction.

An increasing capacitor charge causes an increasing electric field. The changing electric field, in turn, induces a circular magnetic field. But the sign of the Ampère-Maxwell law is positive, the opposite of the sign of Faraday's law, so the induced magnetic field direction is cw when you're looking along the electric field direction.

FIGURE 34.17 The close analogy between an induced electric field and an induced magnetic field.

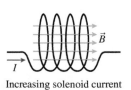

Increasing solenoid current   Increasing $\vec{B}$

Faraday's law describes an induced electric field.

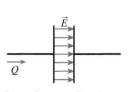

Increasing capacitor charge   Increasing $\vec{E}$

The Ampère-Maxwell law describes an induced magnetic field.

EXAMPLE 34.3 **The fields inside a charging capacitor**

A 2.0-cm-diameter parallel-plate capacitor with a 1.0 mm spacing is being charged at the rate 0.50 C/s. What is the magnetic field strength inside the capacitor at a point 0.50 cm from the axis?

MODEL The electric field inside a parallel-plate capacitor is uniform. As the capacitor is charged, the changing electric field induces a magnetic field.

VISUALIZE FIGURE 34.18 shows the fields. The induced magnetic field lines are circles concentric with the capacitor.

FIGURE 34.18 The magnetic field strength is found by integrating around a closed curve of radius r.

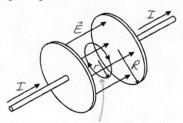

The magnetic field line is a circle concentric with the capacitor. The electric flux through this circle is $\pi r^2 E$.

SOLVE The electric field of a parallel-plate capacitor is $E = Q/\epsilon_0 A = Q/\epsilon_0 \pi R^2$. The electric flux through the circle of radius r (not the full flux of the capacitor) is

$$\Phi_e = \pi r^2 E = \pi r^2 \frac{Q}{\epsilon_0 \pi R^2} = \frac{r^2}{R^2} \frac{Q}{\epsilon_0}$$

Thus the Ampère-Maxwell law is

$$\oint \vec{B} \cdot d\vec{s} = \epsilon_0 \mu_0 \frac{d\Phi_e}{dt} = \epsilon_0 \mu_0 \frac{d}{dt}\left(\frac{r^2}{R^2} \frac{Q}{\epsilon_0}\right) = \mu_0 \frac{r^2}{R^2} \frac{dQ}{dt}$$

The magnetic field is everywhere tangent to the circle of radius r, so the integral of $\vec{B} \cdot d\vec{s}$ around the circle is simply $BL = 2\pi rB$. With this value for the line integral, the Ampère-Maxwell law becomes

$$2\pi rB = \mu_0 \frac{r^2}{R^2} \frac{dQ}{dt}$$

and thus

$$B = \frac{\mu_0}{2\pi} \frac{r}{R^2} \frac{dQ}{dt} = (2.0 \times 10^{-7}\ \text{T m/A}) \frac{0.0050\ \text{m}}{(0.010\ \text{m})^2}(0.50\ \text{C/s})$$

$$= 5.0 \times 10^{-6}\ \text{T}$$

If a changing magnetic field can induce an electric field and a changing electric field can induce a magnetic field, what happens when both fields change simultaneously? That is the question that Maxwell was finally able to answer after he modified Ampère's law to include the displacement current, and it is the subject to which we turn next.

STOP TO THINK 34.2 The electric field in four identical capacitors is shown as a function of time. Rank in order, from largest to smallest, the magnetic field strength at the outer edge of the capacitor at time T.

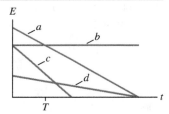

34.4 Maxwell's Equations

James Clerk Maxwell was a young, mathematically brilliant Scottish physicist. In 1855, barely 24 years old, he presented a paper to the Cambridge Philosophical Society entitled "On Faraday's Lines of Force." It had been 30 years and more since the major discoveries of Oersted, Ampère, Faraday, and others, but electromagnetism remained a loose collection of facts and "rules of thumb" without a consistent theory to link these ideas together.

Maxwell's goal was to synthesize this body of knowledge and to form a *theory* of electromagnetic fields. The critical step along the way was his recognition of the need to include a displacement-current term in Ampère's law.

Maxwell's theory of electromagnetism is embodied in four equations that we today call **Maxwell's equations.** These are

$$\oint \vec{E} \cdot d\vec{A} = \frac{Q_{in}}{\epsilon_0} \qquad\qquad \text{Gauss's law}$$

$$\oint \vec{B} \cdot d\vec{A} = 0 \qquad\qquad \text{Gauss's law for magnetism}$$

$$\oint \vec{E} \cdot d\vec{s} = -\frac{d\Phi_m}{dt} \qquad\qquad \text{Faraday's law}$$

$$\oint \vec{B} \cdot d\vec{s} = \mu_0 I_{through} + \epsilon_0 \mu_0 \frac{d\Phi_e}{dt} \qquad \text{Ampère-Maxwell law}$$

Maxwell's claim is that these four equations are a *complete* description of electric and magnetic fields. They tell us how fields are created by charges and currents, and also how fields can be induced by the changing of other fields. We need one more equation for completeness, an equation that tells us how matter responds to electromagnetic fields. The general force equation

$$\vec{F} = q(\vec{E} + \vec{v} \times \vec{B}) \qquad \text{(Lorentz force law)}$$

is known as the *Lorentz force law.* **Maxwell's equations for the fields, together with the Lorentz force law to tell us how matter responds to the fields, form the complete theory of electromagnetism.**

Maxwell's equations bring us to the pinnacle of classical physics. When combined with Newton's three laws of motion, his law of gravity, and the first and second laws of thermodynamics, we have all of classical physics—a total of just 11 equations.

While some physicists might quibble over whether all 11 are truly fundamental, the important point is not the exact number but how few equations we need to describe the overwhelming majority of our experience of the physical world. It seems as if we could have written them all on page 1 of this book and been finished, but it doesn't work that way. Each of these equations is the synthesis of a tremendous number of physical phenomena and conceptual developments. To know physics isn't just to know the equations, but to know what the equations *mean* and how they're used. That's why it's taken us so many chapters and so much effort to get to this point. Each equation is a shorthand way to summarize a book's worth of information!

Let's summarize the physical meaning of the five electromagnetic equations:

Classical physics

Newton's first law
Newton's second law
Newton's third law
Newton's law of gravity
Gauss's law
Gauss's law for magnetism
Faraday's law
Ampère-Maxwell law
Lorentz force law
First law of thermodynamics
Second law of thermodynamics

- **Gauss's law:** Charged particles create an electric field.
- **Faraday's law:** An electric field can also be created by a changing magnetic field.
- **Gauss's law for magnetism:** There are no isolated magnetic poles.
- **Ampère-Maxwell law, first half:** Currents create a magnetic field.
- **Ampère-Maxwell law, second half:** A magnetic field can also be created by a changing electric field.
- **Lorentz force law, first half:** An electric force is exerted on a charged particle in an electric field.
- **Lorentz force law, second half:** A magnetic force is exerted on a charge moving in a magnetic field.

These are the *fundamental ideas* of electromagnetism. Other important ideas, such as Ohm's law, Kirchhoff's laws, and Lenz's law, despite their practical importance, are not fundamental ideas. They can be derived from Maxwell's equations, sometimes with the addition of empirically based concepts such as resistance.

It's true that Maxwell's equations are mathematically more complex than Newton's laws and that their solution, for many problems of practical interest, requires advanced mathematics. Fortunately, we have the mathematical tools to get just far enough into Maxwell's equations to discover their most startling and revolutionary implication—the prediction of electromagnetic waves.

34.5 Electromagnetic Waves

It had been known since the early 19th century, from experiments on interference and diffraction, that light is a wave. We studied the wave properties of light in Part V, but at that time we were not able to determine just what is "waving."

Faraday speculated that light was somehow connected with electricity and magnetism, but Maxwell, using his equations of the electromagnetic field, was the first to understand that light is an oscillation of the electromagnetic field. Maxwell was able to predict that

- Electromagnetic waves can exist at any frequency, not just at the frequencies of visible light. This prediction was the harbinger of radio waves.
- All electromagnetic waves travel in a vacuum with the same speed, a speed that we now call the *speed of light.*

A general wave equation can be derived from Maxwell's equations, but the necessary mathematical techniques are beyond the level of this textbook. We'll adopt a simpler approach in which we *assume* an electromagnetic wave of a certain form and then show that it's consistent with Maxwell's equations. After all, the wave can't exist *unless* it's consistent with Maxwell's equations.

To begin, we're going to assume that electric and magnetic fields can exist independently of charges and currents in a *source-free* region of space. This is a very important assumption because it makes the statement that **fields are real entities.** They're not just cute pictures that tell us about charges and currents, but real things that can exist all by themselves. Our assertion is that the fields can exist in a self-sustaining mode in which a changing magnetic field creates an electric field (Faraday's law) that in turn changes in just the right way to re-create the original magnetic field (the Ampère-Maxwell law).

The source-free Maxwell's equations, with no charges or currents, are

$$\oint \vec{E} \cdot d\vec{A} = 0 \qquad \oint \vec{E} \cdot d\vec{s} = -\frac{d\Phi_m}{dt}$$

$$\oint \vec{B} \cdot d\vec{A} = 0 \qquad \oint \vec{B} \cdot d\vec{s} = \epsilon_0 \mu_0 \frac{d\Phi_e}{dt} \qquad (34.22)$$

Any electromagnetic wave traveling in empty space must be consistent with these equations.

Let's postulate that an electromagnetic plane wave traveling with speed v_{em} has the characteristics shown in FIGURE 34.19. It's a useful picture, and one that you'll see in any textbook, but a picture that can be very misleading if you don't think about it carefully. $\vec{E}$ and $\vec{B}$ are *not* spatial vectors. That is, they don't stretch spatially in the y- or z-direction for a certain distance. Instead, these vectors are showing the values of the electric and magnetic fields along a single line, the x-axis. An $\vec{E}$ vector pointing in the y-direction says that *at this position* on the x-axis, where the vector's tail is, the electric field points in the y-direction and has a certain strength. Nothing is "reaching" to a point in space above the x-axis. In fact, this picture contains no information about the fields anywhere other than right on the x-axis.

However, we are assuming that this is a *plane wave,* which, you'll recall from Chapter 20, is a wave for which the fields are the same *everywhere* in any yz-plane, perpendicular to the x-axis. FIGURE 34.20a shows a small section of the xy-plane where, at this instant of time,

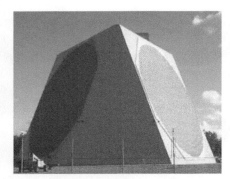

Large radar installations like this one are used to track rockets and missiles.

FIGURE 34.19 A sinusoidal electromagnetic wave.

1. A sinusoidal wave with frequency f and wavelength λ travels with wave speed v_{em}.

Wavelength λ

E_0

v_{em}

2. $\vec{E}$ and $\vec{B}$ are perpendicular to each other and to the direction of travel. The fields have amplitudes E_0 and B_0.

3. $\vec{E}$ and $\vec{B}$ are in phase. That is, they have matching crests, troughs, and zeros.

$\vec{E}$ is pointing up and $\vec{B}$ is pointing toward you. The field strengths vary with x, the direction of travel, but not with y. As the wave moves forward, the fields that are now in the x_1-plane will soon arrive in the x_2-plane, and those now in the x_2-plane will move to x_3.

FIGURE 34.20b shows a section of the yz-plane that slices the x-axis at x_2. These fields are moving out of the page, coming toward you. The fields are the same everywhere in this plane, which is what we mean by a plane wave. If you watched a movie of the event, you would see the $\vec{E}$ and $\vec{B}$ fields at each point in this plane *oscillating* in time, but always synchronized with all the other points in the plane.

Gauss's Laws

Now that we understand the shape of the electromagnetic field, we can check its consistency with Maxwell's equations. This field is a sinusoidal wave, so the components of the fields are

$$E_x = 0 \quad E_y = E_0 \sin\big(2\pi(x/\lambda - ft)\big) \quad E_z = 0$$
$$B_x = 0 \quad B_y = 0 \qquad\qquad\qquad B_z = B_0 \sin\big(2\pi(x/\lambda - ft)\big) \tag{34.23}$$

where E_0 and B_0 are the amplitudes of the oscillating electric and magnetic fields.

FIGURE 34.21 shows an imaginary box—a Gaussian surface—centered on the x-axis. Both electric and magnetic field vectors exist at each point in space, but the figure shows them separately for clarity. $\vec{E}$ oscillates along the y-axis, so all electric field lines enter and leave the box through the top and bottom surfaces; no electric field lines pass through the sides of the box.

FIGURE 34.21 A closed surface can be used to check Gauss's law for the electric and magnetic fields.

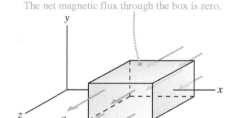

The net electric flux through the box is zero.

The net magnetic flux through the box is zero.

Electric field

Magnetic field

Because this is a plane wave, the magnitude of each electric field vector entering the bottom of the box is exactly matched by the electric field vector leaving the top. The electric flux through the top of the box is equal in magnitude but opposite in sign to the flux through the bottom, and the flux through the sides is zero. Thus the *net* electric flux is $\Phi_e = 0$. There is no charge inside the box because there are no sources in this region of space, so we also have $Q_{in} = 0$. Hence the electric field of a plane wave is consistent with the first of the source-free Maxwell's equations, Gauss's law.

The exact same argument applies to the magnetic field. The net magnetic flux is $\Phi_m = 0$; thus the magnetic field is consistent with the second of Maxwell's equations.

Faraday's Law

Faraday's law is concerned with the changing magnetic flux through a closed curve. We'll apply Faraday's law to a narrow rectangle in the xy-plane, shown in **FIGURE 34.22**, with height h and width Δx. We'll assume Δx to be so small that $\vec{B}$ is essentially constant over the width of the rectangle.

FIGURE 34.20 Interpreting the electromagnetic wave of Figure 34.19.

(a) Wave traveling to the right

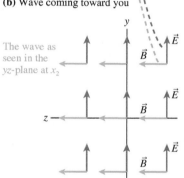

The wave as seen in the xy-plane

$\vec{B}$ out of page

(b) Wave coming toward you

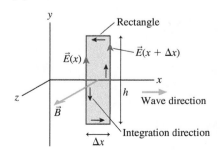

The wave as seen in the yz-plane at x_2

FIGURE 34.22 Faraday's law can be applied to a narrow rectangle in the xy-plane.

Rectangle

$\vec{E}(x)$ $\vec{E}(x + \Delta x)$

$\vec{B}$

h

Wave direction

Integration direction

Δx

The magnetic field $\vec{B}$ points in the z-direction, perpendicular to the rectangle. The magnetic flux through the rectangle is $\Phi_m = B_z A_{\text{rectangle}} = B_z h \Delta x$, hence the flux *changes* at the rate

$$\frac{d\Phi_m}{dt} = \frac{d}{dt}(B_z h \Delta x) = \frac{\partial B_z}{\partial t} h \Delta x \qquad (34.24)$$

The ordinary derivative dB_z/dt, which is the full rate of change of B from all possible causes, becomes a partial derivative $\partial B_z/\partial t$ in this situation because the change in magnetic flux is due entirely to the change of B with time and not at all to the spatial variation of B.

According to our sign convention, we have to go around the rectangle in a ccw direction to make the flux positive. Thus we must also use a ccw direction to evaluate the line integral

$$\oint \vec{E} \cdot d\vec{s} = \int_{\text{right}} \vec{E} \cdot d\vec{s} + \int_{\text{top}} \vec{E} \cdot d\vec{s} + \int_{\text{left}} \vec{E} \cdot d\vec{s} + \int_{\text{bottom}} \vec{E} \cdot d\vec{s} \qquad (34.25)$$

The electric field $\vec{E}$ points in the y-direction, hence $\vec{E} \cdot d\vec{s} = 0$ at all points on the top and bottom edges, and these two integrals are zero.

Along the left edge of the loop, at position x, $\vec{E}$ has the same value at every point. Figure 34.22 shows that the direction of $\vec{E}$ is *opposite* to $d\vec{s}$, thus $\vec{E} \cdot d\vec{s} = -E_y(x)\,ds$. On the right edge of the loop, at position $x + \Delta x$, $\vec{E}$ is *parallel* to $d\vec{s}$ and $\vec{E} \cdot d\vec{s} = E_y(x + \Delta x)\,ds$. Thus the line integral of $\vec{E} \cdot d\vec{s}$ around the rectangle is

$$\oint \vec{E} \cdot d\vec{s} = -E_y(x)h + E_y(x + \Delta x)h = [E_y(x + \Delta x) - E_y(x)]h \qquad (34.26)$$

NOTE ▶ $E_y(x)$ indicates that E_y is a function of the position x. It is *not* E_y multiplied by x. ◀

You learned in calculus that the derivative of the function $f(x)$ is

$$\frac{df}{dx} = \lim_{\Delta x \to 0} \left[\frac{f(x + \Delta x) - f(x)}{\Delta x} \right]$$

We've assumed that Δx is very small. If we now let the width of the rectangle go to zero, $\Delta x \to 0$, Equation 34.26 becomes

$$\oint \vec{E} \cdot d\vec{s} = \frac{\partial E_y}{\partial x} h \Delta x \qquad (34.27)$$

We've used a partial derivative because E_y is a function of both position x and time t.

Now, using Equations 34.24 and 34.27, we can write Faraday's law as

$$\oint \vec{E} \cdot d\vec{s} = \frac{\partial E_y}{\partial x} h \Delta x = -\frac{d\Phi_m}{dt} = -\frac{\partial B_z}{\partial t} h \Delta x$$

The area $h \Delta x$ of the rectangle cancels, and we're left with

$$\frac{\partial E_y}{\partial x} = -\frac{\partial B_z}{\partial t} \qquad (34.28)$$

Equation 34.28, which compares the rate at which E_y varies with position to the rate at which B_z varies with time, is a *required condition* that an electromagnetic wave must satisfy to be consistent with Maxwell's equations. We can use Equations 34.23 for E_y and B_z to evaluate the partial derivatives:

$$\frac{\partial E_y}{\partial x} = \frac{2\pi E_0}{\lambda} \cos\left(2\pi(x/\lambda - ft)\right)$$

$$\frac{\partial B_z}{\partial t} = -2\pi f B_0 \cos\left(2\pi(x/\lambda - ft)\right)$$

Thus the required condition of Equation 34.28 is

$$\frac{\partial E_y}{\partial x} = \frac{2\pi E_0}{\lambda}\cos\left(2\pi(x/\lambda - ft)\right) = -\frac{\partial B_z}{\partial t} = 2\pi f B_0 \cos\left(2\pi(x/\lambda - ft)\right)$$

Canceling the many common factors, and multiplying by λ, we're left with

$$E_0 = (\lambda f)B_0 = v_{\text{em}}B_0 \qquad (34.29)$$

where we used the fact that $\lambda f = v$ for any sinusoidal wave.

Equation 34.29, which came from applying Faraday's law, tells us that the field amplitudes E_0 and B_0 of an electromagnetic wave are not arbitrary. **Once the amplitude B_0 of the magnetic field wave is specified, the electric field amplitude E_0 must be $E_0 = v_{\text{em}}B_0$.** Otherwise the fields won't satisfy Maxwell's equations.

The Ampère-Maxwell Law

We have one equation to go, but this one will now be easier. The Ampère-Maxwell law is concerned with the changing electric flux through a closed curve. FIGURE 34.23 shows a very narrow rectangle of width Δx and length l in the xz-plane. The electric field is perpendicular to this rectangle; hence the electric flux through it is $\Phi_e = E_y A_{\text{rectangle}} = E_y l \Delta x$. This flux is changing at the rate

$$\frac{d\Phi_e}{dt} = \frac{d}{dt}(E_y l \Delta x) = \frac{\partial E_y}{\partial t}l\Delta x \qquad (34.30)$$

The line integral of $\vec{B} \cdot d\vec{s}$ around this closed rectangle is calculated just like the line integral of $\vec{E} \cdot d\vec{s}$ in Figure 34.22. $\vec{B}$ is perpendicular to $d\vec{s}$ on the narrow ends, so $\vec{B} \cdot d\vec{s} = 0$. The field at *all* points on the left edge, at position x, is $\vec{B}(x)$, and this field is parallel to $d\vec{s}$ to make $\vec{B} \cdot d\vec{s} = B_z(x)\,ds$. Similarly, $\vec{B} \cdot d\vec{s} = -B_z(x + \Delta x)\,ds$ at all points on the right edge, where $\vec{B}$ is opposite to $d\vec{s}$.

Thus, if we let $\Delta x \to 0$,

$$\oint \vec{B} \cdot d\vec{s} = B_z(x)l - B_z(x + \Delta x)l = -[B_z(x + \Delta x) - B_z(x)]l$$
$$= -\frac{\partial B_z}{\partial x}l\Delta x \qquad (34.31)$$

Equations 34.30 and 34.31 can now be used in the Ampère-Maxwell law:

$$\oint \vec{B} \cdot d\vec{s} = -\frac{\partial B_z}{\partial x}l\Delta x = \epsilon_0 \mu_0 \frac{d\Phi_e}{dt} = \epsilon_0 \mu_0 \frac{\partial E_y}{\partial t}l\Delta x$$

The area of the rectangle cancels, and we're left with

$$\frac{\partial B_z}{\partial x} = -\epsilon_0 \mu_0 \frac{\partial E_y}{\partial t} \qquad (34.32)$$

Equation 34.32 is a second required condition that the fields must satisfy. If we again evaluate the partial derivatives, using Equations 34.23 for E_y and B_z, we find

$$\frac{\partial E_y}{\partial t} = -2\pi f E_0 \cos\left(2\pi(x/\lambda - ft)\right)$$

$$\frac{\partial B_z}{\partial x} = \frac{2\pi B_0}{\lambda}\cos\left(2\pi(x/\lambda - ft)\right)$$

With these, Equation 34.32 becomes

$$\frac{\partial B_z}{\partial x} = \frac{2\pi B_0}{\lambda}\cos\left(2\pi(x/\lambda - ft)\right) = -\epsilon_0\mu_0\frac{\partial E_y}{\partial t} = 2\pi\epsilon_0\mu_0 f E_0 \cos\left(2\pi(x/\lambda - ft)\right)$$

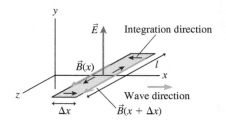

FIGURE 34.23 The Ampère-Maxwell law can be applied to a narrow rectangle in the xz-plane.

A final round of cancellations and another use of $\lambda f = v_{em}$ leave us with

$$E_0 = \frac{B_0}{\epsilon_0 \mu_0 \lambda f} = \frac{B_0}{\epsilon_0 \mu_0 v_{em}} \tag{34.33}$$

The last of Maxwell's equations gives us another constraint between E_0 and B_0.

The Speed of Light

But how can Equation 34.29, which required $E_0 = v_{em} B_0$, and Equation 34.33 both be true at the same time? The one and only way is if

$$\frac{1}{\epsilon_0 \mu_0 v_{em}} = v_{em}$$

from which we find

$$v_{em} = \frac{1}{\sqrt{\epsilon_0 \mu_0}} = 3.00 \times 10^8 \text{ m/s} = c \tag{34.34}$$

This is a remarkable conclusion. The constants ϵ_0 and μ_0 are from electrostatics and magnetostatics, where they determine the size of $\vec{E}$ and $\vec{B}$ due to point charges. Coulomb's law and the Biot-Savart law, where ϵ_0 and μ_0 first appeared, have nothing to do with waves. Yet Maxwell's theory of electromagnetism ends up predicting that electric and magnetic fields can form a self-sustaining electromagnetic wave *if* that wave travels at the specific speed $v_{em} = 1/\sqrt{\epsilon_0 \mu_0}$. No other speed will satisfy Maxwell's equations.

We've made no assumption about the frequency of the wave, so apparently all electromagnetic waves, regardless of their frequency, travel (in vacuum) at the same speed $v_{em} = 1/\sqrt{\epsilon_0 \mu_0}$. We call this speed c, the "speed of light," but it applies equally well from low-frequency radio waves to ultrahigh-frequency x rays.

STOP TO THINK 34.3   An electromagnetic wave is propagating in the positive x-direction. At this instant of time, what is the direction of $\vec{E}$ at the center of the rectangle?

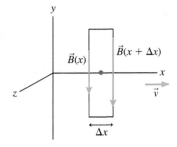

a. In the positive x-direction
b. In the negative x-direction
c. In the positive y-direction
d. In the negative y-direction
e. In the positive z-direction
f. In the negative z-direction

34.6 Properties of Electromagnetic Waves

We've demonstrated that one very specific sinusoidal wave is consistent with Maxwell's equations. It's possible to show that *any* electromagnetic wave, whether it's sinusoidal or not, must satisfy four basic conditions:

1. The fields $\vec{E}$ and $\vec{B}$ are perpendicular to the direction of propagation $\vec{v}_{em}$. Thus an electromagnetic wave is a transverse wave.
2. $\vec{E}$ and $\vec{B}$ are perpendicular to each other in a manner such that $\vec{E} \times \vec{B}$ is in the direction of $\vec{v}_{em}$.
3. The wave travels in vacuum at speed $v_{em} = 1/\sqrt{\epsilon_0 \mu_0} = c$.
4. $E = cB$ at any point on the wave.

In this section, we'll look at some other properties of electromagnetic waves.

Energy and Intensity

Waves transfer energy. Ocean waves erode beaches, sound waves set your eardrums vibrating, and light from the sun warms the earth. The energy flow of an electromagnetic wave is described by the **Poynting vector** $\vec{S}$, defined as

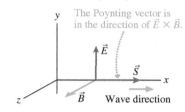

FIGURE 34.24 The Poynting vector.

The Poynting vector is in the direction of $\vec{E} \times \vec{B}$.

Wave direction

$$\vec{S} \equiv \frac{1}{\mu_0}\vec{E} \times \vec{B} \tag{34.35}$$

The Poynting vector, shown in FIGURE 34.24, has two important properties:

1. The Poynting vector points in the direction in which an electromagnetic wave is traveling. You can see this by looking back at Figure 34.19.
2. It is straightforward to show that the units of S are W/m^2, or power (joules per second) per unit area. Thus the magnitude S of the Poynting vector measures the rate of energy transfer per unit area of the wave.

Because $\vec{E}$ and $\vec{B}$ of an electromagnetic wave are perpendicular to each other, and $E = cB$, the magnitude of the Poynting vector is

$$S = \frac{EB}{\mu_0} = \frac{E^2}{c\mu_0} = c\epsilon_0 E^2$$

The Poynting vector is a function of time, oscillating from zero to $S_{max} = E_0^2/c\mu_0$ and back to zero twice during each period of the wave's oscillation. That is, the energy flow in an electromagnetic wave is not smooth. It "pulses" as the electric and magnetic fields oscillate in intensity. We're unaware of this pulsing because the electromagnetic waves that we can sense—light waves—have such high frequencies.

Of more interest is the *average* energy transfer, averaged over one cycle of oscillation, which is the wave's **intensity** I. In our earlier study of waves, we defined the intensity of a wave to be $I = P/A$, where P is the power (energy transferred per second) of a wave that impinges on area A. Because $E = E_0 \sin\left(2\pi(x/\lambda - ft)\right)$, and the average over one period of $\sin^2\left(2\pi(x/\lambda - ft)\right)$ is $\frac{1}{2}$, the intensity of an electromagnetic wave is

$$I = \frac{P}{A} = S_{avg} = \frac{1}{2c\mu_0}E_0^2 = \frac{c\epsilon_0}{2}E_0^2 \tag{34.36}$$

Equation 34.36 relates the intensity of an electromagnetic wave, a quantity that is easily measured, to the amplitude of the wave's electric field.

The intensity of a plane wave, with constant electric field amplitude E_0, would not change with distance. But a plane wave is an idealization; there are no true plane waves in nature. You learned in Chapter 20 that, to conserve energy, the intensity of a wave far from its source decreases with the inverse square of the distance. If a source with power P_{source} emits electromagnetic waves *uniformly* in all directions, the electromagnetic wave intensity at distance r from the source is

$$I = \frac{P_{source}}{4\pi r^2} \tag{34.37}$$

Equation 34.37 simply expresses the recognition that the energy of the wave is spread over a sphere of surface area $4\pi r^2$.

EXAMPLE 34.4 **Fields of a cell phone**

A digital cell phone broadcasts a 0.60 W signal at a frequency of 1.9 GHz. What are the amplitudes of the electric and magnetic fields at a distance of 10 cm, about the distance to the center of the user's brain?

MODEL Treat the cell phone as a point source of electromagnetic waves.

Continued

SOLVE The intensity of a 0.60 W point source at a distance of 10 cm is

$$I = \frac{P_{\text{source}}}{4\pi r^2} = \frac{0.60 \text{ W}}{4\pi(0.10 \text{ m})^2} = 4.78 \text{ W/m}^2$$

We can find the electric field amplitude from the intensity:

$$E_0 = \sqrt{\frac{2I}{c\epsilon_0}} = \sqrt{\frac{2(4.78 \text{ W/m}^2)}{(3.00 \times 10^8 \text{ m/s})(8.85 \times 10^{-12} \text{ C}^2/\text{N m}^2)}}$$

$$= 60 \text{ V/m}$$

The amplitudes of the electric and magnetic fields are related by the speed of light. This allows us to compute

$$B_0 = \frac{E_0}{c} = 2.0 \times 10^{-7} \text{ T}$$

ASSESS The electric field amplitude is modest; the magnetic field amplitude is very small. This implies that the interaction of electromagnetic waves with matter is mostly due to the electric field.

STOP TO THINK 34.4 An electromagnetic wave is traveling in the positive y-direction. The electric field at one instant of time is shown at one position. The magnetic field at this position points

a. In the positive x-direction.
b. In the negative x-direction.
c. In the positive y-direction.
d. In the negative y-direction.
e. Toward the origin.
f. Away from the origin.

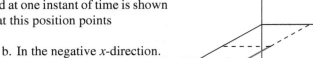

Radiation Pressure

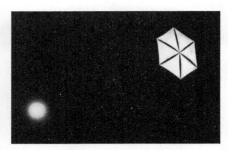

Artist's conception of a future spacecraft powered by radiation pressure from the sun.

Electromagnetic waves transfer not only energy but also momentum. An object gains momentum when it absorbs electromagnetic waves, much as a ball at rest gains momentum when struck by a ball in motion.

Suppose we shine a beam of light on an object that completely absorbs the light energy. If the object absorbs energy during a time interval Δt, its momentum changes by

$$\Delta p = \frac{\text{energy absorbed}}{c}$$

This is a consequence of Maxwell's theory, which we'll state without proof.

The momentum change implies that the light is exerting a force on the object. Newton's second law, in terms of momentum, is $F = \Delta p/\Delta t$. The radiation force due to the beam of light is

$$F = \frac{\Delta p}{\Delta t} = \frac{(\text{energy absorbed})/\Delta t}{c} = \frac{P}{c}$$

where P is the power (joules per second) of the light.

It's more interesting to consider the force exerted on an object per unit area, which is called the **radiation pressure** p_{rad}. The radiation pressure on an object that absorbs all the light is

$$p_{\text{rad}} = \frac{F}{A} = \frac{P/A}{c} = \frac{I}{c} \tag{34.38}$$

where I is the intensity of the light wave. The subscript on p_{rad} is important in this context to distinguish the radiation pressure from the momentum p.

EXAMPLE 34.5 **Solar sailing**

A low-cost way of sending spacecraft to other planets would be to use the radiation pressure on a solar sail. The intensity of the sun's electromagnetic radiation at distances near the earth's orbit is about 1300 W/m². What size sail would be needed to accelerate a 10,000 kg spacecraft toward Mars at 0.010 m/s²?

MODEL Assume that the solar sail is perfectly absorbing.

SOLVE The force that will create a 0.010 m/s² acceleration is $F = ma = 100$ N. We can use Equation 34.38 to find the sail

area that, by absorbing light, will receive a 100 N force from the sun:

$$A = \frac{cF}{I} = \frac{(3.00 \times 10^8 \text{ m/s})(100 \text{ N})}{1300 \text{ W/m}^2} = 2.3 \times 10^7 \text{ m}^2$$

ASSESS If the sail is a square, it would need to be 4.8 km × 4.8 km, or roughly 3 mi × 3 mi. This is large, but not entirely out of the question with thin films that can be unrolled in space. But how will the crew return from Mars?

Antennas

We've seen that an electromagnetic wave is self-sustaining, independent of charges or currents. However, charges and currents are needed at the *source* of an electromagnetic wave. We'll take a brief look at how an electromagnetic wave is generated by an antenna.

FIGURE 34.25 is the electric field of an electric dipole. If the dipole is vertical, the electric field $\vec{E}$ at points along a horizontal line is also vertical. Reversing the dipole, by switching the charges, reverses $\vec{E}$. If the charges were to oscillate back and forth, switching position at frequency f, then $\vec{E}$ would oscillate in a vertical plane. The changing $\vec{E}$ would then create an induced magnetic field $\vec{B}$, which could then create an $\vec{E}$, which could then create a $\vec{B}, \ldots$, and an electromagnetic wave at frequency f would radiate out into space.

FIGURE 34.25 An electric dipole creates an electric field that reverses direction if the dipole charges are switched.

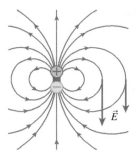

Positive charge on top

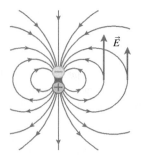

Negative charge on top

This is exactly what an **antenna** does. FIGURE 34.26 shows two metal wires attached to the terminals of an oscillating voltage source. The figure shows an instant when the top wire is negative and the bottom is positive, but these will reverse in half a cycle. The wire is basically an oscillating dipole, and it creates an oscillating electric field. The oscillating $\vec{E}$ induces an oscillating $\vec{B}$, and they take off as an electromagnetic wave at speed $v_{em} = c$. The wave does need oscillating charges as a *wave source*, but once created it is self-sustaining and independent of the source. The antenna might be destroyed, but the wave could travel billions of light years across the universe, bearing the legacy of James Clerk Maxwell.

FIGURE 34.26 An antenna generates a self-sustaining electromagnetic wave.

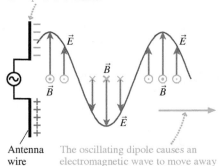

An oscillating voltage causes the dipole to oscillate.

Antenna wire   The oscillating dipole causes an electromagnetic wave to move away from the antenna at speed $v_{em} = c$.

STOP TO THINK 34.5 The amplitude of the oscillating electric field at your cell phone is 4.0 μV/m when you are 10 km east of the broadcast antenna. What is the electric field amplitude when you are 20 km east of the antenna?

a. 1.0 μV/m
b. 2.0 μV/m
c. 4.0 μV/m
d. There's not enough information to tell.

34.7 Polarization

The plane of the electric field vector $\vec{E}$ and the Poynting vector $\vec{S}$ (the direction of propagation) is called the **plane of polarization** of an electromagnetic wave. Figure 34.27 shows two electromagnetic waves moving along the x-axis. The electric field in FIGURE 34.27a oscillates vertically, so we would say that this wave is *vertically polarized*. Similarly the wave in FIGURE 34.27b is *horizontally polarized*. Other polarizations are possible, such as a wave polarized 30° away from horizontal.

FIGURE 34.27 The plane of polarization is the plane in which the electric field vector oscillates.

(a) Vertical polarization

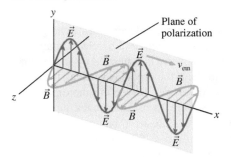

(b) Horizontal polarization

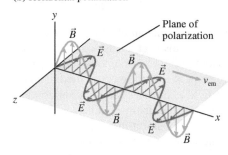

NOTE ▶ This use of the term "polarization" is completely independent of the idea of *charge polarization* that you learned about in Chapter 25. ◀

Some wave sources, such as lasers and radio antennas, emit *polarized* electromagnetic waves with a well-defined plane of polarization. By contrast, most natural sources of electromagnetic radiation are unpolarized, emitting waves whose electric fields oscillate randomly with all possible orientations.

A few natural sources are *partially polarized,* meaning that one direction of polarization is more prominent than others. The light of the sky at right angles to the sun is partially polarized because of how the sun's light scatters from air molecules to create skylight. Bees and other insects make use of this partial polarization to navigate. Light reflected from a flat, horizontal surface, such as a road or the surface of a lake, has a predominantly horizontal polarization. This is the rationale for using polarizing sunglasses.

The most common way of artificially generating polarized visible light is to send unpolarized light through a *polarizing filter*. The first widely used polarizing filter was invented by Edwin Land in 1928, while he was still an undergraduate student. He developed an improved version, called Polaroid, in 1938. Polaroid, as shown in FIGURE 34.28, is a plastic sheet containing very long organic molecules known as polymers. The sheets are formed in such a way that the polymers are all aligned to form a grid, rather like the metal bars in a barbecue grill. The sheet is then chemically treated to make the polymer molecules somewhat conducting.

As a light wave travels through Polaroid, the component of the electric field oscillating parallel to the polymer grid drives the conduction electrons up and down the molecules. The electrons absorb energy from the light wave, so the parallel component of $\vec{E}$ is absorbed in the filter. But the conduction electrons can't oscillate perpendicular to the molecules, so the component of $\vec{E}$ perpendicular to the polymer grid passes through without absorption. Thus the light wave emerging from a polarizing filter is polarized perpendicular to the polymer grid.

FIGURE 34.28 A polarizing filter.

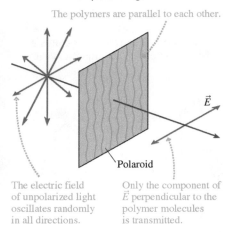

The polymers are parallel to each other.

Polaroid

The electric field of unpolarized light oscillates randomly in all directions.

Only the component of $\vec{E}$ perpendicular to the polymer molecules is transmitted.

Malus's Law

Suppose a *polarized* light wave of intensity I_0 approaches a polarizing filter. What is the intensity of the light that passes through the filter? FIGURE 34.29 shows that an oscillating electric field can be decomposed into components parallel and perpendicular to the polarizer's axis (i.e., the polarization direction transmitted by the polarizer). If we call the polarizer axis the y-axis, then the incident electric field is

$$\vec{E}_{\text{incident}} = E_\perp \hat{i} + E_\| \hat{j} = E_0 \sin\theta\, \hat{i} + E_0 \cos\theta\, \hat{j} \qquad (34.39)$$

where θ is the angle between the incident plane of polarization and the polarizer axis.

If the polarizer is ideal, meaning that light polarized parallel to the axis is 100% transmitted and light perpendicular to the axis is 100% blocked, then the electric field of the light transmitted by the filter is

$$\vec{E}_{\text{transmitted}} = E_\| \hat{j} = E_0 \cos\theta\, \hat{j} \qquad (34.40)$$

Because the intensity depends on the square of the electric field amplitude, you can see that the transmitted intensity is related to the incident intensity by

$$I_{\text{transmitted}} = I_0 \cos^2\theta \qquad \text{(incident light polarized)} \qquad (34.41)$$

This result, which was discovered experimentally in 1809, is called **Malus's law.**

FIGURE 34.30a shows that Malus's law can be demonstrated with two polarizing filters. The first, called the *polarizer,* is used to produce polarized light of intensity I_0. The second, called the *analyzer,* is rotated by angle θ relative to the polarizer. As the photographs of FIGURE 34.30b show, the transmission of the analyzer is (ideally) 100% when $\theta = 0°$ and steadily decreases to zero when $\theta = 90°$. Two polarizing filters with perpendicular axes, called *crossed polarizers,* block all the light.

FIGURE 34.29 An incident electric field can be decomposed into components parallel and perpendicular to a polarizer's axis.

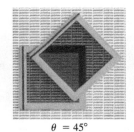

FIGURE 34.30 The intensity of the transmitted light depends on the angle between the polarizing filters.

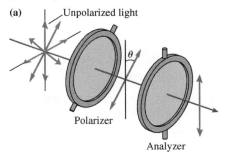

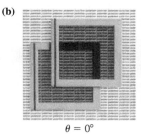

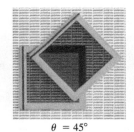

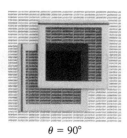

$\theta = 0°$ $\theta = 45°$ $\theta = 90°$

Suppose the light incident on a polarizing filter is *unpolarized,* as is the light incident from the left on the polarizer in Figure 34.30a. The electric field of unpolarized light varies randomly through all possible values of θ. Because the *average* value of $\cos^2\theta$ is $\frac{1}{2}$, the intensity transmitted by a polarizing filter is

$$I_{\text{transmitted}} = \frac{1}{2} I_0 \qquad \text{(incident light unpolarized)} \qquad (34.42)$$

In other words, a polarizing filter passes 50% of unpolarized light and blocks 50%.

In polarizing sunglasses, the polymer grid is aligned horizontally (when the glasses are in the normal orientation) so that the glasses transmit vertically polarized light. Most natural light is unpolarized, so the glasses reduce the light intensity by 50%. But *glare*— the reflection of the sun and the skylight from roads and other horizontal surfaces—has a strong horizontal polarization. This light is almost completely blocked by the Polaroid, so the sunglasses "cut glare" without affecting the main scene you wish to see.

You can test whether your sunglasses are polarized by holding them in front of you and rotating them as you look at the glare reflecting from a horizontal surface. Polarizing sunglasses substantially reduce the glare when the glasses are "normal" but not when the glasses are 90° from normal. (You can also test them against a pair of sunglasses known to be polarizing by seeing if all light is blocked when the lenses of the two pairs are crossed.)

The vertical polarizer blocks the horizontally polarized glare from the surface of the water.

STOP TO THINK 34.6 Unpolarized light of equal intensity is incident on four pairs of polarizing filters. Rank in order, from largest to smallest, the intensities I_a to I_d transmitted through the second polarizer of each pair.

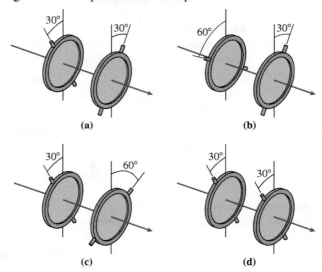

(a) (b)

(c) (d)

CHALLENGE EXAMPLE 34.6 | **Light propulsion**

Future space rockets might propel themselves by firing laser beams, rather than exhaust gases, out the back. The acceleration would be small, but it could continue for months or years in the vacuum of space. Consider a 1200 kg unmanned space probe powered by a 15 MW laser. After one year, how far will it have traveled and how fast will it be going?

MODEL Assume the laser efficiency is so high that it can be powered for a year with a negligible mass of fuel.

SOLVE Light waves transfer not only energy but also momentum, which is how they exert a radiation-pressure force. We found that the radiation force of a light beam of power P is

$$F = \frac{P}{c}$$

From Newton's third law, the emitted light waves must exert an equal-but-opposite reaction force on the source of the light. In this case, the emitted light exerts a force of this magnitude on the space probe to which the laser is attached. This reaction force causes the probe to accelerate at

$$a = \frac{F}{m} = \frac{P}{mc} = \frac{15 \times 10^6 \text{ W}}{(1200 \text{ kg})(3.0 \times 10^8 \text{ m/s})}$$
$$= 4.2 \times 10^{-5} \text{ m/s}^2$$

As expected, the acceleration is extremely small. But one year is a large amount of time: $\Delta t = 3.15 \times 10^7$ s. After one year of acceleration,

$$v = a\Delta t = 1300 \text{ m/s}$$
$$d = \tfrac{1}{2}a(\Delta t)^2 = 2.1 \times 10^{10} \text{ m}$$

The space probe will have traveled 2.1×10^{10} m and will be going 1300 m/s.

ASSESS Even after a year, the speed is not exceptionally fast—only about 2900 mph. But the probe will have traveled a substantial distance, about 25% of the distance to Mars.

SUMMARY

The goal of Chapter 34 has been to study the properties of electromagnetic fields and waves.

General Principles

Maxwell's Equations

These equations govern electromagnetic fields:

$$\oint \vec{E} \cdot d\vec{A} = \frac{Q_{in}}{\epsilon_0}$$ Gauss's law

$$\oint \vec{B} \cdot d\vec{A} = 0$$ Gauss's law for magnetism

$$\oint \vec{E} \cdot d\vec{s} = -\frac{d\Phi_m}{dt}$$ Faraday's law

$$\oint \vec{B} \cdot d\vec{s} = \mu_0 I_{through} + \epsilon_0 \mu_0 \frac{d\Phi_e}{dt}$$ Ampère-Maxwell law

Maxwell's equations tell us that:
An electric field can be created by
- Charged particles
- A changing magnetic field

A magnetic field can be created by
- A current
- A changing electric field

Lorentz Force

This force law governs the interaction of charged particles with electromagnetic fields:

$$\vec{F} = q(\vec{E} + \vec{v} \times \vec{B})$$

- An electric field exerts a force on any charged particle.
- A magnetic field exerts a force on a moving charged particle.

Field Transformations

Fields measured in reference frame A to be $\vec{E}_A$ and $\vec{B}_A$ are found in frame B to be

$$\vec{E}_B = \vec{E}_A + \vec{v}_{BA} \times \vec{B}_A$$

$$\vec{B}_B = \vec{B}_A - \frac{1}{c^2}\vec{v}_{BA} \times \vec{E}_A$$

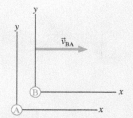

Important Concepts

Induced fields

An induced electric field is created by a changing magnetic field.

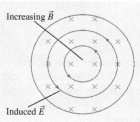

An induced magnetic field is created by a changing electric field.

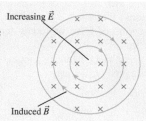

These fields can exist independently of charges and currents.

An electromagnetic wave is a self-sustaining electromagnetic field.
- An em wave is a transverse wave with $\vec{E}$, $\vec{B}$, and $\vec{v}_{em}$ mutually perpendicular.
- An em wave propagates with speed $v_{em} = c = 1/\sqrt{\epsilon_0 \mu_0}$.
- The electric and magnetic field strengths are related by $E = cB$.
- The **Poynting vector** $\vec{S} = (\vec{E} \times \vec{B})/\mu_0$ is the energy transfer in the direction of travel.
- The wave **intensity** is $I = P/A = (1/2c\mu_0)E_0^2 = (c\epsilon_0/2)E_0^2$.

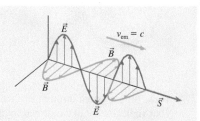

Applications

Polarization

The electric field and the Poynting vector define the **plane of polarization.** The intensity of polarized light transmitted through a polarizing filter is given by Malus's law:

$$I = I_0 \cos^2 \theta$$

where θ is the angle between the electric field and the polarizer axis.

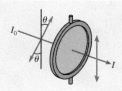

Terms and Notation

Galilean field transformation equations
displacement current
Maxwell's equations

Poynting vector, $\vec{S}$
intensity, I
radiation pressure, p_{rad}

antenna
plane of polarization
Malus's law

CONCEPTUAL QUESTIONS

1. Andre is flying his spaceship to the left through the laboratory magnetic field of FIGURE Q34.1.
   a. Does Andre see a magnetic field? If so, in which direction does it point?
   b. Does Andre see an electric field? If so, in which direction does it point?

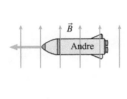

FIGURE Q34.1

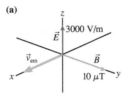

FIGURE Q34.2

2. Sharon drives her rocket through the magnetic field of FIGURE Q34.2 traveling to the right at a speed of 1000 m/s as measured by Bill. As she passes Bill, she shoots a positive charge backward at a speed of 1000 m/s relative to her.
   a. According to Sharon, what kind of force or forces act on the charge? In which directions? Explain.
   b. According to Bill, what kind of force or forces act on the charge? In which directions? Explain.

3. If you curl the fingers of your right hand as shown, are the electric fluxes in FIGURE Q34.3 positive or negative?

(a)

(b)

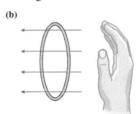

FIGURE Q34.3

4. What is the current through surface S in FIGURE Q34.4 if you curl your right fingers in the direction of the arrow?

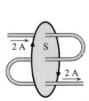

FIGURE Q34.4

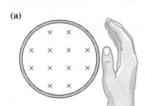

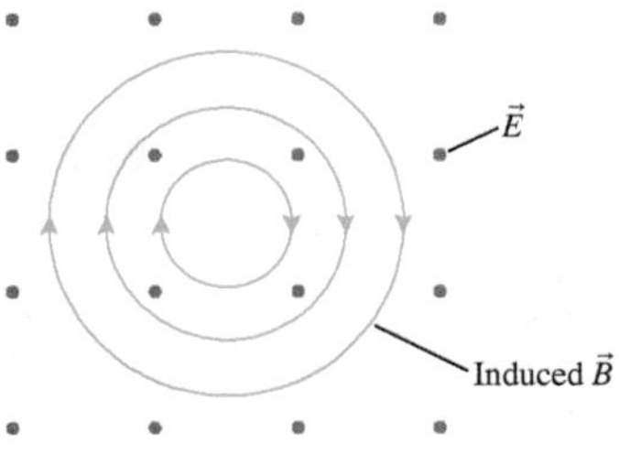

FIGURE Q34.5

5. Is the electric field strength in FIGURE Q34.5 increasing, decreasing, or not changing? Explain.

6. Do the situations in FIGURE Q34.6 represent possible electromagnetic waves? If not, why not?

(a)

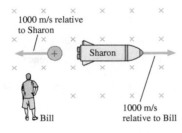

(b)

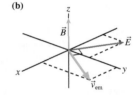

FIGURE Q34.6

7. In what directions are the electromagnetic waves traveling in FIGURE Q34.7?

(a)

(b)

FIGURE Q34.7

8. The intensity of an electromagnetic wave is 10 W/m². What will the intensity be if:
   a. The amplitude of the electric field is doubled?
   b. The amplitude of the magnetic field is doubled?
   c. The amplitudes of both the electric and the magnetic fields are doubled?
   d. The frequency is doubled?

9. Older televisions used a *loop antenna* like the one in FIGURE Q34.9. How does this antenna work?

FIGURE Q34.9

10. A vertically polarized electromagnetic wave passes through the five polarizers in FIGURE Q34.10. Rank in order, from largest to smallest, the transmitted intensities I_a to I_e.

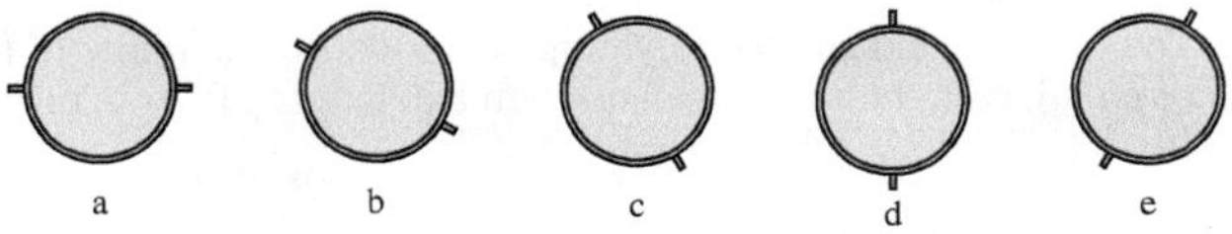

a   b   c   d   e

FIGURE Q34.10

EXERCISES AND PROBLEMS

Problems labeled [ ] integrate material from earlier chapters.

Exercises

Section 34.1 *E* or *B*? It Depends on Your Perspective

1. | A rocket cruises past a laboratory at 1.00×10^6 m/s in the positive x-direction just as a proton is launched with velocity (in the laboratory frame) $\vec{v} = (1.41 \times 10^6 \hat{\imath} + 1.41 \times 10^6 \hat{\jmath})$ m/s. What are the proton's speed and its angle from the y-axis in (a) the laboratory frame and (b) the rocket frame?

2. | FIGURE EX34.2 shows the electric and magnetic field in frame A. A rocket in frame B travels parallel to one of the axes of the A coordinate system. Along which axis must the rocket travel, and in which direction, in order for the rocket scientists to measure (a) $B_B > B_A$, (b) $B_B = B_A$, and (c) $B_B < B_A$?

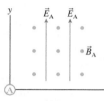

FIGURE EX34.2

3. || Scientists in the laboratory create a uniform electric field $\vec{E} = 1.0 \times 10^6 \hat{k}$ V/m in a region of space where $\vec{B} = \vec{0}$. What are the fields in the reference frame of a rocket traveling in the positive x-direction at 1.0×10^6 m/s?

4. | Laboratory scientists have created the electric and magnetic fields shown in FIGURE EX34.4. These fields are also seen by scientists that zoom past in a rocket traveling in the x-direction at 1.0×10^6 m/s. According to the rocket scientists, what angle does the electric field make with the axis of the rocket?

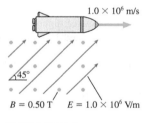

FIGURE EX34.4

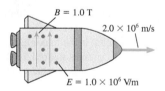

FIGURE EX34.5

5. | A rocket zooms past the earth at $v = 2.0 \times 10^6$ m/s. Scientists on the rocket have created the electric and magnetic fields shown in FIGURE EX34.5. What are the fields measured by an earthbound scientist?

Section 34.2 The Field Laws Thus Far

Section 34.3 The Displacement Current

6. || The magnetic field is uniform over each face of the box shown in FIGURE EX34.6. What are the magnetic field strength and direction on the front surface?

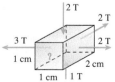

FIGURE EX34.6

7. | Show that the quantity $\epsilon_0(d\Phi_e/dt)$ has units of current.

8. || Show that the displacement current inside a parallel-plate capacitor can be written $C(dV_C/dt)$.

9. | What capacitance, in μF, has its potential difference increasing at 1.0×10^6 V/s when the displacement current in the capacitor is 1.0 A?

10. || A 10-cm-diameter parallel-plate capacitor has a 1.0 mm spacing. The electric field between the plates is increasing at the rate 1.0×10^6 V/m s. What is the magnetic field strength (a) on the axis, (b) 3.0 cm from the axis, and (c) 7.0 cm from the axis?

11. || A 5.0-cm-diameter parallel-plate capacitor has a 0.50 mm gap. What is the displacement current in the capacitor if the potential difference across the capacitor is increasing at 500,000 V/s?

Section 34.5 Electromagnetic Waves

12. | What is the electric field amplitude of an electromagnetic wave whose magnetic field amplitude is 2.0 mT?

13. | What is the magnetic field amplitude of an electromagnetic wave whose electric field amplitude is 10 V/m?

14. | The magnetic field of an electromagnetic wave in a vacuum is $B_z = (3.00 \ \mu\text{T}) \sin((1.00 \times 10^7)x - \omega t)$, where x is in m and t is in s. What are the wave's (a) wavelength, (b) frequency, and (c) electric field amplitude?

15. || The electric field of an electromagnetic wave in a vacuum is $E_y = (20.0 \ \text{V/m}) \cos((6.28 \times 10^8)x - \omega t)$, where x is in m and t is in s. What are the wave's (a) wavelength, (b) frequency, and (c) magnetic field amplitude?

Section 34.6 Properties of Electromagnetic Waves

16. | A radio wave is traveling in the negative y-direction. What is the direction of $\vec{E}$ at a point where $\vec{B}$ is in the positive x-direction?

17. | a. What is the magnetic field amplitude of an electromagnetic wave whose electric field amplitude is 100 V/m?
    b. What is the intensity of the wave?

18. | A radio receiver can detect signals with electric field amplitudes as small as 300 μV/m. What is the intensity of the smallest detectable signal?

19. || A helium-neon laser emits a 1.0-mm-diameter laser beam with a power of 1.0 mW. What are the amplitudes of the electric and magnetic fields of the light wave?

20. || A 200 MW laser pulse is focused with a lens to a diameter of 2.0 μm.
    a. What is the laser beam's electric field amplitude at the focal point?
    b. What is the ratio of the laser beam's electric field to the electric field that keeps the electron bound to the proton of a hydrogen atom? The radius of the electron orbit is 0.053 nm.

21. || A radio antenna broadcasts a 1.0 MHz radio wave with 25 kW of power. Assume that the radiation is emitted uniformly in all directions.
    a. What is the wave's intensity 30 km from the antenna?
    b. What is the electric field amplitude at this distance?

22. || At what distance from a 10 W point source of electromagnetic waves is the magnetic field amplitude 1.0 μT?

23. | A 1000 W carbon-dioxide laser emits light with a wavelength of 10 μm into a 3.0-mm-diameter laser beam. What force does the laser beam exert on a completely absorbing target?

Section 34.7 Polarization

24. | FIGURE EX34.24 shows a vertically polarized radio wave of frequency 1.0×10^6 Hz traveling into the page. The maximum electric field strength is 1000 V/m. What are
    a. The maximum magnetic field strength?
    b. The magnetic field strength and direction at a point where $\vec{E} = $ (500 V/m, down)?

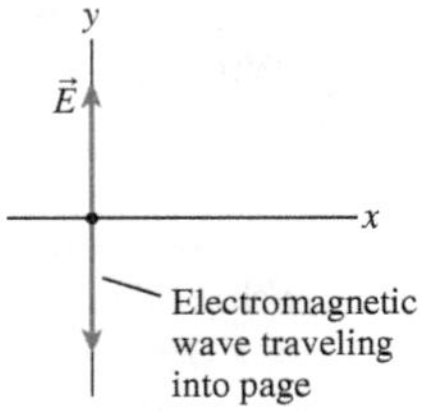

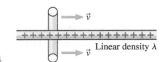

Electromagnetic wave traveling into page

FIGURE EX34.24

25. || Only 25% of the intensity of a polarized light wave passes through a polarizing filter. What is the angle between the electric field and the axis of the filter?

26. || A 200 mW vertically polarized laser beam passes through a polarizing filter whose axis is 35° from horizontal. What is the power of the laser beam as it emerges from the filter?

27. || Unpolarized light with intensity 350 W/m² passes first through a polarizing filter with its axis vertical, then through a second polarizing filter. It emerges from the second filter with intensity 131 W/m². What is the angle from vertical of the axis of the second polarizing filter?

Problems

28. || What is the force (magnitude and direction) on the proton in FIGURE P34.28? Give the direction as an angle cw or ccw from vertical.

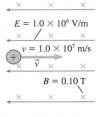

$E = 1.0 \times 10^6$ V/m

$v = 1.0 \times 10^7$ m/s

$B = 0.10$ T

FIGURE P34.28

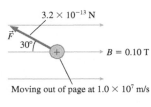

3.2×10^{-13} N

$\vec{F}$ 30°

$B = 0.10$ T

Moving out of page at 1.0×10^7 m/s

FIGURE P34.29

29. || What are the electric field strength and direction at the position of the proton in FIGURE P34.29?

30. | What electric field strength and direction will allow the electron in FIGURE P34.30 to pass through this region of space without being deflected?

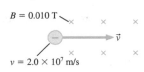

$B = 0.010$ T

$\vec{v}$

$v = 2.0 \times 10^7$ m/s

FIGURE P34.30

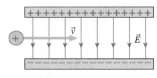

$\vec{v}$

$\vec{E}$

FIGURE P34.31

31. | A proton is fired with a speed of 1.0×10^6 m/s through the parallel-plate capacitor shown in FIGURE P34.31. The capacitor's electric field is $\vec{E} = (1.0 \times 10^5$ V/m, down).
    a. What magnetic field $\vec{B}$, both strength and direction, must be applied to allow the proton to pass through the capacitor with no change in speed or direction?

b. Find the electric and magnetic fields in the proton's reference frame.
   c. How does an experimenter in the proton's frame explain that the proton experiences no force as the charged plates fly by?

32. ||| An electron travels with $\vec{v} = 5.0 \times 10^6 \hat{\imath}$ m/s through a point in space where $\vec{E} = (2.0 \times 10^5 \hat{\imath} - 2.0 \times 10^5 \hat{\jmath})$ V/m and $\vec{B} = -0.10 \hat{k}$ T. What is the force on the electron?

33. || A very long, 1.0-mm-diameter wire carries a 2.5 A current from left to right. Thin plastic insulation on the wire is positively charged with linear charge density 2.5 nC/cm. A mosquito 1.0 cm from the center of the wire would like to move in such a way as to experience an electric field but no magnetic field. How fast and which direction should she fly?

34. || In FIGURE P34.34, a circular loop of radius r travels with speed v along a charged wire having linear charge density λ. The wire is at rest in the laboratory frame, and it passes through the center of the loop.
    a. What are $\vec{E}$ and $\vec{B}$ at a point on the loop as measured by a scientist in the laboratory? Include both strength and direction.
    b. What are the fields $\vec{E}$ and $\vec{B}$ at a point on the loop as measured by a scientist in the frame of the loop?
    c. Show that an experimenter in the loop's frame sees a current $I = \lambda v$ passing through the center of the loop.
    d. What electric and magnetic fields would an experimenter in the loop's frame calculate at distance r from the current of part c?
    e. Show that your fields of parts b and d are the same.

$\vec{v}$

Linear density λ

$\vec{v}$

FIGURE P34.34

35. || The magnetic field inside a 4.0-cm-diameter superconducting solenoid varies sinusoidally between 8.0 T and 12.0 T at a frequency of 10 Hz.
    a. What is the maximum electric field strength at a point 1.5 cm from the solenoid axis?
    b. What is the value of B at the instant E reaches its maximum value?

36. || A simple series circuit consists of a 150 Ω resistor, a 25 V battery, a switch, and a 2.5 pF parallel-plate capacitor (initially uncharged) with plates 5.0 mm apart. The switch is closed at $t = 0$ s.
    a. After the switch is closed, find the maximum electric flux and the maximum displacement current through the capacitor.
    b. Find the electric flux and the displacement current at $t = 0.50$ ns.

37. || A wire with conductivity σ carries current I. The current is increasing at the rate dI/dt.
    a. Show that there is a displacement current in the wire equal to $(\epsilon_0/\sigma)(dI/dt)$.
    b. Evaluate the displacement current for a copper wire in which the current is increasing at 1.0×10^6 A/s.

38. || A 10 A current is charging a 1.0-cm-diameter parallel-plate capacitor.
    a. What is the magnetic field strength at a point 2.0 mm radially from the center of the wire leading to the capacitor?
    b. What is the magnetic field strength at a point 2.0 mm radially from the center of the capacitor?

39. ‖ FIGURE P34.39 shows the voltage across a 0.10 μF capacitor. Draw a graph showing the displacement current through the capacitor as a function of time.

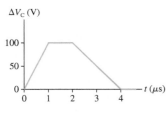

FIGURE P34.39

FIGURE P34.40

40. ‖ FIGURE P34.40 shows the electric field inside a cylinder of radius $R = 3.0$ mm. The field strength is increasing with time as $E = 1.0 \times 10^8 t^2$ V/m, where t is in s. The electric field outside the cylinder is always zero, and the field inside the cylinder was zero for $t < 0$.
   a. Find an expression for the electric flux Φ_e through the entire cylinder as a function of time.
   b. Draw a picture showing the magnetic field lines inside and outside the cylinder. Be sure to include arrowheads showing the field's direction.
   c. Find an expression for the magnetic field strength as a function of time at a distance $r < R$ from the center. Evaluate the magnetic field strength at $r = 2.0$ mm, $t = 2.0$ s.
   d. Find an expression for the magnetic field strength as a function of time at a distance $r > R$ from the center. Evaluate the magnetic field strength at $r = 4.0$ mm, $t = 2.0$ s.

41. ‖ A 1.0 μF capacitor is discharged, starting at $t = 0$ s. The displacement current through the plates is $I_{disp} = (10 \text{ A})\exp(-t/2.0 \text{ }\mu\text{s})$. What was the capacitor's initial voltage $(\Delta V_C)_0$?

42. ‖ At one instant, the electric and magnetic fields at one point of an electromagnetic wave are $\vec{E} = (200\,\hat{i} + 300\,\hat{j} - 50\,\hat{k})$ V/m and $\vec{B} = B_0(7.3\,\hat{i} - 7.3\,\hat{j} + a\,\hat{k})$ μT.
   a. What are the values of a and B_0?
   b. What is the Poynting vector at this time and position?

43. ‖ a. Show that u_E and u_B, the energy densities of the electric and magnetic fields, are equal to each other in an electromagnetic wave. In other words, show that the wave's energy is divided equally between the electric field and the magnetic field.
   b. What is the total energy density in an electromagnetic wave of intensity 1000 W/m²?

44. ‖ Assume that a 7.0-cm-diameter, 100 W lightbulb radiates all its energy as a single wavelength of visible light. Estimate the electric and magnetic field strengths at the surface of the bulb.

45. ‖ The intensity of sunlight reaching the earth is 1360 W/m².
   a. What is the power output of the sun?
   b. What is the intensity of sunlight on Mars?

46. ‖‖‖ A cube of water 10 cm on a side is placed in a microwave beam having $E_0 = 11$ kV/m. The microwaves illuminate one face of the cube, and the water absorbs 80% of the incident energy. How long will it take to raise the water temperature by 50°C? Assume that the water has no heat loss during this time.

47. ‖ A laser beam passes through a converging lens with a focal length f. At what distance past the lens has the laser beam's (a) intensity and (b) electric field strength increased by a factor of 4?

48. | When the Voyager 2 spacecraft passed Neptune in 1989, it was 4.5×10^9 km from the earth. Its radio transmitter, with which it sent back data and images, broadcast with a mere 21 W of power. Assuming that the transmitter broadcast equally in all directions,
   a. What signal intensity was received on the earth?
   b. What electric field amplitude was detected?
   The received signal was somewhat stronger than your result because the spacecraft used a directional antenna, but not by much.

49. ‖ In reading the instruction manual that came with your garage-door opener, you see that the transmitter unit in your car produces a 250 mW signal and that the receiver unit is supposed to respond to a radio wave of the correct frequency if the electric field amplitude exceeds 0.10 V/m. You wonder if this is really true. To find out, you put fresh batteries in the transmitter and start walking away from your garage while opening and closing the door. Your garage door finally fails to respond when you're 42 m away. Are the manufacturer's claims true?

50. ‖ The maximum electric field strength in air is 3.0 MV/m. Stronger electric fields ionize the air and create a spark. What is the maximum power that can be delivered by a 1.0-cm-diameter laser beam propagating through air?

51. ‖ A LASIK vision-correction system uses a laser that emits
BIO 10-ns-long pulses of light, each with 2.5 mJ of energy. The laser beam is focused to a 0.85-mm-diameter circle on the cornea. What is the electric field amplitude of the light wave at the cornea?

52. ‖ The intensity of sunlight reaching the earth is 1360 W/m². Assuming all the sunlight is absorbed, what is the radiation-pressure force on the earth? Give your answer (a) in newtons and (b) as a fraction of the sun's gravitational force on the earth.

53. ‖ For radio and microwaves, the depth of penetration into the
BIO human body is proportional to $\lambda^{1/2}$. If 27 MHz radio waves penetrate to a depth of 14 cm, how far do 2.4 GHz microwaves penetrate?

54. ‖ A laser beam shines straight up onto a flat, black foil of mass m.
   a. Find an expression for the laser power P needed to levitate the foil.
   b. Evaluate P for a foil with a mass of 25 μg.

55. | For a science project, you would like to horizontally suspend an 8.5 by 11 inch sheet of black paper in a vertical beam of light whose dimensions exactly match the paper. If the mass of the sheet is 1.0 g, what light intensity will you need?

56. ‖ You've recently read about a chemical laser that generates a 20-cm-diameter, 25 MW laser beam. One day, after physics class, you start to wonder if you could use the radiation pressure from this laser beam to launch small payloads into orbit. To see if this might be feasible, you do a quick calculation of the acceleration of a 20-cm-diameter, 100 kg, perfectly absorbing block. What speed would such a block have if pushed *horizontally* 100 m along a frictionless track by such a laser?

57. ‖‖‖ An 80 kg astronaut has gone outside his space capsule to do some repair work. Unfortunately, he forgot to lock his safety tether in place, and he has drifted 5.0 m away from the capsule. Fortunately, he has a 1000 W portable laser with fresh batteries that will operate it for 1.0 h. His only chance is to accelerate himself toward the space capsule by firing the laser in the opposite direction. He has a 10-h supply of oxygen. How long will it take him to reach safety?

58. ‖ Unpolarized light of intensity I_0 is incident on three polarizing filters. The axis of the first is vertical, that of the second is 45° from vertical, and that of the third is horizontal. What light intensity emerges from the third filter?

Challenge Problems

59. An electron travels with $\vec{v} = 5.0 \times 10^6 \hat{\imath}$ m/s through a point in space where $\vec{B} = 0.10 \hat{\jmath}$ T. The force on the electron at this point is $\vec{F} = (9.6 \times 10^{-14} \hat{\imath} - 9.6 \times 10^{-14} \hat{k})$ N. What is the electric field?

60. A 4.0-cm-diameter parallel-plate capacitor with a 1.0 mm spacing is charged to 1000 V. A switch closes at $t = 0$ s, and the capacitor is discharged through a wire with 0.20 Ω resistance.
    a. Find an expression for the magnetic field strength inside the capacitor at $r = 1.0$ cm as a function of time.
    b. Draw a graph of B versus t.

61. The radar system at an airport broadcasts 11 GHz microwaves with 150 kW of power. An approaching airplane with a 31 m² cross section is 30 km away. Assume that the radar broadcasts uniformly in all directions and that the airplane scatters microwaves uniformly in all directions. What is the electric field strength of the microwave signal received back at the airport 200 μs later?

62. Large quantities of dust should have been left behind after the creation of the solar system. Larger dust particles, comparable in size to soot and sand grains, are common. They create shooting stars when they collide with the earth's atmosphere. But very small dust particles are conspicuously absent. Astronomers believe that the very small dust particles have been blown out of the solar system by the sun. By comparing the forces on dust particles, determine the diameter of the smallest dust particles that can remain in the solar system over long periods of time. Assume that the dust particles are spherical, black, and have a density of 2000 kg/m³. The sun emits electromagnetic radiation with power 3.9×10^{26} W.

63. Consider current I passing through a resistor of radius r, length L, and resistance R.
    a. Determine the electric and magnetic fields at the surface of the resistor. Assume that the electric field is uniform throughout, including at the surface.
    b. Determine the strength and direction of the Poynting vector at the surface of the resistor.
    c. Show that the flux of the Poynting vector (i.e., the integral of $\vec{S} \cdot d\vec{A}$) over the surface of the resistor is I^2R. Then give an interpretation of this result.

64. Unpolarized light of intensity I_0 is incident on a stack of 7 polarizing filters, each with its axis rotated 15° cw with respect to the previous filter. What light intensity emerges from the last filter?

STOP TO THINK ANSWERS

Stop to Think 34.1: b. $\vec{v}_{AB}$ is parallel to $\vec{B}_A$ hence $\vec{v}_{AB} \times \vec{B}_A$ is zero. Thus $\vec{E}_B = \vec{E}_A$ and points in the positive z-direction. $\vec{v}_{AB} \times \vec{E}_A$ points down, in the negative y-direction, so $-\vec{v}_{AB} \times \vec{E}_A/c^2$ points in the positive y-direction and causes $\vec{B}_B$ to be angled upward.

Stop to Think 34.2: $B_c > B_a > B_d > B_b$. The induced magnetic field strength depends on the *rate dE/dt* at which the electric field is changing. Steeper slopes on the graph correspond to larger magnetic fields.

Stop to Think 34.3: e. $\vec{E}$ is perpendicular to $\vec{B}$ and to $\vec{v}$, so it can only be along the z-axis. According to the Ampère-Maxwell law, $d\Phi_e/dt$ has the same sign as the line integral of $\vec{B} \cdot d\vec{s}$ around the closed curve. The integral is positive for a cw integration. Thus, from the right-hand rule, $\vec{E}$ is either into the page (negative z-direction) and increasing, or out of the page (positive z-direction) and decreasing. We can see from the figure that B is decreasing in strength as the wave moves from left

to right, so E must also be decreasing. Thus $\vec{E}$ points along the positive z-axis.

Stop to Think 34.4: a. The Poynting vector $\vec{S} = (\vec{E} \times \vec{B})/\mu_0$ points in the direction of travel, which is the positive y-direction. $\vec{B}$ must point in the positive x-direction in order for $\vec{E} \times \vec{B}$ to point upward.

Stop to Think 34.5: b. The intensity along a line from the antenna decreases inversely with the square of the distance, so the intensity at 20 km is $\frac{1}{4}$ that at 10 km. But the intensity depends on the square of the electric field amplitude, or, conversely, E_0 is proportional to $I^{1/2}$. Thus E_0 at 20 km is $\frac{1}{2}$ that at 10 km.

Stop to Think 34.6: $I_d > I_a > I_b = I_c$. The intensity depends on $\cos^2\theta$, where θ is the angle *between* the axes of the two filters. The filters in d have $\theta = 0°$. The two filters in both b and c are crossed ($\theta = 90°$) and transmit no light at all.

VI Electricity and Magnetism

Mass and charge are the two most fundamental properties of matter. The first five parts of this text were investigations of the properties and interactions of masses. Part VI has been a study of the physics of charge—what charge is and how charges interact.

Electric and magnetic fields were introduced to enable us to understand the long-range forces of electricity and magnetism. The field concept is subtle, but it is an essential part of our modern understanding of the physical universe. One charge—the source charge—alters the space around it by creating an electric field and, if the charge is moving, a magnetic field. Other charges experience forces exerted *by the fields*. Thus the electric and magnetic fields are the agents by which charges interact.

Faraday's discovery of electromagnetic induction led scientists to recognize that the fields are *real* and can exist independently of charges. The most vivid confirmation of this reality was Maxwell's discovery of electromagnetic waves—the quintessential electromagnetic phenomenon.

Part VI has introduced many new phenomena, concepts, and laws. The knowledge structure table draws together the major ideas about charges and fields, and it briefly summarizes some of the most important applications of electricity and magnetism.

KNOWLEDGE STRUCTURE VI **Electricity and Magnetism**

ESSENTIAL CONCEPTS	Charge, dipole, field, potential, emf	
BASIC GOALS	How do charged particles interact?	
	What are the properties and characteristics of electromagnetic fields?	

GENERAL PRINCIPLES	Coulomb's law	$\vec{E}_{\text{point charge}} = \dfrac{1}{4\pi\epsilon_0}\dfrac{q}{r^2}\hat{r} = \left(\dfrac{1}{4\pi\epsilon_0}\dfrac{q}{r^2},\text{ away from } q\right)$
	Biot-Savart law	$\vec{B}_{\text{point charge}} = \dfrac{\mu_0}{4\pi}\dfrac{q\vec{v}\times\hat{r}}{r^2} = \left(\dfrac{\mu_0}{4\pi}\dfrac{qv\sin\theta}{r^2},\text{ direction of right-hand rule}\right)$
	Faraday's law	$\mathcal{E} = \left|d\Phi_{\text{m}}/dt\right|$ $I_{\text{induced}} = \mathcal{E}/R$ in the direction of Lenz's law
	Lenz's law	An induced current flows around a conducting loop in the direction such that the induced magnetic field opposes the *change* in the magnetic flux.
	Lorentz force law	$\vec{F}_{\text{on }q} = q(\vec{E} + \vec{v}\times\vec{B})$
	Superposition	The electric or magnetic field due to multiple charges is the vector sum of the field of each charge. This principle was used to derive the fields of many special charge distributions, such as wires, planes, and loops.

FIELD AND POTENTIAL The electric field of charges can also be described in terms of an electric potential V:

$$V_{\text{point charge}} = \frac{q}{4\pi\epsilon_0 r}$$

- The electric field is perpendicular to equipotential surfaces and in the direction of decreasing potential.

- The potential energy of charge q is $U = qV$. The total energy $K + qV$ of a group of charges is conserved.

ELECTROMAGNETIC WAVES All the properties of electromagnetic fields are summarized mathematically in four equations called *Maxwell's equations*. From Maxwell's equations we learn that electromagnetic fields can exist independently of charges as an *electromagnetic wave*.

- An em wave travels at speed $c = 1/\sqrt{\epsilon_0\mu_0}$.

- $\vec{E}$ and $\vec{B}$ are perpendicular to each other and to the direction of travel, with $E = cB$.

Electric and magnetic properties of materials

- Charges move through conductors but not through insulators.

- Conductors and insulators are *polarized* in an electric field.

- A magnetic moment in a magnetic field experiences a torque.

Model of current and conductivity

- The charge carriers in metals are electrons.

- emf $\rightarrow$ electric field $\rightarrow$ current density $J = \sigma E \rightarrow I = JA$

Applications to circuits

- Circuits obey Kirchhoff's loop law (conservation of energy) and junction law (conservation of current).

- Resistors control the current: $I = \Delta V/R$ (Ohm's law).

- Capacitors store charge $Q = C\Delta V$ and energy $V_C = \frac{1}{2}C(\Delta V_C)^2$.

The Telecommunications Revolution

In 1800, the year that Alessandro Volta invented the battery and Thomas Jefferson was elected president, the fastest a message could travel was the speed of a man or woman on horseback. News took three days to travel from New York to Boston, and well over a month to reach the frontier outpost of Cincinnati.

But Hans Oersted's 1820 discovery that a current creates a magnetic field introduced revolutionary changes to communications. The American scientist Joseph Henry, who shares with Faraday credit for the discovery of electromagnetic induction, saw a simple electromagnet in 1825. Inspired, he set about improving the device. By 1830, Henry was able to send current through more than a mile of wire to activate an electromagnet and strike a bell.

In 1835, Henry met an entrepreneur interested in the commercial development of electric technology—Samuel F. B. Morse. Morse was one of the most prominent American artists of the early 19th century, but he also had an abiding interest in technology. In the 1830s, he invented the famous code that bears his name—Morse code—and began to experiment with electromagnets.

With advice and encouragement from Henry, Morse developed the first practical telegraph. The first telegraph line, between Washington, D.C., and Baltimore, began operating in 1844; the first message sent was "What hath God wrought?" For the first time, long-distance communications could take place essentially instantaneously.

Telegraph communication advanced as quickly as wire could be strung, and a worldwide network had been established by 1875. But the telegraph didn't hold its monopoly for long, as other inventors began to think about using electromagnetic devices to transmit speech. The first to succeed was Alexander Graham Bell, who invented the telephone in 1876.

The telegraph and telephone provided electromagnetic communication over wires, but the discovery of electromagnetic waves opened up another possibility—wireless communication at the speed of light. Radio technology developed rapidly in the late 19th century, and in 1901 the Italian inventor Guglielmo Marconi sent and received the first transatlantic radio message. World War I prompted further development of radio, because of the need to communicate with military units as they moved about, and by 1925 more than 1000 radio stations were operating in the United States.

Radio and, later, television spanned the globe by 1960, but radio stations reached a few hundred miles at best, and television transmission was limited to each city. National broadcasts within the United States required the signal to be transmitted via microwave relays to local stations for rebroadcast. Network television shows were possible, but not live-from-the-scene broadcasts. Journalists had to film events, then return the film to the studio for broadcast. Television images from overseas could only be seen the next day, after film was flown back to the United States.

The first communications satellite was launched by NASA in 1960, followed two years later by a more practical satellite, Telstar, that used solar power to amplify signals received from earth and beam them back down. The first live transatlantic television transmission was made on July 11, 1962, and was broadcast throughout the United States.

Plans were made for a system of roughly 100 satellites, so that one would always be overhead, but another idea soon proved more practical. In 1945, 12 years before space flight began, the science-fiction writer Arthur C. Clarke proposed placing satellites in orbits 22,300 miles above the earth. A satellite at this altitude orbits with a 24-hour period, so from the ground it appears to hang stationary in space. We now call this a *geosynchronous orbit*. One such satellite would allow microwave communication between two points one-third of a world apart, so just three geosynchronous satellites would span the entire earth.

Much more energy is required to reach geosynchronous orbit than to reach low-earth orbit, but rocket technology was advancing faster than NASA could build Telstar satellites. The first commercial communications satellite was placed in geosynchronous orbit in 1965, and, for the first time, television images could be broadcast live to anywhere in the world. Today all of the world's intercontinental television and much of the intercontinental telephone traffic travel via microwaves to and from a cluster of these artificial stars floating high above the earth.

Today, in the 21st century, information and images span the world as quickly as or more quickly than they once moved through a small village. You can talk to friends or relatives anywhere around the globe, and each day's news brings live images from remote places. Telecommunication unites our world, and the technologies of telecommunications are direct descendants of Coulomb, Ampère, Oersted, Henry, and—most of all—Michael Faraday.

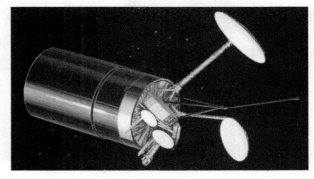

This INTELSAT telecommunications satellite is 12 m (40 ft) long.

VII

Relativity and Quantum Physics

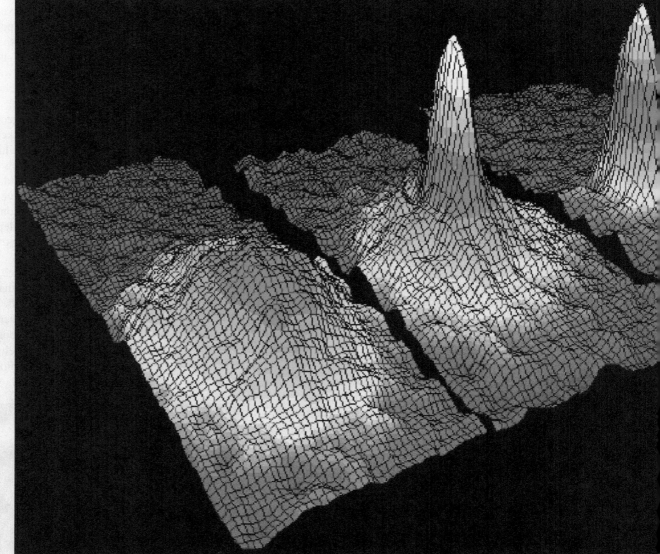

This three-frame sequence shows a gas of a few thousand rubidium atoms condensing into a single quantum state known as a Bose-Einstein condensate. This phenomenon was predicted by Einstein in 1925 but not observed until 1995, when physicists learned how to use lasers to cool the atoms to temperatures below 200 nanokelvin.

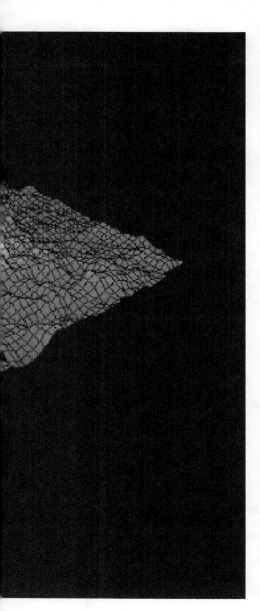

OVERVIEW

Contemporary Physics

Our journey into physics is nearing its end. We began roughly 350 years ago with Newton's discovery of the laws of motion. Part VI brought us to the end of the 19th century, just over 100 years ago. Along the way you've learned about the motion of particles, the conservation of energy, the physics of waves, and the electromagnetic interactions that hold atoms together and generate light waves. We begin the last phase of our journey with confidence.

Newton's mechanics and Maxwell's electromagnetism were the twin pillars of science at the end of the 19th century and the basis for much of engineering and applied science in the 20th century. Despite the successes of these theories, a series of discoveries starting around 1900 and continuing into the first few decades of the 20th century profoundly altered our understanding of the universe at the most fundamental level.

- Einstein's theory of relativity forced scientists to completely revise their concepts of space and time. Our exploration of these fascinating ideas will end with perhaps the most famous equation in physics: Einstein's $E = mc^2$.
- Experimenters found that the classical distinction between *particles* and *waves* breaks down at the atomic level. Light sometimes acts like a particle, while electrons and even entire atoms sometimes act like waves. We will need a new theory of light and matter—quantum physics—to explain these phenomena.

These two theories form the basis for physics as it is practiced today, and they are now having a significant impact on 21st-century engineering.

The complete theory of quantum physics, as it was developed in the 1920s, describes atomic particles in terms of an entirely new concept called a *wave function*. One of our most important tasks in Part VII will be to learn what a wave function is, what laws govern its behavior, and how to relate wave functions to experimental measurements. We will concentrate on one-dimensional models that, while not perfect, will be adequate for understanding the essential features of scanning tunneling microscopes, various semiconductor devices, radioactive decay, and other applications.

We'll complete our study of quantum physics with an introduction to atomic and nuclear physics. You will learn where the electron-shell model of chemistry comes from, how atoms emit and absorb light, what's inside the nucleus, and why some nuclei undergo radioactive decay.

The quantum world with its wave functions and probabilities can seem strange and mysterious, yet quantum physics gives the most definitive and accurate predictions of any physical theory ever devised. The contemporary perspective of quantum physics will be a fitting end to our journey.

36 Relativity

The Large Hadron Collider, the world's highest-energy particle accelerator, is built in a 27-km-circumference tunnel near Geneva, Switzerland. It accelerates protons to 99.999999% of the speed of light.

▶ **Looking Ahead** The goal of Chapter 36 is to understand how Einstein's theory of relativity changes our concepts of space and time.

Principle of Relativity

Einstein's theory of relativity is based on a simple-sounding principle: The laws of physics are the same in every inertial reference frame. This seemingly innocuous statement will force us to completely rethink our ideas of space and time.

The most well-known consequence of this principle is that light travels at the same speed c in all inertial reference frames.

You'll learn why it is that no object or information can travel faster than the speed of light.

Space

The physical length of an object is *less* when the object is moving in a reference frame than when it is at rest in that reference frame. This is **length contraction.**

To us, the Fermilab Accelerator is 3.9 miles in circumference. To protons in the accelerator, moving at 0.999999c, the circumference is only 30 feet.

Mass and Energy

You'll learn the significance of relativity's famous equation, $E = mc^2$. Mass can be transformed into energy, and energy into mass, as long as the total energy is conserved.

The sun is powered by the conversion of 4 billion kilograms of matter into energy every second. Even so, the sun will continue to shine for billions of years.

Reference Frames

You'll learn to work with **events** whose position in space and time of occurrence are measured by experimenters in different **inertial reference frames.**

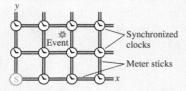

Synchronized clocks

Meter sticks

◀ **Looking Back**
Section 4.4 Reference frames and relative velocity

Time

The time interval between ticks of a clock is *longer* when the clock is moving in a reference frame than when it is at rest in that reference frame. This is **time dilation.**

You'll learn about the **twin paradox.** If an astronaut travels to a distance star and back at a speed close to that of light, she'll be younger than her identical twin when she returns.

Applications of Relativity

Abstract though it may seem, relativity is important for modern technologies such as PET scans (positron-electron tomography) in medicine and nuclear energy. Relativity also underlies our understanding of the physics of stars and galaxies.

Your GPS device receives signals from precision clocks in orbiting satellites. The clocks must be corrected for relativistic effects in order for the GPS system to work.

36.1 Relativity: What's It All About?

What do you think of when you hear the phrase "theory of relativity"? A white-haired Einstein? $E = mc^2$? Black holes? Time travel? Perhaps you've heard that the theory of relativity is so complicated and abstract that only a handful of people in the whole world really understand it.

There is, without doubt, a certain mystique associated with relativity, an aura of the strange and exotic. The good news is that understanding the ideas of relativity is well within your grasp. Einstein's *special theory of relativity,* the portion of relativity we'll study, is not mathematically difficult at all. The challenge is conceptual because relativity questions deeply held assumptions about the nature of space and time. In fact, that's what relativity is all about—space and time.

What's Special About Special Relativity?

Einstein's first paper on relativity, in 1905, dealt exclusively with inertial reference frames, reference frames that move relative to each other with constant velocity. Ten years later, Einstein published a more encompassing theory of relativity that considered accelerated motion and its connection to gravity. The second theory, because it's more general in scope, is called *general relativity.* General relativity is the theory that describes black holes, curved spacetime, and the evolution of the universe. It is a fascinating theory but, alas, very mathematical and outside the scope of this textbook.

Motion at constant velocity is a "special case" of motion—namely, motion for which the acceleration is zero. Hence Einstein's first theory of relativity has come to be known as **special relativity.** It is special in the sense of being a restricted, special case of his more general theory, not special in the everyday sense meaning distinctive or exceptional. Special relativity, with its conclusions about time dilation and length contraction, is what we will study.

Albert Einstein (1879–1955) was one of the most influential thinkers in history.

36.2 Galilean Relativity

Relativity is the process of relating measurements in one reference frame to those in a different reference frame moving *relative to* the first. To appreciate and understand what is new in Einstein's theory, we need a firm grasp of the ideas of relativity that are embodied in Newtonian mechanics. Thus we begin with *Galilean relativity.*

Reference Frames

Suppose you're passing me as we both drive in the same direction along a freeway. My car's speedometer reads 55 mph while your speedometer shows 60 mph. Is 60 mph your "true" speed? That is certainly your speed relative to someone standing beside the road, but your speed relative to me is only 5 mph. Your speed is 120 mph relative to a driver approaching from the other direction at 60 mph.

An object does not have a "true" speed or velocity. The very definition of velocity, $v = \Delta x/\Delta t$, assumes the existence of a coordinate system in which, during some time interval Δt, the displacement Δx is measured. The best we can manage is to specify an object's velocity relative to, or with respect to, the coordinate system in which it is measured.

Let's define a **reference frame** to be a coordinate system in which experimenters equipped with meter sticks, stopwatches, and any other needed equipment make position and time measurements on moving objects. Three ideas are implicit in our definition of a reference frame:

- A reference frame extends infinitely far in all directions.
- The experimenters are at rest in the reference frame.
- The number of experimenters and the quality of their equipment are sufficient to measure positions and velocities to any level of accuracy needed.

The first two ideas are especially important. It is often convenient to say "the laboratory reference frame" or "the reference frame of the rocket." These are shorthand expressions for "a reference frame, infinite in all directions, in which the laboratory (or the rocket) and a set of experimenters happen to be at rest."

NOTE ▶ A reference frame is not the same thing as a "point of view." That is, each person or each experimenter does not have his or her own private reference frame. **All experimenters at rest relative to each other share the same reference frame.** ◀

FIGURE 36.1 shows two reference frames called S and S′. The coordinate axes in S are x, y, z and those in S′ are $x′, y′, z′$. Reference frame S′ moves with velocity v relative to S or, equivalently, S moves with velocity $-v$ relative to S′. There's no implication that either reference frame is "at rest." Notice that the zero of time, when experimenters start their stopwatches, is the instant that the origins of S and S′ coincide.

We will restrict our attention to *inertial reference frames,* implying that the relative velocity v is constant. You should recall from Chapter 5 that an **inertial reference frame** is a reference frame in which Newton's first law, the law of inertia, is valid. In particular, an inertial reference frame is one in which an isolated particle, one on which there are no forces, either remains at rest or moves in a straight line at constant speed.

Any reference frame moving at constant velocity with respect to an inertial reference frame is itself an inertial reference frame. Conversely, a reference frame accelerating with respect to an inertial reference frame is *not* an inertial reference frame. Our restriction to reference frames moving with respect to each other at constant velocity—with no acceleration—is the "special" part of special relativity.

NOTE ▶ An inertial reference frame is an idealization. A true inertial reference frame would need to be floating in deep space, far from any gravitational influence. In practice, an earthbound laboratory is a good approximation of an inertial reference frame because the accelerations associated with the earth's rotation and motion around the sun are too small to influence most experiments. ◀

STOP TO THINK 36.1 Which of these is an inertial reference frame (or a very good approximation)?

a. Your bedroom
b. A car rolling down a steep hill
c. A train coasting along a level track
d. A rocket being launched
e. A roller coaster going over the top of a hill
f. A sky diver falling at terminal speed

The Galilean Transformations

Suppose a firecracker explodes at time t. The experimenters in reference frame S determine that the explosion happened at position x. Similarly, the experimenters in S′ find that the firecracker exploded at $x′$ in their reference frame. What is the relationship between x and $x′$?

FIGURE 36.2 shows the explosion and the two reference frames. You can see from the figure that $x = x′ + vt$, thus

$$x = x′ + vt \qquad x′ = x - vt$$
$$y = y′ \qquad \text{or} \qquad y′ = y \qquad\qquad (36.1)$$
$$z = z′ \qquad z′ = z$$

FIGURE 36.1 The standard reference frames S and S′.

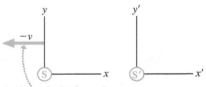

1. The axes of S and S′ have the same orientation.
2. Frame S′ moves with velocity v relative to frame S. The relative motion is parallel to the x- and x′-axes.

3. The origins of S and S′ coincide at $t = 0$. This is our definition of $t = 0$.

4. Alternatively, frame S moves with velocity $-v$ relative to frame S′.

FIGURE 36.2 The position of an exploding firecracker is measured in reference frames S and S′.

At time t, the origin of S′ has moved distance vt to the right. Thus $x = x′ + vt$.

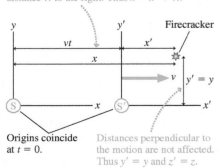

Origins coincide at $t = 0$.

Distances perpendicular to the motion are not affected. Thus $y′ = y$ and $z′ = z$.

These are the *Galilean transformations of position*. If you know a position measured by the experimenters in one inertial reference frame, you can calculate the position that would be measured by experimenters in any other inertial reference frame.

Suppose the experimenters in both reference frames now track the motion of the object in FIGURE 36.3 by measuring its position at many instants of time. The experimenters in S find that the object's velocity is $\vec{u}$. During the *same time interval* Δt, the experimenters in S′ measure the velocity to be $\vec{u}'$.

NOTE ▶ In this chapter, we will use v to represent the velocity of one reference frame relative to another. We will use $\vec{u}$ and $\vec{u}'$ to represent the velocities of objects with respect to reference frames S and S′. ◀

We can find the relationship between $\vec{u}$ and $\vec{u}'$ by taking the time derivatives of Equations 36.1 and using the definition $u_x = dx/dt$:

$$u_x = \frac{dx}{dt} = \frac{dx'}{dt} + v = u'_x + v$$

$$u_y = \frac{dy}{dt} = \frac{dy'}{dt} = u'_y$$

The equation for u_z is similar. The net result is

$$
\begin{array}{ccc}
u_x = u'_x + v & & u'_x = u_x - v \\
u_y = u'_y & \text{or} & u'_y = u_y \\
u_z = u'_z & & u'_z = u_z
\end{array}
\qquad (36.2)
$$

Equations 36.2 are the *Galilean transformations of velocity*. If you know the velocity of a particle in one inertial reference frame, you can find the velocity that would be measured by experimenters in any other inertial reference frame.

NOTE ▶ In Section 4.4 you learned the Galilean transformation of velocity as $\vec{v}_{CB} = \vec{v}_{CA} + \vec{v}_{AB}$, where $\vec{v}_{AB}$ means "the velocity of A relative to B." Equations 36.2 are equivalent for relative motion parallel to the x-axis but are written in a more formal notation that will be useful for relativity. ◀

FIGURE 36.3 The velocity of a moving object is measured in reference frames S and S′.

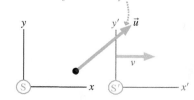
The object's velocity in frame S is $\vec{u}$.

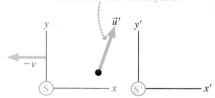
In frame S′, the velocity is $\vec{u}'$.

EXAMPLE 36.1 | The speed of sound

An airplane is flying at speed 200 m/s with respect to the ground. Sound wave 1 is approaching the plane from the front, sound wave 2 is catching up from behind. Both waves travel at 340 m/s relative to the ground. What is the speed of each wave relative to the plane?

MODEL Assume that the earth (frame S) and the airplane (frame S′) are inertial reference frames. Frame S′, in which the airplane is at rest, moves at $v = 200$ m/s relative to frame S.

VISUALIZE FIGURE 36.4 shows the airplane and the sound waves.

FIGURE 36.4 Experimenters in the plane measure different speeds for the waves than do experimenters on the ground.

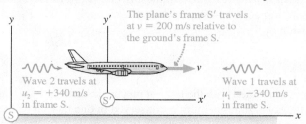
The plane's frame S′ travels at $v = 200$ m/s relative to the ground's frame S.
Wave 2 travels at $u_2 = +340$ m/s in frame S.
Wave 1 travels at $u_1 = -340$ m/s in frame S.

SOLVE The speed of a mechanical wave, such as a sound wave or a wave on a string, is its speed *relative to its medium*. Thus the *speed of sound* is the speed of a sound wave through a reference frame in which the air is at rest. This is reference frame S, where wave 1 travels with velocity $u_1 = -340$ m/s and wave 2 travels with velocity $u_2 = +340$ m/s. Notice that the Galilean transformations use *velocities*, with appropriate signs, not just speeds.

The airplane travels to the right with reference frame S′ at velocity v. We can use the Galilean transformations of velocity to find the velocities of the two sound waves in frame S′:

$$u'_1 = u_1 - v = -340 \text{ m/s} - 200 \text{ m/s} = -540 \text{ m/s}$$

$$u'_2 = u_2 - v = 340 \text{ m/s} - 200 \text{ m/s} = 140 \text{ m/s}$$

ASSESS This isn't surprising. If you're driving at 50 mph, a car coming the other way at 55 mph is approaching you at 105 mph. A car coming up behind you at 55 mph is gaining on you at the rate of only 5 mph. Wave speeds behave the same. Notice that a mechanical wave appears to be stationary to a person moving at the wave speed. To a surfer, the crest of the ocean wave remains at rest under his or her feet.

Ocean waves are approaching the beach at 10 m/s. A boat heading out to sea travels at 6 m/s. How fast are the waves moving in the boat's reference frame?

a. 16 m/s   b. 10 m/s   c. 6 m/s   d. 4 m/s

The Galilean Principle of Relativity

FIGURE 36.5 Experimenters in both reference frames test Newton's second law by measuring the force on a particle and its acceleration.

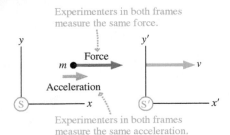

Experimenters in both frames measure the same force.

Experimenters in both frames measure the same acceleration.

Experimenters in reference frames S and S' measure different values for position and velocity. What about the force on and the acceleration of the particle in FIGURE 36.5? The strength of a force can be measured with a spring scale. The experimenters in reference frames S and S' both see the *same reading* on the scale (assume the scale has a bright digital display easily seen by all experimenters), so both conclude that the force is the same. That is, $F' = F$.

We can compare the accelerations measured in the two reference frames by taking the time derivative of the velocity transformation equation $u' = u - v$. (We'll assume, for simplicity, that the velocities and accelerations are all in the x-direction.) The relative velocity v between the two reference frames is *constant*, with $dv/dt = 0$, thus

$$a' = \frac{du'}{dt} = \frac{du}{dt} = a \tag{36.3}$$

Experimenters in reference frames S and S' measure different values for an object's position and velocity, but they *agree* on its acceleration.

If $F = ma$ in reference frame S, then $F' = ma'$ in reference frame S'. Stated another way, if Newton's second law is valid in one inertial reference frame, then it is valid in all inertial reference frames. Because other laws of mechanics, such as the conservation laws, follow from Newton's laws of motion, we can state this conclusion as the *Galilean principle of relativity:*

Galilean principle of relativity The laws of mechanics are the same in all inertial reference frames.

The Galilean principle of relativity is easy to state, but to understand it we must understand what is and is not "the same." To take a specific example, consider the law of conservation of momentum. FIGURE 36.6a shows two particles about to collide. Their total momentum in frame S, where particle 2 is at rest, is $P_i = 9.0$ kg m/s. This is an isolated system, hence the law of conservation of momentum tells us that the momentum after the collision will be $P_f = 9.0$ kg m/s.

FIGURE 36.6 Total momentum measured in two reference frames.

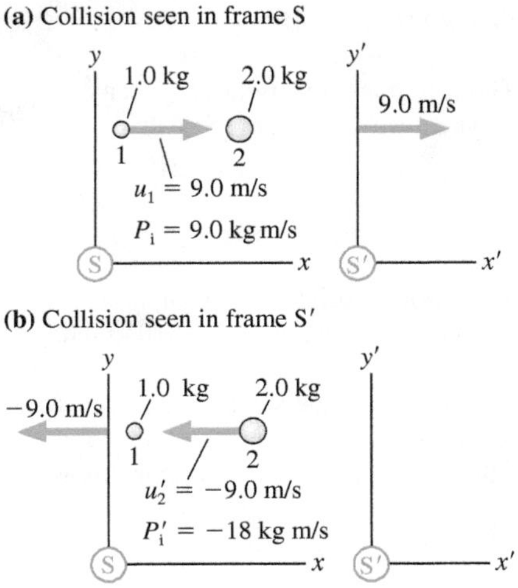

(a) Collision seen in frame S

1.0 kg   2.0 kg   9.0 m/s

1   2
$u_1 = 9.0$ m/s
$P_i = 9.0$ kg m/s

FIGURE 36.6b has used the velocity transformation to look at the same particles in frame S' in which particle 1 is at rest. The initial momentum in S' is $P_i' = -18$ kg m/s. Thus it is not the *value* of the momentum that is the same in all inertial reference frames. Instead, the Galilean principle of relativity tells us that the *law* of momentum conservation is the same in all inertial reference frames. If $P_f = P_i$ in frame S, then it must be true that $P_f' = P_i'$ in frame S'. Consequently, we can conclude that P_f' will be -18 kg m/s after the collision in S'.

(b) Collision seen in frame S'

-9.0 m/s   1.0 kg   2.0 kg

1   2
$u_2' = -9.0$ m/s
$P_i' = -18$ kg m/s

Using Galilean Relativity

The principle of relativity is concerned with the laws of mechanics, not with the values that are needed to satisfy the laws. If momentum is conserved in one inertial reference frame, it is conserved in all inertial reference frames. Even so, a problem may be easier to solve in one reference frame than in others.

Elastic collisions provide a good example of using reference frames. You learned in Chapter 10 how to calculate the outcome of a perfectly elastic collision between two particles in the reference frame in which particle 2 is initially at rest. We can use that information together with the Galilean transformations to solve elastic-collision problems in any inertial reference frame.

TACTICS
BOX 36.1 **Analyzing elastic collisions**

❶ Transform the initial velocities of particles 1 and 2 from frame S to reference frame S′ in which particle 2 is at rest.

❷ The outcome of the collision in S′ is given by

$$u'_{1f} = \frac{m_1 - m_2}{m_1 + m_2} u'_{1i}$$

$$u'_{2f} = \frac{2m_1}{m_1 + m_2} u'_{1i}$$

❸ Transform the two final velocities from frame S′ back to frame S.

Exercises 4–5

EXAMPLE 36.2 **An elastic collision**

A 300 g ball moving to the right at 2.0 m/s has a perfectly elastic collision with a 100 g ball moving to the left at 4.0 m/s. What are the direction and speed of each ball after the collision?

MODEL The velocities are measured in the laboratory frame, which we call frame S.

VISUALIZE **FIGURE 36.7a** shows both the balls and a reference frame S′ in which ball 2 is at rest.

SOLVE The three steps of Tactics Box 36.1 are illustrated in **FIGURE 36.7b**. We're given u_{1i} and u_{2i}. The Galilean transformations of these velocities to frame S′, using $v = -4.0$ m/s, are

$$u'_{1i} = u_{1i} - v = (2.0 \text{ m/s}) - (-4.0 \text{ m/s}) = 6.0 \text{ m/s}$$

$$u'_{2i} = u_{2i} - v = (-4.0 \text{ m/s}) - (-4.0 \text{ m/s}) = 0 \text{ m/s}$$

The 100 g ball is at rest in frame S′, which is what we wanted. The velocities after the collision are

$$u'_{1f} = \frac{m_1 - m_2}{m_1 + m_2} u'_{1i} = 3.0 \text{ m/s}$$

$$u'_{2f} = \frac{2m_1}{m_1 + m_2} u'_{1i} = 9.0 \text{ m/s}$$

We've finished the collision analysis, but we're not done because these are the post-collision velocities in frame S′. Another application of the Galilean transformations tells us that the post-collision velocities in frame S are

$$u_{1f} = u'_{1f} + v = (3.0 \text{ m/s}) + (-4.0 \text{ m/s}) = -1.0 \text{ m/s}$$

$$u_{2f} = u'_{2f} + v = (9.0 \text{ m/s}) + (-4.0 \text{ m/s}) = 5.0 \text{ m/s}$$

Thus the 300 g ball rebounds to the left at a speed of 1.0 m/s and the 100 g ball is knocked to the right at a speed of 5.0 m/s.

FIGURE 36.7 Using reference frames to solve an elastic-collision problem.

(a)

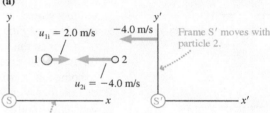

The collision takes place in frame S.

(b)

❶ Transform the velocities to frame S′ in which particle 2 is at rest.

❷ Analyze the collision in frame S′.

❸ Transform the post-collision velocities back to frame S.

ASSESS You can easily verify that momentum is conserved: $P_f = P_i = 0.20$ kg m/s. The calculations in this example were easy. The important point of this example, and one worth careful thought, is the *logic* of what we did and why we did it.

36.3 Einstein's Principle of Relativity

The 19th century was an era of optics and electromagnetism. Thomas Young demonstrated in 1801 that light is a wave, and by midcentury scientists had devised techniques for measuring the speed of light. Faraday discovered electromagnetic induction in 1831, setting in motion a series of events leading to Maxwell's conclusion, in 1864, that light is an electromagnetic wave.

If light is a wave, what is the medium in which it travels? This was perhaps *the* most important scientific question of the second half of the 19th century. The medium in which light waves were assumed to travel was called the **ether.** Experiments to measure the speed of light were assumed to be measuring its speed through the ether. But just what *is* the ether? What are its properties? Can we collect a jar full of ether to study? Despite the significance of these questions, efforts to detect the ether or measure its properties kept coming up empty handed.

Maxwell's theory of electromagnetism didn't help the situation. The crowning success of Maxwell's theory was his prediction that light waves travel with speed

$$c = \frac{1}{\sqrt{\epsilon_0 \mu_0}} = 3.00 \times 10^8 \text{ m/s}$$

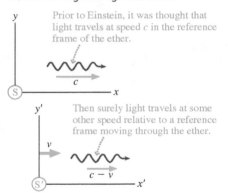

FIGURE 36.8 It seems as if the speed of light should differ from c in a reference frame moving through the ether.

Prior to Einstein, it was thought that light travels at speed c in the reference frame of the ether.

Then surely light travels at some other speed relative to a reference frame moving through the ether.

This is a very specific prediction with no wiggle room. The difficulty with such a specific prediction was the implication that Maxwell's laws of electromagnetism are valid *only* in the reference frame of the ether. After all, as FIGURE 36.8 shows, the light speed should certainly be larger or smaller than c in a reference frame moving through the ether, just as the sound speed is different to someone moving through the air.

As the 19th century closed, it appeared that Maxwell's theory did not obey the classical principle of relativity. There was just one reference frame, the reference frame of the ether, in which the laws of electromagnetism seemed to be true. And to make matters worse, the fact that no one had been able to detect the ether meant that no one could identify the one reference frame in which Maxwell's equations "worked."

It was in this muddled state of affairs that a young Albert Einstein made his mark on the world. Even as a teenager, Einstein had wondered how a light wave would look to someone "surfing" the wave, traveling alongside the wave at the wave speed. You can do that with a water wave or a sound wave, but light waves seemed to present a logical difficulty. An electromagnetic wave sustains itself by virtue of the fact that a changing magnetic field induces an electric field and a changing electric field induces a magnetic field. But to someone moving with the wave, *the fields would not change.* How could there be an electromagnetic wave under these circumstances?

Several years of thinking about the connection between electromagnetism and reference frames led Einstein to the conclusion that *all* the laws of physics, not just the laws of mechanics, should obey the principle of relativity. In other words, the principle of relativity is a fundamental statement about the nature of the physical universe. Thus we can remove the restriction in the Galilean principle of relativity and state a much more general principle:

Principle of relativity All the laws of physics are the same in all inertial reference frames.

All the results of Einstein's theory of relativity flow from this one simple statement.

The Constancy of the Speed of Light

If Maxwell's equations of electromagnetism are laws of physics, and there's every reason to think they are, then, according to the principle of relativity, Maxwell's equations must be true in *every* inertial reference frame. On the surface this seems to be an innocuous statement, equivalent to saying that the law of conservation of momentum is true in every inertial reference frame. But follow the logic:

1. Maxwell's equations are true in all inertial reference frames.
2. Maxwell's equations predict that electromagnetic waves, including light, travel at speed $c = 3.00 \times 10^8$ m/s.
3. Therefore, **light travels at speed c in all inertial reference frames.**

FIGURE 36.9 shows the implications of this conclusion. *All* experimenters, regardless of how they move with respect to each other, find that *all* light waves, regardless of the source, travel in their reference frame with the *same* speed c. If Cathy's velocity toward Bill and away from Amy is $v = 0.9c$, Cathy finds, by making measurements in her reference frame, that the light from Bill approaches her at speed c, not at $c + v = 1.9c$. And the light from Amy, which left Amy at speed c, catches up from behind at speed c *relative to Cathy,* not the $c - v = 0.1c$ you would have expected.

Although this prediction goes against all shreds of common sense, the experimental evidence for it is strong. Laboratory experiments are difficult because even the highest laboratory speed is insignificant in comparison to c. In the 1930s, however, physicists R. J. Kennedy and E. M. Thorndike realized that they could use the earth itself as a laboratory. The earth's speed as it circles the sun is about 30,000 m/s. The *relative* velocity of the earth in January differs by 60,000 m/s from its velocity in July, when the earth is moving in the opposite direction. Kennedy and Thorndike were able to use a very sensitive and stable interferometer to show that the numerical values of the speed of light in January and July differ by less than 2 m/s.

More recent experiments have used unstable elementary particles, called π mesons, that decay into high-energy photons of light. The π mesons, created in a particle accelerator, move through the laboratory at 99.975% the speed of light, or $v = 0.99975c$, as they emit photons at speed c in the π meson's reference frame. As FIGURE 36.10 shows, you would expect the photons to travel through the laboratory with speed $c + v = 1.99975c$. Instead, the measured speed of the photons in the laboratory was, within experimental error, 3.00×10^8 m/s.

In summary, *every* experiment designed to compare the speed of light in different reference frames has found that light travels at 3.00×10^8 m/s in every inertial reference frame, regardless of how the reference frames are moving with respect to each other.

How Can This Be?

You're in good company if you find this impossible to believe. Suppose I shot a ball forward at 50 m/s while driving past you at 30 m/s. You would certainly see the ball traveling at 80 m/s relative to you and the ground. What we're saying with regard to light is equivalent to saying that the ball travels at 50 m/s relative to my car and *at the same time* travels at 50 m/s relative to the ground, even though the car is moving across the ground at 30 m/s. It seems logically impossible.

You might think that this is merely a matter of semantics. If we can just get our definitions and use of words straight, then the mystery and confusion will disappear. Or perhaps the difficulty is a confusion between what we "see" versus what "really happens." In other words, a better analysis, one that focuses on what really happens, would find that light "really" travels at different speeds in different reference frames.

Alas, what "really happens" is that light travels at 3.00×10^8 m/s in every inertial reference frame, regardless of how the reference frames are moving with respect to each other. It's not a trick. There remains only one way to escape the logical contradictions.

The definition of velocity is $u = \Delta x/\Delta t$, the ratio of a distance traveled to the time interval in which the travel occurs. Suppose you and I both make measurements on an object as it moves, but you happen to be moving relative to me. Perhaps I'm standing on the corner, you're driving past in your car, and we're both trying to measure the velocity of a bicycle. Further, suppose we have agreed in advance to measure the position of the bicycle

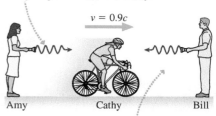

FIGURE 36.9 Light travels at speed c in all inertial reference frames, regardless of how the reference frames are moving with respect to the light source.

This light wave leaves Amy at speed c relative to Amy. It approaches Cathy at speed c relative to Cathy.

This light wave leaves Bill at speed c relative to Bill. It approaches Cathy at speed c relative to Cathy.

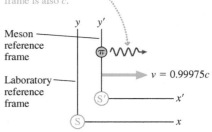

FIGURE 36.10 Experiments find that the photons travel through the laboratory with speed c, not the speed $1.99975c$ that you might expect.

A photon is emitted at speed c relative to the π meson. Measurements find that the photon's speed in the laboratory reference frame is also c.

first as it passes the tree in FIGURE 36.11, then later as it passes the lamppost. Your $\Delta x'$, the bicycle's displacement, differs from my Δx because of your motion relative to me, causing you to calculate a bicycle velocity u' in your reference frame that differs from its velocity u in my reference frame. This is just the Galilean transformations showing up again.

FIGURE 36.11 Measuring the velocity of an object by appealing to the basic definition $u = \Delta x / \Delta t$.

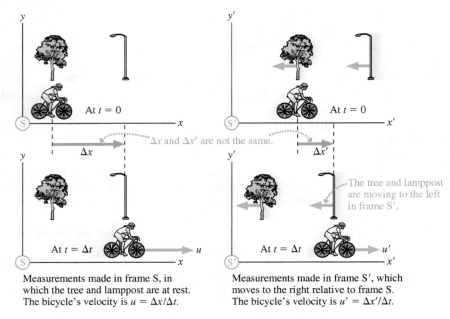

Measurements made in frame S, in which the tree and lamppost are at rest. The bicycle's velocity is $u = \Delta x / \Delta t$.

Measurements made in frame S′, which moves to the right relative to frame S. The bicycle's velocity is $u' = \Delta x' / \Delta t$.

Now let's repeat the measurements, but this time let's measure the velocity of a light wave as it travels from the tree to the lamppost. Once again, your $\Delta x'$ differs from my Δx, and the obvious conclusion is that your light speed u' differs from my light speed u. The difference will be very small if you're driving past in your car, very large if you're flying past in a rocket traveling at nearly the speed of light. Although this conclusion seems obvious, it is wrong. Experiments show that, for a light wave, we'll get the *same* values: $u' = u$.

The only way this can be true is if your Δt is not the same as my Δt. If the time it takes the light to move from the tree to the lamppost in your reference frame, a time we'll now call $\Delta t'$, differs from the time Δt it takes the light to move from the tree to the lamppost in my reference frame, then we might find that $\Delta x'/\Delta t' = \Delta x/\Delta t$. That is, $u' = u$ even though you are moving with respect to me.

We've assumed, since the beginning of this textbook, that time is simply time. It flows along like a river, and all experimenters in all reference frames simply use it. For example, suppose the tree and the lamppost both have big clocks that we both can see. Shouldn't we be able to agree on the time interval Δt the light needs to move from the tree to the lamppost?

Perhaps not. It's demonstrably true that $\Delta x' \neq \Delta x$. It's experimentally verified that $u' = u$ for light waves. Something must be wrong with *assumptions* that we've made about the nature of time. The principle of relativity has painted us into a corner, and our only way out is to reexamine our understanding of time.

36.4 Events and Measurements

To question some of our most basic assumptions about space and time requires extreme care. We need to be certain that no assumptions slip into our analysis unnoticed. Our goal is to describe the motion of a particle in a clear and precise way, making the barest minimum of assumptions.

Events

The fundamental element of relativity is called an **event.** An event is a physical activity that takes place at a definite point in space and at a definite instant of time. An exploding firecracker is an event. A collision between two particles is an event. A light wave hitting a detector is an event.

Events can be observed and measured by experimenters in different reference frames. An exploding firecracker is as clear to you as you drive by in your car as it is to me standing on the street corner. We can quantify where and when an event occurs with four numbers: the coordinates (x, y, z) and the instant of time t. These four numbers, illustrated in FIGURE 36.12, are called the **spacetime coordinates** of the event.

The spatial coordinates of an event measured in reference frames S and S′ may differ. It now appears that the instant of time recorded in S and S′ may also differ. Thus the spacetime coordinates of an event measured by experimenters in frame S are (x, y, z, t) and the spacetime coordinates of the *same event* measured by experimenters in frame S′ are (x', y', z', t').

The motion of a particle can be described as a sequence of two or more events. We introduced this idea in the preceding section when we agreed to measure the velocity of a bicycle and then of a light wave by making measurements when the object passed the tree (first event) and when the object passed the lamppost (second event).

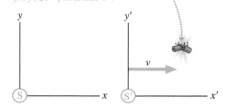

FIGURE 36.12 The location and time of an event are described by its spacetime coordinates.

An event has spacetime coordinates (x, y, z, t) in frame S and different spacetime coordinates (x', y', z', t') in frame S′.

Measurements

Events are what "really happen," but how do we learn about an event? That is, how do the experimenters in a reference frame determine the spacetime coordinates of an event? This is a problem of *measurement.*

We defined a reference frame to be a coordinate system in which experimenters can make position and time measurements. That's a good start, but now we need to be more precise as to *how* the measurements are made. Imagine that a reference frame is filled with a cubic lattice of meter sticks, as shown in FIGURE 36.13. At every intersection is a clock, and all the clocks in a reference frame are *synchronized*. We'll return in a moment to consider how to synchronize the clocks, but assume for the moment it can be done.

Now, with our meter sticks and clocks in place, we can use a two-part measurement scheme:

- The (x, y, z) coordinates of an event are determined by the intersection of the meter sticks closest to the event.
- The event's time t is the time displayed on the clock nearest the event.

You can imagine, if you wish, that each event is accompanied by a flash of light to illuminate the face of the nearest clock and make its reading known.

Several important issues need to be noted:

1. The clocks and meter sticks in each reference frame are imaginary, so they have no difficulty passing through each other.
2. Measurements of position and time made in one reference frame must use only the clocks and meter sticks in that reference frame.
3. There's nothing special about the sticks being 1 m long and the clocks 1 m apart. The lattice spacing can be altered to achieve whatever level of measurement accuracy is desired.
4. We'll assume that the experimenters in each reference frame have assistants sitting beside every clock to record the position and time of nearby events.
5. Perhaps most important, t is the time at which the event *actually happens,* not the time at which an experimenter sees the event or at which information about the event reaches an experimenter.
6. All experimenters in one reference frame agree on the spacetime coordinates of an event. In other words, **an event has a unique set of spacetime coordinates in each reference frame.**

FIGURE 36.13 The spacetime coordinates of an event are measured by a lattice of meter sticks and clocks.

The spacetime coordinates of this event are measured by the nearest meter stick intersection and the nearest clock.

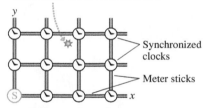

Synchronized clocks

Meter sticks

Reference frame S

Reference frame S′ has its own meter sticks and its own clocks.

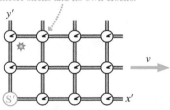

Reference frame S′

STOP TO THINK 36.3 A carpenter is working on a house two blocks away. You notice a slight delay between seeing the carpenter's hammer hit the nail and hearing the blow. At what time does the event "hammer hits nail" occur?

    a. At the instant you hear the blow
    b. At the instant you see the hammer hit
    c. Very slightly before you see the hammer hit
    d. Very slightly after you see the hammer hit

Clock Synchronization

It's important that all the clocks in a reference frame be **synchronized,** meaning that all clocks in the reference frame have the same reading at any one instant of time. Thus we need a method of synchronization. One idea that comes to mind is to designate the clock at the origin as the *master clock.* We could then carry this clock around to every clock in the lattice, adjust that clock to match the master clock, and finally return the master clock to the origin.

This would be a perfectly good method of clock synchronization in Newtonian mechanics, where time flows along smoothly, the same for everyone. But we've been driven to reexamine the nature of time by the possibility that time is different in reference frames moving relative to each other. Because the master clock would *move,* we cannot assume that the moving master clock would keep time in the same way as the stationary clocks.

We need a synchronization method that does not require moving the clocks. Fortunately, such a method is easy to devise. Each clock is resting at the intersection of meter sticks, so by looking at the meter sticks, the assistant knows, or can calculate, exactly how far each clock is from the origin. Once the distance is known, the assistant can calculate exactly how long a light wave will take to travel from the origin to each clock. For example, light will take $1.00\ \mu s$ to travel to a clock 300 m from the origin.

NOTE ▶ It's handy for many relativity problems to know that the speed of light is $c = 300\ \text{m}/\mu\text{s}$. ◀

To synchronize the clocks, the assistants begin by setting each clock to display the light travel time from the origin, but they don't start the clocks. Next, as FIGURE 36.14 shows, a light flashes at the origin and, simultaneously, the clock at the origin starts running from $t = 0$ s. The light wave spreads out in all directions at speed c. A photodetector on each clock recognizes the arrival of the light wave and, without delay, starts the clock. The clock had been preset with the light travel time, so each clock as it starts reads exactly the same as the clock at the origin. Thus all the clocks will be synchronized after the light wave has passed by.

Events and Observations

We noted above that t is the time the event *actually happens.* This is an important point, one that bears further discussion. Light waves take time to travel. Messages, whether they're transmitted by light pulses, telephone, or courier on horseback, take time to be delivered. An experimenter *observes* an event, such as an exploding firecracker, only *at a later time* when light waves reach his or her eyes. But our interest is in the event itself, not the experimenter's observation of the event. The time at which the experimenter sees the event or receives information about the event is not when the event actually occurred.

Suppose at $t = 0$ s a firecracker explodes at $x = 300$ m. The flash of light from the firecracker will reach an experimenter at the origin at $t_1 = 1.0\ \mu s$. The sound of the explosion will reach a sightless experimenter at the origin at $t_2 = 0.88$ s. Neither of these is the time t_{event} of the explosion, although the experimenter can work backward from these times, using known wave speeds, to determine t_{event}. In this example, the spacetime coordinates of the event—the explosion—are (300 m, 0 m, 0 m, 0 s).

FIGURE 36.14 Synchronizing clocks.

1. This clock is preset to $1.00\ \mu s$, the time it takes light to travel 300 m.

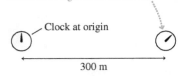

300 m

2. At $t = 0$ s, a light flashes at the origin and the origin clock starts running. A very short time later, seen here, a light wave has begun to move outward.

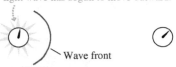

3. The clock starts when the light wave reaches it. It is now synchronized with the origin clock.

| EXAMPLE 36.3 | **Finding the time of an event** |

Experimenter A in reference frame S stands at the origin looking in the positive x-direction. Experimenter B stands at $x = 900$ m looking in the negative x-direction. A firecracker explodes somewhere between them. Experimenter B sees the light flash at $t = 3.0 \, \mu$s. Experimenter A sees the light flash at $t = 4.0 \, \mu$s. What are the spacetime coordinates of the explosion?

MODEL Experimenters A and B are in the same reference frame and have synchronized clocks.

VISUALIZE FIGURE 36.15 shows the two experimenters and the explosion at unknown position x.

SOLVE The two experimenters observe light flashes at two different instants, but there's only one event. Light travels at 300 m/μs, so the additional 1.0 μs needed for the light to reach experimenter A implies that distance $(x - 0$ m$)$ is 300 m longer than distance $(900$ m $- x)$. That is,

$$(x - 0 \text{ m}) = (900 \text{ m} - x) + 300 \text{ m}$$

This is easily solved to give $x = 600$ m as the position coordinate of the explosion. The light takes 1.0 μs to travel 300 m to experimenter B, 2.0 μs to travel 600 m to experimenter A. The light is

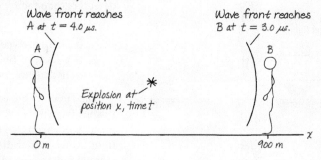

FIGURE 36.15 The light wave reaches the experimenters at different times. Neither of these is the time at which the event actually happened.

received at 3.0 μs and 4.0 μs, respectively; hence it was emitted by the explosion at $t = 2.0 \, \mu$s. The spacetime coordinates of the explosion are (600 m, 0 m, 0 m, 2.0 μs).

ASSESS Although the experimenters *see* the explosion at different times, they agree that the explosion actually *happened* at $t = 2.0 \, \mu$s.

Simultaneity

Two events 1 and 2 that take place at different positions x_1 and x_2 but at the *same time* $t_1 = t_2$, as measured in some reference frame, are said to be **simultaneous** in that reference frame. Simultaneity is determined by when the events actually happen, not when they are seen or observed. In general, simultaneous events are *not* seen at the same time because of the difference in light travel times from the events to an experimenter.

| EXAMPLE 36.4 | **Are the explosions simultaneous?** |

An experimenter in reference frame S stands at the origin looking in the positive x-direction. At $t = 3.0 \, \mu$s she sees firecracker 1 explode at $x = 600$ m. A short time later, at $t = 5.0 \, \mu$s, she sees firecracker 2 explode at $x = 1200$ m. Are the two explosions simultaneous? If not, which firecracker exploded first?

MODEL Light from both explosions travels toward the experimenter at 300 m/μs.

SOLVE The experimenter *sees* two different explosions, but perceptions of the events are not the events themselves. When did the explosions *actually* occur? Using the fact that light travels at 300 m/μs, we can see that firecracker 1 exploded at $t_1 = 1.0 \, \mu$s and firecracker 2 also exploded at $t_2 = 1.0 \, \mu$s. The events *are* simultaneous.

STOP TO THINK 36.4 A tree and a pole are 3000 m apart. Each is suddenly hit by a bolt of lightning. Mark, who is standing at rest midway between the two, sees the two lightning bolts at the same instant of time. Nancy is at rest under the tree. Define event 1 to be "lightning strikes tree" and event 2 to be "lightning strikes pole." For Nancy, does event 1 occur before, after, or at the same time as event 2?

36.5 The Relativity of Simultaneity

We've now established a means for measuring the time of an event in a reference frame, so let's begin to investigate the nature of time. The following "thought experiment" is very similar to one suggested by Einstein.

FIGURE 36.16 on the next page shows a long railroad car traveling to the right with a velocity v that may be an appreciable fraction of the speed of light. A firecracker is tied

FIGURE 36.16 A railroad car traveling to the right with velocity v.

The firecrackers will make burn marks on the ground at the positions where they explode.

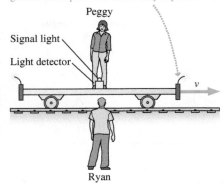

Peggy

Signal light

Light detector

v

Ryan

to each end of the car, just above the ground. Each firecracker is powerful enough so that, when it explodes, it will make a burn mark on the ground at the position of the explosion.

Ryan is standing on the ground, watching the railroad car go by. Peggy is standing in the exact center of the car with a special box at her feet. This box has two light detectors, one facing each way, and a signal light on top. The box works as follows:

1. If a flash of light is received at the detector facing right, as seen by Ryan, before a flash is received at the left detector, then the light on top of the box will turn green.
2. If a flash of light is received at the left detector before a flash is received at the right detector, or if two flashes arrive simultaneously, the light on top will turn red.

The firecrackers explode as the railroad car passes Ryan, and he sees the two light flashes from the explosions simultaneously. He then measures the distances to the two burn marks and finds that he was standing exactly halfway between the marks. Because light travels equal distances in equal times, Ryan concludes that the two explosions were simultaneous in his reference frame, the reference frame of the ground. Further, because he was midway between the two ends of the car, he was directly opposite Peggy when the explosions occurred.

FIGURE 36.17a shows the sequence of events in Ryan's reference frame. Light travels at speed c in all inertial reference frames, so, although the firecrackers were moving, the light waves are spheres centered on the burn marks. Ryan determines that the light wave coming from the right reaches Peggy and the box before the light wave coming from the left. Thus, according to Ryan, the signal light on top of the box turns green.

FIGURE 36.17 Exploding firecrackers seen in two different reference frames.

(a) The events in Ryan's frame

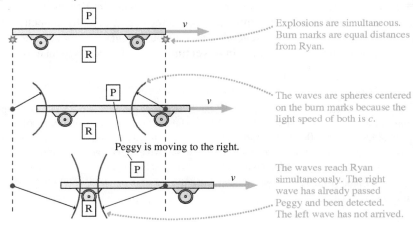

Explosions are simultaneous. Burn marks are equal distances from Ryan.

The waves are spheres centered on the burn marks because the light speed of both is c.

Peggy is moving to the right.

The waves reach Ryan simultaneously. The right wave has already passed Peggy and been detected. The left wave has not arrived.

(b) The events in Peggy's frame

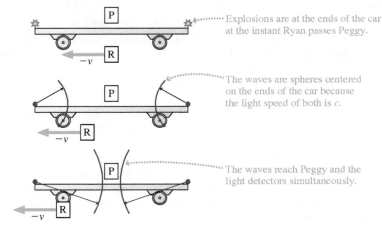

Explosions are at the ends of the car at the instant Ryan passes Peggy.

The waves are spheres centered on the ends of the car because the light speed of both is c.

The waves reach Peggy and the light detectors simultaneously.

How do things look in Peggy's reference frame, a reference frame moving to the right at velocity v relative to the ground? As FIGURE 36.17b shows, Peggy sees Ryan moving to the left with speed v. Light travels at speed c in all inertial reference frames, so the light waves are spheres centered on the ends of the car. If the explosions are simultaneous, as Ryan has determined, the two light waves reach her and the box simultaneously. Thus, according to Peggy, the signal light on top of the box turns red!

Now the light on top must be either green or red. *It can't be both!* Later, after the railroad car has stopped, Ryan and Peggy can place the box in front of them. Either it has a red light or a green light. Ryan can't see one color while Peggy sees the other. Hence we have a paradox. It's impossible for Peggy and Ryan both to be right. But who is wrong, and why?

What do we know with absolute certainty?

1. Ryan detected the flashes simultaneously.
2. Ryan was halfway between the firecrackers when they exploded.
3. The light from the two explosions traveled toward Ryan at equal speeds.

The conclusion that the explosions were simultaneous in Ryan's reference frame is unassailable. The light is green.

Peggy, however, made an assumption. It's a perfectly ordinary assumption, one that seems sufficiently obvious that you probably didn't notice, but an assumption nonetheless. Peggy assumed that the explosions were simultaneous.

Didn't Ryan find them to be simultaneous? Indeed, he did. Suppose we call Ryan's reference frame S, the explosion on the right event R, and the explosion on the left event L. Ryan found that $t_R = t_L$. But Peggy has to use a different set of clocks, the clocks in her reference frame S′, to measure the times t'_R and t'_L at which the explosions occurred. The fact that $t_R = t_L$ in frame S does *not* allow us to conclude that $t'_R = t'_L$ in frame S′.

In fact, in frame S′ the right firecracker must explode *before* the left firecracker. Figure 36.17b, with its assumption about simultaneity, was incorrect. FIGURE 36.18 shows the situation in Peggy's reference frame, with the right firecracker exploding first. Now the wave from the right reaches Peggy and the box first, as Ryan had concluded, and the light on top turns green.

One of the most disconcerting conclusions of relativity is that **two events occurring simultaneously in reference frame S are *not* simultaneous in any reference frame S′ moving relative to S.** This is called the **relativity of simultaneity.**

The two firecrackers *really* explode at the same instant of time in Ryan's reference frame. And the right firecracker *really* explodes first in Peggy's reference frame. It's not a matter of when they see the flashes. Our conclusion refers to the times at which the explosions actually occur.

The paradox of Peggy and Ryan contains the essence of relativity, and it's worth careful thought. First, review the logic until you're certain that there *is* a paradox, a logical impossibility. Then convince yourself that the only way to resolve the paradox is to abandon the assumption that the explosions are simultaneous in Peggy's reference frame. If you understand the paradox and its resolution, you've made a big step toward understanding what relativity is all about.

FIGURE 36.18 The real sequence of events in Peggy's reference frame.

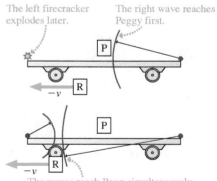

The right firecracker explodes first.

The left firecracker explodes later.   The right wave reaches Peggy first.

The waves reach Ryan simultaneously. The left wave has not reached Peggy.

STOP TO THINK 36.5   A tree and a pole are 3000 m apart. Each is hit by a bolt of lightning. Mark, who is standing at rest midway between the two, sees the two lightning bolts at the same instant of time. Nancy is flying her rocket at $v = 0.5c$ in the direction from the tree toward the pole. The lightning hits the tree just as she passes by it. Define event 1 to be "lightning strikes tree" and event 2 to be "lightning strikes pole." For Nancy, does event 1 occur before, after, or at the same time as event 2?

36.6 Time Dilation

The principle of relativity has driven us to the logical conclusion that time is not the same for two reference frames moving relative to each other. Our analysis thus far has been mostly qualitative. It's time to start developing some quantitative tools that will allow us to compare measurements in one reference frame to measurements in another reference frame.

FIGURE 36.19a shows a special clock called a *light clock*. The light clock is a box with a light source at the bottom and a mirror at the top, separated by distance h. The light source emits a very short pulse of light that travels to the mirror and reflects back to a light detector beside the source. The clock advances one "tick" each time the detector receives a light pulse, and it immediately, with no delay, causes the light source to emit the next light pulse.

Our goal is to compare two measurements of the interval between two ticks of the clock: one taken by an experimenter standing next to the clock and the other by an experimenter moving with respect to the clock. To be specific, FIGURE 36.19b shows the clock at rest in reference frame S′. We call this the **rest frame** of the clock. Reference frame S′ moves to the right with velocity v relative to reference frame S.

Relativity requires us to measure *events,* so let's define event 1 to be the emission of a light pulse and event 2 to be the detection of that light pulse. Experimenters in both reference frames are able to measure where and when these events occur *in their frame.* In frame S, the time interval $\Delta t = t_2 - t_1$ is one tick of the clock. Similarly, one tick in frame S′ is $\Delta t' = t'_2 - t'_1$.

To be sure we have a clear understanding of the relativity result, let's first do a classical analysis. In frame S′, the clock's rest frame, the light travels straight up and down, a total distance $2h$, at speed c. The time interval is $\Delta t' = 2h/c$.

FIGURE 36.20a shows the operation of the light clock as seen in frame S. The clock is moving to the right at speed v in S, thus the mirror moves distance $\frac{1}{2}v(\Delta t)$ during the time $\frac{1}{2}(\Delta t)$ in which the light pulse moves from the source to the mirror. The distance traveled by the light during this interval is $\frac{1}{2}u_{\text{light}}(\Delta t)$, where u_{light} is the speed of light in frame S. You can see from the vector addition in FIGURE 36.20b that the speed of light in frame S is $u_{\text{light}} = (c^2 + v^2)^{1/2}$. (Remember, this is a classical analysis in which the speed of light *does* depend on the motion of the reference frame relative to the light source.)

The Pythagorean theorem applied to the right triangle in Figure 36.20a is

$$h^2 + \left(\frac{1}{2}v\,\Delta t\right)^2 = \left(\frac{1}{2}u_{\text{light}}\Delta t\right)^2 = \left(\frac{1}{2}\sqrt{c^2 + v^2}\,\Delta t\right)^2$$

$$= \left(\frac{1}{2}c\,\Delta t\right)^2 + \left(\frac{1}{2}v\,\Delta t\right)^2$$

(36.4)

The term $\left(\frac{1}{2}v\,\Delta t\right)^2$ is common to both sides and cancels. Solving for Δt gives $\Delta t = 2h/c$, identical to $\Delta t'$. In other words, a classical analysis finds that the clock ticks at exactly the same rate in both frame S and frame S′. This shouldn't be surprising. There's only one kind of time in classical physics, measured the same by all experimenters independent of their motion.

The principle of relativity changes only one thing, but that change has profound consequences. According to the principle of relativity, light travels at the same speed in *all* inertial reference frames. In frame S′, the rest frame of the clock, the light simply goes straight up and back. The time of one tick,

$$\Delta t' = \frac{2h}{c}$$

(36.5)

is unchanged from the classical analysis.

FIGURE 36.19 The ticking of a light clock can be measured by experimenters in two different reference frames.

(a) A light clock

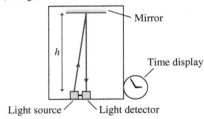

Mirror

Time display

Light source   Light detector

(b) The clock is at rest in frame S′.

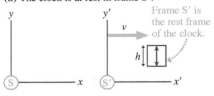

Frame S′ is the rest frame of the clock.

FIGURE 36.20 A classical analysis of the light clock.

(a)

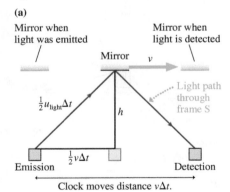

Mirror when light was emitted

Mirror when light is detected

Mirror

$\frac{1}{2}u_{\text{light}}\Delta t$

Light path through frame S

h

Emission $\frac{1}{2}v\Delta t$ Detection

Clock moves distance $v\Delta t$.

(b)

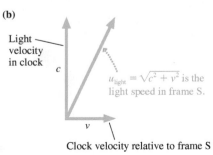

Light velocity in clock

c

$u_{\text{light}} = \sqrt{c^2 + v^2}$ is the light speed in frame S.

v

Clock velocity relative to frame S

FIGURE 36.21 shows the light clock as seen in frame S. The difference from Figure 36.20a is that the light now travels along the hypotenuse at speed c. We can again use the Pythagorean theorem to write

$$h^2 + \left(\frac{1}{2}v\,\Delta t\right)^2 = \left(\frac{1}{2}c\,\Delta t\right)^2 \qquad (36.6)$$

Solving for Δt gives

$$\Delta t = \frac{2h/c}{\sqrt{1 - v^2/c^2}} = \frac{\Delta t'}{\sqrt{1 - v^2/c^2}} \qquad (36.7)$$

The time interval between two ticks in frame S is *not* the same as in frame S′.

It's useful to define $\beta = v/c$, the velocity as a fraction of the speed of light. For example, a reference frame moving with $v = 2.4 \times 10^8$ m/s has $\beta = 0.80$. In terms of β, Equation 36.7 is

$$\Delta t = \frac{\Delta t'}{\sqrt{1 - \beta^2}} \qquad (36.8)$$

NOTE ▶ The expression $(1 - v^2/c^2)^{1/2} = (1 - \beta^2)^{1/2}$ occurs frequently in relativity. The value of the expression is 1 when $v = 0$, and it steadily decreases to 0 as $v \to c$ (or $\beta \to 1$). The square root is an imaginary number if $v > c$, which would make Δt imaginary in Equation 36.8. Time intervals certainly have to be real numbers, suggesting that $v > c$ is not physically possible. One of the predictions of the theory of relativity, as you've undoubtedly heard, is that nothing can travel faster than the speed of light. Now you can begin to see why. We'll examine this topic more closely in Section 36.9. In the meantime, we'll require v to be less than c. ◀

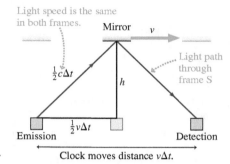

FIGURE 36.21 A light clock analysis in which the speed of light is the same in all reference frames.

Proper Time

Frame S′ has one important distinction. It is the *one and only* inertial reference frame in which the light clock is at rest. Consequently, it is the one and only inertial reference frame in which the times of both events—the emission of the light and the detection of the light—are measured by the *same* reference-frame clock. You can see that the light pulse in Figure 36.19a starts and ends at the same position. In Figure 36.21, the emission and detection take place at different positions in frame S and must be measured by different reference-frame clocks, one at each position.

The time interval between two events that occur at the *same position* is called the **proper time** $\Delta\tau$. Only one inertial reference frame measures the proper time, and it does so with a single clock that is present at both events. An inertial reference frame moving with velocity $v = \beta c$ relative to the proper-time frame must use two clocks to measure the time interval: one at the position of the first event, the other at the position of the second event. The time interval between the two events in this frame is

$$\Delta t = \frac{\Delta\tau}{\sqrt{1 - \beta^2}} \geq \Delta\tau \qquad \text{(time dilation)} \qquad (36.9)$$

The "stretching out" of the time interval implied by Equation 36.9 is called **time dilation.** Time dilation is sometimes described by saying that "moving clocks run slow." This is not an accurate statement because it implies that some reference frames are "really" moving while others are "really" at rest. The whole point of relativity is that all inertial reference frames are equally valid, that all we know about reference frames is how they move relative to each other. A better description of time dilation is the statement that **the time interval between two ticks is the shortest in the reference frame in which the clock is at rest.** The time interval between two ticks is longer (i.e., the clock "runs slower") when it is measured in any reference frame in which the clock is moving.

NOTE ▶ Equation 36.9 was derived using a light clock because the operation of a light clock is clear and easy to analyze. But the conclusion is really about time itself. *Any* clock, regardless of how it operates, behaves the same. ◀

EXAMPLE 36.5 **From the sun to Saturn**

Saturn is 1.43×10^{12} m from the sun. A rocket travels along a line from the sun to Saturn at a constant speed of $0.9c$ relative to the solar system. How long does the journey take as measured by an experimenter on earth? As measured by an astronaut on the rocket?

MODEL Let the solar system be in reference frame S and the rocket be in reference frame S' that travels with velocity $v = 0.9c$ relative to S. Relativity problems must be stated in terms of *events*. Let event 1 be "the rocket and the sun coincide" (the experimenter on earth says that the rocket passes the sun; the astronaut on the rocket says that the sun passes the rocket) and event 2 be "the rocket and Saturn coincide."

FIGURE 36.22 Pictorial representation of the trip as seen in frames S and S'.

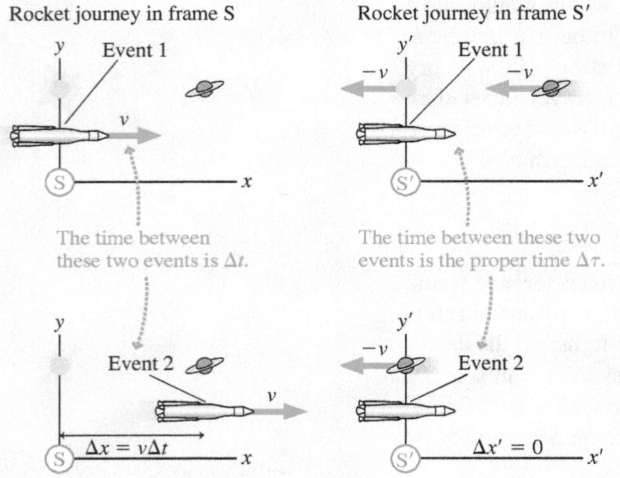

VISUALIZE FIGURE 36.22 shows the two events as seen from the two reference frames. Notice that the two events occur at the *same position* in S', the position of the rocket, and consequently can be measured by *one* clock.

SOLVE The time interval measured in the solar system reference frame, which includes the earth, is simply

$$\Delta t = \frac{\Delta x}{v} = \frac{1.43 \times 10^{12} \text{ m}}{0.9 \times (3.00 \times 10^8 \text{ m/s})} = 5300 \text{ s}$$

Relativity hasn't abandoned the basic definition $v = \Delta x/\Delta t$, although we do have to be sure that Δx and Δt are measured in just one reference frame and refer to the same two events.

How are things in the rocket's reference frame? The two events occur at the *same position* in S' and can be measured by *one* clock, the clock at the origin. Thus the time measured by the astronauts is the *proper time* $\Delta \tau$ between the two events. We can use Equation 36.9 with $\beta = 0.9$ to find

$$\Delta \tau = \sqrt{1 - \beta^2} \, \Delta t = \sqrt{1 - 0.9^2}(5300 \text{ s}) = 2310 \text{ s}$$

ASSESS The time interval measured between these two events by the astronauts is less than half the time interval measured by experimenters on earth. The difference has nothing to do with when earthbound astronomers *see* the rocket pass the sun and Saturn. Δt is the time interval from when the rocket actually passes the sun, as measured by a clock at the sun, until it actually passes Saturn, as measured by a synchronized clock at Saturn. The interval between *seeing* the events from earth, which would have to allow for light travel times, would be something other than 5300 s. Δt and $\Delta \tau$ are different because *time is different* in two reference frames moving relative to each other.

STOP TO THINK 36.6 Molly flies her rocket past Nick at constant velocity v. Molly and Nick both measure the time it takes the rocket, from nose to tail, to pass Nick. Which of the following is true?

a. Both Molly and Nick measure the same amount of time.
b. Molly measures a shorter time interval than Nick.
c. Nick measures a shorter time interval than Molly.

Experimental Evidence

Is there any evidence for the crazy idea that clocks moving relative to each other tell time differently? Indeed, there's plenty. An experiment in 1971 sent an atomic clock around the world on a jet plane while an identical clock remained in the laboratory. This was a difficult experiment because the traveling clock's speed was so small compared to c, but measuring the small differences between the time intervals was just barely within the capabilities of atomic clocks. It was also a more complex experiment than we've analyzed because the clock accelerated as it moved around a circle. The scientists found that, upon its return, the eastbound clock, traveling faster than the laboratory on a rotating earth, was 60 ns behind the stay-at-home clock, which was exactly as predicted by relativity.

Very detailed studies have been done on unstable particles called *muons* that are created at the top of the atmosphere, at a height of about 60 km, when high-energy cosmic rays collide with air molecules. It is well known, from laboratory studies, that stationary muons decay with a *half-life* of 1.5 μs. That is, half the muons decay within 1.5 μs, half of those remaining decay in the next 1.5 μs, and so on. The decays can be used as a clock.

The muons travel down through the atmosphere at very nearly the speed of light. The time needed to reach the ground, assuming $v \approx c$, is $\Delta t \approx (60,000 \text{ m})/(3 \times 10^8 \text{ m/s}) = 200 \ \mu$s. This is 133 half-lives, so the fraction of muons reaching the ground should be $\approx \left(\frac{1}{2}\right)^{133} = 10^{-40}$. That is, only 1 out of every 10^{40} muons should reach the ground. In fact, experiments find that about 1 in 10 muons reach the ground, an experimental result that differs by a factor of 10^{39} from our prediction!

The discrepancy is due to time dilation. In FIGURE 36.23, the two events "muon is created" and "muon hits ground" take place at two different places in the earth's reference frame. However, these two events occur at the *same position* in the muon's reference frame. (The muon is like the rocket in Example 36.5.) Thus the muon's internal clock measures the proper time. The time-dilated interval $\Delta t = 200 \ \mu$s in the earth's reference frame corresponds to a proper time $\Delta \tau \approx 5 \ \mu$s in the muon's reference frame. That is, in the muon's reference frame it takes only 5 μs from creation at the top of the atmosphere until the ground runs into it. This is 3.3 half-lives, so the fraction of muons reaching the ground is $\left(\frac{1}{2}\right)^{3.3} = 0.1$, or 1 out of 10. We wouldn't detect muons at the ground at all if not for time dilation.

The details are beyond the scope of this textbook, but dozens of high-energy particle accelerators around the world that study quarks and other elementary particles have been designed and built on the basis of Einstein's theory of relativity. The fact that they work exactly as planned is strong testimony to the reality of time dilation.

FIGURE 36.23 We wouldn't detect muons at the ground if not for time dilation.

A muon travels $\approx$450 m in 1.5 μs. We would not detect muons at ground level if the half-life of a moving muon were 1.5 μs.

Muon is created.

Because of time dilation, the half-life of a high-speed muon is long enough in the earth's reference frame for about 1 in 10 muons to reach the ground.

Muon hits ground.

The Twin Paradox

The most well-known relativity paradox is the twin paradox. George and Helen are twins. On their 25th birthday, Helen departs on a starship voyage to a distant star. Let's imagine, to be specific, that her starship accelerates almost instantly to a speed of 0.95c and that she travels to a star that is 9.5 light years (9.5 ly) from earth. Upon arriving, she discovers that the planets circling the star are inhabited by fierce aliens, so she immediately turns around and heads home at 0.95c.

A **light year,** abbreviated ly, is the distance that light travels in one year. A light year is vastly larger than the diameter of the solar system. The distance between two neighboring stars is typically a few light years. For our purpose, we can write the speed of light as $c = 1$ ly/year. That is, light travels 1 light year per year.

This value for c allows us to determine how long, according to George and his fellow earthlings, it takes Helen to travel out and back. Her total distance is 19 ly and, due to her rapid acceleration and rapid turn-around, she travels essentially the entire distance at speed $v = 0.95c = 0.95$ ly/year. Thus the time she's away, as measured by George, is

$$\Delta t_G = \frac{19 \text{ ly}}{0.95 \text{ ly/year}} = 20 \text{ years} \qquad (36.10)$$

George will be 45 years old when his sister Helen returns with tales of adventure.

While she's away, George takes a physics class and studies Einstein's theory of relativity. He realizes that time dilation will make Helen's clocks run more slowly than his clocks, which are at rest relative to him. Her heart—a clock—will beat fewer

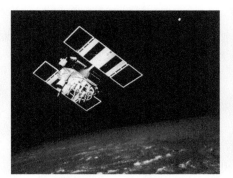

The global positioning system (GPS), which allows you to pinpoint your location anywhere in the world to within a few meters, uses a set of orbiting satellites. Because of their motion, the atomic clocks on these satellites keep time differently from clocks on the ground. To determine an accurate position, the software in your GPS receiver must carefully correct for time-dilation effects.

times and the minute hand on her watch will go around fewer times. In other words, she's aging more slowly than he is. Although she is his twin, she will be younger than he is when she returns.

Calculating Helen's age is not hard. We simply have to identify Helen's clock, because it's always with Helen as she travels, as the clock that measures proper time $\Delta\tau$. From Equation 36.9,

$$\Delta t_{\mathrm{H}} = \Delta\tau = \sqrt{1 - \beta^2}\,\Delta t_{\mathrm{G}} = \sqrt{1 - 0.95^2}\,(20 \text{ years}) = 6.25 \text{ years} \quad (36.11)$$

George will have just celebrated his 45th birthday as he welcomes home his 31-year-and-3-month-old twin sister.

This may be unsettling because it violates our commonsense notion of time, but it's not a paradox. There's no logical inconsistency in this outcome. So why is it called "the twin paradox"?

Helen, knowing that she had quite of bit of time to kill on her journey, brought along several physics books to read. As she learns about relativity, she begins to think about George and her friends back on earth. Relative to her, they are all moving away at 0.95c. Later they'll come rushing toward her at 0.95c. Time dilation will cause their clocks to run more slowly than her clocks, which are at rest relative to her. In other words, as FIGURE 36.24 shows, Helen concludes that people on earth are aging more slowly than she is. Alas, she will be much older than they when she returns.

Finally, the big day arrives. Helen lands back on earth and steps out of the starship. George is expecting Helen to be younger than he is. Helen is expecting George to be younger than she is.

Here's the paradox! It's logically impossible for each to be younger than the other at the time they are reunited. Where, then, is the flaw in our reasoning? It seems to be a symmetrical situation—Helen moves relative to George and George moves relative to Helen—but symmetrical reasoning has led to a conundrum.

But are the situations really symmetrical? George goes about his business day after day without noticing anything unusual. Helen, on the other hand, experiences three distinct periods during which the starship engines fire, she's crushed into her seat, and free dust particles that had been floating inside the starship are no longer, in the star-ship's reference frame, at rest or traveling in a straight line at constant speed. In other words, George spends the entire time in an inertial reference frame, *but Helen does not*. The situation is *not* symmetrical.

The principle of relativity applies *only* to inertial reference frames. Our discussion of time dilation was for inertial reference frames. Thus George's analysis and calculations are correct. Helen's analysis and calculations are *not* correct because she was trying to apply an inertial reference frame result while traveling in a noninertial reference frame.

Helen is younger than George when she returns. This is strange, but not a paradox. It is a consequence of the fact that time flows differently in two reference frames moving relative to each other.

FIGURE 36.24 The twin paradox.

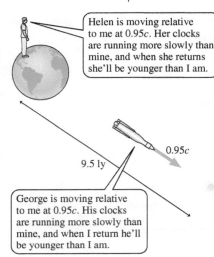

Helen is moving relative to me at 0.95c. Her clocks are running more slowly than mine, and when she returns she'll be younger than I am.

0.95c

9.5 ly

George is moving relative to me at 0.95c. His clocks are running more slowly than mine, and when I return he'll be younger than I am.

36.7 Length Contraction

We've seen that relativity requires us to rethink our idea of time. Now let's turn our attention to the concepts of space and distance. Consider the rocket that traveled from the sun to Saturn in Example 36.5. FIGURE 36.25a shows the rocket moving with velocity v through the solar system reference frame S. We define $L = \Delta x = x_{\mathrm{Saturn}} - x_{\mathrm{sun}}$ as the distance between the sun and Saturn in frame S or, more generally, the *length* of the spatial interval between two points. The rocket's speed is $v = L/\Delta t$, where Δt is the time measured in frame S for the journey from the sun to Saturn.

FIGURE 36.25 L and L' are the distances between the sun and Saturn in frames S and S'.

(a) Reference frame S: The solar system is stationary.

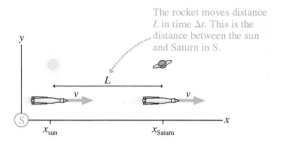

The rocket moves distance L in time Δt. This is the distance between the sun and Saturn in S.

L

x_{sun} x_{Saturn}

(b) Reference frame S': The rocket is stationary.

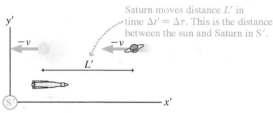

Saturn moves distance L' in time $\Delta t' = \Delta \tau$. This is the distance between the sun and Saturn in S'.

L'

FIGURE 36.25b shows the situation in reference frame S', where the rocket is at rest. The sun and Saturn move to the left at speed $v = L'/\Delta t'$, where $\Delta t'$ is the time measured in frame S' for Saturn to travel distance L'.

Speed v is the relative speed between S and S' and is the same for experimenters in both reference frames. That is,

$$v = \frac{L}{\Delta t} = \frac{L'}{\Delta t'} \tag{36.12}$$

The time interval $\Delta t'$ measured in frame S' is the proper time $\Delta \tau$ because both events occur at the same position in frame S' and can be measured by one clock. We can use the time-dilation result, Equation 36.9, to relate $\Delta \tau$ measured by the astronauts to Δt measured by the earthbound scientists. Then Equation 36.12 becomes

$$\frac{L}{\Delta t} = \frac{L'}{\Delta \tau} = \frac{L'}{\sqrt{1 - \beta^2} \, \Delta t} \tag{36.13}$$

The Δt cancels, and the distance L' in frame S' is

$$L' = \sqrt{1 - \beta^2} \, L \tag{36.14}$$

Surprisingly, we find that **the distance between two objects in reference frame S' is _not the same_ as the distance between the same two objects in reference frame S.**

Frame S, in which the distance is L, has one important distinction. It is the _one and only_ inertial reference frame in which the objects are at rest. Experimenters in frame S can take all the time they need to measure L because the two objects aren't going anywhere. The distance L between two objects, or two points on one object, measured in the reference frame in which the objects are at rest is called the **proper length** ℓ. Only one inertial reference frame can measure the proper length.

We can use the proper length ℓ to write Equation 36.14 as

$$L' = \sqrt{1 - \beta^2} \, \ell \le \ell \tag{36.15}$$

This "shrinking" of the distance between two objects, as measured by an experiment moving with respect to the objects, is called **length contraction.** Although we derived length contraction for the distance between two distinct objects, it applies equally well to the length of any physical object that stretches between two points along the x- and x'- axes. The length of an object is greatest in the reference frame in which the object is at rest. The object's length is less (i.e., the length is contracted) when it is measured in any reference frame in which the object is moving.

The Stanford Linear Accelerator (SLAC) is a 2-mi-long electron accelerator. The accelerator's length is less than 1 m in the reference frame of the electrons.

EXAMPLE 36.6 **The distance from the sun to Saturn**

In Example 36.5 a rocket traveled along a line from the sun to Saturn at a constant speed of 0.9c relative to the solar system. The Saturn-to-sun distance was given as 1.43×10^{12} m. What is the distance between the sun and Saturn in the rocket's reference frame?

MODEL Saturn and the sun are, at least approximately, at rest in the solar system reference frame S. Thus the given distance is the proper length ℓ.

SOLVE We can use Equation 36.15 to find the distance in the rocket's frame S':

$$L' = \sqrt{1 - \beta^2}\, \ell = \sqrt{1 - 0.9^2}(1.43 \times 10^{12} \text{ m})$$

$$= 0.62 \times 10^{12} \text{ m}$$

ASSESS The sun-to-Saturn distance measured by the astronauts is less than half the distance measured by experimenters on earth. L' and ℓ are different because *space is different* in two reference frames moving relative to each other.

FIGURE 36.26 Carmen and Dan each measure the length of the other's meter stick as they move relative to each other.

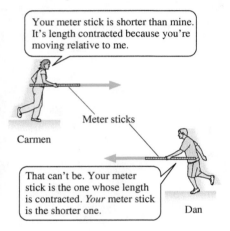

Your meter stick is shorter than mine. It's length contracted because you're moving relative to me.

Meter sticks

Carmen

That can't be. Your meter stick is the one whose length is contracted. *Your* meter stick is the shorter one.

Dan

FIGURE 36.27 Distance d is the same in both coordinate systems.

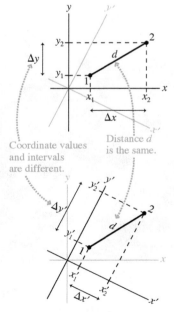

Measurements in the xy-system

Coordinate values and intervals are different.

Distance d is the same.

Measurements in the x'y'-system

The conclusion that space is different in reference frames moving relative to each other is a direct consequence of the fact that time is different. Experimenters in both reference frames agree on the relative velocity v, leading to Equation 36.12: $v = L/\Delta t = L'/\Delta t'$. We had already learned that $\Delta t' < \Delta t$ because of time dilation. Thus L' *has* to be less than L. That is the only way experimenters in the two reference frames can reconcile their measurements.

To be specific, the earthly experimenters in Examples 36.5 and 36.6 find that the rocket takes 5300 s to travel the 1.43×10^{12} m between the sun and Saturn. The rocket's speed is $v = L/\Delta t = 2.7 \times 10^8$ m/s $= 0.9c$. The astronauts in the rocket find that it takes only 2310 s for Saturn to reach them after the sun has passed by. But there's no conflict, because they also find that the distance is only 0.62×10^{12} m. Thus Saturn's speed toward them is $v = L'/\Delta t' = (0.62 \times 10^{12} \text{ m})/(2310 \text{ s}) = 2.7 \times 10^8$ m/s $= 0.9c$.

Another Paradox?

Carmen and Dan are in their physics lab room. They each select a meter stick, lay the two side by side, and agree that the meter sticks are exactly the same length. Then, for an extra-credit project, they go outside and run past each other, in opposite directions, at a relative speed $v = 0.9c$. FIGURE 36.26 shows their experiment and a portion of their conversation.

Now, Dan's meter stick can't be both longer and shorter than Carmen's meter stick. Is this another paradox? No! Relativity allows us to compare the *same* events as they're measured in two different reference frames. This did lead to a real paradox when Peggy rolled past Ryan on the train. There the signal light on the box turns green (a single event) or it doesn't, and Peggy and Ryan have to agree about it. But the events by which Dan measures the length (in Dan's frame) of Carmen's meter stick are *not the same events* as those by which Carmen measures the length (in Carmen's frame) of Dan's meter stick.

There's no conflict between their measurements. In Dan's reference frame, Carmen's meter stick has been length contracted and is less than 1 m in length. In Carmen's reference frame, Dan's meter stick has been length contracted and is less than 1m in length. If this weren't the case, if both agreed that one of the meter sticks was shorter than the other, then we could tell which reference frame was "really" moving and which was "really" at rest. But the principle of relativity doesn't allow us to make that distinction. Each is moving relative to the other, so each should make the same measurement for the length of the other's meter stick.

The Spacetime Interval

Forget relativity for a minute and think about ordinary geometry. FIGURE 36.27 shows two ordinary coordinate systems. They are identical except for the fact that one has been rotated relative to the other. A student using the xy-system would measure coordinates (x_1, y_1) for point 1 and (x_2, y_2) for point 2. A second student, using the x'y'-system, would measure (x'_1, y'_1) and (x'_2, y'_2).

The students soon find that none of their measurements agree. That is, $x_1 \neq x'_1$ and so on. Even the intervals are different: $\Delta x \neq \Delta x'$ and $\Delta y \neq \Delta y'$. Each is a perfectly valid coordinate system, giving no reason to prefer one over the other, but each yields different measurements.

Is there *anything* on which the two students can agree? Yes, there is. The distance d between points 1 and 2 is independent of the coordinates. We can state this mathematically as

$$d^2 = (\Delta x)^2 + (\Delta y)^2 = (\Delta x')^2 + (\Delta y')^2 \qquad (36.16)$$

The quantity $(\Delta x)^2 + (\Delta y)^2$ is called an **invariant** in geometry because it has the same value in any Cartesian coordinate system.

Returning to relativity, is there an invariant in the spacetime coordinates, some quantity that has the *same value* in all inertial reference frames? There is, and to find it let's return to the light clock of Figure 36.21. FIGURE 36.28 shows the light clock as seen in reference frames S' and S''. The speed of light is the same in both frames, even though both are moving with respect to each other and with respect to the clock.

Notice that the clock's height h is common to both reference frames. Thus

$$h^2 = \left(\frac{1}{2}c\,\Delta t'\right)^2 - \left(\frac{1}{2}\Delta x'\right)^2 = \left(\frac{1}{2}c\,\Delta t''\right)^2 - \left(\frac{1}{2}\Delta x''\right)^2 \qquad (36.17)$$

The factor $\frac{1}{2}$ cancels, allowing us to write

$$c^2(\Delta t')^2 - (\Delta x')^2 = c^2(\Delta t'')^2 - (\Delta x'')^2 \qquad (36.18)$$

Let us define the **spacetime interval** s between two events to be

$$s^2 = c^2(\Delta t)^2 - (\Delta x)^2 \qquad (36.19)$$

What we've shown in Equation 36.18 is that **the spacetime interval s has the same value in all inertial reference frames.** That is, the spacetime interval between two events is an invariant. It is a value that all experimenters, in all reference frames, can agree upon.

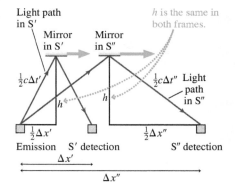

FIGURE 36.28 The light clock seen by experimenters in reference frames S' and S''.

EXAMPLE 36.7 **Using the spacetime interval**

A firecracker explodes at the origin of an inertial reference frame. Then, 2.0 μs later, a second firecracker explodes 300 m away. Astronauts in a passing rocket measure the distance between the explosions to be 200 m. According to the astronauts, how much time elapses between the two explosions?

MODEL The spacetime coordinates of two events are measured in two different inertial reference frames. Call the reference frame of the ground S and the reference frame of the rocket S'. The spacetime interval between these two events is the same in both reference frames.

SOLVE The spacetime interval (or, rather, its square) in frame S is

$$s^2 = c^2(\Delta t)^2 - (\Delta x)^2 = (600 \text{ m})^2 - (300 \text{ m})^2 = 270{,}000 \text{ m}^2$$

where we used $c = 300$ m/μs to determine that $c\,\Delta t = 600$ m. The spacetime interval has the same value in frame S'. Thus

$$s^2 = 270{,}000 \text{ m}^2 = c^2(\Delta t')^2 - (\Delta x')^2$$
$$= c^2(\Delta t')^2 - (200 \text{ m})^2$$

This is easily solved to give $\Delta t' = 1.85$ μs.

ASSESS The two events are closer together in both space and time in the rocket's reference frame than in the reference frame of the ground.

Einstein's legacy, according to popular culture, was the discovery that "everything is relative." But it's not so. Time intervals and space intervals may be relative, as were the intervals Δx and Δy in the purely geometric analogy with which we opened this section, but some things are *not* relative. In particular, the spacetime interval s between two events is not relative. It is a well-defined number, agreed on by experimenters in each and every inertial reference frame.

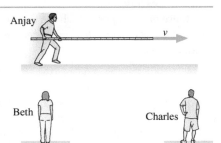

STOP TO THINK 36.7 Beth and Charles are at rest relative to each other. Anjay runs past at velocity v while holding a long pole parallel to his motion. Anjay, Beth, and Charles each measure the length of the pole at the instant Anjay passes Beth. Rank in order, from largest to smallest, the three lengths L_A, L_B, and L_C.

36.8 The Lorentz Transformations

The Galilean transformation $x' = x - vt$ of classical relativity lets us calculate the position x' of an event in frame S' if we know its position x in frame S. Classical relativity, of course, assumes that $t' = t$. Is there a similar transformation in relativity that would allow us to calculate an event's spacetime coordinates (x', t') in frame S' if we know their values (x, t) in frame S? Such a transformation would need to satisfy three conditions:

1. Agree with the Galilean transformations in the low-speed limit $v \ll c$.
2. Transform not only spatial coordinates but also time coordinates.
3. Ensure that the speed of light is the same in all reference frames.

FIGURE 36.29 The spacetime coordinates of an event are measured in inertial reference frames S and S'.

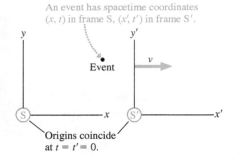

An event has spacetime coordinates (x, t) in frame S, (x', t') in frame S'.

Origins coincide at $t = t' = 0$.

We'll continue to use reference frames in the standard orientation of FIGURE 36.29. The motion is parallel to the x- and x'-axes, and we *define* $t = 0$ and $t' = 0$ as the instant when the origins of S and S' coincide.

The requirement that a new transformation agree with the Galilean transformation when $v \ll c$ suggests that we look for a transformation of the form

$$x' = \gamma(x - vt) \quad \text{and} \quad x = \gamma(x' + vt') \tag{36.20}$$

where γ is a dimensionless function of velocity that satisfies $\gamma \to 1$ as $v \to 0$.

To determine γ, we consider the following two events:

> Event 1: A flash of light is emitted from the origin of both reference frames $(x = x' = 0)$ at the instant they coincide $(t = t' = 0)$.

> Event 2: The light strikes a light detector. The spacetime coordinates of this event are (x, t) in frame S and (x', t') in frame S'.

Light travels at speed c in both reference frames, so the positions of event 2 are $x = ct$ in S and $x' = ct'$ in S'. Substituting these expressions for x and x' into Equation 36.20 gives

$$ct' = \gamma(ct - vt) = \gamma(c - v)t$$
$$ct = \gamma(ct' + vt') = \gamma(c + v)t' \tag{36.21}$$

We solve the first equation for t', by dividing by c, then substitute this result for t' into the second:

$$ct = \gamma(c + v)\frac{\gamma(c - v)t}{c} = \gamma^2(c^2 - v^2)\frac{t}{c}$$

The t cancels, leading to

$$\gamma^2 = \frac{c^2}{c^2 - v^2} = \frac{1}{1 - v^2/c^2}$$

Thus the γ that "works" in the proposed transformation of Equation 36.20 is

$$\gamma = \frac{1}{\sqrt{1 - v^2/c^2}} = \frac{1}{\sqrt{1 - \beta^2}} \tag{36.22}$$

You can see that $\gamma \rightarrow 1$ as $v \rightarrow 0$, as expected.

The transformation between t and t' is found by requiring that $x = x$ if you use Equation 36.20 to transform a position from S to S$'$ and then back to S. The details will be left for a homework problem. Another homework problem will let you demonstrate that the y and z measurements made perpendicular to the relative motion are not affected by the motion. We tacitly assumed this condition in our analysis of the light clock.

The full set of equations are called the **Lorentz transformations.** They are

$$\begin{aligned} x' &= \gamma(x - vt) & x &= \gamma(x' + vt') \\ y' &= y & y &= y' \\ z' &= z & z &= z' \\ t' &= \gamma(t - vx/c^2) & t &= \gamma(t' + vx'/c^2) \end{aligned} \tag{36.23}$$

The Lorentz transformations transform the spacetime coordinates of *one* event. Compare these to the Galilean transformation equations in Equations 36.1.

NOTE ▶ These transformations are named after the Dutch physicist H. A. Lorentz, who derived them prior to Einstein. Lorentz was close to discovering special relativity, but he didn't recognize that our concepts of space and time have to be changed before these equations can be properly interpreted. ◀

Using Relativity

Relativity is phrased in terms of *events;* hence relativity problems are solved by interpreting the problem statement in terms of specific events.

PROBLEM-SOLVING
STRATEGY 36.1 **Relativity**

MODEL Frame the problem in terms of events, things that happen at a specific place and time.

VISUALIZE A pictorial representation defines the reference frames.

- Sketch the reference frames, showing their motion relative to each other.
- Show events. Identify objects that are moving with respect to the reference frames.
- Identify any proper time intervals and proper lengths. These are measured in an object's rest frame.

SOLVE The mathematical representation is based on the Lorentz transformations, but not every problem requires the full transformation equations.

- Problems about time intervals can often be solved using time dilation: $\Delta t = \gamma \Delta\tau$.
- Problems about distances can often be solved using length contraction: $L = \ell/\gamma$.

ASSESS Are the results consistent with Galilean relativity when $v \ll c$?

EXAMPLE 36.8 **Ryan and Peggy revisited**

Peggy is standing in the center of a long, flat railroad car that has firecrackers tied to both ends. The car moves past Ryan, who is standing on the ground, with velocity $v = 0.8c$. Flashes from the exploding firecrackers reach him simultaneously 1.0 μs after the instant that Peggy passes him, and he later finds burn marks on the track 300 m to either side of where he had been standing.

a. According to Ryan, what is the distance between the two explosions, and at what times do the explosions occur relative to the time that Peggy passes him?
b. According to Peggy, what is the distance between the two explosions, and at what times do the explosions occur relative to the time that Ryan passes her?

MODEL Let the explosion on Ryan's right, the direction in which Peggy is moving, be event R. The explosion on his left is event L.

VISUALIZE Peggy and Ryan are in inertial reference frames. As FIGURE 36.30 shows, Peggy's frame S' is moving with $v = 0.8c$ relative to Ryan's frame S. We've defined the reference frames such that Peggy and Ryan are at the origins. The instant they pass, by definition, is $t = t' = 0$ s. The two events are shown in Ryan's reference frame.

FIGURE 36.30 A pictorial representation of the reference frames and events.

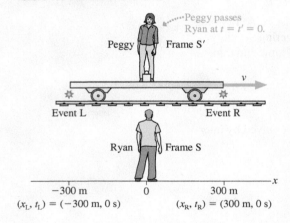

$(x_L, t_L) = (-300 \text{ m}, 0 \text{ s})$ $(x_R, t_R) = (300 \text{ m}, 0 \text{ s})$

SOLVE a. The two burn marks tell Ryan that the distance between the explosions was $L = 600$ m. Light travels at $c = 300$ m/μs, and the burn marks are 300 m on either side of him, so Ryan can determine that each explosion took place 1.0 μs before he saw the flash. But this was the instant of time that Peggy passed him, so Ryan concludes that the explosions were simultaneous with each other and with Peggy's passing him. The spacetime coordinates of the two events in frame S are $(x_R, t_R) = (300 \text{ m}, 0 \text{ } \mu\text{s})$ and $(x_L, t_L) = (-300 \text{ m}, 0 \text{ } \mu\text{s})$.

b. We already know, from our qualitative analysis in Section 36.5, that the explosions are *not* simultaneous in Peggy's reference frame. Event R happens before event L in S', but we don't know how they compare to the time at which Ryan passes Peggy. We can now use the Lorentz transformations to relate the spacetime coordinates of these events as measured by Ryan to the spacetime coordinates as measured by Peggy. Using $v = 0.8c$, we find that γ is

$$\gamma = \frac{1}{\sqrt{1 - v^2/c^2}} = \frac{1}{\sqrt{1 - 0.8^2}} = 1.667$$

For event L, the Lorentz transformations are

$$x'_L = 1.667((-300 \text{ m}) - (0.8c)(0 \text{ } \mu\text{s})) = -500 \text{ m}$$

$$t'_L = 1.667((0 \text{ } \mu\text{s}) - (0.8c)(-300 \text{ m})/c^2) = 1.33 \text{ } \mu\text{s}$$

And for event R,

$$x'_R = 1.667((300 \text{ m}) - (0.8c)(0 \text{ } \mu\text{s})) = 500 \text{ m}$$

$$t'_R = 1.667((0 \text{ } \mu\text{s}) - (0.8c)(300 \text{ m})/c^2) = -1.33 \text{ } \mu\text{s}$$

According to Peggy, the two explosions occur 1000 m apart. Furthermore, the first explosion, on the right, occurs 1.33 μs before Ryan passes her at $t' = 0$ s. The second, on the left, occurs 1.33 μs after Ryan goes by.

ASSESS Events that are simultaneous in frame S are *not* simultaneous in frame S'. The results of the Lorentz transformations agree with our earlier qualitative analysis.

A follow-up discussion of Example 36.8 is worthwhile. Because Ryan moves at speed $v = 0.8c = 240$ m/μs relative to Peggy, he moves 320 m during the 1.33 μs between the first explosion and the instant he passes Peggy, then another 320 m before the second explosion. Gathering this information together, FIGURE 36.31 shows the sequence of events in Peggy's reference frame.

The firecrackers define the ends of the railroad car, so the 1000 m distance between the explosions in Peggy's frame is the car's length L' in frame S'. The car is at rest in frame S', hence length L' is the proper length: $\ell = 1000$ m. Ryan is measuring the length of a moving object, so he should see the car length contracted to

$$L = \sqrt{1 - \beta^2}\,\ell = \frac{\ell}{\gamma} = \frac{1000 \text{ m}}{1.667} = 600 \text{ m}$$

And, indeed, that is exactly the distance Ryan measured between the burn marks.

Finally, we can calculate the spacetime interval s between the two events. According to Ryan,

$$s^2 = c^2(\Delta t^2) - (\Delta x)^2 = c^2(0 \ \mu s)^2 - (600 \text{ m})^2 = -(600 \text{ m})^2$$

Peggy computes the spacetime interval to be

$$s^2 = c^2(\Delta t')^2 - (\Delta x')^2 = c^2(2.67 \ \mu s)^2 - (1000 \text{ m})^2 = -(600 \text{ m})^2$$

Their calculations of the spacetime interval agree, showing that s really is an invariant, but notice that s itself is an imaginary number.

Length

We've already introduced the idea of length contraction, but we didn't precisely define just what we mean by the *length* of a moving object. The length of an object at rest is clear because we can take all the time we need to measure it with meter sticks, surveying tools, or whatever we need. But how can we give clear meaning to the length of a moving object?

A reasonable definition of an object's length is the distance $L = \Delta x = x_R - x_L$ between the right and left ends when the positions x_R and x_L are measured *at the same time t.* In other words, length is the distance spanned by the object at *one instant* of time. Measuring an object's length requires *simultaneous* measurements of two positions (i.e., two events are required); hence the result won't be known until the information from two spatially separated measurements can be brought together.

FIGURE 36.32 shows an object traveling through reference frame S with velocity v. The object is at rest in reference frame S′ that travels with the object at velocity v; hence the length in frame S′ is the proper length ℓ. That is, $\Delta x' = x_R' - x_L' = \ell$ in frame S′.

At time t, an experimenter (and his or her assistants) in frame S makes simultaneous measurements of the positions x_R and x_L of the ends of the object. The difference $\Delta x = x_R - x_L = L$ is the length in frame S. The Lorentz transformations of x_R and x_L are

$$x_R' = \gamma(x_R - vt)$$
$$x_L' = \gamma(x_L - vt)$$

(36.24)

where, it is important to note, t is the *same* for both because the measurements are simultaneous.

Subtracting the second equation from the first, we find

$$x_R' - x_L' = \ell = \gamma(x_R - x_L) = \gamma L = \frac{L}{\sqrt{1 - \beta^2}}$$

Solving for L, we find, in agreement with Equation 36.15, that

$$L = \sqrt{1 - \beta^2} \ \ell$$

(36.25)

This analysis has accomplished two things. First, by giving a precise definition of length, we've put our length-contraction result on a firmer footing. Second, we've had good practice at relativistic reasoning using the Lorentz transformation.

NOTE ▶ Length contraction does not tell us how an object would *look*. The visual appearance of an object is determined by light waves that arrive simultaneously at the eye. These waves left points on the object at different times (i.e., *not* simultaneously) because they had to travel different distances to the eye. The analysis needed to determine an object's visual appearance is considerably more complex. Length and length contraction are concerned only with the *actual* length of the object at one instant of time. ◀

FIGURE 36.31 The sequence of events as seen in Peggy's reference frame.

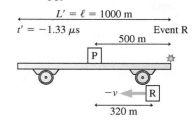

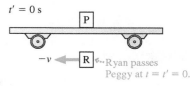

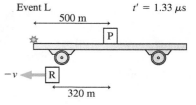

FIGURE 36.32 The length of an object is the distance between *simultaneous* measurements of the positions of the end points.

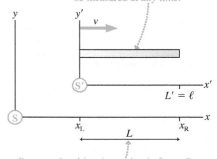

Because the object is moving in frame S, simultaneous measurements of its ends must be made to find its length L in frame S.

The Binomial Approximation

The binomial approximation

If $x \ll 1$, then $(1 + x)^n \approx 1 + nx$.

You've met the binomial approximation earlier in this text and in your calculus class. The binomial approximation is useful when we need to calculate a relativistic expression for a nonrelativistic velocity $v \ll c$. Because $v^2/c^2 \ll 1$ in these cases, we can write

$$\text{If } v \ll c: \begin{cases} \sqrt{1 - \beta^2} = (1 - v^2/c^2)^{1/2} \approx 1 - \dfrac{1}{2}\dfrac{v^2}{c^2} \\ \gamma = \dfrac{1}{\sqrt{1 - \beta^2}} = (1 - v^2/c^2)^{-1/2} \approx 1 + \dfrac{1}{2}\dfrac{v^2}{c^2} \end{cases} \tag{36.26}$$

The following example illustrates the use of the binomial approximation.

EXAMPLE 36.9 **The shrinking school bus**

An 8.0-m-long school bus drives past at 30 m/s. By how much is its length contracted?

MODEL The school bus is at rest in an inertial reference frame S′ moving at velocity $v = 30$ m/s relative to the ground frame S. The given length, 8.0 m, is the proper length ℓ in frame S′.

SOLVE In frame S, the school bus is length contracted to

$$L = \sqrt{1 - \beta^2}\,\ell$$

The bus's velocity v is much less than c, so we can use the binomial approximation to write

$$L \approx \left(1 - \frac{1}{2}\frac{v^2}{c^2}\right)\ell = \ell - \frac{1}{2}\frac{v^2}{c^2}\ell$$

The *amount* of the length contraction is

$$\ell - L = \frac{1}{2}\frac{v^2}{c^2}\ell = \frac{1}{2}\left(\frac{30 \text{ m/s}}{3.0 \times 10^8 \text{ m/s}}\right)^2 (8.0 \text{ m})$$

$$= 4.0 \times 10^{-14} \text{ m} = 40 \text{ fm}$$

where 1 fm = 1 femtometer = 10^{-15} m.

ASSESS The bus "shrinks" by only slightly more than the diameter of the nucleus of an atom. It's no wonder that we're not aware of length contraction in our everyday lives. If you had tried to calculate this number exactly, your calculator would have shown $\ell - L = 0$ because the difference between ℓ and L shows up only in the 14th decimal place. A scientific calculator determines numbers to 10 or 12 decimal places, but that isn't sufficient to show the difference. The binomial approximation provides an invaluable tool for finding the very tiny difference between two numbers that are nearly identical.

The Lorentz Velocity Transformations

FIGURE 36.33 The velocity of a moving object is measured to be u in frame S and u' in frame S′.

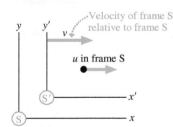

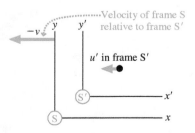

FIGURE 36.33 shows an object that is moving in both reference frame S and reference frame S′. Experimenters in frame S determine that the object's velocity is u, while experimenters in frame S′ find it to be u'. For simplicity, we'll assume that the object moves parallel to the x- and x'-axes.

The Galilean velocity transformation $u' = u - v$ was found by taking the time derivative of the position transformation. We can do the same with the Lorentz transformation if we take the derivative with respect to the time in each frame. Velocity u' in frame S′ is

$$u' = \frac{dx'}{dt'} = \frac{d(\gamma(x - vt))}{d(\gamma(t - vx/c^2))} \tag{36.27}$$

where we've used the Lorentz transformations for position x' and time t'.

Carrying out the differentiation gives

$$u' = \frac{\gamma(dx - v\,dt)}{\gamma(dt - v\,dx/c^2)} = \frac{dx/dt - v}{1 - v(dx/dt)/c^2} \tag{36.28}$$

But dx/dt is u, the object's velocity in frame S, leading to

$$u' = \frac{u - v}{1 - uv/c^2} \tag{36.29}$$

You can see that Equation 36.29 reduces to the Galilean transformation $u' = u - v$ when $v \ll c$, as expected.

The transformation from S′ to S is found by reversing the sign of v. Altogether,

$$u' = \frac{u - v}{1 - uv/c^2} \quad \text{and} \quad u = \frac{u' + v}{1 + u'v/c^2} \qquad (36.30)$$

Equations 36.30 are the Lorentz velocity transformation equations.

NOTE ▶ It is important to distinguish carefully between v, which is the relative velocity between two reference frames, and u and u', which are the velocities of an *object* as measured in the two different reference frames. ◀

EXAMPLE 36.10 | **A really fast bullet**

A rocket flies past the earth at $0.90c$. As it goes by, the rocket fires a bullet in the forward direction at $0.95c$ with respect to the rocket. What is the bullet's speed with respect to the earth?

MODEL The rocket and the earth are inertial reference frames. Let the earth be frame S and the rocket be frame S′. The velocity of frame S′ relative to frame S is $v = 0.90c$. The bullet's velocity in frame S′ is $u' = 0.95c$.

SOLVE We can use the Lorentz velocity transformation to find

$$u = \frac{u' + v}{1 + u'v/c^2} = \frac{0.95c + 0.90c}{1 + (0.95c)(0.90c)/c^2} = 0.997c$$

The bullet's speed with respect to the earth is 99.7% of the speed of light.

NOTE ▶ Many relativistic calculations are much easier when velocities are specified as a fraction of c. ◀

ASSESS In Newtonian mechanics, the Galilean transformation of velocity would give $u = 1.85c$. Now, despite the very high speed of the rocket and of the bullet with respect to the rocket, the bullet's speed with respect to the earth remains less than c. This is yet more evidence that objects cannot travel faster than the speed of light.

Suppose the rocket in Example 36.10 fired a laser beam in the forward direction as it traveled past the earth at velocity v. The laser beam would travel away from the rocket at speed $u' = c$ in the rocket's reference frame S′. What is the laser beam's speed in the earth's frame S? According to the Lorentz velocity transformation, it must be

$$u = \frac{u' + v}{1 + u'v/c^2} = \frac{c + v}{1 + cv/c^2} = \frac{c + v}{1 + v/c} = \frac{c + v}{(c + v)/c} = c \qquad (36.31)$$

Light travels at speed c in both frame S and frame S′. This important consequence of the principle of relativity is "built into" the Lorentz transformations.

36.9 Relativistic Momentum

In Newtonian mechanics, the total momentum of a system is a conserved quantity. Further, as we've seen, the law of conservation of momentum, $P_f = P_i$, is true in all inertial reference frames *if* the particle velocities in different reference frames are related by the Galilean velocity transformations.

The difficulty, of course, is that the Galilean transformations are not consistent with the principle of relativity. It is a reasonable approximation when all velocities are very much less than c, but the Galilean transformations fail dramatically as velocities approach c. It's not hard to show that $P_f' \neq P_i'$ if the particle velocities in frame S′ are related to the particle velocities in frame S by the Lorentz transformations.

There are two possibilities:

1. The so-called law of conservation of momentum is not really a law of physics. It is approximately true at low velocities but fails as velocities approach the speed of light.
2. The law of conservation of momentum really is a law of physics, but the expression $p = mu$ is not the correct way to calculate momentum when the particle velocity u becomes a significant fraction of c.

Momentum conservation is such a central and important feature of mechanics that it seems unlikely to fail in relativity.

The classical momentum, for one-dimensional motion, is $p = mu = m(\Delta x/\Delta t)$. Δt is the time to move distance Δx. That seemed clear enough within a Newtonian framework, but now we've learned that experimenters in different reference frames disagree about the amount of time needed. So whose Δt should we use?

One possibility is to use the time measured *by the particle*. This is the proper time $\Delta \tau$ because the particle is at rest in its own reference frame and needs only one clock. With this in mind, let's redefine the momentum of a particle of mass m moving with velocity $u = \Delta x/\Delta t$ to be

$$p = m\frac{\Delta x}{\Delta \tau} \tag{36.32}$$

We can relate this new expression for p to the familiar Newtonian expression by using the time-dilation result $\Delta \tau = (1 - u^2/c^2)^{1/2}\Delta t$ to relate the proper time interval measured by the particle to the more practical time interval Δt measured by experimenters in frame S. With this substitution, Equation 36.32 becomes

$$p = m\frac{\Delta x}{\Delta \tau} = m\frac{\Delta x}{\sqrt{1 - u^2/c^2}\,\Delta t} = \frac{mu}{\sqrt{1 - u^2/c^2}} \tag{36.33}$$

You can see that Equation 36.33 reduces to the classical expression $p = mu$ when the particle's speed $u \ll c$. That is an important requirement, but whether this is the "correct" expression for p depends on whether the total momentum P is conserved when the velocities of a system of particles are transformed with the Lorentz velocity transformation equations. The proof is rather long and tedious, so we will assert, without actual proof, that the momentum defined in Equation 36.33 does, indeed, transform correctly. **The law of conservation of momentum is still valid in all inertial reference frames *if* the momentum of each particle is calculated with Equation 36.33.**

The factor that multiplies mu in Equation 36.33 looks much like the factor γ in the Lorentz transformation equations for x and t, but there's one very important difference. The v in the Lorentz transformation equations is the velocity of a *reference frame*. The u in Equation 36.33 is the velocity of a particle moving *in* a reference frame.

With this distinction in mind, let's define the quantity

$$\gamma_p = \frac{1}{\sqrt{1 - u^2/c^2}} \tag{36.34}$$

where the subscript p indicates that this is γ for a particle, not for a reference frame. In frame S$'$, where the particle moves with velocity u', the corresponding expression would be called γ_p'. With this definition of γ_p, the momentum of a particle is

$$p = \gamma_p mu \tag{36.35}$$

EXAMPLE 36.11 **Momentum of a subatomic particle**

Electrons in a particle accelerator reach a speed of $0.999c$ relative to the laboratory. One collision of an electron with a target produces a muon that moves forward with a speed of $0.95c$ relative to the laboratory. The muon mass is 1.90×10^{-28} kg. What is the muon's momentum in the laboratory frame and in the frame of the electron beam?

MODEL Let the laboratory be reference frame S. The reference frame S$'$ of the electron beam (i.e., a reference frame in which the electrons are at rest) moves in the direction of the electrons at $v = 0.999c$. The muon velocity in frame S is $u = 0.95c$.

SOLVE γ_p for the muon in the laboratory reference frame is

$$\gamma_p = \frac{1}{\sqrt{1 - u^2/c^2}} = \frac{1}{\sqrt{1 - 0.95^2}} = 3.20$$

Thus the muon's momentum in the laboratory is

$$p = \gamma_p mu = (3.20)(1.90 \times 10^{-28}\text{ kg})(0.95 \times 3.00 \times 10^8\text{ m/s})$$

$$= 1.73 \times 10^{-19}\text{ kg m/s}$$

The momentum is a factor of 3.2 larger than the Newtonian momentum mu. To find the momentum in the electron-beam reference frame, we must first use the velocity transformation equation to find the muon's velocity in frame S':

$$u' = \frac{u - v}{1 - uv/c^2} = \frac{0.95c - 0.999c}{1 - (0.95c)(0.999c)/c^2} = -0.962c$$

In the laboratory frame, the faster electrons are overtaking the slower muon. Hence the muon's velocity in the electron-beam frame is negative. γ_p' for the muon in frame S' is

$$\gamma_p' = \frac{1}{\sqrt{1 - u'^2/c^2}} = \frac{1}{\sqrt{1 - 0.962^2}} = 3.66$$

The muon's momentum in the electron-beam reference frame is

$$p' = \gamma_p' \, mu'$$
$$= (3.66)(1.90 \times 10^{-28} \, \text{kg})(-0.962 \times 3.00 \times 10^8 \, \text{m/s})$$
$$= -2.01 \times 10^{-19} \, \text{kg m/s}$$

ASSESS From the laboratory perspective, the muon moves only slightly slower than the electron beam. But it turns out that the muon moves faster with respect to the electrons, although in the opposite direction, than it does with respect to the laboratory.

The Cosmic Speed Limit

FIGURE 36.34a is a graph of momentum versus velocity. For a Newtonian particle, with $p = mu$, the momentum is directly proportional to the velocity. The relativistic expression for momentum agrees with the Newtonian value if $u \ll c$, but p approaches ∞ as $u \to c$.

The implications of this graph become clear when we relate momentum to force. Consider a particle subjected to a constant force, such as a rocket that never runs out of fuel. If F is constant, we can see from $F = dp/dt$ that the momentum is $p = Ft$. If Newtonian physics were correct, a particle would go faster and faster as its velocity $u = p/m = (F/m)t$ increased without limit. But the relativistic result, shown in FIGURE 36.34b, is that the particle's velocity asymptotically approaches the speed of light ($u \to c$) as p approaches ∞. Relativity gives a very different outcome than Newtonian mechanics.

The speed c is a "cosmic speed limit" for material particles. A force cannot accelerate a particle to a speed higher than c because the particle's momentum becomes infinitely large as the speed approaches c. The amount of effort required for each additional increment of velocity becomes larger and larger until no amount of effort can raise the velocity any higher.

Actually, at a more fundamental level, c is a speed limit for *any* kind of **causal influence.** If I throw a rock and break a window, my throw is the *cause* of the breaking window and the rock is the *causal influence.* If I shoot a laser beam at a light detector that is wired to a firecracker, the light wave is the *causal influence* that leads to the explosion. A causal influence can be any kind of particle, wave, or information that travels from A to B and allows A to be the cause of B.

For two unrelated events—a firecracker explodes in Tokyo and a balloon bursts in Paris—the relativity of simultaneity tells us that they may be simultaneous in one reference frame but not in others. Or in one reference frame the firecracker may explode before the balloon bursts but in some other reference frame the balloon may burst first. These possibilities violate our commonsense view of time, but they're not in conflict with the principle of relativity.

For two causally related events—A *causes* B—it would be nonsense for an experimenter in any reference frame to find that B occurs before A. No experimenter in any reference frame, no matter how it is moving, will find that you are born before your mother is born. If A causes B, then it must be the case that $t_A < t_B$ in *all* reference frames.

Suppose there exists some kind of causal influence that *can* travel at speed $u > c$. FIGURE 36.35 shows a reference frame S in which event A occurs at position $x_A = 0$. The faster-than-light causal influence—perhaps some yet-to-be-discovered "z ray"—leaves A at $t_A = 0$ and travels to the point at which it will cause event B. It arrives at x_B at time $t_B = x_B/u$.

How do events A and B appear in a reference frame S' that travels at an ordinary speed $v < c$ relative to frame S? We can use the Lorentz transformations to find out.

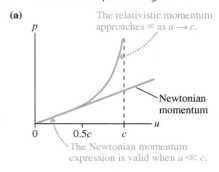

FIGURE 36.34 The speed of a particle cannot reach the speed of light.

(a) The relativistic momentum approaches ∞ as $u \to c$.

Newtonian momentum

The Newtonian momentum expression is valid when $u \ll c$.

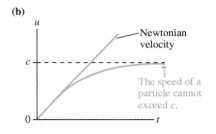

(b) Newtonian velocity

The speed of a particle cannot exceed c.

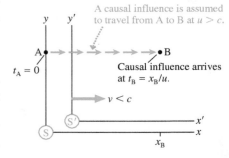

FIGURE 36.35 Assume that a causal influence can travel from A to B at a speed $u > c$.

A causal influence is assumed to travel from A to B at $u > c$.

Causal influence arrives at $t_B = x_B/u$.

$v < c$

Because $x_A = 0$ and $t_A = 0$, it's easy to see that $x'_A = 0$ and $t'_A = 0$. That is, the origins of S and S' overlap at the instant the causal influence leaves event A. More interesting is the time at which this influence reaches B in frame S'. The Lorentz time transformation for event B is

$$t'_B = \gamma\left(t_B - \frac{vx_B}{c^2}\right) = \gamma t_B\left(1 - \frac{v(x_B/t_B)}{c^2}\right) = \gamma t_B\left(1 - \frac{vu}{c^2}\right) \tag{36.36}$$

where we first factored out t_B, then made use of the fact that $u = x_B/t_B$ in frame S.

We're assuming $u > c$, so let $u = \alpha c$ where $\alpha > 1$ is a constant. Then $vu/c^2 = \alpha v/c$. Now follow the logic:

1. If $v > c/\alpha$, which is possible because $\alpha > 1$, then $vu/c^2 > 1$.
2. If $vu/c^2 > 1$, then the term $(1 - vu/c^2)$ is negative and $t'_B < 0$.
3. If $t'_B < 0$, then event B happens *before* event A in reference frame S'.

In other words, if a causal influence can travel faster than c, then there exist reference frames in which the effect happens before the cause. We know this can't happen, so our assumption $u > c$ must be wrong. **No causal influence of any kind—particle, wave, or yet-to-be-discovered z rays—can travel faster than c.**

The existence of a cosmic speed limit is one of the most interesting consequences of the theory of relativity. "Warp drive," in which a spaceship suddenly leaps to faster-than-light velocities, is simply incompatible with the theory of relativity. Rapid travel to the stars will remain in the realm of science fiction unless future scientific discoveries find flaws in Einstein's theory and open the doors to yet-undreamed-of theories. While we can't say with certainty that a scientific theory will never be overturned, there is currently not even a hint of evidence that disagrees with the special theory of relativity.

36.10 Relativistic Energy

Energy is our final topic in this chapter on relativity. Space, time, velocity, and momentum are changed by relativity, so it seems inevitable that we'll need a new view of energy.

In Newtonian mechanics, a particle's kinetic energy $K = \frac{1}{2}mu^2$ can be written in terms of its momentum $p = mu$ as $K = p^2/2m$. This suggests that a relativistic expression for energy will likely involve both the square of p and the particle's mass. We also hope that energy will be conserved in relativity, so a reasonable starting point is with the one quantity we've found that is the same in all inertial reference frames: the spacetime interval s.

Let a particle of mass m move through distance Δx during a time interval Δt, as measured in reference frame S. The spacetime interval is

$$s^2 = c^2(\Delta t)^2 - (\Delta x)^2 = \text{invariant}$$

We can turn this into an expression involving momentum if we multiply by $(m/\Delta\tau)^2$, where $\Delta\tau$ is the proper time (i.e., the time measured by the particle). Doing so gives

$$(mc)^2\left(\frac{\Delta t}{\Delta\tau}\right)^2 - \left(\frac{m\Delta x}{\Delta\tau}\right)^2 = (mc)^2\left(\frac{\Delta t}{\Delta\tau}\right)^2 - p^2 = \text{invariant} \tag{36.37}$$

where we used $p = m(\Delta x/\Delta\tau)$ from Equation 36.32.

Now Δt, the time interval in frame S, is related to the proper time by the time-dilation result $\Delta t = \gamma_p \Delta\tau$. With this change, Equation 36.37 becomes

$$(\gamma_p mc)^2 - p^2 = \text{invariant}$$

Finally, for reasons that will be clear in a minute, we multiply by c^2, to get

$$(\gamma_p mc^2)^2 - (pc)^2 = \text{invariant} \tag{36.38}$$

To say that the right side is an *invariant* means it has the same value in all inertial reference frames. We can easily determine the constant by evaluating it in the reference frame in which the particle is at rest. In that frame, where $p = 0$ and $\gamma_p = 1$, we find that

$$(\gamma_p mc^2)^2 - (pc)^2 = (mc^2)^2 \qquad (36.39)$$

Let's reflect on what this means before taking the next step. The space-time interval s has the same value in all inertial reference frames. In other words, $c^2 (\Delta t)^2 - (\Delta x)^2 = c^2(\Delta t')^2 - (\Delta x')^2$. Equation 36.39 was derived from the definition of the spacetime interval; hence the quantity mc^2 is also an invariant having the same value in all inertial reference frames. In other words, if experimenters in frames S and S' both make measurements on this particle of mass m, they will find that

$$(\gamma_p mc^2)^2 - (pc)^2 = (\gamma'_p mc^2)^2 - (p'c)^2 \qquad (36.40)$$

Experimenters in different reference frames measure different values for the momentum, but experimenters in all reference frames agree that momentum is a conserved quantity. Equations 36.39 and 36.40 suggest that the quantity $\gamma_p mc^2$ is also an important property of the particle, a property that changes along with p in just the right way to satisfy Equation 36.39. But what is this property?

The first clue comes from checking the units. γ_p is dimensionless and c is a velocity, so $\gamma_p mc^2$ has the same units as the classical expression $\frac{1}{2}mv^2$—namely, units of energy. For a second clue, let's examine how $\gamma_p mc^2$ behaves in the low-velocity limit $u \ll c$. We can use the binomial approximation expression for γ_p to find

$$\gamma_p mc^2 = \frac{mc^2}{\sqrt{1 - u^2/c^2}} \approx \left(1 + \frac{1}{2}\frac{u^2}{c^2}\right)mc^2 = mc^2 + \frac{1}{2}mu^2 \qquad (36.41)$$

The second term, $\frac{1}{2}mu^2$, is the low-velocity expression for the kinetic energy K. This is an energy associated with motion. But the first term suggests that the concept of energy is more complex than we originally thought. It appears that **there is an inherent energy associated with mass itself.**

With that as a possibility, subject to experimental verification, let's define the **total energy** E of a particle to be

$$E = \gamma_p mc^2 = E_0 + K = \text{rest energy} + \text{kinetic energy} \qquad (36.42)$$

This total energy consists of a **rest energy**

$$E_0 = mc^2 \qquad (36.43)$$

and a relativistic expression for the *kinetic energy*

$$K = (\gamma_p - 1)mc^2 = (\gamma_p - 1)E_0 \qquad (36.44)$$

This expression for the kinetic energy is very nearly $\frac{1}{2}mu^2$ when $u \ll c$ but, as FIGURE 36.36 shows, differs significantly from the classical value for very high velocities.

Equation 36.43 is, of course, Einstein's famous $E = mc^2$, perhaps the most famous equation in all of physics. Before discussing its significance, we need to tie up some loose ends. First, notice that the right-hand side of Equation 36.39 is the square of the rest energy E_0. Thus we can write a final version of that equation:

$$E^2 - (pc)^2 = E_0^2 \qquad (36.45)$$

The quantity E_0 is an *invariant* with the same value mc^2 in *all* inertial reference frames.

Second, notice that we can write

$$pc = (\gamma_p mu)c = \frac{u}{c}(\gamma_p mc^2)$$

FIGURE 36.36 The relativistic kinetic energy.

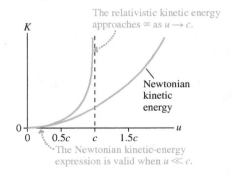

The relativistic kinetic energy approaches ∞ as $u \to c$.

Newtonian kinetic energy

The Newtonian kinetic-energy expression is valid when $u \ll c$.

But $\gamma_p mc^2$ is the total energy E and $u/c = \beta_p$, where the subscript p, as on γ_p, indicates that we're referring to the motion of a particle within a reference frame, not the motion of two reference frames relative to each other. Thus

$$pc = \beta_p E \qquad (36.46)$$

FIGURE 36.37 shows the "velocity-energy-momentum triangle," a convenient way to remember the relationships among the three quantities.

FIGURE 36.37 The velocity-energy-momentum triangle.

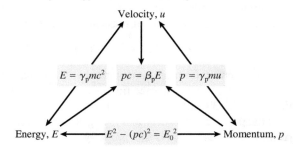

EXAMPLE 36.12 | Kinetic energy and total energy

Calculate the rest energy and the kinetic energy of (a) a 100 g ball moving with a speed of 100 m/s and (b) an electron with a speed of 0.999c.

MODEL The ball, with $u \ll c$, is a classical particle. We don't need to use the relativistic expression for its kinetic energy. The electron is highly relativistic.

SOLVE a. For the ball, with $m = 0.10$ kg,

$$E_0 = mc^2 = 9.0 \times 10^{15} \text{ J}$$

$$K = \frac{1}{2} mu^2 = 500 \text{ J}$$

b. For the electron, we start by calculating

$$\gamma_p = \frac{1}{(1 - u^2/c^2)^{1/2}} = 22.4$$

Then, using $m_e = 9.11 \times 10^{-31}$ kg, we find

$$E_0 = mc^2 = 8.2 \times 10^{-14} \text{ J}$$

$$K = (\gamma_p - 1)E_0 = 170 \times 10^{-14} \text{ J}$$

ASSESS The ball's kinetic energy is a typical kinetic energy. Its rest energy, by contrast, is a staggeringly large number. For a relativistic electron, on the other hand, the kinetic energy is more important than the rest energy.

STOP TO THINK 36.8   An electron moves through the lab at 99% the speed of light. The lab reference frame is S and the electron's reference frame is S′. In which reference frame is the electron's rest mass larger?

a. In frame S, the lab frame
b. In frame S′, the electron's frame
c. It is the same in both frames.

FIGURE 36.38 An inelastic collision between two balls of clay does not seem to conserve the total energy E.

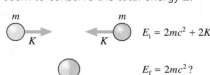

Mass-Energy Equivalence

Now we're ready to explore the significance of Einstein's famous equation $E = mc^2$. FIGURE 36.38 shows two balls of clay approaching each other. They have equal masses and equal kinetic energies, and they slam together in a perfectly inelastic collision to form one large ball of clay at rest. In Newtonian mechanics, we would say that the initial energy $2K$ is dissipated by being transformed into an equal amount of thermal energy, raising the temperature of the coalesced ball of clay. But Equation 36.42, $E = E_0 + K$, doesn't say anything about thermal energy. The total energy before the collision is $E_i = 2mc^2 + 2K$, with the factor of 2 appearing because there are two masses. It seems like the total energy after the collision, when the clay is at rest, should be $2mc^2$, but this value doesn't conserve total energy.

There's ample experimental evidence that energy is conserved, so there must be a flaw in our reasoning. The statement of energy conservation is

$$E_f = Mc^2 = E_i = 2mc^2 + 2K \qquad (36.47)$$

where M is the mass of clay after the collision. But, remarkably, this requires

$$M = 2m + \frac{2K}{c^2} \qquad (36.48)$$

In other words, **mass is not conserved.** The mass of clay after the collision is larger than the mass of clay before the collision. Total energy can be conserved only if kinetic energy is transformed into an "equivalent" amount of mass.

The mass increase in a collision between two balls of clay is incredibly small, far beyond any scientist's ability to detect. So how do we know if such a crazy idea is true?

FIGURE 36.39 shows an experiment that has been done countless times in the last 50 years at particle accelerators around the world. An electron that has been accelerated to $u \approx c$ is aimed at a target material. When a high-energy electron collides with an atom in the target, it can easily knock one of the electrons out of the atom. Thus we would expect to see two electrons leaving the target: the incident electron and the ejected electron. Instead, *four* particles emerge from the target: three electrons and a positron. A *positron,* or positive electron, is the antimatter version of an electron, identical to an electron in all respects other than having charge $q = +e$.

In chemical-reaction notation, the collision is

$$e^- \text{ (fast)} + e^- \text{ (at rest)} \rightarrow e^- + e^- + e^- + e^+$$

An electron and a positron have been *created,* apparently out of nothing. Mass $2m_e$ before the collision has become mass $4m_e$ after the collision. (Notice that charge has been conserved in this collision.)

Although the mass has increased, it wasn't created "out of nothing." This is an inelastic collision, just like the collision of the balls of clay, because the kinetic energy after the collision is less than before. In fact, if you measured the energies before and after the collision, you would find that the decrease in kinetic energy is exactly equal to the energy equivalent of the two particles that have been created: $\Delta K = 2m_e c^2$. The new particles have been created *out of energy!*

Particles can be created from energy, and particles can return to energy. FIGURE 36.40 shows an electron colliding with a positron, its antimatter partner. When a particle and its antiparticle meet, they *annihilate* each other. The mass disappears, and the energy equivalent of the mass is transformed into light. In Chapter 38, you'll learn that light is *quantized,* meaning that light is emitted and absorbed in discrete chunks of energy called *photons.* For light with wavelength λ, the energy of a photon is $E_{photon} = hc/\lambda$, where $h = 6.63 \times 10^{-34}$ J s is called *Planck's constant.* Photons carry momentum as well as energy. Conserving both energy and momentum in the annihilation of an electron and a positron requires the emission in opposite directions of two photons of equal energy.

If the electron and positron are fairly slow, so that $K \ll mc^2$, then $E_i \approx E_0 = mc^2$. In that case, energy conservation requires

$$E_f = 2E_{photon} = E_i \approx 2m_e c^2 \qquad (36.49)$$

Hence the wavelength of the emitted photons is

$$\lambda = \frac{hc}{m_e c^2} \approx 0.0024 \text{ nm} \qquad (36.50)$$

The tracks of elementary particles in a bubble chamber show the creation of an electron-positron pair. The negative electron and positive positron spiral in opposite directions in the magnetic field.

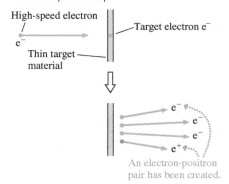

FIGURE 36.39 An inelastic collision between electrons can create an electron-positron pair.

High-speed electron

Target electron e^-

Thin target material

An electron-positron pair has been created.

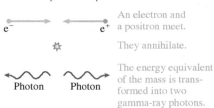

FIGURE 36.40 The annihilation of an electron-positron pair.

An electron and a positron meet.

They annihilate.

The energy equivalent of the mass is transformed into two gamma-ray photons.

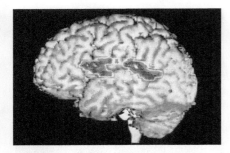

Positron-electron annihilation (a PET scan) provides a noninvasive look into the brain.

This is an extremely short wavelength, even shorter than the wavelengths of x rays. Photons in this wavelength range are called *gamma rays*. And, indeed, the emission of 0.0024 nm gamma rays is observed in many laboratory experiments in which positrons are able to collide with electrons and thus annihilate. In recent years, with the advent of gamma-ray telescopes on satellites, astronomers have found 0.0024 nm photons coming from many places in the universe, especially galactic centers—evidence that positrons are abundant throughout the universe.

Positron-electron annihilation is also the basis of the medical procedure known as a positron-emission tomography, or PET scans. A patient ingests a very small amount of a radioactive substance that decays by the emission of positrons. This substance is taken up by certain tissues in the body, especially those tissues with a high metabolic rate. As the substance decays, the positrons immediately collide with electrons, annihilate, and create two gamma-ray photons that are emitted back to back. The gamma rays, which easily leave the body, are detected, and their trajectories are traced backward into the body. The overlap of many such trajectories shows quite clearly the tissue in which the positron emission is occurring. The results are usually shown as false-color photographs, with redder areas indicating regions of higher positron emission.

Conservation of Energy

The creation and annihilation of particles with mass, processes strictly forbidden in Newtonian mechanics, are vivid proof that neither mass nor the Newtonian definition of energy is conserved. Even so, the *total* energy—the kinetic energy *and* the energy equivalent of mass—remains a conserved quantity.

Law of conservation of total energy The energy $E = \sum E_i$ of an isolated system is conserved, where $E_i = (\gamma_p)_i m_i c^2$ is the total energy of particle i.

Mass and energy are not the same thing, but, as the last few examples have shown, they are *equivalent* in the sense that mass can be transformed into energy and energy can be transformed into mass as long as the total energy is conserved.

Probably the most well-known application of the conservation of total energy is nuclear fission. The uranium isotope ^{236}U, containing 236 protons and neutrons, does not exist in nature. It can be created when a ^{235}U nucleus absorbs a neutron, increasing its atomic mass from 235 to 236. The ^{236}U nucleus quickly fragments into two smaller nuclei and several extra neutrons, a process known as **nuclear fission**. The nucleus can fragment in several ways, but one is

$$n + {}^{235}U \rightarrow {}^{236}U \rightarrow {}^{144}Ba + {}^{89}Kr + 3n$$

Ba and Kr are the atomic symbols for barium and krypton.

This reaction seems like an ordinary chemical reaction—until you check the masses. The masses of atomic isotopes are known with great precision from many decades of measurement in instruments called mass spectrometers. If you add up the masses on both sides, you find that the mass of the products is 0.185 u smaller than the mass of the initial neutron and ^{235}U, where, you will recall, 1 u = 1.66×10^{-27} kg is the atomic mass unit. In kilograms the mass loss is 3.07×10^{-28} kg.

Mass has been lost, but the energy equivalent of the mass has not. As FIGURE 36.41 shows, the mass has been converted to kinetic energy, causing the two product nuclei and three neutrons to be ejected at very high speeds. The kinetic energy is easily calculated: $\Delta K = m_{lost}c^2 = 2.8 \times 10^{-11}$ J.

This is a very tiny amount of energy, but it is the energy released from *one* fission. The number of nuclei in a macroscopic sample of uranium is on the order of N_A, Avogadro's number. Hence the energy available if *all* the nuclei fission is enormous. This energy, of course, is the basis for both nuclear power reactors and nuclear weapons.

FIGURE 36.41 In nuclear fission, the energy equivalent of lost mass is converted into kinetic energy.

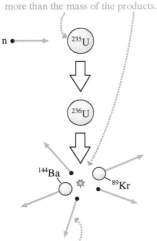

The mass of the reactants is 0.185 u more than the mass of the products.

n •———→ ^{235}U

^{236}U

^{144}Ba ^{89}Kr

0.185 u of mass has been converted into kinetic energy.

We started this chapter with an expectation that relativity would challenge our basic notions of space and time. We end by finding that relativity changes our understanding of mass and energy. Most remarkable of all is that each and every one of these new ideas flows from one simple statement: The laws of physics are the same in all inertial reference frames.

CHALLENGE EXAMPLE 36.13   **Goths and Huns**

The rockets of the Goths and the Huns are each 1000 m long in their rest frame. The rockets pass each other, virtually touching, at a relative speed of 0.8c. The Huns have a laser cannon at the rear of their rocket that fires a deadly laser beam perpendicular to the rocket's motion. The captain of the Huns wants to send a threatening message to the Goths by "firing a shot across their bow." He tells his first mate, "The Goths' rocket is length contracted to 600 m. Fire the laser cannon at the instant the tail of their rocket passes the nose of ours. The laser beam will cross 400 m in front of them."

But things are different in the Goths' reference frame. The Goth captain muses, "The Huns' rocket is length contracted to 600 m, 400 m shorter than our rocket. If they fire as the nose of their ship passes the tail of ours, the lethal laser beam will pass right through our side."

The first mate on the Huns' rocket fires as ordered. Does the laser beam blast the Goths or not?

MODEL Both rockets are inertial reference frames. Let the Huns' rocket be frame S and the Goths' rocket be frame S′. S′ moves with velocity $v = 0.8c$ relative to S. We need to describe the situation in terms of events.

VISUALIZE Begin by considering the situation from the Huns' reference frame, as shown in FIGURE 36.42.

FIGURE 36.42 The situation seen by the Huns.

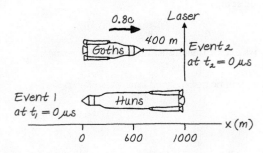

SOLVE The key to resolving the paradox is that two events simultaneous in one reference frame are not simultaneous in a different reference frame. The Huns do, indeed, see the Goths' rocket length contracted to $L_{\text{Goths}} = (1 - (0.8)^2)^{1/2} (1000 \text{ m}) = 600 \text{ m}$. Let event 1 be the tail of the Goths' rocket passing the nose of the Huns' rocket. Since we're free to define the origin of our coordinate system, we define this event to be at time $t_1 = 0 \ \mu s$ and at position $x_1 = 0 \text{ m}$. Then, in the Huns' reference frame, the spacetime coordinates of event 2, the firing of the laser cannon,

are $(x_2, t_2) = (1000 \text{ m}, 0 \ \mu s)$. The nose of the Goths' rocket is at $x = 600 \text{ m}$ at $t = 0 \ \mu s$; thus the laser cannon misses the Goths by 400 m.

Now we can use the Lorentz transformations to find the spacetime coordinates of the events in the Goths' reference frame. The nose of the Huns' rocket passes the tail of the Goths' rocket at $(x_1', t_1') = (0 \text{ m}, 0 \ \mu s)$. The Huns fire their laser cannon at

$$x_2' = \gamma(x_2 - vt_2) = \frac{5}{3}(1000 \text{ m} - 0 \text{ m}) = 1667 \text{ m}$$

$$t_2' = \gamma\left(t_2 - \frac{vx_2}{c^2}\right) = \frac{5}{3}\left(0 \ \mu s - (0.8)\frac{1000 \text{ m}}{300 \text{ m}/\mu s}\right) = -4.444 \ \mu s$$

where we calculated $\gamma = 5/3$ for $v = 0.8c$. Events 1 and 2 are *not* simultaneous in S′. The Huns fire the laser cannon 4.444 μs *before* the nose of their rocket reaches the tail of the Goths' rocket. The laser is fired at $x_2' = 1667 \text{ m}$, missing the nose of the Goths' rocket by 667 m. FIGURE 36.43 shows how the Goths see things.

FIGURE 36.43 The situation seen by the Goths.

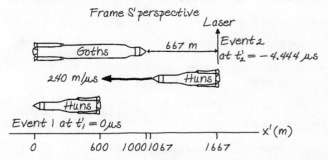

In fact, since the Huns' rocket is length contracted to 600 m, the nose of the Huns' rocket is at $x' = 1667 \text{ m} - 600 \text{ m} = 1067 \text{ m}$ at the instant they fire the laser cannon. At a speed of $v = 0.8c = 240 \text{ m}/\mu s$, in 4.444 μs the nose of the Huns' rocket travels $\Delta x' = (240 \text{ m}/\mu s)(4.444 \ \mu s) = 1067 \text{ m}$—exactly the right distance to be at the tail of the Goths' rocket at $t_1' = 0 \ \mu s$. We could also note that the 667 m "miss distance" in the Goths' frame is length contracted to $(1 - (0.8)^2)^{1/2} (667 \text{ m}) = 400 \text{ m}$ in the Huns' frame—exactly the amount by which the Huns think they miss the Goths' rocket.

ASSESS Thus we end up with a consistent explanation. The Huns miss the Goths' rocket because, to them, the Goths' rocket is length contracted. The Goths find that the Huns miss because event 2 (the firing of the laser cannon) occurs before event 1 (the nose of one rocket passing the tail of the other). The 400 m distance of the miss in the Huns' reference frame is the length-contracted miss distance of 667 m in the Goths' reference frame.

SUMMARY

The goal of Chapter 36 has been to understand how Einstein's theory of relativity changes our concepts of space and time.

General Principles

Principle of Relativity All the laws of physics are the same in all inertial reference frames.

- The speed of light c is the same in all inertial reference frames.
- No particle or causal influence can travel at a speed greater than c.

Important Concepts

Space

Spatial measurements depend on the motion of the experimenter relative to the events. An object's length is the difference between *simultaneous* measurements of the positions of both ends.

Proper length ℓ is the length of an object measured in a reference frame in which the object is at rest. The object's length in a frame in which the object moves with velocity v is

$$L = \sqrt{1 - \beta^2}\,\ell \le \ell$$

This is called **length contraction.**

Time

Time measurements depend on the motion of the experimenter relative to the events. Events that are simultaneous in reference frame S are not simultaneous in frame S' moving relative to S.

Proper time $\Delta\tau$ is the time interval between two events measured in a reference frame in which the events occur at the same position. The time interval between the events in a frame moving with relative velocity v is

$$\Delta t = \Delta\tau/\sqrt{1 - \beta^2} \ge \Delta\tau$$

This is called **time dilation.**

Momentum

The law of conservation of momentum is valid in all inertial reference frames if the momentum of a particle with velocity u is $p = \gamma_p m u$, where

$$\gamma_p = 1/\sqrt{1 - u^2/c^2}$$

The momentum approaches ∞ as $u \to c$.

Energy

The law of conservation of energy is valid in all inertial reference frames if the energy of a particle with velocity u is $E = \gamma_p mc^2 = E_0 + K$.

Rest energy $E_0 = mc^2$

Kinetic energy $K = (\gamma_p - 1)mc^2$

Invariants are quantities that have the same value in all inertial reference frames.

Spacetime interval: $s^2 = (c\Delta t)^2 - (\Delta x)^2$

Particle rest energy: $E_0^2 = (mc^2)^2 = E^2 - (pc)^2$

Mass-energy equivalence

Mass m can be transformed into energy $E = mc^2$.

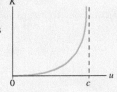

Energy can be transformed into mass $m = \Delta E/c^2$.

Applications

An event happens at a specific place in space and time. Spacetime coordinates are (x, t) in frame S and (x', t') in frame S'.

A reference frame is a coordinate system with meter sticks and clocks for measuring events. Experimenters at rest relative to each other share the same reference frame.

The Lorentz transformations transform spacetime coordinates and velocities between reference frames S and S'.

$$x' = \gamma(x - vt) \qquad x = \gamma(x' + vt')$$
$$y' = y \qquad y = y'$$
$$z' = z \qquad z = z'$$
$$t' = \gamma(t - vx/c^2) \qquad t = \gamma(t' + vx'/c^2)$$
$$u' = \frac{u - v}{1 - uv/c^2} \qquad u = \frac{u' + v}{1 + u'v/c^2}$$

where u and u' are the x- and x'-components of an object's velocity.

$$\beta = \frac{v}{c} \quad \text{and} \quad \gamma = 1/\sqrt{1 - v^2/c^2} = 1/\sqrt{1 - \beta^2}$$

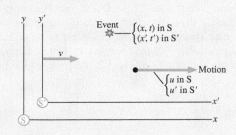

Terms and Notation

special relativity	spacetime coordinates,	time dilation	causal influence
reference frame	(x, y, z, t)	light year, ly	total energy, E
inertial reference frame	synchronized	proper length, ℓ	rest energy, E_0
Galilean principle of relativity	simultaneous	length contraction	law of conservation of total
ether	relativity of simultaneity	invariant	energy
principle of relativity	rest frame	spacetime interval, s	nuclear fission
event	proper time, $\Delta\tau$	Lorentz transformations	

CONCEPTUAL QUESTIONS

1. FIGURE Q36.1 shows two balls. What are the speed and direction of each (a) in a reference frame that moves with ball 1 and (b) in a reference frame that moves with ball 2?

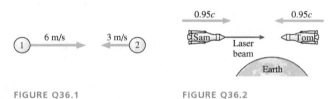

FIGURE Q36.1

FIGURE Q36.2

2. Teenagers Sam and Tom are playing chicken in their rockets. As FIGURE Q36.2 shows, an experimenter on earth sees that each is traveling at $0.95c$ as he approaches the other. Sam fires a laser beam toward Tom.
   a. What is the speed of the laser beam relative to Sam?
   b. What is the speed of the laser beam relative to Tom?

3. Firecracker A is 300 m from you. Firecracker B is 600 m from you in the same direction. You see both explode at the same time. Define event 1 to be "firecracker A explodes" and event 2 to be "firecracker B explodes." Does event 1 occur before, after, or at the same time as event 2? Explain.

4. Firecrackers A and B are 600 m apart. You are standing exactly halfway between them. Your lab partner is 300 m on the other side of firecracker A. You see two flashes of light, from the two explosions, at exactly the same instant of time. Define event 1 to be "firecracker A explodes" and event 2 to be "firecracker B explodes." According to your lab partner, based on measurements he or she makes, does event 1 occur before, after, or at the same time as event 2? Explain.

5. FIGURE Q36.5 shows Peggy standing at the center of her railroad car as it passes Ryan on the ground. Firecrackers attached to the ends of the car explode. A short time later, the flashes from the two explosions arrive at Peggy at the same time.

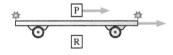

FIGURE Q36.5

   a. Were the explosions simultaneous in Peggy's reference frame? If not, which exploded first? Explain.
   b. Were the explosions simultaneous in Ryan's reference frame? If not, which exploded first? Explain.

6. FIGURE Q36.6 shows a rocket traveling from left to right. At the instant it is halfway between two trees, lightning simultaneously (in the rocket's frame) hits both trees.

   a. Do the light flashes reach the rocket pilot simultaneously? If not, which reaches her first? Explain.
   b. A student was sitting on the ground halfway between the trees as the rocket passed overhead. According to the student, were the lightning strikes simultaneous? If not, which tree was hit first? Explain.

FIGURE Q36.6

7. Your friend flies from Los Angeles to New York. She carries an accurate stopwatch with her to measure the flight time. You and your assistants on the ground also measure the flight time.
   a. Identify the two events associated with this measurement.
   b. Who, if anyone, measures the proper time?
   c. Who, if anyone, measures the shorter flight time?

8. As the meter stick in FIGURE Q36.8 flies past you, you simultaneously measure the positions of both ends and determine that $L < 1$ m.

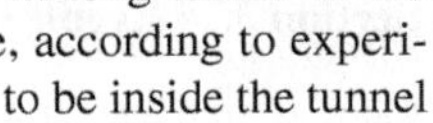

   FIGURE Q36.8

   a. To an experimenter in frame S′, the meter stick's frame, did you make your two measurements simultaneously? If not, which end did you measure first? Explain.
   b. Can experimenters in frame S′ give an explanation for why your measurement is less than 1 m?

9. A 100-m-long train is heading for an 80-m-long tunnel. If the train moves sufficiently fast, is it possible, according to experimenters on the ground, for the entire train to be inside the tunnel at one instant of time? Explain.

10. Particle A has half the mass and twice the speed of particle B. Is the momentum p_A less than, greater than, or equal to p_B? Explain.

11. Event A occurs at spacetime coordinates (300 m, 2 μs).
    a. Event B occurs at spacetime coordinates (1200 m, 6 μs). Could A possibly be the cause of B? Explain.
    b. Event C occurs at spacetime coordinates (2400 m, 8 μs). Could A possibly be the cause of C? Explain.

EXERCISES AND PROBLEMS

Problems labeled ▩ integrate material from earlier chapters.

Exercises

Section 36.2 Galilean Relativity

1. ‖ At $t = 1.0$ s, a firecracker explodes at $x = 10$ m in reference frame S. Four seconds later, a second firecracker explodes at $x = 20$ m. Reference frame S′ moves in the x-direction at a speed of 5.0 m/s. What are the positions and times of these two events in frame S′?

2. ‖ A firecracker explodes in reference frame S at $t = 1.0$ s. A second firecracker explodes at the same position at $t = 3.0$ s. In reference frame S′, which moves in the x-direction at speed v, the first explosion is detected at $x′ = 4.0$ m and the second at $x′ = -4.0$ m.
   a. What is the speed of frame S′ relative to frame S?
   b. What is the position of the two explosions in frame S?

3. | A sprinter crosses the finish line of a race. The roar of the crowd in front approaches her at a speed of 360 m/s. The roar from the crowd behind her approaches at 330 m/s. What are the speed of sound and the speed of the sprinter?

4. | A baseball pitcher can throw a ball with a speed of 40 m/s. He is in the back of a pickup truck that is driving away from you. He throws the ball in your direction, and it floats toward you at a lazy 10 m/s. What is the speed of the truck?

5. | A newspaper delivery boy is riding his bicycle down the street at 5.0 m/s. He can throw a paper at a speed of 8.0 m/s. What is the paper's speed relative to the ground if he throws the paper (a) forward, (b) backward, and (c) to the side?

Section 36.3 Einstein's Principle of Relativity

6. | An out-of-control alien spacecraft is diving into a star at a speed of 1.0×10^8 m/s. At what speed, relative to the spacecraft, is the starlight approaching?

7. | A starship blasts past the earth at 2.0×10^8 m/s. Just after passing the earth, it fires a laser beam out the back of the starship. With what speed does the laser beam approach the earth?

8. | A positron moving in the positive x-direction at 2.0×10^8 m/s collides with an electron at rest. The positron and electron annihilate, producing two gamma-ray photons. Photon 1 travels in the positive x-direction and photon 2 travels in the negative x-direction. What is the speed of each photon?

Section 36.4 Events and Measurements

Section 36.5 The Relativity of Simultaneity

9. ‖ Your job is to synchronize the clocks in a reference frame. You are going to do so by flashing a light at the origin at $t = 0$ s. To what time should the clock at $(x, y, z) = (30$ m, 40 m, 0 m) be preset?

10. | Bjorn is standing at $x = 600$ m. Firecracker 1 explodes at the origin and firecracker 2 explodes at $x = 900$ m. The flashes from both explosions reach Bjorn's eye at $t = 3.0 \ \mu$s. At what time did each firecracker explode?

11. ‖ Bianca is standing at $x = 600$ m. Firecracker 1, at the origin, and firecracker 2, at $x = 900$ m, explode simultaneously. The flash from firecracker 1 reaches Bianca's eye at $t = 3.0 \ \mu$s. At what time does she see the flash from firecracker 2?

12. ‖ You are standing at $x = 9.0$ km. Lightning bolt 1 strikes at $x = 0$ km and lightning bolt 2 strikes at $x = 12.0$ km. Both flashes reach your eye at the same time. Your assistant is standing at $x = 3.0$ km. Does your assistant see the flashes at the same time? If not, which does she see first, and what is the time difference between the two?

13. ‖ You are standing at $x = 9.0$ km and your assistant is standing at $x = 3.0$ km. Lightning bolt 1 strikes at $x = 0$ km and lightning bolt 2 strikes at $x = 12.0$ km. You see the flash from bolt 2 at $t = 10 \ \mu$s and the flash from bolt 1 at $t = 50 \ \mu$s. According to your assistant, were the lightning strikes simultaneous? If not, which occurred first, and what was the time difference between the two?

14. ‖ Jose is looking to the east. Lightning bolt 1 strikes a tree 300 m from him. Lightning bolt 2 strikes a barn 900 m from him in the same direction. Jose sees the tree strike 1.0 μs before he sees the barn strike. According to Jose, were the lightning strikes simultaneous? If not, which occurred first, and what was the time difference between the two?

15. ‖ You are flying your personal rocketcraft at $0.9c$ from Star A toward Star B. The distance between the stars, in the stars' reference frame, is 1.0 ly. Both stars happen to explode simultaneously in your reference frame at the instant you are exactly halfway between them. Do you see the flashes simultaneously? If not, which do you see first, and what is the time difference between the two?

Section 36.6 Time Dilation

16. ‖ A cosmic ray travels 60 km through the earth's atmosphere in 400 μs, as measured by experimenters on the ground. How long does the journey take according to the cosmic ray?

17. | At what speed, as a fraction of c, does a moving clock tick at half the rate of an identical clock at rest?

18. | An astronaut travels to a star system 4.5 ly away at a speed of $0.9c$. Assume that the time needed to accelerate and decelerate is negligible.
   a. How long does the journey take according to Mission Control on earth?
   b. How long does the journey take according to the astronaut?
   c. How much time elapses between the launch and the arrival of the first radio message from the astronaut saying that she has arrived?

19. ‖ a. How fast must a rocket travel on a journey to and from a distant star so that the astronauts age 10 years while the Mission Control workers on earth age 120 years?
   b. As measured by Mission Control, how far away is the distant star?

20. ‖ You fly 5000 km across the United States on an airliner at 250 m/s. You return two days later at the same speed.
   a. Have you aged more or less than your friends at home?
   b. By how much?
   Hint: Use the binomial approximation.

21. ‖ At what speed, in m/s, would a moving clock lose 1.0 ns in 1.0 day according to experimenters on the ground?
   Hint: Use the binomial approximation.

Section 36.7 Length Contraction

22. | At what speed, as a fraction of c, will a moving rod have a length 60% that of an identical rod at rest?

23. | Jill claims that her new rocket is 100 m long. As she flies past your house, you measure the rocket's length and find that it is only 80 m. Should Jill be cited for exceeding the $0.5c$ speed limit?

24. || A muon travels 60 km through the atmosphere at a speed of $0.9997c$. According to the muon, how thick is the atmosphere?

25. || A cube has a density of 2000 kg/m^3 while at rest in the laboratory. What is the cube's density as measured by an experimenter in the laboratory as the cube moves through the laboratory at 90% of the speed of light in a direction perpendicular to one of its faces?

26. | Our Milky Way galaxy is 100,000 ly in diameter. A spaceship crossing the galaxy measures the galaxy's diameter to be a mere 1.0 ly.
    a. What is the speed of the spaceship relative to the galaxy?
    b. How long is the crossing time as measured in the galaxy's reference frame?

27. || A human hair is about 50 μm in diameter. At what speed, in m/s, would a meter stick "shrink by a hair"?
    Hint: Use the binomial approximation.

Section 36.8 The Lorentz Transformations

28. | An event has spacetime coordinates $(x, t) = (1200$ m, 2.0 μs$)$ in reference frame S. What are the event's spacetime coordinates (a) in reference frame S$'$ that moves in the positive x-direction at $0.8c$ and (b) in reference frame S$''$ that moves in the negative x-direction at $0.8c$?

29. || A rocket travels in the x-direction at speed $0.6c$ with respect to the earth. An experimenter on the rocket observes a collision between two comets and determines that the spacetime coordinates of the collision are $(x', t') = (3.0 \times 10^{10}$ m, 200 s$)$. What are the spacetime coordinates of the collision in earth's reference frame?

30. || In the earth's reference frame, a tree is at the origin and a pole is at $x = 30$ km. Lightning strikes both the tree and the pole at $t = 10$ μs. The lightning strikes are observed by a rocket traveling in the x-direction at $0.5c$.
    a. What are the spacetime coordinates for these two events in the rocket's reference frame?
    b. Are the events simultaneous in the rocket's frame? If not, which occurs first?

31. || A rocket cruising past earth at $0.8c$ shoots a bullet out the back door, opposite the rocket's motion, at $0.9c$ relative to the rocket. What is the bullet's speed relative to the earth?

32. || A laboratory experiment shoots an electron to the left at $0.9c$. What is the electron's speed relative to a proton moving to the right at $0.9c$?

33. || A distant quasar is found to be moving away from the earth at $0.8c$. A galaxy closer to the earth and along the same line of sight is moving away from us at $0.2c$. What is the recessional speed of the quasar as measured by astronomers in the other galaxy?

Section 36.9 Relativistic Momentum

34. | A proton is accelerated to $0.999c$.
    a. What is the proton's momentum?
    b. By what factor does the proton's momentum exceed its Newtonian momentum?

35. || At what speed is a particle's momentum twice its Newtonian value?

36. ||| A 1.0 g particle has momentum 400,000 kg m/s. What is the particle's speed?

37. || What is the speed of a particle whose momentum is mc?

Section 36.10 Relativistic Energy

38. | What are the kinetic energy, the rest energy, and the total energy of a 1.0 g particle with a speed of $0.8c$?

39. | A quarter-pound hamburger with all the fixings has a mass of 200 g. The food energy of the hamburger (480 food calories) is 2 MJ.
    a. What is the energy equivalent of the mass of the hamburger?
    b. By what factor does the energy equivalent exceed the food energy?

40. | How fast must an electron move so that its total energy is 10% more than its rest mass energy?

41. | At what speed is a particle's kinetic energy twice its rest energy?

42. || At what speed is a particle's total energy twice its rest energy?

Problems

43. | A 50 g ball moving to the right at 4.0 m/s overtakes and collides with a 100 g ball moving to the right at 2.0 m/s. The collision is perfectly elastic. Use reference frames and the Chapter 10 result for perfectly elastic collisions to find the speed and direction of each ball after the collision.

44. | A billiard ball has a perfectly elastic collision with a second billiard ball of equal mass. Afterward, the first ball moves to the left at 2.0 m/s and the second to the right at 4.0 m/s. Use reference frames and the Chapter 10 result for perfectly elastic collisions to find the speed and direction of each ball before the collision.

45. || The diameter of the solar system is 10 light hours. A spaceship crosses the solar system in 15 hours, as measured on earth. How long, in hours, does the passage take according to passengers on the spaceship?
    Hint: $c = 1$ light hour per hour.

46. | A 30-m-long rocket train car is traveling from Los Angeles to New York at $0.5c$ when a light at the center of the car flashes. When the light reaches the front of the car, it immediately rings a bell. Light reaching the back of the car immediately sounds a siren.
    a. Are the bell and siren simultaneous events for a passenger seated in the car? If not, which occurs first and by how much time?
    b. Are the bell and siren simultaneous events for a bicyclist waiting to cross the tracks? If not, which occurs first and by how much time?

47. ||| The star Alpha goes supernova. Ten years later and 100 ly away, as measured by astronomers in the galaxy, star Beta explodes.
    a. Is it possible that the explosion of Alpha is in any way responsible for the explosion of Beta? Explain.
    b. An alien spacecraft passing through the galaxy finds that the distance between the two explosions is 120 ly. According to the aliens, what is the time between the explosions?

48. || Two events in reference frame S occur 10 μs apart at the same point in space. The distance between the two events is 2400 m in reference frame S$'$.
    a. What is the time interval between the events in reference frame S$'$?
    b. What is the velocity of S$'$ relative to S?

49. ‖‖ A starship voyages to a distant planet 10 ly away. The explorers stay 1 yr, return at the same speed, and arrive back on earth 26 yr after they left. Assume that the time needed to accelerate and decelerate is negligible.
    a. What is the speed of the starship?
    b. How much time has elapsed on the astronauts' chronometers?

50. ‖ In Section 36.6 we saw that muons can reach the ground because of time dilation. But how do things appear in the muon's reference frame, where the muon's half-life is only 1.5 μs? How can a muon travel the 60 km to reach the earth's surface before decaying? Resolve this apparent paradox. Be as quantitative as you can in your answer.

51. ‖ The Stanford Linear Accelerator (SLAC) accelerates electrons to $c = 0.99999997c$ in a 3.2-km-long tube. If they travel the length of the tube at full speed (they don't, because they are accelerating), how long is the tube in the electrons' reference frame?

52. ‖ In an attempt to reduce the extraordinarily long travel times for voyaging to distant stars, some people have suggested traveling at close to the speed of light. Suppose you wish to visit the red giant star Betelgeuse, which is 430 ly away, and that you want your 20,000 kg rocket to move so fast that you age only 20 years during the round trip.
    a. How fast must the rocket travel relative to earth?
    b. How much energy is needed to accelerate the rocket to this speed?
    c. Compare this amount of energy to the total energy used by the United States in the year 2010, which was roughly 1.0×10^{20} J.

53. ‖ A rocket traveling at $0.5c$ sets out for the nearest star, Alpha Centauri, which is 4.25 ly away from earth. It will return to earth immediately after reaching Alpha Centauri. What distance will the rocket travel and how long will the journey last according to (a) stay-at-home earthlings and (b) the rocket crew? (c) Which answers are the correct ones, those in part a or those in part b?

54. ‖ The star Delta goes supernova. One year later and 2 ly away, as measured by astronomers in the galaxy, star Epsilon explodes. Let the explosion of Delta be at $x_D = 0$ and $t_D = 0$. The explosions are observed by three spaceships cruising through the galaxy in the direction from Delta to Epsilon at velocities $v_1 = 0.3c$, $v_2 = 0.5c$, and $v_3 = 0.7c$.
    a. What are the times of the two explosions as measured by scientists on each of the three spaceships?
    b. Does one spaceship find that the explosions are simultaneous? If so, which one?
    c. Does one spaceship find that Epsilon explodes before Delta? If so, which one?
    d. Do your answers to parts b and c violate the idea of causality? Explain.

55. ‖ Two rockets approach each other. Each is traveling at $0.75c$ in the earth's reference frame. What is the speed of one rocket relative to the other?

56. ‖ A rocket fires a projectile at a speed of $0.95c$ while traveling past the earth. An earthbound scientist measures the projectile's speed to be $0.90c$. What was the rocket's speed?

57. ‖ Through what potential difference must an electron be accelerated, starting from rest, to acquire a speed of $0.99c$?

58. ‖ What is the speed of a proton after being accelerated from rest through a 50×10^6 V potential difference?

59. ‖ The half-life of a muon at rest is 1.5 μs. Muons that have been accelerated to a very high speed and are then held in a circular storage ring have a half-life of 7.5 μs.

a. What is the speed of the muons in the storage ring?
b. What is the total energy of a muon in the storage ring? The mass of a muon is 207 times the mass of an electron.

60. ‖ A solar flare blowing out from the sun at $0.9c$ is overtaking a rocket as it flies away from the sun at $0.8c$. According to the crew on board, with what speed is the flare gaining on the rocket?

61. ‖ This chapter has assumed that lengths perpendicular to the direction of motion are not affected by the motion. That is, motion in the x-direction does not cause length contraction along the y- or z-axes. To find out if this is really true, consider two spray-paint nozzles attached to rods perpendicular to the x-axis. It has been confirmed that, when both rods are at rest, both nozzles are exactly 1 m above the base of the rod. One rod is placed in the S reference frame with its base on the x-axis; the other is placed in the S' reference frame with its base on the x'-axis. The rods then swoop past each other and, as FIGURE P36.61 shows, each paints a stripe across the other rod.

We will use proof by contradiction. Assume that objects perpendicular to the motion *are* contracted. An experimenter in frame S finds that the S' nozzle, as it goes past, is less than 1 m above the x-axis. The principle of relativity says that an experiment carried out in two different inertial reference frames will have the same outcome in both.
    a. Pursue this line of reasoning and show that you end up with a logical contradiction, two mutually incompatible situations.
    b. What can you conclude from this contradiction?

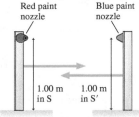

FIGURE P36.61

62. ‖ Derive the Lorentz transformations for t and t'.
    Hint: See the comment following Equation 36.22.

63. ‖ a. Derive a velocity transformation equation for u_y and u_y'. Assume that the reference frames are in the standard orientation with motion parallel to the x- and x'-axes.
    b. A rocket passes the earth at $0.8c$. As it goes by, it launches a projectile at $0.6c$ perpendicular to the direction of motion. What is the projectile's speed in the earth's reference frame?

64. ‖ What is the momentum of a particle whose total energy is four times its rest energy? Give your answer as a multiple of mc.

65. ‖ a. What are the momentum and total energy of a proton with speed $0.99c$?
    b. What is the proton's momentum in a different reference frame in which $E' = 5.0 \times 10^{-10}$ J?

66. ‖‖ At what speed is the kinetic energy of a particle twice its Newtonian value?

67. ‖ A typical nuclear power plant generates electricity at the rate of 1000 MW. The efficiency of transforming thermal energy into electrical energy is $\frac{1}{3}$ and the plant runs at full capacity for 80% of the year. (Nuclear power plants are down about 20% of the time for maintenance and refueling.)
    a. How much thermal energy does the plant generate in one year?
    b. What mass of uranium is transformed into energy in one year?

68. ‖ The sun radiates energy at the rate 3.8×10^{26} W. The source of this energy is fusion, a nuclear reaction in which mass is transformed into energy. The mass of the sun is 2.0×10^{30} kg.
    a. How much mass does the sun lose each year?
    b. What percent is this of the sun's total mass?
    c. Estimate the lifetime of the sun.

69. ‖ The radioactive element radium (Ra) decays by a process known as *alpha decay*, in which the nucleus emits a helium nucleus. (These high-speed helium nuclei were named alpha particles when radioactivity was first discovered, long before the identity of the particles was established.) The reaction is ^{226}Ra → ^{222}Rn + ^{4}He, where Rn is the element radon. The accurately measured atomic masses of the three atoms are 226.025, 222.017, and 4.003. How much energy is released in each decay? (The energy released in radioactive decay is what makes nuclear waste "hot.")

70. ‖ The nuclear reaction that powers the sun is the fusion of four protons into a helium nucleus. The process involves several steps, but the net reaction is simply 4p → ^{4}He + energy. The mass of a helium nucleus is known to be 6.64×10^{-27} kg.
    a. How much energy is released in each fusion?
    b. What fraction of the initial rest mass energy is this energy?

71. ‖‖‖ An electron moving to the right at 0.9c collides with a positron moving to the left at 0.9c. The two particles annihilate and produce two gamma-ray photons. What is the wavelength of the photons?

72. ‖ Consider the inelastic collision $e^- + e^- \rightarrow e^- + e^- + e^+ + e^+$ in which an electron-positron pair is produced in a head-on collision between two electrons moving in opposite directions at the same speed. This is similar to Figure 36.39, but both of the initial electrons are moving.
    a. What is the threshold kinetic energy? That is, what minimum kinetic energy must each electron have to allow this process to occur?
    b. What is the speed of an electron with this kinetic energy?

Challenge Problems

73. Two rockets, A and B, approach the earth from opposite directions at speed 0.8c. The length of each rocket measured in its rest frame is 100 m. What is the length of rocket A as measured by the crew of rocket B?

74. Two rockets are each 1000 m long in their rest frame. Rocket Orion, traveling at 0.8c relative to the earth, is overtaking rocket Sirius, which is poking along at a mere 0.6c. According to the crew on Sirius, how long does Orion take to completely pass? That is, how long is it from the instant the nose of Orion is at the tail of Sirius until the tail of Orion is at the nose of Sirius?

75. Some particle accelerators allow protons (p^+) and antiprotons (p^-) to circulate at equal speeds in opposite directions in a device called a *storage ring*. The particle beams cross each other at various points to cause $p^+ + p^-$ collisions. In one collision, the outcome is $p^+ + p^- \rightarrow e^+ + e^- + \gamma + \gamma$, where γ represents a high-energy gamma-ray photon. The electron and positron are ejected from the collision at 0.9999995c and the gamma-ray photon wavelengths are found to be 1.0×10^{-6} nm. What were the proton and antiproton speeds prior to the collision?

76. A very fast pole vaulter lives in the country. One day, while practicing, he notices a 10.0-m-long barn with the doors open at both ends. He decides to run through the barn at 0.866c while carrying his 16.0-m-long pole. The farmer, who sees him coming, says, "Aha! This guy's pole is length contracted to 8.0 m. There will be a short interval of time when the pole is entirely inside the barn. If I'm quick, I can simultaneously close both barn doors while the pole vaulter and his pole are inside." The pole vaulter, who sees the farmer beside the barn, thinks to himself, "That farmer is crazy. The barn is length contracted and is only 5.0 m long. My 16.0-m-long pole cannot fit into a 5.0-m-long barn. If the farmer closes the doors just as the tip of my pole reaches the back door, the front door will break off the last 11.0 m of my pole."

Can the farmer close the doors without breaking the pole? Show that, when properly analyzed, the farmer and the pole vaulter agree on the outcome. Your analysis should contain both quantitative calculations and written explanation.

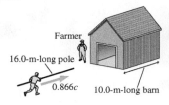

FIGURE CP36.76

STOP TO THINK ANSWERS

Stop to Think 36.1: a, c, and f. These move at constant velocity, or very nearly so. The others are accelerating.

Stop to Think 36.2: a. $u' = u - v = -10$ m/s $- 6$ m/s $= -16$ m/s. The *speed* is 16 m/s.

Stop to Think 36.3: c. Even the light has a slight travel time. The event is the hammer hitting the nail, not your seeing the hammer hit the nail.

Stop to Think 36.4: At the same time. Mark is halfway between the tree and the pole, so the fact that he *sees* the lightning bolts at the same time means they *happened* at the same time. It's true that Nancy *sees* event 1 before event 2, but the events actually occurred before she sees them. Mark and Nancy share a reference frame, because they are at rest relative to each other, and all experimenters in a reference frame, after correcting for any signal delays, *agree* on the spacetime coordinates of an event.

Stop to Think 36.5: After. This is the same as the case of Peggy and Ryan. In Mark's reference frame, as in Ryan's, the events are simultaneous. Nancy *sees* event 1 first, but the time when an event is seen is not when the event actually happens. Because all experimenters in a reference frame agree on the spacetime coordinates of an event, Nancy's position in her reference frame cannot affect the order of the events. If Nancy had been passing Mark at the instant the lightning strikes occur in Mark's frame, then Nancy would be equivalent to Peggy. Event 2, like the firecracker at the front of Peggy's railroad car, occurs first in Nancy's reference frame.

Stop to Think 36.6: c. Nick measures proper time because Nick's clock is present at both the "nose passes Nick" event and the "tail passes Nick" event. Proper time is the smallest measured time interval between two events.

Stop to Think 36.7: $L_A > L_B = L_C$. Anjay measures the pole's proper length because it is at rest in his reference frame. Proper length is the longest measured length. Beth and Charles may *see* the pole differently, but they share the same reference frame and their *measurements* of the length agree.

Stop to Think 36.8: c. The rest energy E_0 is an invariant, the same in all inertial reference frames. Thus $m = E_0/c^2$ is independent of speed.

37 The Foundations of Modern Physics

Studies of the light emitted by gas discharge tubes helped lay the foundations of modern physics.

▶ **Looking Ahead** The goal of Chapter 37 is to learn about the structure and properties of atoms.

Matter and Light

Except for relativity, everything you've studied until now was known by 1900. But within the span of just a few years, right around 1900, investigations into the structure of matter and the properties of light led to many discoveries at odds with classical physics.

Our goal is to establish the experimental basis for new theories of matter and light that arose in the first decades of the 20th century. We cannot see atoms, so what is the *evidence* for our current understanding of the atomic structure of matter?

Electrons

Experiments to study electrical conduction in gases found that unknown "rays" travel outward from the cathode—the negative electrode. You'll learn how J. J. Thomson discovered that these **cathode rays** are a stream of subatomic particles—electrons.

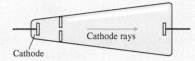
Cathode rays
Cathode

A cathode-ray tube, or CRT, was, until very recently, the "picture tube" of televisions and computer monitors.

X Rays

At very high voltages, the cathode-ray tube itself is a source of rays, highly penetrating rays called **x rays.** You'll learn that x rays are electromagnetic waves with wavelengths much shorter than those of visible light.

The penetrating power of x rays led to their use in medicine almost immediately. Today, x rays have applications ranging from inspecting machine parts to deciphering the structure of biological molecules.

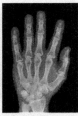

Emission and Absorption

You'll learn how **spectroscopy** is based on the interference of light and how scientists used spectroscopy to study the emission and absorption of light. This provided many new clues about the structure of matter.

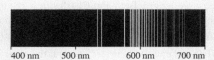
400 nm   500 nm   600 nm   700 nm

Atoms emit a **discrete spectrum** consisting of many discrete wavelengths. Each element has a unique spectrum, an *electromagnetic fingerprint* that can identify that element.

The Nucleus

How are atoms built? You'll learn how Ernest Rutherford used the particles emitted in radioactive decay to discover that atoms have an incredibly tiny **nucleus.**

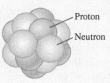
The nucleus, which is unbelievably dense, consists of positive protons and neutral neutrons.
Proton
Neutron

◀ **Looking Back**
Section 28.1–28.2 Electric potential energy

Rutherford's Model of the Atom

The discovery of the electron and the nucleus led Rutherford to propose a solar-system model of the atom in which negative electrons orbit a tiny, dense, positive nucleus.

An element's atomic number is the number of protons in the nucleus. An atom with three protons is lithium.

◀ **Looking Back**
Section 16.2 Atomic masses

37.1 Matter and Light

The idea that matter consists of small, indivisible particles can be traced to the Greek philosophers Leucippus and Democritus in the 5th century BCE. They called these particles *atoms*, Greek for "not divisible." Atomism was not widely accepted, due in no small part to the complete lack of evidence, but atomic ideas never died.

Things began to change in the early years of the 19th century. The English chemist John Dalton argued that chemical reactions could be understood if each chemical element consisted of identical atoms. An important feature of Dalton's work, which made it more science than speculation, was his experimental effort to determine the relative masses of the atoms of different elements.

The evidence for atoms grew stronger as thermodynamics and the kinetic theory of gases developed in the mid-19th century. Slight deviations from the ideal-gas law at high pressures, which could be understood if the atoms were beginning to come into close proximity to one another, led to a rough estimate of atomic sizes. By 1890, it was widely accepted that atoms exist and have diameters of approximately 10^{-10} m.

Other scientists of the 19th century were trying to understand what light is. Newton, as we have noted, favored a *corpuscular* theory whereby small particles of light travel in straight lines. However, the situation changed when, in 1801, Thomas Young demonstrated the interference of light with his celebrated double-slit experiment. But if light is a wave, what is waving? Studies of electricity and magnetism by Ampère, Faraday, and others led Maxwell to the realization that light is an electromagnetic wave.

This was the situation at the end of the 19th century, when a series of discoveries began to reveal that the theories of Newton and Maxwell were not sufficient to explain the properties of atoms. New theories of matter and light at the atomic level, collectively called *modern physics*, arose in the early decades of the 20th century. Modern physics, including relativity and quantum physics, is our topic for the final part of this textbook.

A difficulty, however, is that we cannot directly see, feel, or manipulate atoms. To know what the theories of modern physics are attempting to explain, and whether they are successful, we must start with *experimental evidence* about the behavior of atoms and light. That is the primary purpose of this chapter and the next.

FIGURE 37.1 A grating spectrometer is used to study the emission of light.

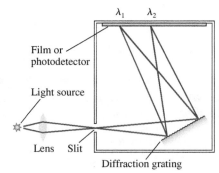

37.2 The Emission and Absorption of Light

The interference and diffraction of light, discovered early in the 19th century, soon led to practical tools for measuring the wavelengths of light. The most important tool, still widely used today, is the **spectrometer,** such as the one shown in FIGURE 37.1. The heart of a spectrometer is a diffraction grating that diffracts different wavelengths of light at different angles. Making the grating slightly curved, like a spherical mirror, focuses the interference fringes onto a *photographic plate* or (more likely today) an electronic array detector. Each wavelength in the light is focused to a different position on the detector, producing a distinctive pattern called the **spectrum** of the light. Spectroscopists discovered very early that there are two distinct types of spectra.

Continuous Spectra and Blackbody Radiation

Cool lava is black, but lava heated to a high temperature glows red and, if hot enough, yellow. A tungsten wire, dark gray at room temperature, emits bright white light when heated by a current—thus becoming the bright filament in an incandescent lightbulb. Hot, self-luminous objects, such as the lava or the lightbulb, form a rainbow-like **continuous spectrum** in which light is emitted at every possible wavelength. FIGURE 37.2 is a continuous spectrum.

FIGURE 37.2 The continuous spectrum of an incandescent lightbulb.

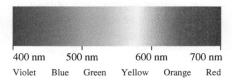

400 nm	500 nm		600 nm	700 nm
Violet	Blue	Green	Yellow	Orange	Red

Black lava glows brightly when hot.

This temperature-dependent emission of electromagnetic waves was called *thermal radiation* when we studied it as the mechanism of heat transfer in Chapter 17. Recall that the heat energy Q radiated in a time interval Δt by an object with surface area A and absolute temperature T is given by

$$\frac{Q}{\Delta t} = e\sigma A T^4 \tag{37.1}$$

where $\sigma = 5.67 \times 10^{-8} \text{ W/m}^2 \text{ K}^4$ is the Stefan-Boltzmann constant. Notice the very strong fourth-power dependence on temperature.

The parameter e in Equation 37.1 is the *emissivity* of the surface, a measure of how effectively it radiates. A perfectly absorbing—and thus perfectly emitting—object with $e = 1$ is called a *blackbody*, and the thermal radiation emitted by a blackbody is called **blackbody radiation.** Charcoal is an excellent approximation of a blackbody.

Our interest in Chapter 17 was the amount of energy radiated. Now we want to examine the spectrum of that radiation. If we measure the spectrum of a blackbody at three temperatures, 3500 K, 4500 K, and 5500 K, the data appear as in FIGURE 37.3. These continuous curves are called *blackbody spectra*. There are four important features of the spectra:

FIGURE 37.3 Blackbody radiation spectra.

A hotter object has a much greater intensity, peaked at shorter wavelengths.

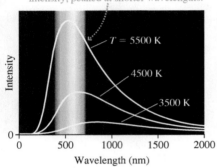

- All blackbodies at the same temperature emit exactly the same spectrum. **The spectrum depends on only an object's temperature, not the material of which it is made.**
- Increasing the temperature increases the radiated intensity at *all* wavelengths. **Making the object hotter causes it to emit more radiation across the entire spectrum.**
- Increasing the temperature causes the peak intensity to shift toward shorter wavelengths. **The higher the temperature, the shorter the wavelength of the peak of the spectrum.**
- The visible rainbow that we see is only a small portion of the continuous blackbody spectrum. Much of the emission is infrared. Extremely hot objects, such as stars, emit a significant fraction of their radiation at ultraviolet wavelengths.

The wavelength corresponding to the peak of the intensity graph is given by

$$\lambda_{\text{peak}}(\text{in nm}) = \frac{2.90 \times 10^6 \text{ nm K}}{T} \tag{37.2}$$

where T must be in kelvin. Equation 37.2 is known as **Wien's law.**

EXAMPLE 37.1 **Finding peak wavelengths**

What are the peak wavelengths and the corresponding spectral regions for thermal radiation from the sun, a glowing ball of gas with a surface temperature of 5800 K, and from the earth, whose average surface temperature is 15°C?

MODEL The sun and the earth are well approximated as blackbodies.

SOLVE The sun's wavelength of peak intensity is given by Wien's law:

$$\lambda_{\text{peak}} = \frac{2.90 \times 10^6 \text{ nm K}}{5800 \text{ K}} = 500 \text{ nm}$$

This is right in the middle of the visible spectrum. The earth's wavelength of peak intensity is

$$\lambda_{\text{peak}} = \frac{2.90 \times 10^6 \text{ nm K}}{288 \text{ K}} = 10,000 \text{ nm}$$

where we converted the surface temperature to kelvin before computing. This is rather far into the infrared portion of the spectrum, which is not surprising because we don't "see" the earth glowing.

ASSESS The difference between these two wavelengths is quite important for understanding the earth's greenhouse effect. Most of the energy from the sun—its spectrum is much like the highest curve in Figure 37.3—arrives as visible light. The earth's atmosphere is transparent to visible wavelengths, so this energy reaches the ground and is absorbed. The earth must radiate an equal amount of energy back to space, but it does so with long-wavelength infrared radiation. These wavelengths are strongly absorbed by some gases in the atmosphere, so the atmosphere acts as a blanket to keep the earth's surface warmer than it would be otherwise.

That all blackbodies at the same temperature emit the same spectrum was an unexpected discovery. Why should this be? It seemed that a combination of thermodynamics and Maxwell's new theory of electromagnetic waves ought to provide a convincing explanation, but scientists of the late 19th century failed to come up with a theoretical justification for the curves seen in Figure 37.3.

Discrete Spectra

Michael Faraday, who discovered electromagnetic induction, wanted to know whether an electric current could pass through a gas. To find out, he sealed metal electrodes into a glass tube, lowered the pressure with a primitive vacuum pump, and then attached an electrostatic generator. When he started the generator, the gas inside the tube began to glow with a bright purple color! Faraday's device, called a **gas discharge tube,** is shown in FIGURE 37.4.

The purple color Faraday saw is characteristic of nitrogen, the primary component of air. You are more likely familiar with the reddish-orange color of a neon discharge tube, but neon was not discovered until long after Faraday's time. If light from a neon discharge tube is passed through a spectrometer, it produces the spectrum seen in FIGURE 37.5. This is called a **discrete spectrum** because it contains only discrete, individual wavelengths. Further, each kind of gas emits a unique spectrum—a *spectral fingerprint*—that distinguishes it from every other gas.

The discrete emission spectrum of a hot, low-density gas stands in sharp contrast to the continuous blackbody spectrum of a glowing solid. Not only do gases emit discrete wavelengths, but it was soon discovered that they also absorb discrete wavelengths. FIGURE 37.6a shows an absorption experiment in which white light passes through a sample of gas. Without the gas, the white light would expose the film with a continuous rainbow spectrum. Any wavelengths absorbed by the gas are missing, and the film is dark at that wavelength. FIGURE 37.6b shows, for sodium vapor, that only certain discrete wavelengths are absorbed.

FIGURE 37.4 Faraday's gas discharge tube.

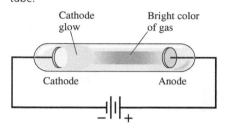

FIGURE 37.5 The discrete spectrum of a neon discharge tube.

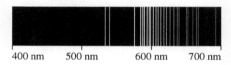

FIGURE 37.6 Measuring an absorption spectrum.

(a) Measuring an absorption spectrum

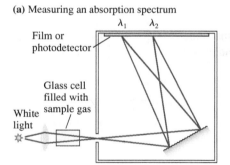

(b) Absorption and emission spectra of sodium

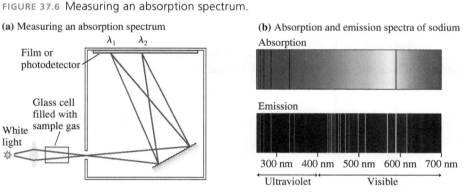

Although the emission and absorption spectra of a gas are both discrete, there is an important difference: **Every wavelength absorbed by the gas is also emitted, but *not* every emitted wavelength is absorbed.** Figure 37.6b shows that the wavelengths in the absorption spectrum are a subset of those in the emission spectrum. All the absorption wavelengths are prominent in the emission spectrum, but there are many emission wavelengths for which no absorption occurs.

What causes atoms to emit or absorb light? Why a discrete spectrum? Why are some wavelengths emitted but not absorbed? Why is each element different? Nineteenth-century physicists struggled with these questions but could not answer them. Ultimately, their inability to understand the emission and absorption of light forced scientists to the unwelcome realization that classical physics was simply incapable of providing an understanding of atoms.

FIGURE 37.7 The hydrogen emission spectrum.

The spectral lines extend to the series limit at 364.7 nm.

Hydrogen emission spectrum

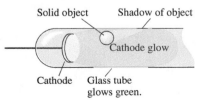

656.5 nm
486.3 nm
434.2 nm
410.3 nm

The only encouraging sign came from an unlikely source. While the spectra of other atoms have dozens or even hundreds of wavelengths, the emission spectrum of hydrogen, seen in FIGURE 37.7, is very simple and regular. If any spectrum could be understood, it should be that of the first element in the periodic table. The break-through came in 1885, not by an established and recognized scientist but by a Swiss schoolteacher, Johann Balmer. Balmer showed that the wavelengths in the hydrogen spectrum could be represented by the simple formula

$$\lambda = \frac{91.18 \text{ nm}}{\left(\frac{1}{2^2} - \frac{1}{n^2}\right)} \qquad n = 3, 4, 5, \ldots \qquad (37.3)$$

This formula predicts a series of spectral lines of gradually decreasing wavelength, converging to the series limit wavelength of 364.7 nm as $n \to \infty$. This series of spectral lines is now called the **Balmer series.**

Later experimental evidence, as ultraviolet and infrared spectroscopy developed, showed that Balmer's result could be generalized to

$$\lambda = \frac{91.18 \text{ nm}}{\left(\frac{1}{m^2} - \frac{1}{n^2}\right)} \qquad m = 1, 2, 3, \ldots \qquad n = m + 1, m + 2, \ldots \qquad (37.4)$$

We now refer to Equation 37.4 as the **Balmer formula,** although Balmer himself suggested only the original version of Equation 37.3 in which $m = 2$. Other than at the highest levels of resolution, where new details appear that need not concern us in this text, the Balmer formula accurately describes *every* wavelength in the emission spectrum of hydrogen.

The Balmer formula is what we call *empirical knowledge.* It is an accurate mathematical representation found empirically—that is, through experimental evidence—but it does not rest on any physical principles or physical laws. Yet the formula was so simple that it must, everyone agreed, have a simple explanation. It would take 30 years to find it.

STOP TO THINK 37.1   These spectra are due to the same element. Which one is an emission spectrum and which is an absorption spectrum?

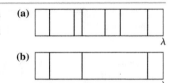

37.3 Cathode Rays and X Rays

Faraday's invention of the gas discharge tube had two major repercussions. One set of investigations, as we've seen, led to the development of spectroscopy. Another set led to the discovery of the electron.

In addition to the bright color of the gas in a discharge tube, Figure 37.4 shows a separate, constant glow around the negative electrode (i.e., the cathode) called the **cathode glow.** As vacuum technology improved, scientists made two discoveries:

1. At lower pressures, the cathode glow became more extended.
2. If the cathode glow extended to the wall of the glass tube, the glass itself emitted a greenish glow—*fluorescence*—at that point.

In fact, a solid object sealed inside a low-pressure tube casts a *shadow* on the glass wall, as shown in FIGURE 37.8. This suggests that the cathode emits *rays* of some form that

FIGURE 37.8 A solid object in the cathode glow casts a shadow.

Solid object   Shadow of object

Cathode glow

Cathode   Glass tube glows green.

travel in straight lines but are easily blocked. These rays, which are invisible but cause the glass to glow where they strike it, were quickly dubbed **cathode rays.** This name lives on today in the *cathode-ray tube* that forms the picture tube in older televisions and computer-display terminals. But naming the rays did nothing to explain them. What were they?

Crookes Tubes

The most systematic studies on the new cathode rays were carried out during the 1870s by the English scientist Sir William Crookes. Crookes devised a set of glass tubes, such as the one shown in FIGURE 37.9, that could be used to make careful studies of cathode rays. These tubes, today called **Crookes tubes,** generate a small glowing spot where the cathode rays strike the face of the tube.

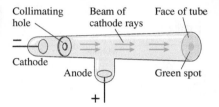

FIGURE 37.9 A Crookes tube.

The work of Crookes and others demonstrated that

1. There is an electric current in a tube in which cathode rays are emitted.
2. The rays are deflected by a magnetic field *as if* they are negative charges.
3. Cathodes made of any metal produce cathode rays. Furthermore, the ray properties are independent of the cathode material.

Crookes's experiments led to more questions than they answered. Were the cathode rays some sort of particles? Or a wave? Were the rays themselves the carriers of the electric current, or were they something else that happened to be emitted whenever there was a current? Item 3 is worthy of note because it suggests that the cathode rays are a *fundamental* entity, not a part of the element from which they are emitted.

It is important to realize how difficult these questions were at the time and how experimental evidence was used to answer them. Crookes suggested that molecules in the gas collided with the cathode, somehow acquired a negative charge (i.e., became negative ions), and then "rebounded" with great speed as they were repelled by the negative cathode. These "charged molecules" would travel in a straight line, be deflected by a magnetic field, and cause the tube to glow where they struck the glass. Crookes's theory predicted, of course, that the negative ions should also be deflected by an electric field, but his experimental efforts were inconclusive. Otherwise, Crookes's model seemed to explain the observations.

However, Crookes's theory was immediately attacked. Critics noted that the cathode rays could travel the length of a 90-cm-long tube with no discernible deviation from a straight line. But the mean free path for molecules, due to collisions with other molecules, is only about 6 mm at the pressure in Crookes's tubes. There was no chance at all that molecules could travel in a straight line for 150 times their mean free path! Crookes's theory, seemingly adequate when it was proposed, was wildly inconsistent with subsequent observations.

But if cathode rays were not particles, what were they? An alternative theory was that the cathode rays were electromagnetic waves. After all, light travels in straight lines, casts shadows, and can, under the right circumstances, cause materials to fluoresce. It was known that hot metals emit light—incandescence—so it seemed plausible that the cathode could be emitting waves. The major obstacle for the wave theory was the deflection of cathode rays by a magnetic field. But the theory of electromagnetic waves was quite new at the time, and many characteristics of these waves were still unknown. Visible light was not deflected by a magnetic field, but it was easy to think that some other form of electromagnetic waves might be so influenced.

The controversy over particles versus waves was intense. British scientists generally favored particles, but their continental counterparts preferred waves. Such controversies are an integral part of science, for they stimulate the best minds to come forward with new ideas and new experiments.

X Rays

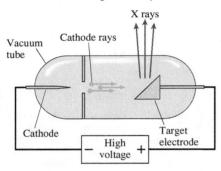

FIGURE 37.10 Röntgen's x-ray tube.

The German physicist Wilhelm Röntgen, also studying cathode rays, made a remarkable discovery in 1895. He had sealed a cathode and a metal target electrode into a vacuum tube, as shown in FIGURE 37.10, and then applied a much higher voltage than normally used to produce cathode rays. He happened, by chance, to leave a sealed envelope containing photographic film near the vacuum tube, and was later surprised to discover that the film had been exposed. This serendipitous discovery was the beginning of the study of x rays.

Röntgen quickly found that the vacuum tube was the source of whatever was exposing the film. Not having any idea what was coming from the tube, he called them **x rays,** using the algebraic symbol x as meaning "unknown." X rays were unlike anything, particle or wave, ever discovered. Röntgen was not successful at reflecting the rays or at focusing the rays with a lens. He showed that they travel in straight lines, like particles, but they also pass right through most solid materials, something no known particle could do.

Scientists soon began to suspect that x rays were an electromagnetic wave with a wavelength much shorter than that of visible light. However, it wasn't until 20 years after their discovery that this was verified by the diffraction of x rays, showing that they have wavelengths in the range 0.01 nm to 10 nm. The production and the properties of x rays seemed far outside the scope of Maxwell's theory of electromagnetic waves.

37.4 The Discovery of the Electron

Shortly after Röntgen's discovery of x rays, the young English physicist J. J. Thomson began using them to study electrical conduction in gases. He found that x rays could discharge an electroscope and concluded that they must be ionizing the air molecules, thereby making the air conductive.

This simple observation was of profound significance. Until then, the only form of ionization known was the creation of positive and negative ions in solutions where, for example, a molecule such as NaCl splits into two smaller charged pieces. Although the underlying process was not yet understood, the fact that two atoms could acquire charge as a molecule splits apart did not jeopardize the idea that the atoms themselves were indivisible. But after observing that even monatomic gases, such as helium, could be ionized by x rays, Thomson realized that **the atom itself must have charged constituents that could be separated!** This was the first direct evidence that the atom is a complex structure, not a fundamental, indivisible unit of matter.

Thomson was also investigating the nature of cathode rays. Other scientists, using a Crookes tube like the one shown in FIGURE 37.11a, had measured an electric current in a cathode-ray beam. Although its presence seemed to demonstrate that the rays are charged particles, proponents of the wave model argued that the current might be a separate, independent event that just happened to be following the same straight line as the cathode rays.

Thomson realized that he could use magnetic deflection of the cathode rays to settle the issue. He built a modified tube, shown in FIGURE 37.11b, in which the collecting electrode was off to the side. With no magnetic field, the cathode rays struck the center of the tube face and created a greenish spot on the glass. No current was measured by the electrode under these circumstances. Thomson then placed the tube in a magnetic field to deflect the cathode rays to the side. He could determine their trajectory by the location of the green spot as it moved across the face of the tube. Just at the point when the field was strong enough to deflect the cathode rays onto the electrode, a current was detected! At an even stronger field, when the cathode rays were deflected completely to the other side of the electrode, the current ceased.

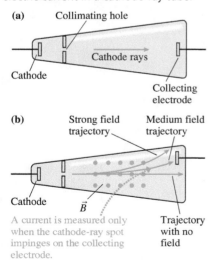

FIGURE 37.11 Experiments to measure the electric current in a cathode-ray tube.

A current is measured only when the cathode-ray spot impinges on the collecting electrode.

This was the first conclusive demonstration that cathode rays really are negatively charged particles. But why were they not deflected by an electric field? Thomson's experience with the x-ray ionization of gases soon led him to recognize that the rapidly moving cathode-ray particles must be colliding with the few remaining gas molecules in the tube with sufficient energy to *ionize* them by splitting them into charged pieces. The electric field created by these charges neutralized the field of the electrodes, hence there was no deflection.

Fortunately, vacuum technology was getting ever better. By using the most sophisticated techniques of his day, Thomson was able to lower the pressure to a point where ionization of the gas was not a problem. Then, just as he had expected, the cathode rays *were* deflected by an electric field!

Thomson's experiment was a decisive victory for the charged-particle model, but it still did not indicate anything about the nature of the particles. What were they?

J. J. Thomson.

Thomson's Crossed-Field Experiment

Thomson could measure the deflection of cathode-ray particles for various strengths of the magnetic field, but magnetic deflection depends both on the particle's charge-to-mass ratio q/m *and* on its speed. Measuring the charge-to-mass ratio, and thus learning something about the particles themselves, requires some means of determining their speed. To do so, Thomson devised the experiment for which he is most remembered.

Thomson built a tube containing the parallel-plate electrodes visible in the photo in FIGURE 37.12a. He then placed the tube in a magnetic field. FIGURE 37.12b shows that the electric and magnetic fields were perpendicular to each other, thus creating what came to be known as a **crossed-field experiment.**

The magnetic field, which is perpendicular to the particle's velocity $\vec{v}$, exerts a magnetic force on the charged particle of magnitude

$$F_B = qvB \qquad (37.5)$$

The magnetic field alone would cause a negatively charged particle to move along an *upward* circular arc. The particle doesn't move in a complete circle because the velocity is large and because the magnetic field is limited in extent. As you learned in Chapter 32, the radius of the arc is

$$r = \frac{mv}{qB} \qquad (37.6)$$

The net result is to *deflect* the beam of particles upward. It is a straightforward geometry problem to determine the radius of curvature r from the measured deflection.

Thomson's new idea was to create an electric field between the parallel-plate electrodes that would exert a *downward* force on the negative charges, pushing them back toward the center of the tube. The magnitude of the electric force on each particle is

$$F_E = qE \qquad (37.7)$$

Thomson adjusted the electric field strength until the cathode-ray beam, in the presence of both electric and magnetic fields, had no deflection and was seen exactly in the center of the tube.

Zero deflection occurs when the magnetic and electric forces exactly balance each other, as FIGURE 37.12c shows. The force vectors point in opposite directions, and their magnitudes are equal when

$$F_B = qvB = F_E = qE$$

Notice that the charge q cancels. Once E and B are set, a charged particle can pass undeflected through the crossed fields only if its speed is

$$v = \frac{E}{B} \qquad (37.8)$$

FIGURE 37.12 Thomson's crossed-field experiment to measure the velocity of cathode rays. The photograph shows his original tube and the coils he used to produce the magnetic field.

(a)

(b)

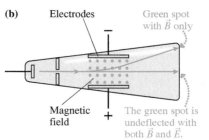

Electrodes

Green spot with $\vec{B}$ only

Magnetic field

The green spot is undeflected with both $\vec{B}$ and $\vec{E}$.

(c)

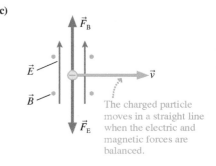

The charged particle moves in a straight line when the electric and magnetic forces are balanced.

By balancing the magnetic force against the electric force, Thomson could determine the speed of the charged-particle beam. Once he knew v, he could use Equation 37.6 to find the charge-to-mass ratio:

$$\frac{q}{m} = \frac{v}{rB} \tag{37.9}$$

Thomson found that the charge-to-mass ratio of cathode rays is $q/m \approx 1 \times 10^{11}$ C/kg. This seems not terribly accurate in comparison to the modern value of 1.76×10^{11} C/kg, but keep in mind both the experimental limitations of his day and the fact that, prior to his work, no one had *any* idea of the charge-to-mass ratio.

EXAMPLE 37.2 **A crossed-field experiment**

An electron is fired between two parallel-plate electrodes that are 5.0 mm apart and 3.0 cm long. A potential difference ΔV between the electrodes establishes an electric field between them. A 3.0-cm-wide, 1.0 mT magnetic field overlaps the electrodes and is perpendicular to the electric field. When $\Delta V = 0$ V, the electron is deflected by 2.0 mm as it passes between the plates. What value of ΔV will allow the electron to pass through the plates without deflection?

MODEL Assume that the fields between the electrodes are uniform and that they are zero outside the electrodes.

VISUALIZE FIGURE 37.13 shows an electron passing through the magnetic field between the plates when $\Delta V = 0$ V. The curvature has been exaggerated to make the geometry clear.

FIGURE 37.13 The electron's trajectory in Example 37.2.

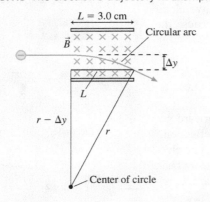

SOLVE We can find the needed electric field, and thus ΔV, if we know the electron's speed. We can find the electron's speed from the radius of curvature of its circular arc in a magnetic field. Figure 37.13 shows a right triangle with hypotenuse r and width L. We can use the Pythagorean theorem to write

$$(r - \Delta y)^2 + L^2 = r^2$$

where Δy is the electron's deflection in the magnetic field. This is easily solved to find the radius of the arc:

$$r = \frac{(\Delta y)^2 + L^2}{2\,\Delta y} = \frac{(0.0020 \text{ m})^2 + (0.030 \text{ m})^2}{2(0.0020 \text{ m})} = 0.226 \text{ m}$$

The speed of an electron traveling along an arc with this radius is found from Equation 37.6:

$$v = \frac{erB}{m} = 4.0 \times 10^7 \text{ m/s}$$

Thus the electric field allowing the electron to pass through without deflection is

$$E = vB = 40,000 \text{ V/m}$$

The electric field of a parallel-plate capacitor of spacing d is related to the potential difference by $E = \Delta V/d$, so the necessary potential difference is

$$\Delta V = Ed = (40,000 \text{ V/m})(0.0050 \text{ m}) = 200 \text{ V}$$

ASSESS A fairly small potential difference is sufficient to counteract the magnetic deflection.

The Electron

Thomson next measured q/m for different cathode materials. Finding them all to be the same, he concluded that all metals emit the *same* cathode rays. Thomson then compared his result to the charge-to-mass ratio of the hydrogen ion, known from electrolysis to have a value of $\approx 1 \times 10^8$ C/kg. This value was roughly 1000 times smaller than for the cathode-ray particles, which could imply that a cathode-ray particle has a much larger charge than a hydrogen ion, or a much smaller mass, or some combination of these.

Electrolysis experiments suggested the existence of a basic unit of charge, so it was tempting to assume that the cathode-ray charge was the same as the charge of a hydrogen ion. However, cathode rays were so different from the hydrogen ion that such an assumption could not be justified without some other evidence. To provide that evidence, Thomson called attention to previous experiments showing that cathode rays can penetrate thin metal foils but atoms cannot. This can be true, Thomson argued, only if cathode-ray particles are vastly smaller and thus much less massive than atoms.

In a paper published in 1897, Thomson assembled all of the evidence to announce the discovery that cathode rays are negatively charged particles, that they are much less massive ($\approx 0.1\%$) than atoms, and that they are identical when generated by different elements. In other words, Thomson had discovered a **subatomic particle,** one of the constituents of which atoms themselves are constructed. In recognition of the role this particle plays in electricity, it was later named the **electron.** By 1900 it was clear to all that electrons were a fundamental building block of atoms. Thomson was awarded the Nobel Prize in 1906.

STOP TO THINK 37.2 Thomson's conclusion that cathode-ray particles are *fundamental* constituents of atoms was based primarily on which observation?

a. They have a negative charge.
b. They are the same from all cathode materials.
c. Their mass is much less than that of hydrogen.
d. They penetrate very thin metal foils.

37.5 The Fundamental Unit of Charge

Thomson measured the electron's charge-to-mass ratio and *surmised* that the mass must be much smaller than that of an atom, but clearly it was desirable to measure the charge q directly. This was done in 1906 by the American scientist Robert Millikan.

The **Millikan oil-drop experiment,** as we call it today, is illustrated in FIGURE 37.14. A squeeze-bulb atomizer sprayed out a very fine mist of oil droplets. Millikan found that some of these droplets were charged from friction in the sprayer. The charged droplets slowly settled toward a horizontal pair of parallel-plate electrodes, where a few droplets passed through a small hole in the top plate. Millikan observed the drops by shining a bright light between the plates and using an eyepiece to see the droplets' reflections. He then established an electric field by applying a voltage to the plates.

A drop will remain suspended between the plates, moving neither up nor down, if the electric field exerts an upward force on a charged drop that exactly balances the downward gravitational force. The forces balance when

$$m_{\text{drop}}g = q_{\text{drop}}E \tag{37.10}$$

and thus the charge on the drop is measured to be

$$q_{\text{drop}} = \frac{m_{\text{drop}}g}{E} \tag{37.11}$$

Notice that m and q are the mass and charge of the oil droplet, not of an electron. But because the droplet is charged by acquiring (or losing) electrons, the charge of the droplet should be related to the electron's charge.

The field strength E could be determined accurately from the voltage applied to the plates, so the limiting factor in measuring q_{drop} was Millikan's ability to determine the mass of these small drops. Ideally, the mass could be found by measuring a drop's diameter and using the known density of the oil. However, the drops were too small ($\approx 1 \ \mu$m) to measure accurately by viewing through the eyepiece.

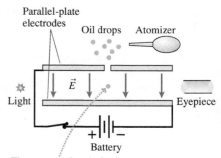

FIGURE 37.14 Millikan's oil-drop apparatus to measure the fundamental unit of charge.

The upward electric force on a negatively charged droplet balances the downward gravitational force.

Instead, Millikan devised an ingenious method to find the size of the droplets. Objects this small are *not* in free fall. The air resistance forces are so large that the drops fall with a very small but constant speed. The motion of a sphere through a viscous medium is a problem that had been solved in the 19th century, and it was known that the sphere's terminal speed depends on its radius and on the viscosity of air. By timing the droplets' fall with a stopwatch, then using the known viscosity of air, Millikan could calculate their radii, compute their masses, and, finally, arrive at a value for their charge. Although it was a somewhat roundabout procedure, Millikan was able to measure the charge on a droplet with an accuracy of ±0.1%.

Millikan measured many hundreds of droplets, some for hours at a time, under a wide variety of conditions. He found that some of his droplets were positively charged and some negatively charged, but **all had charges that were integer multiples of a certain minimum charge value.** Millikan concluded that "the electric charges found on ions all have either exactly the same value or else some small exact multiple of that value." That value, the *fundamental unit of charge* that we now call *e*, is measured to be

$$e = 1.60 \times 10^{-19} \text{ C}$$

We can then combine the measured *e* with the measured charge-to-mass ratio *e/m* to find that the mass of the electron is

$$m_{\text{elec}} = 9.11 \times 10^{-31} \text{ kg}$$

Taken together, the experiments of Thomson, Millikan, and others provided overwhelming evidence that electric charge comes in discrete units and that *all* charges found in nature are multiples of a fundamental unit of charge we call *e*.

EXAMPLE 37.3 **Suspending an oil drop**

Oil has a density of 860 kg/m³. A 1.0-μm-diameter oil droplet acquires 10 extra electrons as it is sprayed. What potential difference between two parallel plates 1.0 cm apart will cause the droplet to be suspended in air?

MODEL Assume a uniform electric field $E = \Delta V/d$ between the plates.

SOLVE The magnitude of the charge on the drop is $q_{\text{drop}} = 10e$. The mass of the charge is related to its density ρ and volume V by

$$m_{\text{drop}} = \rho V = \frac{4}{3}\pi R^3 \rho = 4.50 \times 10^{-16} \text{ kg}$$

where the droplet's radius is $R = 5.0 \times 10^{-7}$ m. The electric field that will suspend this droplet against the force of gravity is

$$E = \frac{m_{\text{drop}} g}{q_{\text{drop}}} = 2760 \text{ V/m}$$

Establishing this electric field between two plates spaced by $d = 0.010$ m requires a potential difference

$$\Delta V = Ed = 27.6 \text{ V}$$

ASSESS Experimentally, this is a very convenient voltage.

37.6 The Discovery of the Nucleus

By 1900, it was clear that atoms are not indivisible but, instead, are constructed of charged particles. Atomic sizes were known to be $\approx 10^{-10}$ m, but the electrons common to all atoms are much smaller and much less massive than the smallest atom. How do they "fit" into the larger atom? What is the positive charge of the atom? Where are the charges located inside the atoms?

Thomson proposed the first model of an atom. Because the electrons are very small and light compared to the whole atom, it seemed reasonable to think that the positively charged part would take up most of the space. Thomson suggested that the atom consists of a spherical "cloud" of positive charge, roughly 10^{-10} m in diameter, in which the smaller negative electrons are embedded. The positive charge exactly balances the negative, so the atom as a whole has no net charge. This model of the atom has often been called the "plum-pudding model" or the "raisin-cake model" for reasons that should be clear from FIGURE 37.15.

Thomson was never able to make any predictions that would enable his model to be tested, and the Thomson atom did not stand the test of time. His model is of interest today primarily to remind us that our current models of the atom are by no means obvious. Science has many sidesteps and dead ends as it progresses.

One of Thomson's students was a New Zealander named Ernest Rutherford. While Rutherford and Thomson were studying the ionizing effects of x rays, in 1896, the French physicist Antoine Henri Becquerel announced the discovery that some new form of "rays" were emitted by crystals of uranium. These rays, like x rays, could expose film, pass through objects, and ionize the air. Yet they were emitted continuously from the uranium without having to "do" anything to it. This was the discovery of **radioactivity,** a topic we'll study in Chapter 42.

With x rays only a year old and cathode rays not yet completely understood, it was not known whether all these various kinds of rays were truly different or merely variations of a single type. Rutherford immediately began a study of these new rays. He quickly discovered that at least two *different* rays are emitted by a uranium crystal. The first, which he called **alpha rays,** were easily absorbed by a piece of paper. The second, **beta rays,** could penetrate through at least 0.1 inch of metal.

Thomson soon found that beta rays have the same charge-to-mass ratio as cathode rays. The beta rays turned out to be high-speed electrons emitted by the uranium crystal. Rutherford, using similar techniques, showed that alpha rays are *positively* charged particles. By 1906 he had measured their charge-to-mass ratio to be

$$\frac{q}{m} = \frac{1}{2}\frac{e}{m_H}$$

where m_H is the mass of a hydrogen atom. This value could indicate either a singly ionized hydrogen molecule H_2^+ ($q = e$, $m = 2m_H$) *or* a doubly ionized helium atom He^{++} ($q = 2e$, $m = 4m_H$).

In an ingenious experiment, Rutherford sealed a sample of radium—an emitter of alpha radiation—into a glass tube. Alpha rays could not penetrate the glass, so the particles were contained within the tube. Several days later, Rutherford used electrodes in the tube to create a discharge and observed the spectrum of the emitted light. He found the characteristic wavelengths of helium, but not those of hydrogen. Alpha rays (or alpha particles, as we now call them) consist of doubly ionized helium atoms (bare helium nuclei) emitted at high speed ($\approx 3 \times 10^7$ m/s) from the sample.

The First Nuclear Physics Experiment

Rutherford soon realized that he could use these high-speed particles to probe inside other atoms. In 1909, Rutherford and his students set up the experiment shown in FIGURE 37.16 to shoot alpha particles at very thin metal foils. Some of the alpha particles penetrated the foil, but the beam of alpha particles that did so became somewhat spread out. This was not surprising. According to Thomson's raisin-cake model of the atom, the electric forces exerted on the positive alpha particle by the positive atomic charges should roughly cancel the forces from the negative electrons, causing the alpha particles to be deflected only slightly.

At Rutherford's suggestion, his students then set up the apparatus to see if any alpha particles were deflected at *large* angles. It took only a few days to find the answer. Not only were alpha particles deflected at large angles, but a very few were reflected almost straight backward toward the source!

How can we understand this result? FIGURE 37.17a on the next page shows that only a small deflection is expected for an alpha particle passing through a Thomson atom. But if an atom has a small, positive core, such as the one in FIGURE 37.17b, a few of the

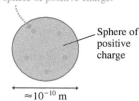

FIGURE 37.15 Thomson's raisin-cake model of the atom.

Thomson proposed that small, negative electrons are embedded in a sphere of positive charge.

Sphere of positive charge

$\approx 10^{-10}$ m

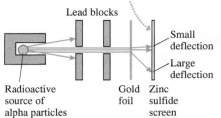

FIGURE 37.16 Rutherford's experiment to shoot high-speed alpha particles through a thin gold foil.

The alpha particles make little flashes of light where they hit the screen.

Lead blocks

Small deflection

Large deflection

Radioactive source of alpha particles

Gold foil

Zinc sulfide screen

(a)

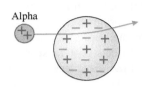

(b)

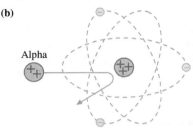

The alpha particle is only slightly deflected by a Thomson atom because forces from the spread-out positive and negative charges nearly cancel.

If the atom has a concentrated positive nucleus, some alpha particles will be able to come very close to the nucleus and thus feel a very strong repulsive force.

alpha particles can come very close to the core. Because the electric force varies with the inverse square of the distance, the very large force of this very close approach can cause a large-angle scattering or a backward deflection of the alpha particle.

Thus the discovery of large-angle scattering of alpha particles led Rutherford to envision an atom in which negative electrons orbit an unbelievably small, massive, positive **nucleus,** rather like a miniature solar system. This is the **nuclear model of the atom.** Notice that nearly all of the atom is empty space—the void!

EXAMPLE 37.4 **A nuclear physics experiment**

An alpha particle is shot with a speed of 2.0×10^7 m/s directly toward the nucleus of a gold atom. What is the distance of closest approach to the nucleus?

MODEL Energy is conserved in electric interactions. Assume that the gold nucleus, which is much more massive than the alpha particle, does not move. Also recall that the exterior electric field and potential of a sphere of charge can be found by treating the total charge as a point charge at the center.

VISUALIZE FIGURE 37.18 is a pictorial representation. The motion is in and out along a straight line.

FIGURE 37.18 A before-and-after pictorial representation of an alpha particle colliding with a nucleus.

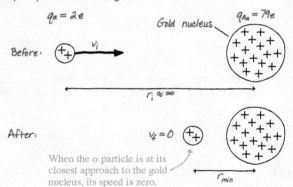

When the α particle is at its closest approach to the gold nucleus, its speed is zero.

SOLVE We are not interested in how long the collision takes or any of the details of the trajectory, so using conservation of energy rather than Newton's laws is appropriate. Initially, when the alpha particle is very far away, the system has only kinetic energy. At the moment of closest approach, just before the alpha particle is reflected, the charges are at rest and the system has only potential energy. The conservation of energy statement $K_f + U_f = K_i + U_i$ is

$$0 + \frac{1}{4\pi\epsilon_0} \frac{q_\alpha q_{Au}}{r_{min}} = \frac{1}{2} m v_i^2 + 0$$

where q_α is the alpha-particle charge and we've treated the gold nucleus as a point charge q_{Au}. The mass m is that of the alpha particle. The solution for r_{min} is

$$r_{min} = \frac{1}{4\pi\epsilon_0} \frac{2 q_\alpha q_{Au}}{m v_i^2}$$

The alpha particle is a helium nucleus, so $m = 4\,u = 6.64 \times 10^{-27}$ kg and $q_\alpha = 2e = 3.20 \times 10^{-19}$ C. Gold has atomic number 79, so $q_{Au} = 79e = 1.26 \times 10^{-17}$ C. We can then calculate

$$r_{min} = 2.7 \times 10^{-14} \text{ m}$$

This is only about 1/10,000 the size of the atom itself!

ASSESS We ignored the atom's electrons in this example. In fact, they make almost no contribution to the alpha particle's trajectory. The alpha particle is exceedingly massive compared to the electrons, and the electrons are spread out over a distance very large compared to the size of the nucleus. Hence the alpha particle easily pushes them aside without any noticeable change in its velocity.

Rutherford went on to make careful experiments of how the alpha particles scattered at different angles. From these experiments he deduced that the diameter of the atomic nucleus is $\approx 1 \times 10^{-14}$ m $= 10$ fm (1 fm $= 1$ femtometer $= 10^{-15}$ m), increasing a little for elements of higher atomic number and atomic mass.

It may seem surprising to you that the Rutherford model of the atom, with its solar-system analogy, was not Thomson's original choice. However, scientists at the time could not imagine matter having the extraordinarily high density implied by a small nucleus. Neither could they understand what holds the nucleus together, why the positive charges do not push each other apart. Thomson's model, in which the positive charge was spread out and balanced by the negative electrons, actually made more sense. It would be several decades before the forces holding the nucleus together began to be understood, but Rutherford's evidence for a very small nucleus was indisputable.

If the alpha particle has a positive charge, which way will it be deflected in the magnetic field?

a. Up   b. Down   c. Into the page   d. Out of the page

The Electron Volt

The joule is a unit of appropriate size in mechanics and thermodynamics, where we dealt with macroscopic objects, but it is poorly matched to the needs of atomic physics. It will be very useful to have an energy unit appropriate to atomic and nuclear events.

FIGURE 37.19 shows an electron accelerating (in a vacuum) from rest across a parallel-plate capacitor with a 1.0 V potential difference. What is the electron's kinetic energy when it reaches the positive plate? We know from energy conservation that $K_f + qV_f = K_i + qV_i$, where $U = qV$ is the electric potential energy. $K_i = 0$ because the electron starts from rest, and the electron's charge is $q = -e$. Thus

$$K_f = -q(V_f - V_i) = -q \, \Delta V = e \, \Delta V = (1.60 \times 10^{-19} \text{ C})(1.0 \text{ V})$$

$$= 1.60 \times 10^{-19} \text{ J}$$

Let us define a new unit of energy, called the **electron volt,** as

$$1 \text{ electron volt} = 1 \text{ eV} \equiv 1.60 \times 10^{-19} \text{ J}$$

With this definition, the kinetic energy gained by the electron in our example is

$$K_f = 1 \text{ eV}$$

In other words, **1 electron volt is the kinetic energy gained by an electron (or proton) if it accelerates through a potential difference of 1 volt.**

NOTE ▶ The abbreviation eV uses a lowercase e but an uppercase V. Units of keV (10^3 eV), MeV (10^6 eV), and GeV (10^9 eV) are common. ◀

The electron volt can be a troublesome unit. One difficulty is its unusual name, which looks less like a unit than, say, "meter" or "second." A more significant difficulty is that the name suggests a relationship to volts. But *volts* are units of electric potential, whereas this new unit is a unit of energy! It is crucial to distinguish between the *potential V*, measured in volts, and an *energy* that can be measured either in joules or in electron volts. You can now use electron volts anywhere that you would previously have used joules.

NOTE ▶ To reiterate, the electron volt is a unit of *energy*, convertible to joules, and not a unit of potential. Potential is always measured in volts. However, the joule remains the SI unit of energy. It will be useful to express energies in eV, but you *must* convert this energy to joules before doing most calculations. ◀

FIGURE 37.19 An electron accelerating across a 1 V potential difference gains 1 eV of kinetic energy.

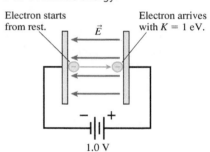

Electron starts from rest.

Electron arrives with $K = 1$ eV.

1.0 V

EXAMPLE 37.5 **The speed of an alpha particle**

Alpha particles are usually characterized by their kinetic energy in MeV. What is the speed of an 8.3 MeV alpha particle?

SOLVE Alpha particles are helium nuclei, having $m = 4\,u = 6.64 \times 10^{-27}$ kg. The kinetic energy of this alpha particle is 8.3×10^6 eV. First, we convert the energy to joules:

$$K = 8.3 \times 10^6 \text{ eV} \times \frac{1.60 \times 10^{-19} \text{ J}}{1.00 \text{ eV}} = 1.33 \times 10^{-12} \text{ J}$$

Now we can find the speed:

$$K = \frac{1}{2}mv^2 = 1.33 \times 10^{-12} \text{ J}$$

$$v = \sqrt{\frac{2K}{m}} = 2.0 \times 10^7 \text{ m/s}$$

This was the speed of the alpha particle in Example 37.4.

EXAMPLE 37.6 **Energy of an electron**

In a simple model of the hydrogen atom, the electron orbits the proton at 2.19×10^6 m/s in a circle with radius 5.29×10^{-11} m. What is the atom's energy in eV?

MODEL The electron has a kinetic energy of motion, and the electron + proton system has an electric potential energy.

SOLVE The potential energy is that of two point charges, with $q_{proton} = +e$ and $q_{elec} = -e$. Thus

$$E = K + U = \frac{1}{2}m_{elec}v^2 + \frac{1}{4\pi\epsilon_0}\frac{(e)(-e)}{r} = -2.17 \times 10^{-18} \text{ J}$$

Conversion to eV gives

$$E = -2.17 \times 10^{-18} \text{ J} \times \frac{1 \text{ eV}}{1.60 \times 10^{-19} \text{ J}} = -13.6 \text{ eV}$$

ASSESS The negative energy reflects the fact that the electron is *bound* to the proton. You would need to *add* energy to remove the electron.

Using the Nuclear Model

The nuclear model of the atom makes it easy to understand and picture such processes as ionization. Because electrons orbit a positive nucleus, an x-ray photon or a rapidly moving particle, such as another electron, can knock one of the orbiting electrons away, creating a positive ion. Removing one electron makes a singly charged ion, with $q = +e$. Removing two electrons creates a doubly charged ion, with $q = +2e$. This is shown for lithium (atomic number 3) in FIGURE 37.20.

FIGURE 37.20 Different ionization stages of the lithium atom ($Z = 3$).

Nucleus has charge $+3e$.

Neutral Li   Singly charged Li$^+$ Doubly charged Li^{++}

The nuclear model also allows us to understand why, during chemical reactions and when an object is charged by rubbing, electrons are easily transferred but protons are not. The protons are tightly bound in the nucleus, shielded by all the electrons, but outer electrons are easily stripped away. Rutherford's nuclear model has explanatory power that was lacking in Thomson's model.

EXAMPLE 37.7 **The ionization energy of hydrogen**

What is the minimum energy required to ionize a hydrogen atom?

SOLVE In Example 37.6 we found that the atom's energy is $E_i = -13.6$ eV. Ionizing the atom means removing the electron and taking it very far away. As $r \to \infty$, the potential energy becomes zero. Further, using the least possible energy to ionize the atom will leave the electron, when it is very far away, very nearly at rest. Thus the atom's energy after ionization is

$E_f = K_f + U_f = 0 + 0 = 0$ eV. This is *larger* than E_i by 13.6 eV, so the minimum energy that is required to ionize a hydrogen atom is 13.6 eV. This is called the atom's *ionization energy*. If the electron receives ≥ 13.6 eV (2.17×10^{-18} J) of energy from a photon, or in a collision with another electron, or by any other means, it will be knocked out of the atom and leave a H$^+$ ion behind.

STOP TO THINK 37.4 Carbon is the sixth element in the periodic table. How many electrons are in a C^{++} ion?

37.7 Into the Nucleus

Chapter 42 will discuss nuclear physics in more detail, but it will be helpful to give a brief overview of the nucleus. The relative masses of many of the elements were known from chemistry experiments by the mid-19th century. By arranging the elements in order of ascending mass, and noting recurring regularities in their chemical properties, the Russian chemist Dmitri Mendeleev first proposed the periodic table of the elements in 1872. But what did it mean to say that hydrogen was atomic number 1, helium number 2, lithium number 3, and so on?

It soon became known that hydrogen atoms can be only singly ionized, producing H^+. A doubly ionized H^{++} is never observed. Helium, by contrast, can be both singly and doubly ionized, creating He^+ and He^{++}, but He^{+++} is not observed. Once Thomson discovered the electron and Millikan established the fundamental unit of charge, it seemed fairly clear that a hydrogen atom contains only one electron and one unit of positive charge, helium has two electrons and two units of positive charge, and so on. Thus the **atomic number** of an element, which is always an integer, describes the number of electrons (of a neutral atom) and the number of units of positive charge in the nucleus. The atomic number is represented by Z, so hydrogen is $Z = 1$, helium $Z = 2$, and lithium $Z = 3$. Elements are listed in the periodic table by their atomic number.

Rutherford's discovery of the nucleus soon led to the recognition that the positive charge is associated with a positive subatomic particle called the **proton.** The proton's charge is $+e$, equal in magnitude but opposite in sign to the electron's charge. Further, because nearly all the atomic mass is associated with the nucleus, the proton is much more massive than the electron. According to Rutherford's nuclear model, atoms with atomic number Z consist of Z negative electrons, with net charge $-Ze$, orbiting a massive nucleus that contains protons and has net charge $+Ze$. The Rutherford atom went a long way toward explaining the periodic table.

But there was a problem. Helium, with atomic number 2, has twice as many electrons as hydrogen. Lithium, $Z = 3$, has three electrons. But it was known from chemistry measurements that helium is *four times* as massive as hydrogen and lithium is *seven times* as massive. If a nucleus contains Z protons to balance the Z orbiting electrons, and if nearly all the atomic mass is contained in the nucleus, then helium should be simply twice as massive as hydrogen and lithium three times as massive.

The Neutron

About 1910, Thomson and his student Francis Aston developed a device called a **mass spectrometer** for measuring the charge-to-mass ratios of atomic ions. As Aston and others began collecting data, they soon found that many elements consist of atoms of *differing* mass! Neon, for example, had been assigned an atomic mass of 20. But Aston found, as the data of FIGURE 37.21 show, that while 91% of neon atoms have mass $m = 20$ u, 9% have $m = 22$ u and a very small percentage have $m = 21$ u. Chlorine was found to be a mixture of 75% chlorine atoms with $m = 35$ u and 25% chlorine atoms with $m = 37$ u, both having atomic number $Z = 17$.

These difficulties were not resolved until the discovery, in 1932, of a third subatomic particle. This particle has essentially the same mass as a proton but *no* electric charge. It is called the **neutron.** Neutrons reside in the nucleus, with the protons, where they contribute to the mass of the atom but not to its charge. As you'll see in Chapter 42, neutrons help provide the "glue" that holds the nucleus together.

FIGURE 37.21 The mass spectrum of neon.

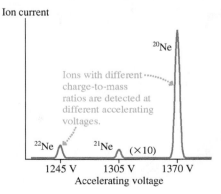

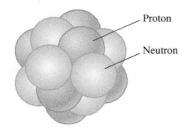

FIGURE 37.22 The nucleus of an atom contains protons and neutrons.

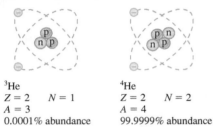

FIGURE 37.23 The two isotopes of helium. ^{3}He is only 0.0001% abundant.

^{3}He
$Z = 2$ $N = 1$
$A = 3$
0.0001% abundance

^{4}He
$Z = 2$ $N = 2$
$A = 4$
99.9999% abundance

The neutron was the missing link needed to explain why atoms of the same element can have different masses. We now know that every atom with atomic number Z has a nucleus containing Z protons with charge $+Ze$. In addition, as shown in FIGURE 37.22, the nucleus contains N neutrons. There are a *range* of neutron numbers that happily form a nucleus with Z protons, creating a series of nuclei having the same Z-value (i.e., they are all the same chemical element) but different masses. Such a series of nuclei are called **isotopes.**

Chemical behavior is determined by the orbiting electrons. All isotopes of one element have the same number Z of orbiting electrons and have the same chemical properties. But different isotopes of the same element can have quite different nuclear properties.

An atom's **mass number** A is defined to be $A = Z + N$. It is the total number of protons and neutrons in a nucleus. The mass number, which is dimensionless, is *not* the same thing as the atomic mass m. By definition, A is an integer. But because the proton and neutron masses are both ≈ 1 u, the mass number A is *approximately* the mass in atomic mass units.

The notation used to label isotopes is ^{A}Z, where the mass number A is given as a *leading* superscript. The proton number Z is not specified by an actual number but, equivalently, by the chemical symbol for that element. The most common isotope of neon has $Z = 10$ protons and $N = 10$ neutrons. Thus it has mass number $A = 20$ and it is labeled ^{20}Ne. The neon isotope ^{22}Ne has $Z = 10$ protons (that's what makes it neon) and $N = 12$ neutrons. Helium has the two isotopes shown in FIGURE 37.23. The rare ^{3}He is only 0.0001% abundant, but it can be isolated and has important uses in scientific research.

STOP TO THINK 37.5 Carbon is the sixth element in the periodic table. How many protons and how many neutrons are there in a nucleus of the isotope ^{14}C?

37.8 Classical Physics at the Limit

At the start of the 19th century, only a few scientists thought that matter consists of atoms. By century's end, there was substantial evidence not only for atoms but also for the existence of charged subatomic particles. The explorations into atomic structure culminated with Rutherford's nuclear model.

Rutherford's nuclear model of the atom matched the experimental evidence about the *structure* of atoms, but it had one serious shortcoming. According to Maxwell's theory of electricity and magnetism, the orbiting electrons in a Rutherford atom should act as small antennas and radiate electromagnetic waves. That sounds encouraging, because we know that atoms can emit light, but the radiation of electromagnetic waves means the atoms would continuously lose energy. As FIGURE 37.24 shows, this would cause the electrons to spiral into the nucleus! Calculations showed that a Rutherford atom can last no more than about a microsecond. In other words, classical Newtonian mechanics and electromagnetism predict that an atom in which electrons orbit a nucleus would be highly unstable and would immediately self-destruct. This clearly does not happen.

The experimental efforts of the late 19th and early 20th centuries had been impressive, and there could be no doubt about the existence of electrons, about the small positive nucleus, and about the unique discrete spectrum emitted by each atom. But the theoretical framework for understanding such observations had lagged behind. As the new century dawned, physicists could not explain the structure of atoms, could not explain the stability of matter, could not explain discrete spectra or blackbody radiation, and could not explain the origin of x rays or radioactivity.

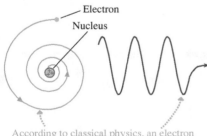

FIGURE 37.24 The fate of a Rutherford atom.

According to classical physics, an electron would spiral into the nucleus while radiating energy as an electromagnetic wave.

Yet few physicists were willing to abandon the successful and long-cherished theories of classical physics. Most considered these "problems" with atoms to be minor discrepancies that would soon be resolved. But classical physics had, indeed, reached its limit, and a whole new generation of brilliant young physicists, with new ideas, was about to take the stage. Among the first was an unassuming young man in Bern, Switzerland. His scholastic record had been mediocre, and the best job he could find upon graduation was as a clerk in the patent office, examining patent applications. His name was Albert Einstein.

CHALLENGE EXAMPLE 37.8   **Radioactive decay**

The cesium isotope ^{137}Cs, with $Z = 55$, is radioactive and decays by beta decay. A beta particle is observed in the laboratory with a kinetic energy of 300 keV. With what kinetic energy was the beta particle ejected from the 12.4-fm-diameter nucleus?

MODEL A beta particle is an electron that was ejected from the nucleus of an atom during a radioactive decay. Energy is conserved in the decay.

VISUALIZE FIGURE 37.25 shows a before-and-after pictorial representation. The electron starts by being ejected from the nucleus with kinetic energy K_i. It has electric potential energy U_i due to its interaction with the nucleus. The potential energy due to the atom's orbiting electrons is negligible because they are so far away

FIGURE 37.25 A before-and-after pictorial representation of the beta decay.

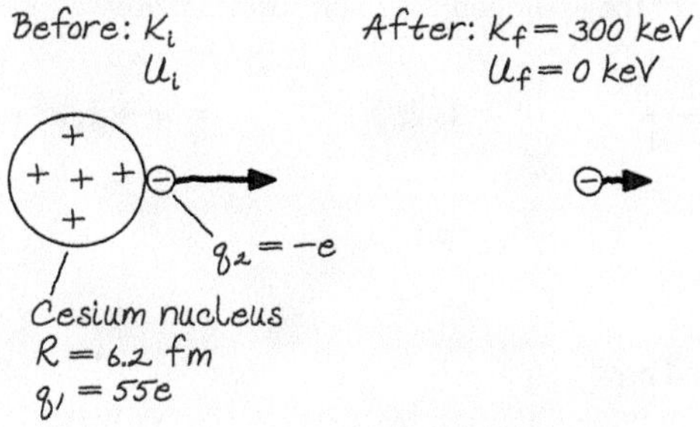

in comparison to a nuclear radius. The detected electron is very far from the nucleus, so $U_f = 0$.

SOLVE The conservation of energy statement is $K_f + U_f = K_i + U_i$. The electron starts outside the nucleus, even though at the surface, so the spherical nucleus can be treated as a point charge with $q_1 = 55e$. The electron has $q_2 = -e$, so the initial electron-nucleus potential energy is

$$U_i = \frac{Kq_1q_2}{r_i}$$

$$= \frac{(9.0 \times 10^9\,\text{N}\,\text{m}^2/\text{C}^2)(55 \times 1.60 \times 10^{-19}\,\text{C})(-1.60 \times 10^{-19}\,\text{C})}{6.20 \times 10^{-15}\,\text{m}}$$

$$= -2.04 \times 10^{-12}\,\text{J} \times \frac{1\,\text{eV}}{1.60 \times 10^{-19}\,\text{J}} = -12.8\,\text{MeV}$$

To be detected in the laboratory with $K_f = 300\,\text{keV} = 0.3\,\text{MeV}$, the electron had to be ejected from the nucleus with

$$K_i = K_f + U_f - U_i = 0.3\,\text{MeV} + 0\,\text{MeV} + 12.8\,\text{MeV}$$

$$= 13.1\,\text{MeV}$$

ASSESS A negative electron is very strongly attracted to the nucleus. It's not surprising that it has to be ejected from the nucleus with an enormous amount of kinetic energy to be able to escape at all.

SUMMARY

The goal of Chapter 37 has been to learn about the structure and properties of atoms.

Important Concepts/Experiments

Nineteenth-century scientists focused on understanding matter and light. Faraday's invention of the gas discharge tube launched two important avenues of inquiry:

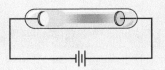

- Atomic structure.
- Atomic spectra.

Cathode Rays and Atomic Structure

Thomson found that cathode rays are negative, subatomic particles. These were soon named electrons. Electrons are

- Constituents of atoms.
- The fundamental units of negative charge.

Rutherford discovered the atomic nucleus. His nuclear model of the atom proposes

- A very small, dense positive nucleus.
- Orbiting negative electrons.

Later, different isotopes were recognized to contain different numbers of **neutrons** in a nucleus with the same number of **protons.**

Atomic Spectra and the Nature of Light

The spectra emitted by the gas in a discharge tube consist of discrete wavelengths.

- Every element has a unique spectrum.
- Every spectral line in an element's absorption spectrum is present in its emission spectrum, but not all emission lines are seen in the absorption spectrum.

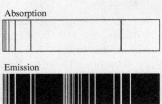

The wavelengths of the hydrogen emission spectrum are

$$\lambda = \frac{91.18 \text{ nm}}{\left(\dfrac{1}{m^2} - \dfrac{1}{n^2}\right)} \qquad m = 1, 2, 3, \ldots \qquad n = m + 1, m + 2, \ldots$$

The end of classical physics. . .
Atomic spectra had to be related to atomic structure, but no one could understand how. Classical physics could not explain

- The stability of matter.
- Discrete atomic spectra.
- Continuous blackbody spectra.

Applications

Millikan's oil-drop experiment measured the fundamental unit of charge:

$$e = 1.60 \times 10^{-19} \text{ C}$$

One electron volt (1 eV) is the energy an electron or proton (charge $\pm e$) gains by accelerating through a potential difference of 1 V:

$$1 \text{ eV} = 1.60 \times 10^{-19} \text{ J}$$

Terms and Notation

spectrometer	Balmer formula	Millikan oil-drop experiment	proton
spectrum	cathode glow	radioactivity	mass spectrometer
continuous spectrum	cathode rays	alpha rays	neutron
blackbody radiation	Crookes tube	beta rays	isotope
Wien's law	x rays	nucleus	mass number, A
gas discharge tube	crossed-field experiment	nuclear model of the atom	
discrete spectrum	subatomic particle	electron volt, eV	
Balmer series	electron	atomic number, Z	

CONCEPTUAL QUESTIONS

1. a. Summarize the experimental evidence *prior* to the research of Thomson by which you might conclude that cathode rays are some kind of particle.
   b. Summarize the experimental evidence *prior* to the research of Thomson by which you might conclude that cathode rays are some kind of wave.

2. Thomson observed deflection of the cathode-ray particles due to magnetic and electric fields, but there was no observed deflection due to gravity. Why not?

3. What was the significance of Thomson's experiment in which an off-center electrode was used to collect charge deflected by a magnetic field?

4. What is the evidence by which we know that an electron from an iron atom is identical to an electron from a copper atom?

5. a. Describe the experimental evidence by which we know that the nucleus is made up not just of protons.
   b. The neutron is not easy to isolate or control because it has no charge that would allow scientists to manipulate it. What evidence allowed scientists to determine that the mass of the neutron is almost the same as the mass of a proton?

6. Rutherford studied alpha particles using the crossed-field technique Thomson had invented to study cathode rays. Assuming that $v_{alpha} \approx v_{cathode\ ray}$ (which turns out to be true), would the deflection of an alpha particle by a magnetic field be larger, smaller, or the same as the deflection of a cathode-ray particle by the same field? Explain.

7. Once Thomson showed that atoms consist of very light negative electrons and a much more massive positive charge, why didn't physicists immediately consider a solar-system model of electrons orbiting a positive nucleus? Why would physicists in 1900 object to such a model?

8. Explain why the observation of alpha particles scattered at very large angles led Rutherford to reject Thomson's model of the atom and to propose a nuclear model.

9. Identify the element, the isotope, and the charge state of each atom in FIGURE Q37.9. Give your answer in symbolic form, such as $^4He^+$ or $^8Be^-$.

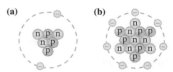

FIGURE Q37.9

EXERCISES AND PROBLEMS

Problems labeled [   ] integrate material from earlier chapters.

Exercises

Section 37.2 The Emission and Absorption of Light

1. | Figure 37.7 identified the wavelengths of four lines in the Balmer series of hydrogen.
   a. Determine the Balmer formula n and m values for these wavelengths.
   b. Predict the wavelength of the fifth line in the spectrum.

2. | What are the wavelengths of spectral lines in the Balmer series with $n = 6, 8$, and 10?

3. ‖ The wavelengths in the hydrogen spectrum with $m = 1$ form a series of spectral lines called the Lyman series. Calculate the wavelengths of the first four members of the Lyman series.

4. | Two of the wavelengths emitted by a hydrogen atom are 102.6 nm and 1876 nm.
   a. What are the m and n values for each of these wavelengths?
   b. For each of these wavelengths, is the light infrared, visible, or ultraviolet?

5. | What temperature, in °C, is a blackbody whose emission spectrum peaks at (a) 300 nm and (b) 3.00 μm?

6. ‖ A 2.0-cm-diameter metal sphere is glowing red, but a spectrum shows that its emission spectrum peaks at an infrared wavelength of 2.0 μm. How much power does the sphere radiate?

7. ‖ A ceramic cube 3.0 cm on each side radiates heat at 630 W. At what wavelength, in μm, does its emission spectrum peak?

Section 37.3 Cathode Rays and X Rays

Section 37.4 The Discovery of the Electron

8. | The current in a Crookes tube is 10 nA. How many electrons strike the face of the glass tube each second?

9. | An electron in a cathode-ray beam passes between 2.5-cm-long parallel-plate electrodes that are 5.0 mm apart. A 2.0 mT, 2.5-cm-wide magnetic field is perpendicular to the electric field between the plates. The electron passes through the electrodes without being deflected if the potential difference between the plates is 600 V.
   a. What is the electron's speed?
   b. If the potential difference between the plates is set to zero, what is the electron's radius of curvature in the magnetic field?

10. | Electrons pass through the parallel electrodes shown in FIGURE EX37.10 with a speed of 5.0×10^6 m/s. What magnetic field strength and direction will allow the electrons to pass through without being deflected? Assume that the magnetic field is confined to the region between the electrodes.

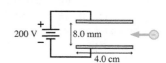

FIGURE EX37.10

Section 37.5 The Fundamental Unit of Charge

11. | A 0.80-μm-diameter oil droplet is observed between two parallel electrodes spaced 11 mm apart. The droplet hangs motionless if the upper electrode is 20 V more positive than the lower electrode. The density of the oil is 885 kg/m³.
    a. What is the droplet's mass?
    b. What is the droplet's charge?
    c. Does the droplet have a surplus or a deficit of electrons? How many?

12. ‖ An oil droplet with 15 excess electrons is observed between two parallel electrodes spaced 12 mm apart. The droplet hangs motionless if the upper electrode is 25 V more positive than the lower electrode. The density of the oil is 860 kg/m³. What is the radius of the droplet?

13. ‖ Suppose that in a hypothetical oil-drop experiment you measure the following values for the charges on the drops: 3.99×10^{-19} C, 6.65×10^{-19} C, 2.66×10^{-19} C, 10.64×10^{-19} C, and 9.31×10^{-19} C. What is the largest value of the fundamental unit of charge that is consistent with your measurements?

Section 37.6 The Discovery of the Nucleus

Section 37.7 Into the Nucleus

14. | Determine:
    a. The speed of a 300 eV electron.
    b. The speed of a 3.5 MeV H⁺ ion.
    c. The specific type of particle that has 2.09 MeV of kinetic energy when moving with a speed of 1.0×10^7 m/s.

15. | Determine:
    a. The speed of a 7.0 MeV neutron.
    b. The speed of a 15 MeV helium atom.
    c. The specific type of particle that has 1.14 keV of kinetic energy when moving with a speed of 2.0×10^7 m/s.

16. ‖ Express in eV (or keV or MeV if more appropriate):
    a. The kinetic energy of an electron moving with a speed of 5.0×10^6 m/s.
    b. The potential energy of an electron and a proton 0.10 nm apart.
    c. The kinetic energy of a proton that has accelerated from rest through a potential difference of 5000 V.

17. ‖ Express in eV (or keV or MeV if more appropriate):
    a. The kinetic energy of a Li⁺⁺ ion that has accelerated from rest through a potential difference of 5000 V.
    b. The potential energy of two protons 10 fm apart.
    c. The kinetic energy, just before impact, of a 200 g ball dropped from a height of 1.0 m.

18. | A parallel-plate capacitor with a 1.0 mm plate separation is charged to 75 V. With what kinetic energy, in eV, must a proton be launched from the negative plate if it is just barely able to reach the positive plate?

19. | How many electrons, protons, and neutrons are contained in the following atoms or ions: (a) ⁶Li, (b) ¹⁶O⁺, and (c) ¹³N⁺⁺?

20. | How many electrons, protons, and neutrons are contained in the following atoms or ions: (a) ¹⁰B, (b) ¹³N⁺, and (c) ¹⁷O⁺⁺⁺?

21. | Write the symbol for an atom or ion with:
    a. five electrons, five protons, and six neutrons.
    b. five electrons, six protons, and eight neutrons.

22. | Write the symbol for an atom or ion with:
    a. one electron, one proton, and two neutrons.
    b. seven electrons, eight protons, and ten neutrons.

23. | Consider the gold isotope ¹⁹⁷Au.
    a. How many electrons, protons, and neutrons are in a neutral ¹⁹⁷Au atom?
    b. The gold nucleus has a diameter of 14.0 fm. What is the density of matter in a gold nucleus?
    c. The density of lead is 11,400 kg/m³. How many times the density of lead is your answer to part b?

24. ‖ Consider the lead isotope ²⁰⁷Pb.
    a. How many electrons, protons, and neutrons are in a neutral ²⁰⁷Pb atom?
    b. The lead nucleus has a diameter of 14.2 fm. What is the electric field strength at the surface of a lead nucleus?

Problems

25. ‖ What is the total energy, in MeV, of
    a. A proton traveling at 99% of the speed of light?
    b. An electron traveling at 99% of the speed of light?
    Hint: This problem uses relativity.

26. | What is the velocity, as a fraction of c, of
    a. A proton with 500 GeV total energy?
    b. An electron with 2.0 GeV total energy?
    Hint: This problem uses relativity.

27. | You learned in Chapter 36 that mass has an equivalent amount of energy. What are the energy equivalents in MeV of the rest masses of an electron and a proton?

28. ‖ The factor γ appears in many relativistic expressions. A value $\gamma = 1.01$ implies that relativity changes the Newtonian values by approximately 1% and that relativistic effects can no longer be ignored. At what kinetic energy, in MeV, is $\gamma = 1.01$ for (a) an electron, (b) a proton, and (c) an alpha particle?

29. | The fission process n + ²³⁵U → ²³⁶U → ¹⁴⁴Ba + ⁸⁹Kr + 3n converts 0.185 u of mass into the kinetic energy of the fission products. What is the total kinetic energy in MeV?

30. ‖ An electron in a cathode-ray beam passes between 2.5-cm-long parallel-plate electrodes that are 5.0 mm apart. A 1.0 mT, 2.5-cm-wide magnetic field is perpendicular to the electric field between the plates. If the potential difference between the plates is 150 V, the electron passes through the electrodes without being deflected. If the potential difference across the plates is set to zero, through what angle is the electron deflected as it passes through the magnetic field?

31. ‖ The two 5.0-cm-long parallel electrodes in FIGURE P37.31 are spaced 1.0 cm apart. A proton enters the plates from one end, an equal distance from both electrodes. A potential difference $\Delta V = 500$ V across the electrodes deflects the proton so that it strikes the outer end of the lower electrode. What magnetic field strength and direction will allow the proton to pass through undeflected while the 500 V potential difference is applied? Assume that both the electric and magnetic fields are confined to the space between the electrodes.

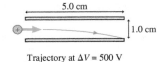

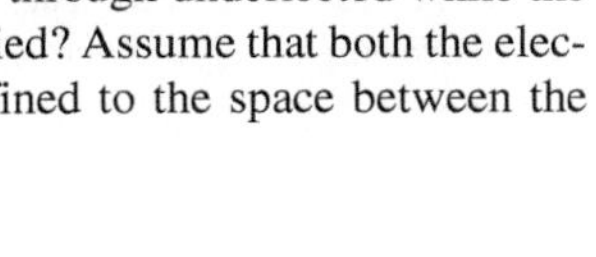

Trajectory at $\Delta V = 500$ V

FIGURE P37.31

32. ‖ An unknown charged particle passes without deflection through crossed electric and magnetic fields of strengths 187,500 V/m and 0.1250 T, respectively. The particle passes out of the electric field, but the magnetic field continues, and the particle makes a semicircle of diameter 25.05 cm. What is the particle's charge-to-mass ratio? Can you identify the particle?

33. ‖ In one of Thomson's experiments he placed a thin metal foil in the electron beam and measured its temperature rise. Consider a cathode-ray tube in which electrons are accelerated through a 2000 V potential difference, then strike a 10 mg copper foil. What is the electron-beam current if the foil temperature rises 6.0°C in 10 s? Assume no loss of energy by radiation or other means. The specific heat of copper is 385 J/kg K.

34. ‖ A neutral lithium atom has three electrons. As you will discover in Chapter 41, two of these electrons form an "inner core," but the third—the valence electron—orbits at much larger radius. From the valence electron's perspective, it is orbiting a spherical ball of charge having net charge $+1e$ (i.e., the three protons in the nucleus and the two inner-core electrons). The energy required to ionize a lithium atom is 5.14 eV. According to Rutherford's nuclear model of the atom, what are the orbital radius and speed of the valence electron?
    Hint: Consider the energy needed to remove the electron *and* the force needed to give the electron a circular orbit.

35. ‖ The diameter of an atom is 1.2×10^{-10} m and the diameter of its nucleus is 1.0×10^{-14} m. What percent of the atom's volume is occupied by mass and what percent is empty space?

36. ‖ A ^{222}Rn atom (radon) in a 0.75 T magnetic field undergoes radioactive decay, emitting an alpha particle in a direction perpendicular to $\vec{B}$. The alpha particle begins cyclotron motion with a radius of 45 cm. With what energy, in MeV, was the alpha particle emitted?

37. ‖‖ The diameter of an aluminum atom of mass 27 u is approximately 1.2×10^{-10} m. The diameter of the nucleus of an aluminum atom is approximately 8×10^{-15} m. The density of solid aluminum is 2700 kg/m^3.
    a. What is the average density of an aluminum atom?
    b. Your answer to part a was larger than the density of solid aluminum. This suggests that the atoms in solid aluminum have spaces between them rather than being tightly packed together. What is the average volume per atom in solid aluminum? If this volume is a sphere, what is the radius?
    Hint: The volume *per* atom is not the same as the volume *of* an atom.
    c. What is the density of the aluminum nucleus? By what factor is the nuclear density larger than the density of solid aluminum?

38. ‖ The charge-to-mass ratio of a nucleus, in units of e/u, is $q/m = Z/A$. For example, a hydrogen nucleus has $q/m = 1/1 = 1$.
    a. Make a graph of charge-to-mass ratio versus proton number Z for nuclei with $Z = 5, 10, 15, 20, \ldots, 90$. For A, use the average atomic mass shown on the periodic table of elements in Appendix B. Show each of these 18 nuclei as a dot, but don't connect the dots together as a curve.
    b. Describe any trend that you notice in your graph.
    c. What's happening in the nuclei that is responsible for this trend?

39. ‖ If the nucleus is a few fm in diameter, the distance between the centers of two protons must be ≈ 2 fm.

a. Calculate the repulsive electric force between two protons that are 2.0 fm apart.
b. Calculate the attractive gravitational force between two protons that are 2.0 fm apart. Could gravity be the force that holds the nucleus together?
c. Your answers to parts a and b imply that there must be some other force that binds the nucleus together and prevents the protons from pushing each other out. What characteristics of this force can you deduce from the discussion of the atom and the nucleus in this chapter?

40. ‖‖ A proton is shot straight outward from the surface of a 1.0-mm-diameter glass bead that has been charged to 0.20 nC. If the proton is launched with 520 eV of kinetic energy, what is its kinetic energy, in eV, when it is 2.0 mm from the surface?

41. ‖ In a head-on collision, the closest approach of a 6.24 MeV alpha particle to the center of a nucleus is 6.00 fm. The nucleus is in an atom of what element? Assume the nucleus remains at rest.

42. ‖ Through what potential difference would you need to accelerate an alpha particle, starting from rest, so that it will just reach the surface of a 15-fm-diameter ^{238}U nucleus?

43. ‖ The oxygen nucleus ^{16}O has a radius of 3.0 fm.
    a. With what speed must a proton be fired toward an oxygen nucleus to have a turning point 1.0 fm from the surface? Assume the nucleus remains at rest.
    b. What is the proton's kinetic energy in MeV?

44. ‖ To initiate a nuclear reaction, an experimental nuclear physicist wants to shoot a proton *into* a 5.50-fm-diameter ^{12}C nucleus. The proton must impact the nucleus with a kinetic energy of 3.00 MeV. Assume the nucleus remains at rest.
    a. With what speed must the proton be fired toward the target?
    b. Through what potential difference must the proton be accelerated from rest to acquire this speed?

Challenge Problems

45. An alpha particle approaches a ^{197}Au nucleus with a speed of 1.50×10^7 m/s. As FIGURE CP37.45 shows, the alpha particle is scattered at a 49° angle at the slower speed of 1.49×10^7 m/s. In what direction does the ^{197}Au nucleus recoil, and with what speed?

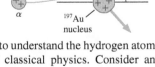

FIGURE CP37.45

46. Physicists first attempted to understand the hydrogen atom by applying the laws of classical physics. Consider an electron of mass m and charge $-e$ in a circular orbit of radius r around a proton of charge $+e$.
    a. Use Newtonian physics to show that the total energy of the atom is $E = -e^2/8\pi\epsilon_0 r$.
    b. Show that the potential energy is -2 times the electron's kinetic energy. This result is called the *virial theorem*.
    c. The minimum energy needed to ionize a hydrogen atom (i.e., to remove the electron) is found experimentally to be 13.6 eV. From this information, what are the electron's speed and the radius of its orbit?

47. Consider an oil droplet of mass m and charge q. We want to determine the charge on the droplet in a Millikan-type experiment. We will do this in several steps. Assume, for simplicity, that the charge is positive and that the electric field between the plates points upward.
    a. An electric field is established by applying a potential difference to the plates. It is found that a field of strength E_0 will cause the droplet to be suspended motionless. Write an expression for the droplet's charge in terms of the suspending field E_0 and the droplet's weight mg.
    b. The field E_0 is easily determined by knowing the plate spacing and measuring the potential difference applied to them. The larger problem is to determine the mass of a microscopic droplet. Consider a mass m falling through a viscous medium in which there is a retarding or drag force. For very small particles, the retarding force is given by $F_{drag} = -bv$ where b is a constant and v the droplet's velocity. The sign recognizes that the drag force vector points upward when the droplet is falling (negative v). A falling droplet quickly reaches a constant speed, called the *terminal speed*. Write an expression for the terminal speed v_{term} in terms of m, g, and b.
    c. A spherical object of radius r moving slowly through the air is known to experience a retarding force $F_{drag} = -6\pi\eta rv$

where η is the *viscosity* of the air. Use this and your answer to part b to show that a spherical droplet of density ρ falling with a terminal velocity v_{term} has a radius

$$r = \sqrt{\frac{9\eta v_{term}}{2\rho g}}$$

    d. Oil has a density 860 kg/m³. An oil droplet is suspended between two plates 1.0 cm apart by adjusting the potential difference between them to 1177 V. When the voltage is removed, the droplet falls and quickly reaches constant speed. It is timed with a stopwatch, and falls 3.00 mm in 7.33 s. The viscosity of air is 1.83×10^{-5} kg/m s. What is the droplet's charge?
    e. How many units of the fundamental electric charge does this droplet possess?
48. A classical atom orbiting at frequency f would emit electromagnetic waves of frequency f because the electron's orbit, seen edge-on, looks like an oscillating electric dipole.
    a. At what radius, in nm, would the electron orbiting the proton in a hydrogen atom emit light with a wavelength of 600 nm?
    b. What is the total mechanical energy of this atom?

STOP TO THINK ANSWERS

Stop to Think 37.1: a is emission, b is absorption. All wavelengths in the absorption spectrum are seen in the emission spectrum, but not all wavelengths in the emission spectrum are seen in the absorption spectrum.

Stop to Think 37.2: b. This observation says that all electrons are the same.

Stop to Think 37.3: b. From the right-hand rule with $\vec{v}$ to the right and $\vec{B}$ out of the page.

Stop to Think 37.4: 4. Neutral carbon would have six electrons. C⁺⁺ is missing two.

Stop to Think 37.5: 6 protons and 8 neutrons. The number of protons is the atomic number, which is 6. That leaves $14 - 6 = 8$ neutrons.

38 Quantization

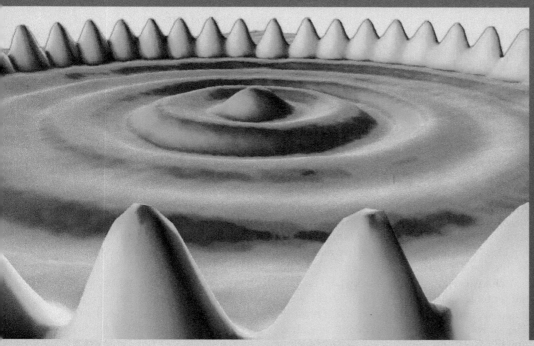

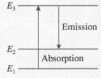
A scanning tunneling microscope image shows an electron standing wave in a "quantum corral" made from 60 iron atoms.

▶ **Looking Ahead** The goal of Chapter 38 is to understand the quantization of energy for light and matter.

Waves and Particles

You've learned that light is an electromagnetic *wave*.

As we found in Chapter 22, light exhibits interference and diffraction, the hallmarks of waviness.

◀ **Looking Back**
Chapter 22 Interference and diffraction

But matters are more complex.

At very low intensity, light hits the screen in "chunks." Sometimes light acts like a particle.

An electron is a basic, sub-atomic *particle*.

Our model of conduction in metals was based on the motion of particle-like electrons moving through a lattice of fixed ions.

Or maybe not.

Shooting electrons through two closely spaced slits produces an interference pattern. Sometimes matter acts like a wave.

You'll learn that light and matter have characteristics of both particles *and* waves.

Photons

The **photon model** of light says that

- Light consists of discrete, massless "chunks" called **photons.**
- The energy of a photon of frequency f is *quantized*: $E_{\text{photon}} = hf$, where h is a constant.

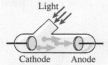

In the *photoelectric effect*, short-wavelength light ejects electrons from a metal surface but long-wavelength light does not. You'll learn how this is evidence for photons.

Matter Waves

You'll learn that the wave-like properties of matter are described by the **de Broglie wavelength** $\lambda = h/mv$. Wave properties are not noticeable for macroscopic matter but are essential to understand matter at the atomic level.

A classical particle confined to a box would bounce back and forth. But reflected matter waves set up a standing wave. You'll see how this leads to quantized energy levels.

Bohr's Atomic Model

By adding quantum ideas to Rutherford's solar-system model of the atom, Bohr created an atomic model in which the electrons can orbit only with certain discrete energies. These are the **energy levels** of the atom.

You'll learn to use *energy-level diagrams* to understand the discrete emission and absorption spectra of gases.

E_3
E_2
E_1
Emission
Absorption

◀ **Looking Back**
Section 37.6 Rutherford's atom

38.1 The Photoelectric Effect

In 1886, Heinrich Hertz, who was the first to demonstrate that electromagnetic waves can be artificially generated, noticed that a negatively charged electroscope could be discharged by shining ultraviolet light on it. Hertz's observation caught the attention of J. J. Thomson, who inferred that the ultraviolet light was causing the electrode to emit electrons, thus restoring itself to electric neutrality. The emission of electrons from a substance due to light striking its surface came to be called the **photoelectric effect.** The emitted electrons are often called *photoelectrons* to indicate their origin, but they are identical in every respect to all other electrons.

Although this discovery might seem to be a minor footnote in the history of science, it soon became a, or maybe *the,* pivotal event that opened the door to new ideas.

Characteristics of the Photoelectric Effect

It was not the discovery itself that dealt the fatal blow to classical physics, but the specific characteristics of the photoelectric effect found around 1900 by one of Hertz's students, Phillip Lenard. Lenard built a glass tube, shown in FIGURE 38.1, with two facing electrodes and a window. After removing the air from the tube, he allowed light to shine on the cathode.

Lenard found a counterclockwise current (clockwise flow of electrons) through the ammeter whenever ultraviolet light was shining on the cathode. There are no junctions in this circuit, so the current must be the same all the way around the loop. The current in the space between the cathode and the anode consists of electrons moving freely through the evacuated space between the electrodes (i.e., not inside a wire) at the *same rate* (same number of electrons per second) as the current in the wire. There is no current if the electrodes are in the dark, so electrons don't spontaneously leap off the cathode. Instead, the light causes electrons to be ejected from the cathode at a steady rate.

Lenard used a battery to establish an adjustable potential difference ΔV between the two electrodes. He then studied how the current I varied as the potential difference and the light's frequency and intensity were changed. Lenard made the following observations:

1. The current I is directly proportional to the light intensity. If the light intensity is doubled, the current also doubles.
2. The current appears without delay when the light is applied. To Lenard, this meant within the ≈ 0.1 s with which his equipment could respond. Later experiments showed that the current begins in less than 1 ns.
3. Photoelectrons are emitted *only* if the light frequency f exceeds a **threshold frequency** f_0. This is shown in the graph of FIGURE 38.2.
4. The value of the threshold frequency f_0 depends on the type of metal from which the cathode is made.
5. If the potential difference ΔV is more than about 1 V positive (anode positive with respect to the cathode), the current does not change as ΔV is increased. If ΔV is made negative (anode negative with respect to the cathode), by reversing the battery, the current decreases until, at some voltage $\Delta V = -V_{stop}$ the current reaches zero. The value of V_{stop} is called the **stopping potential.** This behavior is shown in FIGURE 38.3.
6. The value of V_{stop} is the same for both weak light and intense light. A more intense light causes a larger current, as Figure 38.3 shows, but in both cases the current ceases when $\Delta V = -V_{stop}$.

NOTE ▶ We're defining V_{stop} to be a *positive* number. The potential difference that stops the electrons is $\Delta V = -V_{stop}$, with an explicit minus sign. ◀

FIGURE 38.1 Lenard's experimental device to study the photoelectric effect.

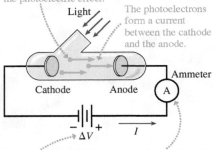

Ultraviolet light causes the metal cathode to emit electrons. This is the photoelectric effect.

The photoelectrons form a current between the cathode and the anode.

The potential difference can be changed or reversed.

The current can be measured while the potential difference, the light frequency, and the light intensity are varied.

FIGURE 38.2 The photoelectric current as a function of the light frequency f for light of constant intensity.

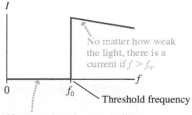

No matter how weak the light, there is a current if $f > f_0$.

Threshold frequency

No matter how intense the light, there is no current if $f < f_0$.

FIGURE 38.3 The photoelectric current as a function of the battery potential.

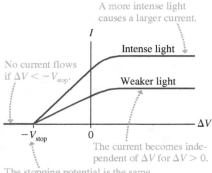

A more intense light causes a larger current.

No current flows if $\Delta V < -V_{stop}$.

The current becomes independent of ΔV for $\Delta V > 0$.

The stopping potential is the same for intense light and weak light.

Classical Interpretation of the Photoelectric Effect

The mere existence of the photoelectric effect is not, as is sometimes assumed, a difficulty for classical physics. You learned in Chapter 25 that electrons are the charge carriers in a metal. The electrons move freely but are bound inside the metal and do not spontaneously spill out of an electrode at room temperature. But a piece of metal heated to a sufficiently high temperature *does* emit electrons in a process called **thermal emission.** The electron gun in an older television or computer display terminal starts with the thermal emission of electrons from a hot tungsten filament.

A useful analogy, shown in FIGURE 38.4, is the water in a swimming pool. Water molecules do not spontaneously leap out of the pool if the water is calm. To remove a water molecule, you must do *work* on it to lift it upward, against the force of gravity. A minimum energy is needed to extract a water molecule, namely the energy needed to lift a molecule that is right at the surface. Removing a water molecule that is deeper requires more than the minimum energy. People playing in the pool add energy to the water, causing waves. If sufficient energy is added, a few water molecules will gain enough energy to splash over the edge and leave the pool.

Similarly, a *minimum* energy is needed to free an electron from a metal. To extract an electron, you would need to exert a force on it and pull it (i.e., do *work* on it) until its speed is large enough to escape. The minimum energy E_0 needed to free an electron is called the **work function** of the metal. Some electrons, like the deeper water molecules, may require more energy than E_0 to escape, but all will require *at least* E_0. Different metals have different work functions; Table 38.1 provides a short list. Notice that work functions are given in electron volts.

Heating a metal, like splashing in the pool, increases the thermal energy of the electrons. At a sufficiently high temperature, the kinetic energy of a small percentage of the electrons may exceed the work function. These electrons can "make it out of the pool" and leave the metal. In practice, there are only a few elements, such as tungsten, for which thermal emission can become significant before the metal melts!

Suppose we could raise the temperature of only the electrons, not the crystal lattice. One possible way to do this is to shine a light wave on the surface. Because electromagnetic waves are absorbed by the conduction electrons, not by the positive ions, the light wave heats only the electrons. Eventually the electrons' energy is transferred to the crystal lattice, via collisions, but if the light is sufficiently intense, the *electron temperature* may be significantly higher than the temperature of the metal. In 1900, it was plausible to think that an intense light source could cause the thermal emission of electrons without melting the metal.

The Stopping Potential

Photoelectrons leave the cathode with kinetic energy. An electron with energy E_{elec} inside the metal loses energy ΔE as it escapes, so it emerges as a photoelectron with $K = E_{elec} - \Delta E$. The work function energy E_0 is the *minimum* energy needed to remove an electron, so the *maximum* possible kinetic energy of a photoelectron is

$$K_{max} = E_{elec} - E_0 \qquad (38.1)$$

Some photoelectrons reach the anode, creating a measurable current, but many do not. However, as FIGURE 38.5 shows:

- A positive anode attracts the photoelectrons. Once all electrons reach the anode, which happens for ΔV greater than about 1 V, a further increase in ΔV does not cause any further increase in the current I. That is why the graph lines become horizontal on the right side of Figure 38.3.
- A negative anode repels the electrons. However, photoelectrons leaving the cathode with sufficient kinetic energy can still reach the anode. The current steadily decreases as the anode voltage becomes increasingly negative until, at the stopping potential, *all* electrons are turned back and the current ceases. This was the behavior observed on the left side of Figure 38.3.

FIGURE 38.4 A swimming pool analogy of electrons in a metal.

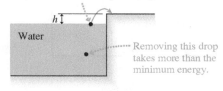

The *minimum* energy to remove a drop of water from the pool is *mgh*.

Removing this drop takes more than the minimum energy.

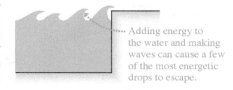

Adding energy to the water and making waves can cause a few of the most energetic drops to escape.

TABLE 38.1 The work function for some of the elements

Element	E_0 (eV)
Potassium	2.30
Sodium	2.75
Aluminum	4.28
Tungsten	4.55
Copper	4.65
Iron	4.70
Gold	5.10

FIGURE 38.5 The photoelectron current depends on the anode potential.

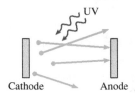

$\Delta V = 0$: The photoelectrons leave the cathode in all directions. Only a few reach the anode.

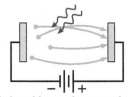

$\Delta V > 0$: A positive anode attracts the photoelectrons to the anode.

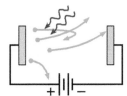

$\Delta V < 0$: A negative anode repels the electrons. Only the very fastest make it to the anode.

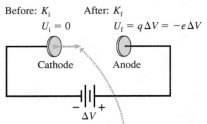

FIGURE 38.6 Energy is conserved.

Before: K_i After: K_f

$U_i = 0$ $U_f = q\Delta V = -e\Delta V$

Cathode   Anode

ΔV

Energy is transformed from kinetic to potential as an electron moves from cathode to anode.

Let the cathode be the point of zero potential energy, as shown in FIGURE 38.6. An electron emitted from the cathode with kinetic energy K_i has initial total energy

$$E_i = K_i + U_i = K_i + 0 = K_i$$

When the electron reaches the anode, which is at potential ΔV relative to the cathode, it has potential energy $U = q\,\Delta V = -e\,\Delta V$ and final total energy

$$E_f = K_f + U_f = K_f - e\,\Delta V$$

From conservation of energy, $E_f = E_i$, the electron's final kinetic energy is

$$K_f = K_i + e\,\Delta V \tag{38.2}$$

The electron speeds up ($K_f > K_i$) if ΔV is positive. The electron slows down if ΔV is negative, but it still reaches the anode ($K_f > 0$) if K_i is large enough.

An electron with initial kinetic energy K_i will stop just as it reaches the anode if the potential difference is $\Delta V = -K_i/e$. The potential difference that turns back the very fastest electrons, those with $K = K_{max}$, and thus stops the current is

$$\Delta V_{\text{stop fastest electrons}} = -\frac{K_{max}}{e}$$

By definition, the potential difference that causes the electron current to cease is $\Delta V = -V_{stop}$, where V_{stop} is the stopping potential. The stopping potential is

$$V_{stop} = \frac{K_{max}}{e} \tag{38.3}$$

Thus the stopping potential tells us the maximum kinetic energy of the photoelectrons.

EXAMPLE 38.1 **The classical photoelectric effect**

A photoelectric-effect experiment is performed with an aluminum cathode. An electron inside the cathode has a speed of 1.5×10^6 m/s. If the potential difference between the anode and cathode is -2.00 V, what is the highest possible speed with which this electron could reach the anode?

MODEL Energy is conserved.

SOLVE If the electron escapes with the maximum possible kinetic energy, its kinetic energy at the anode will be given by Equation 38.2 with $\Delta V = -2.00$ V. The electron's initial kinetic energy is

$$E_{elec} = \frac{1}{2}mv^2 = \frac{1}{2}(9.11 \times 10^{-31} \text{ kg})(1.5 \times 10^6 \text{ m/s})^2$$

$$= 1.025 \times 10^{-18} \text{ J} = 6.41 \text{ eV}$$

Its maximum possible kinetic energy as it leaves the cathode is

$$K_i = K_{max} = E_{elec} - E_0 = 2.13 \text{ eV}$$

where $E_0 = 4.28$ eV is the work function of aluminum. Thus the kinetic energy at the anode, given by Equation 38.2, is

$$K_f = K_i + e\,\Delta V = 2.13 \text{ eV} - (e)(2.00 \text{ V}) = 0.13 \text{ eV}$$

Notice that the electron loses 2.00 eV of *energy* as it moves through the *potential* difference of -2.00 V, so we can compute the final kinetic energy in eV without having to convert to joules. However, we must convert K_f to joules to find the final speed:

$$K_f = \frac{1}{2}mv_f^2 = 0.13 \text{ eV} = 2.1 \times 10^{-20} \text{ J}$$

$$v_f = \sqrt{\frac{2K_f}{m}} = 2.1 \times 10^5 \text{ m/s}$$

Limits of the Classical Interpretation

A classical analysis has provided a possible explanation of observations 1 and 5 above. But nothing in this explanation suggests that there should be a threshold frequency, as Lenard found. If a weak intensity at a frequency just slightly above f_0 can generate a current, why can't a strong intensity at a frequency just slightly below f_0 do so?

What about Lenard's observation that the current starts instantly? If the photo-electrons are due to thermal emission, it should take some time for the light to raise the electron temperature sufficiently high for some to escape. The experimental evidence was in sharp disagreement. And more intense light would be expected to heat the electrons to a higher temperature. Doing so should increase the maximum kinetic energy of the photoelectrons and thus should increase the stopping potential V_{stop}. But as Lenard found, the stopping potential is the same for strong light as it is for weak light.

Although the mere presence of photoelectrons did not seem surprising, classical physics was unable to explain the observed behavior of the photoelectrons. The threshold frequency and the instant current seemed particularly anomalous.

38.2 Einstein's Explanation

Albert Einstein, seen in FIGURE 38.7, was a little-known young man of 26 in 1905. He had recently graduated from the Polytechnic Institute in Zurich, Switzerland, with the Swiss equivalent of a Ph.D. in physics. Although his mathematical brilliance was recognized, his overall academic record was mediocre. Rather than pursue an academic career, Einstein took a job with the Swiss Patent Office in Bern. This was a fortuitous choice because it provided him with plenty of spare time to think about physics.

FIGURE 38.7 A young Einstein.

In 1905, Einstein published his initial paper on the theory of relativity, the subject for which he is most well known to the general public. He also published another paper, on the nature of light. In it Einstein offered an exceedingly simple but amazingly bold idea to explain Lenard's photoelectric-effect data.

A few years earlier, in 1900, the German physicist Max Planck had been trying to understand the details of the rainbow-like blackbody spectrum of light emitted by a glowing hot object. As we noted in the preceding chapter, this problem didn't yield to a classical physics analysis, but Planck found that he could calculate the spectrum perfectly if he made an unusual assumption. The atoms in a solid vibrate back and forth around their equilibrium positions with frequency f. You learned in Chapter 14 that the energy of a simple harmonic oscillator depends on its amplitude and can have *any* possible value. But to predict the spectrum correctly, Planck had to assume that the oscillating atoms are *not* free to have any possible energy. Instead, the energy of an atom vibrating with frequency f has to be one of the specific energies $E = 0$, hf, $2hf$, $3hf$, ..., where h is a constant. That is, the vibration energies are *quantized*.

Planck was able to determine the value of the constant h by comparing his calculations of the spectrum to experimental measurements. The constant that he introduced into physics is now called **Planck's constant.** Its contemporary value is

$$h = 6.63 \times 10^{-34}\,\text{J s} = 4.14 \times 10^{-15}\,\text{eV s}$$

The first value, with SI units, is the proper one for most calculations, but you will find the second to be useful when energies are expressed in eV.

Einstein was the first to take Planck's quantization idea seriously. He went even further and suggested that **electromagnetic radiation itself is quantized!** That is, light is not really a continuous wave but, instead, arrives in small packets or bundles of energy. Einstein called each packet of energy a **light quantum,** and he postulated that the energy of one light quantum is directly proportional to the frequency of the light. That is, each quantum of light has energy

$$E = hf \tag{38.4}$$

where h is Planck's constant and f is the frequency of the light.

The idea of light quanta is subtle, so let's look at an analogy with raindrops. A downpour has a torrent of raindrops, but in a light shower the drops are few. The difference between "intense" rain and "weak" rain is the *rate* at which the drops arrive. An intense rain makes a continuous noise on the roof, so you are not aware of the individual drops, but the individual drops become apparent during a light rain.

Similarly, intense light has so many quanta arriving per second that the light seems continuous, but very weak light consists of only a few quanta per second. And just as raindrops come in different sizes, with larger-mass drops having larger kinetic energy, higher-frequency light quanta have a larger amount of energy. Although this analogy is not perfect, it does provide a useful mental picture of light quanta arriving at a surface.

EXAMPLE 38.2 **Light quanta**

The retina of your eye has three types of color photoreceptors, called *cones*, with maximum sensitivities at 437 nm, 533 nm, and 575 nm. For each, what is the energy of one quantum of light having that wavelength?

MODEL The energy of light is quantized.

SOLVE Light with wavelength λ has frequency $f = c/\lambda$. The energy of one quantum of light at this wavelength is

$$E = hf = \frac{hc}{\lambda}$$

The calculation requires λ to be in m, but it is useful to have Planck's constant in eV s. At 437 nm, we have

$$E = \frac{(4.14 \times 10^{-15} \text{ eV s})(3.00 \times 10^8 \text{ m/s})}{437 \times 10^{-9} \text{ m}} = 2.84 \text{ eV}$$

Carrying out the same calculation for the other two wavelengths gives $E = 2.33$ eV at 533 nm and $E = 2.16$ eV at 575 nm.

ASSESS The electron volt turns out to be more convenient than the joule for describing the energy of light quanta. Because these wavelengths span a good fraction of the visible spectrum of 400–700 nm, you can see that visible light corresponds to light quanta having energy of roughly 2–3 eV.

Einstein's Postulates

Einstein framed three postulates about light quanta and their interaction with matter:

1. Light of frequency f consists of discrete quanta, each of energy $E = hf$. Each photon travels at the speed of light c.
2. Light quanta are emitted or absorbed on an all-or-nothing basis. A substance can emit 1 or 2 or 3 quanta, but not 1.5. Similarly, an electron in a metal cannot absorb half a quantum but, instead, only an integer number.
3. A light quantum, when absorbed by a metal, delivers its entire energy to *one* electron.

NOTE ▶ These three postulates—that light comes in chunks, that the chunks cannot be divided, and that the energy of one chunk is delivered to one electron—are crucial for understanding the new ideas that will lead to quantum physics. They are completely at odds with the concepts of classical physics, where energy can be continuously divided and shared, so they deserve careful thought. ◀

Let's look at how Einstein's postulates apply to the photoelectric effect. If Einstein is correct, the light of frequency f shining on the metal is a flow of light quanta, each of energy hf. Each quantum is absorbed by *one* electron, giving that electron an energy $E_{\text{elec}} = hf$. This leads us to several interesting conclusions:

1. An electron that has just absorbed a quantum of light energy has $E_{\text{elec}} = hf$. (The electron's thermal energy at room temperature is so much less than hf that we can neglect it.) FIGURE 38.8 shows that this electron can escape from the metal, becoming a photoelectron, if

$$E_{\text{elec}} = hf \geq E_0 \qquad (38.5)$$

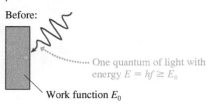

FIGURE 38.8 The creation of a photoelectron.

Before:

One quantum of light with energy $E = hf \geq E_0$

Work function E_0

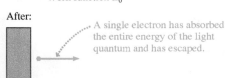

After:

A single electron has absorbed the entire energy of the light quantum and has escaped.

where, you will recall, the work function E_0 is the minimum energy needed to free an electron from the metal. As a result, there is a *threshold frequency*

$$f_0 = \frac{E_0}{h} \tag{38.6}$$

for the ejection of photoelectrons. If f is less than f_0, even by just a small amount, none of the electrons will have sufficient energy to escape no matter how intense the light. But even very weak light with $f \geq f_0$ will give a few electrons sufficient energy to escape **because each light quantum delivers all of its energy to one electron.** This threshold behavior is exactly what Lenard observed.

NOTE ▶ The threshold frequency is directly proportional to the work function. Metals with large work functions, such as iron, copper, and gold, exhibit the photoelectric effect only when illuminated by high-frequency ultraviolet light. Photoemission occurs with lower-frequency visible light for metals with smaller values of E_0, such as sodium and potassium. ◀

2. A more intense light means *more quanta* of the same energy, not more energetic quanta. These quanta eject a larger number of photoelectrons and cause a larger current, exactly as observed.
3. There is a distribution of kinetic energies, because different photoelectrons require different amounts of energy to escape, but the *maximum* kinetic energy is

$$K_{\text{max}} = E_{\text{elec}} - E_0 = hf - E_0 \tag{38.7}$$

As we noted in Equation 38.3, the stopping potential V_{stop} is directly proportional to K_{max}. Einstein's theory predicts that the stopping potential is related to the light frequency by

$$V_{\text{stop}} = \frac{K_{\text{max}}}{e} = \frac{hf - E_0}{e} \tag{38.8}$$

FIGURE 38.9 A pebble transfers energy to the water.

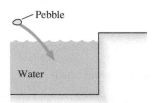

Classically, the energy of the pebble is shared by all the water molecules. One pebble causes only very small waves.

The stopping potential does *not* depend on the intensity of the light. Both weak light and intense light will have the same stopping potential, which Lenard had observed but which could not previously be explained.

4. If each light quantum transfers its energy hf to just one electron, that electron *immediately* has enough energy to escape. The current should begin instantly, with no delay, exactly as Lenard had observed.

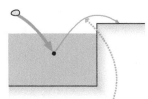

If the pebble could give *all* its energy to one drop, that drop could easily splash out of the pool.

Using the swimming pool analogy again, FIGURE 38.9 shows a pebble being thrown into the pool. The pebble increases the energy of the water, but the increase is shared among all the molecules in the pool. The increase in the water's energy is barely enough to make ripples, not nearly enough to splash water out of the pool. But suppose *all* the pebble's energy could go to *one drop* of water that didn't have to share it. That one drop of water could easily have enough energy to leap out of the pool. Einstein's hypothesis that a light quantum transfers all its energy to one electron is equivalent to the pebble transferring all its energy to one drop of water.

A Prediction

Not only do Einstein's hypotheses explain all of Lenard's observations, they also make a new prediction. According to Equation 38.8, the stopping potential should be a linearly increasing function of the light's frequency f. We can rewrite Equation 38.8 in terms of the threshold frequency $f_0 = E_0/h$ as

$$V_{\text{stop}} = \frac{h}{e}(f - f_0) \tag{38.9}$$

FIGURE 38.10 A graph of Millikan's data for the stopping potential as the light frequency is varied.

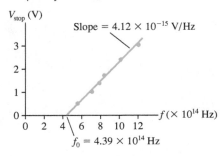

A graph of the stopping potential V_{stop} versus the light frequency f should start from zero at $f = f_0$, then rise linearly with a slope of h/e. In fact, the slope of the graph provides a way to measure Planck's constant h.

Lenard had not measured the stopping potential for different frequencies, so Einstein offered this as an untested prediction of his postulates. Robert Millikan, known for his oil-drop experiment to measure e, took up the challenge. Some of Millikan's data for a cesium cathode are shown in FIGURE 38.10. As you can see, Einstein's prediction of a linear relationship between f and V_{stop} was confirmed.

Millikan measured the slope of his graph and multiplied it by the value of e (which he had measured a few years earlier in the oil-drop experiment) to find h. His value agreed with the value that Planck had determined in 1900 from an entirely different experiment. Light quanta, whether physicists liked the idea or not, were real.

EXAMPLE 38.3 The photoelectric threshold frequency

What are the threshold frequencies and wavelengths for photoemission from sodium and from aluminum?

SOLVE Table 38.1 gives the sodium work function as $E_0 = 2.75$ eV. Aluminum has $E_0 = 4.28$ eV. We can use Equation 38.6, with h in units of eV s, to calculate

$$f_0 = \frac{E_0}{h} = \begin{cases} 6.64 \times 10^{14} \text{ Hz} & \text{sodium} \\ 10.34 \times 10^{14} \text{ Hz} & \text{aluminum} \end{cases}$$

These frequencies are converted to wavelengths with $\lambda = c/f$, giving

$$\lambda = \begin{cases} 452 \text{ nm} & \text{sodium} \\ 290 \text{ nm} & \text{aluminum} \end{cases}$$

ASSESS The photoelectric effect can be observed with sodium for $\lambda < 452$ nm. This includes blue and violet visible light but not red, orange, yellow, or green. Aluminum, with a larger work function, needs ultraviolet wavelengths $\lambda < 290$ nm.

EXAMPLE 38.4 Maximum photoelectron speed

What is the maximum photoelectron speed if sodium is illuminated with light of 300 nm?

SOLVE The light frequency is $f = c/\lambda = 1.00 \times 10^{15}$ Hz, so each light quantum has energy $hf = 4.14$ eV. The maximum kinetic energy of a photoelectron is

$$K_{max} = hf - E_0 = 4.14 \text{ eV} - 2.75 \text{ eV} = 1.39 \text{ eV}$$
$$= 2.22 \times 10^{-19} \text{ J}$$

Because $K = \frac{1}{2}mv^2$, where m is the electron's mass, not the mass of the sodium atom, the maximum speed of a photoelectron leaving the cathode is

$$v_{max} = \sqrt{\frac{2K_{max}}{m}} = 6.99 \times 10^5 \text{ m/s}$$

Note that we had to convert K_{max} to SI units of J before calculating a speed in m/s.

STOP TO THINK 38.1 The work function of metal A is 3.0 eV. Metals B and C have work functions of 4.0 eV and 5.0 eV, respectively. Ultraviolet light shines on all three metals, creating photoelectrons. Rank in order, from largest to smallest, the stopping potentials for A, B, and C.

38.3 Photons

Einstein was awarded the Nobel Prize in 1921 not for his theory of relativity, as many suppose, but for his explanation of the photoelectric effect. Although Planck had made the first suggestion, it was Einstein who showed convincingly that energy is quantized. Quanta of light energy were later given the name **photons**.

But just what are photons? To begin our explanation, let's return to the experiment that showed most dramatically the wave nature of light—Young's double-slit interference experiment. We will make a change, though: We will dramatically lower the light intensity by inserting filters between the light source and the slits. The fringes will be too dim to see by eye, so we will replace the viewing screen with a detector that can build up an image over time.

What would we predict for the outcome of this experiment? If light is a wave, there is no reason to think that the nature of the interference fringes will change. The detector should continue to show alternating light and dark bands.

FIGURE 38.11 shows the actual outcome at four different times. At early times, contrary to our prediction, the detector shows not dim interference fringes but discrete, bright dots. If we didn't know that light is a wave, we would interpret the dots as evidence that light is a stream of some type of particle-like objects. They arrive one by one, seemingly randomly, and each is localized at a specific point on the detector. (Waves, you will recall, are not localized at a specific point in space.)

As the detector builds up the image for a longer period of time, we see that these dots are not entirely random. They are grouped into bands at *exactly* the positions where we expected to see bright constructive-interference fringes. No dot ever appears at points of destructive interference. After a long time, the individual dots overlap and the image looks like the photographs of interference fringes in Chapter 22.

We're detecting individual photons! Most light sources—even very dim sources—emit such vast numbers of photons that you are aware of only their wave-like superposition, just as you notice only the roar of a heavy rain on your roof and not the individual raindrops. But at extremely low intensities the light begins to appear as a stream of individual photons, like the random patter of raindrops when it is barely sprinkling. Each dot on the detector in Figure 38.11 signifies a point where one particle-like photon delivered its energy and caused a measurable signal.

But photons are certainly not classical particles. Classical particles, such as Newton's corpuscles of light, would travel in straight lines through the two slits of a double-slit experiment and make just two bright areas on the detector. Instead, as Figure 38.11 shows, the *particle*-like photons seem to be landing at places where a *wave* undergoes constructive interference, thus forming the bands of dots.

Today, it is quite feasible to do this experiment with a light intensity so low that only one photon at a time is passing through the double-slit apparatus. But if one photon at a time can build up a wave-like interference pattern, what is the photon interfering with? The only possible answer is that **the photon is interfering *with itself.*** Nothing else is present. But if each photon interferes with itself, rather than with other photons, then each photon, despite the fact that it is a particle-like object, must somehow go through *both* slits! Photons seem to be both wave-like *and* particle-like at the same time.

This all seems pretty crazy, but it's the way light actually behaves. **Sometimes light exhibits particle-like behavior and sometimes it exhibits wave-like behavior.** The thing we call *light* is stranger and more complex than it first appeared, and there is no way to reconcile these seemingly contradictory behaviors. We have to accept nature as it is rather than hoping that nature will conform to our expectations. Furthermore, as we will see, this half-wave/half-particle behavior is not restricted to light.

The Photon Model of Light

The **photon model** of light consists of three basic postulates:

1. Light consists of discrete, massless units called *photons*. A photon travels in vacuum at the speed of light.
2. Each photon has energy

$$E_{\text{photon}} = hf \tag{38.10}$$

   where f is the frequency of the light and $h = 6.63 \times 10^{-34}$ Js is Planck's constant. In other words, the light comes in discrete "chunks" of energy hf.
3. The superposition of a sufficiently large number of photons has the characteristics of a classical light wave.

FIGURE 38.11 A double-slit experiment performed with light of very low intensity.

(a) Image after a very short time

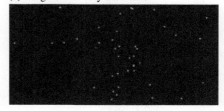

(b) Image after a slightly longer time

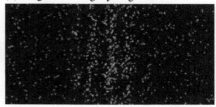

(c) Continuing to build up the image

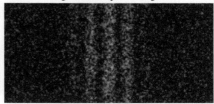

(d) Image after a very long time

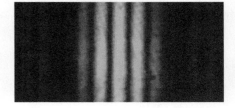

FIGURE 38.12 A wave packet has wave-like and particle-like properties.

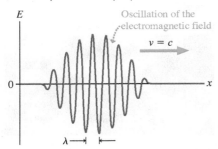

Photons are sometimes visualized as **wave packets.** The electromagnetic wave shown FIGURE 38.12 has a wavelength and a frequency, yet it is also discrete and fairly localized. But this cannot be exactly what a photon is because a wave packet would take a finite amount of time to be emitted or absorbed. This is contrary to much evidence that the entire photon is emitted or absorbed in a single instant; there is no point in time at which the photon is "half absorbed." The wave packet idea, although useful, is still too classical to represent a photon.

In fact, there simply is no "true" mental representation of a photon. Analogies such as raindrops or wave packets can be useful, but none is perfectly accurate. We can detect photons, measure the properties of photons, and put photons to practical use, but the ultimate nature of the photon remains a mystery. To paraphrase Gertrude Stein, "A photon is a photon is a photon."

The Photon Rate

Light, in the raindrop analogy, consists of a stream of photons. For monochromatic light of frequency f, N photons have a total energy $E_{light} = Nhf$. We are usually more interested in the *power* of the light, or the rate (in joules per second, or watts) at which the light energy is delivered. The power is

$$P = \frac{dE_{light}}{dt} = \frac{dN}{dt}hf = Rhf \qquad (38.11)$$

where $R = dN/dt$ is the *rate* at which photons arrive or, equivalently, the number of photons per second.

EXAMPLE 38.5 **The photon rate in a laser beam**

The 1.0 mW light beam of a helium-neon laser ($\lambda = 633$ nm) shines on a screen. How many photons strike the screen each second?

SOLVE The light-beam power, or energy delivered per second, is $P = 1.0$ mW $= 0.0010$ J/s. The frequency of the light is $f = c/\lambda = 4.74 \times 10^{14}$ Hz. The number of photons striking the screen per second, which is the *rate* of arrival of photons, is

$$R = \frac{P}{hf} = 3.2 \times 10^{15} \text{ photons per second}$$

ASSESS That is a lot of photons per second. No wonder we are not aware of individual photons!

STOP TO THINK 38.2 The intensity of a beam of light is increased but the light's frequency is unchanged. Which one (or perhaps more than one) of the following is true?

a. The photons travel faster.
b. Each photon has more energy.
c. The photons are larger.
d. There are more photons per second.

38.4 Matter Waves and Energy Quantization

Prince Louis-Victor de Broglie was a French graduate student in 1924. It had been 19 years since Einstein had shaken the world of physics by introducing photons and blurring the distinction between a particle and a wave. As de Broglie thought about these issues, it seemed that nature should have some kind of symmetry. If light waves could have a particle-like nature, why shouldn't material particles have some kind of wave-like nature? In other words, could **matter waves** exist?

With no experimental evidence to go on, de Broglie reasoned by analogy with Einstein's equation $E = hf$ for the photon and with some of the ideas of his theory of relativity. The details need not concern us, but they led de Broglie to postulate that *if* a material particle of momentum $p = mv$ has a wave-like nature, then its wavelength must be given by

$$\lambda = \frac{h}{p} = \frac{h}{mv} \tag{38.12}$$

where h is Planck's constant. This is called the **de Broglie wavelength.**

EXAMPLE 38.6 **The de Broglie wavelength of an electron**

What is the de Broglie wavelength of a 1.0 eV electron?

SOLVE An electron with $1.0 \text{ eV} = 1.6 \times 10^{-19}$ J of kinetic energy has speed

$$v = \sqrt{\frac{2K}{m}} = 5.9 \times 10^5 \text{ m/s}$$

Although fast by macroscopic standards, this is a slow electron because it gains this speed by accelerating through a potential difference of a mere 1 V. Its de Broglie wavelength is

$$\lambda = \frac{h}{mv} = 1.2 \times 10^{-9} \text{ m} = 1.2 \text{ nm}$$

ASSESS The electron's wavelength is small, but it is similar to the wavelengths of x rays and larger than the approximately 10^{-10} m spacing of atoms in a crystal.

What would it mean for matter—an electron or a proton or a baseball—to have a wavelength? Would it obey the principle of superposition? Would it exhibit interference and diffraction? The classic test of "waviness" is Young's double-slit experiment. FIGURE 38.13 shows the intensity pattern recorded after 50 keV electrons passed through two slits separated by 1.0 μm. The pattern is clearly a double-slit interference pattern, and the spacing of the fringes is exactly as predicted for a wavelength given by de Broglie's formula. And because the electron beam was weak, with one electron at a time passing through the apparatus, it would appear that each electron—like photons—somehow went through both slits, then interfered with itself before striking the detector!

Surprisingly, electrons—also neutrons—exhibit all the behavior we associate with waves. But electrons and neutrons are subatomic particles. What about entire atoms, aggregates of many fundamental particles? Amazing as it seems, research during the 1980s demonstrated that whole atoms, and even molecules, can produce interference patterns.

FIGURE 38.14 shows an *atom interferometer*. You learned in Chapter 22 that an interferometer, such as the Michelson interferometer, works by dividing a wave front

FIGURE 38.13 A double-slit interference pattern created with electrons.

FIGURE 38.14 An atom interferometer.

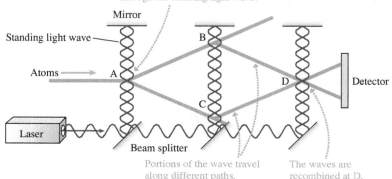

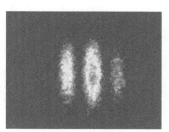

Detector output

into two waves, sending the two waves along separate paths, then recombining them. For light waves, wave division can be accomplished by sending light through the *periodic* slits in a diffraction grating. In an atom interferometer, the atom's matter wave is divided by sending atoms through the *periodic* intensity of a standing light wave.

You can see in the figure that a laser creates three parallel *standing waves* of light, each with nodes spaced a distance $\lambda/2$ apart. The wavelength is chosen so that the light waves exert small forces on an atom in the laser beam. Because the intensity along a standing wave alternates between maximum at the antinodes and zero intensity at the nodes, an atom crossing the laser beam experiences a *periodic* force field. A particle-like atom would be deflected by this periodic force, but a wave is *diffracted*. After being diffracted by the first standing wave at A, an atom is, in some sense, traveling toward both point B *and* point C.

The second standing wave diffracts the atom waves again at points B and C, directing some of them toward D where, with a third diffraction, they are recombined after having traveled along different paths. The detector image shows interference fringes, exactly as would be expected for a wave but completely at odds with the expectation for particles.

The atom interferometer is fascinating because it completely inverts everything we previously learned about interference and diffraction. The scientists who studied the wave nature of light during the 19th century aimed light (a wave) at a diffraction grating (a periodic structure of matter) and found that it diffracted. Now we aim atoms (matter) at a standing wave (a periodic structure of light) and find that the atoms diffract. The roles of light and matter have been reversed!

Quantization of Energy

The fact that matter has wave-like properties is not merely a laboratory curiosity; the implications are profound. Foremost among them is that the energy of matter, like that of light, is quantized.

We'll illustrate quantization with a simple system that physicists call "a particle in a box." FIGURE 38.15a shows a particle of mass m moving in one dimension as it bounces back and forth with speed v between the ends of a box of length L. The width of the box is irrelevant, so we'll call this a *one-dimensional box*. We'll assume that the collisions at the ends are perfectly elastic, so the particle's energy—entirely kinetic—never changes. According to classical physics, there are no restrictions on the particle's speed or energy.

But if matter has wave-like properties, perhaps we should consider the particle in a box to be a *wave* reflecting back and forth between the ends of the box, as shown in FIGURE 38.15b. These are the conditions that create standing waves. You learned in Chapter 21 that a standing wave of length L *must* have one of the wavelengths given by

$$\lambda_n = \frac{2L}{n} \qquad n = 1, 2, 3, 4, \ldots \tag{38.13}$$

If the confined particle has wave-like properties, it should satisfy both Equation 38.13 *and* the de Broglie relationship $\lambda = h/mv$. That is, a particle in a box should obey the relationship

$$\lambda_n = \frac{h}{mv} = \frac{2L}{n}$$

Thus the particle's speed must be

$$v_n = n\left(\frac{h}{2Lm}\right) \qquad n = 1, 2, 3, \ldots \tag{38.14}$$

In other words, the particle cannot bounce back and forth with just any speed. Rather, it can have *only* those specific speeds v_n, given by Equation 38.14, for which the de Broglie wavelength creates a standing wave in the box.

FIGURE 38.15 A particle confined in a box of length L.

(a) A classical particle bounces back and forth.

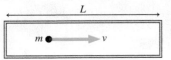

(b) A reflected wave creates a standing wave.

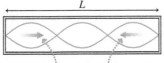

Matter waves travel in both directions.

Thus the particle's energy, which is purely kinetic energy, is

$$E_n = \frac{1}{2}mv_n^2 = n^2\frac{h^2}{8mL^2} \qquad n = 1, 2, 3, \ldots \qquad (38.15)$$

De Broglie's hypothesis about the wave-like properties of matter leads us to the remarkable conclusion that **a particle confined in a box can have only certain energies.** We say that its energy is **quantized.** The energy of the particle in the box can be $1(h^2/8mL^2)$, or $4(h^2/8mL^2)$, or $9(h^2/8mL^2)$, but it *cannot* have an energy between these values.

The possible values of the particle's energy are called **energy levels,** and the integer n that characterizes the energy levels is called the **quantum number.** The quantum number can be found by counting the antinodes, just as you learned to do for standing waves on a string. The standing wave shown in Figure 38.15 is $n = 3$, thus its energy is E_3.

We can rewrite Equation 38.15 in the useful form

$$E_n = n^2E_1 \qquad (38.16)$$

where

$$E_1 = \frac{h^2}{8mL^2} \qquad (38.17)$$

is the **fundamental quantum of energy** for a particle in a one-dimensional box. It is analogous to the fundamental frequency f_1 of a standing wave on a string.

EXAMPLE 38.7   **The energy levels of a virus**

A 30-nm-diameter virus is about the smallest imaginable macroscopic particle. What is the fundamental quantum of energy for this virus if confined in a one-dimensional cell of length 1.0 μm? The density of a virus is very close to that of water.

MODEL Model the virus as a particle in a box.

SOLVE The mass of a virus is $m = \rho V$, where the volume is $\frac{4}{3}\pi r^3$. A quick calculation shows that a 30-nm-diameter virus has mass $m = 1.4 \times 10^{-20}$ kg. The confinement length is $L = 1.0 \times 10^{-6}$ m. From Equation 38.17, the fundamental quantum of energy is

$$E_1 = \frac{h^2}{8mL^2} = \frac{(6.63 \times 10^{-34}\,\text{J s})^2}{8(1.4 \times 10^{-20}\,\text{kg})(1.0 \times 10^{-6}\,\text{m})^2}$$

$$= 3.9 \times 10^{-36}\,\text{J} = 2.5 \times 10^{-17}\,\text{eV}$$

ASSESS This is such an incredibly small amount of energy that there is no hope of distinguishing between energies of E_1 or $4E_1$ or $9E_1$. For any macroscopic particle, even one this tiny, the allowed energies will *seem* to be perfectly continuous. We will not observe the quantization.

EXAMPLE 38.8   **The energy levels of an electron**

As a very simple model of a hydrogen atom, consider an electron confined in a one-dimensional box of length 0.10 nm, about the size of an atom. What are the first three allowed energy levels?

SOLVE We can use Equation 38.17, with $m_{\text{elec}} = 9.11 \times 10^{-31}$ kg and $L = 1.0 \times 10^{-10}$ m, to find that the fundamental quantum of energy is $E_1 = 6.0 \times 10^{-18}$ J $= 38$ eV. Thus the first three allowed energies of an electron in a 0.10 nm box are

$$E_1 = 38\ \text{eV}$$

$$E_2 = 4E_1 = 152\ \text{eV}$$

$$E_3 = 9E_1 = 342\ \text{eV}$$

ASSESS You'll soon see that the results are way off. This model of a hydrogen atom is *too* simple to capture essential details.

It is the *confinement* of the particle in a box that leads to standing matter waves and thus energy quantization. Our goal is to extend this idea to atoms. An atom is certainly more complicated than a one-dimensional box, but an electron is "confined" within an atom. Thus an electron in an atom must be some kind of three-dimensional standing wave and, like the particle in a box, must have quantized energies. De Broglie's idea is steering us toward a new theory of matter.

STOP TO THINK 38.3 What is the quantum number of this particle confined in a box?

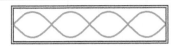

38.5 Bohr's Model of Atomic Quantization

Thomson's electron and Rutherford's nucleus made it clear that the atom has a *structure* of some sort. The challenge at the beginning of the 20th century was to deduce, from experimental evidence, the correct structure. The difficulty of this task cannot be exaggerated. The evidence about atoms, such as observations of atomic spectra, was very indirect, and experiments were carried out with only the simplest measuring devices.

Rutherford's nuclear model was the most successful of various proposals, but Rutherford's model failed to explain why atoms are stable or why their spectra are discrete. A missing piece of the puzzle, although not recognized as such for a few years, was Einstein's 1905 introduction of light quanta. If light comes in discrete packets of energy, which we now call photons, and if atoms emit and absorb light, what does that imply about the structure of the atoms?

This was the question posed by the Danish physicist Niels Bohr, shown as a young man in FIGURE 38.16. After receiving his doctoral degree in physics in 1911, Bohr went to England to work in Rutherford's laboratory. Rutherford had just, within the previous year, completed his development of the nuclear model of the atom. Rutherford's model certainly contained a kernel of truth, but Bohr wanted to understand how a solar-system-like atom could be stable and not radiate away all its energy. He soon recognized that Einstein's light quanta had profound implications for the structure of atoms. In 1913, Bohr proposed a new model of the atom in which he added quantization to Rutherford's nuclear atom.

The basic assumptions of the **Bohr model of the atom** are as follows:

FIGURE 38.16 Niels Bohr.

Understanding Bohr's model

Electrons can exist in only certain allowed orbits.

An electron cannot exist here, where there is no allowed orbit.

This is one   This is another
stationary   stationary
state.   state.

1. The electrons in an atom can exist in only certain *allowed orbits*. A particular arrangement of electrons in these orbits is called a **stationary state.**

Stationary states

These other states are **excited states**.

This state, with the lowest energy E_1, is the **ground state**. It is stable and can persist indefinitely.

2. Each stationary state has a discrete, well-defined energy E_n. That is, atomic energies are *quantized*. The stationary states are labeled by the *quantum number n* in order of increasing energy: $E_1 < E_2 < E_3 < \cdots$.

Photon emission

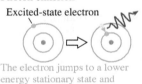

Excited-state electron

The electron jumps to a lower energy stationary state and emits a photon.

Photon absorption

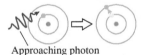

Approaching photon

The electron absorbs the photon and jumps to a higher energy stationary state.

3. An atom can undergo a **transition** or **quantum jump** from one stationary state to another by emitting or absorbing a photon whose energy is exactly equal to the energy difference between the two stationary states.

Collisional excitation

Approaching   Particle loses
particle   energy.

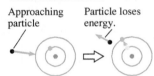

The particle transfers energy to the atom in the collision and excites the atom.

An atom in an excited state jumps to lower states, emitting a photon at each jump.

4. Atoms can also move from a lower energy state to a higher energy state by absorbing energy in a collision with an electron or other atom in a process called **collisional excitation.**

The excited atoms soon jump down to lower states, eventually ending in the stable ground state.

Bohr's model builds upon Rutherford's model, but it adds two new ideas that are derived from Einstein's ideas of quanta. The first, expressed in assumption 1, is that only certain electron orbits are "allowed" or can exist. The second, expressed in assumption 3, is that **the atom can jump from one state to another by emitting or absorbing a photon of just the right frequency to conserve energy.**

According to Einstein, a photon of frequency f has energy $E_{photon} = hf$. If an atom jumps from an initial state with energy E_i to a final state with energy E_f, energy will be conserved if the atom emits or absorbs a photon with $E_{photon} = \Delta E_{atom} = |E_f - E_i|$. This photon must have frequency

$$f_{photon} = \frac{\Delta E_{atom}}{h} \tag{38.18}$$

if it is to add or carry away exactly the right amount of energy. The total energy of the atom-plus-light system is conserved.

NOTE ▶ When an atom is excited to a higher energy level by absorbing a photon, the photon vanishes. Thus energy conservation requires $E_{photon} = \Delta E_{atom}$. When an atom is excited to a higher energy level in a collision with a particle, such as an electron or another atom, the particle still exists after the collision and still has energy. Thus energy conservation requires the less stringent condition $E_{particle} \geq \Delta E_{atom}$. ◀

The implications of Bohr's model are profound. In particular:

1. **Matter is stable.** An atom in its ground state has no states of any lower energy to which it can jump. It can remain in the ground state forever.
2. **Atoms emit and absorb a *discrete spectrum.*** Only those photons whose frequencies match the energy *intervals* between the stationary states can be emitted or absorbed. Photons of other frequencies cannot be emitted or absorbed without violating energy conservation.
3. **Emission spectra can be produced by collisions.** In a gas discharge tube, the current-carrying electrons moving through the tube occasionally collide with the atoms. A collision transfers energy to an atom and can kick the atom to an excited state. Once the atom is in an excited state, it can emit photons of light—a discrete emission spectrum—as it jumps back down to lower-energy states.
4. **Absorption wavelengths are a subset of the wavelengths in the emission spectrum.** Recall that all the lines seen in an absorption spectrum are also seen in emission, but many emission lines are *not* seen in absorption. According to Bohr's model, most atoms, most of the time, are in their lowest energy state, the $n = 1$ ground state. Thus the absorption spectrum consists of *only* those transitions such as $1 \rightarrow 2$, $1 \rightarrow 3, \ldots$ in which the atom jumps from $n = 1$ to a higher value of n by absorbing a photon. Transitions such as $2 \rightarrow 3$ are *not* observed because there are essentially no atoms in $n = 2$ at any instant of time. On the other hand, atoms that have been excited to the $n = 3$ state by collisions can emit photons corresponding to transitions $3 \rightarrow 1$ *and* $3 \rightarrow 2$. Thus the wavelength corresponding to $\Delta E_{atom} = E_3 - E_1$ is seen in both emission and absorption, but transitions with $\Delta E_{atom} = E_3 - E_2$ occur in emission only.
5. **Each element in the periodic table has a unique spectrum.** The energies of the stationary states are the energies of the orbiting electrons. Different elements, with different numbers of electrons, have different stable orbits and thus different stationary states. States with different energies emit and absorb photons of different wavelengths.

EXAMPLE 38.9 The wavelength of an emitted photon

An atom has stationary states with energies $E_j = 4.00$ eV and $E_k = 6.00$ eV. What is the wavelength of a photon emitted in a quantum jump from state k to state j?

MODEL To conserve energy, the emitted photon must have exactly the energy lost by the atom in the quantum jump.

SOLVE The atom can jump from the higher energy state k to the lower energy state j by emitting a photon. The atom's change in energy is $\Delta E_{atom} = |E_j - E_k| = 2.00$ eV, so the photon energy must be $E_{photon} = 2.00$ eV.

The photon frequency is

$$f = \frac{E_{photon}}{h} = \frac{2.00 \text{ eV}}{4.14 \times 10^{-15} \text{ eV s}} = 4.83 \times 10^{14} \text{ Hz}$$

The wavelength of this photon is

$$\lambda = \frac{c}{f} = 621 \text{ nm}$$

ASSESS 621 nm is a visible-light wavelength. Notice that the wavelength depends on the *difference* between the atom's energy levels, not the *values* of the energies.

Energy-Level Diagrams

An **energy-level diagram,** such as the one shown in FIGURE 38.17, is a useful pictorial representation of the stationary-state energies. An energy-level diagram is less a graph than it is a picture. The vertical axis represents energy, but the horizontal axis is not a scale. Think of this as a picture of a ladder in which the energies are the rungs of the ladder. The lowest rung, with energy E_1, is the ground state. Higher rungs are labeled by their quantum numbers, $n = 2, 3, 4, \ldots$.

FIGURE 38.17 An energy-level diagram.

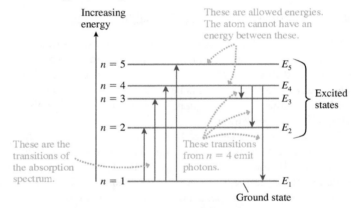

Energy-level diagrams are especially useful for showing transitions, or quantum jumps, in which a photon of light is emitted or absorbed. As examples, Figure 38.17 shows upward transitions in which a photon is absorbed by a ground-state atom ($n = 1$) and downward transitions in which a photon is emitted from an $n = 4$ excited state.

EXAMPLE 38.10 Emission and absorption

An atom has stationary states $E_1 = 0.00$ eV, $E_2 = 3.00$ eV, and $E_3 = 5.00$ eV. What wavelengths are observed in the absorption spectrum and in the emission spectrum of this atom?

MODEL Photons are emitted when an atom undergoes a quantum jump from a higher energy level to a lower energy level. Photons are absorbed in a quantum jump from a lower energy level to a higher energy level. But most of the atoms are in the $n = 1$ ground state, so the only quantum jumps seen in the absorption spectrum start from the $n = 1$ state.

VISUALIZE FIGURE 38.18 shows an energy-level diagram for the atom.

FIGURE 38.18 The atom's energy-level diagram.

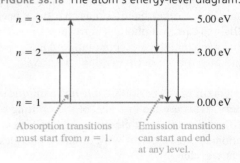

SOLVE This atom will absorb photons on the $1 \rightarrow 2$ and $1 \rightarrow 3$ transitions, with $\Delta E_{1 \rightarrow 2} = 3.00$ eV and $\Delta E_{1 \rightarrow 3} = 5.00$ eV. From $f = \Delta E_{atom}/h$ and $\lambda = c/f$, we find that the wavelengths in the absorption spectrum are

$$1 \rightarrow 2 \quad f = 3.00 \text{ eV}/h = 7.25 \times 10^{14} \text{ Hz}$$

$$\lambda = 414 \text{ nm (blue)}$$

$$1 \rightarrow 3 \quad f = 5.00 \text{ eV}/h = 1.21 \times 10^{15} \text{ Hz}$$

$$\lambda = 248 \text{ nm (ultraviolet)}$$

The emission spectrum will also have the 414 nm and 248 nm wavelengths due to the $2 \rightarrow 1$ and $3 \rightarrow 1$ quantum jumps from excited states 2 and 3 to the ground state. In addition, the emission spectrum will contain the $3 \rightarrow 2$ quantum jump with $\Delta E_{3 \rightarrow 2} = -2.00$ eV that is *not* seen in absorption because there are too few atoms in the $n = 2$ state to absorb. We found in Example 38.9 that a 2.00 eV transition corresponds to a wavelength of 621 nm. Thus the emission wavelengths are

$$2 \rightarrow 1 \quad \lambda = 414 \text{ nm (blue)}$$

$$3 \rightarrow 1 \quad \lambda = 248 \text{ nm (ultraviolet)}$$

$$3 \rightarrow 2 \quad \lambda = 621 \text{ nm (orange)}$$

STOP TO THINK 38.4 A photon with a wavelength of 414 nm has energy $E_{photon} = 3.00$ eV. Do you expect to see a spectral line with $\lambda = 414$ nm in the emission spectrum of the atom represented by this energy-level diagram? If so, what transition or transitions will emit it? Do you expect to see a spectral line with $\lambda = 414$ nm in the absorption spectrum? If so, what transition or transitions will absorb it?

$n = 4$	6.00 eV
$n = 3$	5.00 eV
$n = 2$	2.00 eV
$n = 1$	0.00 eV

38.6 The Bohr Hydrogen Atom

Bohr's hypothesis was a bold new idea, yet there was still one enormous stumbling block: What *are* the stationary states of an atom? Everything in Bohr's model hinges on the existence of these stationary states, of there being only certain electron orbits that are allowed. But nothing in classical physics provides any basis for such orbits. And Bohr's model describes only the *consequences* of having stationary states, not how to find them. If such states really exist, we will have to go beyond classical physics to find them.

To address this problem, Bohr did an explicit analysis of the hydrogen atom. The hydrogen atom, with only a single electron, was known to be the simplest atom. Furthermore, as we discussed in Chapter 37, Balmer had discovered a fairly simple formula that characterized the wavelengths in the hydrogen emission spectrum. Anyone with a successful model of an atom was going to have to *predict*, from theory, Balmer's formula for the hydrogen atom.

Bohr's paper followed a rather circuitous line of reasoning. That is not surprising because he had little to go on at the time. But our goal is a clear explanation of the ideas, not a historical study of Bohr's methods, so we are going to follow a different analysis using de Broglie's matter waves. De Broglie did not propose matter waves until 1924, 11 years after Bohr's paper, but with the clarity of hindsight we can see that treating the electron as a wave provides a more straightforward analysis of the hydrogen atom. Although our route will be different from Bohr's, we will arrive at the same point, and, in addition, we will be in a much better position to understand the work that came after Bohr.

NOTE ▶ Bohr's analysis of the hydrogen atom is sometimes called the *Bohr atom*. It's important not to confuse this analysis, which applies only to hydrogen, with the more general postulates of the *Bohr model of the atom*. Those postulates, which we looked at in Section 38.5, apply to any atom. To make the distinction clear, we'll call Bohr's analysis of hydrogen the *Bohr hydrogen atom*. ◀

FIGURE 38.19 A Rutherford hydrogen atom. The size of the nucleus is greatly exaggerated.

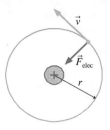

The Stationary States of the Hydrogen Atom

FIGURE 38.19 shows a Rutherford hydrogen atom, with a single electron orbiting a nucleus that consists of a single proton. We will assume a circular orbit of radius r and speed v. We will also assume, to keep the analysis manageable, that the proton remains stationary while the electron revolves around it. This is a reasonable assumption because the proton is roughly 1800 times as massive as the electron. With these assumptions, the atom's energy is the kinetic energy of the electron plus the potential energy of the electron-proton interaction. This is

$$E = K + U = \frac{1}{2}mv^2 + \frac{1}{4\pi\epsilon_0}\frac{q_{elec}q_{proton}}{r} = \frac{1}{2}mv^2 - \frac{e^2}{4\pi\epsilon_0 r} \qquad (38.19)$$

where we used $q_{elec} = -e$ and $q_{proton} = +e$.

NOTE ▶ m is the mass of the electron, *not* the mass of the entire atom. ◀

Now, the electron, as we are coming to understand it, has both particle-like and wave-like properties. First, let us treat the electron as a charged particle. The proton exerts a Coulomb electric force on the electron:

$$\vec{F}_{elec} = \left(\frac{1}{4\pi\epsilon_0}\frac{e^2}{r^2}, \text{ toward center}\right) \qquad (38.20)$$

This force gives the electron an acceleration $\vec{a}_{elec} = \vec{F}_{elec}/m$ that also points to the center. This is a centripetal acceleration, causing the particle to move in its circular orbit. The centripetal acceleration of a particle moving in a circle of radius r at speed v *must* be v^2/r, thus

$$a_{elec} = \frac{F_{elec}}{m} = \frac{e^2}{4\pi\epsilon_0 mr^2} = \frac{v^2}{r} \qquad (38.21)$$

Rearranging, we find

$$v^2 = \frac{e^2}{4\pi\epsilon_0 mr} \qquad (38.22)$$

Equation 38.22 is a *constraint* on the motion. The speed v and radius r must satisfy Equation 38.22 if the electron is to move in a circular orbit. This constraint is not unique to atoms; we earlier found a similar relationship between v and r for orbiting satellites.

Now let's treat the electron as a de Broglie wave. In Section 38.4 we found that a particle confined to a one-dimensional box sets up a standing wave as it reflects back and forth. A standing wave, you will recall, consists of two traveling waves moving in opposite directions. When the round-trip distance in the box is equal to an integer number of wavelengths ($2L = n\lambda$), the two oppositely traveling waves interfere constructively to set up the standing wave.

Suppose that, instead of traveling back and forth along a line, our wave-like particle travels around the circumference of a circle. The particle will set up a standing wave, just like the particle in the box, if there are waves traveling in both directions and if the round-trip distance is an integer number of wavelengths. This is the idea we want to carry over from the particle in a box. As an example, FIGURE 38.20 shows a standing wave around a circle with $n = 10$ wavelengths.

The mathematical condition for a circular standing wave is found by replacing the round-trip distance $2L$ in a box with the round-trip distance $2\pi r$ on a circle. Thus a circular standing wave will occur when

$$2\pi r = n\lambda \qquad n = 1, 2, 3, \ldots \qquad (38.23)$$

But the de Broglie wavelength for a particle *has* to be $\lambda = h/p = h/mv$. Thus the standing-wave condition for a de Broglie wave is

$$2\pi r = n\frac{h}{mv}$$

FIGURE 38.20 An $n = 10$ electron standing wave around the orbit's circumference.

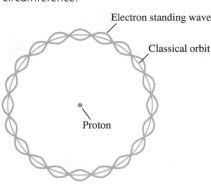

Electron standing wave

Classical orbit

Proton

This condition is true only if the electron's speed is

$$v_n = \frac{nh}{2\pi mr} \qquad n = 1, 2, 3, \ldots \qquad (38.24)$$

The quantity $h/2\pi$ occurs so often in quantum physics that it is customary to give it a special name. We define the quantity $\hbar$, pronounced "h bar," as

$$\hbar \equiv \frac{h}{2\pi} = 1.055 \times 10^{-34} \, \text{J s} = 6.58 \times 10^{-16} \, \text{eV s}$$

With this definition, we can write Equation 38.24 as

$$v_n = \frac{n\hbar}{mr} \qquad n = 1, 2, 3, \ldots \qquad (38.25)$$

This, like Equation 38.22, is another relationship between v and r. This is the constraint that arises from treating the electron as a wave.

Now if the electron can act as both a particle *and* a wave, then both the Equation 38.22 *and* Equation 38.25 constraints have to be obeyed. That is, v^2 as given by the Equation 38.22 particle constraint has to equal v^2 of the Equation 38.25 wave constraint. Equating these gives

$$v^2 = \frac{e^2}{4\pi\epsilon_0 mr} = \frac{n^2\hbar^2}{m^2 r^2}$$

We can solve this equation to find that the radius r is

$$r_n = n^2 \frac{4\pi\epsilon_0 \hbar^2}{me^2} \qquad n = 1, 2, 3, \ldots \qquad (38.26)$$

where we have added a subscript n to the radius r to indicate that it depends on the integer n.

The right-hand side of Equation 38.26, except for the n^2, is just a collection of constants. Let's group them all together and define the **Bohr radius** a_B as

$$a_B = \text{Bohr radius} \equiv \frac{4\pi\epsilon_0 \hbar^2}{me^2} = 5.29 \times 10^{-11} \, \text{m} = 0.0529 \, \text{nm}$$

With this definition, Equation 38.26 for the radius of the electron's orbit becomes

$$r_n = n^2 a_B \qquad n = 1, 2, 3, \ldots \qquad (38.27)$$

For example, $r_1 = 0.053$ nm, $r_2 = 0.212$ nm and $r_3 = 0.476$ nm.

We have discovered stationary states! That is, **a hydrogen atom can exist *only* if the radius of the electron's orbit is one of the values given by Equation 38.27.** Intermediate values of the radius, such as $r = 0.100$ nm, cannot exist because the electron cannot set up a standing wave around the circumference. The possible orbits are *quantized*, with only certain orbits allowed.

The key step leading to Equation 38.27 was the requirement that the electron have wave-like properties in addition to particle-like properties. This requirement leads to quantized orbits, or what Bohr called stationary states. The integer n is thus the *quantum number* that numbers the various stationary states.

Hydrogen Atom Energy Levels

Now we can make progress quickly. Knowing the possible radii, we can return to Equation 38.24 and find the possible electron speeds to be

$$v_n = \frac{n\hbar}{mr_n} = \frac{1}{n}\frac{\hbar}{ma_B} = \frac{v_1}{n} \qquad n = 1, 2, 3, \ldots \qquad (38.28)$$

where $v_1 = \hbar/ma_B = 2.19 \times 10^6$ m/s is the electron's speed in the $n = 1$ orbit. The speed decreases as n increases.

Finally, we can determine the energies of the stationary states. From Equation 38.19 for the energy, with Equations 38.27 and 38.28 for r and v, we have

$$E_n = \frac{1}{2}mv_n^2 - \frac{e^2}{4\pi\epsilon_0 r_n} = \frac{1}{2}m\left(\frac{\hbar^2}{m^2 a_B^2 n^2}\right) - \frac{e^2}{4\pi\epsilon_0 n^2 a_B} \tag{38.29}$$

As a homework problem, you can show that this rather messy expression simplifies to

$$E_n = -\frac{1}{n^2}\left(\frac{1}{4\pi\epsilon_0}\frac{e^2}{2a_B}\right) \tag{38.30}$$

The expression in parentheses is easily evaluated, giving

$$\frac{1}{4\pi\epsilon_0}\frac{e^2}{2a_B} = 13.60 \text{ eV}$$

We can then write the energy levels of the stationary states of the hydrogen atom as

$$E_n = -\frac{13.60 \text{ eV}}{n^2} \qquad n = 1, 2, 3, \ldots \tag{38.31}$$

This has been a lot of math, so we need to see where we are and what we have learned. Table 38.2 shows values of r_n, v_n, and E_n evaluated for quantum number values $n = 1$ to 5. We do indeed seem to have discovered stationary states of the hydrogen atom. Each state, characterized by its quantum number n, has a unique radius, speed, and energy. These are displayed graphically in FIGURE 38.21, in which the orbits are drawn to scale. Notice how the atom's diameter increases very rapidly as n increases. At the same time, the electron's speed decreases.

FIGURE 38.21 The first four stationary states, or allowed orbits, of the Bohr hydrogen atom drawn to scale.

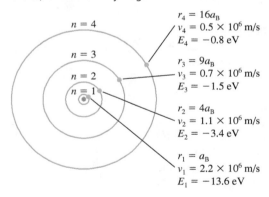

$r_4 = 16a_B$
$v_4 = 0.5 \times 10^6 \text{ m/s}$
$E_4 = -0.8 \text{ eV}$

$r_3 = 9a_B$
$v_3 = 0.7 \times 10^6 \text{ m/s}$
$E_3 = -1.5 \text{ eV}$

$r_2 = 4a_B$
$v_2 = 1.1 \times 10^6 \text{ m/s}$
$E_2 = -3.4 \text{ eV}$

$r_1 = a_B$
$v_1 = 2.2 \times 10^6 \text{ m/s}$
$E_1 = -13.6 \text{ eV}$

TABLE 38.2 Radii, speeds, and energies for the first five states of the Bohr hydrogen atom

n	r_n (nm)	v_n (m/s)	E_n (eV)
1	0.053	2.19×10^6	-13.60
2	0.212	1.09×10^6	-3.40
3	0.476	0.73×10^6	-1.51
4	0.846	0.55×10^6	-0.85
5	1.322	0.44×10^6	-0.54

EXAMPLE 38.11 **Stationary states of the hydrogen atom**

Can an electron in a hydrogen atom have a speed of 3.60×10^5 m/s? If so, what are its energy and the radius of its orbit? What about a speed of 3.65×10^5 m/s?

SOLVE To be in a stationary state, the electron must have speed

$$v_n = \frac{v_1}{n} = \frac{2.19 \times 10^6 \text{ m/s}}{n}$$

where n is an integer. A speed of 3.60×10^5 m/s would require quantum number

$$n = \frac{2.19 \times 10^6 \text{ m/s}}{3.60 \times 10^5 \text{ m/s}} = 6.08$$

This is not an integer, so the electron can *not* have this speed. But if $v = 3.65 \times 10^5$ m/s, then

$$n = \frac{2.19 \times 10^6 \text{ m/s}}{3.65 \times 10^5 \text{ m/s}} = 6$$

This is the speed of an electron in the $n = 6$ excited state. An electron in this state has energy

$$E_6 = -\frac{13.60 \text{ eV}}{6^2} = -0.38 \text{ eV}$$

and the radius of its orbit is

$$r_6 = 6^2(5.29 \times 10^{-11} \text{ m}) = 1.90 \times 10^{-9} \text{ m} = 1.90 \text{ nm}$$

Binding Energy and Ionization Energy

It is important to understand why the energies of the stationary states are negative. Because the potential energy of two charged particles is $U = q_1 q_2/4\pi\epsilon_0 r$, the zero of potential energy occurs at $r = \infty$ where the particles are infinitely far apart. The state of zero total energy corresponds to having the electron at rest ($K = 0$) and infinitely far from the proton ($U = 0$). This situation, which is the case of two "free particles," occurs in the limit $n \to \infty$, for which $r_n \to \infty$ and $v_n \to 0$.

An electron and a proton bound into an atom have *less* energy than two free particles. We know this because we would have to do work (i.e., add energy) to pull the electron and proton apart. If the bound atom's energy is lower than that of two free particles, and if the total energy of two free particles is zero, then it must be the case that the atom has a *negative* amount of energy.

Thus $|E_n|$ is the **binding energy** of the electron in stationary state n. In the ground state, where $E_1 = -13.60$ eV, we would have to add 13.60 eV to the electron to free it from the proton and reach the zero energy state of two free particles. We can say that the electron in the ground state is "bound by 13.60 eV." An electron in an $n = 3$ orbit, where it is farther from the proton and moving more slowly, is bound by only 1.51 eV. That is the amount of energy you would have to supply to remove the electron from an $n = 3$ orbit.

Removing the electron entirely leaves behind a positive ion, H^+ in the case of a hydrogen atom. (The fact that H^+ happens to be a proton does not alter the fact that it is also an atomic ion.) Because nearly all atoms are in their ground state, the binding energy $|E_1|$ of the ground state is called the **ionization energy** of an atom. Bohr's analysis predicts that the ionization energy of hydrogen is 13.60 eV. FIGURE 38.22 illustrates the ideas of binding energy and ionization energy.

We can test this prediction by shooting a beam of electrons at hydrogen atoms. A projectile electron can knock out an atomic electron if its kinetic energy K is greater than the atom's ionization energy, leaving an ion behind. But a projectile electron will be unable to cause ionization if its kinetic energy is less than the atom's ionization energy. This is a fairly straightforward experiment to carry out, and the evidence shows that the ionization energy of hydrogen is, indeed, 13.60 eV.

Quantization of Angular Momentum

The angular momentum of a particle in circular motion, whether it is a planet or an electron, is

$$L = mvr$$

You will recall that angular momentum is conserved in orbital motion because a force directed toward a central point exerts no torque on the particle. Bohr used conservation of energy explicitly in his analysis of the hydrogen atom, but what role does conservation of angular momentum play?

The condition that a de Broglie wave for the electron set up a standing wave around the circumference was given, in Equation 38.23, as

$$2\pi r = n\lambda = n\frac{h}{mv}$$

Multiplying by mv and dividing by 2π, we can rewrite this equation as

$$mvr = n\frac{h}{2\pi} = n\hbar \tag{38.32}$$

But mvr is the angular momentum L for a particle in a circular orbit. It appears that the angular momentum of an orbiting electron cannot have just any value. Instead, it must satisfy

$$L = n\hbar \qquad n = 1, 2, 3, \ldots \tag{38.33}$$

Thus angular momentum also is quantized! The electron's angular momentum must be an integer multiple of Planck's constant $\hbar$.

FIGURE 38.22 Binding energy and ionization energy.

The *binding energy* is the energy needed to remove an electron from its orbit.

The *ionization energy* is the energy needed to create an ion by removing a ground-state electron.

The quantization of angular momentum is a direct consequence of this wave-like nature of the electron. We will find that the quantization of angular momentum plays a major role in the behavior of more complex atoms, leading to the idea of electron shells that you likely have studied in chemistry.

STOP TO THINK 38.5   What is the quantum number of this hydrogen atom?

38.7 The Hydrogen Spectrum

Our analysis of the hydrogen atom has revealed stationary states, but how do we know whether the results make any sense? The most important experimental evidence that we have about the hydrogen atom is its spectrum, so the primary test of the Bohr hydrogen atom is whether it correctly predicts the spectrum.

The Hydrogen Energy-Level Diagram

FIGURE 38.23 The energy-level diagram of the hydrogen atom.

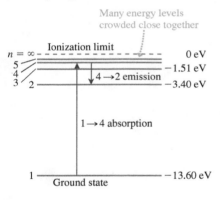

FIGURE 38.23 is an energy-level diagram for the hydrogen atom. As we noted earlier, the energies are like the rungs of a ladder. The lowest rung is the ground state, with $E_1 = -13.60$ eV. The top rung, with $E = 0$ eV, corresponds to a hydrogen ion in the limit $n \to \infty$. This top rung is called the **ionization limit.** In principle there are an infinite number of rungs, but only the lowest few are shown. The higher values of n are all crowded together just below the ionization limit at $n = \infty$.

The figure shows a $1 \to 4$ transition in which a photon is absorbed and a $4 \to 2$ transition in which a photon is emitted. For two quantum states m and n, where $n > m$ and E_n is the higher energy state, an atom can *emit* a photon in an $n \to m$ transition or *absorb* a photon in an $m \to n$ transition.

The Emission Spectrum

According to the third assumption of Bohr's model of atomic quantization, the frequency of the photon emitted in an $n \to m$ transition is

$$f = \frac{\Delta E_{\text{atom}}}{h} = \frac{E_n - E_m}{h} \tag{38.34}$$

We can use Equation 38.30 for the energies E_n and E_m to predict that the emitted photon has frequency

$$f = \frac{1}{h}\left\{\left[-\frac{1}{n^2}\left(\frac{1}{4\pi\epsilon_0}\frac{e^2}{2a_{\text{B}}}\right)\right] - \left[-\frac{1}{m^2}\left(\frac{1}{4\pi\epsilon_0}\frac{e^2}{2a_{\text{B}}}\right)\right]\right\}$$

$$= \frac{1}{4\pi\epsilon_0}\frac{e^2}{2ha_{\text{B}}}\left(\frac{1}{m^2} - \frac{1}{n^2}\right) \tag{38.35}$$

The frequency is a positive number because $m < n$ and thus $1/m^2 > 1/n^2$.

We are more interested in wavelength than frequency, because wavelengths are the quantity measured by experiment. The wavelength of the photon emitted in an $n \to m$ quantum jump is

$$\lambda_{n \to m} = \frac{c}{f} = \frac{8\pi\epsilon_0 hca_{\text{B}}/e^2}{\left(\dfrac{1}{m^2} - \dfrac{1}{n^2}\right)} \tag{38.36}$$

This looks rather gruesome, but notice that the numerator is simply a collection of various constants. The value of the numerator, which we can call λ_0, is

$$\lambda_0 = \frac{8\pi\epsilon_0 hca_B}{e^2} = 9.112 \times 10^{-8} \text{ m} = 91.12 \text{ nm}$$

With this definition, our prediction for the wavelengths in the hydrogen emission spectrum is

$$\lambda_{n \to m} = \frac{\lambda_0}{\left(\dfrac{1}{m^2} - \dfrac{1}{n^2}\right)} \quad m = 1, 2, 3, \dots \quad n = m + 1, m + 2, \dots \quad (38.37)$$

This should look familiar. It is the Balmer formula from Chapter 37! However, there is one *slight* difference: Bohr's analysis of the hydrogen atom has predicted $\lambda_0 = 91.12$ nm, whereas Balmer found, from experiment, that $\lambda_0 = 91.18$ nm. Could Bohr have come this close but then fail to predict the Balmer formula correctly?

The problem, it turns out, is in our assumption that the proton remains at rest while the electron orbits it. In fact, *both* particles rotate about their common center of mass, rather like a dumbbell with a big end and a small end. The center of mass is very close to the proton, which is far more massive than the electron, but the proton is not entirely motionless. The good news is that a more advanced analysis can account for the proton's motion. It changes the energies of the stationary states ever so slightly—about 1 part in 2000—but that is precisely what is needed to give a revised value:

$$\lambda_0 = 91.18 \text{ nm when corrected for the nuclear motion}$$

It works! Unlike all previous atomic models, **the Bohr hydrogen atom correctly predicts the discrete spectrum of the hydrogen atom.** FIGURE 38.24 shows the *Balmer series* and the *Lyman series* transitions on an energy-level diagram. Only the Balmer series, consisting of transitions ending on the $m = 2$ state, gives visible wavelengths, and this is the series that Balmer initially analyzed. The Lyman series, ending on the $m = 1$ ground state, is in the ultraviolet region of the spectrum and was not measured until later. These series, as well as others in the infrared, are observed in a discharge tube where collisions with electrons excite the atoms upward from the ground state to state n. They then decay downward by emitting photons. Only the Lyman series is observed in the absorption spectrum because, as noted previously, essentially all the atoms in a quiescent gas are in the ground state.

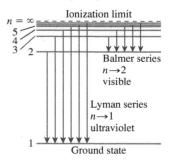

FIGURE 38.24 Transitions producing the Lyman series and the Balmer series of lines in the hydrogen spectrum.

EXAMPLE 38.12 **Hydrogen absorption**

Whenever astronomers look at distant galaxies, they find that the light has been strongly absorbed at the wavelength of the $1 \to 2$ transition in the Lyman series of hydrogen. This absorption tells us that interstellar space is filled with vast clouds of hydrogen left over from the Big Bang. What is the wavelength of the $1 \to 2$ absorption in hydrogen?

SOLVE Equation 38.37 predicts the *absorption* spectrum of hydrogen if we let $m = 1$. The absorption seen by astronomers is from the ground state of hydrogen ($m = 1$) to its first excited state ($n = 2$). The wavelength is

$$\lambda_{1 \to 2} = \frac{91.18 \text{ nm}}{\left(\dfrac{1}{1^2} - \dfrac{1}{2^2}\right)} = 121.6 \text{ nm}$$

ASSESS This wavelength is far into the ultraviolet. Ground-based astronomy cannot observe this region of the spectrum because the wavelengths are strongly absorbed by the atmosphere, but with space-based telescopes, first widely used in the 1970s, astronomers see 121.6 nm absorption in nearly every direction they look.

Hydrogen-Like Ions

An ion with a *single* electron orbiting Z protons in the nucleus is called a **hydrogen-like ion.** Z is the atomic number and describes the number of protons in the nucleus. He^+, with one electron circling a $Z = 2$ nucleus, and Li^{++}, with one electron and a

$Z = 3$ nucleus, are hydrogen-like ions. So is U^{+91}, with one lonely electron orbiting a $Z = 92$ uranium nucleus.

Any hydrogen-like ion is simply a variation on the Bohr hydrogen atom. The only difference between a hydrogen-like ion and neutral hydrogen is that the potential energy $-e^2/4\pi\epsilon_0 r$ becomes, instead, $-Ze^2/4\pi\epsilon_0 r$. Hydrogen itself is the $Z = 1$ case. If we repeat the analysis of the previous sections with this one change, we find:

$$r_n = \frac{n^2 a_B}{Z} \qquad E_n = -\frac{13.60\, Z^2 \text{ eV}}{n^2}$$

$$v_n = Z\frac{v_1}{n} \qquad \lambda_0 = \frac{91.18 \text{ nm}}{Z^2} \tag{38.38}$$

As the nuclear charge increases, the electron moves into a smaller-diameter, higher-speed orbit. Its ionization energy $|E_1|$ increases significantly, and its spectrum shifts to shorter wavelengths. Table 38.3 compares the ground-state atomic diameter $2r_1$, the ionization energy $|E_1|$, and the first wavelength $3 \rightarrow 2$ in the Balmer series for hydrogen and the first two hydrogen-like ions.

TABLE 38.3 Comparison of hydrogen-like ions with $Z = 1$, 2, and 3

Ion	Diameter $2r_1$	Ionization energy $|E_1|$	Wavelength of $3 \rightarrow 2$
H $(Z = 1)$	0.106 nm	13.6 eV	656 nm
He$^+$ $(Z = 2)$	0.053 nm	54.4 eV	164 nm
Li^{++} $(Z = 3)$	0.035 nm	122.4 eV	73 nm

Success and Failure

Bohr's analysis of the hydrogen atom seemed to be a resounding success. By introducing Einstein's ideas about light quanta, Bohr was able to provide the first understanding of discrete spectra and to predict the Balmer formula for the wavelengths in the hydrogen spectrum. And the Bohr hydrogen atom, unlike Rutherford's model, was stable. There was clearly some validity to the idea of stationary states.

But Bohr was completely unsuccessful at explaining the spectra of any other neutral atom. His method did not work even for helium, the second element in the periodic table with a mere two electrons. Something inherent in Bohr's assumptions seemed to work correctly for a single electron but not in situations with two or more electrons.

It is important to make a distinction between the Bohr model of atomic quantization, described in Section 38.5, and the Bohr hydrogen atom. The Bohr model assumes that stationary states exist, but it does not say how to find them. We found the stationary states of a hydrogen atom by requiring that an integer number of de Broglie waves fit around the circumference of the orbit, setting up standing waves. The difficulty with more complex atoms is not the Bohr model but the method of finding the stationary states. Bohr's model of the atomic quantization remains valid, and we will continue to use it, but the procedure of fitting standing waves to a circle is just too simple to find the stationary states of complex atoms. We need to find a better procedure.

Einstein, de Broglie, and Bohr carried physics into uncharted waters. Their successes made it clear that the microscopic realm of light and atoms is governed by quantization, discreteness, and a blurring of the distinction between particles and waves. Although Bohr was clearly on the right track, his inability to extend the Bohr hydrogen atom to more complex atoms made it equally clear that the complete and correct theory remained to be discovered. Bohr's theory was what we now call "semiclassical," a hybrid of classical Newtonian mechanics with the new ideas of quanta. Still missing was a complete theory of motion and dynamics in a quantized universe—a *quantum* mechanics.

Hydrogen fluorescence

Fluorescence is the absorption of light at one wavelength followed by emission at a longer wavelength. Suppose a hydrogen atom in its ground state absorbs an ultraviolet photon with a wavelength of 95.10 nm. Immediately after the absorption, the atom undergoes a quantum jump with $\Delta n = 3$. What is the wavelength of the photon emitted in this quantum jump?

MODEL Photons are emitted and absorbed as an atom undergoes quantum jumps from one energy level to another. The Bohr model gives the energy levels of the hydrogen atom.

VISUALIZE FIGURE 38.25 shows the process. To be absorbed, the photon energy has to match exactly the energy *difference* between the ground state of hydrogen and an excited state with quantum number n. After excitation, the atom emits a photon as it jumps downward in a $n \rightarrow n - 3$ transition.

FIGURE 38.25 The process of fluorescence in hydrogen. Energy levels are not drawn to scale.

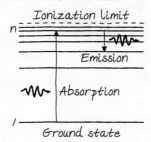

SOLVE The energy of the absorbed photon is

$$E = hf = \frac{hc}{\lambda} = \frac{(4.14 \times 10^{-15} \text{ eV s})(3.00 \times 10^8 \text{ m/s})}{95.10 \times 10^{-9} \text{ m}} = 13.06 \text{ eV}$$

The atom's initial energy is $E_1 = -13.60$ eV, the energy of the ground state of hydrogen. Absorbing a 13.06 eV photon raises the atom's energy to $E_n = E_1 + 13.06$ eV $= -0.54$ eV. The energy levels of hydrogen are given by

$$E_n = -\frac{13.60 \text{ eV}}{n^2}$$

The quantum number of the energy level with -0.54 eV is

$$n = \sqrt{-\frac{13.60 \text{ eV}}{(-0.54 \text{ eV})}} = 5$$

We see that the absorption is a $1 \rightarrow 5$ transition; thus the emission, with $\Delta n = 3$, must be a $5 \rightarrow 2$ transition. The energy of the $n = 2$ state is

$$E_2 = -\frac{13.60 \text{ eV}}{2^2} = -3.40 \text{ eV}$$

Consequently, the energy of the emitted photon is

$$E_{photon} = \Delta E_{atom} = (-0.54 \text{ eV}) - (-3.40 \text{ eV}) = 2.86 \text{ eV}$$

Inverting the energy-wavelength relationship that we started with, we find

$$\lambda = \frac{hc}{E_{photon}} = \frac{(4.14 \times 10^{-15} \text{ eV s})(3.00 \times 10^8 \text{ m/s})}{2.86 \text{ eV}} = 434 \text{ nm}$$

When atomic hydrogen gas is irradiated with ultraviolet light having a wavelength of 95.10 nm, it fluoresces at the visible wavelength of 434 nm. (It also fluoresces at infrared and ultraviolet wavelengths in downward transitions with other values of Δn.)

ASSESS The $5 \rightarrow 2$ transition is a member of the Balmer series, and a 434 nm spectral line was shown in the hydrogen spectrum of Figure 37.7. It is important to notice that the 13.06 eV photon energy does not match any energy level of the hydrogen atom. Instead, it matches the *difference* between two levels because that conserves energy in a quantum jump between those two levels. Photons with nearby wavelengths, such as 94 nm or 96 nm, would not be absorbed at all because their energy does not match the difference of any two energy levels in hydrogen.

SUMMARY

The goal of Chapter 38 has been to understand the quantization of energy for light and matter.

General Principles

Light has particle-like properties

- The energy of a light wave comes in discrete packets called light quanta or photons.
- For light of frequency f, the energy of each photon is $E = hf$, where h is **Planck's constant.**
- For a light wave that delivers power P, photons arrive at rate R such that $P = Rhf$.
- Photons are "particle-like" but are not classical particles.

Matter has wave-like properties

- The **de Broglie wavelength** of a "particle" of mass m is $\lambda = h/mv$.
- The wave-like nature of matter is seen in the interference patterns of electrons, neutrons, and entire atoms.
- When a particle is confined, it sets up a de Broglie standing wave. The fact that standing waves have only certain allowed wavelengths leads to the conclusion that a confined particle has only certain allowed energies. That is, energy is quantized.

Important Concepts

Einstein's Model of Light

- Light consists of quanta of energy $E = hf$.
- Quanta are emitted and absorbed on an all-or-nothing basis.
- When a light quantum is absorbed, it delivers all its energy to *one* electron.

Bohr's Model of the Atom

- An atom can exist in only certain stationary states. The allowed energies are quantized. State n has energy E_n.
- An atom can jump from one stationary state to another by emitting or absorbing a photon with $E_{\text{photon}} = hf = \Delta E_{\text{atom}}$.
- Atoms can be excited in inelastic collisions.
- Atoms seek the $n = 1$ **ground state.** Most atoms, most of the time, are in the ground state.

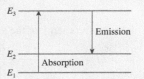

Applications

Photoelectric effect

Light can eject electrons from a metal only if $f \geq f_0 = E_0/h$, where E_0 is the metal's **work function.**

The **stopping potential** that stops even the fastest electrons is

$$V_{\text{stop}} = \frac{h}{e}(f - f_0)$$

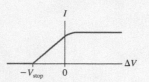

Particle in a box

A particle confined to a one-dimensional box of length L sets up de Broglie standing waves. The allowed energies are

$$E_n = \frac{1}{2}mv_n^2 = n^2 \frac{h^2}{8mL^2} \qquad n = 1, 2, 3, \ldots$$

The Bohr hydrogen atom

The stationary states are found by requiring an integer number of de Broglie wavelengths to fit around the circumference of the electron's orbit: $2\pi r = n\lambda$.

This leads to energy quantization with

$$r_n = n^2 a_B \qquad v_n = \frac{v_1}{n} \qquad E_n = -\frac{13.60 \text{ eV}}{n^2}$$

where $a_B = 0.0529$ nm is the **Bohr radius.** The Bohr hydrogen atom successfully predicts the Balmer formula for the hydrogen spectrum. Angular momentum is also quantized, with $L = n\hbar$.

Terms and Notation

photoelectric effect	wave packet	stationary state	ionization energy
threshold frequency, f_0	matter wave	excited state	ionization limit
stopping potential, V_{stop}	de Broglie wavelength	ground state	hydrogen-like ion
thermal emission	quantized	transition	
work function, E_0	energy level	quantum jump	
Planck's constant, h or $\hbar$	quantum number, n	collisional excitation	
light quantum	fundamental quantum of	energy-level diagram	
photon	energy, E_1	Bohr radius, a_B	
photon model	Bohr model of the atom	binding energy	

CONCEPTUAL QUESTIONS

1. a. A negatively charged electroscope can be discharged by shining an ultraviolet light on it. How does this happen?
   b. You might think that an ultraviolet light shining on an initially uncharged electroscope would cause the electroscope to become positively charged as photoelectrons are emitted. In fact, ultraviolet light has no noticeable effect on an uncharged electroscope. Why not?

2. a. Explain why the graphs of Figure 38.3 are mostly horizontal for $\Delta V > 0$.
   b. Explain why photoelectrons are ejected from the cathode with a range of kinetic energies, rather than all electrons having the same kinetic energy.
   c. Explain the reasoning by which we claim that the stopping potential V_{stop} indicates the maximum kinetic energy of the electrons.

3. How would the graph of Figure 38.2 look if classical physics provided the correct description of the photoelectric effect? Draw the graph and explain your reasoning. Assume that the light intensity remains constant as its frequency and wavelength are varied.

4. How would the graphs of Figure 38.3 look if classical physics provided the correct description of the photoelectric effect? Draw the graph and explain your reasoning. Include curves for both weak light and intense light.

5. FIGURE Q38.5 is the current-versus-potential-difference graph for a photoelectric-effect experiment with an unknown metal. If classical physics provided the correct description of the photoelectric effect, how would the graph look if:
   a. The light was replaced by an equally intense light with a shorter wavelength? Draw it.
   b. The metal was replaced by a different metal with a smaller work function? Draw it.

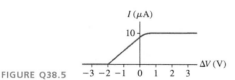

FIGURE Q38.5

6. Metal 1 has a larger work function than metal 2. Both are illuminated with the same short-wavelength ultraviolet light. Do photoelectrons from metal 1 have a higher speed, a lower speed, or the same speed as photoelectrons from metal 2? Explain.

7. Electron 1 is accelerated from rest through a potential difference of 100 V. Electron 2 is accelerated from rest through a potential difference of 200 V. Afterward, which electron has the larger de Broglie wavelength? Explain.

8. An electron and a proton are each accelerated from rest through a potential difference of 100 V. Afterward, which particle has the larger de Broglie wavelength? Explain.

9. FIGURE Q38.9 is a simulation of the electrons detected behind two closely spaced slits. Each bright dot represents one electron. How will this pattern change if
   a. The electron-beam intensity is increased?
   b. The electron speed is reduced?
   c. The electrons are replaced by neutrons?
   d. The left slit is closed?
   Your answers should consider the number of dots on the screen and the spacing, width, and positions of the fringes.

FIGURE Q38.9

10. Imagine that the horizontal box of Figure 38.15 is instead oriented vertically. Also imagine the box to be on a neutron star where the gravitational field is so strong that the particle in the box slows significantly, nearly stopping, before it hits the top of the box. Make a *qualitative* sketch of the $n = 3$ de Broglie standing wave of a particle in this box.
    Hint: The nodes are *not* uniformly spaced.

11. If an electron is in a *stationary state* of an atom, is the electron at rest? If not, what does the term mean?

12. FIGURE Q38.12 shows the energy-level diagram of Element X.
    a. What is the ionization energy of Element X?
    b. An atom in the ground state absorbs a photon, then emits a photon with a wavelength of 1240 nm. What conclusion can you draw about the energy of the photon that was absorbed?
    c. An atom in the ground state has a collision with an electron, then emits a photon with a wavelength of 1240 nm. What conclusion can you draw about the initial kinetic energy of the electron?

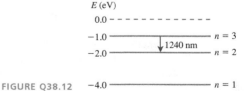

FIGURE Q38.12

EXERCISES AND PROBLEMS

Problems labeled [   ] integrate material from earlier chapters.

Exercises

Section 38.1 The Photoelectric Effect

Section 38.2 Einstein's Explanation

1. ‖ How many photoelectrons are ejected per second in the experiment represented by the graph of FIGURE EX38.1?

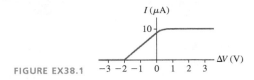

FIGURE EX38.1

2. | Which metals in Table 38.1 exhibit the photoelectric effect for (a) light with $\lambda = 400$ nm and (b) light with $\lambda = 250$ nm?
3. | Photoelectrons are observed when a metal is illuminated by light with a wavelength less than 388 nm. What is the metal's work function?
4. ‖ Electrons in a photoelectric-effect experiment emerge from an aluminum surface with a maximum kinetic energy of 1.30 eV. What is the wavelength of the light?
5. | You need to design a photodetector that can respond to the entire range of visible light. What is the maximum possible work function of the cathode?
6. ‖ A photoelectric-effect experiment finds a stopping potential of 1.56 V when light of 200 nm is used to illuminate the cathode.
   a. From what metal is the cathode made?
   b. What is the stopping potential if the intensity of the light is doubled?

Section 38.3 Photons

7. | a. Determine the energy, in eV, of a photon with a 550 nm wavelength.
   b. Determine the wavelength of a 7.5 keV x-ray photon.
8. | What is the wavelength, in nm, of a photon with energy (a) 0.30 eV, (b) 3.0 eV, and (c) 30 eV? For each, is this wavelength visible, ultraviolet, or infrared light?
9. | What is the energy, in eV, of (a) a 450 MHz radio-frequency photon, (b) a visible-light photon with a wavelength of 450 nm, and (c) an x-ray photon with a wavelength of 0.045 nm?
10. | An FM radio station broadcasts with a power of 10 kW at a frequency of 101 MHz.
    a. How many photons does the antenna emit each second?
    b. Should the broadcast be treated as an electromagnetic wave or discrete photons? Explain.
11. | For what wavelength of light does a 100 mW laser deliver 2.50×10^{17} photons per second?
12. | A red laser with a wavelength of 650 nm and a blue laser with a wavelength of 450 nm emit laser beams with the same light power. How do their rates of photon emission compare? Answer this by computing R_{red}/R_{blue}.

13. | A 100 W incandescent lightbulb emits about 5 W of visible light. (The other 95 W are emitted as infrared radiation or lost as heat to the surroundings.) The average wavelength of the visible light is about 600 nm, so make the simplifying assumption that all the light has this wavelength. How many visible-light photons does the bulb emit per second?

Section 38.4 Matter Waves and Energy Quantization

14. ‖ At what speed is an electron's de Broglie wavelength (a) 1.0 pm, (b) 1.0 nm, (c) 1.0 μm, and (d) 1.0 mm?
15. ‖ Through what potential difference must an electron be accelerated from rest to have a de Broglie wavelength of 500 nm?
16. ‖ What is the de Broglie wavelength of a neutron that has fallen 1.0 m in a vacuum chamber, starting from rest?
17. | a. What is the de Broglie wavelength of a 200 g baseball with a speed of 30 m/s?
    b. What is the speed of a 200 g baseball with a de Broglie wavelength of 0.20 nm?
18. | The diameter of the nucleus is about 10 fm. What is the kinetic energy, in MeV, of a proton with a de Broglie wavelength of 10 fm?
19. | What is the quantum number of an electron confined in a 3.0-nm-long one-dimensional box if the electron's de Broglie wavelength is 1.0 nm?
20. | The diameter of the nucleus is about 10 fm. A simple model of the nucleus is that protons and neutrons are confined within a one-dimensional box of length 10 fm. What are the first three energy levels, in MeV, for a proton in such a box?
21. ‖ What is the length of a one-dimensional box in which an electron in the $n = 1$ state has the same energy as a photon with a wavelength of 600 nm?

Section 38.5 Bohr's Model of Atomic Quantization

22. | FIGURE EX38.22 is an energy-level diagram for a simple atom. What wavelengths appear in the atom's (a) emission spectrum and (b) absorption spectrum?

$$n = 3 \text{———} E_3 = 4.00 \text{ eV}$$

$$n = 2 \text{———} E_2 = 1.50 \text{ eV}$$

$$n = 1 \text{———} E_1 = 0.00 \text{ eV}$$

FIGURE EX38.22

23. ‖ An electron with 2.00 eV of kinetic energy collides with the atom shown in FIGURE EX38.22.
    a. Is the electron able to excite the atom? Why or why not?
    b. If your answer to part a was yes, what is the electron's kinetic energy after the collision?
24. ‖ The allowed energies of a simple atom are 0.00 eV, 4.00 eV, and 6.00 eV.
    a. Draw the atom's energy-level diagram. Label each level with the energy and the quantum number.
    b. What wavelengths appear in the atom's emission spectrum?
    c. What wavelengths appear in the atom's absorption spectrum?

25. ‖ The allowed energies of a simple atom are 0.00 eV, 4.00 eV, and 6.00 eV. An electron traveling with a speed of 1.30×10^6 m/s collides with the atom. Can the electron excite the atom to the $n = 2$ stationary state? The $n = 3$ stationary state? Explain.

Section 38.6 The Bohr Hydrogen Atom

26. | What is the radius of a hydrogen atom whose electron moves at 7.3×10^5 m/s?

27. | What is the radius of a hydrogen atom whose electron is bound by 0.378 eV?

28. | a. What quantum number of the hydrogen atom comes closest to giving a 100-nm-diameter electron orbit?
    b. What are the electron's speed and energy in this state?

29. ‖ a. Calculate the de Broglie wavelength of the electron in the $n = 1$, 2, and 3 states of the hydrogen atom. Use the information in Table 38.2.
    b. Show numerically that the circumference of the orbit for each of these stationary states is exactly equal to n de Broglie wavelengths.
    c. Sketch the de Broglie standing wave for the $n = 3$ orbit.

30. ‖ How much energy does it take to ionize a hydrogen atom that is in its first excited state?

31. | Show, by calculation, that the first three states of the hydrogen atom have angular momenta $\hbar$, $2\hbar$, and $3\hbar$, respectively.

Section 38.7 The Hydrogen Spectrum

32. | Determine the wavelengths of all the possible photons that can be emitted from the $n = 4$ state of a hydrogen atom.

33. ‖ What is the third-longest wavelength in the absorption spectrum of hydrogen?

34. | Is a spectral line with wavelength 656.5 nm seen in the absorption spectrum of hydrogen atoms? Why or why not?

35. ‖ Find the radius of the electron's orbit, the electron's speed, and the energy of the atom for the first three stationary states of He^+.

Problems

36. ‖ A ruby laser emits an intense pulse of light that lasts a mere 10 ns. The light has a wavelength of 690 nm, and each pulse has an energy of 500 mJ.
    a. How many photons are emitted in each pulse?
    b. What is the *rate* of photon emission, in photons per second, during the 10 ns that the laser is "on"?

37. ‖ In a photoelectric-effect experiment, the wavelength of light shining on an aluminum cathode is decreased from 250 nm to 200 nm. What is the change in the stopping potential?

38. | The wavelengths of light emitted by a firefly span the visible
BIO spectrum but have maximum intensity near 550 nm. A typical flash lasts for 100 ms and has a power output of 1.2 mW. How many photons does a firefly emit in one flash if we assume that all light is emitted at the peak intensity wavelength of 550 nm?

39. | *Dinoflagellates* are single-cell organisms that float in the
BIO world's oceans. Many types are bioluminescent. When disturbed, a typical bioluminescent dinoflagellate emits 10^8 photons in a 0.10-s-long flash of wavelength 460 nm. What is the power of the flash?

40. ‖ Potassium and gold cathodes are used in a photoelectric-effect experiment. For each cathode, find:
    a. The threshold frequency.
    b. The threshold wavelength.
    c. The maximum photoelectron ejection speed if the light has a wavelength of 220 nm.
    d. The stopping potential if the wavelength is 220 nm.

41. ‖ The maximum kinetic energy of photoelectrons is 2.8 eV. When the wavelength of the light is increased by 50%, the maximum energy decreases to 1.1 eV. What are (a) the work function of the cathode and (b) the initial wavelength of the light?

42. ‖ In a photoelectric-effect experiment, the stopping potential at a wavelength of 400 nm is 25.7% of the stopping potential at a wavelength of 300 nm. Of what metal is the cathode made?

43. ‖ The graph in **FIGURE P38.43** was measured in a photoelectric-effect experiment.
    a. What is the work function (in eV) of the cathode?
    b. What experimental value of Planck's constant is obtained from these data?

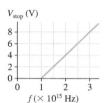

FIGURE P38.43

44. ‖ A metal cathode whose work function is 3.3 eV is illuminated with 15 μW of light having a wavelength of 300 nm. The efficiency of converting photons to photoelectrons is 12%. What current is measured in the experiment?

45. ‖ In a photoelectric-effect experiment, the stopping potential was measured for several different wavelengths of incident light. The data are as follows:

Wavelength (nm)	Stopping potential (V)
500	0.19
450	0.48
400	0.83
350	1.28
300	1.89
250	2.74

Use an appropriate graph of the data to determine (a) the metal used for the cathode and (b) an experimental value for Planck's constant.

46. ‖ The relationship between momentum and energy from Einstein's theory of relativity is $E^2 - (pc)^2 = E_0^2$, where, in this context, $E_0 = mc^2$ is the rest energy rather than the work function.
    a. A photon is a massless particle. What is a photon's momentum p in terms of its energy E?
    b. Einstein also claimed that the energy of a photon is related to its frequency by $E = hf$. Use this and your result from part a to write an expression for the wavelength λ of a photon in terms of its momentum p.
    c. Your result for part b is for a "particle-like wave." Suppose you thought this expression should also apply to a "wave-like particle." What is your expression for λ if you replace p with the classical-mechanics expression for the momentum of a particle of mass m? Is this a familiar-looking expression?

47. ∥ A red blood cell is a 7.0-μm-diameter, 2.0-μm-thick disk with a density of 1100 kg/m³. What is the de Broglie wavelength of a red blood cell moving through a capillary at 4.0 mm/s? Do we need to be concerned with the wave nature of blood cells when describing the flow of blood?
BIO

48. ∥ The electron interference pattern of Figure 38.13 was made by shooting electrons with 50 keV of kinetic energy through two slits spaced 1.0 μm apart. The fringes were recorded on a detector 1.0 m behind the slits.
    a. What was the speed of the electrons? (The speed is large enough to justify using relativity, but for simplicity do this as a nonrelativistic calculation.)
    b. Figure 38.13 is greatly magnified. What was the actual spacing on the detector between adjacent bright fringes?

49. ∥ An experiment was performed in which neutrons were shot through two slits spaced 0.10 nm apart and detected 3.5 m behind the slits. FIGURE P38.49 shows the detector output. Notice the 100 μm scale on the figure. To one significant figure, what was the speed of the neutrons?

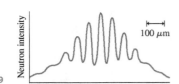

FIGURE P38.49

50. ∥ The electrons in a cathode-ray tube are accelerated through a 250 V potential difference and then shot through a 33-nm-diameter circular aperture. What is the diameter of the bright spot on an electron detector 1.5 m behind the aperture?

51. ∥ An electron confined in a one-dimensional box is observed, at different times, to have energies of 12 eV, 27 eV, and 48 eV. What is the length of the box?

52. ∥ An electron confined in a one-dimensional box emits a 200 nm photon in a quantum jump from $n = 2$ to $n = 1$. What is the length of the box?

53. ∥∥ A proton confined in a one-dimensional box emits a 2.0 MeV gamma-ray photon in a quantum jump from $n = 2$ to $n = 1$. What is the length of the box?

54. ∥ Consider a small virus having a diameter of 10 nm. The atoms of the intracellular fluid are confined within the virus. Suppose we model the virus as a 10-nm-long "box." What is the ground-state energy (in eV) of a sodium ion confined in this box?
BIO

55. ∥ The absorption spectrum of an atom consists of the wavelengths 200 nm, 300 nm, and 500 nm.
    a. Draw the atom's energy-level diagram.
    b. What wavelengths are seen in the atom's emission spectrum?

56. ∥ The first three energy levels of the fictitious element X are shown in FIGURE P38.56.
    a. What is the ionization energy of element X?
    b. What wavelengths are observed in the absorption spectrum of element X? Express your answers in nm.
    c. State whether each of your wavelengths in part b corresponds to ultraviolet, visible, or infrared light.

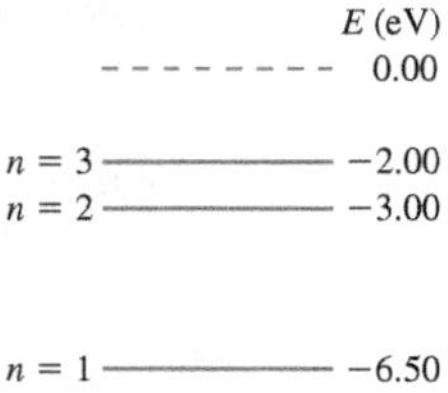

	E (eV)
– – – – – – – –	0.00
$n = 3$ ————————	−2.00
$n = 2$ ————————	−3.00
$n = 1$ ————————	−6.50

FIGURE P38.56

57. ∥ The first three energy levels of the fictitious element X were shown in FIGURE P38.56. An electron with a speed of 1.4×10^6 m/s collides with an atom of element X. Shortly afterward, the atom emits a photon with a wavelength of 1240 nm. What was the electron's speed after the collision? Assume that, because the atom is much more massive than the electron, the recoil of the atom is negligible.

Hint: The energy of the photon is *not* the energy transferred to the atom in the collision.

58. ∥ Starting from Equation 38.29, derive Equation 38.30.

59. ∣ Calculate *all* the wavelengths of *visible* light in the emission spectrum of the hydrogen atom.

Hint: There are infinitely many wavelengths in the spectrum, so you'll need to develop a strategy for this problem rather than using trial and error.

60. ∥ An electron with a speed of 2.1×10^6 m/s collides with a hydrogen atom, exciting the atom to the highest possible energy level. The atom then undergoes a quantum jump with $\Delta n = 1$. What is the wavelength of the photon emitted in the quantum jump?

61. ∥ a. What wavelength photon does a hydrogen atom emit in a $200 \rightarrow 199$ transition?
    b. What is the *difference* in the wavelengths emitted in a $199 \rightarrow 2$ transition and a $200 \rightarrow 2$ transition?

62. ∥ Draw an energy-level diagram, similar to Figure 38.23, for the He⁺ ion. On your diagram:
    a. Show the first five energy levels. Label each with the values of n and E_n.
    b. Show the ionization limit.
    c. Show all possible emission transitions from the $n = 4$ energy level.
    d. Calculate the wavelengths (in nm) for each of the transitions in part c and show them alongside the appropriate arrow.

63. ∣ What are the wavelengths of the transitions $3 \rightarrow 2$, $4 \rightarrow 2$, and $5 \rightarrow 2$ in the hydrogen-like ion O⁺⁷? In what spectral range do these lie?

64. ∥ Two hydrogen atoms collide head-on. The collision brings both atoms to a halt. Immediately after the collision, both atoms emit a 121.6 nm photon. What was the speed of each atom just before the collision?

65. ∥ A beam of electrons is incident upon a gas of hydrogen atoms.
    a. What minimum speed must the electrons have to cause the emission of 656 nm light from the $3 \rightarrow 2$ transition of hydrogen?
    b. Through what potential difference must the electrons be accelerated to have this speed?

Challenge Problems

66. Ultraviolet light with a wavelength of 70.0 nm shines on a gas of hydrogen atoms in their ground states. Some of the atoms are ionized by the light. What is the kinetic energy of the electrons that are freed in this process?

67. In the atom interferometer experiment of Figure 38.14, laser-cooling techniques were used to cool a dilute vapor of sodium atoms to a temperature of 0.0010 K = 1.0 mK. The ultracold atoms passed through a series of collimating apertures to form the *atomic beam* you see entering the figure from the left. The standing light waves were created from a laser beam with a wavelength of 590 nm.
    a. What is the rms speed v_{rms} of a sodium atom ($A = 23$) in a gas at temperature 1.0 mK?

b. By treating the laser beam as if it were a diffraction grating, calculate the first-order diffraction angle of a sodium atom traveling with the rms speed of part a.

c. How far apart are points B and C if the second standing wave is 10 cm from the first?

d. Because interference is observed between the two paths, each individual atom is apparently present at both point B *and* point C. Describe, in your own words, what this experiment tells you about the nature of matter.

68. Consider a hydrogen atom in stationary state n.

a. Show that the orbital period of an electron in quantum state n is $T = n^3 T_1$, and find a numerical value for T_1.

b. On average, an atom stays in the $n = 2$ state for 1.6 ns before undergoing a quantum jump to the $n = 1$ state. On average, how many revolutions does the electron make before the quantum jump?

69. Consider an electron undergoing cyclotron motion in a magnetic field. According to Bohr, the electron's angular momentum must be quantized in units of $\hbar$.

a. Show that allowed radii for the electron's orbit are given by $r_n = (n\hbar/eB)^{1/2}$, where $n = 1, 2, 3,....$

b. Compute the first four allowed radii in a 1.0 T magnetic field.

c. Find an expression for the allowed energy levels E_n in terms of $\hbar$ and the cyclotron frequency f_{cyc}.

70. The *muon* is a subatomic particle with the same charge as an electron but with a mass that is 207 times greater: $m_\mu = 207 m_e$. Physicists think of muons as "heavy electrons." However, the muon is not a stable particle; it decays with a half-life of 1.5 μs into an electron plus two neutrinos. Muons from cosmic rays are sometimes "captured" by the nuclei of the atoms in a solid. A captured muon orbits this nucleus, like an electron, until it decays. Because the muon is often captured into an excited orbit ($n > 1$), its presence can be detected by observing the photons emitted in transitions such as $2 \rightarrow 1$ and $3 \rightarrow 1$.

Consider a muon captured by a carbon nucleus ($Z = 6$). Because of its large mass, the muon orbits well *inside* the electron cloud and is not affected by the electrons. Thus the muon "sees" the full nuclear charge Ze and acts like the electron in a hydrogen-like ion.

a. What are the orbital radius and speed of a muon in the $n = 1$ ground state? Note that the mass of a muon differs from the mass of an electron.

b. What is the wavelength of the $2 \rightarrow 1$ muon transition?

c. Is the photon emitted in the $2 \rightarrow 1$ transition infrared, visible, ultraviolet, or x ray?

d. How many orbits will the muon complete during 1.5 μs? Is this a sufficiently large number that the Bohr model "makes sense," even though the muon is not stable?

STOP TO THINK ANSWERS

Stop to Think 38.1: $V_A > V_B > V_C$. For a given wavelength of light, electrons are ejected with more kinetic energy from metals with smaller work functions because it takes less energy to remove an electron. Faster electrons need a larger negative voltage to stop them.

Stop to Think 38.2: d. Photons always travel at c, and a photon's energy depends only on the light's frequency, not its intensity.

Stop to Think 38.3: $n = 4$. There are four antinodes.

Stop to Think 38.4: Not in absorption. In emission from the $n = 3$ to $n = 2$ transition. The photon energy has to match the energy *difference* between two energy levels. Absorption is from the ground state, at $E_1 = 0.00$ eV. There's no energy level at 3.00 eV to which the atom could jump.

Stop to Think 38.5: $n = 3$. Each antinode is half a wavelength, so this standing wave has three full wavelengths in one circumference.

39 Wave Functions and Uncertainty

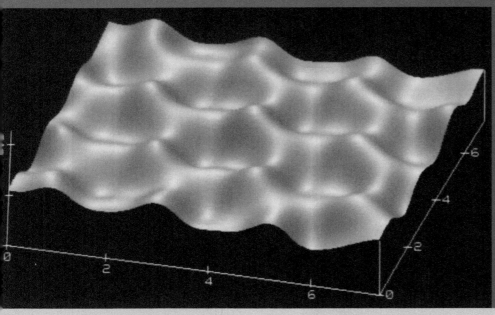

The surface of graphite, imaged with atomic resolution by a scanning tunneling microscope. The hexagonal ridges show the most probable locations of the electrons.

▶ **Looking Ahead** The goal of Chapter 39 is to introduce and learn to use the wave-function description of matter.

Quantum Mechanics

This chapter and the next will introduce the essential ideas of **quantum mechanics** in one dimension. The full theory is beyond the scope of this textbook, but we can delve far enough into quantum mechanics to learn, in the final two chapters, how it solves the problems of atomic and nuclear structure.

Despite the strange and unfamiliar aspects of quantum mechanics, its predictions are verified with amazing precision. It is the most successful physical theory ever devised.

Probability

You'll learn that quantum mechanics deals with *probabilities*. We cannot say exactly where an electron is or how it's moving, but we can make accurate statements about the probability of locating the electron in a region of space.

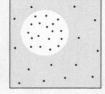

If an experiment detects *N* particles, the *expected number* in a given region of space is *N* times the probability of being in that region.

Wave Functions

You'll learn that the probability of finding a particle is determined by the particle's **wave function** $\psi(x)$.

$\psi(x)$ — The wave function is an oscillatory function.

$|\psi(x)|^2$ — The square of the wave function is the **probability density.**

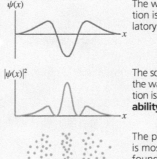

The particle is most likely found where the probability density peaks.

The wave function $\psi(x)$ is a *wave-like function* that can be used to make probabilistic predictions, but nothing is actually waving.

You'll learn how to interpret the wave function in different situations.

◀ **Looking Back**
Section 38.3 Photons
Section 38.4 de Broglie wavelength

Waves and Particles

The wave function reconciles the experimental evidence that matter has both particle-like and wave-like properties. The probability of detecting a *particle* is governed by a *wave-like* function that can exhibit interference.

In the double-slit experiment, interference fringes in the wave function indicate that particle-like electrons are most likely to be detected where a wave would exhibit bright fringes.

Uncertainty

You'll learn that the **Heisenberg uncertainty principle** places a fundamental limit on how well you can know a particle's position and speed.

Because matter has wave-like properties, a particle simply does not have a precise position or a precise speed. Our knowledge of a particle is inherently uncertain.

Wave packet length Δx

◀ **Looking Back**
Section 21.8 Beats

39.1 Waves, Particles, and the Double-Slit Experiment

You may feel surprise at how slowly we have been building up to quantum mechanics. Why not just write it down and start using it? There are two reasons. First, quantum mechanics explains microscopic phenomena that we cannot directly sense or experience. It was important to begin by learning how light and atoms behave. Otherwise, how would you know if quantum mechanics explains anything? Second, the concepts we'll need in quantum mechanics are rather abstract. Before launching into the mathematics, we need to establish a connection between theory and experiment.

We will make the connection by returning to the double-slit interference experiment, an experiment that goes right to the heart of wave–particle duality. The significance of the double-slit experiment arises from the fact that both light and matter exhibit the same interference pattern. Regardless of whether photons, electrons, or neutrons pass through the slits, their arrival at a detector is a particle-like event. That is, they make a collection of discrete dots on a detector. Yet our understanding of how interference "works" is based on the properties of waves. Our goal is to find the connection between the wave description and the particle description of interference.

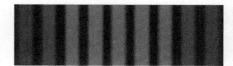

Interference fringes in an optical double-slit interference experiment.

A Wave Analysis of Interference

The interference of light can be analyzed from either a wave perspective or a photon perspective. Let's start with a wave analysis. FIGURE 39.1 shows light waves passing through a double slit with slit separation d. You should recall that the lines in a wavefront diagram represent wave crests, spaced one wavelength apart. The bright fringes of constructive interference occur where two crests or two troughs overlap. The graphs and the picture of the detection screen (notice that they're aligned vertically) show the outcome of the experiment.

You studied interference and the double-slit experiment in Chapters 21 and 22. The two waves traveling from the slits to the viewing screen are traveling waves with displacements

$$D_1 = a\sin(kr_1 - \omega t)$$

$$D_2 = a\sin(kr_2 - \omega t)$$

where a is the amplitude of each wave, $k = 2\pi/\lambda$ is the wave number, and r_1 and r_2 are the distances from the two slits. The "displacement" of a light wave is not a physical displacement, as in a water wave, but a change in the electromagnetic field.

According to the principle of superposition, these two waves add together where they meet at a point on the screen to give a wave with net displacement $D = D_1 + D_2$. Previously (see Equation 22.12) we found that the amplitude of their superposition is

$$A(x) = 2a\cos\left(\frac{\pi dx}{\lambda L}\right) \tag{39.1}$$

where x is the horizontal coordinate on the screen, measured from $x = 0$ in the center.

The function $A(x)$, the top graph in Figure 39.1, is called the *amplitude function*. It describes the amplitude A of the light wave as a function of the position x on the viewing screen. The amplitude function has maxima where two crests from individual waves overlap and add constructively to make a larger wave with amplitude $2a$. $A(x)$ is zero at points where the two individual waves are out of phase and interfere destructively.

If you carry out a double-slit experiment in the lab, what you observe on the screen is the light's *intensity,* not its amplitude. A wave's intensity I is proportional to the *square* of the amplitude. That is, $I \propto A^2$, where $\propto$ is the "is proportional to" symbol.

FIGURE 39.1 The double-slit experiment with light.

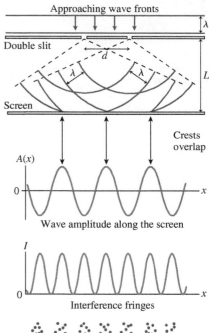

Using Equation 39.1 for the amplitude at each point, we find the intensity $I(x)$ as a function of position x on the screen is

$$I(x) = C\cos^2\left(\frac{\pi dx}{\lambda L}\right) \qquad (39.2)$$

where C is a proportionality constant.

The lower graph in Figure 39.1 shows the intensity as a function of position along the screen. This graph shows the alternating bright and dark interference fringes that you see in the laboratory. In other words, the intensity of the wave is the *experimental reality* that you observe and measure.

Probability

FIGURE 39.2 One hundred throws at a dart board.

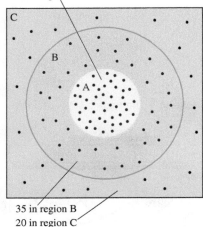

45 in region A

35 in region B
20 in region C

Before discussing photons, we need to introduce some ideas about probability. Imagine throwing darts at a dart board while blindfolded. FIGURE 39.2 shows how the board might look after your first 100 throws. From this information, can you predict where your 101st throw is going to land? We'll assume that all darts hit the board.

No. The position of any individual dart is *unpredictable*. No matter how hard you try to reproduce the previous throw, a second dart will not land at the same place. Yet there is clearly an overall *pattern* to where the darts strike the board. Even blindfolded, you had a general sense of where the center of the board was, so each dart was *more likely* to land near the center than at the edge.

Although we can't predict where any individual dart will land, we can use the information in Figure 39.2 to determine the *probability* that your next throw will land in region A or region B or region C. Because 45 out of 100 throws landed in region A, we could say that the *odds* of hitting region A are 45 out of 100, or 45%.

Now, 100 throws isn't all that many. If you throw another 100 darts, perhaps only 43 will land in region A. Then maybe 48 of the next 100 throws. Imagine that the total number of throws N_{tot} becomes extremely large. Then the **probability** that any particular throw lands in region A is defined to be

$$P_A = \lim_{N_{tot} \to \infty} \frac{N_A}{N_{tot}} \qquad (39.3)$$

In other words, the probability that the outcome will be A is the fraction of outcomes that are A in an enormously large number of trials. Similarly, $P_B = N_B/N_{tot}$ and $P_C = N_C/N_{tot}$ as $N_{tot} \to \infty$. We can give probabilities as either a decimal fraction or a percentage. In this example, $P_A \approx 45\%$, $P_B \approx 35\%$, and $P_C \approx 20\%$. We've used $\approx$ rather than $=$ because 100 throws isn't enough to determine the probabilities with great precision.

What is the probability that a dart lands in either region A *or* region B? The number of darts landing in either A *or* B is $N_{A\,or\,B} = N_A + N_B$, so we can use the definition of probability to learn that

$$\begin{aligned} P_{A\,or\,B} &= \lim_{N_{tot} \to \infty} \frac{N_{A\,or\,B}}{N_{tot}} = \lim_{N_{tot} \to \infty} \frac{N_A + N_B}{N_{tot}} \\ &= \lim_{N_{tot} \to \infty} \frac{N_A}{N_{tot}} + \lim_{N_{tot} \to \infty} \frac{N_B}{N_{tot}} = P_A + P_B \end{aligned} \qquad (39.4)$$

That is, **the probability that the outcome will be A *or* B is the sum of P_A and P_B.** This important conclusion is a general property of probabilities.

Each dart lands *somewhere on* the board. Consequently, the probability that a dart lands in A *or* B *or* C must be 100%. And, in fact,

$$P_{somewhere} = P_{A\,or\,B\,or\,C} = P_A + P_B + P_C = 0.45 + 0.35 + 0.20 = 1.00$$

Thus another important property of probabilities is that **the sum of the probabilities of all possible outcomes must equal 1.**

Suppose exhaustive trials have established that the probability of a dart landing in region A is P_A. If you throw N darts, how many do you *expect* to land in A? This value, called the **expected value,** is

$$N_{A\text{ expected}} = NP_A \qquad (39.5)$$

The expected value is your best prediction of the outcome of an experiment.

If $P_A = 0.45$, your *best prediction* is that 27 of 60 throws (45% of 60) will land in A. Of course, predicting 27 and actually getting 27 aren't the same thing. You would predict 30 heads in 60 flips of a coin, but you wouldn't be surprised if the actual number were 28 or 31. Similarly, the number of darts landing in region A might be 24 or 29 instead of 27. In general, the agreement between actual values and expected values improves as you throw more darts.

STOP TO THINK 39.1 Suppose you roll a die 30 times. What is the expected number of 1's *and* 6's?

A Photon Analysis of Interference

Now let's look at the double-slit results from a photon perspective. We know, from experimental evidence, that the interference pattern is built up photon by photon. The bottom portion of Figure 39.1 shows the pattern made on a detector after the arrival of the first few dozen photons. It is clearly a double-slit interference pattern, but it's made, rather like a newspaper photograph, by piling up dots in some places but not others.

The arrival position of any particular photon is *unpredictable*. That is, nothing about how the experiment is set up or conducted allows us to predict exactly where the dot of an individual photon will appear on the detector. Yet there is clearly an overall pattern. There are some positions at which a photon is *more likely* to be detected, other positions at which it is *less likely* to be found.

If we record the arrival positions of many thousands of photons, we will be able to determine the *probability* that a photon will be detected at any given location. If 50 out of 50,000 photons land in one small area of the screen, then each photon has a probability of 50/50,000 = 0.001 = 0.1% of being detected there. The probability will be zero at the interference minima because no photons at all arrive at those points. Similarly, the probability will be a maximum at the interference maxima. The probability will have some in-between value on the sides of the interference fringes.

FIGURE 39.3a shows a narrow strip with width δx and height H. (We will assume that δx is very small in comparison with the fringe spacing, so the light's intensity over δx is very nearly constant.) Think of this strip as a very narrow detector that can detect and count the photons landing on it. Suppose we place the narrow strip at position x. We'll use the notation $N(\text{in } \delta x \text{ at } x)$ to indicate the number of photons that hit the detector at this position. The value of $N(\text{in } \delta x \text{ at } x)$ varies from point to point. $N(\text{in } \delta x \text{ at } x)$ is large if x happens to be near the center of a bright fringe; $N(\text{in } \delta x \text{ at } x)$ is small if x is in a dark fringe.

Suppose N_{tot} photons are fired at the slits. The *probability* that any one photon ends up in the strip at position x is

$$\text{Prob(in } \delta x \text{ at } x) = \lim_{N_{\text{tot}} \to \infty} \frac{N(\text{in } \delta x \text{ at } x)}{N_{\text{tot}}} \qquad (39.6)$$

As FIGURE 39.3b shows, Equation 39.6 is an empirical method for determining the probability of the photons hitting a particular spot on the detector.

FIGURE 39.3 A strip of width δx at position x.

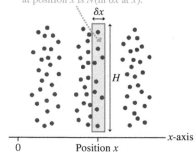

(a) The number of photons in this narrow strip when it is at position x is $N(\text{in } \delta x \text{ at } x)$.

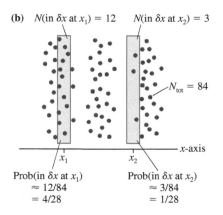

(b) $N(\text{in } \delta x \text{ at } x_1) = 12$ $N(\text{in } \delta x \text{ at } x_2) = 3$

$N_{\text{tot}} = 84$

Prob(in δx at x_1)
$\approx 12/84$
$= 4/28$

Prob(in δx at x_2)
$\approx 3/84$
$= 1/28$

Alternatively, suppose we can calculate the probabilities from a theory. In that case, the *expected value* for the number of photons landing in the narrow strip when it is at position x is

$$N(\text{in } \delta x \text{ at } x) = N \times \text{Prob}(\text{in } \delta x \text{ at } x) \tag{39.7}$$

We cannot predict what any individual photon will do, but we can predict the fraction of the photons that should land in this little region of space. Prob(in δx at x) is the probability that it will happen.

39.2 Connecting the Wave and Photon Views

The wave model of light describes the interference pattern in terms of the wave's intensity $I(x)$, a continuous-valued function. The photon model describes the interference pattern in terms of the probability Prob(in δx at x) of detecting a photon. These two models are very different, yet Figure 39.1 shows a clear correlation between the *intensity of the wave* and the *probability of detecting photons*. That is, photons are more likely to be detected at those points where the wave intensity is high and less likely to be detected at those points where the wave intensity is low.

The intensity of a wave is $I = P/A$, the ratio of light power P (joules per second) to the area A on which the light falls. The narrow strip in Figure 39.3a has area $A = H \delta x$. If the light intensity at position x is $I(x)$, the amount of light energy E falling onto this narrow strip during each second is

$$E(\text{in } \delta x \text{ at } x) = I(x)A = I(x)H\delta x = HI(x)\delta x \tag{39.8}$$

The notation E(in δx at x) refers to the energy landing on this narrow strip if you place it at position x.

From the photon perspective, energy E is due to the arrival of N photons, each of which has energy hf. The number of photons that arrive in the strip each second is

$$N(\text{in } \delta x \text{ at } x) = \frac{E(\text{in } \delta x \text{ at } x)}{hf} = \frac{H}{hf}I(x)\delta x \tag{39.9}$$

We can then use Equation 39.6, the definition of probability, to write the *probability* that a photon lands in the narrow strip δx at position x as

$$\text{Prob}(\text{in } \delta x \text{ at } x) = \frac{N(\text{in } \delta x \text{ at } x)}{N_{\text{tot}}} = \frac{H}{hfN_{\text{tot}}}I(x)\delta x \tag{39.10}$$

Equation 39.10 is a critical link between the wave model and the photon model. It tells us that the probability of detecting a photon is proportional to the intensity of the light at that point and to the width of the detector.

As a final step, recall that the light intensity $I(x)$ is proportional to $|A(x)|^2$, the square of the amplitude function. Consequently,

$$\text{Prob}(\text{in } \delta x \text{ at } x) \propto |A(x)|^2 \delta x \tag{39.11}$$

where the various constants in Equation 39.10 have all been incorporated into the unspecified proportionality constant of Equation 39.11.

In other words, **the probability of detecting a photon at a particular point is directly proportional to the square of the light-wave amplitude function at that point.** If the wave amplitude at point A is twice that at point B, then a photon is four times as likely to land in a narrow strip at A as it is to land in an equal-width strip at B.

NOTE ▶ Equation 39.11 is the connection between the particle perspective and the wave perspective. It relates the probability of observing a particle-like event—the arrival of a photon—to the amplitude of a continuous, classical wave. This connection will become the basis of how we interpret the results of quantum-physics calculations. ◀

Probability Density

We need one last definition. Recall that the mass of a wire or string of a length L can be expressed in terms of the linear mass density μ as $m = \mu L$. Similarly, the charge along a length L of wire can be expressed in terms of the linear charge density λ as $Q = \lambda L$. If the length had been very short—in which case we might have denoted it as δx—and if the density varied from point to point, we could have written

$$\text{mass(in length } \delta x \text{ at } x) = \mu(x)\,\delta x$$

$$\text{charge(in length } \delta x \text{ at } x) = \lambda(x)\,\delta x$$

where $\mu(x)$ and $\lambda(x)$ are the linear densities at position x. Writing the mass and charge this way separates the role of the density from the role of the small length δx.

Equation 39.11 looks similar. Using the mass and charge densities as analogies, as shown in FIGURE 39.4, we can define the **probability density** $P(x)$ such that

$$\text{Prob(in } \delta x \text{ at } x) = P(x)\,\delta x \qquad (39.12)$$

In one dimension, probability density has SI units of m^{-1}. Thus the probability density multiplied by a length, as in Equation 39.12, yields a dimensionless probability.

NOTE ▶ $P(x)$ itself is *not* a probability, just as the linear mass density λ is not, by itself, a mass. You must multiply the probability density by a length, as shown in Equation 39.12, to find an actual probability. ◀

By comparing Equation 39.12 to Equation 39.11, you can see that the photon probability density is directly proportional to the square of the light-wave amplitude:

$$P(x) \propto |A(x)|^2 \qquad (39.13)$$

The probability density, unlike the probability itself, is independent of the width δx and depends on only the amplitude function.

Although we were inspired by the double-slit experiment, nothing in our analysis actually depends on the double-slit geometry. Consequently, Equation 39.13 is quite general. It says that for *any* experiment in which we detect photons, **the probability density for detecting a photon is directly proportional to the square of the amplitude function of the corresponding electromagnetic wave.** We now have an explicit connection between the wave-like and the particle-like properties of the light.

FIGURE 39.4 The probability density is analogous to the linear mass density.

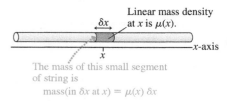

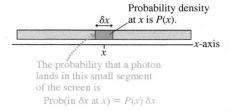

EXAMPLE 39.1 **Calculating the probability density**

In an experiment, 6000 out of 600,000 photons are detected in a 1.0-mm-wide strip located at position $x = 50$ cm. What is the probability density at $x = 50$ cm?

SOLVE The probability that a photon arrives at this particular strip is

$$\text{Prob(in 1.0 mm at } x = 50 \text{ cm)} = \frac{6000}{600,000} = 0.010$$

Thus the probability density $P(x) = \text{Prob(in } \delta x \text{ at } x)/\delta x$ at this position is

$$P(50 \text{ cm}) = \frac{\text{Prob(in 1.0 mm at } x = 50 \text{ cm)}}{0.0010 \text{ m}} = \frac{0.010}{0.0010 \text{ m}}$$
$$= 10 \text{ m}^{-1}$$

STOP TO THINK 39.2 The figure shows the detection of photons in an optical experiment. Rank in order, from largest to smallest, the square of the amplitude function of the electromagnetic wave at positions A, B, C, and D.

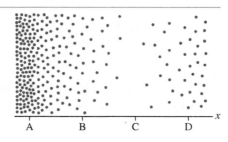

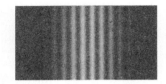

Electrons create interference fringes.

FIGURE 39.5 The double-slit experiment with electrons.

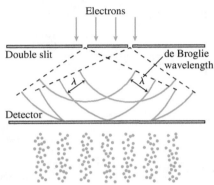

FIGURE 39.6 The square of the wave function is the probability density for detecting the electron at position x.

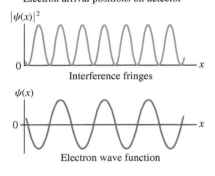

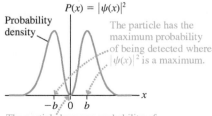

39.3 The Wave Function

Now let's look at the interference of matter. Electrons passing through a double-slit apparatus create the same interference patterns as photons. The pattern is built up electron by electron, but there is no way to predict where any particular electron will be detected. Even so, we can establish the *probability* of an electron landing in a narrow strip of width δx by measuring the positions of many individual electrons.

For light, we were able to relate the photon probability density $P(x)$ to the amplitude of an electromagnetic wave. But there is no wave for electrons like electromagnetic waves for light. So how do we find the probability density for electrons? We have reached the point where we must make an inspired leap beyond classical physics. Let us *assume* that there is some kind of continuous, wave-like function for matter that plays a role analogous to the electromagnetic amplitude function $A(x)$ for light. We will call this function the **wave function** $\psi(x)$, where ψ is a lowercase Greek psi. The wave function is a function of position, which is why we write it as $\psi(x)$.

To connect the wave function to the real world of experimental measurements, we will interpret $\psi(x)$ in terms of the *probability* of detecting a particle at position x. If a matter particle, such as an electron, is described by the wave function $\psi(x)$, then the probability Prob(in δx at x) of finding the particle within a narrow region of width δx at position x is

$$\text{Prob(in } \delta x \text{ at } x) = |\psi(x)|^2 \delta x = P(x) \delta x \tag{39.14}$$

That is, the probability density $P(x)$ for finding the particle is

$$P(x) = |\psi(x)|^2 \tag{39.15}$$

With Equations 39.14 and 39.15, we are *defining* the wave function $\psi(x)$ to play the same role for material particles that the amplitude function $A(x)$ does for photons. The only difference is that $P(x) = |\psi(x)|^2$ is for particles, whereas Equation 39.13 for photons is $P(x) \propto |A(x)|^2$. The difference is that the electromagnetic field amplitude $A(x)$ had previously been defined through the laws of electricity and magnetism. $|A(x)|^2$ is *proportional* to the probability density for finding a photon, but it is not directly *the* probability density. In contrast, we do not have any preexisting definition for the wave function $\psi(x)$. Thus we are free to define $\psi(x)$ so that $|\psi(x)|^2$ is *exactly* the probability density. That is why we used $=$ rather than $\propto$ in Equation 39.15.

FIGURE 39.5 shows the double-slit experiment with electrons. This time we will work backward. From the observed distribution of electrons, which represents the probabilities of their landing in any particular location, we can deduce that $|\psi(x)|^2$ has alternating maxima and zeros. The oscillatory wave function $\psi(x)$ is the square root *at each point* of $|\psi(x)|^2$. Notice the very close analogy with the amplitude function $A(x)$ in Figure 39.1.

NOTE ▶ $|\psi(x)|^2$ is uniquely determined by the data, but the wave function $\psi(x)$ is *not* unique. The alternative wave function $\psi'(x) = -\psi(x)$—an upside-down version of the graph in Figure 39.5—would be equally acceptable. ◀

FIGURE 39.6 is a different example of a wave function. After squaring it *at each point,* as shown in the bottom half of the figure, we see that this wave function represents a particle most likely to be detected very near $x = -b$ or $x = +b$. These are the points where $|\psi(x)|^2$ is a maximum. There is zero likelihood of finding the particle right in the center. The particle is more likely to be detected at some positions than at others, but we cannot predict what its exact location will be at any given time.

NOTE ▶ One of the difficulties in learning to use the concept of a wave function is coming to grips with the fact that there is no "thing" that is waving. There is no disturbance associated with a physical medium. The wave function $\psi(x)$ is simply a *wave-like function* (i.e., it oscillates between positive and negative values) that can be used to make probabilistic predictions about atomic particles. ◄

A Little Science Methodology

Equation 39.14 defines the wave function $\psi(x)$ for a particle in terms of the probability of finding the particle at different positions x. But our interests go beyond merely characterizing experimental data. We would like to develop a new *theory* of matter. But just what is a theory? Although this is not a book on scientific methodology, we can loosely say that a physical theory needs two basic ingredients:

1. A *descriptor,* a mathematical quantity used to describe our knowledge of a physical object.
2. One or more *laws* that govern the behavior of the descriptor.

For example, Newtonian mechanics is a theory of motion. The primary descriptor in Newtonian mechanics is a particle's *position* $x(t)$ as a function of time. This describes our knowledge of the particle at all times. The position is governed by *Newton's laws.* These laws, especially the second law, are mathematical statements of how the descriptor changes in response to forces. If we predict $x(t)$ for a known set of forces, we feel confident that an experiment carried out at time t will find the particle right where predicted.

Newton's theory of motion *assumes* that a particle's position is well defined at every instant of time. The difficulty facing physicists early in the 20th century was the astounding discovery that **the position of an atomic-size particle is *not* well defined.** An electron in a double-slit experiment must, in some sense, go through *both* slits to produce an electron interference pattern. It simply does not have a well-defined position as it interacts with the slits. But if the position function $x(t)$ is not a valid descriptor for matter at the atomic level, what is?

We will assert that the wave function $\psi(x)$ is the *descriptor* of a particle in quantum mechanics. In other words, the wave function tells us everything we can know about the particle. The wave function $\psi(x)$ plays the same leading role in quantum mechanics that the position function $x(t)$ plays in classical mechanics.

Whether this hypothesis has any merit will not be known until we see if it leads to predictions that can be verified. And before we can do that, we need to learn the "law of psi." What new law of physics determines the wave function $\psi(x)$ in a given situation? We will answer this question in the next chapter.

It may seem to you, as we go along, that we are simply "making up" ideas. Indeed, that is at least partially true. The inventors of entirely new theories use their existing knowledge as a guide, but ultimately they have to make an inspired guess as to what a new theory should look like. Newton and Einstein both made such leaps, and the inventors of quantum mechanics had to make such a leap. We can attempt to make the new ideas *plausible,* but ultimately a new theory is simply a bold assertion that must be tested against reality via controlled experiments. The wave-function theory of quantum mechanics passed the only test that really matters in science—it works!

STOP TO THINK 39.3   This is the wave function of a neutron. At what value of x is the neutron most likely to be found?

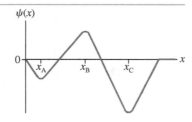

39.4 Normalization

In our discussion of probability we noted that the dart has to hit the wall *somewhere.* The mathematical statement of this idea is the requirement that $P_A + P_B + P_C = 1$. That is, the probabilities of all the mutually exclusive outcomes *must* add up to 1.

Similarly, a photon or electron has to land *somewhere* on the detector after passing through an experimental apparatus. Consequently, the probability that it will be detected at *some* position is 100%. To make use of this requirement, consider an experiment in which an electron is detected on the *x*-axis. As FIGURE 39.7 shows, we can divide the region between positions x_L and x_R into N adjacent narrow strips of width δx.

FIGURE 39.7 Dividing the entire detector into many small strips of width δx.

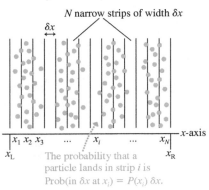

N narrow strips of width δx

δx

x-axis

$x_1\ x_2\ x_3 \quad \cdots \quad x_i \quad \cdots \quad x_N$

x_L

x_R

The probability that a particle lands in strip i is
Prob(in δx at x_i) $= P(x_i)\,\delta x$.

The probability that any particular electron lands in the narrow strip i at position x_i is

$$\text{Prob(in }\delta x\text{ at }x_i) = P(x_i)\,\delta x$$

where $P(x_i) = |\psi(x_i)|^2$ is the probability density at x_i. The probability that the electron lands in the strip at x_1 *or* x_2 *or* x_3 *or* ... is the sum

$$\text{Prob(between }x_L\text{ and }x_R) = \text{Prob(in }\delta x\text{ at }x_1)$$

$$+ \text{Prob(in }\delta x\text{ at }x_2) + \cdots \tag{39.16}$$

$$= \sum_{i=1}^{N} P(x_i)\,\delta x = \sum_{i=1}^{N} |\psi(x_i)|^2\,\delta x$$

That is, **the probability that the electron lands *somewhere* between x_L and x_R is the sum of the probabilities of landing in each narrow strip.**

If we let the strips become narrower and narrower, then $\delta x \rightarrow dx$ and the sum becomes an integral. Thus the probability of finding the particles in the range $x_L \leq x \leq x_R$ is

$$\text{Prob(in range }x_L \leq x \leq x_R) = \int_{x_L}^{x_R} P(x)\,dx = \int_{x_L}^{x_R} |\psi(x)|^2\,dx \tag{39.17}$$

As FIGURE 39.8a shows, we can interpret Prob(in range $x_L \leq x \leq x_R$) as the area under the probability density curve between x_L and x_R.

NOTE ▶ The integral of Equation 39.17 is needed when the probability density changes over the range x_L to x_R. For sufficiently narrow intervals, over which $P(x)$ remains essentially constant, the expression Prob(in δx at x) $= P(x)\,\delta x$ is still valid and is easier to use. ◀

FIGURE 39.8 The area under the probability density curve is a probability.

(a) $P(x) = |\psi(x)|^2$

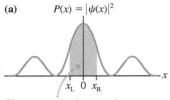

$x_L\ 0\ x_R$

x

The area under the curve between x_L and x_R is the probability of finding the particle between x_L and x_R.

(b) $P(x) = |\psi(x)|^2$

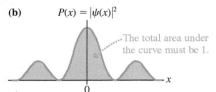

The total area under the curve must be 1.

0

x

Now let the detector become infinitely wide, so that the probability that the electron will arrive *somewhere* on the detector becomes 100%. The statement that the electron has to land *somewhere* on the *x*-axis is expressed mathematically as

$$\int_{-\infty}^{\infty} P(x)\,dx = \int_{-\infty}^{\infty} |\psi(x)|^2\,dx = 1 \tag{39.18}$$

Equation 39.18 is called the **normalization condition.** Any wave function $\psi(x)$ must satisfy this condition; otherwise we would not be able to interpret $|\psi(x)|^2$ as a probability density. As FIGURE 39.8b shows, Equation 39.18 tells us that the total area under the probability density curve must be 1.

NOTE ▶ The normalization condition integrates the *square* of the wave function. We don't have any information about what the integral of $\psi(x)$ might be. ◀

EXAMPLE 39.2 **Normalizing and interpreting a wave function**

FIGURE 39.9 shows the wave function of a particle confined within the region between $x = 0$ nm and $x = L = 1.0$ nm. The wave function is zero outside this region.

a. Determine the value of the constant c that makes this a normalized wave function.
b. Draw a graph of the probability density $P(x)$.
c. Draw a dot picture showing where the first 40 or 50 particles might be found.
d. Calculate the probability of finding the particle in a region of width $\delta x = 0.01$ nm at positions $x_1 = 0.05$ nm, $x_2 = 0.50$ nm, and $x_3 = 0.95$ nm.

FIGURE 39.9 The wave function of Example 39.2.

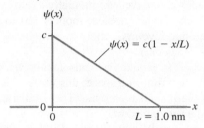

MODEL The probability of finding the particle is determined by the probability density $P(x)$.

VISUALIZE The wave function is shown in Figure 39.9.

SOLVE a. The wave function is $\psi(x) = c(1 - x/L)$ between 0 and L, 0 otherwise. This is a function that decreases linearly from $\psi = c$ at $x = 0$ to $\psi = 0$ at $x = L$. The constant c is the height of this wave function. The particle *has* to be in the region $0 \le x \le L$ with probability 1, and only one value of c will make it so. We can determine c by using Equation 39.18, the normalization condition. Because the wave function is zero outside the interval from 0 to L, the integration limits are 0 to L. Thus

$$1 = \int_0^L |\psi(x)|^2 \, dx = c^2 \int_0^L \left(1 - \frac{x}{L}\right)^2 dx$$

$$= c^2 \int_0^L \left(1 - \frac{2x}{L} + \frac{x^2}{L^2}\right) dx$$

$$= c^2 \left[x - \frac{x^2}{L} + \frac{x^3}{3L^2}\right]_0^L = \frac{1}{3}c^2 L$$

The solution for c is

$$c = \sqrt{\frac{3}{L}} = \sqrt{\frac{3}{1.0 \text{ nm}}} = 1.732 \text{ nm}^{-1/2}$$

Note the unusual units for c. Although these are not SI units, we can correctly compute probabilities as long as δx has units of nm. A multiplicative constant such as c is often called a *normalization constant*.

b. The wave function is

$$\psi(x) = (1.732 \text{ nm}^{-1/2})\left(1 - \frac{x}{1.0 \text{ nm}}\right)$$

Thus the probability density is

$$P(x) = |\psi(x)|^2 = (3.0 \text{ nm}^{-1})\left(1 - \frac{x}{1.0 \text{ nm}}\right)^2$$

This probability density is graphed in FIGURE 39.10a.

FIGURE 39.10 The probability density $P(x)$ and the detected positions of particles.

(a) $P(x)$ (nm^{-1})

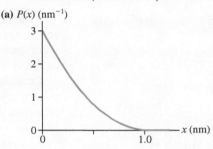

(b)

c. Particles are most likely to be detected at the left edge of the interval, where the probability density $P(x)$ is maximum. The probability steadily decreases across the interval, becoming zero at $x = 1.0$ nm. FIGURE 39.10b shows how a group of particles described by this wave function might appear on a detection screen.

d. $P(x)$ is essentially constant over the small interval $\delta x = 0.01$ nm, so we can use

$$\text{Prob(in } \delta x \text{ at } x) = P(x)\, \delta x = |\psi(x)|^2 \, \delta x$$

for the probability of finding the particle in a region of width δx at the position x. We need to evaluate $|\psi(x)|^2$ at the three positions $x_1 = 0.05$ nm, $x_2 = 0.50$ nm, and $x_3 = 0.95$ nm. Doing so gives

$$\text{Prob(in } 0.01 \text{ nm at } x_1 = 0.05 \text{ nm}) = c^2(1 - x_1/L)^2 \, \delta x$$
$$= 0.0270 = 2.70\%$$

$$\text{Prob(in } 0.01 \text{ nm at } x_2 = 0.50 \text{ nm}) = c^2(1 - x_2/L)^2 \, \delta x$$
$$= 0.0075 = 0.75\%$$

$$\text{Prob(in } 0.01 \text{ nm at } x_3 = 0.95 \text{ nm}) = c^2(1 - x_3/L)^2 \, \delta x$$
$$= 0.00008 = 0.008\%$$

STOP TO THINK 39.4   The value of the constant a is

a. $a = 2.0 \text{ mm}^{-1}$
b. $a = 1.0 \text{ mm}^{-1}$
c. $a = 0.5 \text{ mm}^{-1}$
d. $a = 2.0 \text{ mm}^{-1/2}$
e. $a = 1.0 \text{ mm}^{-1/2}$
f. $a = 0.5 \text{ mm}^{-1/2}$

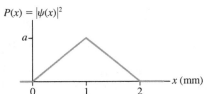

39.5 Wave Packets

The classical physics ideas of particles and waves are mutually exclusive. An object can be one or the other, but not both. These classical models fail to describe the wave–particle duality seen at the atomic level. An alternative model with both particle and wave characteristics is a *wave packet.*

Consider the wave shown in FIGURE 39.11. Unlike the sinusoidal waves we have considered previously, which stretch through time and space, this wave is bunched up, or localized. The localization is a particle-like characteristic. The oscillations are wavelike. Such a localized wave is called a **wave packet.**

A wave packet travels through space with constant speed v, just like a photon in a light wave or an electron in a force-free region. A wave packet has a wavelength, hence it will undergo interference and diffraction. But because it is also localized, a wave packet has the possibility of making a "dot" when it strikes a detector. We can visualize a light wave as consisting of a very large number of these wave packets moving along together. Similarly, we can think of a beam of electrons as a series of wave packets spread out along a line.

Wave packets are not a perfect model of photons or electrons (we need the full treatment of quantum physics to get a more accurate description), but they do provide a useful way of thinking about photons and electrons in many circumstances.

You might have noticed that the wave packet in Figure 39.11 looks very much like one cycle of a beat pattern. You will recall that beats occur if we superimpose two waves of frequencies f_1 and f_2 where the two frequencies are very similar: $f_1 \approx f_2$. FIGURE 39.12, which is copied from Chapter 21 where we studied beats, shows that the loud, soft, loud, soft, ... pattern of beats corresponds to a series of wave packets.

In Chapter 21, the beat frequency (number of pulses per second) was found to be

$$f_{\text{beat}} = f_1 - f_2 = \Delta f \qquad (39.19)$$

where Δf is the *range* of frequencies that are superimposed to form the wave packet. Figure 39.12 defines Δt as the duration of each beat or each wave packet. This interval of time is equivalent to the *period* T_{beat} of the beat. Because period and frequency are inverses of each other, the duration Δt is

$$\Delta t = T_{\text{beat}} = \frac{1}{f_{\text{beat}}} = \frac{1}{\Delta f}$$

We can rewrite this as

$$\Delta f \Delta t = 1 \qquad (39.20)$$

Equation 39.20 is nothing new; we are simply writing what we already knew in a different form. Equation 39.20 is a combination of three things: the relationship $f = 1/T$ between period and frequency, writing T_{beat} as Δt, and the specific knowledge that the beat frequency f_{beat} is the difference Δf of the two frequencies contributing to

FIGURE 39.11 History graph of a wave packet with duration Δt.

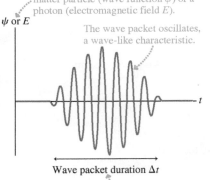

A wave packet can represent either a matter particle (wave function ψ) or a photon (electromagnetic field E).

The wave packet oscillates, a wave-like characteristic.

The wave packet is localized, a particle-like characteristic.

FIGURE 39.12 Beats are a series of wave packets.

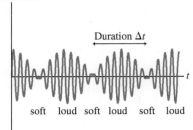

the wave packet. As the frequency separation gets smaller, the duration of each beat gets longer.

When we superimpose two frequencies to create beats, the wave packet repeats over and over. A more advanced treatment of waves, called Fourier analysis, reveals that a single, *nonrepeating* wave packet can be created through the superposition of *many* waves of very similar frequency. FIGURE 39.13 illustrates this idea. At one instant of time, all the waves interfere constructively to produce the maximum amplitude of the wave packet. At other times, the individual waves get out of phase and their super-position tends toward zero.

FIGURE 39.13 A single wave packet is the superposition of many component waves of similar wavelength and frequency.

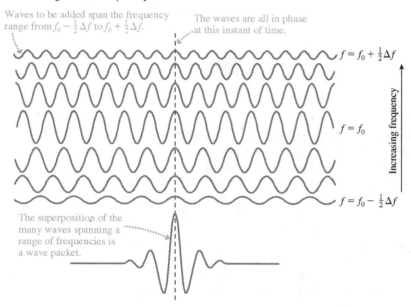

Waves to be added span the frequency range from $f_0 - \frac{1}{2}\Delta f$ to $f_0 + \frac{1}{2}\Delta f$.

The waves are all in phase at this instant of time.

$f = f_0 + \frac{1}{2}\Delta f$

$f = f_0$

Increasing frequency

$f = f_0 - \frac{1}{2}\Delta f$

The superposition of the many waves spanning a range of frequencies is a wave packet.

Suppose a single nonrepeating wave packet of duration Δt is created by the super-position of *many* waves that span a range of frequencies Δf. We'll not prove it, but Fourier analysis shows that for *any* wave packet

$$\Delta f \Delta t \approx 1 \qquad\qquad (39.21)$$

The relationship between Δf and Δt for a general wave packet is not as precise as Equation 39.20 for beats. There are two reasons for this:

1. Wave packets come in a variety of shapes. The exact relationship between Δf and Δt depends somewhat on the shape of the wave packet.
2. We have not given a precise definition of Δt and Δf for a general wave packet. The quantity Δt is "about how long the wave packet lasts," while Δf is "about the range of frequencies needing to be superimposed to produce this wave packet." For our purposes, we will not need to be any more precise than this.

Equation 39.21 is a purely classical result that applies to waves of any kind. It tells you the range of frequencies you need to superimpose to construct a wave packet of duration Δt. Alternatively, Equation 39.21 tells you that a wave packet created as a superposition of various frequencies cannot be arbitrarily short but *must* last for a time interval $\Delta t \approx 1/\Delta f$.

EXAMPLE 39.3 **Creating radio-frequency pulses**

A short-wave radio station broadcasts at a frequency of 10.000 MHz. What is the range of frequencies of the waves that must be superimposed to broadcast a radio-wave pulse lasting 0.800 μs?

MODEL A pulse of radio waves is an electromagnetic wave packet, hence it must satisfy the relationship $\Delta f \Delta t \approx 1$.

VISUALIZE FIGURE 39.14 shows the pulse.

FIGURE 39.14 A pulse of radio waves.

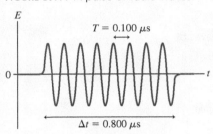

SOLVE The period of a 10.000 MHz oscillation is 0.100 μs. A pulse 0.800 μs in duration is 8 oscillations of the wave. Although the station broadcasts at a nominal frequency of 10.000 MHz, this pulse is not a pure 10.000 MHz oscillation. Instead, the pulse has been created by the superposition of many waves whose frequencies span

$$\Delta f \approx \frac{1}{\Delta t} = \frac{1}{0.800 \times 10^{-6}\ \text{s}} = 1.250 \times 10^6\ \text{Hz} = 1.250\ \text{MHz}$$

This range of frequencies will be centered at the 10.000 MHz broadcast frequency, so the waves that must be superimposed to create this pulse span the frequency range

$$9.375\ \text{MHz} \le f \le 10.625\ \text{MHz}$$

Bandwidth

Short-duration pulses, like the one in Example 39.3, are used to transmit digital information. Digital signals are sent over a phone line by brief tone pulses, over satellite links by brief radio pulses like the one in the example, and through optical fibers by brief laser-light pulses. Regardless of the type of wave and the medium through which it travels, any wave pulse must obey the fundamental relationship $\Delta f \Delta t \approx 1$.

Sending data at a higher rate (i.e., more pulses per second) requires that the pulse duration Δt be shorter. But a shorter-duration pulse must be created by the superposition of a *larger* range of frequencies. Thus the medium through which a shorter-duration pulse travels must be physically able to transmit the full range of frequencies.

The range of frequencies that can be transmitted through a medium is called the **bandwidth** Δf_B of the medium. The shortest possible pulse that can be transmitted through a medium is

$$\Delta t_{\text{min}} \approx \frac{1}{\Delta f_B} \tag{39.22}$$

A pulse shorter than this would require a larger range of frequencies than the medium can support.

The concept of bandwidth is extremely important in digital communications. A higher bandwidth permits the transmission of shorter pulses and allows a higher data rate. A standard telephone line does not have a very high bandwidth, and that is why a modem is limited to sending data at the rate of roughly 50,000 pulses per second. A 0.80 μs pulse can't be sent over a phone line simply because the phone line won't transmit the range of frequencies that would be needed.

An optical fiber is a high-bandwidth medium. A fiber has a bandwidth $\Delta f_B > 1$ GHz and thus can transmit laser-light pulses with duration $\Delta t < 1$ ns. As a result, more than 10^9 pulses per second can be sent along an optical fiber, which is why optical-fiber networks now form the backbone of the Internet.

Uncertainty

There is another way of thinking about the time-frequency relationship $\Delta f \Delta t \approx 1$. Suppose you want to determine *when* a wave packet arrives at a specific point in space, such as at a detector of some sort. At what instant of time can you say that the wave packet is detected? When the front edge arrives? When the maximum amplitude arrives? When the back edge arrives? Because a wave packet is spread out in time, there is not a unique and well-defined time *t* at which the packet arrives. All we can say is that it arrives within some interval of time Δ*t*. We are *uncertain* about the exact arrival time.

Similarly, suppose you would like to know the oscillation frequency of a wave packet. There is no precise value for *f* because the wave packet is constructed from many waves within a range of frequencies Δ*f*. All we can say is that the frequency is within this range. We are *uncertain* about the exact frequency.

The time-frequency relationship Δ*f*Δ*t* ≈ 1 tells us that the uncertainty in our knowledge about the arrival time of the wave packet is related to our uncertainty about the packet's frequency. The more precisely and accurately we know one quantity, the less precisely we will be able to know the other.

FIGURE 39.15 shows two different wave packets. The wave packet of FIGURE 39.15a is very narrow and thus very localized in time. As it travels, our knowledge of when it will arrive at a specified point is fairly precise. But a very wide range of frequencies Δ*f* is required to create a wave packet with a very small Δ*t*. The price we pay for being fairly certain about the time is a very large uncertainty Δ*f* about the frequency of this wave packet.

FIGURE 39.15b shows the opposite situation: The wave packet oscillates many times and the frequency of these oscillations is pretty clear. Our knowledge of the frequency is good, with minimal uncertainty Δ*f*. But such a wave packet is so spread out that there is a very large uncertainty Δ*t* as to its time of arrival.

In practice, Δ*f*Δ*t* ≈ 1 is really a lower limit. Technical limitations may cause the uncertainties in our knowledge of *f* and *t* to be even larger than this relationship implies. Consequently, a better statement about our knowledge of a wave packet is

$$\Delta f \Delta t \geq 1 \tag{39.23}$$

The fact that waves are spread out makes it meaningless to specify an exact frequency and an exact arrival time simultaneously. This is an inherent feature of waviness that applies to all waves.

FIGURE 39.15 Two wave packets with different Δ*t*.

(a)

Δ*t*

This wave packet has a large frequency uncertainty Δ*f*.

(b)

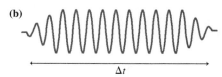

Δ*t*

This wave packet has a small frequency uncertainty Δ*f*.

STOP TO THINK 39.5 What minimum bandwidth must a medium have to transmit a 100-ns-long pulse?

a. 1 MHz   b. 10 MHz   c. 100 MHz   d. 1000 MHz

39.6 The Heisenberg Uncertainty Principle

If matter has wave-like aspects and a de Broglie wavelength, then the expression Δ*f*Δ*t* ≥ 1 must somehow apply to matter. How? And what are the implications?

Consider a particle with velocity v_x as it travels along the *x*-axis with deBroglie wavelength $\lambda = h/p_x$. Figure 39.11 showed a *history graph* (ψ versus *t*) of a wave packet that might represent the particle as it passes a point on the *x*-axis. It will be more useful to have a *snapshot graph* (ψ versus *x*) of the wave packet traveling along the *x*-axis.

The time interval Δ*t* is the duration of the wave packet as the particle passes a point in space. During this interval, the packet moves forward

$$\Delta x = v_x \Delta t = \frac{p_x}{m} \Delta t \tag{39.24}$$

where $p_x = mv_x$ is the *x*-component of the particle's momentum. The quantity Δ*x*, shown in FIGURE 39.16, is the length or spatial extent of the wave packet. Conversely, we can write the wave packet's duration in terms of its length as

$$\Delta t = \frac{m}{p_x} \Delta x \tag{39.25}$$

FIGURE 39.16 A snapshot graph of a wave packet.

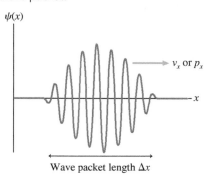

ψ(*x*)

v_x or p_x

x

Wave packet length Δ*x*

You will recall that any wave with sinusoidal oscillations must satisfy the wave condition $\lambda f = v$. For a material particle, where λ is the de Broglie wavelength, the frequency f is

$$f = \frac{v}{\lambda} = \frac{p_x/m}{h/p_x} = \frac{p_x^2}{hm}$$

If the momentum p_x should vary by the small amount Δp_x, the frequency will vary by the small amount Δf. Assuming that $\Delta f \ll f$ and $\Delta p_x \ll p_x$ (reasonable assumptions), we can treat Δf and Δp_x as if they were differentials df and dp_x. Taking the derivative, we find

$$\Delta f = \frac{2p_x \Delta p_x}{hm} \tag{39.26}$$

Multiplying together these expressions for Δt and Δf, we find that

$$\Delta f \Delta t = \frac{2p_x \Delta p_x}{hm} \frac{m \Delta x}{p_x} = \frac{2}{h} \Delta x \Delta p_x \tag{39.27}$$

Because $\Delta f \Delta t \geq 1$ for any wave, one last rearrangement of Equation 39.27 shows that a matter wave must obey the condition

$$\Delta x \Delta p_x \geq \frac{h}{2} \quad \text{(Heisenberg uncertainty principle)} \tag{39.28}$$

This statement about the relationship between the position and momentum of a particle was proposed by Werner Heisenberg, creator of one of the first successful quantum theories. Physicists often just call it the **uncertainty principle.**

NOTE ▶ In statements of the uncertainty principle, the right side is sometimes $h/2$, as we have it, but other times it is just h or contains various factors of π. The specific number is not especially important because it depends on exactly how Δx and Δp are defined. The important idea is that the product of Δx and Δp_x for a particle cannot be significantly less than Planck's constant h. A similar relationship for $\Delta y \Delta p_y$ applies along the y-axis. ◀

What Does It Mean?

Heisenberg's uncertainty principle is a statement about our *knowledge* of the properties of a particle. If we want to know *where* a particle is located, we measure its position x. That measurement is not absolutely perfect but has some uncertainty Δx. Likewise, if we want to know *how fast* the particle is going, we need to measure its velocity v_x or, equivalently, its momentum p_x. This measurement also has some uncertainty Δp_x.

Uncertainties are associated with all experimental measurements, but better procedures and techniques can reduce those uncertainties. Newtonian physics places no limits on how small the uncertainties can be. A Newtonian particle at any instant of time has an exact position x and an exact momentum p_x, and with sufficient care we can measure both x and p_x with such precision that the product $\Delta x \Delta p_x \rightarrow 0$. There are no inherent limits to our knowledge about a classical, or Newtonian, particle.

Heisenberg, however, made the bold and original statement that our knowledge has real limitations. No matter how clever you are, and no matter how good your experiment, you *cannot* measure both x and p_x simultaneously with arbitrarily good precision. Any measurements you make are limited by the condition that $\Delta x \Delta p_x \geq h/2$. **Our knowledge about a particle is *inherently* uncertain.**

Why? Because of the wave-like nature of matter. The "particle" is spread out in space, so there simply is not a precise value of its position x. Similarly, the de Broglie relationship between momentum and wavelength implies that we cannot know the momentum of a wave packet any more exactly than we can know its wavelength or frequency. Our belief that position and momentum have precise values is tied to our classical concept of a particle. As we revise our ideas of what atomic particles are like, we will also have to revise our old ideas about position and momentum.

EXAMPLE 39.4   The uncertainty of a dust particle

A 1.0-μm-diameter dust particle ($m \approx 10^{-15}$ kg) is confined within a 10-μm-long box. Can we know with certainty if the particle is at rest? If not, within what range is its velocity likely to be found?

MODEL All matter is subject to the Heisenberg uncertainty principle.

SOLVE If we know *for sure* that the particle is at rest, then $p_x = 0$ with no uncertainty. That is, $\Delta p_x = 0$. But then, according to the uncertainty principle, the uncertainty in our knowledge of the particle's position would have to be $\Delta x \rightarrow \infty$. In other words, we would have no knowledge at all about the particle's position—it could be anywhere! But that is not the case. We know the particle is *somewhere* in the box, so the uncertainty in our knowledge of its position is at most $\Delta x = L = 10~\mu$m. With a finite Δx, the uncertainty Δp_x *cannot* be zero. We cannot know with certainty if the particle is at rest inside the box. No matter how hard we try to bring the particle to rest, the uncertainty in our knowledge of

the particle's momentum will be $\Delta p_x \approx h/(2\,\Delta x) = h/2L$. We've assumed the most accurate measurements possible so that the $\geq$ in Heisenberg's uncertainty principle becomes $\approx$. Consequently, the range of possible velocities is

$$\Delta v_x = \frac{\Delta p_x}{m} \approx \frac{h}{2mL} \approx 3.0 \times 10^{-14}~\text{m/s}$$

This range of possible velocities will be centered on $v_x = 0$ m/s if we have done our best to have the particle be at rest. Thus all we can know with certainty is that the particle's velocity is somewhere within the interval -1.5×10^{-14} m/s $\leq v \leq 1.5 \times 10^{-14}$ m/s.

ASSESS For practical purposes you might consider this to be a satisfactory definition of "at rest." After all, a particle moving with a speed of 1.5×10^{-14} m/s would need 6×10^{10} s to move a mere 1 mm. That is about 2000 years! Nonetheless, we can't know if the particle is "really" at rest.

EXAMPLE 39.5   The uncertainty of an electron

What range of velocities might an electron have if confined to a 0.10-nm-wide region, about the size of an atom?

MODEL Electrons are subject to the Heisenberg uncertainty principle.

SOLVE The analysis is the same as in Example 39.4. If we know that the electron's position is located within an interval $\Delta x \approx 0.1$ nm, then the best we can know is that its velocity is within the range

$$\Delta v_x = \frac{\Delta p_x}{m} \approx \frac{h}{2mL} \approx 4 \times 10^6~\text{m/s}$$

Because the *average* velocity is zero, the best we can say is that the electron's velocity is somewhere in the interval -2×10^6 m/s $\leq v \leq 2 \times 10^6$ m/s. It is simply not possible to know the electron's velocity any more precisely than this.

ASSESS Unlike the situation in Example 39.4, where Δv was so small as to be of no practical consequence, our uncertainty about the electron's velocity is enormous—about 1% of the speed of light!

Once again, we see that even the smallest of macroscopic objects behaves very much like a classical Newtonian particle. Perhaps a 1-μm-diameter particle is slightly fuzzy and has a slightly uncertain velocity, but it is far beyond the measuring capabilities of even the very best instruments to detect this wave-like behavior. In contrast, the effects of the uncertainty principle at the atomic scale are stupendous. We are unable to determine the velocity of an electron in an atom-size container to any better accuracy than about 1% of the speed of light.

STOP TO THINK 39.6   Which of these particles, A or B, can you locate more precisely?

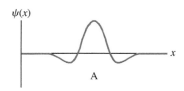
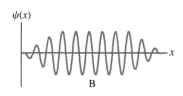

CHALLENGE EXAMPLE 39.6 **The probability of finding a particle**

A particle is described by the wave function

$$\psi(x) = \begin{cases} 0 & x < 0 \\ ce^{-x/L} & x \geq 0 \end{cases}$$

where $L = 1$ nm.

a. Determine the value of the constant c.
b. Draw graphs of $\psi(x)$ and the probability density $P(x)$.
c. If 10^6 particles are detected, how many are expected to be found in the region $x \geq 1$ nm?

MODEL The probability of finding a particle is determined by the probability density $P(x)$.

SOLVE a. The wave function is an exponential $\psi(x) = ce^{-x/L}$ that extends from $x = 0$ to $x = +\infty$. Equation 39.18, the normalization condition, is

$$1 = \int_{-\infty}^{\infty} |\psi(x)|^2 \, dx = c^2 \int_0^{\infty} e^{-2x/L} \, dx = -\frac{c^2 L}{2} e^{-2x/L} \Big|_0^{\infty} = \frac{c^2 L}{2}$$

We can solve this for the normalization constant c:

$$c = \sqrt{\frac{2}{L}} = \sqrt{\frac{2}{1 \text{ nm}}} = 1.414 \text{ nm}^{-1/2}$$

b. The probability density is

$$P(x) = |\psi(x)|^2 = (2.0 \text{ nm}^{-1})e^{-2x/(1.0 \text{ nm})}$$

The wave function and the probability density are graphed in FIGURE 39.17.

c. The probability of finding a particle in the region $x \geq 1$ nm is the shaded area under the probability density curve in Figure 39.17. We must use Equation 39.17 and integrate to find a numerical value. The probability is

FIGURE 39.17 The wave function and probability density of Example 39.6.

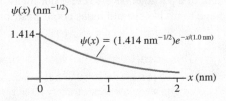

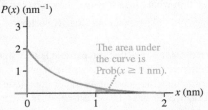

$$\text{Prob}(x \geq 1 \text{ nm}) = \int_{1 \text{ nm}}^{\infty} |\psi(x)|^2 \, dx$$

$$= (2.0 \text{ nm}^{-1}) \int_{1 \text{ nm}}^{\infty} e^{-2x/(1.0 \text{ nm})} \, dx$$

$$= (2.0 \text{ nm}^{-1}) \left(-\frac{1.0 \text{ nm}}{2} \right) e^{-2x/(1.0 \text{ nm})} \Big|_{1 \text{ nm}}^{\infty}$$

$$= e^{-2} = 0.135 = 13.5\%$$

The number of particles expected to be found at $x \geq 1$ nm is

$$N_{\text{detected}} = N \cdot \text{Prob}(x \geq 1 \text{ nm}) = (10^6)(0.135) = 135,000$$

ASSESS There is a 13.5% chance of detecting a particle beyond 1 nm and thus an 86.5% chance of finding it within the interval $0 \leq x \leq 1$ nm. Unlike classical physics, we cannot make an exact prediction of a particle's position.

SUMMARY

The goal of Chapter 39 has been to introduce and learn to use the wave-function description of matter.

General Principles

Wave Functions and the Probability Density

We cannot predict the exact trajectory of an atomic-level particle such as an electron. The best we can do is to predict the **probability** that a particle will be found in some region of space. The probability is determined by the particle's wave function $\psi(x)$.

- $\psi(x)$ is a continuous, wave-like (i.e., oscillatory) function.

- The probability that a particle will be found in the narrow interval δx at position x is
$$\text{Prob(in } \delta x \text{ at } x) = |\psi(x)|^2 \, \delta x$$

- $|\psi(x)|^2$ is the probability density $P(x)$.

- For the probability interpretation of $\psi(x)$ to make sense, the wave function must satisfy the normalization condition:

-
$$\int_{-\infty}^{\infty} P(x) \, dx = \int_{-\infty}^{\infty} |\psi(x)|^2 \, dx = 1$$

That is, it is certain that the particle is *somewhere* on the x-axis.

- For an extended interval
$$\text{Prob}(x_L \leq x \leq x_R) = \int_{x_L}^{x_R} |\psi(x)|^2 \, dx = \text{area under the curve}$$

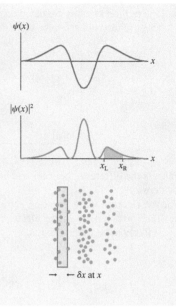

Heisenberg Uncertainty Principle

A particle with wave-like characteristics does not have a precise value of position x or a precise value of momentum p_x. Both are uncertain. The position uncertainty Δx and momentum uncertainty Δp_x are related by $\Delta x \, \Delta p_x \geq h/2$. The more you try to pin down the value of one, the less precisely the other can be known.

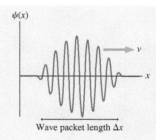

Wave packet length Δx

Important Concepts

The probability that a particle is found in region A is
$$P_A = \lim_{N_{\text{tot}} \to \infty} \frac{N_A}{N_{\text{tot}}}$$

If the probability is known, the expected number of A outcomes in N trials is $N_A = NP_A$.

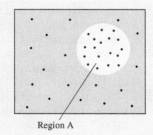

Region A

A wave packet of duration Δt can be created by the superposition of many waves spanning the frequency range Δf. These are related by
$$\Delta f \, \Delta t \approx 1$$

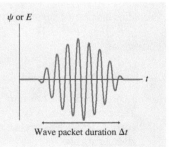

Wave packet duration Δt

Terms and Notation

probability	wave function, $\psi(x)$	bandwidth, Δf_B
expected value	normalization condition	uncertainty principle
probability density, $P(x)$	wave packet	

CONCEPTUAL QUESTIONS

1. FIGURE Q39.1 shows the probability density for photons to be detected on the x-axis.
   a. Is a photon more likely to be detected at $x = 0$ m or at $x = 1$ m? Explain.
   b. One million photons are detected. What is the expected number of photons in a 1-mm-wide interval at $x = 0.50$ m?

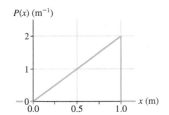

FIGURE Q39.1

2. What is the difference between the probability and the probability density?

3. For the electron wave function shown in FIGURE Q39.3, at what position or positions is the electron most likely to be found? Least likely to be found? Explain.

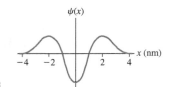

FIGURE Q39.3

4. FIGURE Q39.4 shows the dot pattern of electrons landing on a screen.
   a. At what value or values of x is the electron probability density at maximum? Explain.
   b. Can you tell at what value or values of x the electron wave function $\psi(x)$ is most positive? If so, where? If not, why not?

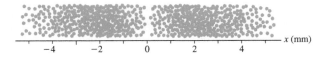

FIGURE Q39.4

5. What is the value of the constant a in FIGURE Q39.5?

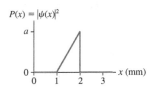

FIGURE Q39.5

6. FIGURE Q39.6 shows wave packets for particles 1, 2, and 3. Which particle can have its velocity known most precisely? Explain.

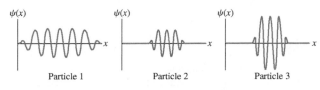

FIGURE Q39.6

EXERCISES AND PROBLEMS

Problems labeled [   ] integrate material from earlier chapters.

Exercises

Section 39.1 Waves, Particles, and the Double-Slit Experiment

1. ‖ An experiment has four possible outcomes, labeled A to D. The probability of A is $P_A = 40\%$ and of B is $P_B = 30\%$. Outcome C is twice as probable as outcome D. What are the probabilities P_C and P_D?

2. ‖ Suppose you toss three coins into the air and let them fall on the floor. Each coin shows either a head or a tail.
   a. Make a table in which you list all the possible outcomes of this experiment. Call the coins A, B, and C.
   b. What is the probability of getting two heads and one tail? Explain.
   c. What is the probability of getting *at least* two heads?

3. | Suppose you draw a card from a regular deck of 52 cards.
   a. What is the probability that you draw an ace?
   b. What is the probability that you draw a spade?

4. | You are dealt 1 card each from 1000 decks of cards. What is the expected number of picture cards (jacks, queens, and kings)?

5. | Make a table in which you list all possible outcomes of rolling two dice. Call the dice A and B. What is the probability of rolling (a) a 7, (b) any double, and (c) a 6 or an 8? You can give the probabilities as fractions, such as 3/36.

Section 39.2 Connecting the Wave and Photon Views

6. | In one experiment, 2000 photons are detected in a 0.10-mm-wide strip where the amplitude of the electromagnetic wave is 10 V/m. How many photons are detected in a nearby 0.10-mm-wide strip where the amplitude is 30 V/m?

7. ‖ In one experiment, 6000 photons are detected in a 0.10-mm-wide strip where the amplitude of the electromagnetic wave is 200 V/m. What is the wave amplitude at a nearby 0.20-mm-wide strip where 3000 photons are detected?

8. ‖ 1.0×10^{10} photons pass through an experimental apparatus. How many of them land in a 0.10-mm-wide strip where the probability density is 20 m^{-1}?

9. | When 5×10^{12} photons pass through an experimental apparatus, 2.0×10^9 land in a 0.10-mm-wide strip. What is the probability density at this point?

Section 39.3 The Wave Function

10. | What are the units of ψ? Explain.

11. | FIGURE EX39.11 shows the probability density for an electron that has passed through an experimental apparatus. If 1.0×10^6 electrons are used, what is the expected number that will land in a 0.010-mm-wide strip at (a) $x = 0.000$ mm and (b) 2.000 mm?

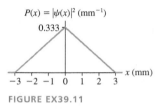

FIGURE EX39.11

12. ‖ In an interference experiment with electrons, you find the most intense fringe is at $x = 7.0$ cm. There are slightly weaker fringes at $x = 6.0$ and 8.0 cm, still weaker fringes at $x = 4.0$ and 10.0 cm, and two very weak fringes at $x = 1.0$ and 13.0 cm. No electrons are detected at $x < 0$ cm or $x > 14$ cm.
   a. Sketch a graph of $|\psi(x)|^2$ for these electrons.
   b. Sketch a possible graph of $\psi(x)$.
   c. Are there other possible graphs for $\psi(x)$? If so, draw one.

13. | FIGURE EX39.13 shows the probability density for an electron that has passed through an experimental apparatus. What is the probability that the electron will land in a 0.010-mm-wide strip at (a) $x = 0.000$ mm, (b) $x = 0.500$ mm, (c) $x = 1.000$ mm, and (d) $x = 2.000$ mm?

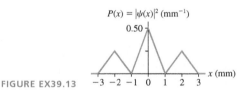

FIGURE EX39.13

Section 39.4 Normalization

14. ‖ FIGURE EX39.14 is a graph of $|\psi(x)|^2$ for an electron.
   a. What is the value of a?
   b. Draw a graph of the wave function $\psi(x)$. (There is more than one acceptable answer.)
   c. What is the probability that the electron is located between $x = 1.0$ nm and $x = 2.0$ nm?

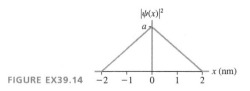

FIGURE EX39.14

15. ‖ FIGURE EX39.15 is a graph of $|\psi(x)|^2$ for a neutron.
   a. What is the value of a?
   b. Draw a graph of the wave function $\psi(x)$. (There is more than one acceptable answer.)
   c. What is the probability that the neutron is located at a position with $|x| \geq 2$ fm?

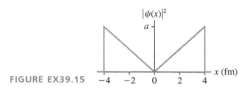

FIGURE EX39.15

16. ‖ FIGURE EX39.16 shows the wave function of an electron.
   a. What is the value of c?
   b. Draw a graph of $|\psi(x)|^2$.
   c. What is the probability that the electron is located between $x = -1.0$ nm and $x = 1.0$ nm?

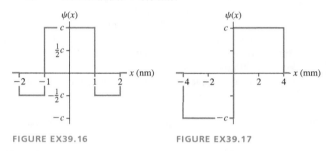

FIGURE EX39.16   FIGURE EX39.17

17. ‖ FIGURE EX39.17 shows the wave function of a neutron.
   a. What is the value of c?
   b. Draw a graph of $|\psi(x)|^2$.
   c. What is the probability that the neutron is located between $x = -1.0$ mm and $x = 1.0$ mm?

Section 39.5 Wave Packets

18. | What minimum bandwidth is needed to transmit a pulse that consists of 100 cycles of a 1.00 MHz oscillation?

19. ‖ A radio-frequency amplifier is designed to amplify signals in the frequency range 80 MHz to 120 MHz. What is the shortest-duration radio-frequency pulse that can be amplified without distortion?

20. ‖ Sound waves of 498 Hz and 502 Hz are superimposed at a temperature where the speed of sound in air is 340 m/s. What is the length Δx of one wave packet?

21. ‖ A 1.5-μm-wavelength laser pulse is transmitted through a 2.0-GHz-bandwidth optical fiber. How many oscillations are in the shortest-duration laser pulse that can travel through the fiber?

Section 39.6 The Heisenberg Uncertainty Principle

22. ‖ A thin solid barrier in the xy-plane has a 10-μm-diameter circular hole. An electron traveling in the z-direction with $v_x = 0$ m/s passes through the hole. Afterward, is it certain that v_x is still zero? If not, within what range is v_x likely to be?

23. ‖ Andrea, whose mass is 50 kg, thinks she's sitting at rest in her 5.0-m-long dorm room as she does her physics homework. Can Andrea be sure she's at rest? If not, within what range is her velocity likely to be?

24. ‖ What is the minimum uncertainty in position, in nm, of an electron whose velocity is known to be between 3.48×10^5 m/s and 3.58×10^5 m/s?

25. ‖ A proton is confined within an atomic nucleus of diameter 4.0 m. Use a one-dimensional model to estimate the smallest range of speeds you might find for a proton in the nucleus.

Problems

26. ‖ A 1.0-mm-diameter sphere bounces back and forth between two walls at $x = 0$ mm and $x = 100$ mm. The collisions are perfectly elastic, and the sphere repeats this motion over and over with no loss of speed. At a random instant of time, what is the probability that the center of the sphere is
   a. At exactly $x = 50.0$ mm?
   b. Between $x = 49.0$ mm and $x = 51.0$ mm?
   c. At $x \geq 75$ mm?

27. ‖ A radar antenna broadcasts electromagnetic waves with a period of 0.100 ns. What range of frequencies would need to be superimposed to create a 1.0-ns-long radar pulse?

28. ‖ Ultrasound pulses with a frequency of 1.000 MHz are transmitted into water, where the speed of sound is 1500 m/s. The spatial length of each pulse is 12 mm.
   a. How many complete cycles are contained in one pulse?
   b. What range of frequencies must be superimposed to create each pulse?

29. ‖ FIGURE P39.29 shows a *pulse train*. The period of the pulse train is $T = 2\Delta t$, where Δt is the duration of each pulse. What is the maximum pulse-transmission rate (pulses per second) through an electronics system with a 200 kHz bandwidth? (This is the bandwidth allotted to each FM radio station.)

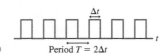

FIGURE P39.29   Period $T = 2\Delta t$

30. ‖ Consider a single-slit diffraction experiment using electrons. (Single-slit diffraction was described in Section 22.4.) Using Figure 39.5 as a model, draw
   a. A dot picture showing the arrival positions of the first 40 or 50 electrons.
   b. A graph of $|\psi(x)|^2$ for the electrons on the detection screen.
   c. A graph of $\psi(x)$ for the electrons. Keep in mind that ψ, as a wave-like function, oscillates between positive and negative.

31. ‖ An experiment finds electrons to be uniformly distributed over the interval 0 cm $\leq x \leq 2$ cm, with no electrons falling outside this interval.
   a. Draw a graph of $|\psi(x)|^2$ for these electrons.
   b. What is the probability that an electron will land within the interval 0.79 to 0.81 cm?
   c. If 10^6 electrons are detected, how many will be detected in the interval 0.79 to 0.81 cm?
   d. What is the probability density at $x = 0.80$ cm?

32. ‖ In an experiment with 10,000 electrons, which land symmetrically on both sides of $x = 0$ cm, 5000 are detected in the range -1.0 cm $\leq x \leq +1.0$ cm, 7500 are detected in the range -2.0 cm $\leq x \leq +2.0$ cm, and all 10,000 are detected in the range -3.0 cm $\leq x \leq +3.0$ cm. Draw a graph of a probability density that is consistent with these data. (There may be more than one acceptable answer.)

33. ‖ FIGURE P39.33 shows $|\psi(x)|^2$ for the electrons in an experiment.
   a. Is the electron wave function normalized? Explain.
   b. Draw a graph of $\psi(x)$ over this same interval. Provide a numerical scale on both axes. (There may be more than one acceptable answer.)
   c. What is the probability that an electron will be detected in a 0.0010-cm-wide region at $x = 0.00$ cm? At $x = 0.50$ cm? At $x = 0.999$ cm?
   d. If 10^4 electrons are detected, how many are expected to land in the interval -0.30 cm $\leq x \leq 0.30$ cm?

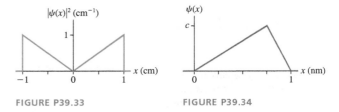

FIGURE P39.33   FIGURE P39.34

34. ‖ FIGURE P39.34 shows the wave function of a particle confined between $x = 0$ nm and $x = 1.0$ nm. The wave function is zero outside this region.
   a. Determine the value of the constant c, as defined in the figure.
   b. Draw a graph of the probability density $P(x) = |\psi(x)|^2$.
   c. Draw a dot picture showing where the first 40 or 50 particles might be found.
   d. Calculate the probability of finding the particle in the interval 0 nm $\leq x \leq 0.25$ nm.

35. ‖ FIGURE P39.35 shows the wave function of a particle confined between $x = -4.0$ mm and $x = 4.0$ mm. The wave function is zero outside this region.
   a. Determine the value of the constant c, as defined in the figure.
   b. Draw a graph of the probability density $P(x) = |\psi(x)|^2$.
   c. Draw a dot picture showing where the first 40 or 50 particles might be found.
   d. Calculate the probability of finding the particle in the interval -2.0 mm $\leq x \leq 2.0$ mm.

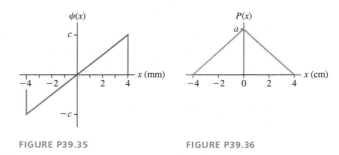

FIGURE P39.35   FIGURE P39.36

36. ‖ FIGURE P39.36 shows the probability density for finding a particle at position x.
   a. Determine the value of the constant a, as defined in the figure.
   b. At what value of x are you most likely to find the particle? Explain.
   c. Within what range of positions centered on your answer to part b are you 75% certain of finding the particle?
   d. Interpret your answer to part c by drawing the probability density graph and shading the appropriate region.

37. ‖ An electron that is confined to $x \geq 0$ nm has the normalized wave function

$$\psi(x) = \begin{cases} 0 & x < 0 \text{ nm} \\ (1.414 \text{ nm}^{-1/2})e^{-x/(1.0 \text{ nm})} & x \geq 0 \text{ nm} \end{cases}$$

where x is in nm.
   a. What is the probability of finding the electron in a 0.010-nm-wide region at $x = 1.0$ nm?
   b. What is the probability of finding the electron in the interval $0.50 \text{ nm} \leq x \leq 1.50 \text{ nm}$?

38. ‖ A particle is described by the wave function

$$\psi(x) = \begin{cases} ce^{x/L} & x \leq 0 \text{ mm} \\ ce^{-x/L} & x \geq 0 \text{ mm} \end{cases}$$

where $L = 2.0$ mm.
   a. Sketch graphs of both the wave function and the probability density as functions of x.
   b. Determine the normalization constant c.
   c. Calculate the probability of finding the particle within 1.0 mm of the origin.
   d. Interpret your answer to part b by shading the region representing this probability on the appropriate graph in part a.

39. ‖ Consider the electron wave function

$$\psi(x) = \begin{cases} c\sqrt{1 - x^2} & |x| \leq 1 \text{ cm} \\ 0 & |x| \geq 1 \text{ cm} \end{cases}$$

where x is in cm.
   a. Determine the normalization constant c.
   b. Draw a graph of $\psi(x)$ over the interval $-2 \text{ cm} \leq x \leq 2 \text{ cm}$. Provide numerical scales on both axes.
   c. Draw a graph of $|\psi(x)|^2$ over the interval $-2 \text{ cm} \leq x \leq 2 \text{ cm}$. Provide numerical scales.
   d. If 10^4 electrons are detected, how many will be in the interval $0.00 \text{ cm} \leq x \leq 0.50 \text{ cm}$?

40. ‖ Consider the electron wave function

$$\psi(x) = \begin{cases} c\sin\left(\dfrac{2\pi x}{L}\right) & 0 \leq x \leq L \\ 0 & x < 0 \text{ or } x > L \end{cases}$$

   a. Determine the normalization constant c. Your answer will be in terms of L.
   b. Draw a graph of $\psi(x)$ over the interval $-L \leq x \leq 2L$.
   c. Draw a graph of $|\psi(x)|^2$ over the interval $-L \leq x \leq 2L$.
   d. What is the probability that an electron is in the interval $0 \leq x \leq L/3$?

41. ‖ The probability density for finding a particle at position x is

$$P(x) = \begin{cases} \dfrac{a}{(1 - x)} & -1 \text{ mm} \leq x < 0 \text{ mm} \\ b(1 - x) & 0 \text{ mm} \leq x \leq 1 \text{ mm} \end{cases}$$

and zero elsewhere.
   a. You will learn in Chapter 40 that the wave function must be a *continuous* function. Assuming that to be the case, what can you conclude about the relationship between a and b?
   b. Determine values for a and b.
   c. Draw a graph of the probability density over the interval $-2 \text{ mm} \leq x \leq 2 \text{ mm}$.
   d. What is the probability that the particle will be found to the left of the origin?

42. ‖ A pulse of light is created by the superposition of many waves that span the frequency range $f_0 - \frac{1}{2}\Delta f \leq f \leq f_0 + \frac{1}{2}\Delta f$, where $f_0 = c/\lambda$ is called the *center frequency* of the pulse. Laser technology can generate a pulse of light that has a wavelength of 600 nm and lasts a mere 6.0 fs (1 fs = 1 femtosecond = 10^{-15} s).
   a. What is the center frequency of this pulse of light?
   b. How many cycles, or oscillations, of the light wave are completed during the 6.0 fs pulse?
   c. What range of frequencies must be superimposed to create this pulse?
   d. What is the spatial length of the laser pulse as it travels through space?
   e. Draw a snapshot graph of this wave packet.

43. ‖‖ What is the smallest one-dimensional box in which you can confine an electron if you want to know for certain that the electron's speed is no more than 10 m/s?

44. ‖ A small speck of dust with mass 1.0×10^{-13} g has fallen into the hole shown in FIGURE P39.44 and appears to be at rest. According to the uncertainty principle, could this particle have enough energy to get out of the hole? If not, what is the deepest hole of this width from which it would have a good chance to escape?

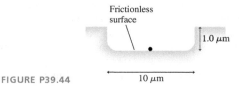

Frictionless surface

$1.0 \ \mu m$

FIGURE P39.44 $10 \ \mu m$

45. ‖ You learned in Chapter 37 that, except for hydrogen, the mass of a nucleus with atomic number Z is larger than the mass of the Z protons. The additional mass was ultimately discovered to be due to neutrons, but prior to the discovery of the neutron it was suggested that a nucleus with mass number A might contain A protons and $(A - Z)$ electrons. Such a nucleus would have the mass of A protons, but its net charge would be only Ze.
   a. We know that the diameter of a nucleus is approximately 10 fm. Model the nucleus as a one-dimensional box and find the minimum range of speeds that an electron would have in such a box.
   b. What does your answer imply about the possibility that the nucleus contains electrons? Explain.

46. ‖ a. Starting with the expression $\Delta f \Delta t \approx 1$ for a wave packet, find an expression for the product $\Delta E \Delta t$ for a photon.
   b. Interpret your expression. What does it tell you?
   c. The Bohr model of atomic quantization says that an atom in an excited state can jump to a lower-energy state by emitting a photon. The Bohr model says nothing about how long this process takes. You'll learn in Chapter 41 that the time any particular atom spends in the excited state before emitting a photon is unpredictable, but the *average lifetime* Δt of many atoms can be determined. You can think of Δt as being the uncertainty in your knowledge of how long the atom spends in the excited state. A typical value is $\Delta t \approx 10$ ns. Consider an atom that emits a photon with a 500 nm wavelength as it jumps down from an excited state. What is the uncertainty in the energy of the photon? Give your answer in eV.
   d. What is the *fractional uncertainty* $\Delta E/E$ in the photon's energy?

Challenge Problems

47. **FIGURE CP39.47** shows 1.0-μm-diameter dust particles ($m = 1.0 \times 10^{-15}$ kg) in a vacuum chamber. The dust particles are released from rest above a 1.0-μm-diameter hole, fall through the hole (there's just barely room for the particles to go through), and land on a detector at distance d below.

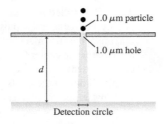

FIGURE CP39.47

  a. If the particles were purely classical, they would all land in the same 1.0-μm-diameter circle. But quantum effects don't allow this. If $d = 1.0$ m, by how much does the diameter of the circle in which most dust particles land exceed 1.0 μm? Is this increase in diameter likely to be detectable?

  b. Quantum effects would be noticeable if the detection-circle diameter increased by 10% to 1.1 μm. At what distance d would the detector need to be placed to observe this increase in the diameter?

48. Physicists use laser beams to create an *atom trap* in which atoms are confined within a spherical region of space with a diameter of about 1 mm. The scientists have been able to cool the atoms in an atom trap to a temperature of approximately 1 nK, which is extremely close to absolute zero, but it would be interesting to know if this temperature is close to any limit set by quantum physics. We can explore this issue with a one-dimensional model of a sodium atom in a 1.0-mm-long box.

  a. Estimate the *smallest* range of speeds you might find for a sodium atom in this box.

  b. Even if we do our best to bring a group of sodium atoms to rest, individual atoms will have speeds within the range you found in part a. Because there's a distribution of speeds, suppose we estimate that the root-mean-square speed v_{rms} of the atoms in the trap is half the value you found in part a. Use this v_{rms} to estimate the temperature of the atoms when they've been cooled to the limit set by the uncertainty principle.

49. The wave function of a particle is

$$\psi(x) = \sqrt{\frac{b}{\pi(x^2 + b^2)}}$$

where b is a positive constant. Find the probability that the particle is located in the interval $-b \leq x \leq b$.

50. The wave function of a particle is

$$\psi(x) = \begin{cases} \dfrac{b}{(1 + x^2)} & -1 \text{ mm} \leq x < 0 \text{ mm} \\ c(1 + x)^2 & 0 \text{ mm} \leq x \leq 1 \text{ mm} \end{cases}$$

and zero elsewhere.

  a. You will learn in Chapter 40 that the wave function must be a *continuous* function. Assuming that to be the case, what can you conclude about the relationship between b and c?

  b. Draw graphs of the wave function and the probability density over the interval -2 mm $\leq x \leq 2$ mm.

  c. What is the probability that the particle will be found to the right of the origin?

51. Consider the electron wave function

$$\psi(x) = \begin{cases} cx & |x| \leq 1 \text{ nm} \\ \dfrac{c}{x} & |x| \geq 1 \text{ nm} \end{cases}$$

where x is in nm.

  a. Determine the normalization constant c.

  b. Draw a graph of $\psi(x)$ over the interval -5 nm $\leq x \leq 5$ nm. Provide numerical scales on both axes.

  c. Draw a graph of $|\psi(x)|^2$ over the interval -5 nm $\leq x \leq 5$ nm. Provide numerical scales.

  d. If 10^6 electrons are detected, how many will be in the interval -1.0 nm $\leq x \leq 1.0$ nm?

STOP TO THINK ANSWERS

Stop to Think 39.1: 10. The probability of a 1 is $P_1 = \frac{1}{6}$. Similarly, $P_6 = \frac{1}{6}$. The probability of a 1 *or* a 6 is $P_{1 \text{ or } 6} = \frac{1}{6} + \frac{1}{6} = \frac{1}{3}$. Thus the expected number is $30(\frac{1}{3}) = 10$.

Stop to Think 39.2: A > B = D > C. $|A(x)|^2$ is proportional to the density of dots.

Stop to Think 39.3: x_C. The probability is largest at the point where the *square* of $\psi(x)$ is largest.

Stop to Think 39.4: b. The area $\frac{1}{2}a(2$ mm$)$ must equal 1.

Stop to Think 39.5: b. $\Delta t = 1.0 \times 10^{-7}$ s. The bandwidth is $\Delta f_B = 1/\Delta t = 1.0 \times 10^7$ Hz = 10 MHz.

Stop to Think 39.6: A. Wave packet A has a smaller spatial extent Δx. The wavelength isn't relevant.

40 One-Dimensional Quantum Mechanics

In this example of atomic engineering, thirty-five xenon atoms have been manipulated with the probe tip of a scanning tunneling microscope.

▶ **Looking Ahead** The goal of Chapter 40 is to understand and apply the essential ideas of quantum mechanics.

The Law of Psi

The basic law of quantum mechanics is the **Schrödinger equation.** It plays a role analogous to Newton's second law in classical mechanics.

We will limit our study to quantum mechanics in one dimension so as to focus on the physics without becoming bogged down by mathematical details.

You'll learn how the solutions to the Schrödinger equation predict the energy levels of a quantum system.

◀ **Looking Back**
Sections 39.3–39.4 Wave functions and normalization

Quantum Models

Classical systems are described in terms of forces. In contrast, a quantum system is described by a potential-energy function $U(x)$.

You'll learn to use **potential wells** to model different physical situations. A region in which $E < U_0$ is forbidden to a classical particle but not always to a quantum particle.

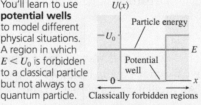

Classically forbidden regions

◀ **Looking Back**
Section 10.6 Energy diagrams

Tunneling

A surprising conclusion of quantum mechanics is that a wave function can penetrate some distance into a classically forbidden region.

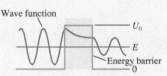

You'll learn that a particle can **tunnel** through a potential-energy barrier, emerging on the other side with no loss of energy. This totally nonclassical behavior is the basis of the scanning tunneling microscope.

Quantum Mechanics

Quantum mechanics is not just for physicists anymore. A knowledge of quantum mechanics is needed to understand the properties of materials and to design semiconductor devices. Quantum mechanics will be even more important in the near future for atomic level engineering of nanostructures and the development of quantum computing.

◀ **Looking Back**
Sections 38.4–38.5 Matter waves and the Bohr model of quantization

Wave Functions

You'll learn to understand why wave functions have the shapes they do.

- The wave function oscillates between the classical turning points.
- The wave function decays exponentially in a classically forbidden region.

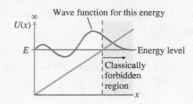

Quantum Applications

You'll study practical applications of quantum mechanics:

- Quantum-well lasers
- Molecular bonds
- Nuclear energy levels

A quantum-well laser is made with a layer of gallium arsenide only about 1 nm thick. Electrons confined within this layer have discrete, quantized energy levels.

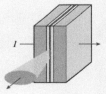

40.1 Schrödinger's Equation: The Law of Psi

Erwin Schrödinger.

In the winter of 1925, just before Christmas, the Austrian physicist Erwin Schrödinger gathered together a few books and headed off to a villa in the Swiss Alps. He had recently learned of de Broglie's 1924 suggestion that matter has wave-like properties, and he wanted some time free from distractions to think about it. Before the trip was over, Schrödinger had discovered the law of quantum mechanics.

Schrödinger's goal was to predict the outcome of atomic experiments, a goal that had eluded classical physics. The mathematical equation that he developed is now called the **Schrödinger equation.** It is the law of quantum mechanics in the same way that Newton's laws are the laws of classical mechanics. It would make sense to call it Schrödinger's law, but by tradition it is called simply the Schrödinger equation.

You learned in Chapter 39 that a matter particle is characterized in quantum physics by its wave function $\psi(x)$. If you know a particle's wave function, you can predict the probability of detecting it in some region of space. That's all well and good, but Chapter 39 didn't provide any method for determining wave functions. The Schrödinger equation is the missing piece of the puzzle. It is an equation for finding a particle's wave function $\psi(x)$.

Consider an atomic particle with mass m and mechanical energy E whose interactions with the environment can be characterized by a one-dimensional potential-energy function $U(x)$. The Schrödinger equation for the particle's wave function is

$$\frac{d^2\psi}{dx^2} = -\frac{2m}{\hbar^2}\big[E - U(x)\big]\psi(x) \qquad \text{(the Schrödinger equation)} \qquad (40.1)$$

This is a differential equation whose solution is the wave function $\psi(x)$ that we seek. Our first goal is to learn what this equation means and how it is used.

Justifying the Schrödinger Equation

The Schrödinger equation can be neither derived nor proved. It is not an outgrowth of any previous theory. Its success depended on its ability to explain the various phenomena that had refused to yield to a classical-physics analysis and to make new predictions that were subsequently verified.

Although the Schrödinger equation cannot be derived, the reasoning behind it can at least be made *plausible*. De Broglie had postulated a wave-like nature for matter in which a particle of mass m, velocity v, and momentum $p = mv$ has a wavelength

$$\lambda = \frac{h}{p} = \frac{h}{mv} \qquad (40.2)$$

Schrödinger's goal was to find a *wave equation* for which the solution would be a wave function having the de Broglie wavelength.

An oscillatory wave-like function with wavelength λ is

$$\psi(x) = \psi_0 \sin\left(\frac{2\pi x}{\lambda}\right) \qquad (40.3)$$

where ψ_0 is the amplitude of the wave function. Suppose we take a second derivative of $\psi(x)$:

$$\frac{d^2\psi}{dx^2} = \frac{d}{dx}\frac{d\psi}{dx} = \frac{d}{dx}\left[\frac{2\pi}{\lambda}\psi_0\cos\left(\frac{2\pi x}{\lambda}\right)\right] = -\frac{(2\pi)^2}{\lambda^2}\psi_0\sin\left(\frac{2\pi x}{\lambda}\right)$$

We can use Equation 40.3 to write this as

$$\frac{d^2\psi}{dx^2} = -\frac{(2\pi)^2}{\lambda^2}\psi(x) \qquad (40.4)$$

Equation 40.4 relates the wavelength λ to a combination of the wave function $\psi(x)$ and its second derivative.

NOTE ▶ These manipulations are not specific to quantum mechanics. Equation 40.4 is well known for classical waves, such as sound waves and waves on a string. ◀

Schrödinger's insight was to identify λ with the de Broglie wavelength of a particle. We can write the de Broglie wavelength in terms of the particle's kinetic energy K as

$$\lambda = \frac{h}{mv} = \frac{h}{\sqrt{2m\left(\frac{1}{2}mv^2\right)}} = \frac{h}{\sqrt{2mK}} \tag{40.5}$$

Notice that **the de Broglie wavelength increases as the particle's kinetic energy decreases.** This observation will play a key role.

If we square this expression for λ and substitute it into Equation 40.4, we find

$$\frac{d^2\psi}{dx^2} = -\frac{(2\pi)^2 \, 2mK}{h^2}\psi(x) = -\frac{2m}{\hbar^2}K\psi(x) \tag{40.6}$$

where $\hbar = h/2\pi$. Equation 40.6 is a differential equation for the function $\psi(x)$. The solution to this equation is the sinusoidal wave function of Equation 40.3, where λ is the de Broglie wavelength for a particle with kinetic energy K.

Our derivation of Equation 40.6 assumed that the particle's kinetic energy K is constant. The energy diagram of FIGURE 40.1a reminds you that a particle's kinetic energy remains constant as it moves along the x-axis only if its potential energy U is constant. In this case, the de Broglie wavelength is the same at all positions.

FIGURE 40.1 The de Broglie wavelength changes as a particle's kinetic energy changes.

(a)

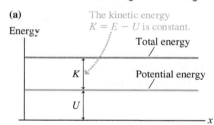

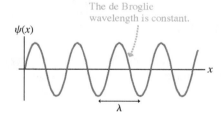

(b)

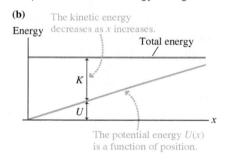

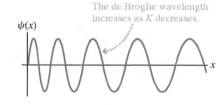

In contrast, FIGURE 40.1b shows the energy diagram for a particle whose kinetic energy is *not* constant. This particle speeds up or slows down as it moves along the x-axis, transforming potential energy to kinetic energy or vice versa. Consequently, its de Broglie wavelength changes with position.

Suppose a particle's potential energy—gravitational or electric or any other kind of potential energy—is described by the function $U(x)$. That is, the potential energy is a *function of position* along the axis of motion. For example, the potential energy of a spring is $\frac{1}{2}kx^2$.

If E is the particle's total mechanical energy, its kinetic energy at position x is

$$K = E - U(x) \tag{40.7}$$

If we use this expression for K in Equation 40.6, that equation becomes

$$\frac{d^2\psi}{dx^2} = -\frac{2m}{\hbar^2}\left[E - U(x)\right]\psi(x)$$

This is Equation 40.1, the Schrödinger equation for the particle's wave function $\psi(x)$.

NOTE ▶ This has not been a derivation of the Schrödinger equation. We've made a *plausibility argument,* based on de Broglie's hypothesis about matter waves, but only experimental evidence will show if this equation has merit. ◀

STOP TO THINK 40.1 Three de Broglie waves are shown for particles of equal mass. Rank in order, from fastest to slowest, the speeds of particles a, b, and c.

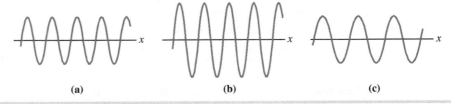

(a)   (b)   (c)

Quantum-Mechanical Models

Long ago, in your study of Newtonian mechanics, you learned the importance of *models.* To understand the motion of an object, we made simplifying assumptions: that the object could be represented by a particle, that friction could be described in a simple way, that air resistance could be neglected, and so on. Models allowed us to understand the primary features of an object's motion without getting lost in the details.

The same holds true in quantum mechanics. The exact description of a microscopic atom or a solid is extremely complicated. Our only hope for using quantum mechanics effectively is to make a number of simplifying assumptions—that is, to make a **quantum-mechanical model** of the situation. Much of this chapter will be about building and using quantum-mechanical models.

The test of a model's success is its agreement with experimental measurement. Laboratory experiments cannot measure $\psi(x)$, and they rarely make direct measurements of probabilities. Thus it will be important to tie our models to measurable quantities such as wavelengths, charges, currents, times, and temperatures.

There's one very important difference between models in classical mechanics and quantum mechanics. Classical models are described in terms of *forces,* and Newton's laws are a connection between force and motion. The Schrödinger equation for the wave function is written in terms of *energies.* Consequently, quantum-mechanical modeling involves finding a potential-energy function $U(x)$ that describes a particle's interactions with its environment.

FIGURE 40.2 reminds you how to interpret an energy diagram. We will use energy diagrams extensively in this and the remaining chapters to portray quantum-mechanical models. **A review of Section 10.6, where energy diagrams were introduced, is highly recommended.**

FIGURE 40.2 Interpreting an energy diagram.

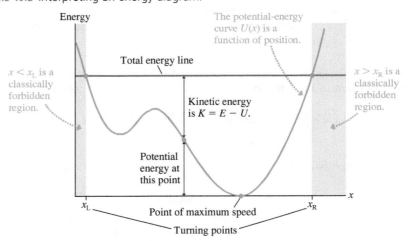

40.2 Solving the Schrödinger Equation

The Schrödinger equation is a second-order differential equation, meaning that it is a differential equation for $\psi(x)$ involving its second derivative. However, this textbook does not assume that you know how to solve differential equations. As we did with Newton's laws, we will restrict ourselves to situations for which you already have the mathematical skills from your calculus class.

The solution to an algebraic equation is simply a number. For example, $x = 3$ is the solution to the equation $2x = 6$. In contrast, the solution to a differential equation is a *function.* You saw this idea in the preceding section, where Equation 40.6 was constructed so that the function $\psi(x) = \psi_0 \sin(2\pi x/\lambda)$ was a solution.

The Schrödinger equation can't be solved until the potential-energy function $U(x)$ has been specified. Different potential-energy functions result in different wave functions, just as different forces lead to different trajectories in classical mechanics. Once $U(x)$ has been specified, the solution of the differential equation is a *function* $\psi(x)$. We will usually display the solution as a graph of $\psi(x)$ versus x.

Restrictions and Boundary Conditions

Not all functions $\psi(x)$ make *acceptable* solutions to the Schrödinger equation. That is, some functions may satisfy the Schrödinger equation but not be physically meaningful. We have previously encountered restrictions in our solutions of algebraic equations. We insist, for physical reasons, that masses be positive rather than negative numbers, that positions be real rather than imaginary numbers, and so on. Mathematical solutions not meeting these restrictions are rejected as being unphysical.

Because we want to interpret $|\psi(x)|^2$ as a probability density, we have to insist that the function $\psi(x)$ be one for which this interpretation is possible. The conditions or restrictions on acceptable solutions are called the **boundary conditions.** You will see, in later examples, how the boundary conditions help us choose the correct solution for $\psi(x)$. The primary conditions the wave function must obey are:

1. $\psi(x)$ is a continuous function.
2. $\psi(x) = 0$ if x is in a region where it is physically impossible for the particle to be.
3. $\psi(x) \rightarrow 0$ as $x \rightarrow +\infty$ and $x \rightarrow -\infty$.
4. $\psi(x)$ is a normalized function.

The last is not, strictly speaking, a boundary condition but is an auxiliary condition we require for the wave function to have a useful interpretation. Boundary condition 3 is needed to enable the normalization integral $\int |\psi(x)|^2\, dx$ to converge.

Once boundary conditions have been established, there are general approaches to solving the Schrödinger equation: Use general mathematical techniques for solving second-order differential equations, solve the equation numerically on a computer, or make a physically informed guess.

More advanced courses make extensive use of the first and second approaches. However, we are not assuming a knowledge of differential equations, so you will not be asked to use these methods. The third, although it sounds almost like cheating, is widely used in simple situations where we can use physical arguments to infer the form of the wave function. The upcoming examples will illustrate this third approach.

A quadratic algebraic equation has two different solutions. Similarly, a second-order differential equation has two independent solutions $\psi_1(x)$ and $\psi_2(x)$. By "independent solutions" we mean that $\psi_2(x)$ is not just a constant multiple of $\psi_1(x)$, such as $3\psi_1(x)$, but that $\psi_1(x)$ and $\psi_2(x)$ are totally different functions.

Suppose that $\psi_1(x)$ and $\psi_2(x)$ are known to be two independent solutions of the Schrödinger equation. A theorem you will learn in differential equations states that a *general solution* of the equation can be written as

$$\psi(x) = A\psi_1(x) + B\psi_2(x) \qquad (40.8)$$

where A and B are constants whose values are determined by the boundary conditions. Equation 40.8 is a powerful statement, although one that will make more sense after you see it applied in upcoming examples. The main point is that **if we can find two independent solutions $\psi_1(x)$ and $\psi_2(x)$ by guessing, then Equation 40.8 is the general solution to the Schrödinger equation.**

Quantization

We've asserted that the Schrödinger equation is the law of quantum mechanics, but thus far we've not said anything about quantization. Although the particle's total energy E appears in the Schrödinger equation, it is treated in the equation as an unspecified constant. However, it will turn out that there are *no* acceptable solutions for most values of E. That is, there are no functions $\psi(x)$ that satisfy both the Schrödinger equation *and* the boundary conditions. Acceptable solutions exist only for *discrete* values of E. The energies for which solutions exist are the quantized energies of the system. Thus, as you'll see, the Schrödinger equation has quantization built in.

Problem Solving in Quantum Mechanics

Our problem-solving strategy for classical mechanics focused on identifying and using forces. In quantum mechanics we're interested in *energy* rather than forces. The critical step in solving a problem in quantum mechanics is to determine the particle's potential-energy function $U(x)$. Identifying the interactions that cause a potential energy is the *physics* of the problem. Once the potential-energy function is known, it is "just mathematics" to solve for the wave function.

PROBLEM-SOLVING STRATEGY 40.1   Quantum-mechanics problems

MODEL Determine a potential-energy function that describes the particle's interactions. Make simplifying assumptions.

VISUALIZE The potential-energy curve is the pictorial representation.

- Draw the potential-energy curve.
- Identify known information.
- Establish the boundary conditions that the wave function must satisfy.

SOLVE The Schrödinger equation is the mathematical representation.

- Utilize the boundary conditions.
- Normalize the wave functions.
- Draw graphs of $\psi(x)$ and $|\psi(x)|^2$.
- Determine the allowed energy levels.
- Calculate probabilities, wavelengths, or other specific quantities.

ASSESS Check that your result has the correct units, is reasonable, and answers the question.

The solutions to the Schrödinger equation are the *stationary states* of the system. Bohr had postulated the existence of stationary states, but he didn't know how to find them. Now we have a strategy for finding them.

Bohr's idea of transitions, or quantum jumps, between stationary states remains very important in Schrödinger's quantum mechanics. The system can jump from one stationary state, characterized by wave function $\psi_i(x)$ and energy E_i, to another state, characterized by $\psi_f(x)$ and E_f, by emitting or absorbing a photon of frequency

$$f = \frac{\Delta E}{h} = \frac{|E_f - E_i|}{h}$$

Thus the solutions to the Schrödinger equation will allow us to predict the emission and absorption spectra of a quantum system. These predictions will test the validity of Schrödinger's theory.

40.3 A Particle in a Rigid Box: Energies and Wave Functions

FIGURE 40.3 shows a particle of mass m confined in a rigid, one-dimensional box of length L. The walls of the box are assumed to be perfectly rigid, and the particle undergoes perfectly elastic reflections from the ends. This situation, which we looked at in Chapter 38, is known as a "particle in a box."

A classical particle bounces back and forth between the walls of the box. There are no restrictions on the speed or kinetic energy of a classical particle. In contrast, a wave-like particle characterized by a de Broglie wavelength sets up a standing wave as it reflects back and forth. In Chapter 38, we found that a standing de Broglie wave automatically leads to energy quantization. That is, only certain discrete energies are allowed. However, our hypothesis of a de Broglie standing wave was just a guess, with no real justification, because we had no theory about how a wave-like particle ought to behave.

We will now revisit this problem from the new perspective of quantum mechanics. The basic questions we want to answer in this, and any quantum-mechanics problem, are:

- What are the allowed energies of the particle?
- What is the wave function associated with each energy?
- In which part of the box is the particle most likely to be found?

We can use Problem-Solving Strategy 40.1 to answer these questions.

Model: Identify a Potential-Energy Function

By a *rigid box* we mean a box whose walls are so sturdy that they can confine a particle no matter how fast the particle moves. Furthermore, the walls are so stiff that they do not flex or give as the particle bounces. No real container has these attributes, so the rigid box is a *model* of a situation in which a particle is extremely well confined. Our first task is to characterize the rigid box in terms of a potential-energy function.

Let's establish a coordinate axis with the boundaries of the box at $x = 0$ and $x = L$. The rigid box has three important characteristics:

1. The particle can move freely between 0 and L at constant speed and thus with constant kinetic energy.
2. No matter how much kinetic energy the particle has, its turning points are at $x = 0$ and $x = L$.
3. The regions $x < 0$ and $x > L$ are forbidden. The particle cannot leave the box.

A potential-energy function that describes the particle in this situation is

$$U_{\text{rigid box}}(x) = \begin{cases} 0 & 0 \le x \le L \\ \infty & x < 0 \quad \text{or} \quad x > L \end{cases} \qquad (40.9)$$

Inside the box, the particle has only kinetic energy. The infinitely high potential-energy barriers prevent the particle from ever having $x < 0$ or $x > L$ no matter how much kinetic energy it may have. It is this potential energy for which we want to solve the Schrödinger equation.

Visualize: Establish Boundary Conditions

FIGURE 40.4 is the energy diagram of a particle in the rigid box. You can see that $U = 0$ and $E = K$ inside the box. The upward arrows labeled ∞ indicate that the potential energy becomes infinitely large at the walls of the box ($x = 0$ and $x = L$).

NOTE ▶ Figure 40.4 is not a picture of the box. It is a graphical representation of the particle's total, kinetic, and potential energy. ◀

FIGURE 40.3 A particle in a rigid box of length L.

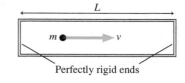

FIGURE 40.4 The energy diagram of a particle in a rigid box of length L.

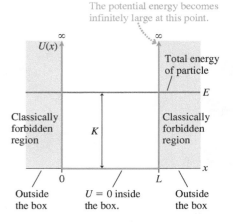

FIGURE 40.5 Applying boundary conditions to the wave function of a particle in a box.

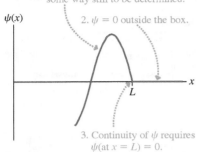

1. Inside the box, ψ is oscillating in some way still to be determined.

$\psi(x)$

2. $\psi = 0$ outside the box.

L

x

3. Continuity of ψ requires $\psi(\text{at } x = L) = 0$.

Next, we need to establish the boundary conditions that the solution must satisfy. Because it is physically impossible for the particle to be outside the box, we require

$$\psi(x) = 0 \quad \text{for } x < 0 \quad \text{or} \quad x > L \tag{40.10}$$

That is, there is zero probability (i.e., $|\psi(x)|^2 = 0$) of finding the particle outside the box.

Furthermore, the wave function must be a *continuous* function. That is, there can be no break in the wave function at any point. Because the solution is zero everywhere outside the box, continuity requires that the wave function inside the box obey the two conditions

$$\psi(\text{at } x = 0) = 0 \quad \text{and} \quad \psi(\text{at } x = L) = 0 \tag{40.11}$$

In other words, as FIGURE 40.5 shows, the oscillating wave function inside the box must go to zero at the boundaries to be continuous with the wave function outside the box. This requirement of the wave function is equivalent to saying that a standing wave on a string must have a node at the ends.

Solve I: Find the Wave Functions

At all points *inside* the box the potential energy is $U(x) = 0$. Thus the Schrödinger equation inside the box is

$$\frac{d^2\psi}{dx^2} = -\frac{2mE}{\hbar^2}\psi(x) \tag{40.12}$$

There are two aspects to solving this equation:

1. For what values of E does Equation 40.12 have physically meaningful solutions?
2. What are the solutions $\psi(x)$ for those values of E?

To begin, let's simplify the notation by defining $\beta^2 = 2mE/\hbar^2$. Equation 40.12 is then

$$\frac{d^2\psi}{dx^2} = -\beta^2\psi(x) \tag{40.13}$$

We're going to solve this differential equation by guessing! Can you think of any functions whose second derivative is a *negative* constant times the function itself? Two such functions are

$$\psi_1(x) = \sin\beta x \quad \text{and} \quad \psi_2(x) = \cos\beta x \tag{40.14}$$

Both are solutions to Equation 40.13 because

$$\frac{d^2\psi_1}{dx^2} = \frac{d^2}{dx^2}(\sin\beta x) = -\beta^2\sin\beta x = -\beta^2\psi_1(x)$$

$$\frac{d^2\psi_2}{dx^2} = \frac{d^2}{dx^2}(\cos\beta x) = -\beta^2\cos\beta x = -\beta^2\psi_2(x)$$

Furthermore, these are *independent* solutions because $\psi_2(x)$ is not a multiple or a rearrangement of $\psi_1(x)$. Consequently, according to Equation 40.8, the general solution to the Schrödinger equation for the particle in a rigid box is

$$\psi(x) = A\sin\beta x + B\cos\beta x \tag{40.15}$$

where

$$\beta = \frac{\sqrt{2mE}}{\hbar} \tag{40.16}$$

The constants A and B must be determined by using the boundary conditions of Equation 40.11. First, the wave function must go to zero at $x = 0$. That is,

$$\psi(\text{at } x = 0) = A \cdot 0 + B \cdot 1 = 0 \tag{40.17}$$

This boundary condition can be satisfied only if $B = 0$. The $\cos \beta x$ term may satisfy the differential equation in a mathematical sense, but it is not a physically meaningful solution for this problem because it does not satisfy the boundary conditions. Thus the physically meaningful solution is

$$\psi(x) = A \sin \beta x$$

The wave function must also go to zero at $x = L$. That is,

$$\psi(\text{at } x = L) = A \sin \beta L = 0 \qquad (40.18)$$

This condition could be satisfied by $A = 0$, but then we wouldn't have a wave function at all! Fortunately, that isn't necessary. This boundary condition is also satisfied if $\sin \beta L = 0$, which requires

$$\beta L = n\pi \quad \text{or} \quad \beta_n = \frac{n\pi}{L} \qquad n = 1, 2, 3, \ldots \qquad (40.19)$$

Notice that n starts with 1, not 0. The value $n = 0$ would give $\beta = 0$ and make $\psi = 0$ at all points, a physically meaningless solution.

Thus the solutions to the Schrödinger equation for a particle in a rigid box are

$$\psi_n(x) = A \sin \beta_n x = A \sin\left(\frac{n\pi x}{L}\right) \qquad n = 1, 2, 3, \ldots \qquad (40.20)$$

We've found a whole *family* of solutions, each corresponding to a different value of the integer n. These wave functions represent the stationary states of the particle in the box. The constant A remains to be determined.

Solve II: Find the Allowed Energies

Equation 40.16 defined β. The boundary condition of Equation 40.19 then placed restrictions on the possible values of β:

$$\beta_n = \frac{\sqrt{2mE_n}}{\hbar} = \frac{n\pi}{L} \qquad n = 1, 2, 3, \ldots \qquad (40.21)$$

where the value of β and the energy associated with the integer n have been labeled β_n and E_n. We can solve for E_n by squaring both sides:

$$E_n = n^2 \frac{\pi^2 \hbar^2}{2mL^2} = n^2 \frac{h^2}{8mL^2} \qquad n = 1, 2, 3, \ldots \qquad (40.22)$$

where, in the last step, we used the definition $\hbar = h/2\pi$. For a particle in a box, **these energies are the only values of E for which there are physically meaningful solutions to the Schrödinger equation.** That is, the particle's energy is quantized! It is worth emphasizing that quantization is not inherent in the wave function itself but arises because the boundary conditions—the physics of the situation—are satisfied by only a small subset of the mathematical solutions to the Schrödinger equation.

It is useful to write the energies of the stationary states as

$$E_n = n^2 E_1 \qquad (40.23)$$

where E_n is the energy of the stationary state with *quantum number n*. The smallest possible energy $E_1 = h^2/8mL^2$ is the energy of the $n = 1$ *ground state*. These allowed energies are shown in the *energy-level diagram* of FIGURE 40.6. Recall, from Chapter 38, that an energy-level diagram is not a graph (the horizontal axis doesn't represent anything) but a "ladder" of allowed energies.

Equation 40.22 is identical to the energies we found in Chapter 38 by requiring the de Broglie wave of a particle in a box to form a standing wave. Only now we have a theory that tells not only the energies but also the wave functions.

FIGURE 40.6 The energy-level diagram for a particle in a box.

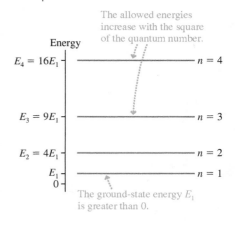

EXAMPLE 40.1 **An electron in a box**

An electron is confined to a rigid box. What is the length of the box if the energy difference between the first and second states is 3.0 eV?

MODEL Model the electron as a particle in a rigid one-dimensional box of length L.

SOLVE The first two quantum states, with $n = 1$ and $n = 2$, have energies E_1 and $E_2 = 4E_1$. Thus the energy difference between the states is

$$\Delta E = 3E_1 = \frac{3h^2}{8mL^2} = 3.0 \text{ eV} = 4.8 \times 10^{-19} \text{ J}$$

The length of the box for which $\Delta E = 3.0$ eV is

$$L = \sqrt{\frac{3h^2}{8m\,\Delta E}} = 6.14 \times 10^{-10} \text{ m} = 0.614 \text{ nm}$$

ASSESS The expression for E_1 is in SI units, so energies must be in J, not eV.

Solve III: Normalize the Wave Functions

We can determine the constant A by requiring the wave functions to be normalized. The normalization condition, which we found in Chapter 39, is

$$\int_{-\infty}^{\infty} |\psi(x)|^2 \, dx = 1$$

This is the mathematical statement that the particle must be *somewhere* on the x-axis. The integration limits extend to $\pm \infty$, but here we need to integrate only from 0 to L because the wave function is zero outside the box. Thus

$$\int_0^L |\psi_n(x)|^2 \, dx = A_n^2 \int_0^L \sin^2\left(\frac{n\pi x}{L}\right) dx = 1 \tag{40.24}$$

or

$$A_n = \left[\int_0^L \sin^2\left(\frac{n\pi x}{L}\right) dx\right]^{-1/2} \tag{40.25}$$

We placed a subscript n on A_n because it is possible that the normalization constant is different for each wave function in the family. This is a standard integral. We will leave it as a homework problem for you to show that its value, for any n, is

$$A_n = \sqrt{\frac{2}{L}} \qquad n = 1, 2, 3, \ldots \tag{40.26}$$

We now have a complete solution to the problem. The normalized wave function for the particle in quantum state n is

$$\psi_n(x) = \begin{cases} \sqrt{\dfrac{2}{L}} \sin\left(\dfrac{n\pi x}{L}\right) & 0 \le x \le L \\ 0 & x < 0 \text{ and } x > L \end{cases} \tag{40.27}$$

40.4 A Particle in a Rigid Box: Interpreting the Solution

Our solution to the quantum-mechanical problem of a particle in a box tells us that:

1. The particle must have energy $E_n = n^2 E_1$, where $n = 1, 2, 3, \ldots$ is the quantum number. $E_1 = h^2/8mL^2$ is the energy of the $n = 1$ ground state.
2. The wave function for a particle in quantum state n is

$$\psi_n(x) = \begin{cases} \sqrt{\dfrac{2}{L}} \sin\left(\dfrac{n\pi x}{L}\right) & 0 \le x \le L \\ 0 & x < 0 \text{ and } x > L \end{cases}$$

These are the stationary states of the system.

3. The probability density for finding the particle at position x inside the box is

$$P_n(x) = |\psi_n(x)|^2 = \frac{2}{L} \sin^2\left(\frac{n\pi x}{L}\right) \qquad (40.28)$$

FIGURE 40.7 Wave functions and probability densities for a particle in a rigid box of length L.

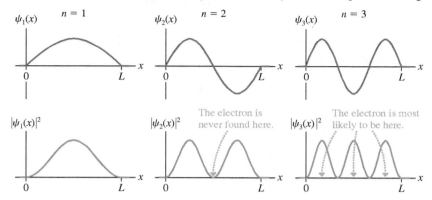

A graphical presentation will make these results more meaningful. FIGURE 40.7 shows the wave functions $\psi(x)$ and the probability densities $P(x) = |\psi(x)|^2$ for quantum states $n = 1$ to 3. Notice that the wave functions go to zero at the boundaries and thus are continuous with $\psi = 0$ outside the box.

The wave functions $\psi(x)$ for a particle in a rigid box are analogous to standing waves on a string that is tied at both ends. You can see that $\psi_n(x)$ has $(n - 1)$ **nodes (zeros), excluding the ends, and n antinodes (maxima and minima).** This is a general result for any wave function, not just for a particle in a rigid box.

FIGURE 40.8 shows another way in which energies and wave functions are shown graphically in quantum mechanics. First, the graph shows the potential-energy function $U(x)$ of the particle. Second, the allowed energies are shown as horizontal lines (total energy lines) across the potential-energy graph. These are labeled with the quantum number n and the energy E_n. Third—and this is a bit tricky—the wave function for each n is drawn *as if* the energy line were the zero of the y-axis. That is, the graph of $\psi_n(x)$ is drawn on top of the E_n energy line. This allows energies and wave functions to be displayed simultaneously, but it does *not* imply that ψ_2 is in any sense "above" ψ_1. Both oscillate sinusoidally about zero, as Figure 40.7 shows.

FIGURE 40.8 An alternative way to show the potential-energy diagram, the energies, and the wave functions.

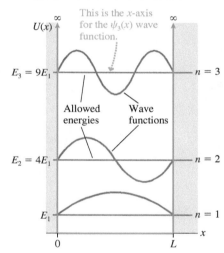

EXAMPLE 40.2 **Energy levels and quantum jumps**

A semiconductor device known as a *quantum-well device* is designed to "trap" electrons in a 1.0-nm-wide region. Treat this as a one-dimensional problem.

a. What are the energies of the first three quantum states?
b. What wavelengths of light can these electrons absorb?

MODEL Model an electron in a quantum-well device as a particle confined in a rigid box of length $L = 1.0$ nm.

VISUALIZE FIGURE 40.9 shows the first three energy levels and the transitions by which an electron in the ground state can absorb a photon.

FIGURE 40.9 Energy levels and quantum jumps for an electron in a quantum-well device.

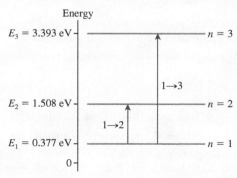

Continued

SOLVE a. The particle's mass is $m = m_e = 9.11 \times 10^{-31}$ kg. The allowed energies, in both J and eV, are

$$E_1 = \frac{h^2}{8mL^2} = 6.03 \times 10^{-20} \text{ J} = 0.377 \text{ eV}$$

$$E_2 = 4E_1 = 1.508 \text{ eV}$$

$$E_3 = 9E_1 = 3.393 \text{ eV}$$

b. An electron spends most of its time in the $n = 1$ ground state. According to Bohr's model of stationary states, the electron can absorb a photon of light and undergo a transition, or quantum jump, to $n = 2$ or $n = 3$ if the light has frequency $f = \Delta E/h$. The wavelengths, given by $\lambda = c/f = hc/\Delta E$, are

$$\lambda_{1 \to 2} = \frac{hc}{E_2 - E_1} = 1098 \text{ nm}$$

$$\lambda_{1 \to 3} = \frac{hc}{E_3 - E_1} = 411 \text{ nm}$$

ASSESS In practice, various complications usually make the $1 \to 3$ transition unobservable. But quantum-well devices do indeed exhibit strong absorption and emission at the $\lambda_{1 \to 2}$ wavelength. In this example, which is typical of quantum-well devices, the wavelength is in the near-infrared portion of the spectrum. Devices such as these are used to construct the semiconductor lasers used in DVD players and laser printers.

NOTE ▶ The wavelengths of light emitted or absorbed by a quantum system are determined by the *difference* between two allowed energies. Quantum jumps involve two stationary states. ◀

Zero-Point Motion

The lowest energy state in Example 40.2, the ground state, has $E_1 = 0.38$ eV. There is no stationary state having $E = 0$. Unlike a classical particle, **a quantum particle in a box cannot be at rest!** No matter how much its energy is reduced, such as by cooling it toward absolute zero, it cannot have energy less than E_1.

The particle motion associated with energy E_1, called the **zero-point motion,** is a consequence of Heisenberg's uncertainty principle. Because the particle is somewhere in the box, its position uncertainty is $\Delta x = L$. If the particle were at rest in the box, we would know that its velocity and momentum are exactly zero with *no* uncertainty: $\Delta p_x = 0$. But then $\Delta x \Delta p_x = 0$ would violate the Heisenberg uncertainty principle. One of the conclusions that follow from the uncertainty principle is that **a confined particle cannot be at rest.**

Although the particle's position and velocity are uncertain, the particle's energy in each state can be calculated with a high degree of precision. This distinction between a precise energy and uncertain position and velocity seems strange, but it is just our old friend the standing wave. In order to *have* a stationary state at all, the de Broglie waves have to form standing waves. Only for very precise frequencies, and thus precise energies, can the standing-wave pattern appear.

EXAMPLE 40.3 **Nuclear energies**

Protons and neutrons are tightly bound within the nucleus of an atom. If we use a one-dimensional model of a nucleus, what are the first three energy levels of a neutron in a 10-fm-diameter nucleus (1 fm = 10^{-15} m)?

MODEL Model the nucleus as a one-dimensional box of length $L = 10$ fm. The neutron is confined within the box.

SOLVE The energy levels, with $L = 10$ fm and $m = m_n = 1.67 \times 10^{-27}$ kg, are

$$E_1 = \frac{h^2}{8mL^2} = 3.29 \times 10^{-13} \text{ J} = 2.06 \text{ MeV}$$

$$E_2 = 4E_1 = 8.24 \text{ MeV}$$

$$E_3 = 9E_1 = 18.54 \text{ MeV}$$

ASSESS You've seen that an electron confined in an atom-size space has energies of a few eV. A neutron confined in a nucleus-size space has energies of a few *million* eV.

EXAMPLE 40.4 **The probabilities of locating the particle**

A particle in a rigid box of length L is in its ground state.

a. Where is the particle most likely to be found?
b. What are the probabilities of finding the particle in an interval of width $0.01L$ at $x = 0.00L$, $0.25L$, and $0.50L$?

c. What is the probability of finding the particle between $L/4$ and $3L/4$?

MODEL The wave functions for a particle in a rigid box have been determined.

VISUALIZE FIGURE 40.10 shows the probability density $P_1(x) = |\psi_1(x)|^2$ in the ground state.

FIGURE 40.10 Probability density for a particle in the ground state.

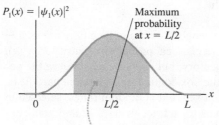

The probability of being in the interval from $L/4$ to $3L/4$ is the area under the curve.

SOLVE a. The particle is most likely to be found at the point where the probability density $P(x)$ is a maximum. You can see from Figure 40.10 that the point of maximum probability for $n = 1$ is $x = L/2$.

b. For a *small* width δx, the probability of finding the particle in δx at position x is

$$\text{Prob(in } \delta x \text{ at } x) = P_1(x)\,\delta x = |\psi_1(x)|^2\,\delta x = \frac{2}{L}\sin^2\left(\frac{\pi x}{L}\right)\delta x$$

The interval $\delta x = 0.01L$ is sufficiently small for this to be valid. The probabilities of finding the particle are

Prob(in $0.01L$ at $x = 0.00L$) = $0.000 = 0.0\%$

Prob(in $0.01L$ at $x = 0.25L$) = $0.010 = 1.0\%$

Prob(in $0.01L$ at $x = 0.50L$) = $0.020 = 2.0\%$

c. You learned in Chapter 39 that the probability of being in an interval is the area under the probability-density curve. We calculate this by integrating:

$$\text{Prob}\left(\text{in interval } \frac{1}{4}L \text{ to } \frac{3}{4}L\right) = \int_{L/4}^{3L/4} P_1(x)\,dx$$

$$= \frac{2}{L}\int_{L/4}^{3L/4}\sin^2\left(\frac{\pi x}{L}\right)dx$$

$$= \left[\frac{x}{L} - \frac{1}{\pi}\sin\left(\frac{\pi x}{L}\right)\cos\left(\frac{\pi x}{L}\right)\right]_{L/4}^{3L/4}$$

$$= \frac{1}{2} + \frac{1}{\pi} = 0.818$$

The integral of $\sin^2$ was taken from the table of integrals in Appendix A.

ASSESS If a particle in a box is in the $n = 1$ ground state, there is an 81.8% chance of finding it in the center half of the box. The probability is greater than 50% because, as you can see in Figure 40.10, the probability density $P_1(x)$ is larger near the center of the box than near the boundaries.

This has been a lengthy presentation of the particle-in-a-box problem. However, it was important that we explore the method of solution completely. Future examples will now go more quickly because many of the issues discussed here will not need to be repeated.

STOP TO THINK 40.2   A particle in a rigid box in the $n = 2$ stationary state is most likely to be found

a. In the center of the box.
b. One-third of the way from either end.
c. One-quarter of the way from either end.
d. It is equally likely to be found at any point in the box.

40.5 The Correspondence Principle

Suppose we confine an electron in a microscopic box, then allow the box to get bigger and bigger. What started out as a quantum-mechanical situation should, when the box becomes macroscopic, eventually look like a classical-physics situation. Similarly, a classical situation such as two charged particles revolving about each other should begin to exhibit quantum behavior as the orbit size becomes smaller and smaller.

These examples suggest that there should be some in-between size, or energy, for which the quantum-mechanical solution corresponds in some way to the solution of classical mechanics. Niels Bohr put forward the idea that the *average* behavior of a quantum system should begin to look like the classical solution in the limit that the quantum number becomes very large—that is, as $n \rightarrow \infty$. Because the radius of the Bohr hydrogen atom is $r = n^2 a_B$, the atom becomes a macroscopic object as n

becomes very large. Bohr's idea, that the quantum world should blend smoothly into the classical world for high quantum numbers, is today known as the **correspondence principle.**

Our quantum knowledge of a particle in a box is given by its probability density

$$P_{quant}(x) = |\psi_n(x)|^2 = \frac{2}{L}\sin^2\left(\frac{n\pi x}{L}\right) \tag{40.29}$$

To what classical quantity can the probability density be compared as $n \to \infty$?

Interestingly, we can also define a classical probability density $P_{class}(x)$. A classical particle follows a well-defined trajectory, but suppose we observe the particle at random times. For example, suppose the box containing a classical particle has a viewing window. The window is normally closed, but at random times, selected by a random-number generator, the window opens for a brief interval δt and you can measure the particle's position. When the window opens, what is the probability that the particle will be in a narrow interval δx at position x?

The probability of finding a classical particle within a small interval δx is equal to the *fraction of its time* that it spends passing through δx. That is, you're more likely to find the particle in those intervals δx where it spends lots of time, less likely to find it in a δx where it spends very little time.

Consider a classical particle oscillating back and forth between two turning points with period T. The time it spends moving from one turning point to the other is $\frac{1}{2}T$. As it moves between the turning points, it passes once through the interval δx at position x, taking time δt to do so. Consequently, the probability of finding the particle within this interval is

$$\text{Prob}_{class}(\text{in } \delta x \text{ at } x) = \text{fraction of time spent in } \delta x = \frac{\delta t}{\frac{1}{2}T} \tag{40.30}$$

The amount of time needed to pass through δx is $\delta t = \delta x/v(x)$, where $v(x)$ is the particle's velocity at position x. Thus the probability of finding the particle in the interval δx at position x is

$$\text{Prob}_{class}(\text{in } \delta x \text{ at } x) = \frac{\delta x/v(x)}{\frac{1}{2}T} = \frac{2}{Tv(x)}\delta x \tag{40.31}$$

You learned in Chapter 39 that the probability is related to the probability density by

$$\text{Prob}_{class}(\text{in } \delta x \text{ at } x) = P_{class}(x)\,\delta x$$

Thus the classical probability density for finding a particle at position x is

$$P_{class}(x) = \frac{2}{Tv(x)} \tag{40.32}$$

where the velocity $v(x)$ is expressed as a function of x. **Classically, a particle is more likely to be found where it is moving slowly, less likely to be found where it is moving quickly.**

NOTE ▶ Our derivation of Equation 40.32 made no assumptions about the particle's motion other than the requirement that it be periodic. This is the classical probability density for any oscillatory motion. ◀

FIGURE 40.11a is the motion diagram of a classical particle in a rigid box of length L. The particle's speed is a *constant* $v(x) = v_0$ as it bounces back and forth between the walls. The particle travels distance $2L$ during one round trip, so the period is $T = 2L/v_0$. Consequently, the classical probability density for a particle in a box is

$$P_{class}(x) = \frac{2}{(2L/v_0)v_0} = \frac{1}{L} \tag{40.33}$$

$P_{class}(x)$ is independent of x, telling us that the particle is equally likely to be found *anywhere* in the box.

FIGURE 40.11 The classical probability density is indicated by the density of dots in a motion diagram.

(a) Uniform speed

Particle in an empty box

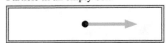

Motion diagram

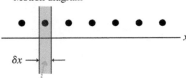

The probability of finding the particle in δx is the fraction of time the particle spends in δx.

(b) Nonuniform speed

Particle on a spring

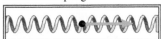

Motion diagram

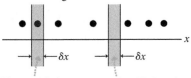

The particle is more likely to be found where it's moving slowly,...

...less likely to be found where it's moving quickly.

In contrast, FIGURE 40.11b shows a particle with nonuniform speed. A mass on a spring slows down near the turning points, so it spends more time near the ends of the box than in the middle. Consequently the classical probability density for this particle is a maximum at the edges and a minimum at the center. We'll look at this classical probability density again later in the chapter.

EXAMPLE 40.5 **The classical probability of locating the particle**

A classical particle is in a rigid 10-cm-long box. What is the probability that, at a random instant of time, the particle is in a 1.0-mm-wide interval at the center of the box?

SOLVE The particle's probability density is

$$P_{class}(x) = \frac{1}{L} = \frac{1}{10 \text{ cm}} = 0.10 \text{ cm}^{-1}$$

The probability that the particle is in an interval of width $\delta x = 1.0 \text{ mm} = 0.10 \text{ cm}$ is

$$\text{Prob(in } \delta x \text{ at } x = 5 \text{ cm)} = P(x)\delta x = (0.10 \text{ cm}^{-1})(0.10 \text{ cm})$$
$$= 0.010 = 1.0\%$$

ASSESS The classical probability is 1.0% because 1.0 mm is 1% of the 10 cm length.

FIGURE 40.12 shows the quantum and the classical probability densities for the $n = 1$ and $n = 20$ quantum states of a particle in a rigid box. Notice that:

- The quantum probability density oscillates between a minimum of 0 and a maximum of $2/L$, so it oscillates around the classical probability density $1/L$.
- For $n = 1$, the quantum and classical probability densities are quite different. The ground state of the quantum system will be very nonclassical.
- For $n = 20$, *on average* the quantum particle's behavior looks very much like that of the classical particle.

FIGURE 40.12 The quantum and classical probability densities for a particle in a box.

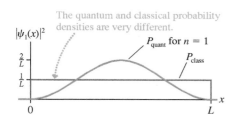
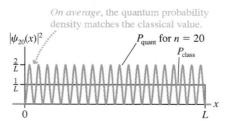

As n gets even bigger and the number of oscillations increases, the probability of finding the particle in an interval δx will be the same for both the quantum and the classical particles as long as δx is large enough to include several oscillations of the wave function. As Bohr predicted, the quantum-mechanical solution "corresponds" to the classical solution in the limit $n \rightarrow \infty$.

40.6 Finite Potential Wells

Figure 40.4, the potential-energy diagram for a particle in a rigid box, is an example of a **potential well,** so named because the graph of the potential-energy "hole" looks like a well from which you might draw water. The rigid box was an *infinite* potential well. There was no chance that a particle inside could escape the infinitely high walls.

A more realistic model of a confined particle is the *finite* potential well shown in FIGURE 40.13a on the next page. A particle with total energy $E < U_0$ is confined within the well, bouncing back and forth between turning points at $x = 0$ and $x = L$. The regions $x < 0$ and $x > L$ are **classically forbidden regions** for a particle with $E < U_0$. However, the particle will escape the well if it manages to acquire energy $E > U_0$.

For example, consider an electron confined within a metal or semiconductor. An electron with energy less than the work function moves freely until it reaches the edge, where it reflects to stay within the solid. But the electron *can* escape if it somehow—such

FIGURE 40.13 A finite potential well of width L and depth U_0.

(a) $U = 0$ inside the well.

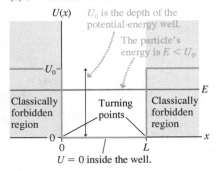

U = 0 inside the well.

(b) $U = 0$ outside the well.

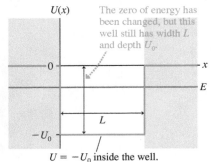

$U = -U_0$ inside the well.

as absorbing energy from a photon—acquires an energy larger than the work function. Similarly, a neutron is confined within the nucleus by the nuclear force, but it *can* escape the nucleus if it has enough energy. The electron, the neutron, and many other particles that are confined can be modeled as a particle in a finite potential well, so it is one of the most important models in quantum mechanics. The Schrödinger equation depends on the *shape* of the potential-energy function, not the cause.

FIGURE 40.13b is the same potential well, simply redrawn to place the zero of potential energy—which, you will recall, is arbitrary—at the level of the "energy plateau." Both have width L and depth U_0 so both have the same wave functions and the same energy levels relative to the bottom of the well. Which one we use is a matter of convenience.

Although it is possible to solve the Schrödinger equation exactly for the finite potential well, the result is cumbersome and not especially illuminating. Instead, we'll present the results of numerical calculations. The derivation of the wave functions and energy levels is not as important as understanding and interpreting the results.

As a first example, consider an electron in a 2.0-nm-wide potential well of depth $U_0 = 1.0$ eV. These are reasonable parameters for an electron in a semiconductor device. FIGURE 40.14a is a graphical presentation of the allowed energies and wave functions. For comparison, FIGURE 40.14b shows the first three energy levels and wave functions for a rigid box ($U_0 \to \infty$) with the same 2.0 nm width.

FIGURE 40.14 Energy levels and wave functions for a finite potential well. For comparison, the energies and wave functions are shown for a rigid box of equal width.

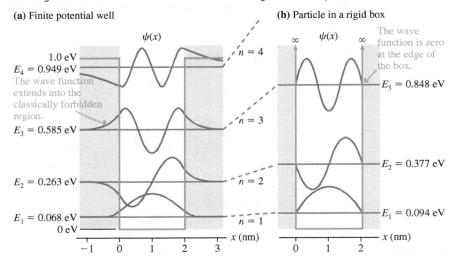

The quantum-mechanical solution for a particle in a finite potential well has some important properties:

- The particle's energy is quantized. A particle in the potential well *must* be in one of the stationary states with quantum numbers $n = 1, 2, 3, \ldots$.
- There are only a finite number of **bound states**—four in this example, although the number will be different in other examples. These wave functions represent electrons confined to, or bound in, the potential well. There are no stationary states with $E > U_0$ because such a particle would not remain in the well.
- The wave functions are qualitatively similar to those of a particle in a rigid box, but the energies are somewhat lower. This is because the wave functions are slightly more spread out horizontally. A slightly longer de Broglie wavelength corresponds to a lower velocity and thus a lower energy.
- Most interesting, perhaps, is that the wave functions of Figure 40.14a extend into the classically forbidden regions. It is as though a tennis ball penetrated partly *through* the racket's strings before bouncing back, but without breaking the strings.

EXAMPLE 40.6 **Absorption spectrum of an electron**

What wavelengths of light are absorbed by a semiconductor device in which electrons are confined in a 2.0-nm-wide region with a potential-energy depth of 1.0 eV?

MODEL The electron is in the finite potential well whose energies and wave functions were shown in Figure 40.14a.

SOLVE Photons can be absorbed if their energy $E_{photon} = hf$ exactly matches the energy difference ΔE between two energy levels. Because most electrons are in the $n = 1$ ground state, the absorption transitions are $1 \rightarrow 2$, $1 \rightarrow 3$, and $1 \rightarrow 4$.

The absorption wavelengths $\lambda = c/f$ are

$$\lambda_{n \rightarrow m} = \frac{hc}{\Delta E} = \frac{hc}{|E_n - E_m|}$$

For this example, we find

$\Delta E_{1-2} = 0.195$ eV	$\lambda_{1 \rightarrow 2} = 6.37\ \mu m$
$\Delta E_{1-3} = 0.517$ eV	$\lambda_{1 \rightarrow 3} = 2.40\ \mu m$
$\Delta E_{1-4} = 0.881$ eV	$\lambda_{1 \rightarrow 4} = 1.41\ \mu m$

ASSESS These transitions are all infrared wavelengths.

STOP TO THINK 40.3 This is a wave function for a particle in a finite quantum well. What is the particle's quantum number?

The Classically Forbidden Region

The extension of a particle's wave functions into the classically forbidden region is an important difference between classical and quantum physics. Let's take a closer look at the wave function in the region $x \geq L$ of Figure 40.13a. The potential energy in the classically forbidden region is U_0; thus the Schrödinger equation for $x \geq L$ is

$$\frac{d^2\psi}{dx^2} = -\frac{2m}{\hbar^2}(E - U_0)\psi(x)$$

We're assuming a confined particle, with E less than U_0, so $E - U_0$ is negative. It will be useful to reverse the order of these and write

$$\frac{d^2\psi}{dx^2} = \frac{2m}{\hbar^2}(U_0 - E)\psi(x) = \frac{1}{\eta^2}\psi(x) \qquad (40.34)$$

where

$$\eta^2 = \frac{\hbar^2}{2m(U_0 - E)} \qquad (40.35)$$

is a *positive* constant. As a homework problem, you can show that the units of η are meters.

The Schrödinger equation of Equation 40.34 is one we can solve by guessing. We simply need to think of two functions whose second derivatives are a positive constant times the functions themselves. Two such functions, as you can quickly confirm, are $e^{x/\eta}$ and $e^{-x/\eta}$. Thus, according to Equation 40.8, the general solution of the Schrödinger equation for $x \geq L$ is

$$\psi(x) = Ae^{x/\eta} + Be^{-x/\eta} \quad \text{for } x \geq L \qquad (40.36)$$

One requirement of the wave function is that $\psi \rightarrow 0$ as $x \rightarrow \infty$. The function $e^{x/\eta}$ diverges as $x \rightarrow \infty$, so the only way to satisfy this requirement is to set $A = 0$. Thus

$$\psi(x) = Be^{-x/\eta} \quad \text{for } x \geq L \qquad (40.37)$$

This is an exponentially decaying function. Notice that all the wave functions in Figure 40.14a look like exponential decays for $x > L$.

The wave function must also be continuous. Suppose the oscillating wave function within the potential well ($x \leq L$) has the value ψ_{edge} when it reaches the classical boundary at $x = L$. To be continuous, the wave function of Equation 40.37 has to match this value at $x = L$. That is,

$$\psi(\text{at } x = L) = Be^{-L/\eta} = \psi_{edge} \qquad (40.38)$$

This boundary condition at $x = L$ is sufficient to determine that the constant B is

$$B = \psi_{edge}e^{L/\eta} \qquad (40.39)$$

If we use the Equation 40.39 result for B in Equation 40.37, we find that the wave function in the classically forbidden region of a finite potential well is

$$\psi(x) = \psi_{edge}e^{-(x-L)/\eta} \quad \text{for } x \geq L \qquad (40.40)$$

In other words, **the wave function oscillates until it reaches the classical turning point at $x = L$, then it decays exponentially within the classically forbidden region.** A similar analysis could be done for $x \leq 0$.

FIGURE 40.15 shows the wave function in the classically forbidden region. You can see that the wave function at $x = L + \eta$ has decreased to

$$\psi(\text{at } x = L + \eta) = e^{-1}\psi_{edge} = 0.37\psi_{edge}$$

Although an exponential decay does not have a sharp ending point, the parameter η measures "about how far" the wave function extends past the classical turning point before the probability of finding the particle has decreased nearly to zero. This distance is called the **penetration distance:**

$$\text{penetration distance } \eta = \frac{\hbar}{\sqrt{2m(U_0 - E)}} \qquad (40.41)$$

A classical particle reverses direction at the $x = L$ turning point. But atomic particles are not classical. Because of wave–particle duality, an atomic particle is "fuzzy" with no well-defined edge. Thus an atomic particle can spread a distance of roughly η into the classically forbidden region.

The penetration distance is unimaginably small for any macroscopic mass, but it can be significant for atomic particles. Notice that the penetration distance depends inversely on the quantity $U_0 - E$, the distance of the energy level below the top of the potential well. You can see in Figure 40.14a that η is much larger for the $n = 4$ state, near the top of the potential well, than for the $n = 1$ state.

NOTE ▶ In making use of Equation 40.41, you *must* use SI units of J s for $\hbar$ and J for the energies. The penetration distance η is then in meters. ◀

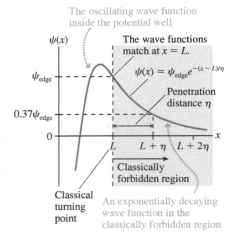

FIGURE 40.15 The wave function in the classically forbidden region.

EXAMPLE 40.7 **Penetration distance of an electron**

An electron is confined in a 2.0-nm-wide region with a potential-energy depth of 1.00 eV. What are the penetration distances into the classically forbidden region for an electron in the $n = 1$ and $n = 4$ states?

MODEL The electron is in the finite potential well whose energies and wave functions were shown in Figure 40.14a.

SOLVE The ground state has $U_0 - E_1 = 1.000 \text{ eV} - 0.068 \text{ eV} = 0.932 \text{ eV}$. Similarly, $U_0 - E_4 = 0.051 \text{ eV}$ in the $n = 4$ state. We can use Equation 40.41 to calculate

$$\eta = \frac{\hbar}{\sqrt{2m(U_0 - E)}} = \begin{cases} 0.20 \text{ nm} & n = 1 \\ 0.86 \text{ nm} & n = 4 \end{cases}$$

ASSESS These values are consistent with Figure 40.14a.

Quantum-Well Devices

In Part VI we developed a model of electrical conductivity in which the valence electrons of a metal form a loosely bound "sea of electrons." The typical speed of an electron is the rms speed:

$$v_{rms} = \sqrt{\frac{3k_B T}{m}}$$

where k_B is Boltzmann's constant. Hence at room temperature, where $v_{rms} \approx 1 \times 10^5$ m/s, the de Broglie wavelength of a typical conduction electron is

$$\lambda \approx \frac{h}{mv_{rms}} \approx 7 \text{ nm}$$

There is a range of wavelengths because the electrons have a range of speeds, but this is a typical value.

You've now seen many times that wave effects are significant only when the sizes of physical structures are comparable to or smaller than the wavelength. Because the de Broglie wavelength of conduction electrons is only a few nm, quantum effects are insignificant in electronic devices whose features are larger than about 100 nm. The electrons in macroscopic devices can be treated as classical particles, which is how we analyzed electric current in Chapter 30.

However, devices smaller than about 100 nm do exhibit quantum effects. Some semiconductor devices, such as the semiconductor lasers used in fiber-optic communications, now incorporate features only a few nm in size. Quantum effects play an important role in these devices.

FIGURE 40.16a shows a *semiconductor diode laser* through which a current travels from left to right. In the center is a very thin layer of the semiconductor gallium arsenide (GaAs). It is surrounded on either side by layers of gallium aluminum arsenide (GaAlAs), and these in turn are embedded within the larger structure of the diode. The electrons within the central GaAs layer begin to emit laser light when the current through the diode exceeds a *threshold current.* The laser beam diverges because of diffraction through the "slit" of the GaAs layer, with the wider axis of the laser beam corresponding to the narrower portion of the lasing region.

You can learn in a solid-state physics or materials engineering course that the electric potential energy of an electron is slightly lower in GaAs than in GaAlAs. This makes the GaAs layer a potential well for electrons, with higher-potential-energy GaAlAs "walls" on either side. As a result, the electrons become trapped within the thin GaAs layer. Such a device is called a **quantum-well laser.**

As an example, FIGURE 40.16b shows a quantum-well device with a 1.0-nm-thick GaAs layer in which the electron's potential energy is 0.300 eV lower than in the surrounding GaAlAs layers. A numerical solution of the Schrödinger equation finds that this potential well has only a *single* quantum state, $n = 1$ with $E_1 = 0.125$ eV. Every electron trapped in this quantum well has the *same* energy—a very nonclassical result! The fact that the electron energies are so well defined, in contrast to the range of electron energies in bulk material, is what makes this a useful device. You can also see from the probability density $|\psi|^2$ that the electrons are more likely to be found in the center of the layer than at the edges. This concentration of electrons makes it easier for the device to begin laser action.

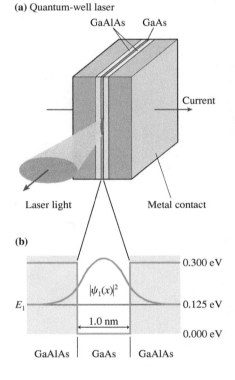

FIGURE 40.16 A semiconductor diode laser with a single quantum well.

(a) Quantum-well laser

GaAlAs GaAs

Current

Laser light   Metal contact

(b)

$|\psi_1(x)|^2$

0.300 eV

E_1 0.125 eV

1.0 nm

0.000 eV

GaAlAs GaAs GaAlAs

Nuclear Physics

The nucleus of an atom consists of an incredibly dense assembly of protons and neutrons. The positively charged protons exert extremely strong electric repulsive forces on each other, so you might wonder how the nucleus keeps from exploding. During the 1930s, physicists found that protons and neutrons also exert an *attractive* force on each other. This force, one of the fundamental forces of nature, is called the *strong force.* It is the force that holds the nucleus together.

The primary characteristic of the strong force, other than its strength, is that it is a *short-range* force. The attractive strong force between two *nucleons* (a nucleon is either a proton or a neutron; the strong force does not distinguish between them) rapidly decreases to zero if they are separated by more than about 2 fm. This is in sharp contrast to the long-range nature of the electric force.

A reasonable model of the nucleus is to think of the protons and neutrons as particles in a nuclear potential well that is created by the strong force. The diameter of the

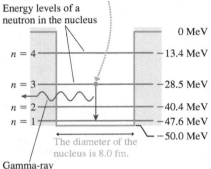

A radioactive decay has left the neutron in the $n = 3$ excited state. The neutron jumps to the $n = 1$ ground state, emitting a gamma-ray photon.

Energy levels of a neutron in the nucleus

0 MeV

$n = 4$ ——— 13.4 MeV

$n = 3$ ——— 28.5 MeV

$n = 2$ ——— 40.4 MeV
$n = 1$ ——— 47.6 MeV
——— 50.0 MeV

The diameter of the nucleus is 8.0 fm.

Gamma-ray emission

potential well is equal to the diameter of the nucleus (this varies with atomic mass), and nuclear physics experiments have found that the depth of the potential well is ≈ 50 MeV.

The real potential well is three-dimensional, but let's make a simplified model of the nucleus as a one-dimensional potential well. FIGURE 40.17 shows the potential energy of a neutron along an x-axis passing through the center of the nucleus. Notice that the zero of energy has been chosen such that a "free" neutron, one outside the nucleus, has $E = 0$. Thus the potential energy inside the nucleus is -50 MeV. The 8.0 fm diameter shown is appropriate for a nucleus having atomic mass number $A \approx 40$, such as argon or potassium. Lighter nuclei will be a little smaller, heavier nuclei somewhat larger. (The potential-energy diagram for a proton is similar, but is complicated a bit by the electric potential energy.)

A numerical solution of the Schrödinger equation finds the four stationary states shown in Figure 40.17. The wave functions have been omitted, but they look essentially identical to the wave functions in Figure 40.14a. The major point to note is that the allowed energies differ by several *million* electron volts! These are enormous energies compared to those of an electron in an atom or a semiconductor. But recall that the energies of a particle in a rigid box, $E_n = n^2h^2/8mL^2$, are proportional to $1/L^2$. Our previous examples, with nanometer-size boxes, found energies in the eV range. When the box size is reduced to femtometers, the energies jump up into the MeV range.

It often happens that the nuclear decay of a radioactive atom leaves a neutron in an excited state. For example, Figure 40.17 shows a neutron that has been left in the $n = 3$ state by a previous radioactive decay. This neutron can now undergo a quantum jump to the $n = 1$ ground state by emitting a photon with energy

$$E_{\text{photon}} = E_3 - E_1 = 19.1 \text{ MeV}$$

and wavelength

$$\lambda_{\text{photon}} = \frac{c}{f} = \frac{hc}{E_{\text{photon}}} = 6.50 \times 10^{-5} \text{ nm}$$

This photon is $\approx 10^7$ times more energetic, and its wavelength $\approx 10^7$ times smaller, than the photons of visible light! These extremely high-energy photons are called **gamma rays.** Gamma-ray emission is, indeed, one of the primary processes in the decay of radioactive elements.

Our one-dimensional model cannot be expected to give accurate results for the energy levels or gamma-ray energies of any specific nucleus. Nonetheless, this model does provide a reasonable understanding of the energy-level structure in nuclei and correctly predicts that nuclei can emit photons having energies of several million electron volts. This model, when extended to three dimensions, becomes the basis for the *shell model* of the nucleus in which the protons and neutrons are grouped in various shells analogous to the electron shells around an atom that you remember from chemistry. You can learn more about nuclear physics and the shell model in Chapter 42.

40.7 Wave-Function Shapes

Bound-state wave functions are standing de Broglie waves. In addition to boundary conditions, two other factors govern the shapes of wave functions:

1. The de Broglie wavelength is inversely dependent on the particle's speed. Consequently, the node spacing is smaller (shorter wavelength) where the kinetic energy is larger, and the spacing is larger (longer wavelength) where the kinetic energy is smaller.

2. A classical particle is more likely to be found where it is moving more slowly. In quantum mechanics, the probability of finding the particle increases as the wave-function amplitude increases. Consequently, the wave-function amplitude is larger where the kinetic energy is smaller, and it is smaller where the kinetic energy is larger.

We can use this information to draw reasonably accurate wave functions for the different allowed energies in a potential-energy well.

TACTICS
BOX 40.1   **Drawing wave functions**

❶ Draw a graph of the potential energy $U(x)$. Show the allowed energy E as a horizontal line. Locate the classical turning points.

❷ Draw the wave function as a continuous, oscillatory function between the turning points. The wave function for quantum state n has n antinodes and $(n - 1)$ nodes (excluding the ends).

❸ Make the wavelength longer (larger node spacing) and the amplitude higher in regions where the kinetic energy is smaller. Make the wavelength shorter and the amplitude lower in regions where the kinetic energy is larger.

❹ Bring the wave function to zero at the edge of an infinitely high potential-energy "wall."

❺ Let the wave function decay exponentially inside a classically forbidden region where $E < U$. The penetration distance η increases as E gets closer to the top of the potential-energy well.

Exercises 10–13

EXAMPLE 40.8   **Sketching wave functions**

FIGURE 40.18 shows a potential-energy well and the allowed energies for the $n = 1$ and $n = 4$ quantum states. Sketch the $n = 1$ and $n = 4$ wave functions.

VISUALIZE The steps of Tactics Box 40.1 have been followed to sketch the wave functions shown in FIGURE 40.19.

FIGURE 40.18 A potential-energy well.

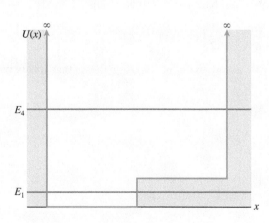

FIGURE 40.19 The $n = 1$ and $n = 4$ wave functions.

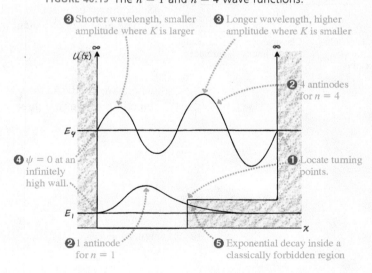

STOP TO THINK 40.4   For which potential energy $U(x)$ is this an appropriate $n = 4$ wave function?

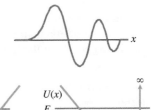

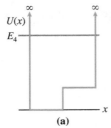 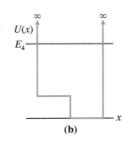 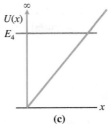 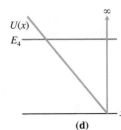

(a)   (b)   (c)   (d)

40.8 The Quantum Harmonic Oscillator

Simple harmonic motion is exceptionally important in classical physics, where it serves as a prototype for more complex oscillations. As you might expect, a microscopic oscillator—the **quantum harmonic oscillator**—is equally important as a model of oscillations at the atomic level.

The defining characteristic of simple harmonic motion is a linear restoring force: $F = -kx$, where k is the spring constant. The corresponding potential-energy function, as you learned in Chapter 10, is

$$U(x) = \frac{1}{2}kx^2 \tag{40.42}$$

FIGURE 40.20 The potential energy of a harmonic oscillator.

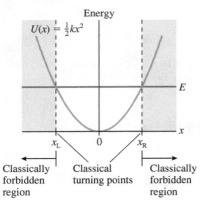

where we'll assume that the equilibrium position is $x_e = 0$. The potential energy of a harmonic oscillator is shown in FIGURE 40.20. It is a potential-energy well with curved sides.

A classical particle of mass m oscillates with angular frequency

$$\omega = \sqrt{\frac{k}{m}} \tag{40.43}$$

between the two turning points where the energy line crosses the parabolic potential-energy curve. As you've learned, this classical description fails if m represents an atomic particle, such as an electron or an atom. In that case, we need to solve the Schrödinger equation to find the wave functions.

The Schrödinger equation for a quantum harmonic oscillator is

$$\frac{d^2\psi}{dx^2} = -\frac{2m}{\hbar^2}\left(E - \frac{1}{2}kx^2\right)\psi(x) \tag{40.44}$$

where we used $U(x) = \frac{1}{2}kx^2$. We will assert, without deriving them, that the wave functions of the first three states are

$$\psi_1(x) = A_1 e^{-x^2/2b^2}$$

$$\psi_2(x) = A_2 \frac{x}{b} e^{-x^2/2b^2} \tag{40.45}$$

$$\psi_3(x) = A_3\left(1 - \frac{2x^2}{b^2}\right)e^{-x^2/2b^2}$$

where

$$b = \sqrt{\frac{\hbar}{m\omega}} \tag{40.46}$$

The constant b has dimensions of length. We will leave it as a homework problem for you to show that b is the classical turning point of an oscillator in the $n = 1$ ground state. The constants A_1, A_2, and A_3 are normalization constants. For example, A_1 can be found by requiring

$$\int_{-\infty}^{\infty} |\psi_1(x)|^2 \, dx = A_1^2 \int_{-\infty}^{\infty} e^{-x^2/b^2} \, dx = 1 \qquad (40.47)$$

The completion of this calculation also will be left as a homework problem.

As expected, stationary states of a quantum harmonic oscillator exist only for certain discrete energy levels, the quantum states of the oscillator. The allowed energies are given by the simple equation

$$E_n = \left(n - \frac{1}{2}\right)\hbar\omega \qquad n = 1, 2, 3, \dots \qquad (40.48)$$

where ω is the classical angular frequency, Equation 40.43, and n is the quantum number.

NOTE ▶ The ground-state energy of the quantum harmonic oscillator is $E_1 = \frac{1}{2}\hbar\omega$. An atomic mass on a spring can *not* be brought to rest. This is a consequence of the uncertainty principle. ◀

FIGURE 40.21 shows the first three energy levels and wave functions of a quantum harmonic oscillator. Notice that the energy levels are equally spaced by $\Delta E = \hbar\omega$. This result differs from the particle in a box, where the energy levels get increasingly farther apart. Also notice that the wave functions, like those of the finite potential well, extend beyond the turning points into the classically forbidden region.

FIGURE 40.21 The first three energy levels and wave functions of a quantum harmonic oscillator.

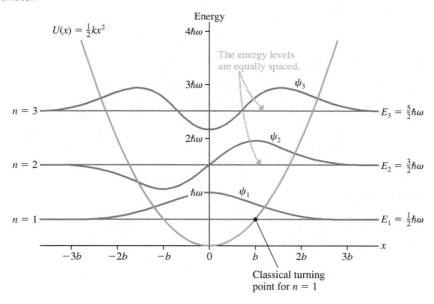

FIGURE 40.22 shows the probability density $|\psi(x)|^2$ for the $n = 11$ state of a quantum harmonic oscillator. Notice how the node spacing and the amplitude both increase as the particle moves away from the equilibrium position at $x = 0$. This is consistent with item 3 of Tactics Box 40.1. The particle slows down as it moves away from the origin, causing its de Broglie wavelength *and* the probability of finding it to increase.

Section 40.5 introduced the classical probability density $P_{class}(x)$ and noted that a classical particle is most likely to be found where it is moving the slowest. Figure 40.22

FIGURE 40.22 The quantum and classical probability densities for the $n = 11$ state of a quantum harmonic oscillator.

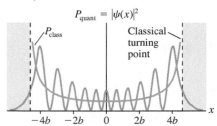

shows $P_{class}(x)$ for a classical particle with the same total energy as the $n = 11$ quantum state. You can see that *on average* the quantum probability density $|\psi(x)|^2$ mimics the classical probability density. This is just what the correspondence principle leads us to expect.

EXAMPLE 40.9 **Light emission by an oscillating electron**

An electron in a harmonic-oscillator potential well emits light of wavelength 600 nm as it jumps from one level to the next lowest level. What is the "spring constant" of the restoring force?

MODEL The electron is a quantum harmonic oscillator.

SOLVE A photon is emitted as the electron undergoes the quantum jump $n \rightarrow n - 1$. We can use Equation 40.48 for the energy levels to find that the electron loses energy

$$\Delta E = E_n - E_{n-1} = \left(n - \frac{1}{2}\right)\hbar\omega_e - \left(n - 1 - \frac{1}{2}\right)\hbar\omega_e = \hbar\omega_e$$

$\Delta E = \hbar\omega_e$ for *all* transitions, independent of n, because the energy levels of the quantum harmonic oscillator are equally spaced. We need to distinguish the harmonic oscillations of the electron from the oscillations of the light wave, hence the subscript e on ω_e.

The emitted photon has energy $E_{photon} = hf_{ph} = \Delta E$. Thus

$$\hbar\omega_e = \frac{h}{2\pi}\omega_e = hf_{ph} = \frac{hc}{\lambda}$$

The wavelength of the light is $\lambda = 600$ nm, so the classical angular frequency of the oscillating electron is

$$\omega_e = 2\pi\frac{c}{\lambda} = 3.14 \times 10^{15} \text{ rad/s}$$

The electron's angular frequency is related to the spring constant of the restoring force by

$$\omega_e = \sqrt{\frac{k}{m}}$$

Thus $k = m\omega_e^2 = 9.0$ N/m.

Molecular Vibrations

We've made many uses of the idea that atoms are held together by spring-like molecular bonds. We've always assumed that the bonds could be modeled as classical springs. The classical model is acceptable for some purposes, but it fails to explain some important features of molecular vibrations. Not surprisingly, the quantum harmonic oscillator is a better model of a molecular bond.

FIGURE 40.23 shows the potential energy of two atoms connected by a molecular bond. Nearby atoms attract each other through a polarization force, much as a charged rod picks up small pieces of paper. If the atoms get too close, a *repulsive* force between the negative electrons pushes them apart. The equilibrium separation at which the attractive and repulsive forces are balanced is r_0, and two classical atoms would be at rest at this separation. But quantum particles, even in their lowest energy state, have $E > 0$. Consequently, the molecule *vibrates* as the two atoms oscillate back and forth along the bond.

U_{dissoc} is the energy at which the molecule will *dissociate* and the two atoms will fly apart. Dissociation can occur at very high temperatures or after the molecule has absorbed a high-energy (ultraviolet) photon, but under typical conditions a molecule has energy $E \ll U_{dissoc}$. In other words, the molecule is in an energy level near the bottom of the potential well.

You can see that the lower portion of the potential well is very nearly a parabola. Consequently, we can model a molecular bond as a quantum harmonic oscillator. The energy associated with the molecular vibration is quantized and can have *only* the values

$$E_{vib} \approx \left(n - \frac{1}{2}\right)\hbar\omega \qquad n = 1, 2, 3, \ldots \qquad (40.49)$$

where ω is the angular frequency with which the atoms would vibrate if the bond were a classical spring. The molecular potential-energy curve is not exactly that of a harmonic oscillator, hence the $\approx$ sign, but the model is very good for low values of the quantum number n. The energy levels calculated by Equation 40.49 are called the **vibrational energy levels** of the molecule. The first few vibrational energy levels are shown in Figure 40.23.

At room temperature, most molecules are in the $n = 1$ vibrational ground state. Their vibrational motion can be excited by absorbing photons of frequency $f = \Delta E/h$.

FIGURE 40.23 The potential energy of a molecular bond and a few of the allowed energies.

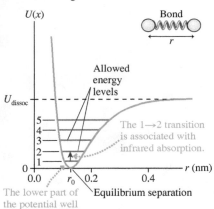

The lower part of the potential well is nearly a parabola.

This frequency is usually in the infrared region of the spectrum, and these *vibrational transitions* give each molecule a unique and distinctive infrared absorption spectrum.

As an example, FIGURE 40.24 shows the infrared absorption spectrum of acetone. The vertical axis is the percentage of the light intensity passing all the way through the sample. The sample is essentially transparent at most wavelengths (transmission ≈ 100%), but there are two prominent absorption features. The transmission drops to ≈75% at $\lambda = 3.3\ \mu m$ and to a mere 7% at $\lambda = 5.8\ \mu m$. The 3.3 μm absorption is due to the $n = 1$ to $n = 2$ transition in the vibration of a $C-CH_3$ carbon-methyl bond. The 5.8 μm absorption is the $1 \rightarrow 2$ transition of a vibrating $C=O$ carbon-oxygen double bond.

Absorption spectra are known for thousands of molecules, and chemists routinely use absorption spectroscopy to identify the chemicals in a sample. A specific bond has the same absorption wavelength regardless of the larger molecule in which it is embedded; thus the presence of that absorption wavelength is a "signature" that the bond is present within a molecule.

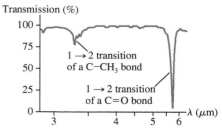

FIGURE 40.24 The absorption spectrum of acetone.

STOP TO THINK 40.5 Which probability density represents a quantum harmonic oscillator with $E = \frac{5}{2}\hbar\omega$?

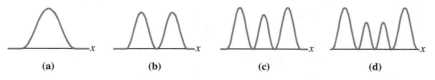

(a)   (b)   (c)   (d)

40.9 More Quantum Models

In this section we'll look at two more examples of quantum-mechanical models.

A Particle in a Capacitor

Many semiconductor devices are designed to confine electrons within a layer only a few nanometers thick. If a potential difference is applied across the layer, the electrons act very much as if they are trapped within a microscopic capacitor.

FIGURE 40.25a shows two capacitor plates separated by distance L. The left plate is positive, so the electric field points to the right with strength $E = \Delta V_0/L$. Because of its negative charge, an electron launched from the left plate is slowed by a *retarding* force. The electron makes it across to the right plate if it starts with sufficient kinetic energy; otherwise, it reaches a turning point and then is pushed back toward the positive plate.

This classical analysis is a valid model of a macroscopic capacitor. But if L becomes sufficiently small, comparable to the de Broglie wavelength of an electron, then the wave-like properties of the electron cannot be ignored. We need a quantum-mechanical model.

Let's establish a coordinate system with $x = 0$ at the left plate and $x = L$ at the right plate. We define the electric potential to be zero at the positive plate. The potential *decreases* in the direction of the field, so the potential inside the capacitor (see Section 28.5) is

$$V(x) = -Ex = -\frac{\Delta V_0}{L}x$$

The electron, with charge $q = -e$, has potential energy

$$U(x) = qV(x) = +\frac{e\,\Delta V_0}{L}x \qquad 0 < x < L \qquad (40.50)$$

This potential energy increases linearly for $0 < x < L$. If we assume that the capacitor plates act like the walls of a rigid box, then $U(x) \rightarrow \infty$ at $x = 0$ and $x = L$.

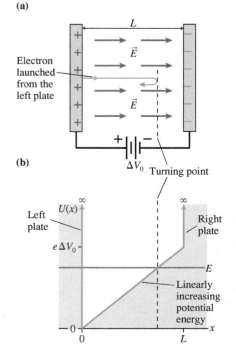

FIGURE 40.25 An electron in a capacitor.

(a)

(b)

FIGURE 40.25b shows the electron's potential-energy function. It is the particle-in-a-rigid-box potential with a sloping "floor" due to the electric field. The figure also shows the total energy line E of an electron in the capacitor. The energy is purely kinetic at $x = 0$, where $K = E$, but it is converted to potential energy as the electron moves to the right. The right turning point occurs where the energy line E crosses the potential-energy curve $U(x)$. If the electron is a classical particle, it must reverse direction at this point.

NOTE ▶ This is also the shape of the potential energy for a microscopic bouncing ball that is trapped between a floor at $y = 0$ and a ceiling at $y = L$. ◀

It is physically impossible for the electron to be outside the capacitor, so the wave function must be zero for $x < 0$ and $x > L$. The continuity of ψ requires the same boundary conditions as for a particle in a rigid box: $\psi = 0$ at $x = 0$ and at $x = L$. The wave functions inside the capacitor are too complicated to find by guessing, so we have solved the Schrödinger equation numerically and will present the results graphically.

FIGURE 40.26 shows the wave functions and probability densities for the first five quantum states of an electron confined in a 5.0-nm-thick layer that has a 0.80 V potential difference across it. Each allowed energy is represented as a horizontal line, with the numerical values shown on the right. They range from $E_1 = 0.23$ eV up to $E_5 = 0.81$ eV. An electron *must* have one of the allowed energies shown in the figure. An electron cannot have $E = 0.30$ eV in this capacitor because no de Broglie wave with that energy can match the necessary boundary conditions.

FIGURE 40.26 Energy levels, wave functions, and probability densities for an electron in a 5.0-nm-wide capacitor with a 0.80 V potential difference.

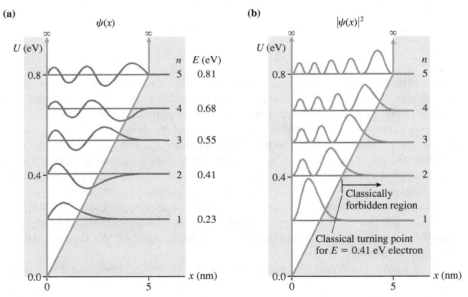

NOTE ▶ Remember that each wave function and probability density is graphed as if its energy line is the zero of the y-axis. ◀

We can make some observations about the Schrödinger equation solutions:

1. The energies E_n become more closely spaced as n increases, at least to $n = 5$. This contrasts with the particle in a box, for which E_n became more widely spaced.
2. The spacing between the nodes of a wave function is not constant but increases toward the right. This is because an electron on the right side of the capacitor has less kinetic energy and thus a slower speed and a larger de Broglie wavelength.

3. The height of the probability density $|\psi|^2$ increases toward the right. That is, we are more likely to find the electron on the right side of the capacitor than on the left. But this also makes sense if, classically, the electron is moving more slowly when on the right side and thus spending more time there than on the left side.

4. The electron penetrates *beyond* the classical turning point into the classically forbidden region.

EXAMPLE 40.10 | **The emission spectrum of an electron in a capacitor**

What are the wavelengths of photons emitted by electrons in the $n = 4$ state of Figure 40.26?

SOLVE Photon emission occurs as the electrons make $4 \rightarrow 3$, $4 \rightarrow 2$, and $4 \rightarrow 1$ quantum jumps. In each case, the photon frequency is $f = \Delta E/h$ and the wavelength is

$$\lambda = \frac{c}{f} = \frac{hc}{\Delta E}$$

The energies of the quantum jumps, which can be read from Figure 40.26a, are $\Delta E_{4 \rightarrow 3} = 0.13$ eV, $\Delta E_{4 \rightarrow 2} = 0.27$ eV, and

$\Delta E_{4 \rightarrow 1} = 0.45$ eV. Thus

$$\lambda_{4 \rightarrow 3} = 9500 \text{ nm} = 9.5 \text{ } \mu\text{m}$$

$$\lambda_{4 \rightarrow 2} = 4600 \text{ nm} = 4.6 \text{ } \mu\text{m}$$

$$\lambda_{4 \rightarrow 1} = 2800 \text{ nm} = 2.8 \text{ } \mu\text{m}$$

ASSESS The $n = 4$ electrons in this device emit three distinct infrared wavelengths.

The Covalent Bond

You probably recall from chemistry that a **covalent molecular bond,** such as the bond between the two atoms in molecules such as H_2 and O_2, is a bond in which the electrons are shared between the atoms. The basic idea of covalent bonding can be understood with a one-dimensional quantum-mechanical model.

The simplest molecule, the hydrogen molecular ion H_2^+, consists of two protons and one electron. Although it seems surprising that such a system could be stable, the two protons form a molecular bond with one electron. This is the simplest covalent bond.

How can we model the H_2^+ ion? To begin, FIGURE 40.27a shows a one-dimensional model of a hydrogen *atom* in which the electron's Coulomb potential energy, with its $1/r$ dependence, has been approximated by a finite potential well of width 0.10 nm ($\approx 2a_B$) and depth 24.2 eV. You learned in Chapter 38 that an electron in the ground state of the Bohr hydrogen atom orbits the proton with radius $r_1 = a_B$ (the Bohr radius) and energy $E_1 = -13.6$ eV. A numerical solution of the Schrödinger equation finds that the ground-state energy of this finite potential well is $E_1 = -13.6$ eV. This model of a hydrogen atom is very oversimplified, but it does have the correct size and ground-state energy.

We can model H_2^+ by bringing two of these potential wells close together. The molecular bond length of H_2^+ is known to be ≈ 0.12 nm, so FIGURE 40.27b shows potential wells with 0.12 nm between their centers. This is a model of H_2^+, not a complete H_2 molecule, because this is the potential energy of a single electron. (Modeling H_2 is more complex because we would need to consider the repulsion between the two electrons.)

FIGURE 40.28 on the next page shows the allowed energies, wave functions, and probability densities for an electron with this potential energy. The $n = 1$ wave function has a high probability of being found within the classically forbidden region *between* the two protons. In other words, an electron in this quantum state really is "shared" by the protons and spends most of its time between them.

In contrast, an electron in the $n = 2$ energy level has zero probability of being found between the two protons because the $n = 2$ wave function has a node at the center. The probability density shows that an $n = 2$ electron is "owned" by one proton or the other rather than being shared.

To learn the consequences of these wave functions we need to calculate the total energy of the molecule: $E_{\text{mol}} = E_{\text{p-p}} + E_{\text{elec}}$. The $n = 1$ and $n = 2$ energies shown in Figure 40.28 are the energies E_{elec} of the electron. At the same time, the protons

FIGURE 40.27 A molecule can be modeled as two closely spaced potential wells, one representing each atom.

(a) Simple one-dimensional model of a hydrogen atom

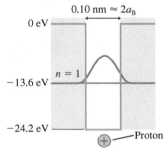

(b) An H_2^+ molecule modeled as an electron with two protons separated by 0.12 nm

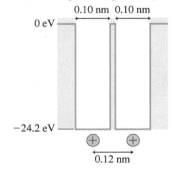

FIGURE 40.28 The wave functions and probability densities of the electron in H_2^+.

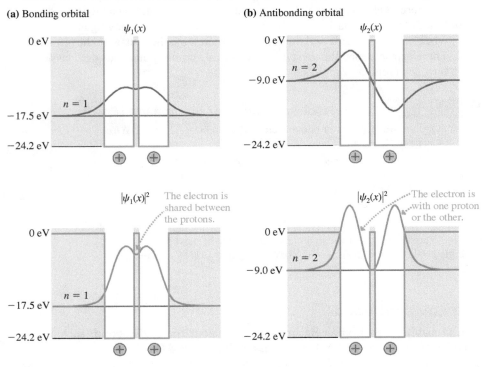

(a) Bonding orbital

(b) Antibonding orbital

repel each other and have electric potential energy E_{p-p}. It's not hard to calculate that $E_{p-p} = 12.0$ eV for two protons separated by 0.12 nm. Thus

$$E_{mol} = E_{p-p} + E_{elec} = \begin{cases} 12.0 \text{ eV} - 17.5 \text{ eV} = -5.5 \text{ eV} & n = 1 \\ 12.0 \text{ eV} - 9.0 \text{ eV} = +3.0 \text{ eV} & n = 2 \end{cases}$$

The $n = 1$ molecular energy is less than zero, showing that this is a *bound state*. The $n = 1$ wave function is called a **bonding molecular orbital.** Although the protons repel each other, the shared electron provides sufficient "glue" to hold the system together. The $n = 2$ molecular energy is positive, so this is *not* a bound state. The system would be more stable as a hydrogen atom and a distant proton. The $n = 2$ wave function is called an **antibonding molecular orbital.**

Both E_{elec} and E_{p-p} depend on the separation between the protons, which we assumed to be 0.12 nm in this calculation. If we were to calculate and graph E_{mol} for many different values of the proton separation, the graph would look like the molecular-bond energy curve shown in Figure 40.23. In other words, a molecular bond has an equilibrium length where the bond energy is a minimum *because* of the interplay between E_{p-p} and E_{elec}.

Although real molecular wave functions are more complex than this one-dimensional model, the $n = 1$ wave function captures the essential idea of a covalent bond. Notice that a "classical" molecule cannot have a covalent bond because the electron would not be able to exist in the classically forbidden region. Covalent bonds can be understood only within the context of quantum mechanics. In fact, the explanation of molecular bonds was one of the earliest successes of quantum mechanics.

40.10 Quantum-Mechanical Tunneling

FIGURE 40.29a shows a ball rolling toward a hill. A ball with sufficient kinetic energy can go over the top of the hill, slowing down as it ascends and speeding up as it rolls down the other side. A ball with insufficient energy rolls partway up the hill, then reverses direction and rolls back down.

FIGURE 40.29 A hill is an energy barrier to a rolling ball.

(a)

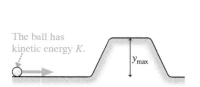

The ball has kinetic energy K.

y_{max}

(b)

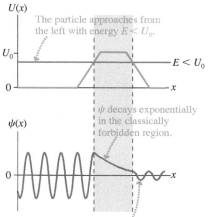

$U(x)$

A ball with this energy slows down while going over the hill, but it makes it over.

$E > U_0$

U_0

$E < U_0$

0

$U_0 = mgy_{max}$

A ball with this energy reverses direction at the turning point.

Turning point

We can think of the hill as an "energy barrier" of height $U_0 = mgy_{max}$. As FIGURE 40.29b shows, a ball incident from the left with energy $E > U_0$ can go over the barrier (i.e., roll over the hill), but a ball with $E < U_0$ will reflect from the energy barrier at the turning point. According to the laws of classical physics, a ball that is incident on the energy barrier from the left with $E < U_0$ will never be found on the right side of the barrier.

NOTE ▶ Figure 40.29b is not a "picture" of the energy barrier. And when we say that a ball with energy $E > U_0$ can go "over" the barrier, we don't mean that the ball is thrown from a higher elevation in order to go over the top of the hill. The ball rolls *on the ground* the entire time, as Figure 40.29a shows, and Figure 40.29b describes the kinetic and potential energy of the ball as it rolls. A higher total energy line means a larger initial kinetic energy, not a higher elevation. ◀

FIGURE 40.30 shows the situation from the perspective of quantum mechanics. As you've learned, quantum particles can penetrate with an exponentially decreasing wave function into the classically forbidden region of an energy barrier. Suppose that the barrier is very narrow. Although the wave function decreases within the barrier, starting at the classical turning point, it hasn't vanished when it reaches the other side. In other words, there is some probability that a quantum particle will pass *through* the barrier and emerge on the other side!

It is very much as if the ball of Figure 40.29a gets to the turning point and then, instead of reversing direction and rolling back down, tunnels its way *through* the hill and emerges on the other side. Although this feat is strictly forbidden in classical mechanics, it is apparently acceptable behavior for quantum particles. The process is called **quantum-mechanical tunneling.**

The process of tunneling through a potential-energy barrier is one of the strangest and most unexpected predictions of quantum mechanics. Yet it does happen, and you will see that it even has many practical applications.

NOTE ▶ The word "tunneling" is used as a metaphor. If a classical particle really did tunnel, it would expend energy doing so and emerge on the other side with less energy. Quantum-mechanical tunneling requires no expenditure of energy. The total energy line is at the same height on both sides of the barrier. A particle that tunnels through a barrier emerges with *no* loss of energy. That is why the de Broglie wavelength is the same on both sides of the potential barrier in Figure 40.30. ◀

To simplify our analysis of tunneling, FIGURE 40.31 shows an idealized energy barrier of height U_0 and width w. We've superimposed the wave function on top of the energy diagram so that you can see how it aligns with the potential energy. The wave function to the left of the barrier is a sinusoidal oscillation with amplitude A_L. The wave function *within* the barrier is the decaying exponential we found in Equation 40.40:

$$\psi_{in}(0 \leq x \leq w) = \psi_{edge}e^{-x/\eta} = A_L e^{-x/\eta} \qquad (40.51)$$

FIGURE 40.30 A quantum particle can penetrate through the energy barrier.

$U(x)$

The particle approaches from the left with energy $E < U_0$.

U_0

$E < U_0$

0

$\psi(x)$

ψ decays exponentially in the classically forbidden region.

0

The particle emerges with the same de Broglie wavelength after tunneling through the energy barrier.

FIGURE 40.31 Tunneling through an idealized energy barrier.

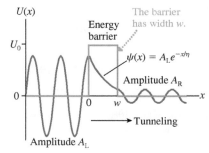

$U(x)$

The barrier has width w.

Energy barrier

U_0

$\psi(x) = A_L e^{-x/\eta}$

Amplitude A_R

0

w

Tunneling

Amplitude A_L

where we've assumed $\psi_{edge} = A_L$. The penetration distance η was given in Equation 40.41 as

$$\eta = \frac{\hbar}{\sqrt{2m(U_0 - E)}}$$

NOTE ▶ You *must* use SI units when calculating values of η. Energies must be in J and $\hbar$ in J s. The penetration distance η has units of meters. ◀

The wave function decreases exponentially within the barrier, but before it can decay to zero, it emerges again on the right side ($x > w$) as an oscillation with amplitude

$$A_R = \psi_{in}(\text{at } x = w) = A_L e^{-w/\eta} \tag{40.52}$$

The probability that the particle is to the left of the barrier is proportional to $|A_L|^2$, and the probability of finding it to the right of the barrier is proportional to $|A_R|^2$. Thus the probability that a particle striking the barrier from the left will emerge on the right is

$$P_{tunnel} = \frac{|A_R|^2}{|A_L|^2} = (e^{-w/\eta})^2 = e^{-2w/\eta} \tag{40.53}$$

This is the probability that a particle will tunnel through the energy barrier.

Now, our analysis, we have to say, has not been terribly rigorous. For example, we assumed that the oscillatory wave functions on the left and the right were exactly at a maximum where they reached the barrier at $x = 0$ and $x = w$. There is no reason this has to be the case. We have taken other liberties, which experts will spot, but—fortunately—it really makes no difference. Our result, Equation 40.53, turns out to be perfectly adequate for most applications of tunneling.

Because the tunneling probability is an exponential function, it is *very* sensitive to the values of w and η. The tunneling probability can be substantially reduced by even a small increase in the thickness of the barrier. The parameter η, which measures how far the particle can penetrate into the barrier, depends both on the particle's mass and on $U_0 - E$. A particle with E only slightly less than U_0 will have a larger value of η and thus a larger tunneling probability than will an identical particle with less energy.

EXAMPLE 40.11 **Electron tunneling**

a. Find the probability that an electron will tunnel through a 1.0-nm-wide energy barrier if the electron's energy is 0.10 eV less than the height of the barrier.
b. Find the tunneling probability if the barrier in part a is widened to 3.0 nm.
c. Find the tunneling probability if the electron in part a is replaced by a proton with the same energy.

SOLVE a. An electron with energy 0.10 eV less than the height of the barrier has $U_0 - E = 0.10$ eV $= 1.60 \times 10^{-20}$ J. Thus its penetration distance is

$$\eta = \frac{\hbar}{\sqrt{2m(U_0 - E)}}$$

$$= \frac{1.05 \times 10^{-34} \text{ J s}}{\sqrt{2(9.11 \times 10^{-31} \text{ kg})(1.60 \times 10^{-20} \text{ J})}}$$

$$= 6.18 \times 10^{-10} \text{ m} = 0.618 \text{ nm}$$

The probability that this electron will tunnel through a barrier of width $w = 1.0$ nm is

$$P_{tunnel} = e^{-2w/\eta} = e^{-2(1.0 \text{ nm})/(0.618 \text{ nm})} = 0.039 = 3.9\%$$

b. Changing the width to $w = 3.0$ nm has no effect on η. The new tunneling probability is

$$P_{tunnel} = e^{-2w/\eta} = e^{-2(3.0 \text{ nm})/(0.618 \text{ nm})} = 6.0 \times 10^{-5}$$

$$= 0.006\%$$

Increasing the width by a factor of 3 decreases the tunneling probability by a factor of 660!

c. A proton is more massive than an electron. Thus a proton with $U_0 - E = 0.10$ eV has $\eta = 0.014$ nm. Its probability of tunneling through a 1.0-nm-wide barrier is

$$P_{tunnel} = e^{-2w/\eta} = e^{-2(1.0 \text{ nm})/(0.014 \text{ nm})} \approx 1 \times 10^{-64}$$

For practical purposes, the probability that a proton will tunnel through this barrier is zero.

ASSESS If the probability of a proton tunneling through a mere 1 nm is only 10^{-64}, you can see that a macroscopic object will "never" tunnel through a macroscopic distance!

Quantum-mechanical tunneling seems so obscure that it is hard to imagine practical applications. Surprisingly, it is the physics behind one of today's most important technical tools, as we describe in the next section.

The Scanning Tunneling Microscope

Diffraction limits the resolution of an optical microscope to objects no smaller than about a wavelength of light—roughly 500 nm. This is more than 1000 times the size of an atom, so there is no hope of resolving atoms or molecules via optical microscopy. Electron microscopes are similarly limited by the de Broglie wavelength of the electrons. Their resolution is much better than that of an optical microscope, but still not quite at the level of resolving individual atoms.

This situation changed dramatically in 1981 with the invention of the **scanning tunneling microscope**, or STM as it is usually called. The STM allowed scientists, for the first time, to "see" surfaces literally atom by atom. The atomic-resolution photos at the beginning of Chapter 39 and this chapter demonstrate the power of an STM. These pictures and many others you have likely seen (but may not have known where they came from) are stupendous, but how are they made?

FIGURE 40.32a shows how the scanning tunneling microscope works. A conducting probe with a *very* sharp tip, just a few atoms wide, is brought to within a few tenths of a nanometer of a surface. Preparing the tips and controlling the spacing are both difficult technical challenges, but scientists have learned how to do both. Once positioned, the probe can mechanically scan back and forth across the surface.

When we analyzed the photoelectric effect, you learned that electrons are bound inside metals by an amount of energy called the *work function* E_0. A typical work function is 4 or 5 eV. This is the energy that must be supplied—by a photon or otherwise—to remove an electron from the metal. In other words, the electron's energy in the metal is E_0 less than its energy outside the metal.

This fact is the basis for the potential-energy diagram of FIGURE 40.32b. The small air gap between the sample and the probe tip is a potential-energy barrier. The energy of an electron in the metal of the sample or the probe tip is lower than the energy of an electron in the air by ≈ 4 eV, the work function. The absorption of a photon with $E_{photon} > 4$ eV would lift the electron *over* the barrier, from the sample to the probe. This is just the photoelectric effect. Alternatively, electrons can tunnel *through* the barrier if it is sufficiently narrow. This creates a *tunneling current* from the sample into the probe.

In operation, the tunneling current is recorded as the probe tip scans across the surface. You saw above that the tunneling current is extremely sensitive to the barrier thickness. As the tip scans over the position of an atom, the gap decreases by ≈ 0.1 nm and the current increases. The gap is larger when the tip is between atoms, so the current drops. Today's STMs can sense changes in the gap of as little as 0.001 nm, or about 1% of an atomic diameter! The images you see are computer-generated from current measurements at each position.

The STM has revolutionized the science and engineering of microscopic objects. STMs are now used to study everything from how surfaces corrode and oxidize, a topic of great practical importance in engineering, to how biological molecules are structured. Another example of quantum mechanics working for you!

FIGURE 40.32 A scanning tunneling microscope.

(a)

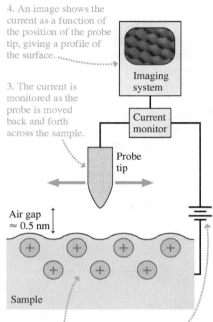

4. An image shows the current as a function of the position of the probe tip, giving a profile of the surface.

Imaging system

Current monitor

Probe tip

3. The current is monitored as the probe is moved back and forth across the sample.

Air gap ≈ 0.5 nm

Sample

1. The sample can be modeled as positive ion cores in an electron "sea."

2. The small positive voltage causes electrons to tunnel across the narrow air gap between the probe tip and the sample.

(b)

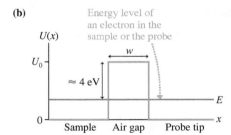

Energy level of an electron in the sample or the probe

$U(x)$

U_0

≈ 4 eV

w

E

0

Sample   Air gap   Probe tip

x

STOP TO THINK 40.6 A particle with energy E approaches an energy barrier with height $U_0 > E$. If U_0 is slowly decreased, the probability that the particle reflects from the barrier

a. Increases.
b. Decreases.
c. Does not change.

CHALLENGE EXAMPLE 40.12 **Tunneling in semiconductors**

Quantum-mechanical tunneling can be important in semiconductors. Consider a 1.0-nm-thick layer of GaAs sandwiched between 4.0-nm-thick layers of GaAlAs. This is the situation explored in Figure 40.16, where we learned that the electron's potential energy is 0.300 eV lower in GaAs than in GaAlAs. An electron in the GaAs layer can tunnel through the GaAlAs to escape, but this doesn't happen instantly. In quantum mechanics, we can't predict exactly when tunneling will occur, only the probability of it happening. Estimate the time at which the probability of escape has reached 50%.

MODEL The electron is a particle in a finite potential well. The tunneling probability depends on the height and thickness of a potential barrier.

VISUALIZE FIGURE 40.33 shows the potential well. An electron in a 0.300-eV-deep, 1.0-nm-wide well is exactly the situation of Figure 40.16, so we know that the electron has a single quantum state with $E_1 = 0.125$ eV. The wave function decreases exponentially with distance into the potential barriers, but a very tiny amplitude—too small to see here—still exists at the far edge of the barrier.

FIGURE 40.33 The potential energy of an electron in a layer of GaAs sandwiched between layers of GaAlAs.

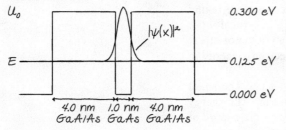

SOLVE We can approach this problem by thinking of the electron as a particle bouncing back and forth between the walls of the potential well. Each time it hits a wall, it has probability P_{tunnel} of tunneling and probability $P_{reflect} = 1 - P_{tunnel}$ of reflecting. The probability of tunneling is $P_{tunnel} = e^{-2w/\eta}$. The penetration distance η depends on $U_0 - E$, the "distance" from the energy level to the top of the barrier, which in this case is

$$U_0 - E = 0.300 \text{ eV} - 0.125 \text{ eV} = 0.175 \text{ eV} = 2.8 \times 10^{-20} \text{ J}$$

Using this value, we can calculate the penetration distance to be

$$\eta = \frac{\hbar}{\sqrt{2m(U_0 - E)}} = 0.465 \text{ nm}$$

We then find the probability of tunneling through a 4.0-nm-wide barrier to be

$$P_{tunnel} = e^{-2w/\eta} = 3.4 \times 10^{-8}$$

It's a very small probability, as expected. The probability of *not* tunneling, of reflecting back into the well, is then

$$P_{reflect} = 1 - P_{tunnel} = 0.999999966$$

You've seen that the probability of A *or* B happening is $P_A + P_B$. Similarly, the probability of A *and* B happening, assuming they are independent events, is $P_A \times P_B$. The probability of a head in a coin toss is $\frac{1}{2}$. If you toss two coins, the probability that A is a head *and* B is a head is $\frac{1}{2} \times \frac{1}{2} = \frac{1}{4}$. If you toss three coins, the probability that all three are heads is $\left(\frac{1}{2}\right)^3 = \frac{1}{8}$. If the electron is still in the potential well after N bounces, it had to reflect N times. The probability of this happening is

$$P_{in \text{ well}} = P_{reflect} \times P_{reflect} \times P_{reflect} \times \cdots \times P_{reflect} = (P_{reflect})^N$$

Because $P_{reflect} < 1$, the probability of still being in the potential well decreases as N increases.

We've focused not on P_{escape} but on $P_{in \text{ well}} = 1 - P_{escape}$ because staying in the well requires N specific events to happen. Escape, on the other hand, could have occurred on any of N attempts, so a direct calculation of P_{escape} is much more complicated. If the probability of escape is 50%, then it's also 50% probable that the electron is still in the potential well. We can find the number of reflections needed to get to the 50% probability by taking the logarithm of both sides of the equation:

$$\log(P_{in \text{ well}}) = \log\left((P_{reflect})^N\right) = N \log(P_{reflect})$$

$$N = \frac{\log(P_{in \text{ well}})}{\log(P_{reflect})} = \frac{\log(0.50)}{\log(0.999999966)} = 2.0 \times 10^7$$

After 20 million reflections, the electron is 50% likely to have escaped. Although that's a large number of reflections, it doesn't take long because the electron is moving only a very small distance between reflections at a fairly high speed. The electron's energy inside the potential well is entirely kinetic, $K = E = 0.125$ eV $= 2.0 \times 10^{-20}$ J, so its speed is

$$v = \sqrt{\frac{2K}{m}} = 2.1 \times 10^5 \text{ m/s}$$

The time between reflections is the time needed to travel across the 1.0-nm-wide GaAs layer:

$$\Delta t = \frac{1.0 \times 10^{-9} \text{ m}}{2.1 \times 10^5 \text{ m/s}} = 4.8 \times 10^{-15} \text{ s}$$

Thus the time needed for 2.0×10^7 reflections is

$$t_{50\%} = N\Delta t = 9.6 \times 10^{-8} \text{ s} = 96 \text{ ns}$$

Because we're making only an estimate, we can say that an electron has a 50% probability of tunneling out of the GaAs layer within about 100 ns.

ASSESS Even though the tunneling probability is very tiny, tunneling takes place very rapidly on a human time scale. An increasing number of semiconductor devices make practical use of this *tunneling current*. Note that no energy is lost in the tunneling process; "tunneling" is a metaphor, not a process that requires work. The electron emerges with 0.125 eV of kinetic energy.

SUMMARY

The goal of Chapter 40 has been to understand and apply the essential ideas of quantum mechanics.

General Principles

The Schrödinger Equation (the law of psi)

$$\frac{d^2\psi}{dx^2} = -\frac{2m}{\hbar^2}\left[E - U(x)\right]\psi(x)$$

This equation determines the wave function $\psi(x)$ and, through $\psi(x)$, the probabilities of finding a particle of mass m with potential energy $U(x)$.

Boundary conditions

- $\psi(x)$ is a continuous function.
- $\psi(x) \to 0$ as $x \to \pm\infty$.
- $\psi(x) = 0$ in a region where it is physically impossible for the particle to be.
- $\psi(x)$ is normalized.

Shapes of wave functions

- The wave function oscillates in the region between the classical turning points.
- State n has n antinodes.
- Node spacing and amplitude increase as kinetic energy K decreases.
- $\psi(x)$ decays exponentially in a classically forbidden region.

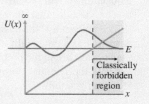

Quantum-mechanical models are characterized by the particle's potential-energy function $U(x)$.

- Wave-function solutions exist for only certain values of E. Thus energy is quantized.
- Photons are emitted or absorbed in quantum jumps.

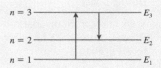

Important Concepts

Quantum-mechanical tunneling

A wave function can penetrate into a classically forbidden region with

$$\psi(x) = \psi_{\text{edge}}e^{-(x-L)/\eta}$$

where the **penetration distance** is

$$\eta = \frac{\hbar}{\sqrt{2m(U_0 - E)}}$$

The probability of tunneling through a barrier of width w is

$$P_{\text{tunnel}} = e^{-2w/\eta}$$

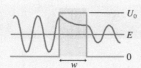

The correspondence principle says that the quantum world blends smoothly into the classical world for high quantum numbers. This is seen by comparing $|\psi(x)|^2$ to the classical probability density

$$P_{\text{class}} = \frac{2}{Tv(x)}$$

P_{class} expresses the idea that a classical particle is more likely to be found where it is moving slowly.

Applications

Particle in a rigid box: $E_n = n^2\dfrac{h^2}{8mL^2}$ $n = 1, 2, 3, \ldots$

Quantum harmonic oscillator: $E_n = (n - \tfrac{1}{2})\hbar\omega$ $n = 1, 2, 3, \ldots$

Other applications were studied through numerical solution of the Schrödinger equation.

Terms and Notation

Schrödinger equation	bound state	bonding molecular orbital
quantum-mechanical model	penetration distance, η	antibonding molecular orbital
boundary conditions	quantum-well laser	quantum-mechanical tunneling
zero-point motion	gamma rays	scanning tunneling microscope (STM)
correspondence principle	quantum harmonic oscillator	
potential well	vibrational energy levels	
classically forbidden regions	covalent molecular bond	

CONCEPTUAL QUESTIONS

1. The correspondence principle says that the *average* behavior of a quantum system should begin to look like the Newtonian solution in the limit that the quantum number becomes very large. What is meant by "the *average* behavior" of a quantum system?

2. A particle in a potential well is in the $n = 5$ quantum state. How many peaks are in the probability density $P(x) = |\psi(x)|^2$?

3. What is the quantum number of the particle in FIGURE Q40.3? How can you tell?

FIGURE Q40.3

4. Rank in order, from largest to smallest, the penetration distances η_a to η_c of the wave functions corresponding to the three energy levels in FIGURE Q40.4.

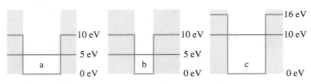

FIGURE Q40.4

5. Consider a quantum harmonic oscillator.
   a. What happens to the spacing between the nodes of the wave function as $|x|$ increases? Why?

   b. What happens to the heights of the antinodes of the wave function as $|x|$ increases? Why?
   c. Sketch a reasonably accurate graph of the $n = 8$ wave function of a quantum harmonic oscillator.

6. FIGURE Q40.6 shows two possible wave functions for an electron in a linear triatomic molecule. Which of these is a bonding orbital and which is an antibonding orbital? Explain how you can distinguish them.

FIGURE Q40.6

7. Four quantum particles, each with energy E, approach the potential-energy barriers seen in FIGURE Q40.7 from the left. Rank in order, from largest to smallest, the tunneling probabilities $(P_{tunnel})_a$ to $(P_{tunnel})_d$.

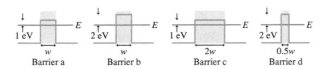

FIGURE Q40.7

EXERCISES AND PROBLEMS

Problems labeled ▓ integrate material from earlier chapters.

Exercises

Sections 40.3–40.4 A Particle in a Rigid Box

1. ‖ An electron in a rigid box absorbs light. The longest wavelength in the absorption spectrum is 600 nm. How long is the box?

2. | The electrons in a rigid box emit photons of wavelength 1484 nm during the $3 \rightarrow 2$ transition.
   a. What kind of photons are they—infrared, visible, or ultraviolet?
   b. How long is the box in which the electrons are confined?

3. ‖ FIGURE EX40.3 shows the wave function of an electron in a rigid box. The electron energy is 6.0 eV. How long is the box?

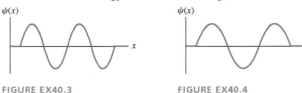

FIGURE EX40.3   FIGURE EX40.4

4. | FIGURE EX40.4 shows the wave function of an electron in a rigid box. The electron energy is 12.0 eV. What is the energy of the electron's ground state?

Section 40.6 Finite Potential Wells

5. | Show that the penetration distance η has units of m.
6. | a. Sketch graphs of the probability density $|\psi(x)|^2$ for the four states in the finite potential well of Figure 40.14a. Stack them vertically, similar to the Figure 40.14a graphs of $\psi(x)$.
   b. What is the probability that a particle in the $n = 2$ state of the finite potential well will be found at the center of the well? Explain.
   c. Is your answer to part b consistent with what you know about waves? Explain.
7. | A finite potential well has depth $U_0 = 2.00$ eV. What is the penetration distance for an electron with energy (a) 0.50 eV, (b) 1.00 eV, and (c) 1.50 eV?
8. || An electron in a finite potential well has a 1.0 nm penetration distance into the classically forbidden region. How far below U_0 is the electron's energy?
9. || The energy of an electron in a 2.00-eV-deep potential well is 1.50 eV. At what distance into the classically forbidden region has the amplitude of the wave function decreased to 25% of its value at the edge of the potential well?
10. | A helium atom is in a finite potential well. The atom's energy is 1.0 eV below U_0. What is the atom's penetration distance into the classically forbidden region?

Section 40.7 Wave-Function Shapes

11. | Sketch the $n = 4$ wave function for the potential energy shown in FIGURE EX40.11.

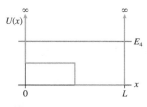

FIGURE EX40.11   FIGURE EX40.12

12. | Sketch the $n = 8$ wave function for the potential energy shown in FIGURE EX40.12.
13. | The graph in FIGURE EX40.13 shows the potential-energy function $U(x)$ of a particle. Solution of the Schrödinger equation finds that the $n = 3$ level has $E_3 = 0.5$ eV and that the $n = 6$ level has $E_6 = 2.0$ eV.
   a. Redraw this figure and add to it the energy lines for the $n = 3$ and $n = 6$ states.
   b. Sketch the $n = 3$ and $n = 6$ wave functions. Show them as oscillating about the appropriate energy line.

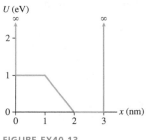

FIGURE EX40.13   FIGURE EX40.14

14. | Sketch the $n = 1$ and $n = 7$ wave functions for the potential energy shown in FIGURE EX40.14.

Section 40.8 The Quantum Harmonic Oscillator

15. | An electron in a harmonic potential well absorbs a photon with a wavelength of 400 nm as it undergoes a $1 \rightarrow 2$ quantum jump. What wavelength is absorbed in a $1 \rightarrow 3$ quantum jump?
16. | An electron is confined in a harmonic potential well that has a spring constant of 2.0 N/m.
   a. What are the first three energy levels of the electron?
   b. What wavelength photon is emitted if the electron undergoes a $3 \rightarrow 1$ quantum jump?
17. | An electron is confined in a harmonic potential well that has a spring constant of 12.0 N/m. What is the longest wavelength of light that the electron can absorb?
18. || An electron confined in a harmonic potential well emits a 1200 nm photon as it undergoes a $3 \rightarrow 2$ quantum jump. What is the spring constant of the potential well?
19. | Two adjacent energy levels of an electron in a harmonic potential well are known to be 2.0 eV and 2.8 eV. What is the spring constant of the potential well?

Section 40.10 Quantum-Mechanical Tunneling

20. || What is the probability that an electron will tunnel through a 0.45 nm gap from a metal to a STM probe if the work function is 4.0 eV?
21. || An electron approaches a 1.0-nm-wide potential-energy barrier of height 5.0 eV. What energy electron has a tunneling probability of (a) 10%, (b) 1.0%, and (c) 0.10%?

Problems

22. || A 2.0-μm-diameter water droplet is moving with a speed of 1.0 μm/s in a 20-μm-long box.
   a. Estimate the particle's quantum number.
   b. Use the correspondence principle to determine whether quantum mechanics is needed to understand the particle's motion or if it is "safe" to use classical physics.
23. || Suppose that $\psi_1(x)$ and $\psi_2(x)$ are both solutions to the Schrödinger equation for the same potential energy $U(x)$. Prove that the superposition $\psi(x) = A\psi_1(x) + B\psi_2(x)$ is also a solution to the Schrödinger equation.
24. || Figure 40.27a modeled a hydrogen atom as a finite potential well with rectangular edges. A more realistic model of a hydrogen atom, although still a one-dimensional model, would be the electron + proton electrostatic potential energy in one dimension:

$$U(x) = -\frac{e^2}{4\pi\epsilon_0 |x|}$$

   a. Draw a graph of $U(x)$ versus x. Center your graph at $x = 0$.
   b. Despite the divergence at $x = 0$, the Schrödinger equation can be solved to find energy levels and wave functions for the electron in this potential. Draw a horizontal line across your graph of part a about one-third of the way from the bottom to the top. Label this line E_2, then, on this line, sketch a plausible graph of the $n = 2$ wave function.
   c. Redraw your graph of part a and add a horizontal line about two-thirds of the way from the bottom to the top. Label this line E_3, then, on this line, sketch a plausible graph of the $n = 3$ wave function.

25. ‖ a. Derive an expression for $\lambda_{2 \to 1}$, the wavelength of light emitted by a particle in a rigid box during a quantum jump from $n = 2$ to $n = 1$.

   b. In what length rigid box will an electron undergoing a $2 \to 1$ transition emit light with a wavelength of 694 nm? This is the wavelength of a ruby laser.

26. ‖ Model an atom as an electron in a rigid box of length 0.100 nm, roughly twice the Bohr radius.

   a. What are the four lowest energy levels of the electron?

   b. Calculate all the wavelengths that would be seen in the emission spectrum of this atom due to quantum jumps between these four energy levels. Give each wavelength a label $\lambda_{n \to m}$ to indicate the transition.

   c. Are these wavelengths in the infrared, visible, or ultraviolet portion of the spectrum?

   d. The stationary states of the Bohr hydrogen atom have negative energies. The stationary states of this model of the atom have positive energies. Is this a physically significant difference? Explain.

   e. Compare this model of an atom to the Bohr hydrogen atom. In what ways are the two models similar? Other than the signs of the energy levels, in what ways are they different?

27. ‖ Show that the normalization constant A_n for the wave functions of a particle in a rigid box has the value given in Equation 40.26.

28. ‖ A particle confined in a rigid one-dimensional box of length 10 fm has an energy level $E_n = 32.9$ MeV and an adjacent energy level $E_{n+1} = 51.4$ MeV.

   a. Determine the values of n and $n + 1$.

   b. Draw an energy-level diagram showing all energy levels from 1 through $n + 1$. Label each level and write the energy beside it.

   c. Sketch the $n + 1$ wave function on the $n + 1$ energy level.

   d. What is the wavelength of a photon emitted in the $n + 1 \to n$ transition? Compare this to a typical visible-light wavelength.

   e. What is the mass of the particle? Can you identify it?

29. ‖ Consider a particle in a rigid box of length L. For each of the states $n = 1$, $n = 2$, and $n = 3$:

   a. Sketch graphs of $|\psi(x)|^2$. Label the points $x = 0$ and $x = L$.

   b. Where, in terms of L, are the positions at which the particle is *most* likely to be found?

   c. Where, in terms of L, are the positions at which the particle is *least* likely to be found?

   d. Determine, by examining your $|\psi(x)|^2$ graphs, if the probability of finding the particle in the left one-third of the box is less than, equal to, or greater than $\frac{1}{3}$. Explain your reasoning.

   e. *Calculate* the probability that the particle will be found in the left one-third of the box.

30. ‖‖ For a particle in a finite potential well of width L and depth U_0, what is the ratio of the probability Prob(in δx at $x = L + \eta$) to the probability Prob(in δx at $x = L$)?

31. ‖ For the quantum-well laser of Figure 40.16, *estimate* the probability that an electron will be found within one of the GaAlAs layers rather than in the GaAs layer. Explain your reasoning.

32. ‖ Use the data from Figure 40.24 to calculate the first three vibrational energy levels of a C=O carbon-oxygen double bond.

33. ‖ Verify that the $n = 1$ wave function $\psi_1(x)$ of the quantum harmonic oscillator really is a solution of the Schrödinger equation. That is, show that the right and left sides of the Schrödinger equation are equal if you use the $\psi_1(x)$ wave function.

34. ‖ Show that the constant b used in the quantum-harmonic-oscillator wave functions (a) has units of length and (b) is the classical turning point of an oscillator in the $n = 1$ ground state.

35. ‖ a. Determine the normalization constant A_1 for the $n = 1$ ground-state wave function of the quantum harmonic oscillator. Your answer will be in terms of b.

   b. Write an expression for the probability that a quantum harmonic oscillator in its $n = 1$ ground state will be found in the classically forbidden region.

   c. (Optional) Use a numerical integration program to evaluate your probability expression of part b.

   Hint: It helps to simplify the integral by making a change of variables to $u = x/b$.

36. ‖ a. Derive an expression for the classical probability density $P_{\text{class}}(x)$ for a simple harmonic oscillator with amplitude A.

   b. Graph your expression between $x = -A$ and $x = +A$.

   c. Interpret your graph. Why is it shaped as it is?

37. ‖ a. Derive an expression for the classical probability density $P_{\text{class}}(y)$ for a ball that bounces between the ground and height h. The collisions with the ground are perfectly elastic.

   b. Graph your expression between $y = 0$ and $y = h$.

   c. Interpret your graph. Why is it shaped as it is?

38. ‖ Figure 40.17 showed that a typical nuclear radius is 4.0 fm. As you'll learn in Chapter 42, a typical energy of a neutron bound inside the nuclear potential well is $E_n = -20$ MeV. To find out how "fuzzy" the edge of the nucleus is, what is the neutron's penetration distance into the classically forbidden region as a fraction of the nuclear radius?

39. ‖ Even the smoothest mirror finishes are "rough" when viewed at a scale of 100 nm. When two very smooth metals are placed in contact with each other, the actual distance between the surfaces varies from 0 nm at a few points of real contact to ≈ 100 nm. The average distance between the surfaces is ≈ 50 nm. The work function of aluminum is 4.3 eV. What is the probability that an electron will tunnel between two pieces of aluminum that are 50 nm apart? Give your answer as a power of 10 rather than a power of e.

40. ‖ A proton's energy is 1.0 MeV below the top of a 10-fm-wide energy barrier. What is the probability that the proton will tunnel through the barrier?

Challenge Problems

41. A typical electron in a piece of metallic sodium has energy $-E_0$ compared to a free electron, where E_0 is the 2.7 eV work function of sodium.

   a. At what distance *beyond* the surface of the metal is the electron's probability density 10% of its value *at* the surface?

   b. How does this distance compare to the size of an atom?

42. In a nuclear physics experiment, a proton is fired toward a $Z = 13$ nucleus with the diameter and neutron energy levels shown in Figure 40.17. The nucleus, which was initially in its ground state, subsequently emits a gamma ray with wavelength 1.73×10^{-4} nm. What was the *minimum* initial speed of the proton?

   Hint: Don't neglect the proton-nucleus collision.

43. A particle of mass m has the wave function $\psi(x) = A \exp(-x^2/a^2)$ when it is in an allowed energy level with $E = 0$.

   a. Draw a graph of $\psi(x)$ versus x.

   b. At what value or values of x is the particle most likely to be found?

   c. Find and graph the potential-energy function $U(x)$.

44. In most metals, the atomic ions form a regular arrangement called a *crystal lattice*. The conduction electrons in the sea of electrons move through this lattice. FIGURE CP40.44 is a one-dimensional model of a crystal lattice. The ions have mass m, charge e, and an equilibrium separation b.

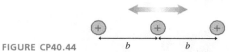

FIGURE CP40.44

a. Suppose the middle charge is displaced a very small distance ($x \ll b$) from its equilibrium position while the outer charges remain fixed. Show that the net electric force on the middle charge is given approximately by

$$F = -\frac{e^2}{b^3 \pi \epsilon_0} x$$

In other words, the charge experiences a linear restoring force.

b. Suppose this crystal consists of aluminum ions with an equilibrium spacing of 0.30 nm. What are the energies of the four lowest vibrational states of these ions?

c. What wavelength photons are emitted during quantum jumps between *adjacent* energy levels? Is this wavelength in the infrared, visible, or ultraviolet portion of the spectrum?

45. a. What is the probability that an electron will tunnel through a 0.50 nm air gap from a metal to a STM probe if the work function is 4.0 eV?

b. The probe passes over an atom that is 0.050 nm "tall." By what factor does the tunneling current increase?

c. If a 10% current change is reliably detectable, what is the smallest height change the STM can detect?

46. Tennis balls traveling faster than 100 mph routinely bounce off tennis rackets. At some sufficiently high speed, however, the ball will break through the strings and keep going. The racket is a potential-energy barrier whose height is the energy of the slowest string-breaking ball. Suppose that a 100 g tennis ball traveling at 200 mph is just sufficient to break the 2.0-mm-thick strings. Estimate the probability that a 120 mph ball will tunnel through the racket without breaking the strings. Give your answer as a power of 10 rather than a power of e.

STOP TO THINK ANSWERS

Stop to Think 40.1: $v_a = v_b > v_c$. The de Broglie wavelength is $\lambda = h/mv$, so slower particles have longer wavelengths. The wave amplitude is not relevant.

Stop to Think 40.2: c. The $n = 2$ state has a node in the middle of the box. The antinodes are centered in the left and right halves of the box.

Stop to Think 40.3: $n = 4$. There are four antinodes and three nodes (excluding the ends).

Stop to Think 40.4: d. The wave function reaches zero abruptly on the right, indicating an infinitely high potential-energy wall. The exponential decay on the left shows that the left wall of the potential energy is *not* infinitely high. The node spacing and the amplitude increase steadily in going from right to left, indicating a *steadily* decreasing kinetic energy and thus a steadily increasing potential energy.

Stop to Think 40.5: c. $E = (n - \frac{1}{2})\hbar\omega$, so $\frac{5}{2}\hbar\omega$ is the energy of the $n = 3$ state. An $n = 3$ state has 3 antinodes.

Stop to Think 40.6: b. The probability of tunneling through the barrier increases as the difference between E and U_0 decreases. If the tunneling probability increases, the reflection probability must decrease.

41 Atomic Physics

Lasers are one of the most important applications of the quantum-mechanical properties of atoms and light.

▶ **Looking Ahead** The goal of Chapter 41 is to understand the structure and properties of atoms.

The Hydrogen Atom

You'll learn to interpret the hydrogen atom as a three-dimensional wave function giving the probability of locating the electron in a region of space.

We'll need three quantum numbers to describe the state of the electron. The wave function is often pictured graphically as an **electron cloud.**

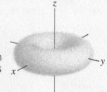

◀ **Looking Back**
Sections 39.3–39.4 Wave functions

Multielectron Atoms

The quantum-mechanical model of the atom is able to explain the properties of multielectron atoms, including their energy levels, ionization energies, and spectra.

You'll use atomic energy-level diagrams like this to understand which states are occupied and how spectra are produced.

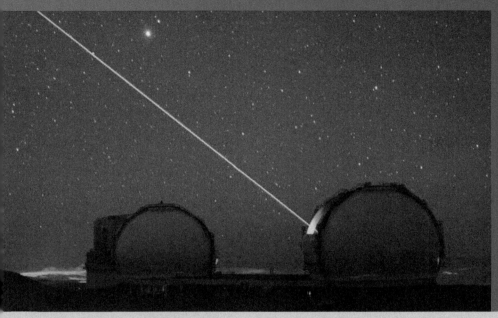

Atomic Spectra

You'll learn to interpret spectra in terms of *excitation* followed by *emission*. You'll also learn that emission doesn't occur instantly; instead, the excited state has a **lifetime** of typically a few nanoseconds.

- Excitation is by the absorption of a photon or by collision with another particle.
- Emission obeys **selection rules** that allow some quantum jumps but not others.

Atomic Models

Our understanding of the atom has evolved as the experimental evidence has grown. You should review:

- The atom as an indivisible object.
- Thomson's plum-pudding model.
- Rutherford's solar-system model.
- Bohr's semi-classical model.

You will learn how Schrödinger's quantum-mechanical model of the atom finally succeeds at explaining *all* the experimental evidence about atoms.

◀ **Looking Back**
Sections 38.5–38.7 The Bohr model

Electron Spin

In addition to having an inherent mass and an inherent charge, the electron has an inherent magnetic moment called the **electron spin.** As a result, a fourth quantum number is needed to specify a quantum state completely

You'll learn how the **Pauli exclusion principle,** which says that only one electron can occupy each quantum state, is the key to understanding the periodic table of the elements.

Lasers

You'll learn that lasers work because of the **stimulated emission** of light, a process in which an incoming photon causes an excited atom to emit an identical photon.

In some lasers, an intense burst of light from a flashlamp creates a **population inversion** with more atoms in an excited state than in the ground state.

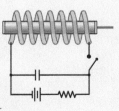

41.1 The Hydrogen Atom: Angular Momentum and Energy

Bohr's concept of stationary states provided a means of understanding both the stability of atoms and the quantum jumps that lead to discrete spectra. Yet, as we have seen, the Bohr model was not successful for any neutral atom other than hydrogen. Is Schrödinger's quantum mechanics better at explaining atomic structure than other models? The answer, as you can probably anticipate, is a decisive yes. This chapter is an overview of how quantum mechanics finally provides us with an understanding of atomic structure and atomic properties.

Let's begin with a quantum-mechanical model of the hydrogen atom. FIGURE 41.1 shows an electron at distance r from a proton. The proton is much more massive than the electron, so we will assume that the proton remains at rest at the origin.

As you learned in Chapter 40, the problem-solving procedure in quantum mechanics consists of two basic steps:

1. Specify a potential-energy function.
2. Solve the Schrödinger equation to find the wave functions, allowed energy levels, and other quantum properties.

The first step is easy. The proton and electron are charged particles with $q = \pm e$, so the potential energy of a hydrogen atom as a function of the electron distance r is

$$U(r) = -\frac{1}{4\pi\epsilon_0}\frac{e^2}{r} \tag{41.1}$$

The difficulty arises with the second step. The Schrödinger equation of Chapter 40 was for one-dimensional problems. Atoms are three-dimensional, and the three-dimensional Schrödinger equation turns out to be a partial differential equation whose solution is outside the scope of this textbook. Consequently, we'll present results without derivation or proof. The good news is that you have learned enough quantum mechanics to interpret and use the results.

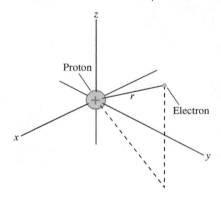

FIGURE 41.1 The electron in a hydrogen atom is distance r from the proton.

Stationary States of Hydrogen

In one dimension, energy quantization appeared as a consequence of *boundary conditions* on the wave function. That is, only for certain discrete energies, characterized by the quantum number n, did solutions to the Schrödinger equation satisfy the boundary conditions. In three dimensions, the wave function must satisfy *three* different boundary conditions. Consequently, solutions to the three-dimensional Schrödinger equation have *three* quantum numbers and *three* quantized parameters.

Solutions to the Schrödinger equation for the hydrogen atom potential energy exist only if three conditions are satisfied:

1. The atom's energy must be one of the values

$$E_n = -\frac{1}{n^2}\left(\frac{1}{4\pi\epsilon_0}\frac{e^2}{2a_B}\right) = -\frac{13.60\text{ eV}}{n^2} \qquad n = 1, 2, 3, \ldots \tag{41.2}$$

where $a_B = 4\pi\epsilon_0\hbar^2/me^2 = 0.0529$ nm is the Bohr radius. The integer n is called the **principal quantum number**. These energies are the same as those predicted by the Bohr model of the hydrogen atom.

2. The orbital angular momentum L of the electron's orbit must be one of the values

$$L = \sqrt{l(l+1)}\,\hbar \qquad l = 0, 1, 2, 3, \ldots, n-1 \tag{41.3}$$

The integer l is called the **orbital quantum number.**

3. The z-component of the angular momentum L_z must be one of the values

$$L_z = m\hbar \qquad m = -l, -l+1, \ldots, 0, \ldots, l-1, l \qquad (41.4)$$

The integer m is called the **magnetic quantum number.**

In other words, each stationary state of the hydrogen atom is identified by a triplet of quantum numbers (n, l, m). Each quantum number is associated with a physical property of the atom.

NOTE ▶ The energy of the stationary state depends only on the principal quantum number n, not on l or m. ◀

EXAMPLE 41.1 **Listing quantum numbers**

List all possible states of a hydrogen atom that have energy $E = -3.40$ eV.

SOLVE Energy depends only on the principal quantum number n. States with $E = -3.40$ eV have

$$n = \sqrt{\frac{-13.60 \text{ eV}}{-3.40 \text{ eV}}} = 2$$

An atom with principal quantum number $n = 2$ could have either $l = 0$ or $l = 1$, but $l \geq 2$ is excluded by the rule $l \leq n - 1$. If

$l = 0$, the only possible value for the magnetic quantum number m is $m = 0$. If $l = 1$, then the atom could have $m = -1$, $m = 0$, or $m = +1$. Thus the possible quantum numbers are

n	l	m
2	0	0
2	1	1
2	1	0
2	1	-1

These four states all have the same energy.

TABLE 41.1 Symbols used to represent quantum number l

l	Symbol
0	s
1	p
2	d
3	f

Hydrogen turns out to be unique. For all other elements, the allowed energies depend on both n and l (but not m). Consequently, it is useful to label the stationary states by their values of n and l. The lowercase letters shown in Table 41.1 are customarily used to represent the various values of quantum number l. These symbols come from spectroscopic notation used in prequantum-mechanics days, when some spectral lines were classified as sharp, others as principal, and so on.

Using these symbols, we call the ground state of the hydrogen atom, with $n = 1$ and $l = 0$, the $1s$ state. The $3d$ state has $n = 3$, $l = 2$. In Example 41.1, we found one $2s$ state (with $l = 0$) and three $2p$ states (with $l = 1$), all with the same energy.

Angular Momentum Is Quantized

A planet orbiting the sun has two different angular momenta: *orbital angular momentum* due to its orbit around the sun (a 365-day period for the earth) and *rotational angular momentum* as it rotates on its axis (a 24-hour period for the earth). We introduced angular momentum in Chapter 12, and a brief review of Section 12.11 is highly recommended.

A classical model of the hydrogen atom would be similar. Although a circular orbit is possible, it's more likely that the electron would follow an elliptical orbit with the proton at one focus of the ellipse. Further, the orbit need not lie in the xy-plane. FIGURE 41.2 shows a classical orbit tilted at angle θ below the xy-plane. The electron, like a planet, has orbital angular momentum, and Figure 41.2 reminds you that the orbital angular momentum vector $\vec{L}$ is perpendicular to the plane of the orbit. (The electron also has a quantum version of rotational angular momentum, called *spin*, that we'll introduce in Section 41.3.) The orbital angular momentum vector has component $L_z = L \cos\theta$ along the z-axis.

Classically, L and L_z can have any values. Not so in quantum mechanics. Quantum conditions 2 and 3 tell us that **the electron's orbital angular momentum is quantized.** The magnitude of the orbital angular momentum must be one of the discrete values

$$L = \sqrt{l(l+1)}\hbar = 0, \sqrt{2}\hbar, \sqrt{6}\hbar, \sqrt{12}\hbar, \ldots$$

where l is an integer. Simultaneously, the z-component L_z must have one of the values $L_z = m\hbar$, where m is an integer between $-l$ and l. No other values of L or L_z allow the wave function to satisfy the boundary conditions.

FIGURE 41.2 The angular momentum of an elliptical orbit.

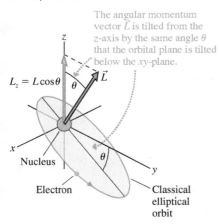

The angular momentum vector $\vec{L}$ is tilted from the z-axis by the same angle θ that the orbital plane is tilted below the xy-plane.

$L_z = L\cos\theta$

$\vec{L}$

Nucleus

Electron

Classical elliptical orbit

The quantization of angular momentum places restrictions on the shape and orientation of the electron's orbit. To see this, consider a hydrogen atom with orbital quantum number $l = 2$. In this state, the *magnitude* of the electron's angular momentum must be $L = \sqrt{6}\hbar = 2.45\hbar$. Furthermore, the angular momentum vector must point in a *direction* such that $L_z = m\hbar$, where m is one of only five integers in the range $-2 \leq m \leq 2$.

The combination of these two requirements allows $\vec{L}$ to point only in certain directions in space, as shown in FIGURE 41.3. This is a rather unusual figure that requires a little thought to understand. Suppose $m = 0$ and thus $L_z = 0$. With no z-component, the angular momentum vector $\vec{L}$ must lie somewhere in the xy-plane. Furthermore, because the length of $\vec{L}$ is constrained to be $2.45\hbar$, the tip of $\vec{L}$ must lie somewhere on the circle labeled $m = 0$. These values of $\vec{L}$ correspond to classical orbits tipped into a vertical plane.

Similarly, $m = 2$ requires $\vec{L}$ to lie along the surface of the cone whose height is $2\hbar$ and whose side has length $2.45\hbar$. These values of $\vec{L}$ correspond to classical orbits tilted slightly out of the xy-plane. Notice that $\vec{L}$ **cannot point directly along the z-axis.** The maximum possible value of L_z, when $m = l$, is $(L_z)_{max} = l\hbar$. But $l < \sqrt{l(l + 1)}$, so $(L_z)_{max} < L$. The angular momentum vector *must* have either an x- or a y-component (or both). In other words, the corresponding classical orbit cannot lie in the xy-plane.

An angular momentum vector $\vec{L}$ tilted at angle θ from the z-axis corresponds to an orbit tilted at angle θ out of the xy-plane. The quantization of angular momentum restricts the orbital planes to only a few discrete angles. For quantum state (n, l, m), the angle of the angular momentum vector is

$$\theta_{lm} = \cos^{-1}\left(\frac{L_z}{L}\right) = \cos^{-1}\left(\frac{m\hbar}{\sqrt{l(l + 1)}\hbar}\right) = \cos^{-1}\left(\frac{m}{\sqrt{l(l + 1)}}\right) \quad (41.5)$$

Angles θ_{22}, θ_{21}, and θ_{20} are labeled in Figure 41.3. Orbital planes at other angles are not allowed because they don't satisfy the quantization conditions for angular momentum.

FIGURE 41.3 The five possible orientations of the angular momentum vector for $l = 2$. The angular momentum vectors all have length $L = \sqrt{6}\hbar = 2.45\hbar$.

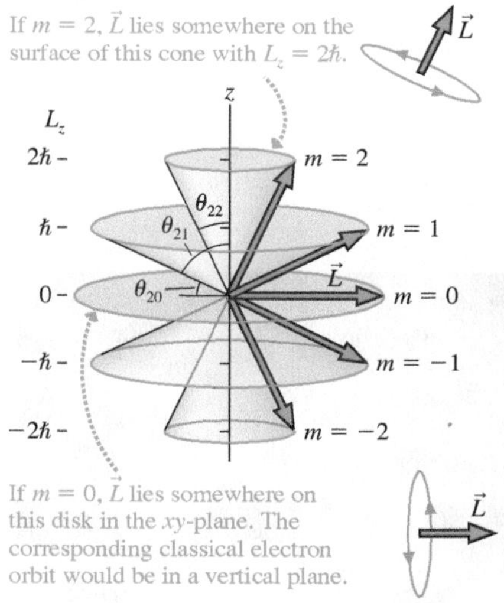

If $m = 2$, $\vec{L}$ lies somewhere on the surface of this cone with $L_z = 2\hbar$.

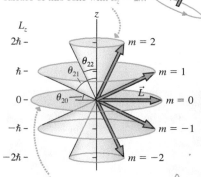

If $m = 0$, $\vec{L}$ lies somewhere on this disk in the xy-plane. The corresponding classical electron orbit would be in a vertical plane.

EXAMPLE 41.2 **The angle of the angular momentum vector**

What is the angle between $\vec{L}$ and the z-axis for a hydrogen atom in the stationary state $(n, l, m) = (4, 2, 1)$?

SOLVE The angle θ_{21} is labeled in Figure 41.3. The state $(4, 2, 1)$ has $l = 2$ and $m = 1$, thus

$$\theta_{21} = \cos^{-1}\left(\frac{1}{\sqrt{6}}\right) = 65.9°$$

ASSESS This quantum state corresponds to a classical orbit tilted 65.9° away from the xy-plane.

NOTE ▶ The ground state of hydrogen, with $l = 0$, has *zero* angular momentum. A classical particle cannot orbit unless it has angular momentum, but apparently a quantum particle does not have this requirement. ◀

Energy Levels of the Hydrogen Atom

The energy of the hydrogen atom is quantized. Only those energies given by Equation 41.2 allow the wave function to satisfy the boundary conditions. The allowed energies of hydrogen depend only on the principal quantum number n, but for other atoms the energies will depend on both n and l. In anticipation of using both quantum numbers, FIGURE 41.4 is an *energy-level diagram* for the hydrogen atom in which the rows are labeled by n and the columns by l. The left column contains all of the $l = 0$ s states, the next column is the $l = 1$ p states, and so on.

Because the quantum condition of Equation 41.3 requires $n > l$, the s states begin with $n = 1$, the p states begin with $n = 2$, and the d states with $n = 3$. That is, the lowest-energy d state is $3d$ because states with $n = 1$ or $n = 2$ cannot have $l = 2$. For hydrogen, where the energy levels do not depend on l, the energy-level diagram shows that the $3s$, $3p$, and $3d$ states have equal energy. Figure 41.4 shows only the first few energy levels for each value of l, but there really are an infinite number of levels, as $n \rightarrow \infty$, crowding together beneath $E = 0$. The dashed line at $E = 0$ is the atom's *ionization limit,* the energy of a hydrogen atom in which the electron has been moved infinitely far away to form an H$^+$ ion.

FIGURE 41.4 Energy-level diagram for the hydrogen atom.

Quantum number l	0	1	2	3
Symbol	s	p	d	f

n	E				
	$E = 0$ eV		Ionization limit		
4	-0.85 eV	$4s$	$4p$	$4d$	$4f$
3	-1.51 eV	$3s$	$3p$	$3d$	
2	-3.40 eV	$2s$	$2p$		
1	-13.60 eV	$1s$	Ground state		

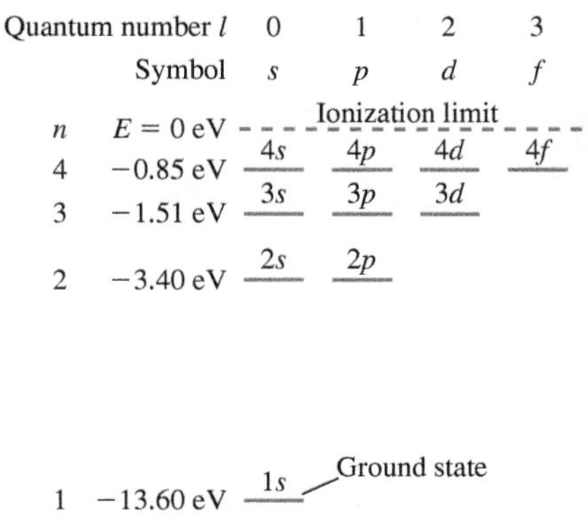

The lowest energy state, the $1s$ state with $E_1 = -13.60$ eV, is the *ground state* of hydrogen. The value $|E_1| = 13.60$ eV is the **ionization energy,** the *minimum* energy that would be needed to form a hydrogen ion by removing the electron from the ground state. All of the states with $n > 1$ (i.e., the states with energy higher than the ground state) are *excited states*.

STOP TO THINK 41.1   What are the quantum numbers n and l for a hydrogen atom with $E = -(13.60/9)$ eV and $L = \sqrt{2}\hbar$?

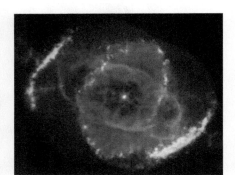

The red color of this nebula is due to the emission of light from hydrogen atoms. The atoms are excited by intense ultraviolet light from the star in the center. They then emit red light ($\lambda = 656$ nm) in a $3 \rightarrow 2$ transition, part of the Balmer series of spectral lines emitted by hydrogen.

41.2 The Hydrogen Atom: Wave Functions and Probabilities

You learned in Chapter 40 that the probability of finding a particle in a small interval of width δx at the position x is given by

$$\text{Prob(in } \delta x \text{ at } x) = |\psi(x)|^2 \delta x = P(x)\,\delta x$$

where $P(x) = |\psi(x)|^2$ is the probability density. This interpretation of $|\psi(x)|^2$ as a probability density lies at the heart of quantum mechanics. However, $P(x)$ was for a one-dimensional wave function.

For a three-dimensional atom, the wave function is $\psi(x, y, z)$, a function of three variables. We now want to consider the probability of finding a particle in a small *volume* of space δV at the position described by the three coordinates (x, y, z). This probability is

$$\text{Prob(in } \delta V \text{ at } x, y, z) = |\psi(x, y, z)|^2 \delta V \qquad (41.6)$$

We can still interpret the square of the wave function as a probability density.

In one-dimensional quantum mechanics we could simply graph $P(x)$ versus x. Portraying the probability density of a three-dimensional wave function is more of a challenge. One way to do so, shown in FIGURE 41.5, is to use denser shading to indicate regions of larger probability density. That is, the amplitude of ψ is larger, and the electron is more likely to be found in regions where the shading is darker. These figures show the probability densities of the $1s$, $2s$, and $2p$ states of hydrogen. As you can see, the probability density in three dimensions creates what is often called an **electron cloud** around the nucleus.

FIGURE 41.5 The probability densities of the electron in the $1s$, $2s$, and $2p$ states of hydrogen.

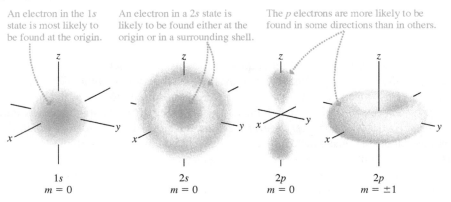

These figures contain a lot of information. For example, notice how the p electrons have directional properties. These directional properties allow p electrons to "reach out" toward nearby atoms, forming molecular bonds. The quantum mechanics of bonding goes beyond what we can study in this text, but the electron-cloud pictures of the p electrons begin to suggest how bonds could form.

Radial Wave Functions

In practice, the probability of finding the electron at a certain point in space is often less useful than the probability of finding the electron at a certain *distance* from the nucleus. That is, what is the probability that the electron is to be found within the small range of distances δr at the distance r?

It turns out that the solutions to the three-dimensional Schrödinger equation, the wave functions $\psi(x, y, z)$, can be written in a form that focuses on the electron's radial distance r from the proton. The portion of the wave function that depends only on r is called the **radial wave function.** These functions, which depend on the quantum numbers n and l, are designated $R_{nl}(r)$. The first three radial wave functions are

$$R_{1s}(r) = \frac{1}{\sqrt{\pi a_B^3}} e^{-r/a_B}$$

$$R_{2s}(r) = \frac{1}{\sqrt{8\pi a_B^3}} \left(1 - \frac{r}{2a_B}\right) e^{-r/2a_B} \qquad (41.7)$$

$$R_{2p}(r) = \frac{1}{\sqrt{24\pi a_B^3}} \left(\frac{r}{2a_B}\right) e^{-r/2a_B}$$

where a_B is the Bohr radius.

The radial wave functions may seem mysterious, because we haven't shown where they come from, but they are essentially the same as the one-dimensional wave functions $\psi(x)$ you learned to work with in Chapter 40. In fact, these radial wave functions are mathematically similar to the one-dimensional wave functions of the simple harmonic oscillator. One important difference, however, is that r ranges from 0 to ∞. For one-dimensional wave functions, x ranged from $-\infty$ to ∞.

> **NOTE** ▶ Don't be confused by the notation. R is not a radius but, like ψ, is the symbol for a wave function, the *radial* wave function. It is a function of the distance r from the proton. ◀

FIGURE 41.6 shows the radial wave functions for the 1s and 2s states. Notice that the radial wave function is nonzero at $r = 0$, the position of the nucleus. This is surprising, but it is consistent with our observation in Figure 41.5 that the 1s and 2s electrons have a strong probability of being found at the origin.

Our purpose for introducing the radial wave functions was to determine the probability of finding the electron a certain *distance* from the nucleus. **FIGURE 41.7** shows a shell of radius r and thickness δr centered on the nucleus. The probability of finding the electron at distance r from the nucleus is equivalent to the probability that the electron is located somewhere within this shell. The volume of a thin shell is its surface area multiplied by its thickness δr. The surface area of a sphere is $4\pi r^2$, so the volume of this thin shell is

$$\delta V = 4\pi r^2 \delta r$$

Just as $|\psi(x)|^2$ is the probability in one dimension of finding a particle within an interval δx, the probability of locating the electron within this spherical shell can be written in terms of the *radial* wave function $R_{nl}(r)$ as

$$\text{Prob(in } \delta r \text{ at } r) = |R_{nl}(r)|^2 \delta V = 4\pi r^2 |R_{nl}(r)|^2 \delta r \qquad (41.8)$$

If we define the **radial probability density** $P_r(r)$ for state nl as

$$P_r(r) = 4\pi r^2 |R_{nl}(r)|^2 \qquad (41.9)$$

then, exactly analogous to the one-dimensional quantum mechanics of Chapter 40, we can write the probability of finding the electron within a small interval δr at distance r as

$$\text{Prob(in } \delta r \text{ at } r) = P_r(r)\delta r \qquad (41.10)$$

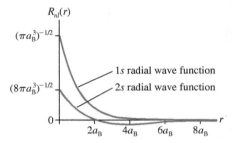

FIGURE 41.6 The 1s and 2s radial wave functions of hydrogen.

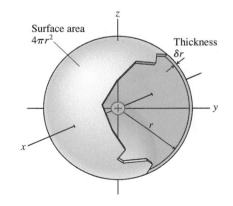

FIGURE 41.7 The radial probability density gives the probability of finding the electron in a spherical shell of thickness δr at radius r.

FIGURE 41.8 The radial probability densities for $n = 1$, 2, and 3.

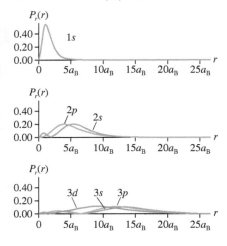

FIGURE 41.8 The radial probability densities for $n = 1$, 2, and 3.

FIGURE 41.9 More circular orbits have larger angular momenta.

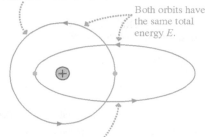

The circular orbit has the largest angular momentum. The electron stays at a constant distance from the nucleus.

Both orbits have the same total energy E.

The elliptical orbit has a smaller angular momentum. Compared to the circular orbit, the electron gets both closer to and farther from the nucleus.

The radial probability density tells us the relative likelihood of finding the electron at distance r from the nucleus. The volume factor $4\pi r^2$ reflects the fact that more space is available in a shell of larger r, and this additional space increases the probability of finding the electron at that distance.

The probability of finding the electron between r_{min} and r_{max} is

$$\text{Prob}(r_{min} \leq r \leq r_{max}) = \int_{r_{min}}^{r_{max}} P_r(r)\, dr = 4\pi \int_{r_{min}}^{r_{max}} r^2 |R_{nl}(r)|^2 dr \quad (41.11)$$

The electron must be *somewhere* between $r = 0$ and $r = \infty$, so the integral of $P_r(r)$ between 0 and ∞ must equal 1. This normalization condition was used to determine the constants in front of the radial wave functions of Equations 41.7.

FIGURE 41.8 shows the radial probability densities for the $n = 1$, 2, and 3 states of the hydrogen atom. You can see that the $1s$, $2p$, and $3d$ states, with maxima at a_B, $4a_B$, and $9a_B$, respectively, are following the pattern $r_{peak} = n^2 a_B$ of the radii of the orbits in the Bohr hydrogen atom. There we simply bent a one-dimensional de Broglie wave into a circle of that radius. Now we have a three-dimensional wave function for which the electron is *most likely* to be this distance from the nucleus, although it *could* be found at other values of r. The physical situation is very different in quantum mechanics, but it is good to see that various aspects of the Bohr model of the hydrogen atom can be reproduced.

But why is it the $3d$ state that agrees with the Bohr atom rather than $3s$ or $3p$? All states with the same value of n form a collection of "orbits" having the same energy. In FIGURE 41.9, the state with $l = n - 1$ has the largest angular momentum of the group. Consequently, the maximum-l state corresponds to a circular classical orbit and matches the circular orbits of the Bohr atom. Notice that the radial probability densities for the $2p$ and $3d$ states have a single peak, corresponding to a classical orbit at a constant distance.

States with smaller l correspond to elliptical orbits. You can see in Figure 41.8 that the radial probability density of a $3s$ electron has a peak close to the nucleus. The $3s$ electron also has a good chance of being found *farther* from the nucleus than a $3d$ electron, suggesting an orbit that alternately swings in near the nucleus, then moves out past the circular orbit with the same energy. This distinction between circular and elliptical orbits will be important when we discuss the energy levels in multielectron atoms.

NOTE ▶ In quantum mechanics, nothing is really orbiting. However, the probability densities for the electron to be, or not to be, any given distance from the nucleus mimic certain aspects of classical orbits and provide a useful analogy. ◀

You can see in Figure 41.8 that the most likely distance from the nucleus of an $n = 1$ electron is approximately a_B. The distance of an $n = 2$ electron is most likely to be between about $3a_B$ and $7a_B$. An $n = 3$ electron is most likely to be found between about $8a_B$ and $15a_B$. In other words, the radial probability densities give the clear impression that each value of n has a fairly well-defined range of radii where the electron is most likely to be found. This is the basis of the **shell model** of the atom that is used in chemistry.

However, there's one significant puzzle. In Figure 41.5, the fuzzy sphere representing the $1s$ ground state is densest at the center, where the electron is most likely to be found. This maximum density at $r = 0$ agrees with the $1s$ radial wave function of Figure 41.6, which is a maximum at $r = 0$, but it seems to be in sharp disagreement with the $1s$ graph of Figure 41.8, which is *zero* at the nucleus and peaks at $r = a_B$.

To resolve this puzzle, we must distinguish between the probability density $|\psi(x, y, z)|^2$ and the *radial* probability density $P_r(r)$. The $1s$ wave function, and thus the $1s$ probability density, really does peak at the nucleus. But $|\psi(x, y, z)|^2$ is the probability of being in a small volume δV, such as a small box with sides δx, δy, and δz, whereas $P_r(r)$ is the probability of being in a spherical shell of thickness δr. Compared to $r = 0$, the probability density $|\psi(x, y, z)|^2$ is smaller at any *one* point having $r = a_B$. But the volume of *all* points with $r \approx a_B$ (i.e., the volume of the spherical shell at $r = a_B$) is so large that the radial probability density P_r peaks at this distance.

To use a mass analogy, consider a fuzzy ball that is densest at the center. Even though the density away from the center has decreased, a spherical shell of modest radius *r* can have *more total mass* than a small-radius spherical shell of the same thickness simply because it has so much more volume.

EXAMPLE 41.3 Maximum probability

Show that an electron in the 2*p* state is most likely to be found at $r = 4a_B$.

SOLVE We can use the 2*p* radial wave function from Equations 41.7 to write the radial probability density

$$P_r(r) = 4\pi r^2 |R_{2p}(r)|^2 = 4\pi r^2 \left[\frac{1}{\sqrt{24\pi a_B^3}} \left(\frac{r}{2a_B}\right) e^{-r/2a_B} \right]^2$$

$$= Cr^4 e^{-r/a_B}$$

where $C = (24a_B^5)^{-1}$ is a constant. This expression for $P_r(r)$ was graphed in Figure 41.8.

Maximum probability occurs at the point where the first derivative of $P_r(r)$ is zero:

$$\frac{dP_r}{dr} = C(4r^3)(e^{-r/a_B}) + C(r^4)\left(\frac{-1}{a_B}e^{-r/a_B}\right)$$

$$= Cr^3\left(4 - \frac{r}{a_B}\right)e^{-r/a_B} = 0$$

This expression is zero only if $r = 4a_B$, so $P_r(r)$ is maximum at $r = 4a_B$. An electron in the 2*p* state is most likely to be found at this distance from the nucleus.

STOP TO THINK 41.2 How many maxima will there be in a graph of the radial probability density for the 4*s* state of hydrogen?

41.3 The Electron's Spin

Recall, from Chapter 32, that an orbiting electron generates a microscopic *magnetic moment* $\vec{\mu}$. FIGURE 41.10 reminds you that a magnetic moment, like a compass needle, has north and south poles. Consequently, a magnetic moment in an external magnetic field experiences forces and torques. In the early 1920s, the German physicists Otto Stern and Walter Gerlach developed a technique to measure the magnetic moments of atoms. Their apparatus, shown in FIGURE 41.11, prepares an *atomic beam* by evaporating atoms out of a hole in an "oven." These atoms, traveling in a vacuum, pass through a *nonuniform* magnetic field. Reducing the size of the upper pole tip makes the field stronger toward the top of the magnet, weaker toward the bottom.

FIGURE 41.10 An orbiting electron generates a magnetic moment.

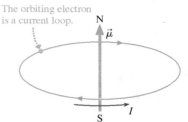

The orbiting electron is a current loop.

A current loop generates a magnetic moment with north and south magnetic poles.

FIGURE 41.11 The Stern-Gerlach experiment.

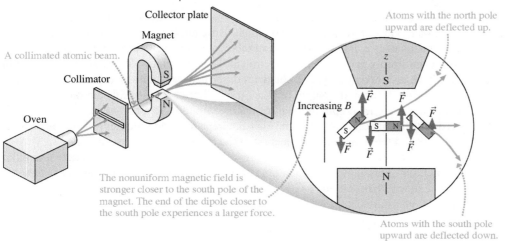

Collector plate

Magnet

A collimated atomic beam.

Collimator

Oven

The nonuniform magnetic field is stronger closer to the south pole of the magnet. The end of the dipole closer to the south pole experiences a larger force.

Atoms with the north pole upward are deflected up.

Increasing *B*

Atoms with the south pole upward are deflected down.

A magnetic moment experiences a *net force* in the nonuniform magnetic field because the field exerts forces of different strengths on the moment's north and south poles. If we define a *z*-axis to point upward, then an atom whose magnetic moment

FIGURE 41.12 Distribution of the atoms on the collector plate.

(a)

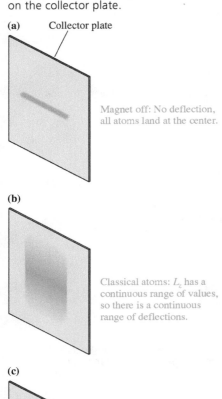

Collector plate

Magnet off: No deflection, all atoms land at the center.

(b)

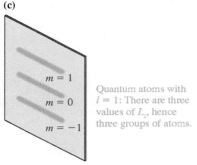

Classical atoms: L_z has a continuous range of values, so there is a continuous range of deflections.

(c)

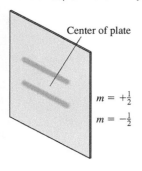

$m = 1$
$m = 0$
$m = -1$

Quantum atoms with $l = 1$: There are three values of L_z, hence three groups of atoms.

FIGURE 41.13 The outcome of the Stern-Gerlach experiment for hydrogen atoms.

Center of plate

$m = +\frac{1}{2}$

$m = -\frac{1}{2}$

vector $\vec{\mu}$ is tilted upward ($\mu_z > 0$) has an upward force on its north pole that is larger than the downward force on its south pole. As the figure shows, this atom is deflected upward as it passes through the magnet. A downward-tilted magnetic moment ($\mu_z < 0$) experiences a net downward force and is deflected downward. A magnetic moment perpendicular to the field ($\mu_z = 0$) feels no net force and passes through the magnet without deflection. In other words, an atom's deflection as it passes through the magnet is proportional to μ_z, the z-component of its magnetic moment.

It's not hard to show, although we will omit the proof, that an atom's magnetic moment is proportional to the electron's orbital angular momentum: $\vec{\mu} \propto \vec{L}$. Because the deflection of an atom depends on μ_z, measuring the deflections in a nonuniform field provides information about the L_z values of the atoms in the atomic beam. The measurements are made by allowing the atoms to stick on a collector plate at the end of the apparatus. After the experiment has been run for several hours, the collector plate is removed and examined to learn how the atoms were deflected.

With the magnet off, the atoms pass through without deflection and land along a narrow line at the center, as shown in FIGURE 41.12a. If the orbiting electrons are classical particles, they should have a continuous range of angular momenta. Turning on the magnet should produce a continuous range of vertical deflections, and the distribution of atoms collected on the plate should look like FIGURE 41.12b. But if angular momentum is *quantized,* as Bohr had suggested several years earlier, the atoms should be deflected to discrete positions on the collector plate.

For example, an atom with $l = 1$ has three distinct values of L_z corresponding to quantum numbers $m = -1$, 0, and 1. This leads to a prediction of the three distinct groups of atoms shown in FIGURE 41.12c. There should always be an *odd* number of groups because there are $2l + 1$ values of L_z.

In 1927, with Schrödinger's quantum theory brand new, the Stern-Gerlach technique was used to measure the magnetic moment of hydrogen atoms. The ground state of hydrogen is 1s, with $l = 0$, so the atoms should have *no* magnetic moment and there should be *no* deflection at all. Instead, the experiment produced the two-peaked distribution shown in FIGURE 41.13.

Because the hydrogen atoms were deflected, they *must* have a magnetic moment. But where does it come from if $L = 0$? Even stranger was the deflection into two groupings, rather than an odd number. The deflection is proportional to L_z, and $L_z = m\hbar$ where m ranges in integer steps from $-l$ to $+l$. The experimental results would make sense only if $l = \frac{1}{2}$, allowing m to take the two possible values $-\frac{1}{2}$ and $+\frac{1}{2}$. But according to Schrödinger's theory, the quantum numbers l and m must be integers.

An explanation for these observations was soon suggested, then confirmed: The electron has an *inherent* magnetic moment. After all, the electron has an inherent gravitational character, its mass m_e, and an inherent electric character, its charge $q_e = -e$. These are simply part of what an electron is. Thus it is plausible that an electron should also have an inherent magnetic character described by a built-in magnetic moment $\vec{\mu}_e$. A classical electron, if thought of as a little ball of charge, could spin on its axis as it orbits the nucleus. A spinning ball of charge would have a magnetic moment associated with its angular momentum. This inherent magnetic moment of the electron is what caused the unexpected deflection in the Stern-Gerlach experiment.

If the electron has an inherent magnetic moment, it must have an inherent angular momentum. This angular momentum is called the electron's **spin,** which is designated $\vec{S}$. The outcome of the Stern-Gerlach experiment tells us that the z-component of this spin angular momentum is

$$S_z = m_s\hbar \quad \text{where } m_s = +\frac{1}{2} \text{ or } -\frac{1}{2} \tag{41.12}$$

The quantity m_s is called the **spin quantum number.**

The z-component of the spin angular momentum vector is determined by the electron's orientation. The $m_s = +\frac{1}{2}$ state, with $S_z = +\frac{1}{2}\hbar$, is called the **spin-up** state, and the $m_s = -\frac{1}{2}$ state is called the **spin-down** state. It is convenient to picture a little angular momentum vector that can be drawn ↑ for an $m_s = +\frac{1}{2}$ state and ↓ for an $m_s = -\frac{1}{2}$ state. We will use this notation in the next section. Because the electron must be either spin-up or spin-down, a hydrogen atom in the Stern-Gerlach experiment will be deflected either up or down. This causes the two groups of atoms seen in Figure 41.13. No atoms have $S_z = 0$, so there are no undeflected atoms in the center.

NOTE ▶ The atom has spin angular momentum *in addition* to any orbital angular momentum that the electrons may have. Only in *s* states, for which $L = 0$, can we see the effects of "pure spin." ◀

The spin angular momentum *S* is analogous to Equation 41.3 for *L*:

$$S = \sqrt{s(s+1)}\hbar = \frac{\sqrt{3}}{2}\hbar \qquad (41.13)$$

where *s* is a quantum number with the single value $s = \frac{1}{2}$. *S* is the *inherent* angular momentum of the electron. Because of the single value of *s*, physicists usually say that the electron has "spin one-half." FIGURE 41.14, which should be compared to Figure 41.3, shows that the terms "spin up" and "spin down" refer to S_z, not the full spin angular momentum. As was the case with $\vec{L}$, it's not possible for $\vec{S}$ to point along the *z*-axis.

NOTE ▶ The term "spin" must be used with caution. Although a classical charged particle could generate a magnetic moment by spinning, the electron most assuredly is *not* a classical particle. It is not spinning in any literal sense. It simply has an inherent magnetic moment, just as it has an inherent mass and charge, and that magnetic moment makes it look *as if* the electron is spinning. It is a convenient figure of speech, not a factual statement. **The electron has a spin, but it is not a spinning electron!** ◀

The electron's spin has significant implications for atomic structure. The solutions to the Schrödinger equation could be described by the three quantum numbers *n*, *l*, and *m*, but the Stern-Gerlach experiment implies that this is not a complete description of an atom. Knowing that a ground-state atom has quantum numbers $n = 1$, $l = 0$, and $m = 0$ is not sufficient to predict whether the atom will be deflected up or down in a nonuniform magnetic field. We need to add the spin quantum number m_s to make our description complete. (Strictly speaking, we also need to add the quantum number *s*, but it provides no additional information because its value never changes.) So we really need *four* quantum numbers (n, l, m, m_s) to characterize the stationary states of the atom. The spin orientation does not affect the atom's energy, so a ground-state electron in hydrogen could be in either the $(1, 0, 0, +\frac{1}{2})$ spin-up state or the $(1, 0, 0, -\frac{1}{2})$ spin-down state.

The fact that *s* has the single value $s = \frac{1}{2}$ has other interesting implications. The correspondence principle tells us that a quantum particle begins to "act classical" in the limit of large quantum numbers. But *s* cannot become large! **The electron's spin is an intrinsic quantum property of the electron that has *no* classical counterpart.**

FIGURE 41.14 The spin angular momentum has two possible orientations.

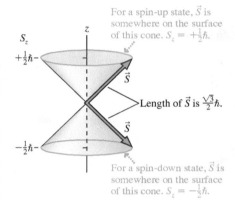

For a spin-up state, $\vec{S}$ is somewhere on the surface of this cone. $S_z = +\frac{1}{2}\hbar$.

Length of $\vec{S}$ is $\frac{\sqrt{3}}{2}\hbar$.

For a spin-down state, $\vec{S}$ is somewhere on the surface of this cone. $S_z = -\frac{1}{2}\hbar$.

STOP TO THINK 41.3 Can the spin angular momentum vector lie in the *xy*-plane? Why or why not?

41.4 Multielectron Atoms

The Schrödinger-equation solution for the hydrogen atom matches the experimental evidence, but so did the Bohr hydrogen atom. The real test of Schrödinger's theory is how well it works for multielectron atoms. A neutral multielectron atom consists of *Z* electrons surrounding a nucleus with *Z* protons and charge $+Ze$. *Z*, the *atomic number,* is the order in which elements are listed in the periodic table. Hydrogen is $Z = 1$, helium $Z = 2$, lithium $Z = 3$, and so on.

The potential-energy function of a multielectron atom is that of Z electrons interacting with the nucleus *and* Z electrons interacting *with each other*. The electron-electron interaction makes the atomic-structure problem more difficult than the solar-system problem, and it proved to be the downfall of the simple Bohr model. The planets in the solar system do exert attractive gravitational forces on each other, but their masses are so much less than that of the sun that these planet-planet forces are insignificant for all but the most precise calculations. Not so in an atom. The electron charge is the same as the proton charge, so the electron-electron repulsion is just as important to atomic structure as is the electron-nucleus attraction.

The potential energy due to electron-electron interactions fluctuates rapidly in value as the electrons move and the distances between them change. Rather than treat this interaction in detail, we can reasonably consider each electron to be moving in an *average* potential due to all the other electrons. That is, electron i has potential energy

$$U(r_i) = -\frac{Ze^2}{4\pi\epsilon_0 r_i} + U_{\text{elec}}(r_i) \qquad (41.14)$$

where the first term is the electron's interaction with the Z protons in the nucleus and U_{elec} is the average potential energy due to all the other electrons. Because each electron is treated independently of the other electrons, this approach is called the **independent particle approximation,** or IPA. This approximation allows the Schrödinger equation for the atom to be broken into Z separate equations, one for each electron.

A major consequence of the IPA is that **each electron can be described by a wave function having the same four quantum numbers n, l, m, and m_s used to describe the single electron of hydrogen.** Because m and m_s do not affect the energy, we can still refer to electrons by their n and l quantum numbers, using the same labeling scheme that we used for hydrogen.

A major difference, however, is that the energy of an electron in a multielectron atom depends on both n *and l.* Whereas the $2s$ and $2p$ states in hydrogen had the same energy, their energies are different in a multielectron atom. The difference arises from the electron-electron interactions that do not exist in a single-electron hydrogen atom.

FIGURE 41.15 shows an energy-level diagram for the electrons in a multielectron atom. For comparison, the hydrogen-atom energies are shown on the right edge of the figure. The comparison is quite interesting. States in a multielectron atom that have small values of l are significantly lower in energy than the corresponding state in hydrogen. For each n, the energy increases as l increases until the maximum-l state has an energy very nearly that of the same n in hydrogen. Can we understand this pattern?

Indeed we can. Recall that states of lower l correspond to elliptical classical orbits and the highest-l state corresponds to a circular orbit. Except for the smallest values of n, an electron in a circular orbit spends most of its time *outside* the electron cloud of the remaining electrons. This is illustrated in FIGURE 41.16. The outer electron is orbiting a ball of charge consisting of Z protons and $(Z-1)$ electrons. This ball of charge has *net* charge $q_{\text{net}} = +e$, so the outer electron "thinks" it is orbiting a proton. An electron in a maximum-l state is nearly indistinguishable from an electron in the hydrogen atom; thus its energy is very nearly that of hydrogen.

The low-l states correspond to elliptical orbits. A low-l electron penetrates in very close to the nucleus, which is no longer shielded by the other electrons. The electron's interaction with the Z protons in the nucleus is much stronger than the interaction it would have with the single proton in a hydrogen nucleus. This strong interaction *lowers* its energy in comparison to the same state in hydrogen.

As we noted earlier, a quantum electron does not really orbit. Even so, the probability density of a $3s$ electron has in-close peaks that are missing in the probability density of a $3d$ electron, as you should confirm by looking back at Figure 41.8. Thus a low-l electron really does have a likelihood of being at small r, where its interaction with the Z protons is strong, whereas a high-l electron is most likely to be farther from the nucleus.

FIGURE 41.15 An energy-level diagram for electrons in a multielectron atom.

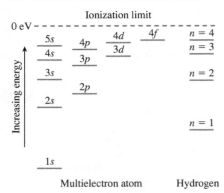

FIGURE 41.16 High-l and low-l orbitals in a multielectron atom.

A high-l electron corresponds to a circular orbit. It stays outside the core of inner electrons and sees a net charge of $+e$, so it behaves like an electron in a hydrogen atom.

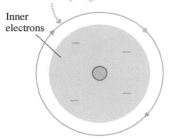

High-l state

A low-l electron corresponds to an elliptical orbit. It penetrates into the core and interacts strongly with the nucleus. The electron-nucleus force is attractive, so this interaction lowers the electron's energy.

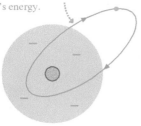

Low-l state

The Pauli Exclusion Principle

By definition, the ground state of a quantum system is the state of lowest energy. What is the ground state of an atom having Z electrons and Z protons? Because the $1s$ state is the lowest energy state in the independent particle approximation, it seems that the ground state should be one in which all Z electrons are in the $1s$ state. However, this idea is not consistent with the experimental evidence.

In 1925, the young Austrian physicist Wolfgang Pauli hypothesized that no two electrons in a quantum system can be in the same quantum state. That is, **no two electrons can have exactly the same set of quantum numbers** (n, l, n, m_s). If one electron is present in a state, it *excludes* all others. This statement, which is called the **Pauli exclusion principle,** turns out to be an extremely profound statement about the nature of matter.

The exclusion principle is not applicable to the hydrogen atom, which has only a single electron. But in helium, with $Z = 2$ electrons, we must make sure that the two electrons are in different quantum states. This is not difficult. For a $1s$ state, with $l = 0$, the only possible value of the magnetic quantum number is $m = 0$. But there are *two* possible values of m_s, namely $+\frac{1}{2}$ and $-\frac{1}{2}$. If a first electron is in the spin-up $1s$ state $(1, 0, 0, +\frac{1}{2})$, a second $1s$ electron can still be added to the atom as long as it is in the spin-down state $(1, 0, 0, -\frac{1}{2})$. This is shown schematically in FIGURE 41.17a, where the dots represent electrons on the rungs of the "energy ladder" and the arrows represent spin-up or spin-down.

The Pauli exclusion principle does not prevent both electrons of helium from being in the $1s$ state as long as they have opposite values of m_s, so we predict this to be the ground state. A list of an atom's occupied energy levels is called its **electron configuration.** The electron configuration of the helium ground state is written $1s^2$, where the superscript 2 indicates two electrons in the $1s$ energy level. An excited state of the helium atom might be the electron configuration $1s2s$. This state is shown in FIGURE 41.17b. Here, because the two electrons have different values of n, there is no restriction on their values of m_s.

The states $(1, 0, 0, +\frac{1}{2})$ and $(1, 0, 0, -\frac{1}{2})$ are the only two states with $n = 1$. The ground state of helium has one electron in each of these states, so all the possible $n = 1$ states are filled. Consequently, the electron configuration $1s^2$ is called a **closed shell.** Because the two electron magnetic moments point in opposite directions, we can predict that helium has *no* net magnetic moment and will be undeflected in a Stern-Gerlach apparatus. This prediction is confirmed by experiment.

The next element, lithium, has $Z = 3$ electrons. The first two electrons can go into $1s$ states, with opposite values of m_s, but what about the third electron? The $1s^2$ shell is closed, and there are no additional quantum states having $n = 1$. The only option for the third electron is the next energy state, $n = 2$. The $2s$ and $2p$ states had equal energies in the hydrogen atom, but they do *not* in a multielectron atom. As Figure 41.15 showed, a lower-l state has lower energy than a higher-l state with the same n. The $2s$ state of lithium is lower in energy than $2p$, so lithium's third ground-state electron will be $2s$. This requires $l = 0$ and $m = 0$ for the third electron, but the value of m_s is not relevant because there is only a single electron in $2s$. FIGURE 41.18a shows the electron configuration with the $2s$ electron being spin-up, but it could equally well be spin-down. The electron configuration for the lithium ground state is written $1s^2 2s$. This indicates two $1s$ electrons and a single $2s$ electron.

FIGURE 41.19a shows the probability density of electrons in the $1s^2 2s$ ground state of lithium. You can see the $2s$ electron shell surrounding the inner $1s^2$ core. For comparison, FIGURE 41.19b shows the *first excited state* of lithium, in which the $2s$ electron has been excited to the $2p$ energy level. This forms the $1s^2 2p$ configuration, also shown in FIGURE 41.18b.

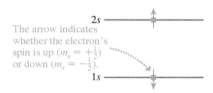

FIGURE 41.17 The ground state and the first excited state of helium.

(a) He ground state

The horizontal lines are the allowed energies. $2s$

Each circle represents an electron in that energy level. $1s$

(b) He excited state

$2s$

The arrow indicates whether the electron's spin is up $(m_s = +\frac{1}{2})$ or down $(m_s = -\frac{1}{2})$. $1s$

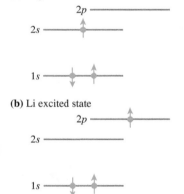

FIGURE 41.18 The ground state and the first excited state of lithium.

(a) Li ground state

$2p$

$2s$

$1s$

(b) Li excited state

$2p$

$2s$

$1s$

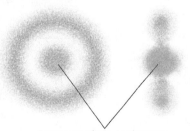

FIGURE 41.19 Electron clouds for the lithium electron configurations $1s^2 2s$ and $1s^2 2p$.

(a) Li ground state $1s^2 2s$

(b) Li excited state $1s^2 2p$

Inner core of two $1s$ electrons

The Schrödinger equation accurately predicts the energies of the $1s^2 2s$ and the $1s^2 2p$ configurations of lithium, but the Schrödinger equation does not tell us which states the electrons actually occupy. The electron spin and the Pauli exclusion principle were the final pieces of the puzzle. Once these were added to Schrödinger's theory, the initial phase of quantum mechanics was complete. Physicists finally had a successful theory for understanding the structure of atoms.

41.5 The Periodic Table of the Elements

The 19th century was a time when scientists were discovering new elements and studying their chemical properties. Several chemists in the 1860s began to point out the regular recurrence of chemical properties. For example, there are obvious similarities among the alkali metals lithium, sodium, potassium, and cesium. But attempts at organization were hampered by the fact that many elements had yet to be discovered.

The Russian chemist Dmitri Mendeléev was the first to propose, in 1867, a *periodic* arrangement of the elements. He did so by explicitly pointing out "gaps" where, according to his hypothesis, undiscovered elements should exist. He could then predict the expected properties of the missing elements. The subsequent discovery of these elements verified Mendeléev's organizational scheme, which came to be known as the *periodic table of the elements.*

FIGURE 41.20 shows a modern periodic table. (A larger version can be found in Appendix B.) The significance of the periodic table to a physicist is the implication that there is a basic regularity or periodicity to the *structure* of atoms. Any successful theory of the atom needs to explain *why* the periodic table looks the way it does.

FIGURE 41.20 The modern periodic table of the elements, showing the atomic number Z of each.

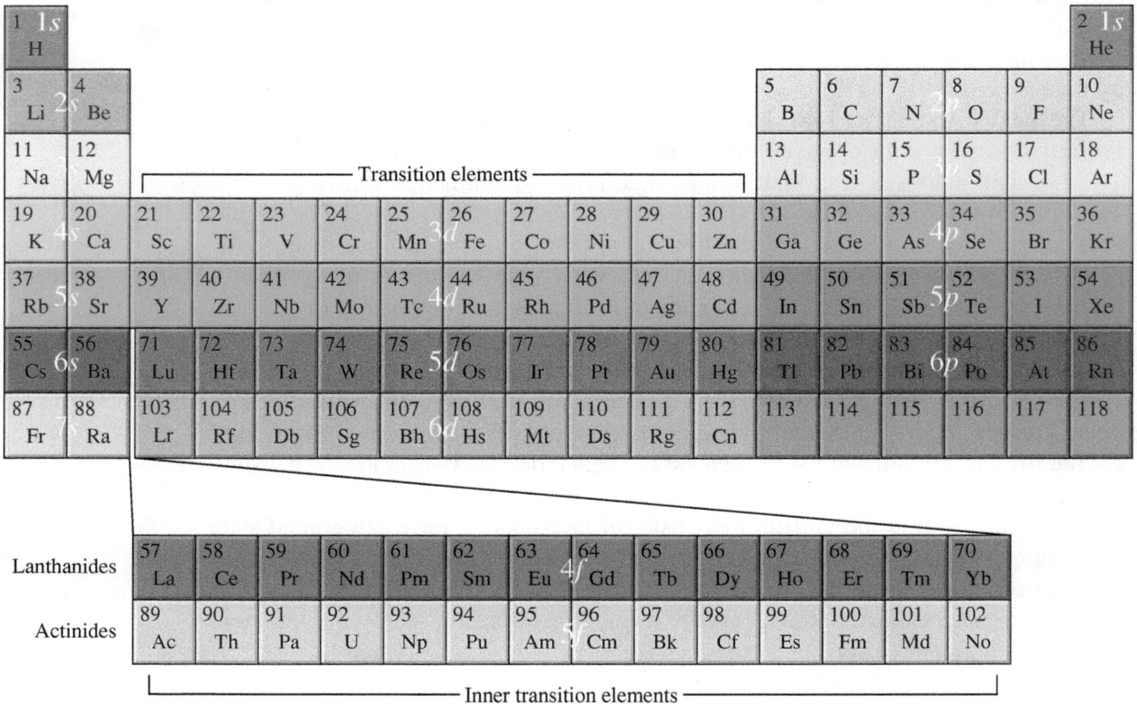

The First Two Rows

Quantum mechanics successfully explains the structure of the periodic table. We need three basic ideas to see how this works:

1. The energy levels of an atom are found by solving the Schrödinger equation for multielectron atoms. Figure 41.15, a very important figure for understanding the periodic table, showed that the energy depends on the quantum numbers n and l.
2. For each value l of the orbital quantum number, there are $2l + 1$ possible values of the magnetic quantum number m and, for each of these, two possible values of the spin quantum number m_s. Consequently, each energy *level* in Figure 41.15 is actually $2(2l + 1)$ different *states*. Each of these states has the same energy.
3. The ground state of the atom is the lowest-energy electron configuration that is consistent with the Pauli exclusion principle.

We used these ideas in the last section to look at the elements helium ($Z = 2$) and lithium ($Z = 3$). Four-electron beryllium ($Z = 4$) comes next. The first two electrons go into $1s$ states, forming a closed shell, and the third goes into $2s$. There is room in the $2s$ level for a second electron as long as its spin is opposite that of the first $2s$ electron. Thus the third and fourth electrons occupy states $(2, 0, 0, +\frac{1}{2})$ and $(2, 0, 0, -\frac{1}{2})$. These are the only two possible $2s$ states. All the states with the same values of n and l are called a **subshell,** so the fourth electron closes the $2s$ subshell. (The outer two electrons are called a subshell, rather than a shell, because they complete only the $2s$ possibilities. There are still spaces for $2p$ electrons.) The ground state of beryllium, shown in **FIGURE 41.21**, is $1s^2 2s^2$.

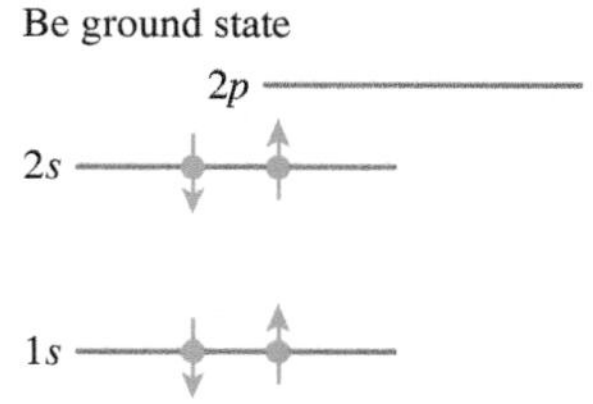

These principles can continue to be applied as we work our way through the elements. There are $2l + 1$ values of m associated with each value of l, and each of these can have $m_s = \pm\frac{1}{2}$. This gives, altogether, $2(2l + 1)$ distinct quantum states in each nl subshell. Table 41.2 lists the number of states in each subshell.

Boron ($1s^2 2s^2 2p$) opens the $2p$ subshell. The remaining possible $2p$ states are filled as we continue across the second row of the periodic table. These elements are shown in **FIGURE 41.22**. With neon ($1s^2 2s^2 2p^6$), which has six $2p$ electrons, the $n = 2$ shell is complete, and we have another closed shell. The second row of the periodic table is eight elements wide because of the two $2s$ electrons *plus* the six $2p$ electrons needed to fill the $n = 2$ shell.

FIGURE 41.21 The ground state of beryllium ($Z = 4$).

Be ground state

TABLE 41.2 Number of states in each subshell of an atom

Subshell	l	Number of states
s	0	2
p	1	6
d	2	10
f	3	14

FIGURE 41.22 Filling the $2p$ subshell with the elements boron through neon.

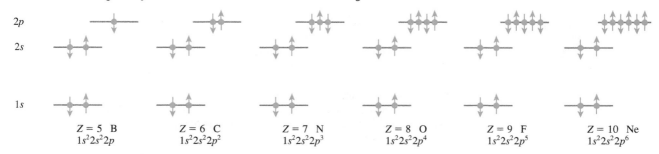

Elements with $Z > 10$

The third row of the periodic table is similar to the second. The two $3s$ states are filled in sodium and magnesium. The two columns on the left of the periodic table represent the two electrons that can go into an s subshell. Then the six $3p$ states are filled, one by one, in aluminum through argon. The six columns on the right represent the six electrons of the p subshell. Argon ($Z = 18$, $1s^2 2s^2 2p^6 3s^2 3p^6$) is another inert gas, although this may seem surprising because the $3d$ subshell is still open.

The fourth row is where the periodic table begins to get complicated. You might expect the closure of the $3p$ subshell in argon to be followed, starting with potassium ($Z = 19$), by filling the $3d$ subshell. But if you look back at Figure 41.15, where the energies of the different nl states are shown, you will see that the $3d$ state is slightly *higher* in energy than the $4s$ state. Because the ground state is the *lowest energy state* consistent with the Pauli exclusion principle, potassium finds it more favorable to fill a $4s$ state than to fill a $3d$ state. Thus the ground-state configuration of potassium is $1s^2 2s^2 2p^6 3s^2 3p^6 4s$ rather than the expected $1s^2 2s^2 2p^6 3s^2 3p^6 3d$.

At this point, we begin to see a competition between increasing n and decreasing l. The highly elliptical characteristic of the $4s$ state brings part of its orbit in so close to the nucleus that its energy is less than that of the more circular $3d$ state. The $4p$ state, though, reverts to the "expected" pattern. We find that

$$E_{4s} < E_{3d} < E_{4p}$$

so the states across the fourth row are filled in the order $4s$, then $3d$, and finally $4p$.

Because there had been no previous d states, the $3d$ subshell "splits open" the periodic table to form the 10-element-wide group of *transition elements*. Most commonly occurring metals are transition elements, and their metallic properties are determined by their partially filled d subshell. The $3d$ subshell closes with zinc, at $Z = 30$, then the next six elements fill the $4p$ subshell up to krypton, at $Z = 36$.

Things get even more complex starting in the sixth row, but the ideas are familiar. The $l = 3$ subshell (f electrons) becomes a possibility with $n = 4$, but it turns out that the $5s$, $5p$, and $6s$ states are all lower in energy than $4f$. Not until barium ($Z = 56$) fills the $6s$ subshell (and lanthanum ($Z = 57$) adds a $5d$ electron) is it energetically favorable to add a $4f$ electron. Immediately after barium you have to switch down to the *lanthanides* at the bottom of the table. The lanthanides fill in the $4f$ states.

The $4f$ subshell is complete with $Z = 70$ ytterbium. Then $Z = 71$ lutetium through $Z = 80$ mercury complete the transition-element $5d$ subshell, followed by the $6p$ subshell in the six elements thallium through radon at the end of the sixth row. Radon, the last inert gas, has $Z = 86$ electrons and the ground-state configuration

$$1s^2 2s^2 2p^6 3s^2 3p^6 4s^2 3d^{10} 4p^6 5s^2 4d^{10} 5p^6 6s^2 4f^{14} 5d^{10} 6p^6$$

This is frightening to behold, but we can now understand it!

EXAMPLE 41.4 **The ground state of arsenic**

Predict the ground-state electron configuration of arsenic.

SOLVE The periodic table shows that arsenic (As) has $Z = 33$, so we must identify the states of 33 electrons. Arsenic is in the fourth row, following the first group of transition elements. Argon ($Z = 18$) filled the $3p$ subshell, then calcium ($Z = 20$) filled the $4s$ subshell. The next 10 elements, through zinc ($Z = 30$), filled the $3d$ subshell. The $4p$ subshell starts filling with gallium ($Z = 31$), and arsenic is the third element in this group, so it will have three $4p$ electrons. Thus the ground-state configuration of arsenic is

$$1s^2 2s^2 2p^6 3s^2 3p^6 4s^2 3d^{10} 4p^3$$

The white lettering on the periodic table of Figure 41.20 summarizes the results, showing the subshells as they are filled. It is especially important to note how the electron's spin is absolutely essential for understanding the periodic table. Explaining the periodic table of the elements is a remarkable success of the quantum model of the atom.

Ionization Energies

Ionization energy is the minimum energy needed to remove a ground-state electron from an atom and leave a positive ion behind. The ionization energy of hydrogen is 13.60 eV because the ground-state energy is $E_1 = -13.60$ eV. FIGURE 41.23 shows the ionization energies of the first 60 elements in the periodic table.

FIGURE 41.23 Ionization energies of the elements up to $Z = 60$.

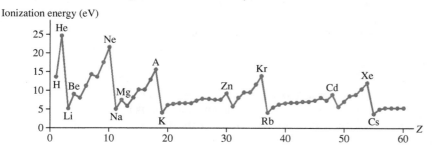

The ionization energy is different for each element, but there's a clear pattern to the values. Ionization energies are ≈ 5 eV for the alkali metals, on the left edge of the periodic table, then increase steadily to ≥ 15 eV for the inert gases before plunging back to ≈ 5 eV. Can the quantum theory of atoms explain this recurring pattern in the ionization energies?

Indeed it can. The inert-gas elements (helium, neon, argon, . . .) in the right column of the periodic table have *closed shells*. A closed shell is a very stable structure, and that is why these elements are chemically nonreactive (i.e., inert). It takes a large amount of energy to pull an electron out of a stable closed shell; thus the inert gases have the largest ionization energies.

The alkali metals, in the left column of the periodic table, have a single *s*-electron outside a closed shell. This electron is easily disrupted, which is why these elements are highly reactive and have the lowest ionization energies. Between the edges of the periodic table are elements such as beryllium ($1s^2 2s^2$) with a closed $2s$ subshell. You can see in Figure 41.23 that the closed subshell gives beryllium a larger ionization energy than its neighbors lithium ($1s^2 2s$) or boron ($1s^2 2s^2 2p$). However, a closed subshell is not nearly as tightly bound as a closed shell, so the ionization energy of beryllium is much less than that of helium or neon.

All in all, you can see that the basic idea of shells and subshells, which follows from the Schrödinger-equation energy levels and the Pauli principle, provides a good understanding of the recurring features in the ionization energies.

STOP TO THINK 41.4   Is the electron configuration $1s^2 2s^2 2p^4 3s$ a ground-state configuration or an excited-state configuration?

a. Ground-state   b. Excited-state
c. It's not possible to tell without knowing which element it is.

41.6 Excited States and Spectra

The periodic table organizes information about the *ground states* of the elements. These states are chemically most important because most atoms spend most of the time in their ground states. All the chemical ideas of valence, bonding, reactivity, and so on are consequences of these ground-state atomic structures. But the periodic table does not tell us anything about the excited states of atoms. It is the excited states that hold the key to understanding atomic spectra, and that is the topic to which we turn next.

FIGURE 41.24 The [Ne]3s ground state of the sodium atom and some of the excited states.

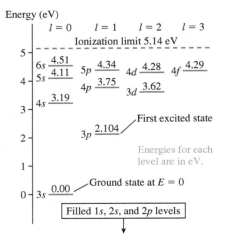

Energy (eV)

Ionization limit 5.14 eV

$l = 0$ $l = 1$ $l = 2$ $l = 3$

6s $\underline{4.51}$ 5p $\underline{4.34}$ 4d $\underline{4.28}$ 4f $\underline{4.29}$
5s $\underline{4.11}$
4p $\underline{3.75}$
4s $\underline{3.19}$ 3d $\underline{3.62}$

3p $\underline{2.104}$ ← First excited state

Energies for each level are in eV.

3s $\underline{0.00}$ ← Ground state at $E = 0$

Filled 1s, 2s, and 2p levels

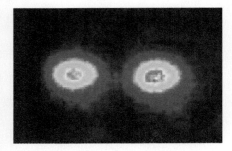

The dots of light are being emitted by two beryllium ions held in a device called an ion trap. Each ion, which is excited by an invisible ultraviolet laser, emits about 10^6 visible-light photons per second.

Sodium ($Z = 11$) is a multielectron atom that we will use as a prototypical atom. The ground-state electron configuration of sodium is $1s^2 2s^2 2p^6 3s$. The first 10 electrons completely fill the $n = 1$ and $n = 2$ shells, creating a *neon core*, while the 3s electron is a valence electron. It is customary to represent this configuration as [Ne]3s or, more simply, as just 3s.

The excited states of sodium are produced by raising the valence electron to a higher energy level. The electrons in the neon core are unchanged. Thus the excited states can be labeled [Ne]nl or, more simply, just nl. **FIGURE 41.24** is an energy-level diagram showing the ground state and some of the excited states of sodium. Notice that the 1s, 2s, and 2p states of the neon core are not shown on the diagram. These states are filled and unchanging, so only the states available to the valence electron are shown.

Figure 41.24 has a new feature: The zero of energy has been shifted to the ground state. As we have discovered many times, the zero of energy can be located where it is most convenient. For analyzing spectra it is convenient to let the ground state have $E = 0$. With this choice, the excited-state energies tell us how far each state is above the ground state. The ionization limit now occurs at the value of the atom's ionization energy, which is 5.14 eV for sodium.

The first energy level above 3s is 3p, so the *first excited state* of sodium is $1s^2 2s^2 2p^6 3p$, written as [Ne]3p or, more simply, 3p. The valence electron is excited, while the core electrons are unchanged. This state is followed, in order of increasing energy, by [Ne]4s, [Ne]3d, and [Ne]4p. Notice that the order of excited states is exactly the same order (3p–4s–3d–4p) that explained the fourth row of the periodic table.

Other atoms with a single valence electron have energy-level diagrams similar to that of sodium. Things get more complicated when there is more than one valence electron, so we'll defer those details to more advanced courses. Nevertheless, you already can *utilize* the information shown on an energy-level diagram without having to understand precisely *why* each level is where it is.

Excitation by Absorption

Left to itself, an atom will be in its lowest-energy ground state. How does an atom get into an excited state? The process of getting an atom into an excited state is called **excitation,** and there are two basic mechanisms: absorption and collision. We'll begin by looking at excitation by absorption.

One postulate of the Bohr model is that an atom can jump from one stationary state, of energy E_1, to a higher-energy state E_2 by absorbing a photon of frequency

$$f = \frac{\Delta E_{atom}}{h} = \frac{E_2 - E_1}{h} \tag{41.15}$$

Because we are interested in spectra, it is more useful to write Equation 41.15 in terms of the wavelength:

$$\lambda = \frac{c}{f} = \frac{hc}{\Delta E_{atom}} = \frac{1240 \text{ eV nm}}{\Delta E \text{ (in eV)}} \tag{41.16}$$

The final expression, which uses the value $hc = 1240$ eV nm, gives the wavelength in nanometers *if* ΔE_{atom} is in electron volts.

Bohr's idea of quantum jumps remains an integral part of our interpretation of the results of quantum mechanics. By absorbing a photon, an atom jumps from its ground state to one of its excited states. However, a careful analysis of how the electrons in an atom interact with a light wave shows that not every conceivable transition can occur. The **allowed transitions** must satisfy a **selection rule:** A transition (either absorption or emission) from a state in which the valence electron has orbital quantum number l_1 to another with orbital quantum number l_2 is allowed only if

$$\Delta l = |l_2 - l_1| = 1 \quad \text{(selection rule for emission and absorption)} \tag{41.17}$$

That is, the electron's orbital quantum number must change by exactly 1. Thus an atom in an s state ($l = 0$) can absorb a photon and be excited to a p state ($l = 1$) but *not* to another s state or to a d state. An atom in a p state ($l = 1$) can emit a photon by dropping to a lower-energy s state *or* to a lower-energy d state but not to another p state.

EXAMPLE 41.5 **Absorption in hydrogen**

What is the longest wavelength in the absorption spectrum of hydrogen? What is the transition?

SOLVE The longest wavelength corresponds to the smallest energy change ΔE_{atom}. Because the atom starts from the $1s$ ground state, the smallest energy change occurs for absorption to the first $n = 2$ excited state. The energy change is

$$\Delta E_{\text{atom}} = E_2 - E_1 = \frac{-13.6\,\text{eV}}{2^2} - \frac{-13.6\,\text{eV}}{1^2} = 10.2\,\text{eV}$$

The wavelength of this transition is

$$\lambda = \frac{1240\,\text{eV nm}}{10.2\,\text{eV}} = 122\,\text{nm}$$

This is an ultraviolet wavelength. Because of the selection rule, the transition is $1s \rightarrow 2p$, not $1s \rightarrow 2s$.

EXAMPLE 41.6 **Absorption in sodium**

What is the longest wavelength in the absorption spectrum of sodium? What is the transition?

SOLVE The sodium ground state is [Ne]$3s$. The lowest excited state is the $3p$ state. $3s \rightarrow 3p$ is an allowed transition ($\Delta l = 1$), so this is the longest wavelength. You can see from the data in Figure 41.24 that $\Delta E_{\text{atom}} = 2.104\,\text{eV}$ for this transition.

The corresponding wavelength is

$$\lambda = \frac{1240\,\text{eV nm}}{2.104\,\text{eV}} = 589\,\text{nm}$$

ASSESS This wavelength (yellow color) is a prominent feature in the spectrum of sodium. Because the ground state has $l = 0$, absorption *must* be to a p state. The s states and d states of sodium cannot be excited by absorption.

Collisional Excitation

A particle traveling with a speed of 1.0×10^6 m/s has a kinetic energy of 2.85 eV. If this particle collides with a ground-state sodium atom, a portion of its energy can be used to excite the atom to its $3p$ state. This process is called **collisional excitation** of the atom.

Collisional excitation differs from excitation by absorption in one very fundamental way. In absorption, the photon disappears. Consequently, *all* of the photon's energy must be transferred to the atom. Conservation of energy requires $E_{\text{photon}} = \Delta E_{\text{atom}}$. In contrast, the particle is still present after collisional excitation and can carry away some kinetic energy. That is, the particle does *not* have to transfer its entire energy to the atom. If the particle has an incident kinetic energy of 2.85 eV, it could transfer 2.10 eV to the sodium atom, thereby exciting it to the $3p$ state, and still depart the collision with an energy of 0.75 eV.

To excite the atom, the incident energy of the particle merely has to *exceed* ΔE_{atom}. That is $E_{\text{particle}} \geq \Delta E_{\text{atom}}$. There's a threshold energy for exciting the atom, but no upper limit. It is all a matter of energy conservation. FIGURE 41.25 shows the idea graphically.

Collisional excitation by electrons is the predominant method of excitation in electrical discharges such as fluorescent lights, street lights, and neon signs. A gas is placed in a tube at reduced pressure (≈ 1 mm of Hg), then a fairly high voltage (≈ 1000 V) between electrodes at the ends of the tube causes the gas to ionize, creating a current in which both ions and electrons are charge carriers. The mean free path of electrons between collisions is large enough for the electrons to gain several eV of kinetic energy as they accelerate in the electric field. This energy is then transferred to the gas atoms upon collision. The process does not work at atmospheric pressure because the mean free path between collisions is too short for the electrons to gain enough kinetic energy to excite the atoms.

NOTE ▶ There are no selection rules for collisional excitation. Any state can be excited if the colliding particle has sufficient energy. ◀

FIGURE 41.25 Excitation by photon absorption and electron collision.

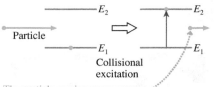

The photon disappears. Energy conservation requires $E_{\text{photon}} = E_2 - E_1$.

Absorption

Collisional excitation

The particle carries away energy. Energy conservation requires $E_{\text{particle}} \geq E_2 - E_1$.

Excitation of hydrogen

Can an electron traveling at 2.0×10^6 m/s cause a hydrogen atom to emit the prominent red spectral line ($\lambda = 656$ nm) in the Balmer series?

MODEL The electron must have sufficient energy to excite the upper state of the transition.

SOLVE The electron's energy is $E_{\text{elec}} = \frac{1}{2}mv^2 = 11.4$ eV. This is significantly larger than the 1.89 eV energy of a photon with wavelength 656 nm, but don't confuse the energy of the photon with the energy of the excitation. The red spectral line in the

Balmer series is emitted by an $n = 3$ to $n = 2$ quantum jump with $\Delta E_{\text{atom}} = 1.89$ eV. But to cause this emission, the electron must excite an atom from its *ground state,* with $n = 1$, up to the $n = 3$ level. The necessary excitation energy is

$$\Delta E_{\text{atom}} = E_3 - E_1 = (-1.51 \text{ eV}) - (-13.60 \text{ eV})$$

$$= 12.09 \text{ eV}$$

The electron does *not* have sufficient energy to excite the atom to the state from which the emission would occur.

FIGURE 41.26 Generation of an emission spectrum.

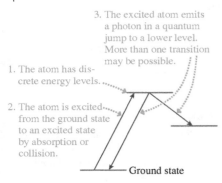

3. The excited atom emits a photon in a quantum jump to a lower level. More than one transition may be possible.

1. The atom has discrete energy levels.

2. The atom is excited from the ground state to an excited state by absorption or collision.

Ground state

FIGURE 41.27 The emission spectrum of sodium.

(a)

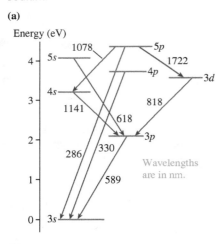

(b)

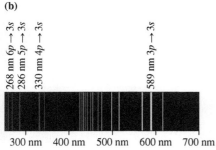

Emission Spectra

The absorption of light is an important process, but it is the emission of light that really gets our attention. The overwhelming bulk of sensory information that we perceive comes to us in the form of light. With the small exception of cosmic rays, all of our knowledge about the cosmos comes to us in the form of light and other electromagnetic waves emitted in various processes.

Understanding emission hinges on the three ideas shown in FIGURE 41.26. Once we have determined the energy levels of an atom, by solving the Schrödinger equation, we can immediately predict its emission spectrum. Conversely, we can use the measured emission spectrum to determine an atom's energy levels.

As an example, FIGURE 41.27a shows some of the transitions and wavelengths observed in the emission spectrum of sodium. This diagram makes the point that each wavelength represents a quantum jump between two well-defined energy levels. Notice that the selection rule $\Delta l = 1$ is being obeyed in the sodium spectrum. The $5p$ levels can undergo quantum jumps to $3s$, $4s$, or $3d$ but *not* to $3p$ or $4p$.

FIGURE 41.27b shows the emission spectrum of sodium as it would be recorded in a spectrometer. (Many of the lines seen in this spectrum start from higher excited states that are not seen in the rather limited energy-level diagram of Figure 41.27a.) By comparing the spectrum to the energy-level diagram, you can recognize that the spectral lines at 589 nm, 330 nm, 286 nm, and 268 nm form a *series* of lines due to all the possible $np \rightarrow 3s$ transitions. They are the dominant features in the sodium spectrum.

The most obvious visual feature of sodium emission is its bright yellow color, produced by the emission wavelength of 589 nm. This is the basis of the *flame test* used in chemistry to test for sodium: A sample is held in a Bunsen burner, and a bright yellow glow indicates the presence of sodium. The 589 nm emission is also prominent in the pinkish-yellow glow of the common sodium-vapor street lights. These operate by creating an electrical discharge in sodium vapor. Most sodium-vapor lights use high-pressure lamps to increase their light output. The high pressure, however, causes the formation of Na_2 molecules, and these molecules, which have a different spectral fingerprint, emit the pinkish portion of the light.

Some cities close to astronomical observatories use low-pressure sodium lights, and these emit the distinctive yellow 589 nm light of sodium. The glow of city lights is a severe problem for astronomers, but the very specific 589 nm emission from sodium is easily removed with a *sodium filter*. The light from the telescope is passed through a container of sodium vapor, and the sodium atoms *absorb* only the unwanted 589 nm photons without disturbing any other wavelengths! However, this cute trick does not work for the other wavelengths emitted by high-pressure sodium lamps or light from other sources.

Color in Solids

It is worth concluding this section with a few remarks about color in solids. Whether it is the intense multihued colors of a stained glass window, the bright colors of flowers or paint, or the deep luminescent red of a ruby, most of the colors we perceive in our lives come from solids rather than free atoms. The basic principles are the same, but the details are different for solids.

An excited atom in a gas has little choice but to give up its energy by emitting a photon. Its only other option, which is rare for gas atoms, is to collide with another atom and transfer its energy into the kinetic energy of recoil. But the atoms in a solid are in intimate contact with each other at all times. Although an excited atom in a solid has the option of emitting a photon, it is often more likely that the energy will be converted, via interactions with neighboring atoms, to the thermal energy of the solid. A process in which an atom is de-excited without radiating is called a **nonradiative transition.**

This is what happens in pigments, such as those in paints, plants, and dyes. Pigment molecules absorb certain wavelengths of light but not other wavelengths. The energy-level structure of a molecule is complex, so the absorption consists of "bands" of wavelengths rather than discrete spectral lines. But instead of re-radiating the energy by photon emission, as a free atom would, the pigment molecules undergo nonradiative transitions and convert the energy into increased thermal energy. That is why darker objects get hotter in the sun than lighter objects.

When light falls on an object, it can be either absorbed or reflected. If *all* wavelengths are reflected, the object is perceived as white. Any wavelengths absorbed by the pigments are removed from the reflected light. A pigment with blue-absorbing properties converts the energy of blue-wavelength photons into thermal energy, but photons of other wavelengths are reflected without change. A blue-absorbing pigment reflects the red and yellow wavelengths, causing the object to be perceived as the color orange!

Some solids, though, are a little different. The color of many minerals and crystals is due to so-called *impurity atoms* embedded in them. For example, the gemstone ruby is a very simple and common crystal of aluminum oxide, called corundum, that happens to have chromium atoms present at the concentration of about one part in a thousand. Pure corundum is transparent, so all of a ruby's color comes from these chromium impurity atoms.

FIGURE 41.28 shows what happens when ruby is illuminated by white light. The chromium atoms have a group of excited states that absorb all wavelengths shorter than about 600 nm—that is, everything except orange and red. Unlike the pigments in red glass, which convert all the absorbed energy into thermal energy, the chromium atoms dissipate only a small amount of heat as they undergo a nonradiative transition to another excited state. From there they emit a photon with $\lambda = hc/(E_2 - E_1) \approx 690$ nm (dark red color) as they jump back to the ground state.

The net effect is that short-wavelength photons, rather than being completely absorbed, are *re-radiated* as longer-wavelength photons. This is why rubies sparkle and have such intense color, whereas red glass is a dull red color. The color of other minerals and gems is due to different impurity atoms, but the principle is the same.

The colors in a stained-glass window are due to the selective absorption of light.

FIGURE 41.28 Absorption and emission in a crystal of ruby.

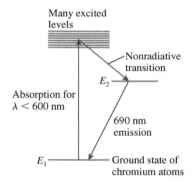

STOP TO THINK 41.5 In this hypothetical atom, what is the photon energy E_{photon} of the longest-wavelength photons emitted by atoms in the 5*p* state?

a. 1.0 eV
b. 2.0 eV
c. 3.0 eV
d. 4.0 eV

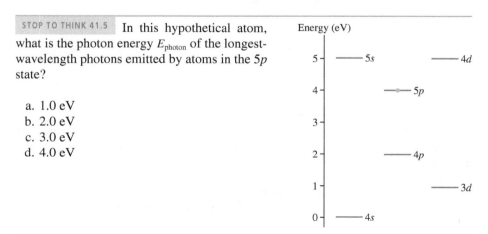

41.7 Lifetimes of Excited States

Excitation of an atom, by either absorption or collision, leaves it in an excited state. From there it jumps back to a lower energy level by emitting a photon. How long does this process take? There are actually two questions here. First, how long does an atom remain in an excited state before undergoing a quantum jump to a lower state? Second, how long does the transition last as the quantum jump is occurring?

Our best understanding of the quantum physics of atoms is that quantum jumps are instantaneous. The absorption or emission of a photon is an all-or-nothing event, so there is not a time when a photon is "half emitted." The prediction that quantum jumps are instantaneous has troubled many physicists, but careful experimental tests have never revealed any evidence that the jump itself takes a measurable amount of time.

The time spent in the excited state, waiting to make a quantum jump, is another story. FIGURE 41.29 shows experimental data for the length of time that doubly charged xenon ions Xe^{++} spend in a certain excited state. In this experiment, a pulse of electrons was used to excite the atoms to the excited state. The number of excited-state atoms was then monitored by detecting the photons emitted—one by one!—as the excited atoms jumped back to the ground state. The number of photons emitted at time t is directly proportional to the number of excited-state atoms present at time t. As the figure shows, the number of atoms in the excited state decreases *exponentially* with time, and virtually all have decayed within 25 ms of their creation.

Figure 41.29 has two important implications. First, atoms spend time in the excited state before undergoing a quantum jump back to a lower state. Second, the length of time spent in the excited state is not a constant value but varies from atom to atom. If every excited xenon ion lived for 5 ms in the excited state, then we would detect *no* photons for 5 ms, a big burst right at 5 ms as they all decay, then no photons after that. Instead, the data tell us that there is a *range* of times spent in the excited state. Some undergo a quantum jump and emit a photon after 1 ms, others after 5 ms or 10 ms, and a few wait as long as 20 or 25 ms.

Consider an experiment in which N_0 excited atoms are created at time $t = 0$. As the curve in Figure 41.29 shows, the number of excited atoms remaining at time t is well described by the exponential function

$$N_{\text{exc}} = N_0 e^{-t/\tau} \tag{41.18}$$

where τ is the point in time at which $e^{-1} = 0.368 = 36.8\%$ of the original atoms remain in the excited state. Thus 63.2% of the atoms, nearly two-thirds, have emitted a photon and jumped to the lower state by time $t = \tau$. The interval of time τ is called the **lifetime** of the excited state. From Figure 41.29 we can deduce that the lifetime of this state in Xe^{++} is ≈ 4 ms because that is the point in time at which the curve has decayed to 36.8% of its initial value.

This lifetime in Xe^{++} is abnormally long, which is why the state was studied. More typical excited-state lifetimes are a few nanoseconds. Table 41.3 gives some measured values of excited-state lifetimes. Whatever the value of τ, the number of excited-state atoms decreases exponentially. Why is this?

FIGURE 41.29 Experimental data for the photon emission rate from an excited state in Xe^{++}.

Photon counts (thousands)

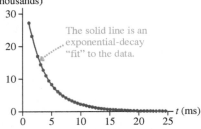

The solid line is an exponential-decay "fit" to the data.

TABLE 41.3 Some excited-state lifetimes

Atom	State	Lifetime (ns)
Hydrogen	$2p$	1.6
Sodium	$3p$	17
Neon	$3p$	20
Potassium	$4p$	26

The Decay Equation

Quantum mechanics is about probabilities. We cannot say exactly where the electron is located, but we can use quantum mechanics to calculate the *probability* that the electron is located in a small interval Δx at position x. Similarly, we cannot say exactly when an excited electron will undergo a quantum jump and emit a photon. However, we can use quantum mechanics to find the *probability* that the electron will undergo a quantum jump during a small time interval Δt at time t.

Let us assume that the probability of an excited atom emitting a photon during time interval Δt is *independent* of how long the atom has been waiting in the excited state. For example, a newly excited atom may have a 10% probability of emitting a photon within the 1 ns interval from 0 ns to 1 ns. If it survives until $t = 7$ ns, our assumption is that it still has a 10% probability of emitting a photon during the 1 ns interval from 7 ns to 8 ns.

This assumption, which can be justified with a detailed analysis, is similar to flipping coins. The probability of a head on your first flip is 50%. If you flip seven heads in a row, the probability of a head on your eighth flip is still 50%. It is *unlikely* that you will flip seven heads in a row, but doing so does not influence the eighth flip. Likewise, it may be *unlikely* for an excited atom to live for 7 ns, but doing so does not affect its probability of emitting a photon during the next 1 ns.

If Δt is small, the probability of photon emission during time interval Δt is directly proportional to Δt. That is, if the emission probability in 1 ns is 1%, it will be 2% in 2 ns and 0.5% in 0.5 ns. (This logic fails if Δt gets too big. If the probability is 70% in 20 ns, we can *not* say that the probability would be 140% in 40 ns because a probability > 1 is meaningless.) We will be interested in the limit $\Delta t \rightarrow dt$, so the concept is valid and we can write

$$\text{Prob(emission in } \Delta t \text{ at time } t) = r\,\Delta t \qquad (41.19)$$

where r is called the **decay rate** because the number of excited atoms decays with time. It is a probability *per second,* with units of s^{-1}, and thus is a rate. For example, if an atom has a 5% probability of emitting a photon during a 2 ns interval, its decay rate is

$$r = \frac{P}{\Delta t} = \frac{0.05}{2 \text{ ns}} = 0.025 \text{ ns}^{-1} = 2.5 \times 10^7 \text{ s}^{-1}$$

NOTE ▶ Equation 41.19 is directly analogous to Prob(found in Δx at x) $= P\,\Delta x$, where P, which had units of m^{-1}, was the probability density. ◀

FIGURE 41.30 shows N_{exc} atoms in an excited state. During a small time interval Δt, the number of these atoms that we expect to undergo a quantum jump and emit a photon is N_{exc} multiplied by the probability of decay. That is,

$$\begin{aligned}
\text{number of photons in } \Delta t \text{ at time } t &= N_{\text{exc}} \times \text{Prob(emission in } \Delta t \text{ at } t) \\
&= rN_{\text{exc}}\,\Delta t
\end{aligned} \qquad (41.20)$$

Now the *change* in N_{exc} is the *negative* of Equation 41.20. For example, suppose 1000 excited atoms are present at time t and each has a 5% probability of emitting a photon in the next 1 ns. On average, the number of photons emitted during the next 1 ns will be $1000 \times 0.05 = 50$. Consequently, the number of excited atoms changes by $\Delta N_{\text{exc}} = -50$, with the minus sign indicating a decrease.

Thus the *change* in the number of atoms in the excited state is

$$\Delta N_{\text{exc}}(\text{in } \Delta t \text{ at } t) = -N_{\text{exc}} \times \text{Prob(decay in } \Delta t \text{ at } t) = -rN_{\text{exc}}\,\Delta t \quad (41.21)$$

Now let $\Delta t \rightarrow dt$. Then $\Delta N_{\text{exc}} \rightarrow dN_{\text{exc}}$ and Equation 41.21 becomes

$$\frac{dN_{\text{exc}}}{dt} = -rN_{\text{exc}} \qquad (41.22)$$

Equation 41.22 is a *rate equation* because it describes the *rate* at which the excited-state population changes. If r is large, the population will decay at a rapid rate and will have a short lifetime. Conversely, a small value of r implies that the population will decay slowly and will live a long time.

The rate equation is a differential equation, but we solved a similar equation for RC circuits in Chapter 31. First, we rewrite Equation 41.22 as

$$\frac{dN_{\text{exc}}}{N_{\text{exc}}} = -r\,dt$$

Then we integrate both sides from $t = 0$, when the initial excited-state population is N_0, to an arbitrary time t when the population is N_{exc}. That is,

$$\int_{N_0}^{N_{\text{exc}}} \frac{dN_{\text{exc}}}{N_{\text{exc}}} = -r \int_0^t dt \qquad (41.23)$$

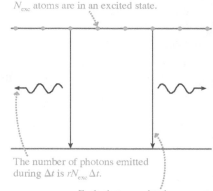

FIGURE 41.30 The number of atoms that emit photons during Δt is directly proportional to the number of excited atoms.

N_{exc} atoms are in an excited state.

The number of photons emitted during Δt is $rN_{\text{exc}}\,\Delta t$.

Each photon emitted represents the loss of 1 excited atom. Thus $\Delta N_{\text{exc}} = -rN_{\text{exc}}\,\Delta t$.

Both are well-known integrals, giving

$$\ln N_{\text{exc}}\Big|_{N_0}^{N_{\text{exc}}} = \ln N_{\text{exc}} - \ln N_0 = \ln\left(\frac{N_{\text{exc}}}{N_0}\right) = -rt$$

We can solve for the number of excited atoms at time t by taking the exponential of both sides, then multiplying by N_0. Doing so gives

$$N_{\text{exc}} = N_0 e^{-rt} \tag{41.24}$$

Notice that $N_{\text{exc}} = N_0$ at $t = 0$, as expected. Equation 41.24, the *decay equation*, shows that the excited-state population decays exponentially with time, as we saw in the experimental data of Figure 41.29.

It will be more convenient to write Equation 41.24 as

$$N_{\text{exc}} = N_0 e^{-t/\tau} \tag{41.25}$$

where

$$\tau = \frac{1}{r} = \text{the } \textit{lifetime} \text{ of the excited state} \tag{41.26}$$

This is the definition of the lifetime we used in Equation 41.18 to describe the experimental results. The lifetime is the inverse of the decay rate r.

EXAMPLE 41.8 **The lifetime of an excited state in mercury**

The mercury atom has two valence electrons. One is always in the $6s$ state, the other is in a state with quantum numbers n and l. One of the excited states in mercury is the state designated $6s6p$. The decay rate of this state is $7.7 \times 10^8 \text{ s}^{-1}$.

a. What is the lifetime of this state?

b. If 1.0×10^{10} mercury atoms are created in the $6s6p$ state at $t = 0$, how many photons will be emitted during the first 1.0 ns?

SOLVE a. The lifetime is

$$\tau = \frac{1}{r} = \frac{1}{7.7 \times 10^8 \text{ s}^{-1}} = 1.3 \times 10^{-9} \text{ s} = 1.3 \text{ ns}$$

b. If there are $N_0 = 1.0 \times 10^{10}$ excited atoms at $t = 0$, the number still remaining at $t = 1.0$ ns is

$$N_{\text{exc}} = N_0 e^{-t/\tau} = (1.0 \times 10^{10})e^{-(1.0 \text{ ns})/(1.3 \text{ ns})} = 4.63 \times 10^9$$

This result implies that 5.37×10^9 atoms undergo quantum jumps during the first 1.0 ns. Each of these atoms emits one photon, so the number of photons emitted during the first 1.0 ns is 5.37×10^9.

STOP TO THINK 41.6 An equal number of excited A atoms and excited B atoms are created at $t = 0$. The decay rate of B atoms is twice that of A atoms: $r_B = 2r_A$. At $t = \tau_A$ (i.e., after one lifetime of A atoms has elapsed), the ratio N_B/N_A of the number of excited B atoms to the number of excited A atoms is

a. >2   b. 2   c. 1   d. $\frac{1}{2}$ e. $<\frac{1}{2}$

41.8 Stimulated Emission and Lasers

We have seen that an atom can jump from a lower-energy level E_1 to a higher-energy level E_2 by absorbing a photon. FIGURE 41.31a illustrates the basic absorption process, with a photon of frequency $f = \Delta E_{\text{atom}}/h$ disappearing as the atom jumps from level 1 to level 2. Once in level 2, as shown in FIGURE 41.31b, the atom can emit a photon of the same frequency as it jumps back to level 1. This transition is called **spontaneous emission**.

In 1917, four years after Bohr's proposal of stationary states in atoms but still prior to de Broglie and Schrödinger, Einstein was puzzled by how quantized atoms reach thermodynamic equilibrium in the presence of electromagnetic radiation. Einstein found that absorption and spontaneous emission were not sufficient to allow a collection of atoms to reach thermodynamic equilibrium. To resolve this difficulty, Einstein proposed a third mechanism for the interaction of atoms with light.

The left half of FIGURE 41.31c shows a photon with frequency $f = \Delta E_{atom}/h$ approaching an *excited* atom. If a photon can induce the $1 \rightarrow 2$ transition of absorption, then Einstein proposed that it should also be able to induce a $2 \rightarrow 1$ transition. In a sense, this transition is a *reverse absorption*. But to undergo a reverse absorption, the atom must *emit* a photon of frequency $f = \Delta E_{atom}/h$. The end result, as seen in the right half of Figure 41.31c, is an atom in level 1 plus *two* photons! Because the first photon induced the atom to emit the second photon, this process is called **stimulated emission.**

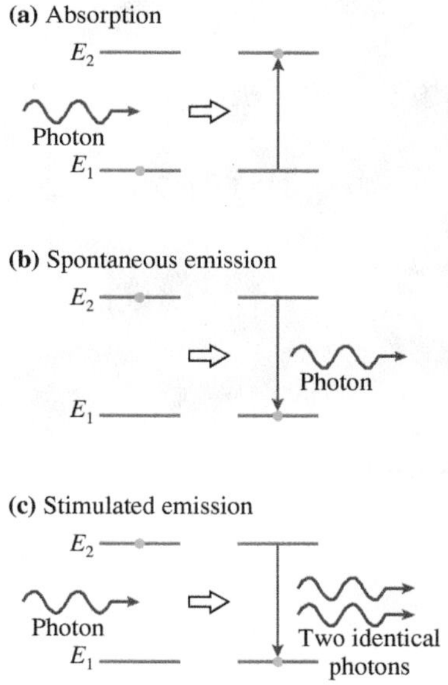

Stimulated emission occurs only if the first photon's frequency exactly matches the $E_2 - E_1$ energy difference of the atom. This is precisely the same condition that absorption has to satisfy. More interesting, the emitted photon is *identical* to the incident photon. This means that as the two photons leave the atom they have exactly the same frequency and wavelength, are traveling in exactly the same direction, and are exactly in phase with each other. In other words, **stimulated emission produces a second photon that is an exact clone of the first.**

Stimulated emission is of no importance in most practical situations. Atoms typically spend only a few nanoseconds in an excited state before undergoing spontaneous emission, so the atom would need to be in an extremely intense light wave for stimulated emission to occur prior to spontaneous emission. Ordinary light sources are not nearly intense enough for stimulated emission to be more than a minor effect; hence it was many years before Einstein's prediction was confirmed. No one had doubted Einstein because he had clearly demonstrated that stimulated emission was necessary to make the energy equations balance, but it seemed no more important than would pennies to a millionaire balancing her checkbook. At least, that is, until 1960, when a revolutionary invention appeared that made explicit use of stimulated emission: the laser.

Lasers

The word **laser** is an acronym for **l**ight **a**mplification by the **s**timulated **e**mission of **r**adiation. The first laser, a ruby laser, was demonstrated in 1960, and several other kinds of lasers appeared within a few months. The driving force behind much of the research was the American physicist Charles Townes. Townes was awarded the Nobel Prize in 1964 for the invention of the maser, an earlier device using microwaves, and his theoretical work leading to the laser.

Today, lasers do everything from being the light source in fiber-optic communications to measuring the distance to the moon and from playing your DVD to performing delicate eye surgery. But what is a laser? Basically it is a device that produces a beam of highly *coherent* and essentially monochromatic (single-color) light as a result of stimulated emission. **Coherent** light is light in which all the electromagnetic waves have the same phase, direction, and amplitude. It is the coherence of a laser beam that allows it to be very tightly focused or to be rapidly modulated for communications.

Let's take a brief look at how a laser works. FIGURE 41.32 represents a system of atoms that have a lower energy level E_1 and a higher energy level E_2. Suppose there are N_1 atoms in level 1 and N_2 atoms in level 2. Left to themselves, all the atoms would soon end up in level 1 because of the spontaneous emission $2 \rightarrow 1$. To prevent this, we can imagine that some type of excitation mechanism, perhaps an electrical discharge, is continuing to produce new excited atoms in level 2.

Let a photon of frequency $f = (E_2 - E_1)/h$ be incident on this group of atoms. Because it has the correct frequency, it could be absorbed by one of the atoms in

FIGURE 41.31 Three types of radiative transitions.

(a) Absorption

(b) Spontaneous emission

(c) Stimulated emission

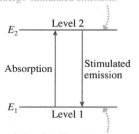

FIGURE 41.32 Energy levels 1 and 2, with populations N_1 and N_2.

N_2 atoms in level 2. Photons of energy $E_{photon} = E_2 - E_1$ can cause these atoms to undergo stimulated emission.

Level 2

E_2

Absorption

Stimulated emission

E_1

Level 1

N_1 atoms in level 1. These atoms can absorb photons of energy $E_{photon} = E_2 - E_1$.

Charles Townes.

level 1. Another possibility is that it could cause stimulated emission from one of the level 2 atoms. Ordinarily $N_2 \ll N_1$, so absorption events far outnumber stimulated emission events. Even if a few photons were generated by stimulated emission, they would quickly be absorbed by the vastly larger group of atoms in level 1.

But what if we could somehow arrange to place *every* atom in level 2, making $N_1 = 0$? Then the incident photon, upon encountering its first atom, will cause stimulated emission. Where there was initially one photon of frequency f, now there are two. These will strike two additional excited-state atoms, again causing stimulated emission. Then there will be four photons. As FIGURE 41.33 shows, there will be a *chain reaction* of stimulated emission until all N_2 atoms emit a photon of frequency f.

FIGURE 41.33 Stimulated emission creates a chain reaction of photon production in a population of excited atoms.

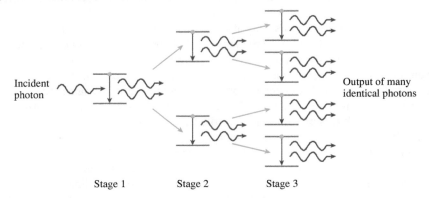

Stage 1   Stage 2   Stage 3

In stimulated emission, each emitted photon is *identical* to the incident photon. The chain reaction of Figure 41.33 will lead not just to N_2 photons of frequency f, but to N_2 identical photons, all traveling together in the same direction with the same phase. If N_2 is a large number, as would be the case in any practical device, the one initial photon will have been amplified into a gigantic coherent pulse of light! A collection of excited-state atoms is called an *optical amplifier.*

As FIGURE 41.34 shows, the stimulated emission is sustained by placing the *lasing medium*—the sample of atoms that emits the light—in an **optical cavity** consisting of two facing mirrors. One of the mirrors will be partially transmitting so that some of the light emerges as the *laser beam.*

Although the chain reaction of Figure 41.33 illustrates the idea most clearly, it is not necessary for every atom to be in level 2 for amplification to occur. All that is needed is to have $N_2 > N_1$ so that stimulated emission exceeds absorption. Such a situation is called a **population inversion.** The process of obtaining a population inversion is called **pumping,** and we will look at two specific examples. Pumping is the technically difficult part of designing and building a laser because normal excitation mechanisms do not create population inversions. In fact, lasers would likely have been discovered accidentally long before 1960 if population inversions were easy to create.

FIGURE 41.34 Lasing takes place in an optical cavity.

The counterpropagating waves interact repeatedly with the atoms, allowing the light intensity to build up to a high level.

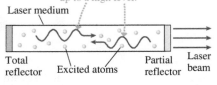

Laser medium

Total reflector   Excited atoms   Partial reflector   Laser beam

The Ruby Laser

The first laser to be developed was a ruby laser. FIGURE 41.35a shows the energy-level structure of the chromium atoms that gives ruby its optical properties. Normally, the number of atoms in the ground-state level E_1 far exceeds the number of excited-state atoms with energy E_2. That is, $N_2 \ll N_1$. Under these circumstances 690 nm light is absorbed rather than amplified. But suppose that we could *rapidly* excite more than half the chromium atoms to level E_2. Then we would have a population inversion $(N_2 > N_1)$ between levels E_1 and E_2.

This can be accomplished by *optically pumping* the ruby with a very intense pulse of white light from a *flashlamp.* A flashlamp is like a camera flash, only vastly more intense. In the basic arrangement of FIGURE 41.35b, a helical flashlamp is coiled around a ruby rod that has mirrors bonded to its end faces. The lamp is fired by discharging a high-voltage capacitor through it, creating a very intense light pulse lasting just a few microseconds. This intense light excites nearly all the chromium atoms from the ground state to the upper energy levels. From there, they quickly ($\approx 10^{-8}$ s) decay nonradiatively to level 2. With $N_2 > N_1$, a population inversion has been created.

Once a photon initiates the laser pulse, the light intensity builds quickly into a brief but incredibly intense burst of light. A typical output pulse lasts 10 ns and has an energy of 1 J. This gives a *peak power* of

$$P = \frac{\Delta E}{\Delta t} = \frac{1 \text{ J}}{10^{-8} \text{ s}} = 10^8 \text{ W} = 100 \text{ MW}$$

One hundred megawatts of light power! That is more than the electrical power used by a small city. The difference, of course, is that a city consumes that power continuously but the laser pulse lasts a mere 10 ns. The laser cannot fire again until the capacitor is recharged and the laser rod cooled. A typical firing rate is a few pulses per second, so the laser is "on" only a few billionths of a second out of each second.

Ruby lasers have been replaced by other pulsed lasers that, for various practical reasons, are easier to operate. However, they all operate with the same basic idea of rapid optical pumping to upper states, rapid nonradiative decay to level 2 where the population inversion is formed, then rapid buildup of an intense optical pulse.

The Helium-Neon Laser

The familiar red laser used in lecture demonstrations, laboratories, and supermarket checkout scanners is the helium-neon laser, often called a HeNe laser. Its output is a *continuous,* rather than pulsed, wavelength of 632.8 nm. The medium of a HeNe laser is a mixture of $\approx 90\%$ helium and $\approx 10\%$ neon gases. As FIGURE 41.36a shows, the gases are sealed in a glass tube, then an electrical discharge is established along the bore of the tube. Two mirrors are bonded to the ends of the discharge tube, one a total reflector and the other having $\approx 2\%$ transmission so that the laser beam can be extracted.

The atoms that lase are the neon atoms, but the pumping method involves the helium atoms. The electrons in the discharge collisionally excite the $1s2s$ state of helium. This state has a very low spontaneous decay rate (i.e., a very long lifetime) because a decay back to the $1s^2$ state would violate the Δl selection rule, so it is possible to build up a fairly large population (but not an inversion) of excited helium atoms in the $1s2s$ state. The energy of the $1s2s$ state is 20.6 eV.

Interestingly, an excited state of neon, the $5s$ state, also has an energy of 20.6 eV. If a $1s2s$ excited helium atom collides with a ground-state neon atom, as frequently happens, the excitation energy can be transferred from one atom to the other! Written as a chemical reaction, the process is

$$\text{He}^* + \text{Ne} \rightarrow \text{He} + \text{Ne}^*$$

where the asterisk indicates the atom is in an excited state. This process, called **excitation transfer,** is very efficient for the $5s$ state because the process is *resonant*—a perfect energy match. Thus the two-step process of collisional excitation of helium, followed by excitation transfer between helium and neon, pumps the neon atoms into the excited $5s$ state. This is shown in FIGURE 41.36b.

The $5s$ energy level in neon is ≈ 1.95 eV above the $3p$ state. The $3p$ state is very nearly empty of population, both because it is not efficiently populated in the discharge and because it undergoes very rapid spontaneous emission to the $3s$ states. Thus the large number of atoms pumped into the $5s$ state creates a population inversion with respect to the lower $3p$ state. These are the necessary conditions for laser action.

Because the lower level of the laser transition is normally empty of population, placing only a small fraction of the neon atoms in the $5s$ state creates a population inversion. Thus a fairly modest pumping action is sufficient to create the inversion and start the laser. Furthermore, a HeNe laser can maintain a *continuous* inversion and thus sustain

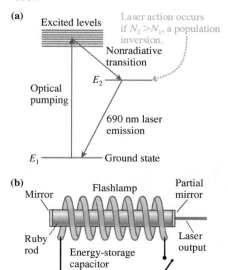

FIGURE 41.35 A flashlamp-pumped ruby laser.

(a)

(b)

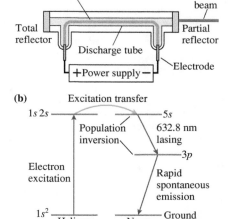

FIGURE 41.36 A HeNe laser.

(a)

(b)

continuous lasing. The electrical discharge continuously creates 5s excited atoms in the upper level, via excitation transfer, and the rapid spontaneous decay of the 3p atoms from the lower level keeps its population low enough to sustain the inversion.

A typical helium-neon laser has a power output of 1 mW = 10^{-3} J/s at 632.8 nm in a 1-mm-diameter laser beam. As you can show in a homework problem, this output corresponds to the emission of 3.2×10^{15} photons per second. Other continuous lasers operate by similar principles, but can produce much more power. The argon laser, which is widely used in scientific research, can produce up to 20 W of power at green and blue wavelengths. The carbon dioxide laser produces output power in excess of 1000 W at the infrared wavelength of 10.6 μm. It is used in industrial applications for cutting and welding.

EXAMPLE 41.9 An ultraviolet laser

An ultraviolet laser generates a 10 MW, 5.0-ns-long light pulse at a wavelength of 355 nm. How many photons are in each pulse?

SOLVE The energy of each light pulse is the power multiplied by the duration:

$$E_{\text{pulse}} = P \,\Delta t = (1.0 \times 10^7 \text{ W})(5.0 \times 10^{-9} \text{ s}) = 0.050 \text{ J}$$

Each photon in the pulse has energy

$$E_{\text{photon}} = hf = \frac{hc}{\lambda} = 3.50 \text{ eV} = 5.60 \times 10^{-19} \text{ J}$$

Because $E_{\text{pulse}} = NE_{\text{photon}}$, the number of photons is

$$N = E_{\text{pulse}}/E_{\text{photon}} = 8.9 \times 10^{16} \text{ photons}$$

CHALLENGE EXAMPLE 41.10 Electron probability in hydrogen

What is the probability that a 1s hydrogen electron is found at a distance from the proton that is less than half the Bohr radius?

MODEL The Schrödinger model of the hydrogen atom represents the electron as a wave function. We can't say exactly where the electron is, but we can calculate the probability of finding it in a specified region of space.

SOLVE We're interested in finding the electron not at a certain *point* in space but within a certain *distance* from the nucleus. For this we use the radial probability density

$$P_r(r) = 4\pi r^2 |R_{nl}(r)|^2$$

where $R_{nl}(r)$ is the radial wave function, rather than the square of the wave function $\psi(x, y, z)$. The probability of finding the electron at a distance between r_{min} and r_{max} is

$$\text{Prob}(r_{\text{min}} \le r \le r_{\text{max}}) = \int_{r_{\text{min}}}^{r_{\text{max}}} P_r(r)\, dr$$

$$= 4\pi \int_{r_{\text{min}}}^{r_{\text{max}}} r^2 |R_{nl}(r)|^2\, dr$$

The 1s radial wave function was given in Equations 41.7:

$$R_{1s}(r) = \frac{1}{\sqrt{\pi a_B{}^3}} e^{-r/a_B}$$

where a_B is the Bohr radius. We specify that the electron is less than half the Bohr radius from the proton by setting $r_{\text{min}} = 0$ and $r_{\text{max}} = \frac{1}{2} a_B$. Thus the probability we seek is

$$\text{Prob}\left(r \le \tfrac{1}{2} a_B\right) = 4\pi \int_0^{a_B/2} r^2 |R_{1s}(r)|^2\, dr$$

$$= \frac{4\pi}{\pi a_B{}^3} \int_0^{a_B/2} r^2 e^{-2r/a_B}\, dr$$

To evaluate this integral, it will be useful to change variables. Let $u = 2r/a_B$, so that the exponential can be written more simply as e^{-u}. Turning this around, we have $r = \frac{1}{2} a_B u$ and thus

$$r^2\, dr = \left(\tfrac{1}{2} a_B u\right)^2 \left(\tfrac{1}{2} a_B\, du\right) = \tfrac{1}{8} a_B{}^3 u^2\, du$$

A change of variables requires a corresponding change of limits: When $r = 0$, $u = 0$ also; when $r = \frac{1}{2} a_B$, $u = 1$. With these substitutions, the probability calculation becomes

$$\text{Prob}\left(r \le \tfrac{1}{2} a_B\right) = \frac{1}{2} \int_0^1 u^2 e^{-u}\, du$$

This looks much nicer! Notice that all the a_B have disappeared, so our answer will be a numerical value.

This is not an easy integral, but it is a common one. It can be found in integral tables, such as in Appendix A, or evaluated with mathematical software. The result is

$$\text{Prob}\left(r \le \tfrac{1}{2} a_B\right) = \frac{1}{2}\left[-(u^2 + 2u + 2)e^{-u}\right]_0^1$$

$$= \frac{1}{2}\left[2 - 5e^{-1}\right] = 0.080$$

The probability that a 1s hydrogen electron is less than half the Bohr radius from the proton is 0.080, or 8.0%.

ASSESS The probability is small, but that is not unexpected. The graph of the radial probability density in Figure 41.8 shows that the probability peaks at $r = a_B$ and then decreases rather slowly. We can see that the area under that curve from $r = 0$ to $r = \frac{1}{2} a_B$ is not large. The electron can be found much closer to the proton than one Bohr radius, but not with a large probability.

SUMMARY

The goal of Chapter 41 has been to understand the structure and properties of atoms.

Important Concepts

Hydrogen Atom

The three-dimensional Schrödinger equation has stationary-state solutions for the hydrogen atom potential energy only if three conditions are satisfied:

- Energy $E_n = -13.60 \text{ eV}/n^2$ $n = 1, 2, 3, \ldots$

- Angular momentum $L = \sqrt{l(l+1)}\hbar$ $l = 0, 1, 2, 3, \ldots, n-1$

- z-component of angular momentum
  $L_z = m\hbar$ $m = -l, -l+1, \ldots, 0, \ldots, l-1, l$

Each state is characterized by **quantum numbers** (n, l, m), but the energy depends only on n.

The probability of finding the electron within a small distance interval δr at distance r is

$$\text{Prob(in } \delta r \text{ at } r) = P_r(r)\delta r$$

where $P_r(r) = 4\pi r^2 |R_{nl}(r)|^2$ is the **radial probability density.**

Graphs of $P_r(r)$ suggest that the electrons are arranged in shells.

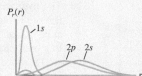

Multielectron Atoms

The potential energy is electron-nucleus plus electron-electron. In the **independent particle approximation,** each electron is described by the same quantum numbers (n, l, m, m_s) used for the hydrogen atom. The energy of a state depends on n and l. For each n, energy increases as l increases.

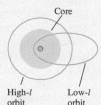

- High-l states correspond to circular orbits. These stay outside the core.

- Low-l states correspond to elliptical orbits. These penetrate the core to interact more strongly with the nucleus. This interaction lowers their energy.

Electron spin

The electron has an inherent angular momentum $\vec{S}$ and magnetic moment $\vec{\mu}$ *as if* it were spinning. The spin angular momentum has a fixed magnitude $S = \sqrt{s(s+1)}\hbar$, where $s = \frac{1}{2}$. The z-component is $S_z = m_s\hbar$, where $m_s = \pm\frac{1}{2}$. These two states are called **spin-up** and **spin-down.** Each atomic state is fully characterized by the four quantum numbers (n, l, m, m_s).

The Pauli exclusion principle says that no more than one electron can occupy each quantum state. The periodic table of the elements is based on the fact that the ground state is the lowest-energy electron configuration compatible with the Pauli principle.

Applications

Atomic spectra are generated by excitation followed by a photon-emitting quantum jump.

- Excitation by absorption or collision

- Quantum-jump selection rule $\Delta l = \pm 1$

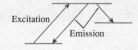

Lifetimes of excited states

The excited-state population decreases exponentially as

$$N_{\text{exc}} = N_0 e^{-t/\tau}$$

where $\tau = 1/r$ is the **lifetime** and r is the **decay rate.** It's not possible to predict when a particular atom will decay, but the *probability* is

$$\text{Prob(in } \delta t \text{ at } t) = r\,\delta t$$

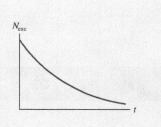

Stimulated emission of an excited state can be caused by a photon with $E_{\text{photon}} = E_2 - E_1$. Laser action can occur if $N_2 > N_1$, a condition called a **population inversion.**

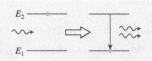

Terms and Notation

principal quantum number, n	spin quantum number, m_s	subshell	spontaneous emission
orbital quantum number, l	spin-up	excitation	stimulated emission
magnetic quantum number, m	spin-down	allowed transition	laser
ionization energy	independent particle	selection rule	coherent
electron cloud	approximation (IPA)	collisional excitation	optical cavity
radial wave function, $R_{nl}(r)$	Pauli exclusion principle	nonradiative transition	population inversion
radial probability density, $P_r(r)$	electron configuration	lifetime, τ	pumping
shell model	closed shell	decay rate, r	excitation transfer
spin			

CONCEPTUAL QUESTIONS

1. Consider the two hydrogen-atom states $5d$ and $4f$. Which has the higher energy? Explain.
2. What is the difference between the *probability density* and the *radial probability density?*
3. What is the difference between l and L?
4. What is the difference between s and S?
5. FIGURE Q41.5 shows the outcome of a Stern-Gerlach experiment with atoms of element X.
   a. Do the peaks represent different values of the atom's total angular momentum or different values of the z-component of its angular momentum? Explain.
   b. What angular momentum quantum numbers characterize these four peaks?
6. Does each of the configurations in FIGURE Q41.6 represent a possible electron configuration of an element? If so, (i) identify the element and (ii) determine whether this is the ground state or an excited state. If not, why not?

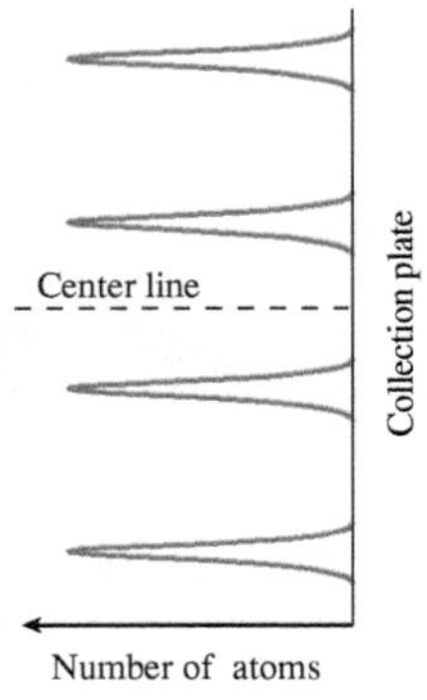

Center line

Collection plate

Number of atoms

FIGURE Q41.5

7. What *is* an atom's ionization energy? In other words, if you know the ionization energy of an atom, what is it that you know about the atom?
8. Figure 41.23 shows that the ionization energy of cadmium ($Z = 48$) is larger than that of its neighbors. Why is this?
9. A neon discharge tube emits a bright reddish-orange spectrum, but a glass tube filled with neon is completely transparent. Why doesn't the neon in the tube absorb orange and red wavelengths?
10. The hydrogen atom $1s$ wave function is a maximum at $r = 0$. But the $1s$ radial probability density, shown in Figure 41.8, peaks at $r = a_B$ and is zero at $r = 0$. Explain this paradox.
11. In a multielectron atom, the lowest-l state for each n ($2s$, $3s$, $4s$, etc.) is significantly lower in energy than the hydrogen state having the same n. But the highest-l state for each n ($2p$, $3d$, $4f$, etc.) is very nearly equal in energy to the hydrogen state with the same n. Explain.
12. In FIGURE Q41.12, a photon with energy 2.0 eV is incident on an atom in the p state. Does the atom undergo an absorption transition, a stimulated emission transition, or neither? Explain.

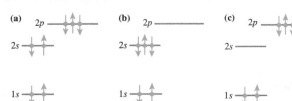

(a) $2p$ ↑↑ **(b)** $2p$ —— **(c)** $2p$ ↑↓ ↑↑

$2s$ ↑↓ $2s$ ↑↓↓ $2s$ ——

$1s$ ↑↓ $1s$ ↑↑ $1s$ ↑↓

FIGURE Q41.6

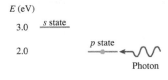

E (eV)

3.0 ___s state___

2.0 _____ p state

Photon

FIGURE Q41.12   0.0 ___s state___

EXERCISES AND PROBLEMS

Problems labeled ▨ integrate material from earlier chapters.

Exercises

Sections 41.1–41.2 The Hydrogen Atom

1. | What is the angular momentum of a hydrogen atom in (a) a $6s$ state and (b) a $4f$ state? Give your answers as a multiple of $\hbar$.

2. | List the quantum numbers, excluding spin, of (a) all possible $3p$ states and (b) all possible $3d$ states.
3. | A hydrogen atom has orbital angular momentum 3.65×10^{-34} J s.
   a. What letter (s, p, d, or f) describes the electron?
   b. What is the atom's minimum possible energy? Explain.
4. | What is the maximum possible angular momentum L (as a multiple of $\hbar$) of a hydrogen atom with energy -0.544 eV?

5. | What are E and L (as a multiple of $\hbar$) of a hydrogen atom in the $6f$ state?

Section 41.3 The Electron's Spin

6. ‖ When all quantum numbers are considered, how many different quantum states are there for a hydrogen atom with $n = 1$? With $n = 2$? With $n = 3$? List the quantum numbers of each state.

7. | How many lines of atoms would you expect to see on the collector plate of a Stern-Gerlach apparatus if the experiment is done with (a) lithium and (b) beryllium? Explain.

Section 41.4 Multielectron Atoms

Section 41.5 The Periodic Table of the Elements

8. | Predict the ground-state electron configurations of Mg, Sr, and Ba.

9. | Predict the ground-state electron configurations of Al, Ga, and In.

10. | Identify the element for each of these electron configurations. Then determine whether this configuration is the ground state or an excited state.
   a. $1s^2 2s^2 2p^5$
   b. $1s^2 2s^2 2p^6 3s^2 3p^6 4s^2 3d^{10} 4p$

11. | Identify the element for each of these electron configurations. Then determine whether this configuration is the ground state or an excited state.
   a. $1s^2 2s^2 2p^5 3s$
   b. $1s^2 2s^2 2p^6 3s^2 3p^6 4s^2 3d^2$

Section 41.6 Excited States and Spectra

12. | Show that $hc = 1240$ eV nm.

13. ‖ What is the electron configuration of the second excited state of lithium?

14. ‖ An electron accelerates through a 12.5 V potential difference, starting from rest, and then collides with a hydrogen atom, exciting the atom to the highest energy level allowed. List all the possible quantum-jump transitions by which the excited atom could emit a photon and the wavelength (in nm) of each.

15. | a. Is a $4p \rightarrow 4s$ transition allowed in sodium? If so, what is its wavelength (in nm)? If not, why not?
   b. Is a $3d \rightarrow 4s$ transition allowed in sodium? If so, what is its wavelength (in nm)? If not, why not?

Section 41.7 Lifetimes of Excited States

16. | An excited state of an atom has a 25 ns lifetime. What is the probability that an excited atom will emit a photon during a 0.50 ns interval?

17. | 1.0×10^6 sodium atoms are excited to the $3p$ state at $t = 0$ s. How many of these atoms remain in the $3p$ state at (a) $t = 10$ ns, (b) $t = 30$ ns, and (c) $t = 100$ ns?

18. | A hydrogen atom is in the $2p$ state. How much time must elapse for there to be a 1% chance that this atom will undergo a quantum jump to the ground state?

19. ‖ 1.0×10^6 atoms are excited to an upper energy level at $t = 0$ s. At the end of 20 ns, 90% of these atoms have undergone a quantum jump to the ground state.
   a. How many photons have been emitted?
   b. What is the lifetime of the excited state?

20. ‖ 1.00×10^6 sodium atoms are excited to the $3p$ state at $t = 0$ s. At what time have 8.0×10^5 photons been emitted?

Section 41.8 Stimulated Emission and Lasers

21. | A 1.0 mW helium-neon laser emits a visible laser beam with a wavelength of 633 nm. How many photons are emitted per second?

22. ‖ In LASIK surgery, a laser is used to reshape the cornea of the
BIO eye to improve vision. The laser produces extremely short pulses of light, each containing 1.0 mJ of energy.
   a. There are 9.7×10^{14} photons in each pulse. What is the wavelength of the laser?
   b. Each pulse lasts a mere 20 ns. What is the average power delivered to the cornea during a pulse?

23. | A laser emits 1.0×10^{19} photons per second from an excited state with energy $E_2 = 1.17$ eV. The lower energy level is $E_1 = 0$ eV.
   a. What is the wavelength of this laser?
   b. What is the power output of this laser?

Problems

24. ‖ a. Draw a diagram similar to Figure 41.3 to show all the possible orientations of the angular momentum vector $\vec{L}$ for the case $l = 3$. Label each $\vec{L}$ with the appropriate value of m.
   b. What is the minimum angle between $\vec{L}$ and the z-axis?

25. ‖ There exist subatomic particles whose spin is characterized by $s = 1$, rather than the $s = \frac{1}{2}$ of electrons. These particles are said to have a spin of one.
   a. What is the magnitude (as a multiple of $\hbar$) of the spin angular momentum S for a particle with a spin of one?
   b. What are the possible values of the spin quantum number?
   c. Draw a vector diagram similar to Figure 41.14 to show the possible orientations of $\vec{S}$.

26. ‖ A hydrogen atom in its fourth excited state emits a photon with a wavelength of 1282 nm. What is the atom's maximum possible orbital angular momentum (as a multiple of $\hbar$) after the emission?

27. ‖ A hydrogen atom has $l = 2$. What are the (a) minimum (as a multiple of $\hbar$) and (b) maximum values of the quantity $(L_x^2 + L_y^2)^{1/2}$?

28. | Calculate (a) the radial wave function and (b) the radial probability density at $r = \frac{1}{2} a_B$ for an electron in the $1s$ state of hydrogen. Give your answers in terms of a_B.

29. ‖ For an electron in the $1s$ state of hydrogen, what is the probability of being in a spherical shell of thickness $0.010 a_B$ at distance (a) $\frac{1}{2} a_B$, (b) a_B, and (c) $2a_B$ from the proton?

30. ‖ Prove that the normalization constant of the $1s$ radial wave function of the hydrogen atom is $(\pi a_B^3)^{-1/2}$, as given in Equations 41.7.
   Hint: A useful definite integral is

$$\int_0^\infty x^n e^{-\alpha x} dx = \frac{n}{\alpha^{n+1}}$$

31. ‖ Prove that the normalization constant of the $2p$ radial wave function of the hydrogen atom is $(24\pi a_B^3)^{-1/2}$, as shown in Equations 41.7.
   Hint: See the hint in Problem 30.

32. ‖ Prove that the radial probability density peaks at $r = a_B$ for the 1s state of hydrogen.

33. ‖ a. Calculate and graph the hydrogen radial wave function $R_{2p}(r)$ over the interval $0 \leq r \leq 8a_B$.
   b. Determine the value of r (in terms of a_B) for which $R_{2p}(r)$ is a maximum.
   c. Example 41.3 and Figure 41.8 showed that the radial probability density for the 2p state is a maximum at $r = 4a_B$. Explain why this differs from your answer to part b.

34. ‖ In general, an atom can have both orbital angular momentum and spin angular momentum. The *total* angular momentum is defined to be $\vec{J} = \vec{L} + \vec{S}$. The total angular momentum is quantized in the same way as $\vec{L}$ and $\vec{S}$. That is, $J = \sqrt{j(j+1)}\hbar$, where j is the total angular momentum quantum number. The z-component of $\vec{J}$ is $J_z = L_z + S_z = m_j \hbar$, where m_j goes in integer steps from $-j$ to $+j$. Consider a hydrogen atom in a p state, with $l = 1$.
   a. L_z has three possible values and S_z has two. List all possible combinations of L_z and S_z. For each, compute J_z and determine the quantum number m_j. Put your results in a table.
   b. The number of values of J_z that you found in part a is too many to go with a single value of j. But you should be able to divide the values of J_z into two groups that correspond to two values of j. What are the allowed values of j? Explain. In a classical atom, there would be no restrictions on how the two angular momenta $\vec{L}$ and $\vec{S}$ can combine. Quantum mechanics is different. You've now shown that there are only two allowed ways to add these two angular momenta.

35. | Draw a series of pictures, similar to Figure 41.22, for the ground states of K, Sc, Co, and Ge.

36. | Draw a series of pictures, similar to Figure 41.22, for the ground states of Ca, Ni, As, and Kr.

37. | a. What downward transitions are possible for a sodium atom in the 6s state? (See Figure 41.24.)
   b. What are the wavelengths of the photons emitted in each of these transitions?

38. ‖ The $5d \rightarrow 3p$ transition in the emission spectrum of sodium has a wavelength of 499 nm. What is the energy of the 5d state?

39. ‖ A sodium atom emits a photon with wavelength 818 nm shortly after being struck by an electron. What minimum speed did the electron have before the collision?

40. ‖ The ionization energy of an atom is known to be 5.5 eV. The emission spectrum of this atom contains only the four wavelengths 310.0 nm, 354.3 nm, 826.7 nm, and 1240.0 nm. Draw an energy-level diagram with the fewest possible energy levels that agrees with these experimental data. Label each level with an appropriate l quantum number.
   Hint: Don't forget about the Δl selection rule.

41. | FIGURE P41.41 shows the first few energy levels of the lithium atom. Make a table showing all the allowed transitions in the emission spectrum. For each transition, indicate
   a. The wavelength, in nm.
   b. Whether the transition is in the infrared, the visible, or the ultraviolet spectral region.
   c. Whether or not the transition would be observed in the lithium absorption spectrum.

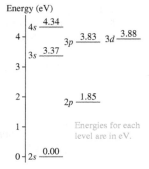

FIGURE P41.41

42. ‖ FIGURE P41.42 shows a few energy levels of the mercury atom.
   a. Make a table showing all the allowed transitions in the emission spectrum. For each transition, indicate the photon wavelength, in nm.
   b. What minimum speed must an electron have to excite the 492-nm-wavelength blue emission line in the Hg spectrum?

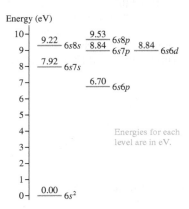

FIGURE P41.42

43. ‖‖ Suppose you put five electrons into a 0.50-nm-wide one-dimensional rigid box (i.e., an infinite potential well).
   a. Use an energy-level diagram to show the electron configuration of the ground state.
   b. What is the ground-state energy of this configuration?

44. ‖ Three electrons are in a one-dimensional rigid box (i.e., an infinite potential well) of length 0.50 nm. Two are in the $n = 1$ state and one is in the $n = 6$ state. The selection rule for the rigid box allows only those transitions for which Δn is odd.
   a. Draw an energy-level diagram. On it, show the filled levels and show all transitions that could emit a photon.
   b. What are all the possible wavelengths that could be emitted by this system?

45. ‖ a. What is the decay rate for the 2p state of hydrogen?
   b. During what interval of time will 10% of a sample of 2p hydrogen atoms decay?

46. ‖ An atom in an excited state has a 1.0% chance of emitting a photon in 0.10 ns. What is the lifetime of the excited state?

47. ‖ a. Find an expression in terms of τ for the *half-life* $t_{1/2}$ of a sample of excited atoms. The half-life is the time at which half of the excited atoms have undergone a quantum jump and emitted a photon.
   b. What is the half-life of the 3p state of sodium?

48. ‖ In fluorescence microscopy, an important tool in biology, a laser beam is absorbed by target molecules in a sample. These molecules are then imaged by a microscope as they emit longer-wavelength photons in quantum jumps back to lower energy levels, a process known as *fluorescence*. A variation on this technique is *two-photon excitation*. If two photons are absorbed simultaneously, their energies add. Consequently, a molecule that is normally excited by a photon of energy E_{photon} can be excited by the simultaneous absorption of two photons having half as much energy. For this process to be useful, the sample must be irradiated at the very high intensity of at least 10^{32} photons/m^2 s. This is achieved by concentrating the laser power into very short pulses (100 fs pulse length) and then focusing the laser beam to a small spot. The laser is fired at the rate of 10^8 pulses each second. Suppose a biologist wants to use two-photon excitation

to excite a molecule that in normal fluorescence microscopy would be excited by a laser with a wavelength of 420 nm. If she focuses the laser beam to a 2.0-μm-diameter spot, what minimum energy must each pulse have?

49. ‖ An electrical discharge in a neon-filled tube maintains a *steady* population of 1.0×10^9 atoms in an excited state with $\tau = 20$ ns. How many photons are emitted per second from atoms in this state?

50. ‖ A ruby laser emits a 100 MW, 10-ns-long pulse of light with a wavelength of 690 nm. How many chromium atoms undergo stimulated emission to generate this pulse?

Challenge Problems

51. Two excited energy levels are separated by the very small energy difference ΔE. As atoms in these levels undergo quantum jumps to the ground state, the photons they emit have nearly identical wavelengths λ.
    a. Show that the wavelengths differ by

    $$\Delta \lambda = \frac{\lambda^2}{hc} \Delta E$$

    b. In the Lyman series of hydrogen, what is the wavelength difference between photons emitted in the $n = 20$ to $n = 1$ transition and photons emitted in the $n = 21$ to $n = 1$ transition?

52. What is the probability of finding a $1s$ hydrogen electron at distance $r > a_B$ from the proton?

53. Prove that the most probable distance from the proton of an electron in the $2s$ state of hydrogen is $5.236a_B$.

54. Find the distance, in terms of a_B, between the two peaks in the radial probability density of the $2s$ state of hydrogen.
    Hint: This problem requires a numerical solution.

55. Suppose you have a machine that gives you pieces of candy when you push a button. Eighty percent of the time, pushing the button gets you two pieces of candy. Twenty percent of the time, pushing the button yields 10 pieces. The *average* number of pieces per push is $N_{avg} = 2 \times 0.80 + 10 \times 0.20 = 3.6$. That is, 10 pushes should get you, on average, 36 pieces. Mathematically, the average value when the probabilities differ is $N_{avg} = \Sigma(N_i \times \text{Probability of } i)$. We can do the same thing in quantum mechanics, with the difference that the sum becomes an integral. If you measured the distance of the electron from the proton in many hydrogen atoms, you would get many values, as indicated

by the radial probability density. But the *average* value of r would be

$$r_{avg} = \int_0^\infty r P_r(r)\, dr$$

Calculate the average value of r in terms of a_B for the electron in the $1s$ and the $2p$ states of hydrogen.

56. An atom in an excited state has a 1.0% chance of emitting a photon in 0.20 ns. How long will it take for 25% of a sample of excited atoms to decay?

57. The 1997 Nobel Prize in physics went to Steven Chu, Claude Cohen-Tannoudji, and William Phillips for their development of techniques to slow, stop, and "trap" atoms with laser light. To see how this works, consider a beam of rubidium atoms (mass 1.4×10^{-25} kg) traveling at 500 m/s after being evaporated out of an oven. A laser beam with a wavelength of 780 nm is directed against the atoms. This is the wavelength of the $5s \rightarrow 5p$ transition in rubidium, with $5s$ being the ground state, so the photons in the laser beam are easily absorbed by the atoms. After an average time of 15 ns, an excited atom spontaneously emits a 780-nm-wavelength photon and returns to the ground state.
    a. The energy-momentum-mass relationship of Einstein's theory of relativity is $E^2 = p^2c^2 + m^2c^4$. A photon is massless, so the momentum of a photon is $p = E_{photon}/c$. Assume that the atoms are traveling in the positive x-direction and the laser beam in the negative x-direction. What is the initial momentum of an atom leaving the oven? What is the momentum of a photon of light?
    b. The total momentum of the atom and the photon must be conserved in the absorption processes. As a consequence, how many photons must be absorbed to bring the atom to a halt?

    NOTE ▶ Momentum is also conserved in the emission processes. However, spontaneously emitted photons are emitted in random directions. Averaged over many absorption/emission cycles, the net recoil of the atom due to emission is zero and can be ignored. ◀

    c. Assume that the laser beam is so intense that a ground-state atom absorbs a photon instantly. How much time is required to stop the atoms?
    d. Use Newton's second law in the form $F = \Delta p/\Delta t$ to calculate the force exerted on the atoms by the photons. From this, calculate the atoms' acceleration as they slow.
    e. Over what distance is the beam of atoms brought to a halt?

STOP TO THINK ANSWERS

Stop to Think 41.1: $n = 3, l = 1$, or a $3p$ state.

Stop to Think 41.2: 4. You can see in Figure 41.8 that the ns state has n maxima.

Stop to Think 41.3: No. $m_s = \pm\frac{1}{2}$, so the z-component S_z cannot be zero.

Stop to Think 41.4: b. The atom would have less energy if the $3s$ electron were in a $2p$ state.

Stop to Think 41.5: c. Emission is a quantum jump to a lower-energy state. The $5p \rightarrow 4p$ transition is not allowed because $\Delta l = 0$ violates the selection rule. The lowest-energy allowed transition is $5p \rightarrow 3d$, with $E_{photon} = \Delta E_{atom} = 3.0$ eV.

Stop to Think 41.6: e. Because $r_B = 2r_A$, the ratio is $e^{-2}/e^{-1} = e^{-1} < \frac{1}{2}$.

42 Nuclear Physics

A photographic emulsion records the tracks of alpha particles emitted by a speck of radium.

▶ **Looking Ahead** The goal of Chapter 42 is to understand the physics of the nucleus and some applications of nuclear physics.

Nuclear Structure

You'll learn how the nucleus is constructed, what holds it together, and why some nuclei are more stable than others.

The nucleus consists of positively charged *protons* and electrically neutral *neutrons*. Together, these are called **nucleons.** The nuclear diameter is only a few femtometers.

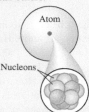

Atom

Nucleons

◀ **Looking Back**
Sections 37.6–37.7 The nucleus

Nuclear Stability

More than 3000 isotopes are known, but only 266 have a stable nucleus. In a graph of neutron number against proton number, the stable nuclei all cluster near a well-defined **line of stability.**

As nuclei grow, the neutron number increases faster than the proton number. You'll learn how this is necessary to hold the nucleus together.

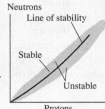

Neutrons

Line of stability

Stable

Unstable

Protons

Nuclear Decay

You'll learn the three basic ways in which an unstable nucleus can decay.

- Alpha decay: Emission of a ^{4}He nucleus (alpha particle).
- Beta decay: Emission of an electron or positron (beta particle).
- Gamma decay: Emission of a high-energy photon (gamma ray).

Nuclear decay releases large amounts of energy. This plutonium sphere—used to power spacecraft—will glow for decades from the energy of alpha decay.

The Shell Model

The force holding the nucleus together is a fundamental force of nature called the **strong force.** It is a *short-range force* whose influence extends over only a few femtometers.

You'll learn to use a **shell model** of nuclear structure, analogous to the electron shells of atoms, to explain nuclear properties.

^{12}C

2   2
4   4
2   2

Neutrons | Protons

◀ **Looking Back**
Section 40.6 Finite potential wells

Half-Lives

The number of unstable nuclei in a sample decreases exponentially with time. We describe nuclear decay by its **half-life,** the time for half the atoms to decay. Half-lives range from microseconds to billions of years.

Nuclei that decay don't vanish—they become some other kind of nucleus called the **daughter nucleus.** You'll learn how to identify the daughter nucleus of a decay.

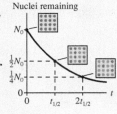

Nuclei remaining

N_0

$\frac{1}{2}N_0$
$\frac{1}{4}N_0$

0
0    $t_{1/2}$ $2t_{1/2}$ t

Nuclear Applications

You'll learn about some of the applications of nuclear physics, which range from measuring ages to curing diseases. You'll also learn how **radiation dose** is measured and what it means.

This image of the brain of a stroke patient was made with nuclei that decay by emitting gamma-ray photons. The damaged area, with reduced activity, is clearly visible.

42.1 Nuclear Structure

The 1890s was a decade of mysterious rays. Cathode rays were being studied in several laboratories, and, in 1895, Röntgen discovered x rays. In 1896, after hearing of Röntgen's discovery, the French scientist A. H. Becquerel wondered if mineral crystals that fluoresce after exposure to sunlight were emitting x rays. He put a piece of film in an opaque envelope, then placed a crystal on top and left it in the sun. To his delight, the film in the envelope was exposed.

Becquerel thought he had discovered x rays coming from crystals, but his joy was short lived. He soon found that the film could be exposed equally well simply by being stored in a closed drawer with the crystals. Further investigation showed that the crystal, which happened to be a mineral containing uranium, was spontaneously emitting some new kind of ray. Rather than finding x rays, as he had hoped, Becquerel had discovered what became known as *radioactivity.*

Ernest Rutherford soon took up the investigation and found not one but three distinct kinds of rays emitted from crystals containing uranium. Not knowing what they were, he named them for their ability to penetrate matter and ionize air. The first, which caused the most ionization and penetrated the least, he called *alpha rays.* The second, with intermediate penetration and ionization, were *beta rays,* and the third, with the least ionization but the largest penetration, became *gamma rays.*

Within a few years, Rutherford was able to show that alpha rays are helium nuclei emitted from the crystal at very high velocities. These became the projectiles that he used in 1909 to probe the structure of the atom. The outcome of that experiment, as you learned in Chapter 37, was Rutherford's discovery that atoms have a very small, dense nucleus at the center.

Rutherford's discovery of the nucleus may have settled the question of atomic structure, but it raised many new issues for scientific research. Foremost among them were:

- What is nuclear matter? What are its properties?
- What holds the nucleus together? Why doesn't the repulsive electrostatic force blow it apart?
- What is the connection between the nucleus and radioactivity?

These questions marked the beginnings of **nuclear physics,** the study of the properties of the atomic nucleus.

Nucleons

The nucleus is a tiny speck in the center of a vastly larger atom. As FIGURE 42.1 shows, the nuclear diameter of roughly 10^{-14} m is only about 1/10,000 the diameter of the atom. Even so, the nucleus is more than 99.9% of the atom's mass. What we call *matter* is overwhelmingly empty space!

The nucleus is composed of two types of particles: *protons* and *neutrons,* which together are referred to as **nucleons.** The role of the neutrons, which have nothing to do with keeping electrons in orbit, is an important issue that we'll address in this chapter. Table 42.1 summarizes the basic properties of protons and neutrons.

As you can see, protons and neutrons are virtually identical other than that the proton has one unit of the fundamental charge e whereas the neutron is electrically neutral. The neutron is slightly more massive than the proton, but the difference is very small, only about 0.1%. Notice that the proton and neutron, like the electron, have an *inherent angular momentum* and magnetic moment with spin quantum number $s = \frac{1}{2}$. As a consequence, protons and neutrons obey the Pauli exclusion principle.

The number of protons Z is the element's **atomic number.** In fact, an element is identified by the number of protons in the nucleus, not by the number of orbiting electrons. Electrons are easily added and removed, forming negative and positive ions, but doing so doesn't change the element. The **mass number** A is defined to be $A = Z + N$,

FIGURE 42.1 The nucleus is a tiny speck within an atom.

This picture of an atom would need to be 10 m in diameter if it were drawn to the same scale as the dot representing the nucleus.

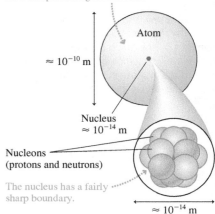

Atom

$\approx 10^{-10}$ m

Nucleus
$\approx 10^{-14}$ m

Nucleons
(protons and neutrons)

The nucleus has a fairly sharp boundary.

$\approx 10^{-14}$ m

TABLE 42.1 Protons and neutrons

	Proton	**Neutron**
Number	Z	N
Charge q	$+e$	0
Spin s	$\frac{1}{2}$	$\frac{1}{2}$
Mass, in u	1.00728	1.00866

where N is the **neutron number.** The mass number is the total number of nucleons in a nucleus.

NOTE ▶ The mass number, which is dimensionless, is *not* the same thing as the atomic mass m. We'll look at actual atomic masses later. ◀

Isotopes and Isobars

It was discovered early in the 20th century that not all atoms of the same element (same Z) have the same mass. There are a *range* of neutron numbers that happily form a nucleus with Z protons, creating a group of nuclei having the same Z-value (i.e., they are all the same chemical element) but different A-values. The atoms of an element with different values of A are called **isotopes** of that element.

Chemical behavior is determined by the orbiting electrons. All isotopes of one element have the same number of orbiting electrons (if the atoms are electrically neutral) and thus have the same chemical properties, but different isotopes of the same element can have quite different nuclear properties.

The notation used to label isotopes is $^A Z$, where the mass number A is given as a *leading* superscript. The proton number Z is not specified by an actual number but, equivalently, by the chemical symbol for that element. Hence ordinary carbon, which has six protons and six neutrons in the nucleus, is written ^{12}C and pronounced "carbon twelve." The radioactive form of carbon used in carbon dating is ^{14}C. It has six protons, making it carbon, and eight neutrons.

More than 3000 isotopes are known. The majority of these are **radioactive,** meaning that the nucleus is not stable but, after some period of time, will either fragment or emit some kind of subatomic particle in an effort to reach a more stable state. Many of these radioactive isotopes are created by nuclear reactions in the laboratory and have only a fleeting existence. Only 266 isotopes are **stable** (i.e., nonradioactive) and occur in nature. We'll begin to look at the issue of nuclear stability in the next section.

The *naturally occurring* nuclei include the 266 stable isotopes and a handful of radioactive isotopes with such long half-lives, measured in billions of years, that they also occur naturally. The most well-known example of a naturally occurring radioactive isotope is the uranium isotope ^{238}U. For each element, the fraction of naturally occurring nuclei represented by one particular isotope is called the **natural abundance** of that isotope.

Although there are many radioactive isotopes of the element iodine, iodine occurs *naturally* only as ^{127}I. Consequently, we say that the natural abundance of ^{127}I is 100%. Most elements have multiple naturally occurring isotopes. The natural abundance of ^{14}N is 99.6%, meaning that 996 out of every 1000 naturally occurring nitrogen atoms are the isotope ^{14}N. The remaining 0.4% of naturally occurring nitrogen is the isotope ^{15}N, with one extra neutron.

A series of nuclei having the same A-value (the same mass number) but different values of Z and N are called **isobars.** For example, the three nuclei ^{14}C, ^{14}N, and ^{14}O are isobars with $A = 14$. Only ^{14}N is stable; the other two are radioactive.

Atomic Mass

You learned in Chapter 16 that atomic masses are specified in terms of the *atomic mass unit* u, defined such that the atomic mass of the isotope ^{12}C is exactly 12 u. The conversion to SI units is

$$1 \text{ u} = 1.6605 \times 10^{-27} \text{ kg}$$

Alternatively, we can use Einstein's $E_0 = mc^2$ to express masses in terms of their energy equivalent. The energy equivalent of 1 u of mass is

$$E_0 = (1.6605 \times 10^{-27} \text{ kg})(2.9979 \times 10^8 \text{ m/s})^2$$
$$= 1.4924 \times 10^{-10} \text{ J} = 931.49 \text{ MeV}$$

(42.1)

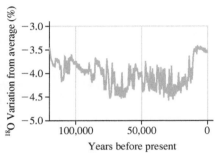

When water freezes to make snow crystals, the fraction of molecules containing ^{18}O is greater for snow that forms at higher atmospheric temperatures. Snow accumulating over tens of thousands of years has built up a thick ice sheet in Greenland. A core sample of this ice gives a record of the isotopic composition of the snow that fell over this time period. Higher numbers on the graph correspond to higher average temperatures. Broad trends, such as the increase in temperature at the end of the last ice age, are clearly seen.

Thus the atomic mass unit can be written

$$1 \text{ u} = 931.49 \text{ MeV}/c^2$$

It may seem unusual, but the units MeV/c^2 are units of mass.

> NOTE ▶ We're using more significant figures than usual. Many nuclear calculations look for the small difference between two masses that are almost the same. Those two masses must be calculated or specified to four or five significant figures if their difference is to be meaningful. ◀

Table 42.2 shows the atomic masses of the electron, the nucleons, and three important light elements. Appendix C contains a more complete list. Notice that the mass of a hydrogen atom is the sum of the masses of a proton and an electron. But a quick calculation shows that the mass of a helium atom (2 protons, 2 neutrons, and 2 electrons) is 0.03038 u less than the sum of the masses of its constituents. The difference is due to the binding energy of the nucleus, a topic we'll look at in Section 42.2.

The isotope ^{2}H is a hydrogen atom in which the nucleus is not simply a proton but a proton and a neutron. Although the isotope is a form of hydrogen, it is called **deuterium.** The natural abundance of deuterium is 0.015%, or about 1 out of every 6700 hydrogen atoms. Water made with deuterium (sometimes written D_2O rather than H_2O) is called *heavy water.*

> NOTE ▶ Don't let the name *deuterium* cause you to think this is a different element. Deuterium is an isotope of hydrogen. Chemically, it behaves just like ordinary hydrogen. ◀

The *chemical* atomic mass shown on the periodic table of the elements is the *weighted average* of the atomic masses of all naturally occurring isotopes. For example, chlorine has two stable isotopes: ^{35}Cl, with $m = 34.97$ u, is 75.8% abundant and ^{37}Cl, at 36.97 u, is 24.2% abundant. The average, weighted by abundance, is $0.758 \times 34.97 + 0.242 \times 36.97 = 35.45$. This is the value shown on the periodic table and is the correct value for most chemical calculations, but it is not the mass of any particular isotope of chlorine.

> NOTE ▶ The atomic masses of the proton and the neutron are both ≈ 1 u. Consequently, the value of the mass number A is *approximately* the atomic mass in u. The approximation $m \approx A$ u is sufficient in many contexts, such as when we're calculating the masses of atoms in the kinetic theory of gases, but in nuclear physics calculations, we almost always need the more accurate mass values that you find in Table 42.2 or Appendix C. ◀

TABLE 42.2 Some atomic masses

Particle	Symbol	Mass (u)	Mass (MeV/c^2)
Electron	e	0.00055	0.51
Proton	p	1.00728	938.28
Neutron	n	1.00866	939.57
Hydrogen	^{1}H	1.00783	938.79
Deuterium	^{2}H	2.01410	1876.12
Helium	^{4}He	4.00260	3728.40

Nuclear Size and Density

Unlike the atom's electron cloud, which is quite diffuse, the nucleus has a fairly sharp boundary. Experimentally, the radius of a nucleus with mass number A is found to be

$$R = r_0 A^{1/3} \tag{42.2}$$

where $r_0 = 1.2$ fm. Recall that 1 fm = 1 femtometer = 10^{-15} m.

As FIGURE 42.2 shows, the radius is proportional to $A^{1/3}$. Consequently, the volume of the nucleus (proportional to R^3) is directly proportional to A, the number of nucleons. A nucleus with twice as many nucleons will occupy twice as much volume. This finding has three implications:

- Nucleons are incompressible. Adding more nucleons doesn't squeeze the inner nucleons into a smaller volume.
- The nucleons are tightly packed, looking much like the drawing in Figure 42.1.
- Nuclear matter has a constant density.

FIGURE 42.2 The nuclear radius and volume as a function of A.

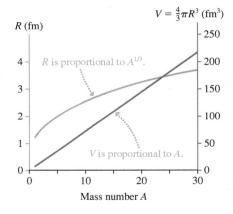

FIGURE 42.3 Density profiles of three nuclei.

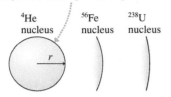

Imagine the nucleus is a drop of liquid. Its density is the same up to the edge of the drop.

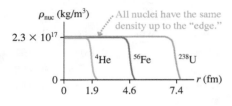

In fact, we can use Equation 42.2 to estimate the density of nuclear matter. Consider a nucleus with mass number A. Its mass, within 1%, is A atomic mass units. Thus

$$\rho_{nuc} \approx \frac{A\,u}{\frac{4}{3}\pi R^3} = \frac{A\,u}{\frac{4}{3}\pi r_0^3 A} = \frac{1\,u}{\frac{4}{3}\pi r_0^3} = \frac{1.66 \times 10^{-27}\ \text{kg}}{\frac{4}{3}\pi(1.2 \times 10^{-15}\ \text{m})^3} \quad (42.3)$$
$$= 2.3 \times 10^{17}\ \text{kg/m}^3$$

The fact that A cancels means that **all nuclei have this density.** It is a staggeringly large density, roughly 10^{14} times larger than the density of familiar liquids and solids. One early objection to Rutherford's model of a nuclear atom was that matter simply couldn't have a density this high. Although we have no direct experience with such matter, nuclear matter really is this dense.

FIGURE 42.3 shows the density profiles of three nuclei. The constant density right to the edge is analogous to that of a drop of incompressible liquid, and, indeed, one successful model of many nuclear properties is called the **liquid-drop model.** Notice that the range of nuclear radii, from small helium to large uranium, is not quite a factor of 4. The fact that ^{56}Fe is a fairly typical atom in the middle of the periodic table is the basis for our earlier assertion that the nuclear diameter is roughly 10^{-14} m, or 10 fm.

STOP TO THINK 42.1   Three electrons orbit a neutral ^{6}Li atom. How many electrons orbit a neutral ^{7}Li atom?

42.2 Nuclear Stability

We've noted that fewer than 10% of the known nuclei are stable (i.e., not radioactive). Because nuclei are characterized by two independent numbers, N and Z, it is useful to show the known nuclei on a plot of neutron number N versus proton number Z. FIGURE 42.4 shows such a plot. Stable nuclei are represented by blue diamonds and unstable, radioactive nuclei by red dots.

FIGURE 42.4 Stable and unstable nuclei shown on a plot of neutron number N versus proton number Z.

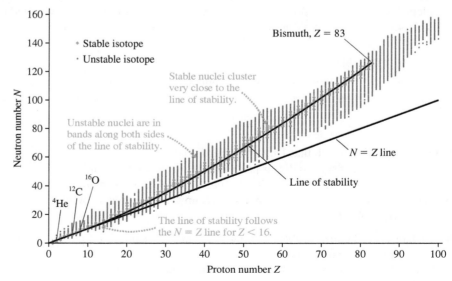

We can make several observations from this graph:

- The stable nuclei cluster very close to the curve called the **line of stability.**
- There are no stable nuclei with $Z > 83$ (bismuth).
- Unstable nuclei are in bands along both sides of the line of stability.
- The lightest elements, with $Z < 16$, are stable when $N \approx Z$. The familiar elements ^{4}He, ^{12}C, and ^{16}O all have equal numbers of protons and neutrons.
- As Z increases, the number of neutrons needed for stability grows increasingly larger than the number of protons. The N/Z ratio is ≈ 1.2 at $Z = 40$ but has grown to ≈ 1.5 at $Z = 80$.

STOP TO THINK 42.2   The isobars corresponding to one specific value of A are found on the plot of Figure 42.4 along

a. A vertical line.

b. A horizontal line.

c. A diagonal line that goes up and to the left.

d. A diagonal line that goes up and to the right.

Binding Energy

A nucleus is a *bound system.* That is, you would need to supply energy to disperse the nucleons by breaking the nuclear bonds between them. FIGURE 42.5 shows this idea schematically.

You learned a similar idea in atomic physics. The energy levels of the hydrogen atom are negative numbers because the bound system has less energy than a free proton and electron. The energy you must supply to an atom to remove an electron is called the *ionization energy.*

In much the same way, the energy you would need to supply to a nucleus to disassemble it into individual protons and neutrons is called the **binding energy.** Whereas ionization energies of atoms are only a few eV, the binding energies of nuclei are tens or hundreds of MeV, energies large enough that their mass equivalent is not negligible.

Consider a nucleus with mass m_{nuc}. It is found experimentally that m_{nuc} is *less* than the total mass $Zm_p + Nm_n$ of the Z protons and N neutrons that form the nucleus, where m_p and m_n are the masses of the proton and neutron. That is, the energy equivalent $m_{nuc}c^2$ of the nucleus is less than the energy equivalent $(Zm_p + Nm_n)c^2$ of the individual nucleons. The binding energy B of the nucleus (not the entire atom) is defined as

$$B = (Zm_p + Nm_n - m_{nuc})c^2 \qquad (42.4)$$

This is the energy you would need to supply to disassemble the nucleus into its pieces.

The practical difficulty is that laboratory scientists use mass spectroscopy to measure *atomic* masses, not nuclear masses. The atomic mass m_{atom} is m_{nuc} plus the mass Zm_e of Z orbiting electrons. (Strictly speaking, we should allow for the binding energy of the electrons, but these binding energies are roughly a factor of 10^6 smaller than the nuclear binding energies and can be neglected in all but the most precise measurements and calculations.)

Fortunately, we can switch from the nuclear mass to the atomic mass by the simple trick of both adding and subtracting Z electron masses. We begin by writing Equation 42.4 in the equivalent form

$$B = (Zm_p + Zm_e + Nm_n - m_{nuc} - Zm_e)c^2 \qquad (42.5)$$

FIGURE 42.5 The nuclear binding energy.

The binding energy is the energy that would be needed to disassemble a nucleus into individual nucleons.

Energy	Nucleus	Disassembled nucleus

$$B \quad + \quad m_{nuc}c^2 \quad = \quad (Zm_p + Nm_n)c^2$$

Now $m_{nuc} + Zm_e = m_{atom}$, the atomic mass, and $Zm_p + Zm_e = Z(m_p + m_e) = Zm_H$, where m_H is the mass of a hydrogen *atom*. Finally, we use the conversion factor 1 u = 931.49 MeV/c^2 to write c^2 = 931.49 MeV/u. The binding energy is then

$$B = (Zm_H + Nm_n - m_{atom}) \times (931.49 \text{ MeV/u}) \qquad (42.6)$$
$$\text{(binding energy)}$$

where all three masses are in atomic mass units.

EXAMPLE 42.1 **The binding energy of iron**

What is the binding energy of the ^{56}Fe nucleus?

SOLVE The isotope ^{56}Fe has Z = 26 and N = 30. The atomic mass of ^{56}Fe, found in Appendix C, is 55.9349 u. Thus the mass difference between the ^{56}Fe nucleus and its constituents is

$$B = 26(1.0078 \text{ u}) + 30(1.0087 \text{ u}) - 55.9349 \text{ u} = 0.529 \text{ u}$$

where, from Table 42.2, 1.0078 u is the mass of the hydrogen atom. Thus the binding energy of ^{56}Fe is

$$B = (0.529 \text{ u}) \times (931.49 \text{ MeV/u}) = 493 \text{ MeV}$$

ASSESS The binding energy is extremely large, the energy equivalent of more than half the mass of a proton or a neutron.

The nuclear binding energy increases as A increases simply because there are more nuclear bonds. A more useful measure for comparing one nucleus to another is the quantity B/A, called the *binding energy per nucleon*. Iron, with B = 493 MeV and A = 56, has 8.80 MeV per nucleon. This is the amount of energy, on average, you would need to supply in order to remove *one* nucleon from the nucleus. Nuclei with larger values of B/A are more tightly held together than nuclei with smaller values of B/A.

FIGURE 42.6 The curve of binding energy.

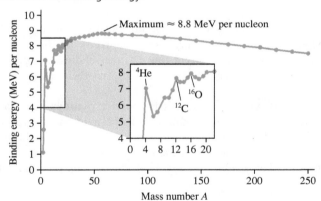

FIGURE 42.6 is a graph of the binding energy per nucleon versus mass number A. The line connecting the points is often called the **curve of binding energy.** This curve has three important features:

■ There are peaks in the binding energy curve at A = 4, 12, and 16. The one at A = 4, corresponding to ^{4}He, is especially pronounced. As you'll see, these peaks, which represent nuclei more tightly bound than their neighbors, are due to *closed shells* in much the same way that the graph of atomic ionization energies (see Figure 41.23) peaked for closed electron shells.

■ The binding energy per nucleon is *roughly* constant at ≈ 8 MeV per nucleon for $A > 20$. This suggests that, as a nucleus grows, there comes a point where the nuclear bonds are *saturated*. Each nucleon interacts only with its nearest neighbors, the ones it's actually touching. This, in turn, implies that the nuclear force is a *short-range* force.

■ The curve has a broad maximum at $A \approx 60$. This will be important for our understanding of radioactivity. In principle, heavier nuclei could become *more* stable (more binding energy per nucleon) by breaking into smaller pieces. Lighter nuclei could become *more* stable by fusing together into larger nuclei. There may not always be a mechanism for such nuclear transformations to take place, but *if* there is a mechanism, it is energetically favorable for it to occur.

42.3 The Strong Force

Rutherford's discovery of the atomic nucleus was not immediately accepted by all scientists. Their primary objection was that the protons would blow themselves apart at tremendously high speeds due to the extremely large electrostatic forces between them at a separation of a few femtometers. No known force could hold the nucleus together.

It soon became clear that a previously unknown force of nature operates within the nucleus to hold the nucleons together. This new force had to be stronger than the repulsive electrostatic force; hence it was named the **strong force**. It is also called the *nuclear force*.

The strong force has four important properties:

1. It is an *attractive* force between any two nucleons.
2. It does not act on electrons.
3. It is a *short-range* force, acting only over nuclear distances.
4. Over the range where it acts, it is *stronger* than the electrostatic force that tries to push two protons apart.

The fact that the strong force is short-range, in contrast to the long-range $1/r^2$ electric, magnetic, and gravitational forces, is apparent from the fact that we see no evidence for nuclear forces outside the nucleus.

FIGURE 42.7 summarizes the three interactions that take place within the nucleus. Whether the strong force between two protons is the same strength as the force between two neutrons or between a proton and a neutron is an important question that can be answered experimentally. The primary means of investigating the strong force is to accelerate a proton to very high speed, using a cyclotron or some other particle accelerator, then to study how the proton is scattered by various target materials.

The conclusion of many decades of research is that the strong force between two nucleons is independent of whether they are protons or neutrons. Charge is the basis for electromagnetic interactions, but it is of no relevance to the strong force. Protons and neutrons are identical as far as nuclear forces are concerned.

FIGURE 42.7 The strong force is the same between any two nucleons.

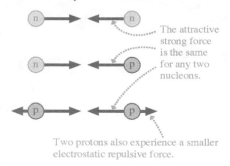

The attractive strong force is the same for any two nucleons.

Two protons also experience a smaller electrostatic repulsive force.

Potential Energy

Unfortunately, there's no simple formula to calculate the strong force or the potential energy of two nucleons interacting via the strong force. FIGURE 42.8 is an experimentally determined potential-energy diagram for two interacting nucleons, with r the distance between their centers. The potential-energy minimum at $r \approx 1$ fm is a point of stable equilibrium.

Recall that the force is the negative of the slope of a potential-energy diagram. The steeply rising potential for $r < 1$ fm represents a strongly repulsive force. That is, the nucleon "cores" strongly repel each other if they get too close together. The force is attractive for $r > 1$ fm, where the slope is positive, and it is strongest where the slope is steepest, at $r \approx 1.5$ fm. The strength of the force quickly decreases for $r > 1.5$ fm and is zero for $r > 3$ fm. That is, the strong force represented by this potential energy is effective only over a very short range of distances.

Notice how small the electrostatic energy of two protons is in comparison to the potential energy of the strong force. At $r \approx 1.0$ fm, the point of stable equilibrium, the magnitude of the nuclear potential energy is ≈ 100 times larger than the electrostatic potential energy.

FIGURE 42.8 The potential-energy diagram for two nucleons interacting via the strong force.

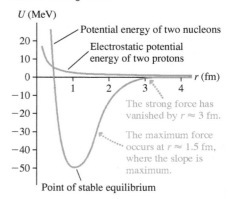

But why does the nucleus have neutrons at all? The answer is related to the short range of the strong force. Protons throughout the nucleus exert repulsive electrostatic forces on each other, but, because of the short range of the strong force, a proton feels an attractive force only from the very few other protons with which it is in close contact. Even though the strong force at its maximum is much larger than the electrostatic force, there wouldn't be enough attractive nuclear bonds for an all-proton nucleus to be stable. Because neutrons participate in the strong force but exert no repulsive forces, **the neutrons provide the extra "glue" that holds the nucleus together.** In small nuclei, where most nucleons are in contact, one neutron per proton is sufficient for stability. Hence small nuclei have $N \approx Z$. But as the nucleus grows, the repulsive force increases faster than the binding energy. More neutrons are needed for stability, causing heavy nuclei to have $N > Z$.

42.4 The Shell Model

Figure 42.8 shows the potential energy of *two* interacting nucleons. To solve Schrödinger's equation for the nucleus, we would need to know the total potential energy of *all* interacting nucleon pairs within the nucleus, including both the strong force and the electrostatic force. This is far too complex to be a tractable problem.

We faced a similar situation with multielectron atoms. Calculating an atom's exact potential energy is exceedingly complicated. To simplify the problem, we made a *model* of the atom in which each electron moves independently with an *average* potential energy due to the nucleus and all other electrons. That model, although not perfect, correctly predicted electron shells and explained the periodic table of the elements.

The **shell model** of the nucleus, using multielectron atoms as an analogy, was proposed in 1949 by Maria Goeppert-Mayer. The shell model considers each nucleon to move independently with an *average* potential energy due to the strong force of all the other nucleons. For the protons, we also have to include the electrostatic potential energy due to the other protons.

FIGURE 42.9 shows the average potential energy of a neutron and a proton. Here r is the distance from the center of the nucleus, not the nucleon–nucleon distance as it was in Figure 42.8. On average, a nucleon's interactions with neighboring nucleons are independent of the nucleon's position inside the nucleus; hence the constant potential energy inside the nucleus. You can see that, to a good approximation, a nucleon appears to be a particle in a finite potential well, a quantum-mechanics problem you studied in Chapter 40.

Maria Goeppert-Mayer received the 1963 Nobel Prize in Physics for her work in nuclear physics.

FIGURE 42.9 The average potential energy of a neutron and a proton.

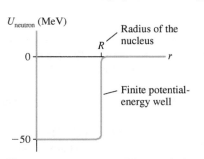

The average neutron potential energy is due to the strong force.

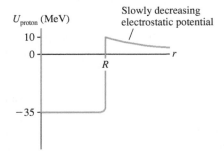

The average proton potential energy is due to the strong force and the electric force. This potential-well depth is for $Z \approx 30$.

Three observations are worthwhile:

1. The depth of the neutron's potential-energy well is ≈ 50 MeV for all nuclei. The radius of the potential-energy well is the nuclear radius $R = r_0 A^{1/3}$.

2. For protons, the positive electrostatic potential energy "lifts" the potential-energy well. The lift varies from essentially none for very light elements to a significant fraction of the well depth for very heavy elements. The potential energy shown in the figure would be appropriate for a nucleus with $Z \approx 30$.

3. Outside the nucleus, where the strong force has vanished, a proton's potential energy is $U = (Z - 1)e^2/4\pi\epsilon_0 r$ due to its electrostatic interaction with the $(Z - 1)$ other protons within the nucleus. This positive potential energy decreases slowly with increasing distance.

The task of quantum mechanics is to solve for the energy levels and wave functions of the nucleons in these potential-energy wells. Once the energy levels are found, we build up the nuclear state, just as we did with atoms, by placing all the nucleons in the lowest energy levels consistent with the Pauli principle. The Pauli principle affects nucleons, just as it did electrons, because they are spin-$\frac{1}{2}$ particles. Each energy level can hold only a certain number of spin-up particles and spin-down particles, depending on the quantum numbers. Additional nucleons have to go into higher energy levels.

Low-Z Nuclei

As an example, we'll consider the energy levels of low-Z nuclei ($Z < 8$). Because these nuclei have so few protons, we can use a reasonable approximation that neglects the electrostatic potential energy due to proton-proton repulsion and considers only the much larger nuclear potential energy. In that case, the proton and neutron potential-energy wells and energy levels are the same.

FIGURE 42.10 shows the three lowest energy levels and the maximum number of nucleons that the Pauli principle allows in each. Energy values vary from nucleus to nucleus, but the spacing between these levels is several MeV. It's customary to draw the proton and neutron potential-energy diagrams and energy levels back to back. Notice that the radial axis for the proton potential-energy well points to the right, while the radial axis for the neutron potential-energy well points to the left.

Let's apply this model to the $A = 12$ isobar. Recall that an isobar is a series of nuclei with the same total number of neutrons and protons. FIGURE 42.11 shows the energy-level diagrams of ^{12}B, ^{12}C, and ^{12}N. Look first at ^{12}C, a nucleus with six protons and six neutrons. You can see that exactly six protons are allowed in the $n = 1$ and $n = 2$ energy levels. Likewise for the six neutrons. Thus ^{12}C has a closed $n = 2$ proton shell and a closed $n = 2$ neutron shell.

> NOTE ▶ Protons and neutrons are different particles, so the Pauli principle is not violated if a proton and a neutron have the same quantum numbers. ◀

FIGURE 42.10 The three lowest energy levels of a low-Z nucleus. The neutron energy levels are on the left, the proton energy levels on the right.

The neutron radial distance is measured to the left.

The proton potential energy is nearly identical to the neutron potential energy when Z is small.

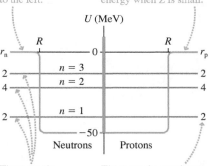

These are the first three allowed energy levels. They are spaced several MeV apart.

These are the maximum numbers of nucleons allowed by the Pauli principle.

FIGURE 42.11 The $A = 12$ isobar has to place 12 nucleons in the lowest available energy levels.

A ^{12}B nucleus could lower its energy if a neutron could turn into a proton.

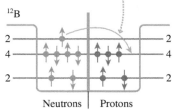

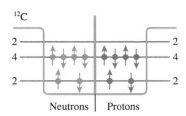

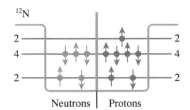

^{12}N has seven protons and five neutrons. The sixth proton fills the $n = 2$ proton shell, so the seventh proton has to go into the $n = 3$ energy level. The $n = 2$ neutron shell has one vacancy because there are only five neutrons. ^{12}B is just the opposite, with the seventh neutron in the $n = 3$ energy level. You can see from the diagrams that the ^{12}B and ^{12}N nuclei have significantly more energy—by several MeV—than ^{12}C.

In atoms, electrons in higher energy levels decay to lower energy levels by emitting a photon as the electron undergoes a quantum jump. That can't happen here because the higher-energy nucleon in ^{12}B is a neutron whereas the vacant lower energy level is that of a proton. But an analogous process could occur *if* a neutron could somehow turn into a proton. And that's exactly what happens! We'll explore the details in Section 42.6, but both ^{12}B and ^{12}N decay into ^{12}C in the process known as *beta decay*.

^{12}C is just one of three low-Z nuclei in which both the proton and neutron shells are full. The other two are ^{4}He (filling both $n = 1$ shells with $Z = 2$, $N = 2$) and ^{16}O (filling both $n = 3$ shells with $Z = 8$, $N = 8$). If the analogy with closed electron shells is valid, these nuclei should be more tightly bound than nuclei with neighboring values of A. And indeed, we've already noted that the curve of binding energy (Figure 42.6) has peaks at $A = 4$, 12, and 16. The shell model of the nucleus satisfactorily explains these peaks. Unfortunately, the shell model quickly becomes much more complex as we go beyond $n = 3$. Heavier nuclei do have closed shells, but there's no evidence for them in the curve of binding energy.

High-Z Nuclei

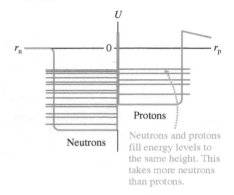

FIGURE 42.12 The proton energy levels are displaced upward in a high-Z nucleus.

We can use the shell model to give a qualitative explanation for one more observation, although the details are beyond the scope of this text. FIGURE 42.12 shows the neutron and proton potential-energy wells of a high-Z nucleus. In a nucleus with many protons, the electrostatic potential energy lifts the proton potential-energy well higher than the neutron potential-energy well. Protons and neutrons now have a different set of energy levels.

As a nucleus is "built," by the addition of protons and neutrons, the proton energy well and the neutron energy well must fill to just about the same height. If there were neutrons in energy levels above vacant proton levels, the nucleus would lower its energy by using beta decay to change the neutron into a proton. Similarly, beta decay would change a proton into a neutron if there were a vacant neutron energy level beneath a filled proton level. **The net result of beta decay is to keep the levels on both sides filled to just about the same energy.**

Because the neutron potential-energy well starts at a lower energy, *more neutron states* are available than proton states. Consequently, a high-Z nucleus will have more neutrons than protons. This conclusion is consistent with our observation in Figure 42.4 that $N > Z$ for heavy nuclei.

42.5 Radiation and Radioactivity

Becquerel's 1896 discovery of "rays" from crystals of uranium prompted a burst of activity. In England, J. J. Thomson and, especially, his student and protégé Ernest Rutherford worked to identify the unknown rays. Using combinations of electric and magnetic fields, much as Thomson had done in his investigations of cathode rays, they found three distinct types of radiation. FIGURE 42.13 shows the basic experimental procedure, and Table 42.3 on the next page summarizes the results.

FIGURE 42.13 Identifying radiation by its deflection in a magnetic field.

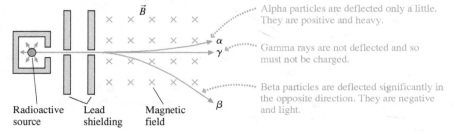

TABLE 42.3 Three types of radiation

Radiation	Identification	Charge	Stopped by
Alpha, α	^{4}He nucleus	$+2e$	Sheet of paper
Beta, β	Electron	$-e$	Few mm of aluminum
Gamma, γ	High-energy photon	0	Many cm of lead

Within a few years, as Rutherford and others deduced the basic structure of the atom, it became clear that these emissions of radiation were coming from the atomic nucleus. We now define *radioactivity* or *radioactive decay* to be the spontaneous emission of particles or high-energy photons from unstable nuclei as they decay from higher-energy to lower-energy states. Radioactivity has nothing to do with the orbiting valence electrons.

NOTE ▶ The term "radiation" merely means something that is *radiated outward*, similar to the word "radial." Electromagnetic waves are often called "electromagnetic radiation." Infrared waves from a hot object are referred to as "thermal radiation." Thus it was no surprise that these new "rays" were also called radiation. Unfortunately, the general public has come to associate the word "radiation" with *nuclear radiation*, something to be feared. It is important, when you use the term, to be sure you're not conveying a wrong impression to a listener or a reader. ◀

Ionizing Radiation

Electromagnetic waves, from microwaves through ultraviolet radiation, are absorbed by matter. The absorbed energy increases an object's thermal energy and its temperature, which is why objects sitting in the sun get warm.

In contrast to visible-light photon energies of a few eV, the energies of the alpha and beta particles and the gamma-ray photons of nuclear decay are typically in the range 0.1–10 MeV, a factor of roughly 10^6 larger. These energies are much larger than the ionization energies of atoms and molecules. Rather than simply being absorbed and increasing an object's thermal energy, nuclear radiation *ionizes* matter and *breaks* molecular bonds. Nuclear radiation (and also x rays, which behave much the same in matter) is called **ionizing radiation.**

An alpha or beta particle traveling through matter creates a trail of ionization, as shown in FIGURE 42.14. Because the ionization energy of an atom is ≈ 10 eV, a particle with 1 MeV of kinetic energy can ionize $\approx 100{,}000$ atoms or molecules before finally stopping. The low-mass electrons are kicked sideways, but the much more massive positive ions barely move and form the trail. This ionization is the basis for the **Geiger counter,** one of the most well-known detectors of nuclear radiation. FIGURE 42.15 shows how a Geiger counter works. The important thing to remember is that a Geiger counter detects only *ionizing radiation.*

Ionizing radiation damages materials. Ions drive chemical reactions that wouldn't otherwise occur. Broken molecular bonds alter the workings of molecular machinery, especially in large biological molecules. It is through these mechanisms—ionization and bond breaking—that nuclear radiation can cause mutations or tumors. We'll look at the biological issues in Section 42.7.

NOTE ▶ Ionizing radiation causes structural damage to materials, but **irradiated objects do not become radioactive.** Ionization drives chemical processes involving the electrons. An object could become radioactive only if its nuclei were somehow changed, and that does not happen. ◀

STOP TO THINK 42.3   A very bright spotlight shines on a Geiger counter. Does it click?

FIGURE 42.14 Alpha and beta particles create a trail of ionization as they pass through matter.

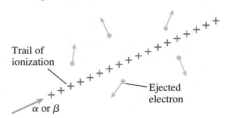

Trail of ionization

Ejected electron

α or β

FIGURE 42.15 A Geiger counter.

1. Ejected electrons cause a chain reaction of ionization of the gas as they accelerate toward the positive wire.

2. Thousands of electrons reach the wire, causing a surge of current.

3. The negative current pulse in the wire causes the "click" of the Geiger counter.

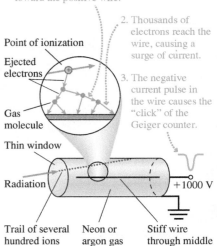

Point of ionization

Ejected electrons

Gas molecule

Thin window

Radiation

+1000 V

Trail of several hundred ions

Neon or argon gas

Stiff wire through middle

Nuclear Decay and Half-Lives

Rutherford discovered experimentally that the number of radioactive atoms in a sample decreases exponentially with time. The reason is that radioactive decay is a *random process*. That is, we can predict only the *probability* that a nucleus will decay, not the exact moment. We encountered exactly this situation when we investigated the lifetimes of excited states of atoms in Section 41.7.

As we did with atoms, let r be the *decay rate*, the probability of decay within the next second by the emission of an alpha or beta particle or a gamma-ray photon. Then the probability of decay within a small time interval Δt is

$$\text{Prob(decay in time interval } \Delta t) = r \, \Delta t \tag{42.7}$$

This equation was also the starting point in our analysis of the spontaneous emission of photons by atoms. The mathematical analysis is exactly the same as in Section 41.7, to which you should refer, leading to the exponential-decay equation

$$N = N_0 e^{-t/\tau} \tag{42.8}$$

where $\tau = 1/r$ is the *lifetime* of the nucleus.

FIGURE 42.16 shows the decrease of N with time. The number of radioactive nuclei decreases from N_0 at $t = 0$ to $e^{-1}N_0 = 0.368N_0$ at time $t = \tau$. In practical terms, the number decreases by roughly two-thirds during one lifetime.

> NOTE ▶ An important aspect of exponential decay is that you can choose any instant you wish to be $t = 0$. The number of radioactive nuclei present at that instant is N_0. If at one instant you have 10,000 radioactive nuclei whose lifetime is $\tau = 10$ min, you'll have roughly 3680 nuclei 10 min later. The fact that you may have had more than 10,000 nuclei earlier isn't relevant. ◀

In practice, it's much easier to measure the time at which half of a sample has decayed than the time at which 36.8% has decayed. Let's define the **half-life** $t_{1/2}$ as the time interval in which half of a sample of radioactive atoms decays. The half-life is shown in Figure 42.16.

The half-life is easily related to the lifetime τ because we know, by definition, that $N = \frac{1}{2}N_0$ at $t = t_{1/2}$. Thus, according to Equation 42.8,

$$\frac{N_0}{2} = N_0 e^{-t_{1/2}/\tau} \tag{42.9}$$

The N_0 cancels, and we can then take the natural logarithm of both sides to find

$$\ln\left(\frac{1}{2}\right) = -\ln 2 = -\frac{t_{1/2}}{\tau} \tag{42.10}$$

With one final rearrangement we have

$$t_{1/2} = \tau \ln 2 = 0.693\tau \tag{42.11}$$

Equation 42.8 can be written in terms of the half-life as

$$N = N_0 \left(\frac{1}{2}\right)^{t/t_{1/2}} \tag{42.12}$$

Thus $N = N_0/2$ at $t = t_{1/2}$, $N = N_0/4$ at $t = 2t_{1/2}$, $N = N_0/8$ at $t = 3t_{1/2}$, and so on. **No matter how many nuclei there are, the number decays by half during the next half-life.**

> NOTE ▶ Half the nuclei decay during one half-life, but don't fall into the trap of thinking that all will have decayed after two half-lives. ◀

FIGURE 42.16 The number of radioactive atoms decreases exponentially with time.

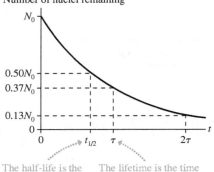

Number of nuclei remaining

The half-life is the time in which half the nuclei decay.

The lifetime is the time at which the number of nuclei is e^{-1}, or 37%, of the initial number.

FIGURE 42.17 shows the half-life graphically. This figure also conveys two other important ideas:

1. Nuclei don't vanish when they decay. The decayed nuclei have merely become some other kind of nuclei, called the *daughter nuclei.*
2. The decay process is random. We can predict that half the nuclei will decay in one half-life, but we can't predict which ones.

Each radioactive isotope, such as ^{14}C, has its own half-life. That half-life doesn't change with time as a sample decays. If you've flipped a coin 10 times and, against all odds, seen 10 heads, you may feel that a tail is overdue. Nonetheless, the probability that the next flip will be a head is still 50%. After 10 half-lives have gone by, $(1/2)^{10} = 1/1024$ of a radioactive sample is still there. There was nothing special or distinctive about these nuclei, and, despite their longevity, each remaining nucleus has exactly a 50% chance of decay during the next half-life.

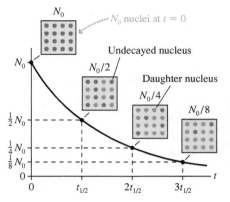

FIGURE 42.17 Half the nuclei decay during each half-life.

EXAMPLE 42.2 **The decay of iodine**

The iodine isotope ^{131}I, which has an eight-day half-life, is used in nuclear medicine. A sample of ^{131}I containing 2.00×10^{12} atoms is created in a nuclear reactor.

a. How many ^{131}I atoms remain 36 hours later when the sample is delivered to a hospital?
b. The sample is constantly getting weaker, but it remains usable as long as there are at least 5.0×10^{11} ^{131}I atoms. What is the maximum delay before the sample is no longer usable?

MODEL The number of ^{131}I atoms decays exponentially.

SOLVE a. The half-life is $t_{1/2} = 8$ days $= 192$ h. After 36 h have elapsed,

$$N = (2.00 \times 10^{12})\left(\frac{1}{2}\right)^{36/192} = 1.76 \times 10^{12} \text{ nuclei}$$

b. The time after creation at which 5.0×10^{11} ^{131}I atoms remain is given by

$$5.0 \times 10^{11} = 0.50 \times 10^{12} = (2.0 \times 10^{12})\left(\frac{1}{2}\right)^{t/8 \text{ days}}$$

To solve for t, we first write this as

$$\frac{0.50}{2.00} = 0.25 = \left(\frac{1}{2}\right)^{t/8 \text{ days}}$$

Now we take the logarithm of both sides. Either natural logarithms or base–10 logarithms can be used, but we'll use natural logarithms:

$$\ln(0.25) = -1.39 = \frac{t}{t_{1/2}}\ln(0.5) = -0.693\frac{t}{t_{1/2}}$$

Solving for t gives

$$t = 2.00t_{1/2} = 16 \text{ days}$$

ASSESS The weakest usable sample is one-quarter of the initial sample. You saw in Figure 42.17 that a radioactive sample decays to one-quarter of its initial number in 2 half-lives.

Activity

The **activity** R of a radioactive sample is the number of decays per second. This is simply the absolute value of dN/dt, or

$$R = \left|\frac{dN}{dt}\right| = rN = rN_0e^{-t/\tau} = R_0e^{-t/\tau} = R_0\left(\frac{1}{2}\right)^{t/t_{1/2}} \qquad (42.13)$$

where $R_0 = rN_0$ is the activity at $t = 0$. The activity of a sample decreases exponentially along with the number of remaining nuclei.

The SI unit of activity is the **becquerel,** defined as

$$1 \text{ becquerel} = 1 \text{ Bq} \equiv 1 \text{ decay/s or } 1 \text{ s}^{-1}$$

An older unit of activity, but one that continues in widespread use, is the **curie.** The curie was originally defined as the activity of 1 g of radium. Today, the conversion factor is

$$1 \text{ curie} = 1 \text{ Ci} \equiv 3.7 \times 10^{10} \text{ Bq}$$

One curie is a substantial activity. The radioactive samples used in laboratory experiments are typically $\approx 1\ \mu$Ci or, equivalently, $\approx 40{,}000$ Bq. These samples can be handled with only minor precautions. Larger sources of radioactivity require lead shielding and special precautions to prevent exposure to high levels of radiation.

EXAMPLE 42.3 **A laboratory source**

The isotope ^{137}Cs is a standard laboratory source of gamma rays. The half-life of ^{137}Cs is 30 years.

a. How many ^{137}Cs atoms are in a 5.0 μCi source?
b. What is the activity of the source 10 years later?

MODEL The number of ^{137}Cs atoms decays exponentially.

SOLVE a. The number of atoms can be found from $N_0 = R_0/r$. The activity in SI units is

$$R = 5.0 \times 10^{-6}\ \text{Ci} \times \frac{3.7 \times 10^{10}\ \text{Bq}}{1\ \text{Ci}} = 1.85 \times 10^5\ \text{Bq}$$

To find the decay rate, first convert the half-life to seconds:

$$t_{1/2} = 30\ \text{years} \times \frac{3.15 \times 10^7\ \text{s}}{1\ \text{year}} = 9.45 \times 10^8\ \text{s}$$

Then

$$r = \frac{1}{\tau} = \frac{\ln 2}{t_{1/2}} = 7.33 \times 10^{-10}\ \text{s}^{-1}$$

Thus the number of ^{137}Cs atoms is

$$N_0 = \frac{R_0}{r} = \frac{1.85 \times 10^5\ \text{Bq}}{7.33 \times 10^{-10}\ \text{s}^{-1}} = 2.5 \times 10^{14}\ \text{atoms}$$

b. The activity decreases exponentially, just like the number of nuclei. After 10 years,

$$R = R_0 \left(\frac{1}{2}\right)^{t/t_{1/2}} = (5.0\ \mu\text{Ci})\left(\frac{1}{2}\right)^{10/30} = 4.0\ \mu\text{Ci}$$

ASSESS Although N_0 is a very large number, it is a very small fraction ($\approx 10^{-10}$) of a mole. The sample is about 60 ng (nanograms) of ^{137}Cs.

Radioactive Dating

A researcher is extracting a small sample of an ancient bone. She will determine the age of the bone by measuring the ratio of ^{14}C to ^{12}C.

Many geological and archeological samples can be dated by measuring the decays of naturally occurring radioactive isotopes. Because we have no way to know N_0, the initial number of radioactive nuclei, radioactive dating depends on the use of ratios.

The most well-known dating technique is carbon dating. The carbon isotope ^{14}C has a half-life of 5730 years, so any ^{14}C present when the earth formed 4.5 billion years ago would long since have decayed away. Nonetheless, ^{14}C is present in atmospheric carbon dioxide because high-energy cosmic rays collide with gas molecules high in the atmosphere. These cosmic rays are energetic enough to create ^{14}C nuclei from nuclear reactions with nitrogen and oxygen nuclei. The creation and decay of ^{14}C have reached a steady state in which the ^{14}C/^{12}C ratio is 1.3×10^{-12}. That is, atmospheric carbon dioxide has ^{14}C at the concentration of 1.3 parts per trillion. As small as this is, it's easily measured by modern chemical techniques.

All living organisms constantly exchange carbon dioxide with the atmosphere, so the ^{14}C/^{12}C ratio in living organisms is also 1.3×10^{-12}. When an organism dies, the ^{14}C in its tissue begins to decay and no new ^{14}C is added. Objects are dated by comparing the measured ^{14}C/^{12}C ratio to the 1.3×10^{-12} value of living material.

Carbon dating is used to date skeletons, wood, paper, fur, food material, and anything else made of organic matter. It is quite accurate for ages to about 15,000 years, roughly three half-lives of ^{14}C. Beyond that, the difficulty of measuring such a small ratio and some uncertainties about the cosmic ray flux in the past combine to decrease the accuracy. Even so, items are dated to about 50,000 years with a fair degree of reliability.

Other isotopes with longer half-lives are used to date geological samples. Potassium-argon dating, using ^{40}K with a half-life of 1.25 billion years, is especially useful for dating rocks of volcanic origin.

EXAMPLE 42.4 **Carbon dating**

Archeologists excavating an ancient hunters' camp have recovered a 5.0 g piece of charcoal from a fireplace. Measurements on the sample find that the ^{14}C activity is 0.35 Bq. What is the approximate age of the camp?

MODEL Charcoal, from burning wood, is almost pure carbon. The number of ^{14}C atoms in the wood has decayed exponentially since the branch fell off a tree. Because wood rots, it is reasonable to assume that there was no significant delay between when the branch fell off the tree and the hunters burned it.

SOLVE The ^{14}C/^{12}C ratio was 1.3×10^{-12} when the branch fell from the tree. We first need to determine the present ratio, then use the known ^{14}C half-life $t_{1/2} = 5730$ years to calculate the time needed to reach the present ratio. The number of ordinary ^{12}C nuclei in the sample is

$$N(^{12}\text{C}) = \left(\frac{5.0 \text{ g}}{12 \text{ g/mol}}\right)(6.02 \times 10^{23} \text{ atoms/mol})$$

$$= 2.5 \times 10^{23} \text{ nuclei}$$

The number of ^{14}C nuclei can be found from the activity to be $N(^{14}\text{C}) = R/r$, but we need to determine the ^{14}C decay rate r. After converting the half-life to seconds, $t_{1/2} = 5730$ years $= 1.807 \times 10^{11}$ s, we can compute

$$r = \frac{1}{\tau} = \frac{1}{t_{1/2}/\ln 2} = 3.84 \times 10^{-12} \text{ s}^{-1}$$

Thus

$$N(^{14}\text{C}) = \frac{R}{r} = \frac{0.35 \text{ Bq}}{3.84 \times 10^{-12} \text{ s}^{-1}} = 9.1 \times 10^{10} \text{ nuclei}$$

and the present ^{14}C/^{12}C ratio is $N(^{14}\text{C})/N(^{12}\text{C}) = 0.36 \times 10^{-12}$. Because this ratio has been decaying with a half-life of 5730 years, the time needed to reach the present ratio is found from

$$0.36 \times 10^{-12} = (1.3 \times 10^{-12})\left(\frac{1}{2}\right)^{t/t_{1/2}}$$

To solve for t, we first write this as

$$\frac{0.36}{1.3} = 0.277 = \left(\frac{1}{2}\right)^{t/t_{1/2}}$$

Now we take the logarithm of both sides:

$$\ln(0.277) = -1.28 = \frac{t}{t_{1/2}}\ln(0.5) = -0.693\frac{t}{t_{1/2}}$$

Thus the age of the hunters' camp is

$$t = 1.85 t_{1/2} = 10,600 \text{ years}$$

ASSESS This is a realistic example of how radioactive dating is done.

STOP TO THINK 42.4   A sample starts with 1000 radioactive atoms. How many half-lives have elapsed when 750 atoms have decayed?

a. 0.25
b. 1.5
c. 2.0
d. 2.5

42.6 Nuclear Decay Mechanisms

This section will look in more detail at the mechanisms of the three types of radioactive decay.

Alpha Decay

An alpha particle, symbolized as α, is a ^{4}He nucleus, a strongly bound system of two protons and two neutrons. An unstable nucleus that ejects an alpha particle will lose two protons and two neutrons, so we can write the decay as

$$^A\text{X}_Z \rightarrow {}^{A-4}\text{Y}_{Z-2} + \alpha + \text{energy} \tag{42.14}$$

FIGURE 42.18 shows the alpha-decay process. The original nucleus X is called the **parent nucleus,** and the decay-product nucleus Y is the **daughter nucleus.** This reaction can occur only when the mass of the parent nucleus is greater than the mass of the daughter nucleus plus the mass of an alpha particle. This requirement is met for heavy,

FIGURE 42.18 Alpha decay.

Before:

$^A\text{X}_Z$ — Parent nucleus

The alpha particle, a fast helium nucleus, carries away most of the energy released in the decay.

After:

$^{A-4}\text{Y}_{Z-2}$

The daughter nucleus has two fewer protons and four fewer nucleons. It has a small recoil.

high-Z nuclei well above the maximum on the Figure 42.6 curve of binding energy. It is energetically favorable for these nuclei to eject an alpha particle because the daughter nucleus is more tightly bound than the parent nucleus.

Although the mass requirement is based on the nuclear masses, we can express it—as we did the binding energy equation—in terms of atomic masses. The energy released in an alpha decay, essentially all of which goes into the alpha particle's kinetic energy, is

$$\Delta E \approx K_\alpha = (m_X - m_Y - m_{He})c^2 \qquad (42.15)$$

EXAMPLE 42.5 **Alpha decay of uranium**

The uranium isotope ^{238}U undergoes alpha decay to ^{234}Th. The atomic masses are 238.0508 u for ^{238}U and 234.0436 u for ^{234}Th. What is the kinetic energy, in MeV, of the alpha particle?

MODEL Essentially all of the energy release ΔE goes into the alpha particle's kinetic energy.

SOLVE The atomic mass of helium is 4.0026 u. Thus

$$K_\alpha = (238.0508 \text{ u} - 234.0436 \text{ u} - 4.0026 \text{ u})c^2$$

$$= \left(0.0046 \text{ u} \times \frac{931.5 \text{ MeV}/c^2}{1 \text{ u}}\right)c^2 = 4.3 \text{ MeV}$$

ASSESS This is a typical alpha-particle energy. Notice how the c^2 canceled from the calculation so that we never had to evaluate c^2.

FIGURE 42.19 The potential-energy diagram of an alpha particle in the parent nucleus.

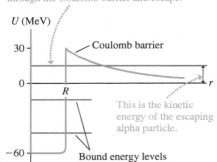

An alpha particle in this energy level can tunnel through the Coulomb barrier and escape.

Alpha decay is a purely quantum-mechanical effect. FIGURE 42.19 shows the potential energy of an alpha particle, where the ^{4}He nucleus of an alpha particle is so tightly bound that we can think of it as existing "prepackaged" inside the parent nucleus. Both the depth of the energy well and the height of the Coulomb barrier are twice those of a proton because the charge of an α particle is $2e$.

Because of the high Coulomb barrier (alpha decay occurs only in high-Z nuclei), there may be one or more allowed energy levels with $E > 0$. Energy levels with $E < 0$ are completely bound, but an alpha particle in an energy level with $E > 0$ can *tunnel* through the Coulomb barrier and escape. That is exactly how alpha decay occurs.

Energy must be conserved, so the kinetic energy of the escaping α particle is the height of the energy level above $E = 0$. That is, potential energy is transformed into kinetic energy as the particle escapes. Notice that the width of the barrier decreases as E increases. The tunneling probability depends very sensitively on the barrier width, as you learned in conjunction with the scanning tunneling microscope. Thus an alpha particle in a higher energy level should have a *shorter half-life* and escape with *more kinetic energy*. The full analysis is beyond the scope of this text, but this prediction is in excellent agreement with measured energies and half-lives.

Beta Decay

Beta decay was initially associated with the emission of an electron e$^-$, the beta particle. It was later discovered that some nuclei can undergo beta decay by emitting a positron e$^+$, the antiparticle of the electron, although this decay mode is not as common. A positron is identical to an electron except that it has a positive charge. To be precise, the emission of an electron is called *beta-minus decay* and the emission of a positron is *beta-plus decay*.

A typical example of beta-minus decay occurs in the carbon isotope ^{14}C, which undergoes the beta-decay process ^{14}C $\rightarrow$ ^{14}N + e$^-$. Carbon has $Z = 6$ and nitrogen has $Z = 7$. Because Z increases by 1 but A doesn't change, it appears that a neutron within the nucleus has changed itself into a proton and an electron. That is, the basic beta-minus decay process appears to be

$$n \rightarrow p^+ + e^- \qquad (42.16)$$

Indeed, a free neutron turns out *not* to be a stable particle. It decays with a half-life of approximately 10 min into a proton and an electron. This decay is energetically allowed because $m_n > m_p + m_e$. Furthermore, it conserves charge.

Whether a neutron *within* a nucleus can decay depends on the masses of the parent and daughter nuclei. The electron is ejected from the nucleus in beta-minus decay, but the proton is not. Thus the decay process shown in FIGURE 42.20a is

$$^A X_Z \rightarrow {}^A Y_{Z+1} + e^- + \text{energy} \qquad \text{(beta-minus decay)} \qquad (42.17)$$

Energy is released because the mass decreases in this process, but we have to be careful when calculating the mass loss. Although not explicitly shown in Equation 42.17, the daughter $^A Y$ is actually the ionized atom $^A Y^+$ because it gained a proton but didn't gain an orbital electron. Its mass is the atomic mass of $^A Y$ *minus* the mass of an electron. But the full right-hand side of the reaction includes an additional electron, the beta particle, so total mass of the decay products is simply the atomic mass of $^A Y$.

Consequently, the energy released in beta-minus decay, based on the mass loss, is

$$\Delta E = (m_X - m_Y)c^2 \qquad (42.18)$$

The energy release has to be positive, so we see that **beta-minus decay occurs only if** $m_X > m_Y$. ^{14}C can undergo beta-minus decay to ^{14}N because $m(^{14}C) > m(^{14}N)$. But $m(^{12}C) < m(^{12}N)$, so ^{12}C is stable and its neutrons cannot decay.

NOTE ▶ The electron emitted in beta-minus decay has nothing to do with the atom's orbital electrons. The beta particle is created in the nucleus and ejected directly from the nucleus when a neutron is transformed into a proton and an electron. ◀

Beta-plus decay is the conversion of a proton into a neutron and a positron:

$$p^+ \rightarrow n + e^+ \qquad (42.19)$$

The full decay process, shown in FIGURE 42.20b, is

$$^A X_Z \rightarrow {}^A Y_{Z-1} + e^+ + \text{energy} \qquad \text{(beta-plus decay)} \qquad (42.20)$$

Beta-plus decay does *not* happen for a free proton because $m_p < m_n$. It *can* happen within a nucleus as long as energy is conserved for the entire nuclear system.

In our earlier discussion of Figure 42.11 we noted that the ^{12}B and ^{12}N nuclei could reach a lower energy state if a proton could change into a neutron, and vice versa. Now we see that such a change can occur if the energy conditions are favorable. And, indeed, ^{12}B undergoes beta-minus decay to ^{12}C while ^{12}N undergoes beta-plus decay to ^{12}C.

In general, beta decay is a process used by nuclei with too many neutrons or too many protons in order to move closer to the line of stability in Figure 42.4.

A third form of beta decay occurs in some nuclei that have too many protons but not enough mass to undergo beta-plus decay. In this case, a proton changes into a neutron by "capturing" an electron from the innermost shell of orbiting electrons (an $n = 1$ electron). The process is

$$p^+ + \text{orbital } e^- \rightarrow n \qquad (42.21)$$

This form of beta decay is called **electron capture,** abbreviated EC. The net result, $^A X_Z \rightarrow {}^A Y_{Z-1}$, is the same as beta-plus decay but without the emission of a positron. Electron capture is the only nuclear decay mechanism that involves the orbital electrons.

The Weak Interaction

We've presented beta decay as if it were perfectly normal for one kind of matter to change spontaneously into a completely different kind of matter. For example, it would be energetically favorable for a large truck to spontaneously turn into a Cadillac and a VW Beetle, ejecting the Beetle at high speed. But it doesn't happen.

FIGURE 42.20 Beta decay.

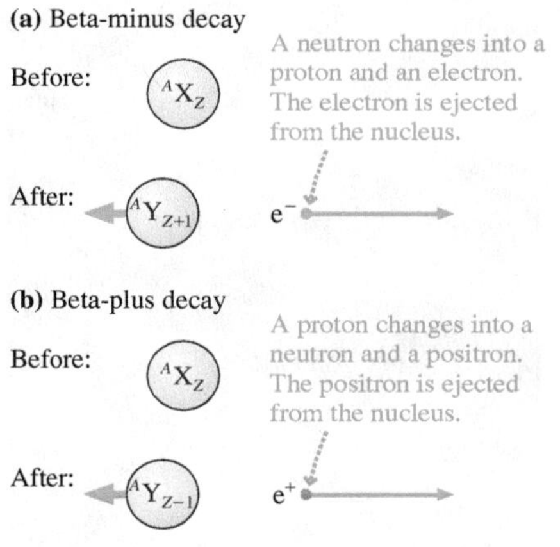

(a) Beta-minus decay

Before:

A neutron changes into a proton and an electron. The electron is ejected from the nucleus.

After:

e⁻

(b) Beta-plus decay

A proton changes into a neutron and a positron. The positron is ejected from the nucleus.

Before:

After:

e⁺

The Super Kamiokande neutrino detector in Japan looks for the neutrinos emitted from nuclear fusion reactions in the core of the sun.

FIGURE 42.21 A more accurate picture of beta decay includes neutrinos.

Before: $^A X_Z$

After: $^A Y_{Z+1}$ e⁻

$\bar{\nu}$

If only the electron and the daughter nucleus are measured, energy and momentum appear not to be conserved. The "missing" energy and momentum are carried away by the undetected antineutrino.

Once you stop to think of it, the process $n \rightarrow p^+ + e^-$ seems ludicrous, not because it violates mass-energy conservation but because we have no idea *how* a neutron could turn into a proton. Alpha decay may be a strange process because tunneling in general goes against our commonsense notions, but it is a perfectly ordinary quantum-mechanical process. Now we're suggesting that one of the basic building blocks of matter can somehow morph into a different basic building block.

To make matters more confusing, measurements in the 1930s found that beta decay didn't seem to conserve either energy or momentum. Faced with these difficulties, the Italian physicist Enrico Fermi made two bold suggestions:

1. A previously unknown fundamental force of nature is responsible for beta decay. This force, which has come to be known as the **weak interaction,** has the ability to turn a neutron into a proton, and vice versa.

2. The beta-decay process emits a particle that, at that time, had not been detected. This new particle has to be electrically neutral, in order to conserve charge, and it has to be much less massive than an electron. Fermi called it the **neutrino,** meaning "little neutral one." Energy and momentum really are conserved, but the neutrino carries away some of the energy and momentum of the decaying nucleus. Thus experiments that detect only the electron seem to violate conservation laws.

The neutrino is represented by the symbol ν, a lowercase Greek nu. The beta-decay processes that Fermi proposed are

$$n \rightarrow p^+ + e^- + \bar{\nu}$$
$$p^+ \rightarrow n + e^+ + \nu \tag{42.22}$$

The symbol $\bar{\nu}$ is an *antineutrino,* although the reason one is a neutrino and the other an antineutrino need not concern us here. **FIGURE 42.21** shows that the electron and antineutrino (or positron and neutrino) *share* the energy released in the decay.

The neutrino interacts with matter so weakly that a neutrino can pass straight through the earth with only a very slight chance of a collision. Trillions of neutrinos created by nuclear fusion reactions in the core of the sun are passing through your body every second. Neutrino interactions are so rare that the first laboratory detection did not occur until 1956, over 20 years after Fermi's proposal.

It was initially thought that the neutrino had not only zero charge but also zero mass. However, experiments in the 1990s showed that the neutrino mass, although very tiny, is not zero. The best current evidence suggests a mass about one-millionth the mass of an electron. Experiments now under way will attempt to determine a more accurate value.

EXAMPLE 42.6 **Beta decay of** ^{14}C

How much energy is released in the beta-minus decay of ^{14}C?

MODEL The decay is $^{14}C \rightarrow ^{14}N + e^- + \bar{\nu}$.

SOLVE In Appendix C we find $m(^{14}C) = 14.003\,242$ u and $m(^{14}N) = 14.003\,074$ u. The mass difference is a mere $0.000\,168$ u, but this is the mass that is converted into the kinetic energy of the escaping particles. The energy released is

$$E = (\Delta m)c^2 = (0.000\,168 \text{ u}) \times (931.5 \text{ MeV/u}) = 0.156 \text{ MeV}$$

ASSESS This energy is shared between the electron and the antineutrino.

Gamma Decay

Gamma decay is the easiest form of nuclear decay to understand. You learned that an atomic system can emit a photon with $E_{photon} = \Delta E_{atom}$ when an electron undergoes a quantum jump from an excited energy level to a lower energy level. Nuclei are no different. A proton or a neutron in an excited nuclear state, such as the one shown in FIGURE 42.22, can undergo a quantum jump to a lower-energy state by emitting a high-energy photon. This is the gamma-decay process.

The spacing between atomic energy levels is only a few eV. Nuclear energy levels, by contrast, are typically 1 MeV apart. Hence gamma-ray photons have $E_{\text{gamma}} \approx 1$ MeV. Photons with this much energy have tremendous penetrating power and deposit an extremely large amount of energy at the point where they are finally absorbed.

Nuclei left to themselves are usually in their ground states and thus cannot emit gamma-ray photons. However, alpha and beta decay often leave the daughter nucleus in an excited nuclear state, so gamma emission is usually found to accompany alpha and beta emission.

The cesium isotope ^{137}Cs is a good example. We noted earlier that ^{137}Cs is used as a laboratory source of gamma rays. Actually, ^{137}Cs undergoes beta-minus decay to ^{137}Ba. FIGURE 42.23 shows the full process. A ^{137}Cs nucleus undergoes beta-minus decay by emitting an electron and an antineutrino, which share between them a total energy of 0.51 MeV. The half-life for this process is 30 years. This leaves the daughter ^{137}Ba nucleus in an excited state 0.66 MeV above the ground state. The excited Ba nucleus then decays within a few seconds to the ground state by emitting a 0.66 MeV gamma-ray photon. Thus a ^{137}Cs sample *is* a source of gamma-ray photons, but the photons are actually emitted by barium nuclei rather than cesium nuclei.

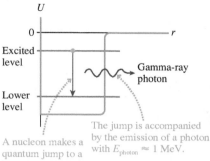

FIGURE 42.22 Gamma decay.

A nucleon makes a quantum jump to a lower energy level. The jump is accompanied by the emission of a photon with $E_{\text{photon}} \approx 1$ MeV.

FIGURE 42.23 The decay of ^{137}Cs involves both beta and gamma decay.

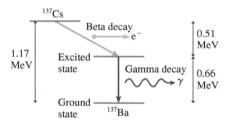

Decay Series

A radioactive nucleus decays into a daughter nucleus. In many cases, the daughter nucleus is also radioactive and decays to produce its own daughter nucleus. The process continues until reaching a daughter nucleus that is stable. The sequence of isotopes, starting with the original unstable isotope and ending with the stable isotope, is called a **decay series.**

Decay series are especially important for very heavy nuclei. As an example, FIGURE 42.24 shows the decay series of ^{235}U, an isotope of uranium with a 700-million-year half-life. This is a very long time, but it is only about 15% the age of the earth, thus most (but not all) of the ^{235}U nuclei present when the earth was formed have now decayed. There are many unstable nuclei along the way, but all ^{235}U nuclei eventually end as the ^{207}Pb isotope of lead, a stable nucleus.

Notice that some nuclei can decay by either alpha *or* beta decay. Thus there are a variety of paths that a decay can follow, but they all end at the same point.

FIGURE 42.24 The decay series of ^{235}U.

Alpha decay reduces A by 4 and Z by 2.
Beta decay increases Z by 1.

Some nuclei can undergo either α or β decay.

^{207}Pb is stable.

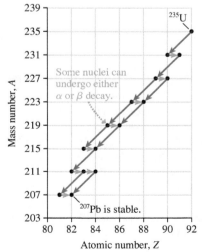

STOP TO THINK 42.5 The cobalt isotope ^{60}Co ($Z = 27$) decays to the nickel isotope ^{60}Ni ($Z = 28$). The decay process is

a. Alpha decay. b. Beta-minus decay. c. Beta-plus decay.
d. Electron capture. e. Gamma decay.

42.7 Biological Applications of Nuclear Physics

Nuclear physics has brought both peril and promise to society. Radiation can cause tumors, but it also can be used to cure some cancers. This section is a brief survey of medical and biological applications of nuclear physics.

Radiation Dose

Nuclear radiation, which is ionizing radiation, disrupts a cell's machinery by altering and damaging the biological molecules. The consequences of this disruption vary from genetic mutations to uncontrolled cell multiplication (i.e., tumors) to cell death.

Beta and gamma radiation can penetrate the entire body and damage internal organs. Alpha radiation has less penetrating ability, but it deposits all its energy in a very small, localized volume. Internal organs are usually safe from alpha radiation, but the skin is very susceptible, as are the lungs if radioactive dust is inhaled.

Biological effects of radiation depend on two factors. The first is the physical factor of how much energy is absorbed by the body. The second is the biological factor of how tissue reacts to different forms of radiation.

The **absorbed dose** of radiation is the energy of ionizing radiation absorbed per kilogram of tissue. The SI unit of absorbed dose is the **gray,** abbreviated Gy. It is defined as

$$1 \text{ gray} = 1 \text{ Gy} \equiv 1.00 \text{ J/kg of absorbed energy}$$

The absorbed dose depends only on the energy absorbed, not at all on the type of radiation or on what the absorbing material is.

Biologists and biophysicists have found that a 1 Gy dose of gamma rays and a 1 Gy dose of alpha particles have different biological consequences. To account for such differences, the **relative biological effectiveness** (RBE) is defined as the biological effect of a given dose relative to the biological effect of an equal dose of x rays.

Table 42.4 shows the relative biological effectiveness of different forms of radiation. Larger values correspond to larger biological effects. Beta radiation and neutrons have a range of values because the biological effect varies with the energy of the particle. Alpha radiation has the largest RBE because the energy is deposited in the smallest volume.

The product of the absorbed dose with the RBE is called the **dose equivalent.** Dose equivalent is measured in **sieverts,** abbreviated Sv. To be precise,

$$\text{dose equivalent in Sv} = \text{absorbed dose in Gy} \times \text{RBE}$$

1 Sv of radiation produces the same biological damage regardless of the type of radiation. An older but still widely used unit for dose equivalent is the **rem,** defined as 1 rem = 0.010 Sv. Small radiation doses are measured in millisievert (mSv) or millirem (mrem).

TABLE 42.4 Relative biological effectiveness of radiation

Radiation type	RBE
X rays	1
Gamma rays	1
Beta particles	1–2
Neutrons	5–20
Alpha particles	20

EXAMPLE 42.7 **Radiation exposure**

A 75 kg laboratory technician working with the radioactive isotope ^{137}Cs receives an accidental 1.0 mSv exposure. ^{137}Cs emits 0.66 MeV gamma-ray photons. How many gamma-ray photons are absorbed in the technician's body?

MODEL The radiation dose is a combination of deposited energy and biological effectiveness. The RBE for gamma rays is 1. Gamma rays are penetrating, so this is a whole-body exposure.

SOLVE The absorbed dose is the dose in Sv divided by the RBE. In this case, because RBE = 1, the dose is 0.0010 Gy = 0.0010 J/kg. This is a whole-body exposure, so the total energy deposited in the

technician's body is 0.075 J. The energy of each absorbed photon is 0.66 MeV, but this value must be converted into joules. The number of photons in 0.075 J is

$$N = \frac{0.075 \text{ J}}{(6.6 \times 10^5 \text{ eV/photon})(1.60 \times 10^{-19} \text{ J/eV})}$$

$$= 7.1 \times 10^{11} \text{ photons}$$

ASSESS The energy deposited, 0.075 J, is very small. Radiation does its damage not by thermal effects, which would require substantially more energy, but by ionization.

Table 42.5 gives some basic information about radiation exposure. We are all exposed to a continuous natural background of radiation from cosmic rays and from naturally occurring radioactive atoms (uranium and other atoms in the uranium decay series) in the ground, the atmosphere, and even the food we eat. This background averages about 3 mSv per year, although there are wide regional variations depending on the soil type and the elevation. (Higher elevations have a larger exposure to cosmic rays.)

Medical x rays vary significantly. The average person in the United States receives approximately 0.6 mSv per year from all medical sources. All other sources, such as fallout from atmospheric nuclear tests many decades ago, nuclear power plants, and industrial uses of radioactivity, add up to less than 0.1 mSv per year.

The question inevitably arises: What is a safe dose? This remains a controversial topic and the subject of ongoing research. The effects of large doses of radiation are easily observed. The effects of small doses are hard to distinguish from other natural and environmental causes. Thus there's no simple or clear definition of a safe dose. A prudent policy is to avoid unnecessary exposure to radiation but not to worry over exposures less than the natural background. It's worth noting that the μCi radioactive sources used in laboratory experiments provide exposures *much* less than the natural background, even if used on a regular basis.

TABLE 42.5 Radiation exposure

Radiation source	Typical exposure (mSv)
CT scan	10
Natural background (1 year)	3
Mammogram x ray	0.8
Chest x ray	0.3
Dental x ray	0.03

Medical Uses of Radiation

Radiation can be put to good use killing cancer cells. This area of medicine is called *radiation therapy*. Gamma rays are the most common form of radiation, often from the isotope ^{60}Co. As FIGURE 42.25 shows, the gamma rays are directed along many different lines, all of which intersect the tumor. The goal is to provide a lethal dose to the cancer cells without overexposing nearby tissue. The patient and the radiation source are rotated around each other under careful computer control to deliver the proper dose.

Other tumors are treated by surgically implanting radioactive "seeds" within or next to the tumor. Alpha particles, which are very damaging locally but don't penetrate far, can be used in this fashion.

Radioactive isotopes are also used as *tracers* in diagnostic procedures. This technique is based on the fact that all isotopes of an element have identical chemical behavior. As an example, a radioactive isotope of iodine is used in the diagnosis of certain thyroid conditions. Iodine is an essential element in the body, and it concentrates in the thyroid gland. A doctor who suspects a malfunctioning thyroid gland gives the patient a small dose of sodium iodide in which some of the normal ^{127}I atoms have been replaced with ^{131}I. (Sodium iodide, which is harmless, dissolves in water and can simply be drunk.) The ^{131}I isotope, with a half-life of eight days, undergoes beta decay and subsequently emits a gamma-ray photon that can be detected.

The radioactive iodine concentrates inside the thyroid gland within a few hours. The doctor then monitors the gamma-ray photon emissions over the next few days to see how the iodine is being processed within the thyroid and how quickly it is eliminated from the body.

Other important radioactive tracers include the chromium isotope ^{51}Cr, which is taken up by red blood cells and can be used to monitor blood flow, and the xenon isotope ^{133}Xe, which is inhaled to reveal lung functioning. Radioactive tracers are *noninvasive*, meaning that the doctor can monitor the inside of the body without surgery.

Magnetic Resonance Imaging

The proton, like the electron, has an inherent angular momentum (spin) and an inherent magnetic moment. You can think of the proton as being like a little compass needle that can be in one of two positions, the positions we call spin up and spin down.

A compass needle aligns itself with an external magnetic field. This is the needle's lowest-energy position. Turning a compass needle by hand is like rolling a ball uphill; you're giving it energy, but, like the ball rolling downhill, it will realign itself with the

FIGURE 42.25 Radiation therapy is designed to deliver a lethal dose to the tumor without damaging nearby tissue.

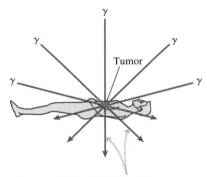

Gamma radiation is incident along many lines, all of which intersect the tumor.

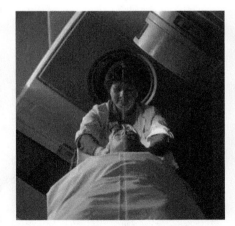

Radiation therapy is a beneficial use of nuclear physics.

lowest-energy position when you remove your finger. There is, however, an *unstable equilibrium* position, like a ball at the top of a hill, in which the needle is anti-aligned with the field. The slightest jostle will cause it to flip around, but the needle will be steady in its upside-down configuration if you can balance it perfectly.

A proton in a magnetic field behaves similarly, but with a major difference: Because the proton's energy is quantized, the proton cannot assume an intermediate position. It's either aligned with the magnetic field (the spin-up orientation) or anti-aligned (spin-down). FIGURE 42.26a shows these two quantum states. Turning on a magnetic field lowers the energy of a spin-up proton and increases the energy of an anti-aligned, spin-down proton. In other words, the magnetic field creates an *energy difference* between these states.

FIGURE 42.26 Nuclear magnetic resonance is possible because spin-up and spin-down protons have slightly different energies in a magnetic field.

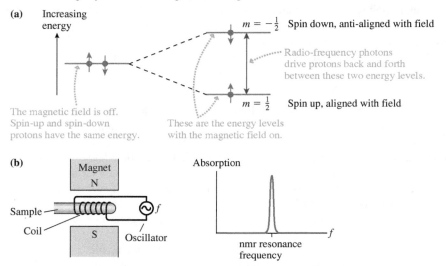

The energy difference is very tiny, only about 10^{-7} eV. Nonetheless, photons whose energy matches the energy difference cause the protons to move back and forth between these two energy levels as the photons are absorbed and emitted. In effect, the photons are causing the proton's spin to flip back and forth rapidly. The photon frequency, which depends on the magnetic field strength, is typically about 100 MHz, similar to FM radio frequencies.

FIGURE 42.26b shows how this behavior is put to use. A sample containing protons is placed in a magnetic field. A coil is wrapped around the sample, and a variable frequency AC source drives a current through this coil. The protons absorb power from the coil when its frequency is just right to flip the spin back and forth; otherwise, no power is absorbed. A *resonance* is seen by scanning the coil through a small range of frequencies.

This technique of observing the spin flip of nuclei (the technique also works for nuclei other than hydrogen) in a magnetic field is called **nuclear magnetic resonance,** or nmr. It has many applications in physics, chemistry, and materials science. Its medical use exploits the fact that tissue is mostly water, and two out of the three nuclei in a water molecule are protons. Thus the human body is basically a sample of protons, with the proton density varying as the tissue density varies.

The medical procedure known as **magnetic resonance imaging,** or MRI, places the patient in a spatially varying magnetic field. The variations in the field cause the proton absorption frequency to vary from point to point. From the known shape of the field and measurements of the frequencies that are absorbed, and how strongly, sophisticated computer software can transform the raw data into detailed images such as the one shown in FIGURE 42.27.

FIGURE 42.27 Magnetic resonance imaging shows internal organs in exquisite detail.

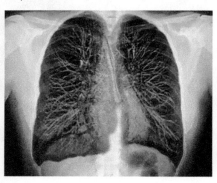

As an interesting footnote, the technique was still being called *nuclear magnetic resonance* when it was first introduced into medicine. Unfortunately, doctors soon found that many patients were afraid of it because of the word "nuclear." Hence the alternative term "magnetic resonance imaging" was coined. It is true that the public perception of nuclear technology is not always positive, but equally true that nuclear physics has made many important and beneficial contributions to society.

CHALLENGE EXAMPLE 42.8   **A radioactive tracer**

An 85 kg patient swallows a 30 μCi beta emitter that is to be used as a tracer. The isotope's half-life is 5.0 days. The average energy of the beta particles is 0.35 MeV, and they have an RBE (relative biological effectiveness) of 1.5. Ninety percent of the beta particles are stopped inside the patient's body and 10% escape. What total dose equivalent does this patient receive?

MODEL Beta radiation penetrates the body—enough that 10% of the particles escape—so this is a whole-body exposure. Even the escaping particles probably deposit some energy in the body, but we'll assume that the dose is from only those particles that stop inside the body.

SOLVE The dose equivalent is the absorbed dose in Gy multiplied by the RBE of 1.5. The absorbed dose is the energy absorbed per kilogram of tissue, so we need to find the total energy absorbed from the time the patient swallows the emitter until it has all decayed. The sample's initial activity R_0 is related to the nuclear decay rate r and the initial number of radioactive atoms N_0 by $R_0 = rN_0$. Thus the number of radioactive atoms in the sample, all of which are going to decay and emit a beta particle, is

$$N_0 = \frac{R_0}{r} = \tau R_0 = \frac{t_{1/2}}{\ln 2} R_0$$

In developing this relationship, we used first the fact that the lifetime τ is the inverse of the decay rate, then the connection between the lifetime and the half-life.

The initial activity is given in microcuries. Converting to becquerels, we have

$$R_0 = (30 \times 10^{-6}\,\text{Ci}) \times \frac{3.7 \times 10^{10}\,\text{Bq}}{1\,\text{Ci}}$$

$$= 1.1 \times 10^6\,\text{Bq} = 1.1 \times 10^6\,\text{decays/s}$$

The half-life in seconds is

$$t_{1/2} = 5.0\,\text{days} \times \frac{86{,}400\,\text{s}}{1\,\text{day}} = 4.3 \times 10^5\,\text{s}$$

Thus the total number of beta decays over the course of several weeks, as the sample completely decays, is

$$N_0 = \frac{t_{1/2}}{\ln 2}\,R_0 = \frac{(4.3 \times 10^5\,\text{s})(1.1 \times 10^6\,\text{decays/s})}{\ln 2} = 6.8 \times 10^{11}$$

Ninety percent of these decays deposit, on average, 0.35 MeV in the body, so the absorbed energy is

$$E_{\text{abs}} = (0.90)(6.8 \times 10^{11})\left((3.5 \times 10^5\,\text{eV}) \times \frac{1.60 \times 10^{-19}\,\text{J}}{1\,\text{eV}} \right)$$

$$= 0.034\,\text{J}$$

This is not a lot of energy in an absolute sense, but it is all damaging, ionizing radiation. The absorbed dose is

$$\text{absorbed dose} = \frac{0.034\,\text{J}}{85\,\text{kg}} = 4.0 \times 10^{-4}\,\text{Gy}$$

and thus the dose equivalent is

$$\text{dose equivalent} = 1.5 \times (4.0 \times 10^{-4}\,\text{Gy}) = 0.60\,\text{mSv}$$

ASSESS This dose, typical of many medical uses of radiation, is about 20% of the yearly radiation dose from the natural background. Although one should always avoid unnecessary radiation, this dose would not cause concern if there were a medical reason for it.

SUMMARY

The goal of Chapter 42 has been to understand the physics of the nucleus and some applications of nuclear physics.

General Principles

The Nucleus

The nucleus is a small, dense, positive core at the center of an atom.

Z protons: charge $+e$, spin $\frac{1}{2}$

N neutrons: charge 0, spin $\frac{1}{2}$

The mass number is $A = Z + N$.

The nuclear radius is $R = r_0 A^{1/3}$, where $r_0 = 1.2$ fm. Typical radii are a few fm.

Proton

Neutron

Nuclear forces

Attractive strong force
- Acts between any two nucleons
- Is short range, < 3 fm
- Is felt between nearest neighbors

Repulsive electric force
- Acts between two protons
- Is long range
- Is felt across the nucleus

Nuclear Stability

Most nuclei are not stable. Unstable nuclei undergo radioactive decay. Stable nuclei cluster along the **line of stability** in a plot of the isotopes.

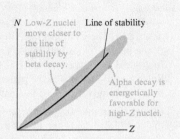

Three mechanisms by which unstable nuclei decay:

Decay	Particle	Mechanism	Energy	Penetration
α	^{4}He nucleus	tunneling	few MeV	low
β	e^-	$n \rightarrow p^+ + e^-$	≈ 1 MeV	medium
	e^+	$p^+ \rightarrow n + e^+$	≈ 1 MeV	medium
γ	photon	quantum jump	≈ 1 MeV	high

Important Concepts

Shell model

Each nucleon moves with an average potential energy due to all other nucleons.

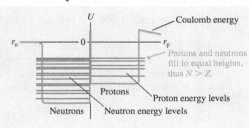

Curve of binding energy

The average binding energy per nucleon has a broad maximum at $A \approx 60$.

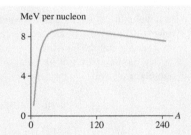

MeV per nucleon

Applications

Radioactive decay

The number of undecayed nuclei decreases exponentially with time t:

$$N = N_0 \exp(-t/\tau)$$
$$= N_0 (1/2)^{t/t_{1/2}}$$

The lifetime τ is $1/r$, where r is the decay rate.
The **half-life**

$$t_{1/2} = \tau \ln 2 = 0.693\tau$$

is the time in which half of any sample decays.

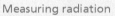

Measuring radiation

The **activity** $R = rN$ of a radioactive sample, measured in becquerels or curies, is the number of decays per second.

The **absorbed dose** is measured in gray, where

$$1 \text{ Gy} \equiv 1.00 \text{ J/kg of absorbed energy}$$

The **relative biological effectiveness** (RBE) is the biological effect of a dose relative to the biological effects of x rays.

The **dose equivalent** is measured in Sv, where Sv = Gy × RBE. One Sv of radiation produces the same biological effect regardless of the type of radiation. Dose equivalent is also measured in rem, where 1 rem = 0.010 Sv.

Terms and Notation

nuclear physics	liquid-drop model	half-life, $t_{1/2}$	gray, Gy
nucleon	line of stability	activity, R	relative biological effectiveness
atomic number, Z	binding energy, B	becquerel, Bq	(RBE)
mass number, A	curve of binding energy	curie, Ci	dose equivalent
neutron number, N	strong force	parent nucleus	sievert, Sv
isotope	shell model	daughter nucleus	rem
radioactive	alpha decay	electron capture	nuclear magnetic resonance (nmr)
stable	beta decay	weak interaction	magnetic resonance imaging (MRI)
natural abundance	gamma decay	neutrino	
isobar	ionizing radiation	decay series	
deuterium	Geiger counter	absorbed dose	

CONCEPTUAL QUESTIONS

1. Consider the atoms ^{16}O, ^{18}O, ^{18}F, ^{18}Ne, and ^{20}Ne. Some of the following questions may have more than one answer. Give all answers that apply.
   a. Which are isotopes?
   b. Which are isobars?
   c. Which have the same chemical properties?
   d. Which have the same number of neutrons?
2. a. Is the binding energy of a nucleus with $A = 200$ more than, less than, or equal to the binding energy of a nucleus with $A = 60$? Explain.
   b. Is a nucleus with $A = 200$ more tightly bound, less tightly bound, or bound equally tightly as a nucleus with $A = 60$? Explain.
3. a. How do we know the strong force exists?
   b. How do we know the strong force is short range?
4. Does each nuclear energy-level diagram in FIGURE Q42.4 represent a nuclear ground state, an excited nuclear state, or an impossible nucleus? Explain.

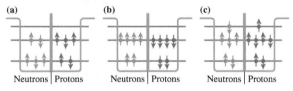

FIGURE Q42.4

5. Are the following decays possible? If not, why not?
   a. $^{232}Th\,(Z = 90) \rightarrow \,^{236}U\,(Z = 92) + \alpha$
   b. $^{238}Pu\,(Z = 94) \rightarrow \,^{236}U\,(Z = 92) + \alpha$
   c. $^{11}B\,(Z = 5) \rightarrow \,^{11}B\,(Z = 5) + \gamma$
   d. $^{33}P\,(Z = 15) \rightarrow \,^{32}S\,(Z = 16) + e^-$

6. Nucleus A decays into nucleus B with a half-life of 10 s. At $t = 0$ s, there are 1000 A nuclei and no B nuclei. At what time will there be 750 B nuclei?
7. What kind of decay, if any, can occur for the nuclei in FIGURE Q42.7?

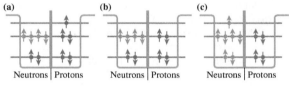

FIGURE Q42.7

8. Apple A in FIGURE Q42.8 is strongly irradiated by nuclear radiation for 1 hour. Apple B is not irradiated. Afterward, in what ways are apples A and B different?

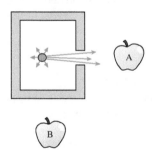

FIGURE Q42.8

9. The three isotopes ^{212}Po, ^{137}Cs, and ^{90}Sr decay as $^{212}Po \rightarrow \,^{208}Pb + \alpha$, $^{137}Cs \rightarrow \,^{137}Ba + e^- + \gamma$, and $^{90}Sr \rightarrow \,^{90}Y + e^-$. Which of these isotopes would be most useful as a biological tracer? Why?

EXERCISES AND PROBLEMS

See Appendix C for data on atomic masses, isotopic abundance, radioactive decay modes, and half-lives.

Problems labeled [   ] integrate material from earlier chapters.

Exercises

Section 42.1 Nuclear Structure

1. | How many protons and how many neutrons are in (a) ^{3}He, (b) ^{32}P, (c) ^{32}S, and (d) ^{238}U?
2. | How many protons and how many neutrons are in (a) ^{6}Li, (b) ^{54}Cr, (c) ^{54}Fe, and (d) ^{220}Rn?
3. | Calculate the nuclear diameters of (a) ^{4}He, (b) ^{40}Ar, and (c) ^{220}Rn.
4. | Which stable nuclei have a diameter of 7.46 fm?
5. | Calculate the mass, radius, and density of the nucleus of (a) ^{7}Li and (b) ^{207}Pb. Give all answers in SI units.

Section 42.2 Nuclear Stability

6. | Use data in Appendix C to make your own chart of stable and unstable nuclei, similar to Figure 42.4, for all nuclei with $Z \leq 8$. Use a blue or black dot to represent stable isotopes, a red dot to represent isotopes that undergo beta-minus decay, and a green dot to represent isotopes that undergo beta-plus decay or electron-capture decay.
7. | a. What is the smallest value of A for which there are two stable nuclei? What are they?
   b. For which values of A less than this are there *no* stable nuclei?
8. | Calculate (in MeV) the total binding energy and the binding energy per nucleon for ^{3}H and for ^{3}He.
9. | Calculate (in MeV) the total binding energy and the binding energy per nucleon for ^{54}Cr and for ^{54}Fe.
10. ‖ Calculate (in MeV) the binding energy per nucleon for ^{3}He and ^{4}He. Which is more tightly bound?
11. ‖ Calculate (in MeV) the binding energy per nucleon for ^{14}O and ^{16}O. Which is more tightly bound?
12. | Calculate the chemical atomic mass of neon.

Section 42.3 The Strong Force

13. ‖ Use the potential-energy diagram in Figure 42.8 to estimate the strength of the strong force between two nucleons separated by 1.5 fm.
14. ‖ Use the potential-energy diagram in Figure 42.8 to sketch an approximate graph of the strong force between two nucleons versus the distance r between their centers.
15. ‖ Use the potential-energy diagram in Figure 42.8 to estimate the ratio of the gravitational potential energy to the nuclear potential energy for two neutrons separated by 1.0 fm.

Section 42.4 The Shell Model

16. | a. Draw energy-level diagrams, similar to Figure 42.11, for all $A = 10$ nuclei listed in Appendix C. Show all the occupied neutron and proton levels.

b. Which of these nuclei are stable? What is the decay mode of any that are radioactive?

17. | a. Draw energy-level diagrams, similar to Figure 42.11, for all $A = 14$ nuclei listed in Appendix C. Show all the occupied neutron and proton levels.
   b. Which of these nuclei are stable? What is the decay mode of any that are radioactive?

Section 42.5 Radiation and Radioactivity

18. | The radium isotope ^{226}Ra has a half-life of 1600 years. A sample begins with 1.00×10^{10} ^{226}Ra atoms. How many are left after (a) 200 years, (b) 2000 years, and (c) 20,000 years?
19. | The barium isotope ^{131}Ba has a half-life of 12 days. A 250 μg sample of ^{131}Ba is prepared. What is the mass of ^{131}Ba after (a) 1 day, (b) 10 days, and (c) 100 days?
20. | The radioactive hydrogen isotope ^{3}H, called *tritium*, has a half-life of 12 years.
   a. What are the decay mode and the daughter nucleus of tritium?
   b. What are the lifetime and the decay rate of tritium?
21. | A sample of 1.0×10^{10} atoms that decay by alpha emission has a half-life of 100 min. How many alpha particles are emitted between $t = 50$ min and $t = 200$ min?
22. ‖ The half-life of ^{60}Co is 5.27 years. The activity of a ^{60}Co sample is 3.50×10^9 Bq. What is the mass of the sample?
23. ‖ What is the half-life in days of a radioactive sample with 5.0×10^{15} atoms and an activity of 5.0×10^8 Bq?

Section 42.6 Nuclear Decay Mechanisms

24. | Identify the unknown isotope X in the following decays.
   a. ^{230}Th $\rightarrow$ X $+ \alpha$
   b. ^{35}S $\rightarrow$ X $+ e^- + \bar{\nu}$
   c. X $\rightarrow$ ^{40}K $+ e^+ + \nu$
   d. ^{24}Na $\rightarrow$ ^{24}Mg $+ e^- + \bar{\nu} \rightarrow$ X $+ \gamma$
25. | Identify the unknown isotope X in the following decays.
   a. X $\rightarrow$ ^{224}Ra $+ \alpha$
   b. X $\rightarrow$ ^{207}Pb $+ e^- + \bar{\nu}$
   c. ^{7}Be $+ e^- \rightarrow$ X $+ \nu$
   d. X $\rightarrow$ ^{60}Ni $+ \gamma$
26. | a. What are the isotopic symbols of all $A = 17$ isobars?
   b. Which of these are stable nuclei?
   c. For those that are not stable, identify both the decay mode and the daughter nucleus.
27. | a. What are the isotopic symbols of all $A = 19$ isobars?
   b. Which of these are stable nuclei?
   c. For those that are not stable, identify both the decay mode and the daughter nucleus.
28. ‖ What is the energy (in MeV) released in the alpha decay of ^{239}Pu?
29. ‖ An unstable nucleus undergoes alpha decay with the release of 5.52 MeV of energy. The combined mass of the parent and daughter nuclei is 452 u. What was the parent nucleus?
30. ‖ What is the total energy (in MeV) released in the beta-minus decay of ^{3}H?

31. ‖ What is the total energy (in MeV) released in the beta-minus decay of ^{24}Na?

32. | What is the total energy (in MeV) released in the beta decay of a neutron?

Section 42.7 Biological Applications of Nuclear Physics

33. | 1.5 Gy of gamma radiation are directed into a 150 g tumor
BIO during radiation therapy. How much energy does the tumor absorb?

34. | The doctors planning a radiation therapy treatment have de-
BIO termined that a 100 g tumor needs to receive 0.20 J of gamma radiation. What is the dose in gray?

35. ‖ A 50 kg laboratory worker is exposed to 20 mJ of beta radia-
BIO tion with RBE = 1.5. What is the dose equivalent in mrem?

36. | How many gray of gamma-ray photons cause the same
BIO biological damage as 30 Gy of alpha radiation?

Problems

37. ‖‖ a. What initial speed must an alpha particle have to just touch the surface of a ^{197}Au gold nucleus before being turned back? Assume the nucleus stays at rest.
    b. What is the initial energy (in MeV) of the alpha particle?
    Hint: The alpha particle is not a point particle.

38. ‖‖ Particle accelerators fire protons at target nuclei for investigators to study the nuclear reactions that occur. In one experiment, the proton needs to have 20 MeV of kinetic energy as it impacts a ^{207}Pb nucleus. With what initial kinetic energy (in MeV) must the proton be fired toward the lead target? Assume the nucleus stays at rest.
    Hint: The proton is not a point particle.

39. ‖ Stars are powered by nuclear reactions that fuse hydrogen into helium. The fate of many stars, once most of the hydrogen is used up, is to collapse, under gravitational pull, into a *neutron star*. The force of gravity becomes so large that protons and electrons are fused into neutrons in the reaction $p^+ + e^- \rightarrow n + \nu$. The entire star is then a tightly packed ball of neutrons with the density of nuclear matter.
    a. Suppose the sun collapses into a neutron star. What will its radius be? Give your answer in km.
    b. The sun's rotation period is now 27 days. What will its rotation period be after it collapses?
    Rapidly rotating neutron stars emit pulses of radio waves at the rotation frequency and are known as *pulsars*.

40. ‖ The element gallium has two stable isotopes: ^{69}Ga with an atomic mass of 68.92 u and ^{71}Ga with an atomic mass of 70.92 u. A periodic table shows that the chemical atomic mass of gallium is 69.72 u. What is the percent abundance of ^{69}Ga?

41. ‖ You learned in Chapter 41 that the binding energy of the electron in a hydrogen atom is 13.6 eV.
    a. By how much does the mass decrease when a hydrogen atom is formed from a proton and an electron? Give your answer both in atomic mass units and as a percentage of the mass of the hydrogen atom.
    b. By how much does the mass decrease when a helium nucleus is formed from two protons and two neutrons? Give your

answer both in atomic mass units and as a percentage of the mass of the helium nucleus.
    c. Compare your answers to parts a and b. Why do you hear it said that mass is "lost" in nuclear reactions but not in chemical reactions?

42. ‖‖ Use the graph of binding energy to estimate the total energy released if a nucleus with mass number 240 fissions into two nuclei with mass number 120.

43. ‖‖ Use the graph of binding energy to estimate the total energy released if three ^{4}He nuclei fuse together to form a ^{12}C nucleus.

44. ‖ Could a ^{56}Fe nucleus fission into two ^{28}Al nuclei? Your answer, which should include some calculations, should be based on the curve of binding energy.

45. ‖‖ What energy (in MeV) alpha particle has a de Broglie wavelength equal to the diameter of a ^{238}U nucleus?

46. ‖ What is the age in years of a bone in which the ^{14}C/^{12}C ratio is measured to be 1.65×10^{-13}?

47. ‖ The activity of a sample of the cesium isotope ^{137}Cs, with a half-life of 30 years, is 2.0×10^8 Bq. Many years later, after the sample has fully decayed, how many beta particles will have been emitted?

48. ‖ A 115 mCi radioactive tracer is made in a nuclear reactor.
BIO When it is delivered to a hospital 16 hours later its activity is 95 mCi. The lowest usable level of activity is 10 mCi.
    a. What is the tracer's half-life?
    b. For how long after delivery is the sample usable?

49. ‖ The radium isotope ^{223}Ra, an alpha emitter, has a half-life of 11.43 days. You happen to have a 1.0 g cube of ^{223}Ra, so you decide to use it to boil water for tea. You fill a well-insulated container with 100 mL of water at 18°C and drop in the cube of radium.
    a. How long will it take the water to boil?
    b. Will the water have been altered in any way by this method of boiling? If so, how?

50. ‖ How many half-lives must elapse until (a) 90% and (b) 99% of a radioactive sample of atoms has decayed?

51. ‖ A sample contains radioactive atoms of two types, A and B. Initially there are five times as many A atoms as there are B atoms. Two hours later, the numbers of the two atoms are equal. The half-life of A is 0.50 hour. What is the half-life of B?

52. ‖ Radioactive isotopes often occur together in mixtures. Suppose a 100 g sample contains ^{131}Ba, with a half-life of 12 days, and ^{47}Ca, with a half-life of 4.5 days. If there are initially twice as many calcium atoms as there are barium atoms, what will be the ratio of calcium atoms to barium atoms 2.5 weeks later?

53. ‖ The technique known as potassium-argon dating is used to date old lava flows. The potassium isotope ^{40}K has a 1.28 billion year half-life and is naturally present at very low levels. ^{40}K decays by two routes: 89% undergo beta-minus decay into ^{40}Ca while 11% undergo electron capture to become ^{40}Ar. Argon is a gas, and there is no argon in flowing lava because the gas escapes. Once the lava solidifies, any argon produced in the decay of ^{40}K is trapped inside and cannot escape. A geologist brings you a piece of solidified lava in which you find the ^{40}Ar/^{40}K ratio to be 0.013. What is the age of the rock?

54. ‖ The half-life of the uranium isotope ^{235}U is 700 million years. The earth is approximately 4.5 billion years old. How much more ^{235}U was there when the earth formed than there is today? Give your answer as the then-to-now ratio.

55. ‖ A chest x ray uses 10 keV photons with an RBE of 0.85. A
BIO 60 kg person receives a 0.30 mSv dose from one chest x ray that exposes 25% of the patient's body. How many x ray photons are absorbed in the patient's body?

56. ‖ The rate at which a radioactive tracer is lost from a patient's
BIO body is the rate at which the isotope decays *plus* the rate at which the element is excreted from the body. Medical experiments have shown that stable isotopes of a particular element are excreted with a 6.0 day half-life. A radioactive isotope of the same element has a half-life of 9.0 days. What is the effective half-life of the isotope in a patient's body?

57. ‖ The plutonium isotope ^{239}Pu has a half-life of 24,000 years
BIO and decays by the emission of a 5.2 MeV alpha particle. Plutonium is not especially dangerous if handled because the activity is low and the alpha radiation doesn't penetrate the skin. However, there are serious health concerns if even the tiniest particles of plutonium are inhaled and lodge deep in the lungs. This could happen following any kind of fire or explosion that disperses plutonium as dust. Let's determine the level of danger.
   a. Soot particles are roughly 1 μm in diameter, and it is known that these particles can go deep into the lungs. How many atoms are in a 1.0-μm-diameter particle of ^{239}Pu? The density of plutonium is 19,800 kg/m^3.
   b. What is the activity, in Bq, of a 1.0-μm-diameter particle?
   c. The activity of the particle is very small, but the penetrating power of alpha particles is also very small. The alpha particles are all stopped, and each deposits its energy in a 50-μm-diameter sphere around the particle. What is the dose, in mSv/year, to this small sphere of tissue in the lungs? Assume that the tissue density is that of water.
   d. Is this exposure likely to be significant? How does it compare to the natural background of radiation exposure?

Challenge Problems

58. The uranium isotope ^{238}U is naturally present at low levels in
BIO many soils. One of the nuclei in the decay series of ^{238}U is the radon isotope ^{222}Rn, which decays by emitting a 5.50 MeV alpha particle with $t_{1/2} = 3.82$ days. Radon is a gas, and it tends to seep from soil into basements. The Environmental Protection Agency recommends that homeowners take steps to remove radon, by pumping in fresh air, if the radon activity exceeds 4 pCi per liter of air.
   a. How many ^{222}Rn atoms are there in 1 m^3 of air if the activity is 4 pCi/L?
   b. The range of alpha particles in air is ≈3 cm. Suppose we model a person as a 180-cm-tall, 25-cm-diameter cylinder with a mass of 65 kg. Only decays within 3 cm of the cylinder can cause exposure, and only ≈50% of the decays direct the alpha particle toward the person. Determine the dose in mSv per year for a person who spends the entire year in a room where the activity is 4 pCi/L.
   c. Does the EPA recommendation seem appropriate? Why?

59. Estimate the stopping distance in air of a 5.0 MeV alpha particle. Assume that the particle loses on average 30 eV per collision.

60. Beta-plus decay is $^A\text{X}_Z \rightarrow {}^A\text{Y}_{Z-1} + e^+ + \nu$.
   a. Determine the mass threshold for beta-plus decay. That is, what is the minimum atomic mass m_X for which this decay is energetically possible? Your answer will be in terms of the atomic mass m_Y and the electron mass m_e.
   b. Can ^{13}N undergo beta-plus decay into ^{13}C? If so, how much energy is released in the decay?

61. All the very heavy atoms found in the earth were created long ago by nuclear fusion reactions in a supernova, an exploding star. The debris spewed out by the supernova later coalesced into the gases from which the sun and the planets of our solar system were formed. Nuclear physics suggests that the uranium isotopes ^{235}U and ^{238}U should have been created in roughly equal numbers. Today, 99.28% of uranium is ^{238}U and only 0.72% is ^{235}U. How long ago did the supernova occur?

62. It might seem strange that in beta decay the positive proton, which is repelled by the positive nucleus, remains in the nucleus while the negative electron, which is attracted to the nucleus, is ejected. To understand beta decay, let's analyze the decay of a free neutron that is at rest in the laboratory. We'll ignore the antineutrino and consider the decay $n \rightarrow p^+ + e^-$. The analysis requires the use of relativistic energy and momentum, from Chapter 36.
   a. What is the total kinetic energy, in MeV, of the proton and electron?
   b. Write the equation that expresses the conservation of relativistic energy for this decay. Your equation will be in terms of the three masses m_n, m_p, and m_e and the relativistic factors γ_p and γ_e.
   c. Write the equation that expresses the conservation of relativistic momentum for this decay. Let v represent speed, rather than velocity, then write any minus signs explicitly.
   d. You have two simultaneous equations in the two unknowns v_p and v_e. To help in solving these, first prove that $\gamma v = (\gamma^2 - 1)^{1/2}c$.
   e. Solve for v_p and v_e. (It's easiest to solve for γ_p and γ_e, then find v from γ.) First get an algebraic expression for each, in terms of the masses. Then evaluate each, giving v as a fraction of c.
   f. Calculate the kinetic energy in MeV of the proton and the electron. Verify that their sum matches your answer to part a.
   g. Now explain why the electron is ejected in beta decay while the proton remains in the nucleus.

63. Alpha decay occurs when an alpha particle tunnels through the Coulomb barrier. FIGURE CP42.63 shows a simple one-dimensional model of the potential-energy well of an alpha particle in a nucleus with $A \approx 235$. The 15 fm width of this one-dimensional potential-energy well is the *diameter* of the nucleus. Further, to keep the model simple, the Coulomb barrier has been modeled as a 20-fm-wide, 30-MeV-high rectangular potential-energy barrier. The goal of this problem is to calculate the half-life of an alpha particle in the energy level $E = 5.0$ MeV.
   a. What is the kinetic energy of the alpha particle while inside the nucleus? What is its kinetic energy after it escapes from the nucleus?
   b. Consider the alpha particle within the nucleus to be a point particle bouncing back and forth with the kinetic energy you

stated in part a. What is the particle's *collision rate,* the number of times per second it collides with a wall of the potential?

c. What is the tunneling probability P_{tunnel}?

d. P_{tunnel} is the probability that on any one collision with a wall the alpha particle tunnels through instead of reflecting. The probability of *not* tunneling is $1 - P_{tunnel}$. Hence the probability that the alpha particle is still inside the nucleus after N collisions is $(1 - P_{tunnel})^N \approx 1 - NP_{tunnel}$, where we've used the binomial approximation because $P_{tunnel} \ll 1$. The half-life is the *time* at which half the nuclei have not yet decayed. Use this to determine (in years) the half-life of the nucleus.

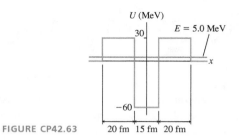

FIGURE CP42.63

STOP TO THINK ANSWERS

Stop to Think 42.1: 3. Different isotopes of an element have different numbers of neutrons but the same number of protons. The number of electrons in a neutral atom matches the number of protons.

Stop to Think 42.2: c. To keep A constant, increasing N by 1 (going up) requires decreasing Z by 1 (going left).

Stop to Think 42.3: No. A Geiger counter responds only to ionizing radiation. Visible light is not ionizing radiation.

Stop to Think 42.4: c. One-quarter of the atoms are left. This is one-half of one-half, or $(1/2)^2$.

Stop to Think 42.5: b. An increase of Z with no change in A occurs when a neutron changes to a proton and an electron, ejecting the electron.

VII Relativity and Quantum Physics

Niels Bohr was right on target with his remark, "Anyone who is not shocked by quantum theory has not understood it." Quantum mechanics *is* shocking. The predictability of Newtonian physics has been replaced by a mysterious world in which physical entities that by all rights should be waves sometimes act like particles. Electrons and neutrons somehow produce wave-like interference with themselves. These discoveries stood common sense on its head.

According to quantum mechanics, the wave function and its associated probabilities are *all we can know* about an atomic particle. This idea is so unsettling that many great scientists were reluctant to accept it. Einstein famously said, "God does not play dice with the universe." But Einstein was wrong. As strange as it seems, this is the way that nature really is.

As we conclude our journey into physics, the knowledge structure for Part VII summarizes the important ideas of relativity and quantum physics. Whether you're shocked or not, these are the scientific theories behind the emerging technologies of the 21st century.

KNOWLEDGE STRUCTURE VII Relativity and Quantum Physics

ESSENTIAL CONCEPTS	Reference frame, event, atom, photon, quantization, wave function, probability density
BASIC GOALS	What are the properties and characteristics of space and time?
	How do we know about light and atoms?
	How are atomic and nuclear phenomena explained by energy levels, wave functions, and photons?

GENERAL PRINCIPLES	**Principle of relativity**	All the laws of physics are the same in all inertial reference frames.
	Schrödinger's equation	$\dfrac{d^2\psi}{dx^2} = -\dfrac{2m}{\hbar^2}[E - U(x)]\psi(x)$
	Pauli exclusion principle	No more than one electron or nucleon can occupy the same quantum state.
	Uncertainty principle	$\Delta x\, \Delta p \geq h/2$

RELATIVITY It follows from the principle of relativity that:

- The speed of light c is the same in all inertial reference frames. No particle or causal influence can travel faster than c.

- Length contraction: The length of an object in a reference frame in which the object moves with speed v is

$$L = \sqrt{1 - \beta^2}\, \ell \leq \ell$$

where ℓ is the proper length and $\beta = v/c$.

- Time dilation: The proper time interval $\Delta\tau$ between two events is measured in a reference frame in which the two events occur at the same position. The time interval Δt in a frame moving with relative speed v is

$$\Delta t = \Delta\tau/\sqrt{1 - \beta^2} \geq \Delta\tau$$

- $E = mc^2$ is the energy equivalent of mass. Mass can be transformed into energy and energy into mass.

QUANTUM PHYSICS Quantum systems are described by a wave function $\psi(x)$.

- The probability that a particle will be found in the narrow interval δx at position x is Prob(in δx at x) $= P(x)\,\delta x$. The probability density is $P(x) = |\psi(x)|^2$.

- The wave function must be normalized

$$\int_{-\infty}^{\infty} |\psi(x)|^2\, dx = 1$$

- The wave function can penetrate into a classically forbidden region with penetration distance

$$\eta = \frac{\hbar}{\sqrt{2m(U_0 - E)}}$$

- A particle can tunnel through an energy barrier of height U_0 and width w with probability $P_{\text{tunnel}} = e^{-2w/\eta}$.

Properties of light

- A photon of light of frequency f has energy $E_{\text{photon}} = hf$.

- Photons are emitted and absorbed on an all-or-nothing basis.

Properties of atoms

- Quantized energy levels, found by solving the Schrödinger equation, depend on quantum numbers n and l.

- An atom can jump from one state to another by emitting or absorbing a photon of energy $E_{\text{photon}} = \Delta E_{\text{atom}}$.

- The ground-state electron configuration is the lowest-energy configuration consistent with the Pauli principle.

Properties of nuclei

- The nucleus is held together by the strong force, an attractive short-range force between any two nucleons.

- Nuclei are stable only if the proton and neutron numbers fall along the line of stability.

- Unstable nuclei decay by alpha, beta, or gamma decay. The number of nuclei decreases exponentially with time.

Quantum Computers

All the systems we studied in Part VII were in a single, well-defined quantum state. For example, a hydrogen atom was in the $1s$ state or, perhaps, the $2p$ state. But there's another possibility. Some quantum systems can exist in a *superposition* of two or more quantum states.

We hinted at the possibility of superposition when we re-examined the double-slit interference experiment in the light of quantum physics. We noted that a photon or electron must, in some sense, go through both slits and then interfere with itself to produce the dot-by-dot buildup of an interference pattern on the screen. Suppose we say that an electron that has passed through the top slit in the figure is in quantum state ψ_a. An electron that has passed through the bottom slit is in state ψ_b.

FIGURE PSVII.1 The electron emerging from the double slit is in a superposition state.

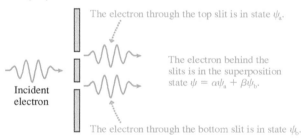

The electron through the top slit is in state ψ_a.

Incident electron

The electron behind the slits is in the superposition state $\psi = \alpha\psi_a + \beta\psi_b$.

The electron through the bottom slit is in state ψ_b.

To say that the electron goes through both slits is to say that the electron emerges from the double slit in the *superposition state* $\psi = \alpha\psi_a + \beta\psi_b$, where the coefficients α and β must satisfy $\alpha^2 + \beta^2 = 1$. (Notice that this is like finding the magnitude of a vector from its components.) If we were to detect the electron, α^2 and β^2 are the probabilities that we would find it to be in state ψ_a or state ψ_b, respectively. But until we detect it, the electron exists in the superposition of *both* states ψ_a and ψ_b. It is this superposition that allows the electron to interfere with itself to produce the interference pattern.

But what does this have to do with computers? As you know, everything a modern digital computer does, from surfing the Internet to crunching numbers, is accomplished by manipulating binary strings of 0s and 1s. The *concept* of computing with binary bits goes back to Charles Babbage in the mid-19th century, but it wasn't until the mid-20th century that scientists and engineers developed the technology that gives this concept a physical representation.

A binary bit is always a 1 or a 0; there's no in-between state. These are represented in a modern microprocessor by small capacitors that are either charged or uncharged. Suppose we wanted to represent information not with capacitors but with a quantum system that has two states. We could say that the system represents a 0 when it is in state ψ_a and a 1 when it is in ψ_b. Such a quantum system is an ordinary binary bit as long as the system is in one state or the other.

But the quantum system, unlike a classical bit, has the possibility of being in a superposition state. Using 0 and 1, rather than ψ_a and ψ_b, we could say that the system can be in the state $\psi = \alpha \cdot 0 + \beta \cdot 1$. This basic unit of quantum computing is called a *qubit*. It may seem at first that we could do the same thing with a classical system by allowing the capacitor charge to vary, but a partially charged capacitor is still a single, well-defined state. In contrast, the qubit—like the electron that goes through both slits—is simultaneously in both state 0 *and* state 1.

To illustrate the possibilities, suppose you have three classical bits and three qubits. The three bits can represent eight different numbers (000 to 111), but only one at a time. The three qubits represent all eight numbers *simultaneously*. To perform a mathematical operation, you must do it eight times on the three bits to learn all the possible outcomes. But you would learn all eight outcomes simultaneously from *one* operation on the three qubits. In general, computing with n qubits provides a theoretical improvement of 2^n over computing with n bits.

We say "theoretical" because quantum computing is still mostly in the concept stage, much as digital computers were 150 years ago. What kind of quantum systems can actually be placed in an appropriate superposition state? How do you manipulate qubits? How do you read information in and out? What kinds of computations would be improved by quantum computing?

These are all questions that are being actively researched today. Quantum computing is in its infancy, and the technology for making a real quantum computer is largely unknown. Just as Charles Babbage couldn't possibly have imagined today's computers, the uses of tomorrow's quantum computers are still unforeseen. But, quite possibly, there are uses that some of you may help to invent.

FIGURE PSVII.2 This string of beryllium ions held in an ion trap is being studied as a possible quantum computer. The quantum states of the ions are manipulated with laser beams.

Mathematics Review

Algebra

Using exponents:

$$a^{-x} = \frac{1}{a^x} \qquad a^x a^y = a^{(x+y)} \qquad \frac{a^x}{a^y} = a^{(x-y)} \qquad (a^x)^y = a^{xy}$$

$$a^0 = 1 \qquad a^1 = a \qquad a^{1/n} = \sqrt[n]{a}$$

Fractions:

$$\left(\frac{a}{b}\right)\left(\frac{c}{d}\right) = \frac{ac}{bd} \qquad \frac{a/b}{c/d} = \frac{ad}{bc} \qquad \frac{1}{1/a} = a$$

Logarithms:

If $a = e^x$, then $\ln(a) = x$ $\qquad$ $\ln(e^x) = x$ $\qquad$ $e^{\ln(x)} = x$

$$\ln(ab) = \ln(a) + \ln(b) \qquad \ln\left(\frac{a}{b}\right) = \ln(a) - \ln(b) \qquad \ln(a^n) = n\ln(a)$$

The expression $\ln(a + b)$ cannot be simplified.

Linear equations: The graph of the equation $y = ax + b$ is a straight line. a is the slope of the graph. b is the y-intercept.

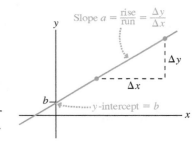

Proportionality: To say that y is proportional to x, written $y \propto x$, means that $y = ax$, where a is a constant. Proportionality is a special case of linearity. A graph of a proportional relationship is a straight line that passes through the origin. If $y \propto x$, then

$$\frac{y_1}{y_2} = \frac{x_1}{x_2}$$

Quadratic equation: The quadratic equation $ax^2 + bx + c = 0$ has the two solutions $x = \dfrac{-b \pm \sqrt{b^2 - 4ac}}{2a}$.

Geometry and Trigonometry

Area and volume:

Rectangle

$A = ab$

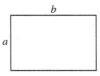

Rectangular box

$V = abc$

Triangle

$A = \frac{1}{2}ab$

Right circular cylinder

$V = \pi r^2 l$

Circle

$C = 2\pi r$

$A = \pi r^2$

Sphere

$A = 4\pi r^2$

$V = \frac{4}{3}\pi r^3$

Arc length and angle: The angle θ in radians is defined as $\theta = s/r$.

The arc length that spans angle θ is $s = r\theta$.

2π rad $= 360°$

Right triangle: Pythagorean theorem $c = \sqrt{a^2 + b^2}$ or $a^2 + b^2 = c^2$

$$\sin\theta = \frac{b}{c} = \frac{\text{far side}}{\text{hypotenuse}} \qquad \theta = \sin^{-1}\left(\frac{b}{c}\right)$$

$$\cos\theta = \frac{a}{c} = \frac{\text{adjacent side}}{\text{hypotenuse}} \qquad \theta = \cos^{-1}\left(\frac{a}{c}\right)$$

$$\tan\theta = \frac{b}{a} = \frac{\text{far side}}{\text{adjacent side}} \qquad \theta = \tan^{-1}\left(\frac{b}{a}\right)$$

General triangle: $\alpha + \beta + \gamma = 180° = \pi$ rad

Law of cosines $c^2 = a^2 + b^2 - 2ab\cos\gamma$

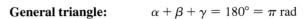

Identities:

$$\tan\alpha = \frac{\sin\alpha}{\cos\alpha} \qquad\qquad \sin^2\alpha + \cos^2\alpha = 1$$

$$\sin(-\alpha) = -\sin\alpha \qquad\qquad \cos(-\alpha) = \cos\alpha$$

$$\sin(\alpha \pm \beta) = \sin\alpha\cos\beta \pm \cos\alpha\sin\beta \qquad \cos(\alpha \pm \beta) = \cos\alpha\cos\beta \mp \sin\alpha\sin\beta$$

$$\sin(2\alpha) = 2\sin\alpha\cos\alpha \qquad\qquad \cos(2\alpha) = \cos^2\alpha - \sin^2\alpha$$

$$\sin(\alpha \pm \pi/2) = \pm\cos\alpha \qquad\qquad \cos(\alpha \pm \pi/2) = \mp\sin\alpha$$

$$\sin(\alpha \pm \pi) = -\sin\alpha \qquad\qquad \cos(\alpha \pm \pi) = -\cos\alpha$$

Expansions and Approximations

Binomial expansion: $(1 + x)^n = 1 + nx + \dfrac{n(n-1)}{2}x^2 + \cdots$

Binomial approximation: $(1 + x)^n \approx 1 + nx$ if $x \ll 1$

Trigonometric expansions: $\sin\alpha = \alpha - \dfrac{\alpha^3}{3!} + \dfrac{\alpha^5}{5!} - \dfrac{\alpha^7}{7!} + \cdots$ for α in rad

$\cos\alpha = 1 - \dfrac{\alpha^2}{2!} + \dfrac{\alpha^4}{4!} - \dfrac{\alpha^6}{6!} + \cdots$ for α in rad

Small-angle approximation: If $\alpha \ll 1$ rad, then $\sin\alpha \approx \tan\alpha \approx \alpha$ and $\cos\alpha \approx 1$.

The small-angle approximation is excellent for $\alpha < 5°$ (≈ 0.1 rad) and generally acceptable up to $\alpha \approx 10°$.

Calculus

The letters a and n represent constants in the following derivatives and integrals.

Derivatives

$$\frac{d}{dx}(a) = 0$$

$$\frac{d}{dx}(ax) = a$$

$$\frac{d}{dx}\left(\frac{a}{x}\right) = -\frac{a}{x^2}$$

$$\frac{d}{dx}(ax^n) = anx^{n-1}$$

$$\frac{d}{dx}\big(\ln(ax)\big) = \frac{1}{x}$$

$$\frac{d}{dx}(e^{ax}) = ae^{ax}$$

$$\frac{d}{dx}\big(\sin(ax)\big) = a\cos(ax)$$

$$\frac{d}{dx}\big(\cos(ax)\big) = -a\sin(ax)$$

Integrals

$$\int x\, dx = \frac{1}{2}x^2$$

$$\int x^2\, dx = \frac{1}{3}x^3$$

$$\int \frac{1}{x^2}\, dx = -\frac{1}{x}$$

$$\int x^n\, dx = \frac{x^{n+1}}{n+1} \qquad n \neq -1$$

$$\int \frac{dx}{x} = \ln x$$

$$\int \frac{dx}{a+x} = \ln(a+x)$$

$$\int \frac{x\, dx}{a+x} = x - a\ln(a+x)$$

$$\int \frac{dx}{\sqrt{x^2 \pm a^2}} = \ln\left(x + \sqrt{x^2 \pm a^2}\right)$$

$$\int \frac{x\, dx}{\sqrt{x^2 \pm a^2}} = \sqrt{x^2 \pm a^2}$$

$$\int \frac{dx}{x^2 + a^2} = \frac{1}{a}\tan^{-1}\left(\frac{x}{a}\right)$$

$$\int \frac{dx}{(x^2 + a^2)^2} = \frac{1}{2a^3}\tan^{-1}\left(\frac{x}{a}\right) + \frac{x}{2a^2(x^2 + a^2)}$$

$$\int \frac{dx}{(x^2 \pm a^2)^{3/2}} = \frac{\pm x}{a^2\sqrt{x^2 \pm a^2}}$$

$$\int \frac{x\, dx}{(x^2 \pm a^2)^{3/2}} = -\frac{1}{\sqrt{x^2 \pm a^2}}$$

$$\int e^{ax}\, dx = \frac{1}{a}e^{ax}$$

$$\int xe^{-x}\, dx = -(x+1)e^{-x}$$

$$\int x^2 e^{-x}\, dx = -(x^2 + 2x + 2)e^{-x}$$

$$\int \sin(ax)\, dx = -\frac{1}{a}\cos(ax)$$

$$\int \cos(ax)\, dx = \frac{1}{a}\sin(ax)$$

$$\int \sin^2(ax)\, dx = \frac{x}{2} - \frac{\sin(2ax)}{4a}$$

$$\int \cos^2(ax)\, dx = \frac{x}{2} + \frac{\sin(2ax)}{4a}$$

$$\int_0^\infty x^n e^{-ax}\, dx = \frac{n!}{a^{n+1}}$$

$$\int_0^\infty e^{-ax^2}\, dx = \frac{1}{2}\sqrt{\frac{\pi}{a}}$$

Periodic Table of Elements

Atomic number — 27
Co — Symbol
58.9 — Atomic mass

Transition elements

Inner transition elements

An atomic mass in brackets is that of the longest-lived isotope of an element with no stable isotopes.

Period																		
1	1 H 1.0																	2 He 4.0
2	3 Li 6.9	4 Be 9.0											5 B 10.8	6 C 12.0	7 N 14.0	8 O 16.0	9 F 19.0	10 Ne 20.2
3	11 Na 23.0	12 Mg 24.3											13 Al 27.0	14 Si 28.1	15 P 31.0	16 S 32.1	17 Cl 35.5	18 Ar 39.9
4	19 K 39.1	20 Ca 40.1	21 Sc 45.0	22 Ti 47.9	23 V 50.9	24 Cr 52.0	25 Mn 54.9	26 Fe 55.8	27 Co 58.9	28 Ni 58.7	29 Cu 63.5	30 Zn 65.4	31 Ga 69.7	32 Ge 72.6	33 As 74.9	34 Se 79.0	35 Br 79.9	36 Kr 83.8
5	37 Rb 85.5	38 Sr 87.6	39 Y 88.9	40 Zr 91.2	41 Nb 92.9	42 Mo 95.9	43 Tc [98]	44 Ru 101.1	45 Rh 102.9	46 Pd 106.4	47 Ag 107.9	48 Cd 112.4	49 In 114.8	50 Sn 118.7	51 Sb 121.8	52 Te 127.6	53 I 126.9	54 Xe 131.3
6	55 Cs 132.9	56 Ba 137.3	71 Lu 175.0	72 Hf 178.5	73 Ta 180.9	74 W 183.9	75 Re 186.2	76 Os 190.2	77 Ir 192.2	78 Pt 195.1	79 Au 197.0	80 Hg 200.6	81 Tl 204.4	82 Pb 207.2	83 Bi 209.0	84 Po [209]	85 At [210]	86 Rn [222]
7	87 Fr [223]	88 Ra [226]	103 Lr [262]	104 Rf [265]	105 Db [268]	106 Sg [271]	107 Bh [272]	108 Hs [270]	109 Mt [276]	110 Ds [281]	111 Rg [280]	112 Cn [285]	113	114	115	116	117	118

Lanthanides 6

57 La 138.9	58 Ce 140.1	59 Pr 140.9	60 Nd 144.2	61 Pm 144.9	62 Sm 150.4	63 Eu 152.0	64 Gd 157.3	65 Tb 158.9	66 Dy 162.5	67 Ho 164.9	68 Er 167.3	69 Tm 168.9	70 Yb 173.0

Actinides 7

89 Ac [227]	90 Th 232.0	91 Pa 231.0	92 U 238.0	93 Np [237]	94 Pu [244]	95 Am [243]	96 Cm [247]	97 Bk [247]	98 Cf [251]	99 Es [252]	100 Fm [257]	101 Md [258]	102 No [259]

Atomic and Nuclear Data

Atomic Number (Z)	Element	Symbol	Mass Number (A)	Atomic Mass (u)	Percent Abundance	Decay Mode	Half-Life $t_{1/2}$
0	(Neutron)	n	1	1.008 665		β^-	10.4 min
1	Hydrogen	H	1	1.007 825	99.985	stable	
	Deuterium	D	2	2.014 102	0.015	stable	
	Tritium	T	3	3.016 049		β^-	12.33 yr
2	Helium	He	3	3.016 029	0.000 1	stable	
			4	4.002 602	99.999 9	stable	
			6	6.018 886		β^-	0.81 s
3	Lithium	Li	6	6.015 121	7.50	stable	
			7	7.016 003	92.50	stable	
			8	8.022 486		β^-	0.84 s
4	Beryllium	Be	7	7.016 928		EC	53.3 days
			9	9.012 174	100	stable	
			10	10.013 534		β^-	1.5×10^6 yr
5	Boron	B	10	10.012 936	19.90	stable	
			11	11.009 305	80.10	stable	
			12	12.014 352		β^-	0.020 2 s
6	Carbon	C	10	10.016 854		β^+	19.3 s
			11	11.011 433		β^+	20.4 min
			12	12.000 000	98.90	stable	
			13	13.003 355	1.10	stable	
			14	14.003 242		β^-	5 730 yr
			15	15.010 599		β^-	2.45 s
7	Nitrogen	N	12	12.018 613		β^+	0.011 0 s
			13	13.005 738		β^+	9.96 min
			14	14.003 074	99.63	stable	
			15	15.000 108	0.37	stable	
			16	16.006 100		β^-	7.13 s
			17	17.008 450		β^-	4.17 s
8	Oxygen	O	14	14.008 595		EC	70.6 s
			15	15.003 065		β^+	122 s
			16	15.994 915	99.76	stable	
			17	16.999 132	0.04	stable	
			18	17.999 160	0.20	stable	
			19	19.003 577		β^-	26.9 s
9	Fluorine	F	17	17.002 094		EC	64.5 s
			18	18.000 937		β^+	109.8 min
			19	18.998 404	100	stable	
			20	19.999 982		β^-	11.0 s
10	Neon	Ne	19	19.001 880		β^+	17.2 s
			20	19.992 435	90.48	stable	
			21	20.993 841	0.27	stable	
			22	21.991 383	9.25	stable	

Atomic Number (Z)	Element	Symbol	Mass Number (A)	Atomic Mass (u)	Percent Abundance	Decay Mode	Half-Life $t_{1/2}$
11	Sodium	Na	22	21.994 434		β^+	2.61 yr
			23	22.989 770	100	stable	
			24	23.990 961		β^-	14.96 hr
12	Magnesium	Mg	24	23.985 042	78.99	stable	
			25	24.985 838	10.00	stable	
			26	25.982 594	11.01	stable	
13	Aluminum	Al	27	26.981 538	100	stable	
			28	27.981 910		β^-	2.24 min
14	Silicon	Si	28	27.976 927	92.23	stable	
			29	28.976 495	4.67	stable	
			30	29.973 770	3.10	stable	
			31	30.975 362		β^-	2.62 hr
15	Phosphorus	P	30	29.978 307		β^+	2.50 min
			31	30.973 762	100	stable	
			32	31.973 908		β^-	14.26 days
16	Sulfur	S	32	31.972 071	95.02	stable	
			33	32.971 459	0.75	stable	
			34	33.967 867	4.21	stable	
			35	34.969 033		β^-	87.5 days
			36	35.967 081	0.02	stable	
17	Chlorine	Cl	35	34.968 853	75.77	stable	
			36	35.968 307		β^-	3.0×10^5 yr
			37	36.965 903	24.23	stable	
18	Argon	Ar	36	35.967 547	0.34	stable	
			38	37.962 732	0.06	stable	
			39	38.964 314		β^-	269 yr
			40	39.962 384	99.60	stable	
			42	41.963 049		β^-	33 yr
19	Potassium	K	39	38.963 708	93.26	stable	
			40	39.964 000	0.01	β^+	1.28×10^9 yr
			41	40.961 827	6.73	stable	
20	Calcium	Ca	40	39.962 591	96.94	stable	
			42	41.958 618	0.64	stable	
			43	42.958 767	0.13	stable	
			44	43.955 481	2.08	stable	
			47	46.954 547		β^-	4.5 days
			48	47.952 534	0.18	stable	
24	Chromium	Cr	50	49.946 047	4.34	stable	
			52	51.940 511	83.79	stable	
			53	52.940 652	9.50	stable	
			54	53.938 883	2.36	stable	
26	Iron	Fe	54	53.939 613	5.9	stable	
			55	54.938 297		EC	2.7 yr
			56	55.934 940	91.72	stable	
			57	56.935 396	2.1	stable	
			58	57.933 278	0.28	stable	

Atomic Number (Z)	Element	Symbol	Mass Number (A)	Atomic Mass (u)	Percent Abundance	Decay Mode	Half-Life $t_{1/2}$
27	Cobalt	Co	59	58.933 198	100	stable	
			60	59.933 820		β^-	5.27 yr
28	Nickel	Ni	58	57.935 346	68.08	stable	
			60	59.930 789	26.22	stable	
			61	60.931 058	1.14	stable	
			62	61.928 346	3.63	stable	
			64	63.927 967	0.92	stable	
29	Copper	Cu	63	62.929 599	69.17	stable	
			65	64.927 791	30.83	stable	
47	Silver	Ag	107	106.905 091	51.84	stable	
			109	108.904 754	48.16	stable	
48	Cadmium	Cd	106	105.906 457	1.25	stable	
			109	108.904 984		EC	462 days
			110	109.903 004	12.49	stable	
			111	110.904 182	12.80	stable	
			112	111.902 760	24.13	stable	
			113	112.904 401	12.22	stable	
			114	113.903 359	28.73	stable	
			116	115.904 755	7.49	stable	
53	Iodine	I	127	126.904 474	100	stable	
			129	128.904 984		β^-	1.6×10^7 yr
			131	130.906 124		β^-	8 days
54	Xenon	Xe	128	127.903 531	1.9	stable	
			129	128.904 779	26.4	stable	
			130	129.903 509	4.1	stable	
			131	130.905 069	21.2	stable	
			132	131.904 141	26.9	stable	
			133	132.905 906		β^-	5.4 days
			134	133.905 394	10.4	stable	
			136	135.907 215	8.9	stable	
55	Cesium	Cs	133	132.905 436	100	stable	
			137	136.907 078		β^-	30 yr
56	Barium	Ba	131	130.906 931		EC	12 days
			133	132.905 990		EC	10.5 yr
			134	133.904 492	2.42	stable	
			135	134.905 671	6.59	stable	
			136	135.904 559	7.85	stable	
			137	136.905 816	11.23	stable	
			138	137.905 236	71.70	stable	
79	Gold	Au	197	196.966 543	100	stable	
81	Thallium	Tl	203	202.972 320	29.524	stable	
			205	204.974 400	70.476	stable	
			207	206.977 403		β^-	4.77 min
82	Lead	Pb	204	203.973 020	1.4	stable	
			205	204.974 457		EC	1.5×10^7 yr

Atomic Number (Z)	Element	Symbol	Mass Number (A)	Atomic Mass (u)	Percent Abundance	Decay Mode	Half-Life $t_{1/2}$
			206	205.974 440	24.1	stable	
			207	206.975 871	22.1	stable	
			208	207.976 627	52.4	stable	
			210	209.984 163		α, β^-	22.3 yr
			211	210.988 734		β^-	36.1 min
83	Bismuth	Bi	208	207.979 717		EC	3.7×10^5 yr
			209	208.980 374	100	stable	
			211	210.987 254		α	2.14 min
			215	215.001 836		β^-	7.4 min
84	Polonium	Po	209	208.982 405		α	102 yr
			210	209.982 848		α	138.38 days
			215	214.999 418		α	0.001 8 s
			218	218.008 965		α, β^-	3.10 min
85	Astatine	At	218	218.008 685		α, β^-	1.6 s
			219	219.011 294		α, β^-	0.9 min
86	Radon	Rn	219	219.009 477		α	3.96 s
			220	220.011 369		α	55.6 s
			222	222.017 571		α, β^-	3.823 days
87	Francium	Fr	223	223.019 733		α, β^-	22 min
88	Radium	Ra	223	223.018 499		α	11.43 days
			224	224.020 187		α	3.66 days
			226	226.025 402		α	1 600 yr
			228	228.031 064		β^-	5.75 yr
89	Actinium	Ac	227	227.027 749		α, β^-	21.77 yr
			228	228.031 015		β^-	6.15 hr
90	Thorium	Th	227	227.027 701		α	18.72 days
			228	228.028 716		α	1.913 yr
			229	229.031 757		α	7 300 yr
			230	230.033 127		α	75.000 yr
			231	231.036 299		α, β^-	25.52 hr
			232	232.038 051	100	α	1.40×10^{10} yr
			234	234.043 593		β^-	24.1 days
91	Protactinium	Pa	231	231.035 880		α	32.760 yr
			234	234.043 300		β^-	6.7 hr
92	Uranium	U	233	233.039 630		α	1.59×10^5 yr
			234	234.040 946		α	2.45×10^5 yr
			235	235.043 924	0.72	α	7.04×10^8 yr
			236	236.045 562		α	2.34×10^7 yr
			238	238.050 784	99.28	α	4.47×10^9 yr
93	Neptunium	Np	236	236.046 560		EC	1.15×10^5 yr
			237	237.048 168		α	2.14×10^6 yr
94	Plutonium	Pu	238	238.049 555		α	87.7 yr
			239	239.052 157		α	2.412×10^4 yr
			240	240.053 808		α	6 560 yr
			242	242.058 737		α	3.73×10^6 yr

ActivPhysics OnLine™ Activities (MP)® www.masteringphysics.com

The following list gives the activity numbers and titles of the ActivPhysics activities available in the Pearson eText and the Study Area of MasteringPhysics, followed by the corresponding textbook page references.

PhET Simulations (MP) www.masteringphysics.com

The following list gives the titles of the PhET simulations available in the Pearson eText and in the Study Area of MasteringPhysics, with the corresponding textbook section and page references.

*Indicates an associated tutorial is available in the MasteringPhysics Item Library.

Answers

Answers to Odd-Numbered Exercises and Problems

Chapter 20

1. 110 N
3. 2.0 m
5.

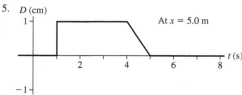

D (cm)

At $x = 5.0$ m

t (s)

7.

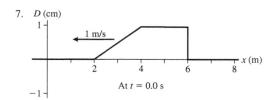

D (cm)

1 m/s

x (m)

At $t = 0.0$ s

9.

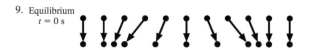

Equilibrium
$t = 0$ s

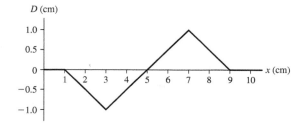

D (cm)

x (cm)

11. a. 3.1 rad/m   b. 9.5 m/s
13. a. 11 Hz   b. 1.1 m   c. 13 m/s
15. $\frac{\pi}{2}$ rad, $\frac{3}{2}\pi$ rad
17. 2.5 m
19. 1500 m/s
21. a. 1.5 GHz   b. 990 nm
23. a. 2.96 m   b. 116 Hz
25. a. 1.5×10^{-11} s   b. 3.4 mm

27. a. 1.88×10^8 m/s   b. 4.48×10^{14} Hz
29. 6.0×10^5 J
31. 110 dB
33. a. 65 dB   b. 105 dB
35. 5.0 W
37. a. 650 Hz   b. 560 Hz
39. 38.1 m/s
41. a. 0.80 m   b. $\frac{1}{2}\pi$ rad
    c. $D(x, t) = (2.0 \text{ mm})\sin(2.5\pi x - 10\pi t + \frac{1}{2}\pi)$
43. $\dfrac{v_0}{2}$

45.

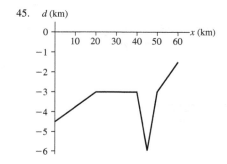

d (km)

x (km)

47. 410 ms
49. a. 440 Hz   b. 3.4 m
51. a. $-y$-direction   b. y-axis   c. 0.701 m, 350 m/s, 2.00 ms
53. a. 12.6 N   b. 2.00 cm   c. 12.8 m/s
55. $D(x, t) = (0.010 \text{ mm})\sin[(\pi \text{ rad/m})x - (400\pi \text{ rad/s})t + \frac{1}{2}\pi \text{ rad}]$
57. -19 m/s, 0 m/s, 19 m/s
59. 8
61. 9.4 m/s
63. a. 0.095 W/m²   b. 1.6 MW/m²
65. a. 6.67×10^4 W   b. 8.5×10^{10} W/m²
67. 50 m
69. 1.3
71. 21 min
75. Receding at 1.5×10^6 m/s
77. 0.07°C
81. 29 s

Chapter 21

1.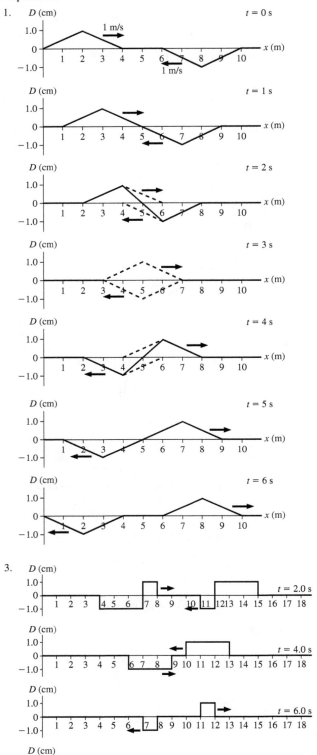

3. (continued in image)

5.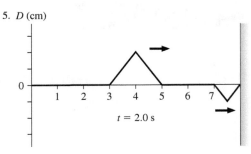

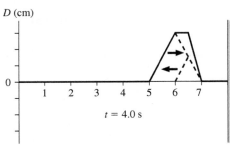

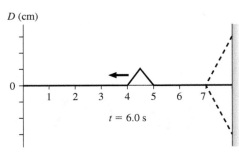

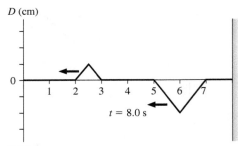

7. 50 Hz
9. a. 4.8 m, 2.4 m, 1.6 m   b. 75 Hz
11. 12 kg
13. a. 2.42 m, 1.21 m, 0.807 m   b. 4.84 m, 1.61 m, 0.968 m
15. 512 Hz
17. 2180 N
19. a. 80 cm   b. 100 cm
21. 216 nm
23. a. In phase

b.

	r_1	r_2	Δr	C/D
P	3λ	4λ	λ	C
Q	$\frac{7}{2}\lambda$	2λ	$\frac{3}{2}\lambda$	D
R	$\frac{5}{2}\lambda$	$\frac{7}{2}\lambda$	λ	C

25. Perfect destructive
27. 203 Hz
29. 1.26 cm

31. $A(x = 10 \text{ cm}) = 0.62 \text{ cm}$, $A(x = 20 \text{ cm}) = 1.18 \text{ cm}$,
    $A(x = 30 \text{ cm}) = 1.62 \text{ cm}$, $A(x = 40 \text{ cm}) = 1.90 \text{ cm}$,
    $A(x = 50 \text{ cm}) = 2.00 \text{ cm}$
33. 1.4 cm
35. 180 Hz
37. 28.4 cm
39. 18 cm
41. 140 N/m
43. 6.1 cm
45. $9\mu_0/4$
47. 13.0 cm
49. 580 Hz, 4.9 kHz
51. 12.1 kHz
53. 450 N
55. 93 m
57. 7.9 cm
59. a. 850 Hz   b. $-\pi/2$ rad
61. 7.2 cm
63. 20
65. 170 Hz
67. 1/3
69. a. a b. 1.0 m   c. 9
71. a. 5   b. 4.6 mm
73. 7.0 m/s
75. 4.0 cm, 35 cm, 65 cm
77. 2.0 kg
79. a. $\lambda_1 = 20.0 \text{ m}$, $\lambda_2 = 10.0 \text{ m}$, $\lambda_3 = 6.67 \text{ m}$
    b. $v_1 = 5.59 \text{ m/s}$, $v_2 = 3.95 \text{ m/s}$, $v_3 = 3.22 \text{ m/s}$
    d. $T_1 = 3.58 \text{ s}$, $T_2 = 2.53 \text{ s}$, $T_3 = 2.07 \text{ s}$

Chapter 22

1. $0.023 \text{ rad} = 1.3°$
3. 1000 nm
5. 0.36 mm
7. 0.286°
9. 1.6°, 3.2°
11. 530
13. 7.9 μm
15. 0.20 mm
17. 0.50 mm
19. 4.0 mm
21. 7.6 m
23. $0.015 \text{ rad} = 0.87°$
25. 0.25 mm
27. 400 nm
29. 0.2895 mm
31. a. Single slit   b. 0.15 mm
33. 1.67 m
35. 3 mW/m^2
37. 12.0 μm
39. 667.8 nm
41. 25 cm
43. 3
45. a. 1230 lines/mm   b. 46.5°
47. 670 lines/mm
49. 16°
51. 800 lines/mm
53. a. 2   b. 1.15   c. 1
55. 670 nm
57. 0.12 mm
59. a. 550 nm   b. 0.40 mm
61. 50 cm

63. a. 22.3°   b. 16.6°
65. 19
67. a. Dark   b. 1.597
69. a. No   b. 0.044°   c. 4.6 mm   d. 1.5 m
71. b. 0.022°, 0.058°
73. b. $-11.5°$, $-53.1°$
75. a. 0.52 mm   b. 0.074°   c. 1.3 m

Chapter 23

1. a. 3.3 ns   b. 75 cm, 67 cm, 46 cm
3. 0.40 ns
5. 30°
7. 6.1 m
9. 433 cm
11. 16°
13. 1.39
15. 76.7°
17. 3.2 cm
19. 1.52
21. 1.48
23. 1600 nm
25. 6.0 cm behind the lens, inverted
27. 7.5 cm in front of the lens, upright
29. 68 cm
31. 200 cm
33. 36 cm
35. 40 cm in front of mirror, inverted
37. 12 cm behind mirror, upright
39. a. 3   b. B$(+1.0 \text{ m}, -2.0 \text{ m})$, C$(-1.0 \text{ m}, +2.0 \text{ m})$, D$(+1.0 \text{ m}, +2.0 \text{ m})$
41. 10 m
43. 1.7
45. a. 87 cm   b. 65 cm   c. 43 cm
47. 4.0 m
49. a. Total internal reflection   b. Refraction at 72°   c. 18 cm
51. 1.58
53. 1.0°
55. 2.00
57. b. -15 cm, 1.5 cm, agree
59. b. 50 cm, 0.67 cm, agree
61. b. -20 cm, 0.33 cm, agree
63. 15.1 cm
65. -15 cm, 0.75 cm, behind, upright
67. Concave, 3.6 cm
69. 67 cm, 1.0 m
71. a. 5.9 cm   b. 6.0 cm
73. 16 cm
75. 13 cm
79. a. $t = \dfrac{n_1}{c}\sqrt{x^2 + a^2} + \dfrac{n_2}{c}\sqrt{(w-x)^2 + b^2}$
    b. $0 = \dfrac{n_1 x}{c\sqrt{x^2 + a^2}} - \dfrac{n_2(w-x)}{c\sqrt{(w-x)^2 + b^2}}$
81. b. 1.574

Chapter 24

1. b. $s_2' = 49 \text{ cm}$, $h_2' = 4.6 \text{ cm}$
3. b. $s_2' = 30 \text{ cm}$, $h_2' = 6.0 \text{ cm}$
5. b. $s_2' = -3.33 \text{ cm}$, $h_2' = 0.66 \text{ cm}$
7. 5.0
9. 3.0 mm
11. 6.0 mm
13. a. Myopia   b. 100 cm

15. 6.3 cm

17. 5.0 cm

19. 6.0 mm

21. a. 8.0 cm   b. 1.2 cm

23. Upright image, 1.0 cm tall, 6.4 cm to left of the second lens

25. a. Both images 2.0 cm tall; one upright 10 cm left of lens, the other inverted 20 cm to right of lens.

27. a. $f_2 + f_1$ b. $\dfrac{f_2}{|f_1|} w_1$

29. 16 cm placed 80 cm from screen

31. 23 cm

33. 5.0 cm

35. a. +3.0 D as objective   b. −1.5   c. 0.56 m

37. 4.6 mm

39. 15 km

41. a. 3.8 cm   b. Sun is too bright

43. 3.5 m

45. b. $\Delta n_2 = \dfrac{1}{2}\Delta n_1$ c. Crown converging, flint diverging   d. 4.18 cm

Chapter 34

1. a. $(2.0 \times 10^6$ m/s, 45° from the y-axis) 45°
   b. $(1.47 \times 10^6$ m/s, 16.2° from the y'-axis) 16.2°

3. $-1.0 \times 10^6 \hat{k}$ V/m, $-1.11 \times 10^{-5}\hat{j}$ T

5. 16.3° above the +x-axis

9. 1.0 μF

11. 17 μA

13. 3.3×10^{-8} T

15. a. 10.0 nm   b. 3.00×10^{16} Hz   c. 6.67×10^{-8} T

17. a. 3.33×10^{-7} T   b. 13.3 W/m²

19. 980 V/m, 3.3 μT

21. a. 2.2×10^{-6} W/m²   b. 0.041 V/m

23. 3.3×10^{-6} N

25. 60°

27. 30°

29. $(1.73 \times 10^6$ V/m, left)

31. a. (0.10 T, into page)   b. 0 V/m, (0.10 T, into page)

33. 1.0×10^7 m/s parallel to the current

35. a. 0.94 V/m   b. 10 T

37. b. 1.5×10^{-13} A

39.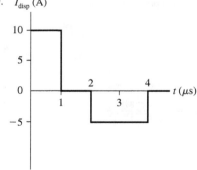

41. 20 V

43. b. 6.67×10^{-6} J/m³

45. a. 3.85×10^{26} W   b. 589 W/m²

47. a. $(1/2)f$ b. $(3/4)f$

49. Yes

51. 1.8×10^7 V/m

53. 1.3 m

55. 4.9×10^7 W/m²

57. 8.8 h

59. $(-6.0 \times 10^5\,\hat{i} + 1.0 \times 10^5\,\hat{j})$ V/m

61. 5.2 μV/m

63. a. $E = IR/L$, $B = \dfrac{\mu_0 I}{2\pi r} IR/L$ b. $(I^2R/2\pi rL$, radially inward)

Chapter 36

1. $x'_1 = 5.0$ m at $t = 1.0\,s$, $x'_2 = -5.0$ m at $t = 5.0\,s$

3. $v_{\text{sound}} = 345$ m/s, $v_{\text{sprinter}} = 15$ m/s

5. a. 13 m/s   b. 3.0 m/s   c. 9.4 m/s

7. 3.0×10^8 m/s

9. 167 ns

11. 2.0 μs

13. No, bolt 2 hits 20 μs before bolt 1.

15. Yes

17. 0.866c

19. a. 0.9965c   b. 59.8 ly

21. 46 m/s

23. Yes

25. 4600 kg/m³

27. 3.0×10^6 m/s

29. $x = 8.3 \times 10^{10}$ m, $t = 330$ s

31. 0.36c

33. 0.71c

35. 0.80c

37. 0.707c

39. a. 1.8×10^{16} J   b. 9.0×10^9

41. 0.943c

43. $u_{50\text{ final}} = 1.33$ m/s to the right, $u_{100\text{ final}} = 3.33$ m/s to the righ

45. 11.2 h

47. a. No   b. 67.1 y

49. a. 0.80c   b. 16 y

51. 0.78 m

53. a. 17 y   b. 15 y   c. Both

55. 0.96c

57. 3.1×10^6 V

59. a. 0.98c   b. 8.5×10^{-11} J

61. b. Lengths perpendicular to the motion are not affected.

63. a. $u'_y = u_y/\gamma\left(1 - u_xv/c^2\right)$ b. 0.877c

65. a. 3.5×10^{-18} kg m/s, 1.1×10^{-9} J   b. 1.6×10^{-18} kg m/s

67. a. 7.6×10^{16} J   b. 0.84 kg

69. 7.5×10^{13} J

71. 1 pm

73. 22 m

75. 0.85c

Chapter 37

1. a. $(m, n) = (2, 3), (2, 4), (2, 5), (2, 6)$ b. 397.1 nm

3. 121.6 nm, 102.6 nm, 97.3 nm, 95.0 nm

5. a. 9.39×10^{4}°C   b. 694°C

7. 2.4 μm

9. a. 6.0×10^7 m/s   b. 17 cm

11. a. 2.4×10^{-16} kg   b. 1.3×10^{-18} C   c. 8

13. 1.33×10^{19} C

15. a. 3.7×10^7 m/s   b. 2.7×10^7 m/s   c. Electron

17. a. 10 keV   b. 0.14 MeV   c. 1.2×10^{19} eV

19. a. 3 electrons, 3 protons, 3 neutrons
    b. 7 electrons, 8 protons, 8 neutrons
    c. 5 electrons, 7 protons, 6 neutrons

21. a. ^{11}B   b. ^{14}C$^+$

23. a. 79 electrons, 79 protons, 118 neutrons
    b. 2.29×10^{17} kg/m³
    c. $2\,01 \times 10^{13}$

25. a. 6660 MeV   b. 3.6 MeV
27. a. 0.512 MeV   b. 939 MeV
29. 173 MeV
31. 46 mT, into the page
33. 1.2 μA
35. 0.000000000058% contains mass, 99.999999999942% empty space
37. a. 5.0×10^4 kg/m^3
    b. 1.7×10^{-29} m^3, 1.6×10^{-10} m
    c. 1.7×10^{17} kg/m^3, 6.2×10^{13}
39. a. 58 N   b. 4.7×10^{-35} N
41. Aluminum
43. a. 2.3×10^7 m/s   b. 2.9 MeV
45. 2.52×10^5 m/s, 65.1° below $+x$-axis
47. a. mg/E_0 b. mg/b d. 2.4×10^{18} C   e. 15

Chapter 38

1. 6.25×10^{13} electrons/s
3. 3.20 eV
5. 1.78 eV
7. a. 2.26 eV   b. 0.166 nm
9. a. 1.86×10^{-6} eV   b. 2.76 eV   c. 27.6 keV
11. 497 nm
13. 1×10^{19} photons/s
15. 6.0×10^{-6} V
17. a. 1.1×10^{-34} m   b. 1.7×10^{-23} m/s
19. 6
21. 0.427 nm
23. a. Yes   b. 0.50 eV
25. $n = 2$: yes; $n = 3$: no
27. 1.90 nm
29. a. 0.332 nm, 0.665 nm, 0.997 nm
    c.

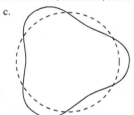

33. 97.26 nm
35.

n	r_n (nm)	v_n (m/s)	E_n (eV)
1	0.026	4.38×10^6	-54.4
2	0.106	2.19×10^6	-13.6
3	0.238	1.46×10^6	-6.0

37. 1.24 V
39. 4.3×10^{-10} W
41. a. 2.3 eV   b. 244 nm
43. a. 4.14 eV   b. 6.4×10^{-34} J s
45. a. Potassium   b. 4.24×10^{-15} eV s
47. 2.0×10^{-18} m, no
49. 200 m/s
51. 0.35 nm

53. 18 fm
55. a.

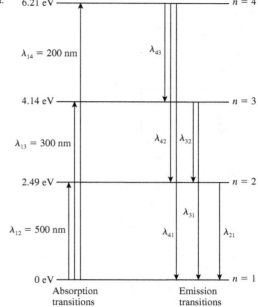

    b. 200 nm, 300 nm, 334 nm, 500 nm, 601 nm, 753 nm
57. 6.2×10^5 m/s
59. 410.3 nm, 434.2 nm, 486.3 nm, 656.5 nm
61. a. 0.362 m   b. 0.000368 nm
63. $3 \rightarrow 2$:10.28 nm, $4 \rightarrow 2$:7.62 nm, $5 \rightarrow 2$: 6.80 nm; all ultraviolet
65. a. 2.06×10^6 m/s   b. 12.09 V
67. a. 1.0 m/s   b. 3.2°   c. 1.1 cm
69. b. 25.7 nm, 36.3 nm, 44.5 nm, 51.4 nm   c. $n(\pi \hbar f_{cyc})$

Chapter 39

1. $P_C = 0.20$, $P_D = 0.10$
3. a. 7.7%   b. 25%
5. a. 1/6   b. 1/6 c. 5/18
7. 100 V/m
9. 4.0 m^{-1}
11. a. 3300   b. 1100
13. a. 5.0×10^{-3} b. 2.5×10^{-3} c. 0   d. 2.5×10^{-3}
15. a. 0.25 fm^{-1} b.   c. 0.75

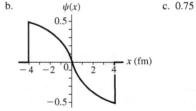

17. a. 0.354 mm$^{-1/2}$
    b.

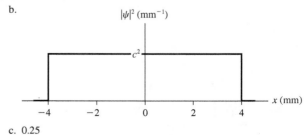

    c. 0.25

19. 25 ns
21. 1.0×10^5
23. -0.65×10^{-36} m/s $\leq v_x \leq 0.65 \times 10^{-36}$ m/s
25. 0.0 m/s $\leq v_x \leq 2.5 \times 10^7$ m/s
27. 9.5 GHz $\leq f \leq$ 10.5 GHz
29. 1.0×10^5 pulses/s
31. a.

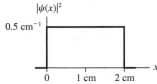

   b. 1%   c. 10^4 d. 0.5 cm^{-1}
33. a. Yes   b.

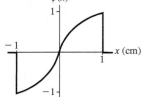

   c. 0.000, 0.00050, 0.0010   d. 900
35. a. $\sqrt{3/8}$ mm$^{-1/2}$
   b.

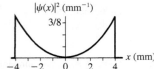

   c.

   d. 0.13
37. a. 0.27%   b. 32%
39. a. 0.87 cm$^{-1/2}$
   b.

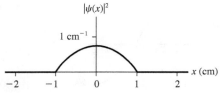

   c.

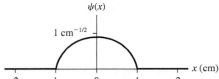

   d. 3.4×10^3
41. a. $a = b$ b. $a = b = 0.84$
   c.   d. 58.1%

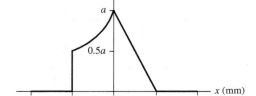

43. 18 μm
45. a. 0 m/s to 1.8×10^{10} m/s
   b. The speed in part a exceeds the speed of light, so it is impossible.
47. a. 1.5×10^{-13} m   b. 4.4×10^{11} m
49. 50%
51. a. $c = \sqrt{3/8}$
   b.

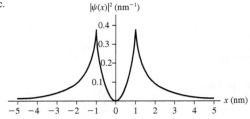

   c.

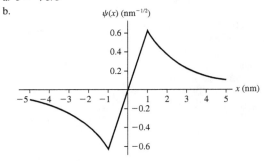

   d. 2.5×10^5

Chapter 40

1. 0.739 nm
3. 1.0 nm
7. a. 0.159 nm   b. 0.159 nm   c. 0.275 nm
9. 0.38 nm
11.

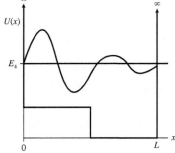

13.

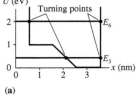
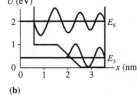

   (a)   (b)

15. 200 nm
17. 519 nm
19. 1.4 N/m

21. a. 4.95 eV   b. 4.80 eV   c. 4.55 eV

25. a. $\lambda_{2\to1} = 8mcL^2/3h$ b. 0.795 nm

29. a.

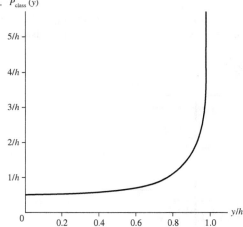

$n =$	1	2	3
b. Most likely	$\frac{1}{2}L$	$\frac{1}{4}L, \frac{3}{4}L$	$\frac{1}{6}L, \frac{3}{6}L, \frac{5}{6}L$
c. Least likely	$0, L$	$0, \frac{1}{2}L, L$	$0, \frac{1}{3}L, \frac{2}{3}L, L$
d. Prob in left $\frac{1}{3}$ from graph	$>\frac{1}{3}$	$>\frac{1}{3}$	$\frac{1}{3}$
e. Prob in left $\frac{1}{3}$ calculated	0.195	0.402	0.333

31. 10%

35. a. $A_1 = \dfrac{1}{(\pi b^2)^{1/4}}$ b. $\text{Prob}(x < -b \text{ or } x > b) = \dfrac{2}{\sqrt{\pi b^2}}\displaystyle\int_b^\infty e^{-x^2/b^2}dx$

   c. 15.7%

37. a. $P_{\text{class}}(x) = \dfrac{1}{2h\sqrt{1-(y/h)}}$

   b.

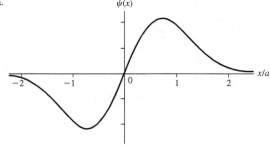

39. 10^{-463}

41. a. 0.136 nm   b. One atomic diameter

43. a.

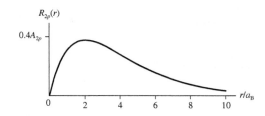

b. $\pm a/\sqrt{2}$ c. $U(x) = \dfrac{2\hbar^2}{ma^2}\left(\left(\dfrac{x}{a}\right)^2 - \dfrac{3}{2}\right)$

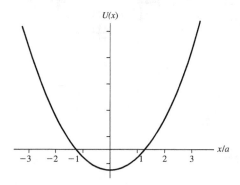

45. a. 3.4×10^{-5} b. 2.8   c. 0.005 nm

Chapter 41

1. a. 0   b. $\sqrt{12}\hbar$

3. a. f b. -0.85 eV

5. -0.378 eV; $\sqrt{12}\hbar$

7. a. 2   b. 1

9. $1s^2 2s^2 2p^6 3s^2 3p$, $1s^2 2s^2 2p^6 3s^2 3p^6 4s^2 3d^{10} 4p$,
   $1s^2 2s^2 2p^6 3s^2 3p^6 4s^2 3d^{10} 4p^6 5s^2 4d^{10} 5p$

11. a. Excited state of Ne   b. Ground state of Ti

13. $1s^2 3s$

15. a. Yes, 2.21 μm   b. No

17. a. 5.6×10^5 b. 1.7×10^5 c. 3.0×10^3

19. a. 9.0×10^5 b. 8.7 ns

21. 3.2×10^{15} s^{-1}

23. a. 1.06 μm   b. 1.9 W

25. a. $\sqrt{2}\hbar$ b. $-1, 0, 1$

   c.

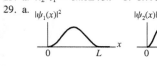

27. a. $\sqrt{2}\hbar$ b. $\sqrt{6}\hbar$

29. a. 3.7×10^{-3} b. 5.4×10^{-3} c. 2.9×10^{-3}

33. a. $R_{2p}(r) = \dfrac{A_{2p}}{2a_B} r e^{-r/2a_B}$

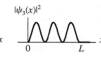

b. $2a_B$

35.

K
$(1s^2\ 2s^2\ 2p^6\ 3s^2\ 3p^6\ 4s^1)$

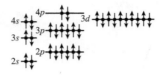

Ge
$(1s^2\ 2s^2\ 2p^6\ 3s^2\ 3p^6\ 4s^2\ 3d^{10}\ 4p^2)$

Sc
$(1s^2\ 2s^2\ 2p^6\ 3s^2\ 3p^6\ 4s^2\ 3d)$

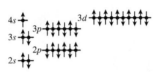

Cu
$(1s^2\ 2s^2\ 2p^6\ 3s^2\ 3p^6\ 4s\ 3d^{10})$

37. a.

Transition	$6s \to 5p$	$6s \to 4p$	$6s \to 3p$
b. λ(nm)	7290	1630	515

39. 1.13×10^6 m/s

41.

Transition	(a) Wavelength	(b) Type	(c) Absorption
$2p \to 2s$	670 nm	VIS	Yes
$3s \to 2p$	816 nm	IR	No
$3p \to 2s$	324 nm	UV	Yes
$3p \to 3s$	2696 nm	IR	No
$3d \to 2p$	611 nm	VIS	No
$3d \to 3p$	24800 nm	IR	No
$4s \to 2p$	498 nm	VIS	No
$4s \to 3p$	2430 nm	IR	No

43. a.   Energy   b. 28.7 eV

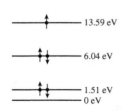

45. a. 6.3×10^8 s^{-1} b. 0.17 ns
47. a. $\tau \ln 2$ b. 12 ns
49. 5.0×10^{16}
51. b. 0.021 nm
55. $1.5a_B$, $5.0a_B$
57. a. $p_{atom} = 7.0 \times 10^{-23}$ kg m/s; $p_{photon} = -8.5 \times 10^{-28}$ kg m/s
    b. 82 000 photons   c. 1.2 ms   d. -5.7×10^{-20} N, -4.0×10^5 m/s^2
    e. 31 cm

Chapter 42

1.

		Protons	Neutrons
a.	^{3}He	2	1
b.	^{32}P	15	17
c.	^{32}S	16	16
d.	^{238}U	92	146

3. a. 3.8 fm   b. 8.2 fm   c. 14.5 fm
5. a. $m = 9.988 \times 10^{-27}$ kg; $r = 2.2 \times 10^{-15}$ m; $\rho = 2.3 \times 10^{17}$ kg/m^3
   b. $m = 3.437 \times 10^{-25}$ kg; $r = 7.1 \times 10^{-15}$ m; $\rho = 2.3 \times 10^{17}$ kg/m^3
7. a. ^{36}S and ^{36}Ar   b. 5, 8
9. ^{54}Cr: 474 MeV, 8.78 MeV; ^{54}Fe: 472 MeV, 8.74 MeV
11. ^{14}O = 7.05 MeV; ^{16}O = 7.98 MeV; ^{16}O is more tightly bound
13. 8000 N
15. 2.3×10^{-38}
17. a. ^{14}C

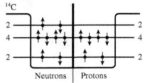

^{14}N

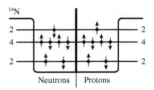

^{14}O

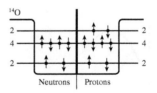

b. ^{14}N is stable; ^{14}C undergoes beta-minus decay and ^{14}O undergoes beta-plus decay

19. a. 236 μg   b. 140 μg   c. 0.775 μg
21. 4.6×10^9
23. 80 d
25. a. ^{228}Th   b. ^{207}Tl   c. ^{7}Li   d. ^{60}Ni
27. a. ^{19}O, ^{19}F, ^{19}Ne   b. ^{19}F
    c. ^{19}O decays by β^- to ^{19}F; ^{19}Ne decays by β^+ to ^{19}F
29. ^{228}Th
31. 5.51 MeV
33. 0.225 J
35. 60 mrem
37. a. 3.5×10^7 m/s   b. 25 MeV
39. a. 12.7 km   b. 780 μs
41. a. 1.46×10^{-8} u, 1.45×10^{-6}%   b. 0.0304 u, 0.76%
43. 6.0 MeV

45. 0.93 MeV
47. 2.7×10^{17}
49. a. 19 s   b. No
51. 1.2 h
53. 210 million years
55. 3.3×10^{12}
57. a. 2.6×10^7 b. 0.024 Bq   c. 1.9×10^5 mSv
    d. Yes, many times more than the background radiation
59. 15 cm
61. $\approx$ 6 billion years ago
63. a. $K_{in} = 65.0$ MeV; $K_{out} = 5.0$ MeV   b. 3.7×10^{21} collisions/s
    c. 6.6×10^{-39} d. 650 million years

Credits

Page **xvi**: Educational Development Center, Inc.
Page **xxix**: IBM Research, Almaden Research Center.

PART V OPENER
Page 558: AguaSonic Acoustics/Photo Researchers, Inc.

CHAPTER 20
Page **560** Top: EpicStockMedia/Shutterstock. Page **560** Middle left: iStockphoto. Page **560** Middle: B. Benoit/Photo Researchers, Inc. Page **560** Middle right: David Parker/Photo Researchers, Inc. Page **560** Bottom left: Oleksiy Maksymenko/Alamy. Page **560** Bottom right: Aaron Kohr/Shutterstock. Page **561**: Dudarev Mikhail/Shutterstock. Page **562**: Uri Haber-Schaim - From PSSC Physics 7th Edition by Haber-Schaim, Dodge, Gardner, Shore. Kendall/Hunt Publishing Company, Dubuque, Iowa (C)1991. Page **566**: Aflo Foto Agency/Alamy. Page **575**: B. Benoit/Photo Researchers, Inc. Page **576**: David Parker/Photo Researchers, Inc. Page **581**: NOAA/AP Images. Page **583**: Space Telescope Science Institute.

CHAPTER 21
Page **591** Top: Peter Aprahamian/SPL/Photo Researchers, Inc. Page **591** Middle left: Pearson Science/Creative Digital Vision. Page **591** Middle: Richard Megna/Fundamental Photographs. Page **591** Middle right: Randy Knight. Page **591** Bottom left: Olga Miltsova/Shutterstock. Page **591** Bottom right: Pearson Science/Eric Schrader. Page **593**: Richard Megna/Fundamental Photographs. Page **594**: Prelinger Archives. Page **596**: Education Development Center, Inc. Page **597**: Pearson Science/Creative Digital Vision. Page **603**: Brian Atkinson/Alamy. Page **609**: Pearson Science/Eric Schrader. Page **611**: Richard Megna/Fundamental Photographs. Page **614** Both: Randy Knight.

CHAPTER 22
Page **627** Top: Pxlxl/Dreamstime. Page **627** Middle left: Irina Pusepp/Alamy. Page **627** Middle: Michael W. Davidson. Page **627** Middle right: Dieter Zawischa. Page **627** Middle left: Jane Pang/iStockphoto. Page **627** Bottom left: Shutterstock. Page **627** Bottom middle: langdu/Shutterstock. Page **627** Bottom right: CENCO Physics/Fundamental Photographs. Page **628** Top: Richard Megna/Fundamental Photographs. Page **628** Bottom: Todd Gipstein/National Geographic Stock. Page **635**: Holographix, LLC. Page **636**: Andrew Bargery/Alamy. Page **636**: inset: Jian Zi. Page **639**: Ken Kay/Fundamental Photographs. Page **644**: CENCO Physics/Fundamental Photographs. Page **645** Top: Philippe Plailly/Photo Researchers, Inc. Page **645** Bottom: Rod Nave. Page **651**: Pyma/Shutterstock.

CHAPTER 23
Page **655** Top: 68images.com - Axel Schmies/Alamy. Page **655** Middle left: Ivinst/iStockphoto. Page **655** Middle: Sciencephotos/Alamy. Page **655** Middle right: GIPhotoStock/Photo Researchers, Inc. Page **655** Bottom left: Shutterstock. Page **655** Bottom 2nd from left: Leslie Garland/Alamy. Page **655** Bottom 3rd from left: piluhinAlamy. Page **655** Bottom right:

Shutterstock. Page **655** Bottom right: iStockphoto. Page **661**: Pearson Science/Creative Digital Vision. Page **664**: Richard Megna/Fundamental Photographs. Page **669**: Pearson Science/Eric Schrader. Page **670**: Shutterstock. Page **671** Both: Richard Megna/Fundamental Photographs. Page **675**: Getty Images - Stockbyte. Page **683**: Shutterstock. Page **685**: Bajande/Photo Researchers, Inc.

CHAPTER 24
Page **694** Top: Don Hammond/Alamy. Page **694** Middle left: iStockphoto. Page **694** Middle: Shutterstock. Page **694** Middle right: Radius Images/Alamy. Page **694** Bottom left: Shutterstock. Page **694** Bottom middle: Shutterstock. Page **698** Both: Richard Megna/Fundamental Photographs. Page **699** Top: Canon U.S.A., Inc. Page **699** Middle: NASA. Page **699** Bottom: Garden World/Alamy. Page **701**: Tetra Images/Alamy. Page **705** Top: Tetra Images/Alamy. Page **705** Bottom: Biophoto Associates/Photo Researchers, Inc. Page **710**: Dr. Jeremy Burgess/Photo Researchers, Inc.

PART V SUMMARY
Page 717: WL Delft Hydraulics.

PART VI OPENER
Page 718: Lucidio Studio/Getty Images.

CHAPTER 34
Page **1003** Top: Innerspace Imaging/Photo Researchers, Inc. Page **1003** Bottom: Richard Megna/Fundamental Photographs. Page **1016**: USACE Engineer Research and Development Center. Page **1022**: NASA. Page **1025**: All: Richard Megna/Fundamental Photographs. Page **1028**: Andy Eaves/Alamy.

PART VI SUMMARY
Page 1057: Boeing.

PART VII OPENER
Page 1058: National Institute of Standards and Technology.

CHAPTER 36
Page **1060** Top: CERN/European Organization for Nuclear Research. Page **1060** Middle: Fermilab/U.S. Department of Energy. Page **1060** Middle right: SOHO/NASA. Page **1060** Bottom left: AF archive/Alamy. Page **1060** Bottom right: Shutterstock. Page **1061**: Topham/The Image Works, Inc. Page **1077**: U.S. Department of Defense Visual Information Center. Page **1079**: Stanford Linear Accelerator Center/Photo Researchers, Inc. Page **1093**: Science Photo Library/Photo Researchers, Inc. Page **1094**: Wellcome Dept. of Cognitive Neurology/Science Photo Library.

CHAPTER 37
Page **1102** Top: iStockphoto. Page **1102** Right: iStockphoto. Page **1104** Top: Stockbyte/Getty Images. Page **1109** Top: Science Photo Library/Photo Researchers, Inc. Page **1109** Bottom: SSPL/The Image Works, Inc.

CHAPTER 38
Page **1125** Top: IBM Corporation. Page **1125** Left: Dieter Zawischa.
Page **1125** Middle: Antoine Weis. Page **1125** Right: Pearson Science.
Page **1129:** Topham/The Image Works, Inc. Page **1133:** Antoine Weis.
Page **1135** Top: Pearson Science. Page **1135** Bottom: National Institute of
Standards and Technology. Page **1138:** Science Source/Photo Researchers, Inc.

CHAPTER 39
Page **1156** Top: Veeco Instruments, Inc. Page **1156** Right: Claus Jonsson.
Page **1162:** Claus Jonsson.

CHAPTER 40
Page **1179:** IBM Corporate Archives. Page **1180:** Mary Evans Picture
Library/Alamy. Page **1209:** Colin Cuthbert/Photo Researchers, Inc.

CHAPTER 41
Page **1216:** Richard Wainscoat/Alamy. Page **1220:** NASA. Page **1232:**
National Bureau of Standards. Page **1235:** Vassil. Page **1240:** Meggers
Gallery/American Institute of Physics/SPL/Photo Researchers, Inc.

CHAPTER 42
Page **1248** Top: C. Powell, P. Fowler & D. Perkin/Photo Researchers, Inc.
Page **1248** Middle: U. S. Department of Energy. Page **1248** Bottom: SPL/
Photo Researchers. Page **1250:** British Antarctic Survey/Photo Researchers.
Page **1256:** SPL/Photo Researchers. Page **1262:** James King-Holmes/Photo
Researchers, Inc. Page **1266:** The Sudbury Neutrino Observatory Institute
SNOI. Page **1269:** Lonnie Duka/Photolibrary. Page **1270:** Zephyr/Photo
Researchers, Inc.

PART VII SUMMARY
Page **1279:** National Institute of Standards and Technology.

Index

Astronomical Data

Planetary body	Mean distance from sun (m)	Period (years)	Mass (kg)	Mean radius (m)
Sun	—	—	1.99×10^{30}	6.96×10^8
Moon	3.84×10^8*	27.3 days	7.36×10^{22}	1.74×10^6
Mercury	5.79×10^{10}	0.241	3.18×10^{23}	2.43×10^6
Venus	1.08×10^{11}	0.615	4.88×10^{24}	6.06×10^6
Earth	1.50×10^{11}	1.00	5.98×10^{24}	6.37×10^6
Mars	2.28×10^{11}	1.88	6.42×10^{23}	3.37×10^6
Jupiter	7.78×10^{11}	11.9	1.90×10^{27}	6.99×10^7
Saturn	1.43×10^{12}	29.5	5.68×10^{26}	5.85×10^7
Uranus	2.87×10^{12}	84.0	8.68×10^{25}	2.33×10^7
Neptune	4.50×10^{12}	165	1.03×10^{26}	2.21×10^7

*Distance from earth

Typical Coefficients of Friction

Material	Static μ_s	Kinetic μ_k	Rolling μ_r
Rubber on concrete	1.00	0.80	0.02
Steel on steel (dry)	0.80	0.60	0.002
Steel on steel (lubricated)	0.10	0.05	
Wood on wood	0.50	0.20	
Wood on snow	0.12	0.06	
Ice on ice	0.10	0.03	

Melting/Boiling Temperatures and Heats of Transformation

Substance	T_m (°C)	L_f (J/kg)	T_b (°C)	L_v (J/kg)
Water	0	3.33×10^5	100	22.6×10^5
Nitrogen (N_2)	−210	0.26×10^5	−196	1.99×10^5
Ethyl alcohol	−114	1.09×10^5	78	8.79×10^5
Mercury	−39	0.11×10^5	357	2.96×10^5
Lead	328	0.25×10^5	1750	8.58×10^5

Properties of Materials

Substance	ρ (kg/m³)	c (J/kg K)
Air at STP*	1.28	
Ethyl alcohol	790	2400
Gasoline	680	
Glycerin	1260	
Mercury	13,600	140
Oil (typical)	900	
Seawater	1030	
Water	1000	4190
Aluminum	2700	900
Copper	8920	385
Gold	19,300	129
Ice	920	2090
Iron	7870	449
Lead	11,300	128
Silicon	2330	703

*Standard temperature (0°C) and pressure (1 atm)

Molar Specific Heats of Gases

Gas	C_P (J/mol K)	C_V (J/mol K)
Monatomic Gases		
He	20.8	12.5
Ne	20.8	12.5
Ar	20.8	12.5
Diatomic Gases		
H_2	28.7	20.4
N_2	29.1	20.8
O_2	29.2	20.9

Indices of Refraction

Material	Index of refraction
Vacuum	1 exactly
Air	1.0003
Water	1.33
Glass	1.50
Diamond	2.42

Resistivity and Conductivity of Conductors

Metals	Resistivity (Ω m)	Conductivity ($\Omega^{-1}m^{-1}$)
Aluminum	2.8×10^{-8}	3.5×10^7
Copper	1.7×10^{-8}	6.0×10^7
Gold	2.4×10^{-8}	4.1×10^7
Iron	9.7×10^{-8}	1.0×10^7
Silver	1.6×10^{-8}	6.2×10^7
Tungsten	5.6×10^{-8}	1.8×10^7
Nichrome	1.5×10^{-6}	6.7×10^5
Carbon	3.5×10^{-5}	2.9×10^4

Atomic and Nuclear Data

Atom	Z	Mass (u)	Mass (MeV/c^2)
Electron	—	0.00055	0.51
Proton	—	1.00728	938.28
Neutron	—	1.00866	939.57
^{1}H	1	1.00783	938.79
^{2}H	1	2.01410	
^{4}He	2	4.00260	
^{12}C	6	12.00000	
^{14}C	6	14.00324	
^{14}N	7	14.00307	
^{16}O	8	15.99492	
^{20}Ne	10	19.99244	
^{27}Al	13	26.98154	
^{40}Ar	18	39.96238	
^{207}Pb	82	206.97444	
^{238}U	92	238.05078	

Hydrogen Atom Energies and Radii

n	E_n (eV)	r_n (nm)
1	−13.60	0.053
2	−3.40	0.212
3	−1.51	0.476
4	−0.85	0.848
5	−0.54	1.322

Work Functions of Metals

Metal	E_0 (eV)
Potassium	2.30
Sodium	2.75
Aluminum	4.28
Tungsten	4.55
Iron	4.65
Copper	4.70
Gold	5.10